Bulletin of the Museum of Comparative Zoology
AT HARVARD COLLEGE.
Vol. 108

CLASSIFICATION OF INSECTS

*Keys to the Living and Extinct Families of Insects, and to the
Living Families of Other Terrestrial Arthropods*

BY

Charles T. Brues

*Professor of Entomology, Emeritus,
Honorary Curator of Parasitic Hymenoptera, Harvard University*

A. L. Melander

Professor of Biology, Emeritus, College of the City of New York

AND

Frank M. Carpenter

*Professor of Entomology, Alexander Agassiz Professor of Zoology,
Curator of Fossil Insects, Harvard University*

53394

CAMBRIDGE, MASS., U. S. A.
PRINTED FOR THE MUSEUM
1954

TABLE OF CONTENTS

PART I

KEYS TO RECENT INSECTA

PART II

KEYS TO RECENT FAMILIES OF OTHER TERRESTRIAL ARTHROPODA

PART III

KEYS TO EXTINCT FAMILIES OF INSECTA

PART IV

ERRATA

page 150: captions to figures 224 and 225 transposed.

page 817, line 30: *Kirgisellodes* should be substituted for *Kirgisélla.*

page 818: captions to figures 1195 and 1196 transposed.

page 873: insert Ichneumonidae, 628, 639 after *Ichneumon;* delete 628 and 639 after Ichneumonoidea.

PREFACE TO FIRST EDITION

Due to the great abundance and diversity of insects their taxonomy presents many difficulties and complexities. Classification is consequently a discouraging aspect of entomology to the young student who must attempt in a short space of time to gain a sufficient knowledge of relationships that may enable him to recognize the more common and important types of insect life.

Long teaching experience has served clearly to demonstrate to the authors that the fundamental principles of classification cannot be fully appreciated through the study of descriptive text-books, nor can any comprehension of the infinite variety of nature be acquired except by close observational contact with the things themselves. Moreover, the study of a few selected types by the laboratory method fails to give more than a very superficial view of the organic world, and as biological knowledge advances, tends to emphasize the similarities between animals and to minimize the differences that exist between them. It is, therefore, highly desirable that the principles of taxonomy be presented to the student in a practical way to demonstrate particularly certain of its more fundamental and important phases.

The present volume is the outcome of a series of steps, developed by the authors during the course of many years to train students in the practical taxonomy of insects and to provide a manual for the identification of the larger groups of insects; one which would prove useful and reliable in the hands of professional entomologists and other persons, especially biologists working in other fields, for the actual identification of specimens of insects.

The precursor of the present manual was published by the authors in 1915 and printed privately as a "Key to the Families of North American Insects." It has proved to be very useful and workable in the teaching laboratory both by ourselves and others and has, we believe, proved to be a valuable aid to entomologists and other interested persons who have occasion to identify specimens of insects. We have regretted the geographical limitations of the original book which have made it less useful to workers in other parts of the world, and also the almost entire omission of aids for the identification of the immature stages. The lack of lists of literature was also recognized as a fault as well as the omission of keys which would serve to identify specimens of the various other terrestrial arthropods which are frequently collected by those interested in insects.

The new volume has, therefore, been entirely rewritten to include the families of the entire world, and in many cases subfamilies of the larger or more important groups. A selected list of literature on the several groups has been added, and so far as possible, keys for the identification of the immature stages. We have also prepared an additional part dealing with the numerous other groups of terrestrial Arthropoda.

The keys aim to reproduce as accurately as possible the most generally accepted system of classification of each group. They are necessarily to some extent heterogeneous as they represent the accumulated opinions and revisions of hundreds of workers during the course of many decades. Taxonomy is the oldest branch of biological science and as it has in the past had many more devotees than the recently developed branches, it has a much more complex background. The present treatment can in no sense be considered as original, nor does it follow in detail any previous comprehensive system. There are numerous changes from the arrangement in our previous book, although this has served in a general way, more closely in some groups than others, as a model for the present one. In a few groups where recent extensive revisions have been published, these have been quite generally followed. In others, where there is considerable disagreement among authorities, we have attempted so far as possible to present what seems to be the most generally acceptable classification or the one which appears to be most rational. The arrangement of the Hymenoptera and Diptera represents mainly our own viewpoint, and this is to some extent true of the Coleoptera. The systems followed in certain other groups are indicated from time to time in the text. Where recent monographs of certain groups have appeared, the classification there proposed has been accepted with few changes, although we have by no means made it a rule to regard the newest arrangement as the most satisfactory.

The illustrations have been derived from many sources and are in great part redrawn from published figures, although it must be stated that many have been simplified, differently lettered or otherwise modified to adapt them to the purpose of the present manual. In each case, where not original, the source of each is indicated by the name of the author in parentheses.

Most of the figures from our previous book are reproduced here. They were drawn mainly by Beirne Barrett Brues, the wife of one of the authors. To these have been added an extensive series prepared by Anna Scholl O'Connor, a considerable number by Selina Tetzlaff Johnson, and a few by others, including the writers. The figures have been selected principally to represent the general appearance of the species of the various groups and the special structures used in classification.

The marking of accents and the indications for the proper pronunciation of the names of genera, families and higher groups has been done in great part by Alice M. Brues, daughter of one of the authors.

The manuscript was transferred into typewritten form chiefly by Mrs. O'Connor who has also aided greatly in the reading of the proof and preparation of the index.

For advice and criticism on numerous occasions we are greatly indebted to a number of friends and co-workers, as well as to several students, especially Mr. R. P. Dow, who was of great assistance in the preparation of the section on Hymenoptera.

Professor W. M. Wheeler has examined the section on ants, but far more, has offered encouragement and criticism during the tedious process of preparation.

Finally, we are deeply grateful to Dr. Thomas Barbour for issuing the volume as a contribution from the Museum of Comparative Zoölogy.

No one is more keenly aware than the writers of the great chance that errors of statement or omission may creep into a work of this kind. We have diligently guarded against the occurrence of such errors during the course of preparation, but for any that may remain we trust that we may be forgiven.

PREFACE TO THE REVISED EDITION

Two decades have passed since the first edition of the present work was written. During this time many contributions dealing with the taxonomy of insects have been published. These include some monographic treatments of families and larger groups, in addition to a really vast series of shorter, less comprehensive papers relating to smaller groups or to the faunas of more restricted areas.

In several orders the system of classification currently in general use differs but little, or scarcely at all, from that presented in the earlier volume. In others, more recent treatments differ very considerably from those most commonly followed by the majority of taxonomists twenty years ago. In such cases extensive revision of the keys has been made, but in frequent instances (*e.g.* Acarina) we have not taken it for granted that the newest arrangement is the most satisfactory, or that it will come into general use, and we have not adopted all such innovations.

During recent years a few taxonomists have proposed an extensive multiplication of family names in some groups, like the Suborder Adephaga among the Coleoptera, and in the Acarina and Diplopoda among the other terrestrial Arthropoda treated in the third part of the present volume. This degradation of the family concept is utterly at variance with accepted practice in other orders and has not been incorporated in the keys. Such family names have been included to some extent in the text in order to indicate their taxonomic position.

A new section, dealing with extinct families of insects, has been included in the revised edition. The purpose of this part is to indicate the extent and nature of the extinct orders and families and to show the pattern of classification currently followed. A discussion of some of the problems involved in the taxonomy of the extinct groups introduces that section.

We are greatly indebted to Professor Charles L. Remington for his aid in revising the keys to the Thysanura and Entotrophi, and especially for his efforts on the Lepidoptera, including the preparation of a new larval key. Dr. Kenneth Christiansen has revised the keys to the Collembola, on which a great deal has been published in recent years.

In addition to these colleagues and those who furthered the preparation of the earlier edition, we wish to extend our grateful appreciation to all who have aided in the accomplishment of its present ecdysis. It now emerges with an increase in length of the order of $\sqrt[3]{2}$, approximately that of a typical insect as it passes into a succeeding instar during growth. This is, of course, entirely coincidental, but as most of the increased length of the new volume is due to newly accumulated references in the literature and to a sound advance in insect palæontology, it reflects in a sense the growth of entomological publication during twenty years. At this rate it is appalling to anticipate what the future may hold for systematic entomology.

The American Philosophical Society has supported the preparation of this revision by a grant which has expedited the completion of the manuscript.

Finally, we are indebted to Miss Ruth C. Dunn, whose judgment and accuracy in checking references and other details, in typing most of our manuscript, and in the performance of difficult editorial work has continuously furthered the completion of our task.

INTRODUCTION

Approximately three-fourths of a million species of insects have so far been described and named, and their number is being gradually increased from year to year. So far as those competent to judge are able to estimate, it seems probable that this number represents perhaps one-fifth or one-tenth of those which actually exist upon our planet at the present time. Their descriptions fill libraries and their final identification requires the knowledge of specialists. Obviously no single volume can provide means for their complete determination, and attempts to deal with selected series of abundant species from particular regions are always disappointing and untrustworthy. It is possible to deal quite fully with the families into which the insects are divided within a reasonable space and it is with their recognition that the present work is concerned.

Identification of the families has been effected by means of analytical keys, which have been arranged as dichotomies. There are also provided similar keys, first for the determination of the classes of Arthropoda, and later others for the determination of the orders of each class. The families are then tabulated under each order. Unless the class or order is known, the student should, therefore, first consult the "Key to Classes of Arthropoda" on page 26. If it be known that the specimen is an insect or an arachnid, or that it surely belongs to a particular class or order, the appropriate key (as indicated in the "Table of Contents") will form the starting point for the work of identification.

Each key contains a number of couplets, or pairs of contrasting statements which indicate clearly two characters or groups of characters, one of which will agree with the specimen in hand. In the first couplet, for example, two contrasting descriptions are given, one of which should agree with the insect to be determined. The number at the end of the line following this description indicates the couplet which should next be studied, and so on until the final name is reached. All the keys have been arranged in this way, as the writers' experience in the classroom shows that specimens can be most easily, rapidly and accurately classified with a key of this type where the contrasting descriptions appear together on the page and may very easily be compared.

Another type of identification key has the pairs of contrasting characters distinguished from other pairs by differences of indention on the page. Keys thus arranged can be constructed to follow natural relationships more closely, but they require much more space for printing and in long keys are exceedingly difficult to follow. We have, therefore, not adopted such an arrangement.

While the dichotomies frequently represent natural relationships or lines of phyletic development, we have not attempted to indicate natural divisions wherever the convenience and practical arrangement of the keys would have been sacrificed. It is at best not convenient to express the natural relationships of animals or plants by any linear arrangement. It may be said, however, that a carefully arranged dichotomy, in most cases, may be made to conform quite closely to such linear arrangement as may seem most appropriate.

The keys present, therefore, to some extent an artificial, as opposed to a natural, sequence, although wherever possible a natural order has been retained. The conspectus of families, on the other hand, aims to present a natural classification as nearly as this can be expressed by a linear sequence. As a linear arrangement is the only one which can be used in a list of this sort, it must be understood that it cannot actually indicate the relationship of the several units by their proximity in the list. We must regard the present fauna as representing a horizontal section of the "phyletic tree" which we see only as a multitudinous series of sections through its twigs and branchlets. The linear arrangement of such a complex cannot even suggest the equally irregular branches to which these twigs were attached in the past. Many of the latter represent extinct groups, and these are far less completely known. They are dealt with separately in a section devoted entirely to a consideration of the families and higher groups that are no longer extant in the living fauna. Knowledge of insect palæontology has advanced rapidly during recent years, but it is necessarily less complete than that relating to living insects and must always remain so. It has greatly improved our insight into the interrelationship of major and minor groups and is destined to clarify our views still further in the future.

There is a very pronounced tendency continually to restrict the extent of families and consequently increase their number. This is greatly deplored by many zoölogists, and regarded as inevitable, if not highly undesirable, by others. The reasons for such a change are manifold. The continual discovery of new forms rapidly increases the number of known species and this in itself merely on the basis of numbers makes it easier to deal with classification if we have a greater number of units of convenient size. The more careful study of anatomical structure frequently leads to the discovery that certain groups are polyphyletic, that is to say, are not of common origin, but represent a convergence or parallelism in the possession of certain closely similar characteristics. If we are to develop a natural classification, such groups must, of course, be divided into a number of smaller families, each easily distinguishable from the others, in fact, more easily characterized than the original large family. Such changes are reasonable and will without doubt be acceptable in the future to all who view them without prejudice. Many such changes represent merely the elevating of groups from subfamily to family rank, and they have been made much more extensively by workers in some groups than in others. For this reason, if for no other, the value of family rank varies in the several groups. There is another reason for such differences which relates to the age of the several groups. Those of greater evolutionary age usually present more constant, clear-cut characters and can be grouped into smaller numbers of families while those now in an active state of evolution or differentiation show so many permutations and intergrades that the value of the family has been cheapened and numerous very closely related series have been accorded family rank. As already indicated we have endeavored to follow the general custom of workers in each group in regard to the number of families that should be recognized at the present time.

The characters useful for the separation of family and other major groups are frequently of very minor nature, due to the fact that characteristics of apparently trivial importance commonly persist over long periods of time, presumably because they are not acted upon by natural selection or other evolutionary factors. The value of such characters is everywhere evident, but in the keys many correlated characters of more noticeable and conspicuous kinds have been added, even though, as indicated, they are not invariably present, and cannot be relied on implicitly. When in the keys such correlation characters are encountered, there is need for judgment in deciding which way to proceed.

Any ideal system of classification should be in accordance with the phylogenetic changes that have occurred during the evolution of the organisms concerned. The importance of this goal is paramount and the efforts of taxonomists to reach it are leading to the gradual disappearance of artificiality in systematics. This is a real advance, but in recent years some taxonomists have assumed, usually for what appear to be good reasons, that definite differential characters cannot be found to distinguish forms which are similar but not genetically related in their phylogeny. When such assumptions are tacitly accepted in the absence of observable differences, it is impossible to translate these conceptions into understandable form for use by others. This is seen frequently in keys where exceptions must be noted, and it presents great, if not insurmountable, difficulties in the practical construction of keys. From a theoretical standpoint, artificial characters are in final analysis only a snare and delusion, but we cannot discard them till better substitutes can be made available. In the keys presented in this volume we have tried to by-pass such dilemmas, but not with complete satisfaction.

As families and other major groups, as well as genera, are concepts and not precepts they are constantly at the mercy of a changing viewpoint and the characters used to define their limits are valid only as accepted by present students. It is hence impossible to standardize the family concept. There are isolated instances where highly specialized students of certain groups have gone literally rampant and have made excessive additions to the number of family designations. Such procedure creates a most unfortunate diversity in the general pattern of classification as it is widely at variance with the views held by other workers in the same or related fields. In some cases where such extravagant changes have been proposed these have been indicated by notations or more lengthy explanations interpolated in the text of the keys.

Even the selection of family names is not done in a uniform way by all entomologists. This is very unfortunate as it leads to the use in some cases of several names for the same group. Thus the family name may be formed from the oldest contained genus, or it may represent the oldest usage, or it may be still another name long in use, but originally formed by neither of the first two methods. We have not been entirely consistent in the selection of these family designations, but have tried to follow the most general present usage in each group. Synonyms that are or have been in general use are given in italic capital letters placed in parentheses just preceding the accepted family names in the keys. If uniformity is ever secured in the use of family names, there will be a number of changes in the ones here used, and the citation of synonyms here must consequently be understood to indicate that there is or has recently been a division in usage. Wherever a family name has been suppressed and the group which it designates has been merged with another, the word "Including" has been added in the parenthesis together with the name thus suppressed.

Over a considerable period of years a sustained effort has been made to secure uniformity in zoological nomenclature. This has been effected through the agency of the International Commission on Zoological Nomenclature, inaugurated and fostered by numerous zoological societies throughout the world. Competing organizations have been established, but their influence has remained at a lower level. The efforts of the International Commission have been applied to priority in nomenclature, validity and dates of publication, homonyms, synonyms, types of families and genera and a host of other matters that enter into nomenclatural practice. The sincere efforts of the Commission have met numerous obstacles imposed by recalcitrant individuals and groups of taxonomists who, like all workers in the natural sciences, are loath to accept ex-cathedral pronouncements emanating from any source. This, coupled with the discovery of old, long-forgotten taxonomic papers whose contents reveal the necessity of changes in generic and family names has caused a serious confusion which does not quickly subside. More recently the resurrection of previously discarded names where these cannot be validated by accepted rules, has aroused further opposition. It is not possible to predict the outcome, but fortunately these matters are of minor import in the present volume since we have consistently tried to reflect current usage in each group, and to cite also any alternate designations that are frequently encountered in the literature.

The International Zoological Commission was established to stabilize nomenclature, but because of the difficulty of arriving at decisions in some instances it has permitted uncertainty to prevail. Notably is this apparent in the case of Meigen's 1800 paper,[1] which affects the families of various Diptera. Meigen wrote this early paper in French for the use of amateur entomologists, noting the names of eighty-eight genera he knew, many of which he coined for the occasion. The names were accompanied by an extremely brief description, but nowhere were species cited by name; merely the number of species was announced as known to Meigen.

Three years later he published a generic account of one hundred and fourteen genera,[2] this time in German, changing the names of many of the previous genera. These two papers become particularly important to us in that many of the cited names are the type-genera of families or subfamilies. Meigen himself made no reference to his first paper in any of his later writings.

The early work became forgotten. Only five or six copies are now known to exist. However, one copy fell into the hands of Friedrich Hendel, who reprinted it, and with the aid of Meigen's 1803 paper, resurrected many of the earlier and discarded names. Hendel's publication started a series of protests among systematic dipterists, many of whom felt that the principle of conservation should prevent a wholesale adoption of names, latent for more than a century. J. M. Aldrich referred the matter to the International Commission on Nomenclature, which in a series of Opinions has ruled that the 1800 paper was actually published, that both were written by J. W. Meigen, that the names proposed were binomial and hence valid, and that it was for dipterists themselves to pass upon their recognition. However, the adoption of some of the names in the 1800 paper will not settle the issue. Already the Commission is considering the abandonment of five of Meigen's early names, of which four are the types of families. To show that great uncertainty exists we have cited those families which would date from the 1800 paper, together with the customarily used name, giving both in bold-face type.[3]

[1] J. G. Meigen. Nouvelle classification des mouches à deux ailes. 40 pp. Paris (1800).

[2] J. W. Meigen. Versuch einer neuen Gattungseintheilung der europäischen zweiflügligen Insekten. Illiger's Magazin, 2, pp. 259–281 (1803).

[3] The families involved are the following, the first name of each pair derived from type genera of Meigen's 1800 paper, the second from his 1803 paper. Three of the names (Simuliidæ, Scenopinidæ and Pipunculidæ) date from Latreille's Histoire Naturelle, 1802.

Liriopeidæ, Ptychopteridæ; Tendipedidæ, Chironomidæ; Heleidæ, Ceratopogonidæ; Melusinidæ, Simuliidæ; Fungivoridæ, Mycetophilidæ; Euphrosynidæ, Macroceridæ; Lycoriidæ, Sciaridæ; Itonididæ, Cecidomyiidæ; Erinnidæ, Xylophagidæ; Omphralidæ, Scenopinidæ; Musidoridæ, Lonchopteridæ; Clythiidæ, Platypezidæ; Dorilaidæ, Pipunculidæ; Larvævoridæ, Tachinidæ; Euribiidæ, Trypetidæ; Titaniidæ, Chloropidæ.

This list does not include fourteen subfamilies nor ten genera which are not types of families.

A short, selected list of genera is given for most families. These represent large or important genera, those characteristic of particular regions or those containing common or important species. In most cases the geographical range is given in greatly abbreviated form. The following abbreviations have been used, all of which should be easily understood without explanation: cosmop., cosmopolitan; tropicopol., tropicopolitan; Holarc., Holarctic (northern hemisphere); Palæarc., Palæarctic (Europe and northern Asia); Nearc., Nearctic (America, north of Mexico); Neotrop., Neotropical (America, south of the United States); Am., new world; Ethiop., Ethiopian (Africa, south of the Sahara); Ind., India; Indomal., Indomalayan (India and east Indian Islands); Austr., Australian. A few variants of these, as Indoaustr. and Malay., need no explanation. Where genera occur in most of the regions named or in several widely separated ones, their range is indicated as widespr., widespread.

A number of vernacular names for common or important species or groups are given from place to place, enclosed in parentheses. These are mainly ones that are actually in use among persons not acquainted with entomology, although certain others that have been adopted by the American Association of Economic Entomologists as designations for specific insects are listed also. However, no attempt has been made to include a great many that are newly coined, cumbersome, or otherwise of such origin or formation that they may never be expected to come into general popular use as vernacular names.

In addition to the keys to families we have added a considerable number of keys which serve to distinguish the subfamilies of many of the more important or extensive families. These are printed in more condensed form than the family keys and the couplets are numbered a, b, c, etc. to distinguish them from the main keys in which they are inserted next to the family to which they pertain. Thus, although inserted directly into the family keys they remain entirely independent so far as couplet numbers are concerned.

In all cases we have endeavored to cite the family names in exact form. Family names are by rule formed by adding the suffix "idæ" to the Latin or Latinized stem of the name of the type genus, and subfamilies uniformly end in "inæ." The compound when thus formed should properly include all of the stem. Unless attention is given to the declension of such words according to Latin rules, errors may occur and unfortunately a few incorrectly formed family names have been used from time to time in publications, sometimes over long periods. We have attempted to correct all such errors of orthography, and trust that we have not overlooked any others. Thus family names based on generic names ending in -cera or -cerus become -ceridæ; in -ceros become -cerotidæ, etc. The names of superfamilies have been consistently treated in a similar way, by adding -oidea to the Latin stem of the name of the type genus of the typical family name. No fixed rule is generally accepted for the formation of group names and we have not always corrected the spelling of such names. Whether well established names should be emended is certainly open to question on the basis of long usage.

The pronunciation of all family, group and generic names is indicated in the text, following a very simple and quite satisfactory method which was apparently first used by Asa Gray in 1848 in the first edition of his "Text Book of Botany." Later revisions of Gray's manual have continued the same method but for some reason it has not been very generally adopted by others. An accent mark is placed over the vowel in the accented syllable, thus indicating whether the accent should be placed on the penultimate or antepenultimate syllable. A long vowel is indicated by a grave accent (*e.g.* è, È) and a short vowel by an acute accent (*e.g.* é, É). Thus with the length of the important vowel and the accent indicated, the word may be pronounced with small chance of error. Usage is not consistent in the pronunciation of the character "oi" which occurs in the names of superfamilies, etc. We are advocating the sound given to the diphthong in the word "coin," rather than the pronunciation of the two vowels separately. The difficulty of indicating this by means of accented type has led us to mark the diphthong oi with a grave accent over the "o," thus: òi, ÒI.

As the names are regarded as Latin, the rules for the pronunciation of Latin words are followed, although most generic and family names are actually of Greek derivation. Many new Latin words or those of non-classical origin have to be treated by analogy, for example, those based on the names of entomologists (Winthemia, after Winthem, Meigenia, after Meigen). In some cases, where names do not readily lend themselves to Latin pronunciation, none is indicated. One of the authors has already dealt at some length with the rules governing the pronunciation of insect names.[4]

A selected list of literature on the classification of insects and the other arthropods dealt with in the present volume is included in the text. This is intended to introduce the student to the taxonomic literature as completely as is possible in the space which could be devoted to that purpose and since the amount of published material is enormous, only those papers which may be most generally useful have been cited. During the past thirty years, approximately 100,000 separate publications on pure entomology have been issued, by far the greater part of these dealing with taxonomy. Many other earlier monographs and synopses have not yet been supplanted, either wholly or in part by more recent studies.

[4] A. L. Melander. The Pronunciation of Insect Names. Bull. Brooklyn Ent. Soc., **11**, pp. 93–101 (1916); Sourcebook of Biological Terms. Coll. City of New York, 157 pp. (1937). See also: E. C. Jaeger. Source-book of Biological Names and Terms. C. C. Thomas, 256 pp. (1944); R. S. Woods. Naturalist's Lexicon. Abbey Garden Press, 282 pp. (1944).

It has, therefore, not been an easy task to determine exactly what ought to be included in such a list. In general we have listed monographs, revisions or synopses of families and larger groups, relating to the fauna of the whole world, or to extensive regions. Often such treatments relating to quite restricted areas are cited where the circumstances seem to warrant their inclusion. Similar publications relating to subfamilies or smaller groups in some cases appear in the lists also where the abundance or importance of the groups concerned render them of special interest. Large works relating to the faunas of extensive regions are included and to some extent the parts of such works are listed separately under the several groups for more ready reference. In general, papers of less than ten pages have not been included.

Catalogues and bibliographies are cited rather extensively as they serve to introduce the student to the smaller, highly specialized papers which he will find it necessary to consult for the serious study of any particular group. The literature of some of the larger orders like the Coleoptera, Lepidoptera and Diptera has been more frequently listed than that of the other groups and here we have generally restricted the citations to the most useful works, catalogues, bibliographies and those containing keys for the identification of genera and species. Almost no references to papers containing only scattered descriptions or very incomplete synopses are included since these will be found by an examination of the catalogues and specialized bibliographies.

In many instances long titles have been abbreviated or paraphrased to save space and to render the scanning of the lists easier, but we have tried in all cases to do this in such a way as not to interfere with the usefulness of the lists, for the present purpose. The references are given with sufficient completeness to insure the ready location of each paper.

Several languages are necessarily represented, although nearly all of the papers cited are in one of the widely used languages, *i.e.* English, German, French, Italian, Latin, Spanish or Portuguese. The language of the individual papers may be ascertained from the titles, which although abbreviated are usually given in the language used by the author.

The literature relating to each order is inserted at the end of the keys of that order. In the case of the larger orders, general references are placed together, followed by other lists relating to superfamilies or other groups as indicated in each case, and every individual list is arranged in alphabetical order by authors. The more general works relating to more than a single order are placed at the end of the key to the Orders of Insects on page 38. The literature relating to the Arachnida and other groups of terrestrial arthropods is arranged in a similar way, in parts following the several keys.

It is impossible to avoid the use of highly technical terms, but we have reduced their number as greatly as clarity permits. A special glossary will be found on page 829, containing definitions of such special terms as are not defined in the text or by reference to figures, or of those that cannot be readily understood by the use of a good dictionary. The nomenclature applied to the body parts, wings, veins, etc., is that used generally in the literature, and represents the current usage in each group. Until quite recently the workers in nearly every group of insects made use of special terminologies for the wing-veins but within the last several decades a more or less uniform system of nomenclature is coming into use. This change has been adopted in the present book as representing the most rational method. In the order Hymenoptera this system is cumbersome and confusing and the current empirical system in use by students of this order has been adopted. The student will, however, encounter some difficulties in consulting the older, and even some of the more recent, treatises and papers. Unfortunately this change is one that cannot be avoided.

The equipment necessary for the identification of specimens of insects is quite simple and inexpensive, at least that required for the study of the larger species. Extremely small forms present greater difficulties on account of the very minute size of the structures which must be examined.

For species of moderate or large size, all that is necessary to observe most structural details is a good hand lens. This should be preferably one having a rating of 12x or 14x magnification. Several types of such lenses are made. The best, known as an achromatic triplet, which gives a clear, sharp image, is made of three lenses cemented together into a single piece. Such a lens may be purchased for about ten or twelve dollars, or a pair, giving 8x and 12x magnification respectively, mounted in a single holder for about fifteen dollars. Cheaper types, known as Coddingtons or doublets may be purchased at much lower prices, but their optical properties are comparatively poor and they are very unsatisfactory, except for examining large or very flat structures. For small insects and for others as well, a binocular microscope is the most satisfactory. Such an instrument, provided with two or three paired objectives and two pairs of eyepieces made by any of several first class manufacturers may be purchased for $250 or slightly more.

As a rule no special method of preparation is necessary since most of the characters made use of in the keys are readily observed on dried pinned specimens. However, in a few cases some previous treatment is necessary. The wings of Lepidoptera must usually be freed from their scaly covering before the venation can be made out. For this, they may be soaked in *eau de Javelle*, or some commercial chlorinated bleach sold for laundry use, to loosen the scales which may then be removed by a camel's hair brush, after which they may be dehydrated, cleared and mounted in balsam or varnish, on slides. Certain small insects such as Thysanoptera may also be mounted very satisfactorily on slides in balsam or spar varnish, preferably the latter as it does not clear transparent structures so completely. Scale insects should be boiled in a solution of caustic potash, washed, dehydrated, cleared and mounted in the same way to show the minute structures upon which these insects are classified. Minute Diptera should be mounted on "double mounts," *i.e.* a blotter 5 x 8 mm. carries a minuten nadel at one end and a #1 insect pin at the other. The blotter is coated with clear white shellac varnish to fuse the pins.

For the methods of collecting, preparing and preserving insects the reader is referred to Dr. H. H. Ross' "How to Collect and Preserve Insects" (Illinois Nat. Hist. Surv. Circ., no. 39, pp. 1–55, figs. 1–63; 1944) or similar publications. Special collecting techniques are discussed in detail in Banks' "Directions for Collecting and Preserving Insects" (Bull. U. S. Nat. Mus., no. 67, pp. 1–135, figs. 1–188; 1909). Instructions for the preparation of chitinous structures for study are contained in Lee's "Microtomist's Vade-Mecum" (Blakiston and Co., 11th edit., 1950), as well as in other less inclusive and pretentious works.

Part I

INSECTA

CONSPECTUS OF THE HIGHER GROUPS OF INSECTA

Subclass **APTERYGOTA**

Order **PROTURA**
(Eosentomidæ, Acerentomidæ, Protentomidæ)

Order **THYSANURA**
MACHILOIDEA (Machilidæ, Meinertellidæ)
LEPISMATOIDEA (Nicoletiidæ, Lepismatidæ)

Order **ENTOTROPHI**
CAMPODEOIDEA (Campodeidæ)
JAPYGOIDEA (Japygidæ, Projapygidæ)

Order **COLLEMBOLA**
Suborder **Arthropleona** (Hypogastruridæ, Entomobryidæ, Actaletidæ, Tomoceridæ, Isotomidæ, Poduridæ, Oncopoduridæ)
Suborder **Symphypleona** (Sminthuridæ, Dicyrtomidæ, Neelidæ)

Subclass **PTERYGOTA**

Order **PLECTOPTERA**
EPHEMEROIDEA (Palingeniidæ, Polymitarcidæ, Ephemeridæ, Potamanthidæ, Prosopistomatidæ)
BAETOIDEA (Baetidæ, Caenidæ, Leptophlebiidæ, Ephemerellidæ, Oligoneuridæ)
SIPHLUROIDEA (Baetiscidæ, Siphluridæ, Ametropodidæ, Heptageniidæ)

Order **ODONATA**
Suborder **Zygoptera**
COENAGRIONOIDEA (Protoneuridæ, Coenagrionidæ, Synlestidæ, Megapodagrionidæ, Lestidæ, Pseudostigmatidæ, Lestoideidæ, Platystictidæ, Platycnemididæ)
AGRIONOIDEA (Amphipterygidæ, Chlorocyphidæ, Epallagidæ, Polythoridæ, Agrionidæ, Heliocharitidæ)
HEMIPHLEBIOIDEA (Hemiphlebiidæ)
Suborder **Anisozygoptera**
EPIOPHLEBIOIDEA (Epiophlebiidæ)
Suborder **Anisoptera**
ÆSHNOIDEA (Petaluridæ, Gomphidæ, Cordulegastridæ, Æshnidæ)
LIBELLULOIDEA (Corduliidæ, Libellulidæ)

Order **PLECOPTERA**
(Perlidæ, Pteronarcidæ, Eustheniidæ, Austroperlidæ, Peltoperlidæ, Leptoperlidæ, Capniidæ, Nemouridæ, Leuctridæ, Tæniopterygidæ)

Order **BLATTARIA**

PHYLLODROMIOIDEA (Blaberidæ, Oxyhaloidæ, Panchloridæ, Epilampridæ, Nyctiboridæ, Perisphæriidæ, Diplopteridæ, Panesthiidæ, Cryptocercidæ, Phyllodromiidæ, Areolariidæ, Chorisoneuridæ, Ectobiidæ, Nothoblattidæ, Attaphilidæ)

BLATTOIDEA (Blattidæ, Archiblattidæ, Nocticolidæ, Oulopterygidæ)

CORYDIOIDEA (Latindiidæ, Homœogamiidæ, Polyphagidæ, Corydiidæ, Atticolidæ, Euthyrrhaphidæ)

Order **ORTHOPTERA**

Suborder **Manteodea** (Manteidæ)

Suborder **Grylloblattodea** (Grylloblattidæ)

Suborder **Saltatoria**

TETTIGONIOIDEA (Tettigoniidæ, Gryllacridæ, Gryllidæ, Myrmecophilidæ, Œcanthidæ, Mogoplistidæ, Trigonidiidæ, Eneopteridæ, Stenopelmatidæ, Phasmodidæ)

TRIDACTYLOIDEA (Gryllotalpidæ, Tridactylidæ, Cylindrachetidæ)

ACRIDOIDEA (Acrididæ, Tetrigidæ, Proscopiidæ)

PNEUMOROIDEA (Pneumoridæ)

Suborder **Phasmatodea**

PHASMATOIDEA (Bacillidæ, Phyllidæ, Phasmatidæ)

BACTERIOIDEA (Bacunculidæ, Bacteriidæ, Timemidæ)

Order **DERMAPTERA**

Suborder **Forficulina**

PROTODERMAPTERA

PYGIDICRANOIDEA (Echinosomatidæ, Pyragridæ, Pygidicranidæ, Karschiellidæ, Anatæliidæ, Diplatyidæ)

PARADERMAPTERA

APACHYOIDEA (Apachyidæ)

LABIDUROIDEA (Platylabiidæ, Allostethidæ, Esphalmenidæ, Psalididæ, Labiduridæ, Parisolabidæ, Brachylabidæ)

EUDERMAPTERA

LABIOIDEA (Pericomidæ, Nesogastridæ, Vandicidæ, Strongylopsalididæ, Sparattidæ, Spongiphoridæ, Labiidæ)

FORFICULOIDEA (Chelisochidæ, Cheliduridæ, Anechuridæ, Forficulidæ, Eudohrniidæ, Neolobophoridæ, Ancistrogastridæ, Opisthocosmiidæ, Diaperasticidæ)

Suborder **Arixenina** (Arixeniidæ)

Suborder **Diploglossata** (Hemimeridæ)

Order **EMBIODEA**

(Anisembiidæ, Oligotomidæ, Teratembiidæ, Embiidæ, Clothodidæ, Oligembiidæ, Notoligotomidæ)

Order **ISOPTERA**

(Mastotermitidæ, Calotermitidæ, Termopsidæ, Hodotermitidæ, Rhinotermitidæ, Termitidæ)

Order **CORRODENTIA**

Suborder **Parapsocida** (Phyllipsocidæ, Perientomidæ, Lepidopsocidæ, Psoquillidæ, Atropidæ, Liposcelidæ, Archipsocidæ)

Suborder **Eupsocida** (Mesopsocidæ, Myopsocidæ, Cæciliidæ, Psocidæ, Amphientomidæ, Thyrsophoridæ)

Order **ZORAPTERA**
  (Zorotypidæ)
Order **MALLOPHAGA**
  Suborder **Amblycera** (Gyropidæ, Boopiidæ, Trimenoponidæ, Menoponidæ, Læmobothridæ, Ricinidæ, Heptapsogastridæ)
  Suborder **Ischnocera** (Trichodectidæ, Trichophilopteridæ, Nesiotinidæ, Philopteridæ, Dasyonygidæ)
Order **THYSANOPTERA**
  Suborder **Terebrantia**
    Æolothripoidea (Æolothripidæ, Orothripidæ, Melanothripidæ, Franklinothripidæ, Mymarothripidæ)
    Thripoidea (Heterothripidæ, Thripidæ, Panchætothripidæ, Ceratothripidæ, Merothripidæ)
  Suborder **Tubulifera**
    Phlœothripoidea (Phlœothripidæ, Ecacanthothripidæ, Eupatithripidæ, Pygothripidæ, Hystrichothripidæ, Megathripidæ, Idolothripidæ, Chirothripoididæ)
    Urothripoidea (Urothripidæ)
Order **HEMIPTERA**
  Suborder **Homoptera**
    AUCHENORRHYNCHA
    Cicadoidea (Cicadidæ)
    Membracoidea (Membracidæ)
    Cercopoidea (Machærotidæ, Tomaspididæ, Clastopteridæ, Cercopidæ)
    Jassoidea (Tettigellidæ, Gyponidæ, Penthimiidæ, Thaumastoscopidæ, Ledridæ, Bythoscopidæ, Jassidæ, Paropiidæ, Stenocotidæ, Kœbeliidæ, Ulopidæ, Nirvanidæ, Signoretiidæ, Euacanthidæ, Pythamidæ, Æthialoniidæ, Macropsidæ, Agalliidæ)
    Fulgoroidea (Tettigometridæ, Cixiidæ, Areopodidæ, Derbidæ, Achilixiidæ, Meenoplidæ, Kinnaridæ, Dictyopharidæ, Fulgoridæ, Achilidæ, Tropiduchidæ, Nogodinidæ, Flatidæ, Acanaloniidæ, Issidæ, Ricaniidæ, Lophopidæ, Eurybrachidæ)
    STERNORRHYNCHA
    Chermoidea (Chermidæ)
    Aleyrodoidea (Aleyrodidæ)
    Aphidoidea (Aphididæ, Eriosomatidæ, Phylloxeridæ, Adelgidæ)
    Coccoidea (Ortheziidæ, Monophlebidæ, Diaspididæ, Conchaspididæ, Lecaniidæ, Lacciferidæ, Apiomorphidæ, Asterolecaniidæ, Phenacoleachiidæ, Coccidæ, Cylindrococcidæ, Eriococcidæ, Kermesidæ)
    COLEORRHYNCHA (Peloridiidæ, Pleidæ)
  Suborder **Heteroptera**
    GYMNOCERATA
    Scutelleroidea (Corimelænidæ, Plataspididæ, Cydnidæ, Scutelleridæ, Pentatomidæ, Podopidæ, Tahitocoridæ)
    Coreoidea (Corizidæ, Coreidæ, Alydidæ)
    Gerroidea (Gerridæ, Veliidæ)
    Aradoidea (Isodermidæ, Aradidæ, Termatophylidæ, Dysodiidæ,

Saldidæ, Thaumastotheriidæ, Mesoveliidæ, Hebridæ, Hydrometridæ, Leotichidæ)

LYGÆOIDEA (Lygæidæ, Hyocephalidæ, Neididæ, Colobothristidæ, Pyrrhocoridæ, Macroveliidæ)

TINGOIDEA (Piesmidæ, Tingidæ)

REDUVIOIDEA (Henicocephalidæ, Phymatidæ, Reduviidæ, Ploiariidæ, Nabidæ, Joppeicidæ)

POLYCTENOIDEA (Polyctenidæ)

CIMICOIDEA (Aepophilidæ, Cimicidæ, Velocipedidæ, Anthocoridæ, Miridæ, Microphysidæ, Isometopidæ, Leptopodidæ)

DIPSOCOROIDEA (Dipsocoridæ, Schizopteridæ)

HELOTREPHOIDEA (Helotrephidæ)

CRYPTOCERATA (Nerthridæ, Ochteridæ, Naucoridæ, Nepidæ, Belostomatidæ, Notonectidæ, Corixidæ, Termitaphididæ)

Order **ANOPLURA** (Hæmatomyzidæ, Echinophthiriidæ, Hæmatopinidæ, Hæmatopinoididæ, Pediculidæ, Phthiriidæ, Neolignathidæ)

Order **NEUROPTERA**

Suborder **Sialodea** (Corydalidæ, Sialidæ)

Suborder **Raphidiodea** (Raphidiidæ, Inoceliidæ)

Suborder **Planipennia**

ITHONOIDEA (Ithonidæ)

HEMEROBIOIDEA (Hemerobiidæ, Sympherobiidæ, Dilaridæ, Psychopsidæ, Osmylidæ, Polystœchotidæ, Sisyridæ, Chrysopidæ, Apochrysidæ, Berothidæ, Trichomatidæ, Mantispidæ)

NEMOPTEROIDEA (Nemopteridæ)

MYRMELEONTOIDEA (Myiodactylidæ, Nymphidæ, Myrmeleontidæ, Stilbopterygidæ, Ascalaphidæ)

CONIOPTERYGOIDEA (Coniopterygidæ)

Order **MECOPTERA**

Suborder **Protomecoptera** (Notiothaumidæ, Meropeidæ)

Suborder **Eumecoptera** (Panorpidæ, Boreidæ, Bittacidæ)

Order **TRICHOPTERA**

Suborder **Æquipalpia**

RHYACOPHILOIDEA (Rhyacophilidæ, Philopotamidæ, Polycentropodidæ, Hydropsychidæ, Psychomyiidæ, Xiphocentronidæ, Calamoceratidæ, Odontoceridæ, Leptoceridæ, Molannidæ, Beræidæ)

HYDROPTILOIDEA (Hydroptilidæ)

Suborder **Inæquipalpia**

PHRYGANOIDEA (Phryganeidæ, Limnephilidæ, Brachycentridæ, Lepidostomatidæ, Helicopsychidæ, Goeridæ)

SERICOSTOMATOIDEA (Sericostomatidæ)

Order **LEPIDOPTERA**

Suborder **Homoneura**

MICROPTERYGOIDEA (Micropterygidæ)

ERIOCRANIOIDEA (Eriocraniidæ, Mnesarchæidæ, Neopseustidæ)

HEPIALOIDEA (Hepialidæ, Prototheoridæ, Palæosetidæ)

Suborder **Heteroneura**

Division MONOTRYSIA

NEPTICULOIDEA (Nepticulidæ, Œnophilidæ, Tischeriidæ)

INCURVARIOIDEA (Incurvariidæ, Prodoxidæ, Adelidæ, Heliozelidæ)
Division DITRYSIA
COSSOIDEA (Cossidæ)
TINEOIDEA (Tineidæ, Setomorphidæ, Amydriidæ, Acrolophidæ, Ashinagidæ, Psychidæ, Plutellidæ, Lyonetiidæ, Opostegidæ, Amphitheridæ, Epermeniidæ, Gracilariidæ, Coleophoridæ, Yponomeutidæ, Acrolepiidæ, Argyresthiidæ, Cyclotornidæ, Scythrididæ, Douglasiidæ, Elachistidæ, Epimarptidæ, Glyphipterygidæ, Heliodinidæ, Ægeriidæ, Phyllocnistidæ, Blastobasidæ, Orneodidæ, Anomologidæ, Metachandidæ, Xylorictidæ, Stenomidæ, Strepsimanidæ, Œcophoridæ, Cosmopterygidæ, Cecidosetidæ, Ridiaschinidæ, Agonoxenidæ, Hyposmocomidæ, Gelechiidæ)
TORTRICOIDEA (Tortricidæ, Chlidanotidæ, Phaloniidæ, Olethreutidæ, Carposinidæ)
ZYGÆNOIDEA (Eucleidæ, Epipyropidæ, Chrysopolomidæ, Megalopygidæ, Zygænidæ, Pyromorphidæ, Charideidæ, Heterogynidæ)
CASTNIOIDEA (Castniidæ)
PYRALIDOIDEA (Oxychirotidæ, Pterophoridæ, Thyrididæ, Pyralididæ, Hyblæidæ)
GEOMETROIDEA (Geometridæ, Uraniidæ, Epiplemidæ, Epicopeiidæ, Apoprogenidæ, Sematuridæ, Drepanidæ, Thyatiridæ, Axiidæ)
CALLIDULOIDEA (Callidulidæ, Pterothysanidæ)
BOMBYCOIDEA (Mimallonidæ, Ratardidæ, Bombycidæ, Eupterotidæ, Lemoniidæ, Brahmæidæ, Oxytenididæ, Cerophanidæ, Saturniidæ, Endromididæ, Lasiocampidæ)
SPHINGOIDEA (Sphingidæ)
NOCTUOIDEA (Noctuidæ, Agaristidæ, Lithosiidæ, Arctiidæ, Nyctemeridæ, Nolidæ, Ctenuchidæ, Notodontidæ, Dioptidæ, Lymantriidæ, Anthelidæ)
HESPERIOIDEA (Hesperiidæ)
PAPILIONOIDEA (Papilionidæ, Pieridæ, Lycænidæ, Riodinidæ, Libytheidæ, Danaidæ, Satyridæ, Amathusiidæ, Morphoidæ, Nymphalidæ)

Order **DIPTERA**
Suborder **Nematocera**
TIPULIMORPHA
TIPULOIDEA (Petauristidæ, Tipulidæ, Cylindrotomidæ, Limoniidæ)
PSYCHOMORPHA
PSYCHODOIDEA (Tanyderidæ, Ptychopteridæ or Liriopeidæ, Psychodidæ)
CULICOIDEA (Corethridæ, Culicidæ, Dixidæ)
CHIRONOMOIDEA or TENDIPEDOIDEA (Chironomidæ or Tendipedidæ, Ceratopogonidæ or Heleidæ, Thaumaleidæ, Simuliidæ or Melusinidæ)
BLEPHAROCEROIDEA (Blepharoceridæ, Deuterophlebiidæ, Nymphomyiidæ)
SILVICOLOMORPHA
SILVICOLOIDEA (Silvicolidæ, Mycetobiidæ)
MYCETOPHILOIDEA or FUNGIVOROIDEA (Mycetophilidæ or Fungivori-

dæ, Allactoneuridæ, Ceroplatidæ, Macroceridæ or Euphrosynidæ, Ditomyiidæ, Diadocidiidæ, Bolitophilidæ, Sciophilidæ, Lygistorhinidæ, Manotidæ, Sciaridæ or Lycoriidæ)

CECIDOMYOIDEA or ITONIDOIDEA (Cecidomyiidæ or Itonididæ)

BIBIONOIDEA (Hesperinidæ, Pachyneuridæ, Bibionidæ, Scatopsidæ, Corynoscelidæ)

Suborder **Brachycera**

Division ORTHORRHAPHA

RHAGIOMORPHA

STRATIOMYIOIDEA (Xylophagidæ or Erinnidæ, Cœnomyiidæ, Solvidæ, Stratiomyiidæ, Chiromyzidæ)

RHAGIONOIDEA (Rhagionidæ, Hilarimorphidæ)

TABANOIDEA (Tabanidæ, Pantophthalmidæ)

THEREVOMORPHA

THEREVOIDEA (Therevidæ, Scenopinidæ or Omphralidæ)

ASILOIDEA (Mydaidæ, Apioceridæ, Asilidæ)

BOMBYLIOIDEA (Bombyliidæ, Nemestrinidæ, Acroceridæ)

EMPIDIDOIDEA (Empididæ, Dolichopodidæ)

Division CYCLORRHAPHA

Series ASCHIZA

PHOROMORPHA

LONCHOPTEROIDEA or MUSIDOROIDEA (Lonchopteridæ or Musidoridæ)

PHOROIDEA (Phoridæ, Termitoxeniidæ, Thaumatoxenidæ)

SYRPHOMORPHA

PLATYPEZOIDEA or CLYTHIOIDEA (Platypezidæ or Clythiidæ, Sciadoceridæ)

SYRPHOIDEA (Pipunculidæ or Dorylaidæ, Syrphidæ, Conopidæ)

Series SCHIZOPHORA

Section MYODARIA

Subsection CALYPTRATÆ (Thecostomata)

MUSCOMORPHA

MUSCOIDEA (Calliphoridæ, Sarcophagidæ, Rhinophoridæ; Tachinidæ or Larvævoridæ, Dexiidæ, Phasiidæ; Muscidæ, Glossinidæ, Anthomyiidæ, Cordyluridæ; Œstridæ, Hypodermatidæ, Cuterebridæ, Gasterophilidæ)

Subsection ACALYPTRATÆ (Haplostomata)

OTIDIMORPHA

TYLOIDEA (Tanypezidæ, Tylidæ, Neriidæ, Nothybidæ)

OTITOIDEA (Pyrgotidæ, Platystomatidæ, Richardiidæ, Phytalmiidæ, Pterocallidæ, Otitidæ, Ulidiidæ; Trypetidæ or Euribiidæ; Tachiniscidæ, Lonchæidæ, Pallopteridæ)

SCIOMYZOMORPHA

SCIOMYZOIDEA (Sciomyzidæ, Dryomyzidæ, Neottiophilidæ, Rhopalomeridæ, Rhinotoridæ)

SEPSOIDEA (Sepsidæ, Piophilidæ, Thyreophoridæ, Megamerinidæ; Diopsidæ; Psilidæ)

LAUXANIOMORPHA

LAUXANIOIDEA (Lauxaniidæ, Celyphidæ, Chamæmyiidæ)

HELOMYZOIDEA (Cœlopidæ, Helomyzidæ, Trixoscelidæ, Chyromyiidæ)

ANTHOMYZOIDEA (Clusiidæ, Anthomyzidæ, Opomyzidæ)

DROSOPHILOMORPHA

DROSOPHILOIDEA (Drosophilidæ, Diastatidæ, Astiidæ, Periscelididæ, Aulacogastridæ, Cnemospathidæ)

EPHYDROIDEA (Canaceidæ, Ephydridæ, Tethinidæ; Sphæroceridæ, Leptoceridæ, Mormotomyiidæ; Chloropidæ)

MILICHIOIDEA (Agromyzidæ, Odiniidæ, Cryptochætidæ, Carnidæ, Milichiidæ)

Section PUPIPARA

BRAULOIDEA (Braulidæ, Nycteribiidæ)

HIPPOBOSCOIDEA (Hippoboscidæ, Streblidæ)

Order **SIPHONAPTERA**
(Stephanocircidæ, Ischnopsyllidæ, Dolichopsyllidæ, Hystrichopsyllidæ, Pulicidæ, Hectopsyllidæ, Tungidæ)

Order **COLEOPTERA**

Suborder **Adephaga**

CARABOIDEA (Cicindelidæ, Carabidæ, Amphizoidæ, Hygrobiidæ, Haliplidæ, Dytiscidæ)

GYRINOIDEA (Gyrinidæ)

CUPOIDEA (Cupidæ)

RHYSODOIDEA (Rhysodidæ, Jacobsoniidæ)

Suborder **Polyphaga**

HYDROPHILOIDEA (Hydrophilidæ, Hydroscaphidæ)

STAPHYLINOIDEA (Silphidæ, Thorictidæ, Sphæritidæ, Leptinidæ, Clambidæ, Scaphidiidæ, Scydmænidæ, Brathinidæ, Staphylinidæ, Platypsyllidæ, Pselaphidæ, Clavigeridæ, Micropeplidæ, Limulodidæ)

CUCUJOIDEA (Cucujidæ, Parandridæ, Helotidæ, Passandridæ, Silvanidæ)

CANTHAROIDEA (Lampyridæ, Cantharidæ, Lycidæ, Drilidæ, Lymexylidæ, Micromalthidæ, Atractoceridæ, Telegeusidæ, Dasytidæ, Malachiidæ, Cleridæ, Corynetidæ)

MORDELLOIDEA (Cephaloidæ, Œdemeridæ, Mordellidæ, Rhipiphoridæ, Meloidæ, Eurystethidæ, Pythidæ, Pyrochroidæ, Pedilidæ, Anthicidæ, Aderidæ, Hemipeplidæ)

ELATEROIDEA (Cerophytidæ, Cebrionidæ, Plastoceridæ, Rhipiceridæ, Elateridæ, Melasidæ, Throscidæ, Buprestidæ)

DRYOPOIDEA (Psephenidæ, Dryopidæ, Elmidæ, Heteroceridæ, Georyssidæ)

DASCYLLOIDEA (Dascyllidæ, Helodidæ, Chelonariidæ, Dermestidæ, Byturidæ, Byrrhidæ, Nosodendridæ, Ptinidæ, Ectrephidæ, Gnostidæ, Eucinetidæ, Limnichidæ, Brachyspectridæ, Hypocephalidæ)

HISTEROIDEA (Histeridæ, Niponiidæ, Synteliidæ)

COLYDIOIDEA (Colydiidæ, Murmidiidæ, Ostomatidæ, Monotomidæ, Crytophagidæ, Nitidulidæ, Brachypteridæ, Cybocephalidæ, Rhizophagidæ, Ciidæ, Mycetophagidæ, Erotylidæ, Languriidæ, Cato-

pochrotidæ, Phalacridæ, Lyctidæ, Anobiidæ, Bostrichidæ, Lathridiidæ, Smicripidæ, Derodontidæ, Endomychidæ, Mycetæidæ, Coccinellidæ, Orthoperidæ, Phænocephalidæ, Sphæriidæ, Ptiliidæ,
Hydroscaphidæ, Discolomidæ, Cyathoceridæ, Aculognathidæ,
Monœdidæ, Diphyllidæ)

TENEBRIONOIDEA (Tenebrionidæ, Cossyphodidæ, Cistelidæ, Petriidæ,
Lagriidæ, Elacatidæ, Nilionidæ, Sphindidæ, Serropalpidæ, Scraptiidæ, Monommatidæ, Trictenotomidæ)

CERAMBYCOIDEA (Prionidæ, Lamiidæ, Cerambycidæ, Donaciidæ,
Megascelidæ, Sagridæ, Crioceridæ, Cryptocephalidæ, Chlamisidæ,
Megalopodidæ, Clytridæ, Chrysomelidæ, Lamprosomatidæ, Eu-
molpidæ, Galerucidæ, Alticidæ, Hispidæ, Cassididæ, Bruchidæ)

CURCULIONOIDEA (Brenthidæ, Cyladidæ, Nemonychidæ, Curculionidæ, Platypodidæ, Chapuisiidæ, Scolytidæ, Scolytoplatypodidæ,
Ipidæ, Anthribidæ, Aglycyderidæ, Proterhinidæ)

SCARABÆOIDEA (Passalidæ, Lucanidæ, Sinodendridæ, Trogidæ, Scarabæidæ, Geotrupidæ, Pleocomidæ, Glaphyridæ, Orphnidæ, Ochodæidæ, Hybosoridæ, Aphodiidæ, Ægialiidæ, Melolonthidæ, Euchiridæ, Rutelidæ, Pachypodidæ, Dynastidæ, Phænomeridæ, Cetoniidæ, Trichiidæ, Acanthoceridæ)

Order STREPSIPTERA

MENGEOIDEA (Mengeidæ, Mengenillidæ)
STICHOTREMATOIDEA (Stichotrematidæ)
XENOIDEA (Callipharixenidæ, Myrmecolacidæ, Stylopidæ)
HALICTOPHAGOIDEA (Halictophagidæ)
ELENCHOIDEA (Elenchidæ)

Order HYMENOPTERA

Suborder Chalastogastra

MEGALODONTOIDEA (Pamphiliidæ, Xyelidæ, Megalodontidæ)
TENTHREDINOIDEA (Pergidæ, Cimbicidæ, Argidæ, Blasticotomidæ,
Tenthredinidæ, Diprionidæ, Acorduleceridæ)
SIRICOIDEA (Xiphydriidæ, Cephidæ, Siricidæ, Syntexidæ)
ORYSSOIDEA (Oryssidæ)

Suborder Clistogastra

Division TEREBRANTIA

ICHNEUMONOIDEA (Megalyridæ, Stephanidæ, Aulacidæ, Gasteruptionidæ, Evaniidæ, Braconidæ, Ichneumonidæ, Agriotypidæ, Alysiidæ, Trigonalidæ)

CHALCIDOIDEA (Torymidæ, Agaontidæ, Chalcididæ, Leucospididæ,
Ormyridæ, Eurytomidæ, Perilampidæ, Eucharididæ, Cleonymidæ,
Encyrtidæ, Pteromalidæ, Miscogastridæ, Elasmidæ, Leptofœnidæ,
Eulophidæ, Trichogrammatidæ, Mymaridæ, Mymarommatidæ)

PROCTOTRYPOIDEA (Pelecinidæ, Monomachidæ, Heloridæ, Roproniidæ, Vanhorniidæ, Proctotrypidæ, Belytidæ, Diapriidæ, Scelionidæ,
Ceraphronidæ, Platygastridæ)

CYNIPOIDEA (Ibaliidæ, Cynipidæ, Figitidæ, Pterostigmatidæ, Ober-
thuerellidæ, Eucoilidæ, Liopteridæ, Charipidæ, Aspiceridæ, Ana-
charitidæ)

Division ACULEATA

BETHYLOIDEA (Rhopalosomatidæ, Bethylidæ, Dryinidæ, Embolemidæ, Sclerogibbidæ)

CHRYSIDOIDEA (Cleptidæ, Chrysididæ, Alienidæ)

SCOLIOIDEA (Sapygidæ, Plumariidæ, Scoliidæ, Tiphiidæ, Anthoboscidæ, Sierolomorphidæ, Thynnidæ, Methocidæ, Myrmosidæ, Mutillidæ, Apterogynidæ)

FORMICOIDEA (Formicidæ)

VESPOIDEA (Vespidæ)

POMPILOIDEA (Pompilidæ)

SPHECOIDEA (Ampulicidæ, Sphecidæ, Mellinidæ, Gorytidæ, Nyssonidæ, Trypoxylidæ, Stizidæ, Dimorphidæ, Bembicidæ, Larridæ, Miscophidæ, Philanthidæ, Cerceridæ, Alyssonidæ, Pemphredonidæ, Crabronidæ, Oxybelidæ)

APOIDEA (Andrenidæ, Halictidæ, Colletidæ, Melittidæ, Megachilidæ, Apidæ)

KEY TO THE CLASSES OF ARTHROPODA

1. Antennæ absent; often four or five pairs of legs, sometimes more very rarely less..2
   One or two pairs of antennæ present; legs variable, often three or many pairs[1]...9
2. Marine animals, occasionally living near the tidal zone...........3
   Terrestrial, rarely aquatic species living in fresh water; never living in the ocean below the tidal zone........................4
3. Respiratory organs well developed, consisting of blood gills; length of body and tail more than twice length of longest leg; large animals, the body covered by a convex carapace. King crabs, Horseshoe crabs.............................XIPHOSÙRA
   Respiratory organs absent or vestigial; length of body and abdomen usually much less than one-half length of longest leg (length rarely equal)..............................PYCNOGÓNIDA
4. Four pairs of legs in the adult, sometimes with another more anterior pair of appendages (pedipalpi) resembling walking legs.......5
   Three pairs of legs or less...................................6
5. With a well developed respiratory system composed of book lungs or of tubular tracheæ opening by spiracles, or of both in the same animal; reproductive organs opening near the base of the abdomen below; integument usually heavily chitinized at least on part of the body. Spiders, Scorpions, Mites, Ticks, etc.
   ARÁCHNIDA (Page 693)
   Without any special respiratory organs, reproductive organs opening into the alimentary canal; very small or microscopic animals with weakly chitinized integument. Water bears, Bear animalcules.
   TARDÌGRADA (Page 753)
6. With three pairs of legs, or with only two pairs, in the latter case the body is vermiform and shows many minute transverse wrinkles or annulations; small or minute animals...........7
   Without legs in the adult which is vermiform and shows many minute transverse wrinkles or annulations, or with two pairs in the embryo or young larva which is short and not thus annulate; internal parasites of vertebrates (see couplet 5).
   PENTÁSTÓMIDA (Page 750)
7. Three pairs of legs....................................8
   Two pairs of legs; body long, tapering, the integument with minute

[1] In the immature stages of some insects, and even in the adult females in very rare cases, the antennæ are absent or vestigial. If it is suspected that any such forms may be insects, they must be examined by reference to the "Key to the Orders of Insecta," p. 28. The number of marine insects is almost negligible.

transverse rings or wrinkles; living in plant or animal tissues. Some Acarina (see couplet 5).

ARÁCHNIDA, part. (Page 693)

8. Body elongate; abdomen consisting of eleven segments, its basal three segments each bearing a pair of vestigial legs. (Order Protura). (If internal parasites, *cf.* Strepsiptera, p. 618).

INSÉCTA, part. (Page 28)

Body short, rounded or oval; abdomen not segmented and without appendages below. The young of some Acarina.

ARÁCHNIDA, part. (Page 693)

9. Only one pair of antennæ.................................10
Two pairs of antennæ; five or more pairs of legs; aquatic (very rarely terrestrial) animals living in the sea or in fresh water, provided with true gills, except in some parasitic forms.

CRUSTÀCEA (Page 692)

10. With three pairs of legs in the adult, and usually with wings; legs reduced in size and structure or often completely absent in the larva.............................INSÉCTA (Page 28)
More than three pairs of legs; no wings; body usually very elongate...11

11. Legs of the first three segments behind the head similar, composed of distinct joints, but of a different type from the more posterior pairs which are not clearly jointed. Larvæ of some insects.

INSÉCTA, part. (Page 28)

Legs essentially similar, at most only the first pair strikingly different from the more posterior ones.............................12

12. Legs composed of distinct, heavily chitinized segments which are articulated by sharply differentiated joints; integument usually heavily chitinized...13
Legs fleshy with numerous annulations, but without any clearly articulated joints; long cylindrical, soft-bodied animals. Tropical.

ONYCHÓPHORA (Page 690)

13. Not more than one pair of legs on any segment of the body.....14
Two pairs of legs on some, usually on most of the segments of the body (as indicated by the tergites); body usually more or less cylindrical.........................DIPLÓPODA (Page 756)

14. Antennæ simple, not branched.............................15
Antennæ branched apically, terminating in three multiarticulate setiform appendages; minute animals without respiratory organs.

PAURÓPODA (Page 755)

15. Legs terminating in a single tarsal claw; first pair of legs modified to form jaw-like poison fangs; at least nineteen body segments and fifteen or more pairs of legs in the adult. Centipedes

CHILÓPODA (Page 770)

Legs each bearing two tarsal claws; first pair of legs more or less reduced in size, not jaw-like and without poison gland; 15 to 22 body segments and twelve pairs of legs.

SỲMPHYLA (Page 774)

CLASS INSÉCTA

(HEXÁPODA)

Small or moderate-sized, frequently very small or minute, never very large, Arthropoda. Body of adult and sometimes also of the immature stages more or less clearly divided into three groups of segments, head, thorax and abdomen; those forming the head fused into a single piece. Three thoracic segments, each bearing a pair of legs; the first segment often much more freely articulated than the others; second and third each usually bearing a pair of wings, sometimes absent on the third or entirely wanting. Abdomen composed of eleven segments or less, frequently six to eight, often terminated by a pair of cerci. One pair of antennæ almost always present; three pairs of mouthparts; a pair of mandibles fitted for chewing or piercing, and two pairs of maxillæ, the latter usually bearing a jointed palpus. Compound eyes and three simple ocelli usually present. Legs almost always terminating in claws, usually nine- or eight-jointed, occasionally less. Wings usually supplied with a series of branched veins or chitinous thickenings, fore pair often thicker than the hind ones. Respiration by branched, tubular tracheæ opening by segmentally arranged pairs of spiracles. Development direct in the primitive forms or with a metamorphosis often involving great changes in form and habits. Younger stages without functional wings; in the forms undergoing metamorphosis with the legs and antennæ much reduced and the body grub-like, caterpillar-like, or vermiform. Insects.

KEY TO THE ORDERS OF INSECTA [1]

1. Wings developed 2
   Wingless, or with vestigial, or with rudimentary wings not suitable for flight (wingless adults and immature stages) 33
2. The wings of the mesothorax (the fore wings) horny, leathery or parchment-like, at least at the base; differing materially in texture

[1] Caution must be exercised in the use of this key. There are very many scattered exceptions to the general characters that must be used to define numerous extensive groups, especially in the immature stages of development. When in doubt, reference to the descriptive paragraph that precedes each ordinal key will aid in placing various degenerate, aberrant or highly modified forms. Any attempt to include more than a few of these types would encumber the key with more detail than is advisable for ordinary use. Specialized references to more elaborate considerations of immature stages are cited in the several lists of literature on later pages of this volume. Tentative keys for the identification of immature stages of some of the better known orders will be found also, following in each case the key to the adults.

from the membranous hind wings which exceptionally may be absent. Prothorax large and not fused with the mesothorax (except in the rare Strepsiptera, which have minute fore wings)... 3

The mesothoracic wings membranous........................12

3. Mesothoracic wings (called tegmina or hemelytra) containing veins, or at least the metathoracic wings not folded crossways when hidden under the upper wings...........................4

Mesothoracic wings (called elytra) veinless, of uniform, horny consistency, the metathoracic wings, when present, folded crossways as well as lengthwise when at rest and hidden beneath the elytra; mouth mandibulate.............................11

4. Mouthparts forming a jointed beak, fitted for piercing and sucking... 5

Mouthparts with mandibles fitted for chewing and moving laterally... 6

5. Head usually horizontal and with the beak arising from the under part so as to project downwards, the gula well developed; mesothoracic wings usually leathery at the base and abruptly membranous on the apical portion, the membranous parts usually overlapping one another and lying flat over the abdomen when at rest. True bugs.

HEMÍPTERA, Suborder HETERÓPTERA (Page 167)

Head usually vertical and with the beak arising from the back part so as to project backward between the front legs; gula absent, or represented by a small membrane.

HEMÍPTERA, Suborder HOMÓPTERA (Page 146)

6. Hind wings not folded, similar to the fore wings; thickened basal part of wings very short, separated from the rest of the wing by a preformed transverse suture; social species, living in colonies.

Termites............................ISÓPTERA (Page 121)

Hind wings folding, fan-like, broader than the fore wings........7

7. Usually rather large or moderately large species; antennæ usually lengthened and thread-like; prothorax large and free from the mesothorax; cerci present; fore wings rarely minute, usually long... 8

Very small active species; antennæ short, with few joints, at least one joint bearing a long lateral process; no cerci; fore wings minute; prothorax small. Rare, short-lived insects, parasites of other insects, usually wasps and bees.

Males of STREPSÍPTERA (Page 618)

8. Hind femora not larger than the fore femora; mute species; body more or less flattened with the wings superposed when at rest; tergites and sternites subequal................................9

Hind femora almost always much larger than the fore femora,

jumping species, if not (Gryllotalpidæ) the front legs broadened for burrowing; species usually capable of chirping or making a creaking noise; body more or less cylindrical, the wings held sloping against the sides of the body when at rest, tergites usually larger than the sternites. Grasshoppers, Katydids, Crickets.

ORTHÓPTERA, Suborder **SALTATÒRIA** (Page 93)

9. Body elongate; head free, not concealed from above by the prothorax; deliberate movers.....................................10

Body oval, much flattened; head nearly concealed beneath the oval pronotum; legs similar and fitted for rapid running, the coxæ large and the tibiæ noticeably spiny or bristly. Roaches.

BLATTÀRIA (Page 77)

10. Prothorax much longer than the mesothorax; front legs almost always heavily spined, formed for seizing prey; cerci usually with several joints. Mantes, Leaf insects.

ORTHÓPTERA, Suborder **MANTEÒDEA** (Page 84)

Prothorax short; legs similar, formed for walking; cerci one-jointed. Stick insects, Walking sticks. (If the wings lack crossveins and have a short thickened basal stub, separated by a curved transverse suture, see *Mastotermes*, p. 122.)

ORTHÓPTERA, Suborder **PHASMATÒDEA** (Page 102)

11. Abdomen terminated by movable, almost always heavily chitinized forceps; antennæ long and slender; fore wings short, leaving most of the abdomen uncovered, hind wings nearly circular, delicate, radially folded from near the center; elongate insects. Earwigs.

DERMÁPTERA (Page 112)

Abdomen not terminated by forceps;[1] antennæ of various forms but usually eleven-jointed; fore wings usually completely sheathing the abdomen; generally hard-bodied species. Beetles, Weevils.

COLEÓPTERA (Page 543)

12. With four wings...13

With but two wings (the mesothoracic) usually outspread when at rest...31

13. Wings long, very narrow, the margins fringed with long hairs, almost veinless; tarsi one- or two-jointed, with swollen tip; mouthparts asymmetrical, without biting mandibles, fitted for lacerating and sucking plant tissues; no cerci; minute species. Thrips.

THYSANÓPTERA (Page 135)

Wings broader and most often supplied with veins, if rarely somewhat linear the tarsi have more than two joints and the last tarsal joint is not swollen..14

14. Wings, legs and body clothed, at least in part, with elongate flattened scales (often intermixed with hairs) which nearly always

[1] If very rarely (one African genus) with apical forceps-like appendages, the wings are not as in Dermaptera.

form a color pattern on the wings; mouthparts (rarely vestigial) forming a coiled tongue composed of the maxillæ, biting mandibles present only in Micropterygoidea, p. 228. Moths and butterflies. **LEPIDÓPTERA** (Page 226)

Wings, legs and body not clothed with scales although sometimes hairy and having a few scales intermixed; sometimes with bristles, especially on the legs, or rarely with waxen flakes or dust; color pattern when present extending to the wing membrane 15

15. Hind wings with the anal area separated, folded fan-like in plaits when in repose, nearly always wider and noticeably larger than the fore wings; antennæ prominent; wing veins usually numerous; nymphs or larvæ nearly always aquatic 16

Hind wings without a separated anal area, not folded and not larger than the fore wings 18

16. Tarsi five-jointed; cerci not pronounced 17

Tarsi three-jointed; cerci well developed, usually long and many jointed; prothorax large, free; species of moderate to large size. Stone-flies . . . . **PLECÓPTERA** (Page 73)

17. Wings with a number of subcostal crossveins; prothorax rather large; species of moderate to large size.
NEURÓPTERA, Suborder **SIALÒDEA** (Page 204)

Wings without subcostal crossveins, with the surface hairy; prothorax small; species of small to moderate size.
TRICHÓPTERA (Page 216)

18. Antennæ short and inconspicuous; wings netveined with numerous crossveins; mouthparts mandibulate; nymphs aquatic. (Subulicornia) 19

Antennæ larger, if of rather small size the wings have few crossveins or the mouthparts form a jointed sucking beak; immature stages almost always terrestrial. 20

19. Hind wings much smaller than the fore wings; abdomen ending in long, thread-like processes; tarsi normally four- or five-jointed; sluggish fliers. May flies . . . . **PLECTÓPTERA** (Page 55)

Hind wings nearly like the fore wings; no caudal setæ; tarsi three-jointed; vigorous, active fliers, often of large size. Dragon flies, Damsel flies . . . . **ODONÀTA** (Page 62)

20. Head produced into a mandibulate beak (Fig. 354), hind wings not folded; wings usually with color pattern, the crossveins numerous; male genitalia usually greatly swollen, forming a reflexed bulb. Scorpion flies . . . . **MECÓPTERA** (Page 214)

Head not drawn out as a mandibulate beak; male abdomen not forcipate 21

21. Mouth mandibulate 22

Mouth haustellate, the mandibles not formed for chewing; no cerci; crossveins few 29

22. Tarsi five-jointed, if rarely three- or four-jointed, the hind wings are smaller than the front ones and the wings lie flat over the body; no cerci 23
Tarsi two-, three- or four-jointed; veins and crossveins not numerous 26

23. Prothorax small or only moderately long. (In Mantispidæ the prothorax is very long, but the front legs are strongly raptorial) 24
Prothorax very long and cylindrical, much longer than the head; front legs normal; antennæ with more than eleven joints; crossveins numerous.
NEURÓPTERA, Suborder RAPHIDIÒDEA (Page 205)

24. Wings similar, with many veins and ˙crossveins; prothorax more or less free. If the neuration is very rarely reduced (*Coniopteryx*) the wings are powdered 25
Wings with relatively few angular cells, the costal cell without crossveins; hind wings smaller than the fore pair; prothorax fused with the mesothorax; abdomen frequently constricted at the base and ending in a sting or specialized ovipositor. Ants, Wasps, Bees, etc. . . . . .HYMENÓPTERA (Page 621)

25. Costal cell, at least in the fore wing, almost always with many crossveins . . .NEURÓPTERA, Suborder PLANIPÉNNIA (Page 206)
Costal cell without crossveins. (If wings are clothed with scales, see Micropterygidæ, p. 228.) . . . . .MECÓPTERA (Page 214)

26. Wings equal in size, or rarely the hind wings larger, held superposed on the top of the abdomen when at rest; media fused with the radial sector for a short distance near the middle of the wing; tarsi three-, four-, or five-jointed 27
Hind wings smaller than the fore wings; wings held at rest folded back against the abdomen; radius and media not fusing; tarsi two- or three-jointed 28

27. Tarsi apparently four-jointed; cerci usually minute; wings with a transverse preformed suture near the base where they break off soon after the insect reaches the adult stage; social species, living in colonies. Termites. . . . . .ISÓPTERA (Page 121)
Tarsi three-jointed, the front metatarsi swollen; cerci conspicuous; usually solitary species . . . . .EMBIÒDEA (Page 119)

28. Cerci absent; tarsi two- or three-jointed; wings remaining attached throughout life; radial sector and media branched, except when fore wings are much thickened . . . .CORRODÉNTIA (Page 125)
Cerci present; tarsi two-jointed; wings deciduous at maturity, the neuration greatly reduced; radial sector and media simple, unbranched . . . . .ZORÁPTERA (Page 130)

29. Wings not covered with scales, not outspread when at rest; prothorax large; antennæ with few joints; mouthparts forming a jointed piercing beak 30

Wings and body covered with colored scales which form a definite pattern on the wings; antennæ many-jointed; mouthparts when present forming a coiled tongue. Moths and Butterflies.

LEPIDÓPTERA (Page 226)

30. Beak arising from the back of the head.

HEMÍPTERA, Suborder HOMÓPTERA (Page 140)

Beak arising from the front part of the head.

HEMÍPTERA, Suborder HETERÓPTERA (Page 167)

31. Mouth not functional; abdomen furnished with a pair of caudal filaments 32

Mouthparts forming a proboscis, only exceptionally vestigial; abdomen without caudal filaments; hind wings replaced by knobbed halteres. Flies, Mosquitoes, Midges. . . . . . **DÍPTERA** (Page 305)

32. No halteres; antennæ inconspicuous; crossveins abundant. A few rare May flies . . . . **PLECTÓPTERA** (Page 55)

Hind wings represented by minute hook-like halteres; antennæ evident; neuration reduced to a forked vein; crossveins lacking; minute delicate insects. Males of Scale insects.

HEMÍPTERA, Suborder HOMÓPTERA (Page 140)

Wingless Adult Forms and Immature Stages of Several Orders [1]

33. Body more or less insect-like, *i.e.* with more or less distinct head, thorax and abdomen, and jointed legs, and capable of locomotion 34

Without distinct body parts, or without jointed legs, or incapable of locomotion. 78

34. Terrestrial, breathing through spiracles; rarely without special respiratory organs. 35

Living in the water; usually gill-breathing, larval forms 64

Parasites on warm-blooded animals 72

35. Mouthparts retracted into the head and scarcely or not at all visible; underside of the abdomen with styles or other appendages; less than three joints on maxillary palpi if antennæ present; very delicate, small or minute insects. (APTERYGÒTA) 36

Mouthparts conspicuously visible externally; if mouthparts mandibulate, maxillary palpi more than two-jointed; antennæ always present; underside of abdomen rarely with styles 38

[1] Any key to immature insects designed to include the innumerable variations presented by highly modified members of many orders becomes so lengthy, complex and unwieldy that it cannot serve the purpose of this book. Keys are included in later sections for the immature stages in certain orders, but these are necessarily incomplete and not fully reliable due to lack of knowledge at the present time. It is suggested that immature specimens be tried out in these later keys when it seems probable that they run out to one of the groups included in the couplets on the following pages.

36. Antennæ absent; no long cerci, pincers, springing apparatus or anterior ventral sucker on abdomen; head pear-shaped
    PROTÙRA (Page 42)
    Antennæ conspicuous; pincers, long cerci, or basal ventral sucker present on abdomen 37
37. Abdomen consisting of six segments or less, with a forked sucker (collophore) at base of abdomen below; no terminal pincers or long cerci; usually with conspicuous springing apparatus (furcula) near the end of the abdomen . . . . **COLLÉMBOLA** (Page 50)
    Abdomen consisting of more than eight visible segments, with long, multi-articulate cerci or strong pincers at the end; eyes and ocelli absent . . . . **ENTÓTROPHI** (Page 47)
38. Mouthparts mandibulate, formed for chewing 39
    Mouthparts haustellate, formed for sucking 60
39. Body usually covered with scales; abdomen with three prominent caudal filaments and bearing at least two pairs of ventral styles.
    THYSANÙRA (Page 44)
    Body never covered with scales; never with three caudal filaments; ventral styles absent on the abdomen 40
40. Underside of abdomen entirely without legs 41
    Abdomen bearing false legs beneath, which differ from those of the thorax; body caterpillar-like, cylindrical, the thorax and abdomen not distinctly separated; larval forms 58
41. Antennæ long and distinct 42
    Antennæ short, not pronounced; larval forms 55
42. Abdomen terminated by strong movable forceps; prothorax free.
    Earwigs . . . . **DERMÁPTERA** (Page 112)
    Abdomen not ending in forceps 43
43. Abdomen not strongly constricted at the base, broadly joined to the thorax 44
    Abdomen strongly constricted at the base; prothorax fused with the mesothorax. Ants, etc. . . . . **HYMENÓPTERA** (Page 621)
44. Head not prolonged into a beak 45
    Head produced into a mandibulate beak.
    MECÓPTERA (Page 214)
45. Very small species, the body soft and weakly sclerotized; tarsi two or three-jointed 46
    Usually much larger species; tarsi usually with more than three joints, or the body is hard and heavily sclerotized and the cerci are absent 47
46. Cerci absent. Book lice . . . . **CORRODÉNTIA** (Page 125)
    Cerci one-jointed, prominent . . . . **ZORÁPTERA** (Page 130)
47. Hind legs fitted for jumping, the femora enlarged; wing-pads of larvæ when present in inverse position, the metathoracic over-

lapping the mesothoracic.
ORTHÓPTERA, Suborder SALTATÓRIA (Page 93)
Hind legs not enlarged for jumping; wing-pads, if present, in normal position 48
48. Prothorax much longer than the mesothorax; front legs fitted for grasping prey.
ORTHÓPTERA, Suborder MANTEÒDEA (Page 84)
Prothorax not greatly lengthened 49
49. Cerci present; antennæ usually with more than fifteen joints, often many-jointed 50
No cerci; body often hard-shelled; antennæ usually with eleven joints . . . . COLEÓPTERA (Page 543)
50. Cerci with more than three joints 51
Cerci short, with one to three joints 53
51. Body flattened and oval; head inflexed; prothorax oval. Roaches.
BLATTÀRIA (Page 77)
Body elongate; head nearly horizontal 52
52. Cerci long; ovipositor chitinized, exserted; tarsi five-jointed.
ORTHÓPTERA, Suborder GRYLLOBLATTÒDEA (Page 92)
Cerci short; no ovipositor; tarsi four-jointed. ISÓPTERA (Page 121)
53. Tarsi five-jointed (three-jointed in Timemidæ, non-social species with the front tarsi not swollen); body usually very slender and long. Walking sticks.
ORTHÓPTERA, Suborder PHASMATÒDEA (Page 102)
Tarsi two or three jointed; body not linear 54
54. Front tarsi with the first joint swollen, containing a silk-spinning gland, producing a web in which the insects live; body long and slender . . . . EMBIÒDEA (Page 119)
Front tarsi not swollen, without silk-spinning gland; body much stouter; social species with an apterous, infertile caste. Termites.
ISÓPTERA (Page 121)
55. Body cylindrical, caterpillar-like 56
Body more or less depressed, not caterpillar-like 57
56. Head with six ocelli on each side; labium with spinnerets; antennæ inserted in membranous area at base of mandibles.
Larvæ of some LEPIDÓPTERA
Head with more than six ocelli on each side; metathoracic legs distinctly larger than prothoracic legs.
Larvæ of Boreidæ, MECÓPTERA
57. Mandibles united with the corresponding maxillæ to form sucking jaws (Fig. 975).
Larvæ of NEURÓPTERA, Suborder PLANIPÉNNIA
Mandibles almost always separate from the maxillæ (Figs. 972, 973, 976, 977, 979, 980, 983, 984, 986, 992).
Larvæ of COLEÓPTERA; NEURÓPTERA,
Suborder RAPHIDIÒDEA; STREPSÍPTERA; DÍPTERA

58. False legs (prolegs) numbering five pairs or less, located on various abdominal segments, but not on the first, second, or seventh; the false legs tipped with many minute hooks (crochets) (hookless prolegs rarely on second and seventh segments).

 Larvæ of most **LEPIDÓPTERA** (Page 271)

 False legs numbering from six to ten pairs, one pair of which occurs on the second abdominal segment; the prolegs not tipped with minute hooks. 59

59. Head with a single ocellus on each side. (Figs. 966–971).

 Larvæ of some **HYMENÓPTERA** (Page 659)

 Head with several ocelli on each side. . . . . Larvæ of **MECÓPTERA**

60. Body bare or with few scattered hairs, or with waxy coating. . . . 61

 Body densely clothed with hairs or scales; proboscis if present coiled under the head. Moths. . . . . **LEPIDÓPTERA** (Page 226)

61. Last tarsal joint swollen; mouth consisting of a triangular unjointed beak; minute species. Thrips. . . . **THYSANÓPTERA** (Page 135)

 Tarsi not bladder-like at the tip, and with distinct claws. 62

62. Prothorax distinct. 63

 Prothorax small, hidden when viewed from above.

 DÍPTERA (Page 305)

63. Beak arising from the front part of the head.

 HEMÍPTERA, Suborder **HETERÓPTERA** (Page 167)

 Beak arising from the back part of the head.

 HEMÍPTERA, Suborder **HOMÓPTERA** (Page 140)

64. Mouth mandibulate. 65

 Mouth haustellate, forming a strong pointed inflexed beak.

 Nymphs of **HEMÍPTERA**

65. Mandibles exserted straight forward and united with the corresponding maxillæ to form piercing jaws.

 Larvæ of some **NEURÓPTERA**

 Mandibles normal, moving laterally to function as biting jaws. . . . 66

66. Body not encased in a shell made of sand, pebbles, leaves, etc. 67

 Case-bearing forms; tracheal gills usually present. Periwinkles, Caddis-worms. (Fig. 974). . . . . Larvæ of **TRICHÓPTERA**

67. Abdomen furnished with external lateral gills or respiratory processes (a few Coleoptera and Trichoptera here also). 68

 Abdomen without external gills. 69

68. Abdomen terminated by two or three long caudal filaments.

 Larvæ of **PLECTÓPTERA**

 Abdomen with short end processes.

 Larvæ of **NEURÓPTERA,** Suborder **SIALÒDEA**

69. Lower lip strong, extensile, and furnished with a pair of opposable hooks. . . . . Larvæ of **ODONÀTA**

 Lower lip not capable of being thrust forward and not hooked. . 70

70. Abdomen without false legs. 71

Abdomen bearing paired false legs on several segments.

A few larvæ of **LEPIDÓPTERA**

71. The three divisions of the thorax loosely united; antennæ and caudal filaments long and slender.........Larvæ of **PLECÓPTERA**

Thoracic divisions not constricted; antennæ and caudal filaments short (also some aquatic larvæ of Diptera and a few Trichoptera here)..............................Larvæ of **COLEÓPTERA**

72. Body flattened (or larval maggots)........................73

Body strongly compressed; mouth formed as a sharp inflexed beak; jumping species. Fleas.........**SIPHONÁPTERA** (Page 538)

73. Mandibulate mouthparts formed for chewing 74

Haustellate mouthparts formed for piercing and sucking.......76

74. Mouth inferior; cerci long...................................75

Mouth anterior; no cerci; generally elongate-oval insects with somewhat triangular head; parasites of birds or mammals. Biting lice.........................**MALLÓPHAGA** (Page 131)

75. Cerci straight; eyes absent; antennæ short; external parasites of rodents.

DERMÁPTERA, Suborder **DIPLOGLOSSÀTA** (Page 112)

Cerci strongly bent or angulate at the middle; eyes present; antennæ nearly as long as the body; external parasites of bats.

Some **DERMÁPTERA** (Page 112)

76. Antennæ exserted, visible, though rather short................77

Antennæ inserted in pits, not visible from above (also the larval maggots, without antennæ)...Pupiparous **DÍPTERA** (Page 384)

77. Beak unjointed; tarsi formed as a hook for grasping the hairs of the host; permanent parasites. Lice.......**ANOPLÚRA** (Page 202)

Beak jointed; tarsi not hooked; temporary parasites.

HEMÍPTERA (Page 140)

78. Legless grubs, maggots or borers; locomotion effected by a squirming motion. Larvæ of Strepsiptera, Siphonaptera, and of some Coleoptera (see couplet 57), Diptera, Lepidoptera and Hymenoptera. (If living in the body of wasps or bees, with the flattened head exposed, compare the females of Strepsiptera; if aquatic wrigglers, see larvæ and pupæ of mosquitoes, etc., p. 391, p. 406).

Sedentary forms, incapable of locomotion 79

79. Small degraded forms bearing little superficial resemblance to insects, with a long slender beak, and usually covered with a waxy scale or powder or cottony tufts; living on various plants. Scale insects......................**HEMÍPTERA** (Page 140)

Body quiescent, but able to bend from side to side; not capable of feeding, enclosed in a skin which is tightly drawn over all the members, or which leaves the limbs free but folded against the body; sometimes free; sometimes enclosed in a cocoon or in a shell formed from the dried larval skin....................80

80. The skin encasing the legs, wings, etc., holding the members tightly
against the body; prothorax small; a proboscis showing........81
Legs, wings, etc., more or less free from the body; biting mouthparts showing....................................82
81. Proboscis usually long, rarely absent; four wing cases; sometimes in
a cocoon. (Figs. 990, 996)...........Pupæ of **LEPIDÓPTERA**
Proboscis short; two wing cases, pupa often enclosed in an oval shell
(puparium) formed of the hardened larval skin. (Figs, 991, 997).
Pupæ of **DÍPTERA** (Page 406)
82. Prothorax small, fused into one piece with the mesothorax; sometimes enclosed in a loose cocoon....Pupæ of **HYMENÓPTERA**
Prothorax larger and not closely fused with the mesothorax......83
83. Wing cases with few or no veins. (Fig. 994).
Pupæ of **COLEÓPTERA**
Wing cases with a number of branched veins. (Fig. 993).
Pupæ of **NEURÓPTERA**

LITERATURE ON INSECTS

General Works on Insects and References Dealing with at least
Several Orders Together

BALFOUR-BROWNE, F. Keys to the Orders of Insects. Cambridge Univ. Press,
58 pp. (1920).
BANKS, N. Synopsis, Catalogue and Bibliography of Neuropteroid Insects of
North America. Trans. American Entom. Soc., 19, pp. 328–373 (1892).
(Includes Neuroptera, Odonata, Plectoptera, Plecoptera, Trichoptera,
Mecoptera, Isoptera, Embiodea, Megaloptera).
A List of Works on North American Entomology. Bull. Bur. Ent., U.S.
Dept. Agric., No. 81, 120 pp. (1910). (A most valuable list of selected
works, classified by groups, including also the Arachnida).
BERLESE, A. Gli Insetti. 2 vols., 2018 pp., Milan (1909–25).
BIOLOGICAL ABSTRACTS. Published by the Union of American Biological So-
cieties, University of Pennsylvania, Philadelphia, 1–26 (1926–). An index
to biological literature beginning with 1926, with an abstract of those
papers to which reference is made.
BLAIR, K. G. Key to Larvæ of Insects with Complete Metamorphosis. Trans.
South London Ent. Soc., 1933–34, p. 100 (1934).
BRIMLEY, C. S. Insects of North Carolina. Div. Ent., Univ. North Carolina.
560 pp. (1938). Supplement, 39 pp. (1942). Second Supplement (By
D. L. Wray), 59 pp. (1950).
BRITTON, W. E. Check List of the Insects of Connecticut. Bull. State Geol.
Nat. Hist. Surv., Connecticut, No. 31, 397 pp. (1920).
Additions to Check-list of Insects of Connecticut. Bull. Conn. State Geol.
Nat. Hist. Survey, No. 60, 169 pp. (1939).
BROHMER, P., EHRMANN, P, and ULMER, G., Editors. Die Tierwelt Mitteleuro-
pas, 1928; vol. 2 contains the lower Arthropoda; vol. 3, Arachnida; vol. 4,

Insects. (The parts are by numerous contributors, and so far as published are listed under the separate groups).

BROHMER, P. *et al.* Fauna von Deutschland. 561 pp., 982 figs. Insects, pp. 129–401. Leipzig, Quelle & Mayer. (1932).

BRUES, C. T. and MELANDER, A. L. Key to the Families of North American Insects. 140 pp., Boston, Mass. and Pullman, Wash. (1915).

BURR, M. The Insect Legion. xiv + 321 pp., 21 pls. J. Nisbet & Co., London. (1939).

BUXTON, P. A. *et al.* Insects of Samoa. 35 parts, 1712 pp., 627 figs. British Mus. Nat. Hist. (1927–35). Numerous sections, not listed separately under the several orders.

CARUS, J. V. Bibliographia Zoologica. Vols. 1–24 issued with the Zoologischer Anzeiger, Leipzig (1900–13); vols. 25–40 issued separately by the Concilium Bibliographicum, Zurich (1913–30).

CLAUSEN, C. P. Entomophagous Insects. 688 pp. McGraw-Hill, New York. (1940).

COCKERELL, T. D. A. Zoölogy of Colorado. 262 pp., Boulder, Colo., (1927).

COMSTOCK, J. H. The Wings of Insects. 423 pp., Comstock Pub. Co., Ithaca, N. Y. (1918).

An Introduction to Entomology. Comstock Pub. Co., Ithaca, N. Y., 1044 pp. (1924).

CONCILIUM BIBLIOGRAPHICUM. Zurich, Switzerland. Index cards to zoölogical literature, 1896–. (Deals with the whole animal kingdom; the cards issued, one card for each title, usually with brief indication of contents.)

COSTA LIMA, A. DA. Catalogo dos insectos que vivem nas plantas do Brasil. Arch. Escola Sup. Agric. Med. Vet., 6, pp. 107–276 (1922).

Terciero catalogo dos insectos qui vivem nas plantas do Brasil. Minis. Agric., Rio de Janeiro. 460 pp. (1936).

Insetos do Brasil. Escuela Nac. Agron., Rio de Janeiro. 470 pp., 218 figs. (1939).

DOANE, R. W. *et al.* Forest Insects. 403 pp. McGraw-Hill, New York. (1934).

ESCHERICH, K. Die Forstinsekten Mitteleuropas. 1055 pp., 1188 figs. (1914–42).

ESSIG, E. O. Insects of Western North America. 1035 pp. New York, Macmillan (1926).

College Entomology. 900 pp. New York, Macmillan (1942).

EWING, H. E. Manual of External Parasites. 225 pp. Springfield, Ill., C. C. Thomas (1929).

FELT, E. P. Key to American Insect Galls. Bull. New York State Mus., No. 200, 310 pp. (1917). (Contains an extensive bibliography.)

Plant Galls and their Makers. 364 pp., 344 figs. Comstock Pub. Co. Ithaca, N. Y. (1940).

FERRIS, G. F. The Principles of Systematic Entomology. Stanford Univ. Publ. Biol. Sci., 5, pp. 103–269 (1928).

FILIP'EV, N. N. Insect Key. (In Russian) 943 pp. Moscow (1928).

FLETCHER, T. B. South Indian Insects. 587 pp. Madras (1914).

Tentative Keys to the Orders and Families of Indian Insects. Bull. Agric. Res. Inst. Pusa, No. 162, 101 pp. (1926).

FROGGATT, W. W. Australian Insects. 463 pp. Sydney (1908).

GODMAN, F. D. and SALVIN, O., Editors. Biologia Centrali-Americana, Contributions to a Knowledge of the Fauna and Flora of Mexico and Central America. (Contains Arachnida, Diplopoda, Chilopoda and Insects in many volumes, some of which we have listed separately). London (1896–1915).

GOWDEY, C. C. Catalogus insectorum Jamaicensis. Ent. Bull. Dept. Agric. Jamaica, **4**, 47 pp. (1928).

GRASSÉ, P. P. Traité de Zoologie, **9, 10**, Insectes inférieures et Coléoptères. (Parts are listed separately.) (1949–50).

HAGEN, H. A. Bibliotheca Entomologica. 2 vols. Leipzig (1862–63). (Literature up to the year 1863).

HANDLIRSCH, A. Die fossilen Insekten und die Phylogenie der rezenten Formen. Leipzig (1906–08).

Geschichte. Litteratur, Technik, Paläontologie, Phylogenie und Systematik der Insekten. Schröder's Handbuch der Entomologie, **3**, 1201 pp. Jena (1925).

Insecta. Kükenthal, Handbuch der Zoologie, **4**, Berlin (1929).

HAYES, W. P. Bibliography of Classification of Immature Insects. Ent. News, **49**, pp. 250–251; **50**, pp. 5–10; 76–82; **52**, pp. 52–55, *ad seq.* (1939–41).

Bibliography of Classification of Immature Insects. Journ. Kansas Ent. Soc., **14**, pp. 3–11 (1941).

HORN, W. and SCHENKLING, S. Index Litteraturæ Entomologicæ. (Before 1863). Berlin-Dahlem, 4 vols. (1928–29).

HOULBERT, C. Bibliothèque de Zoologie. In Encyclopédie Scientifique, Paris, Doin. (Insects form part 5 and numerous volumes.)

IMMS, A. D. A General Textbook of Entomology. E. P. Dutton, New York and Methuen and Co., London (1926). Second Edition. E. P. Dutton, New York and Methuen and Co., London. x + 720 pp., 607 figs. (1930).

LAMEERE, A. Précis de Zoologie, vols. 4 and 5. Univ. Brussels, Inst. Torley-Rousseau, 1004 pp. (1935).

Les Insects Aptilotes. Les Paleoptilotes, les Orthoptères, les Hemiptères, les Stegoptères, les Diptères, les Lepidoptères. Les Animaux de la Belge, Brussels, **3**, 132 pp. (1940).

LEONARD, M. D. List of the Insects and Spiders of New York State. Mem. Cornell Agric. Expt. Sta., No. 101, 1121 pp. (1926).

LINDROTH, C. H. Die Insektenfauna Islands [Iceland]. Zool. Bidrag, **13**, pp. 105–589, 50 figs. (1931).

LUTZ, F. E. Field Book of Insects. (Northeastern North America.) 509 pp. New York (1918). Third Edition. 510 pp., 100 pls. G. P. Putnam's Sons, New York. (1935).

MATSUMURA, S. The Illustrated Thousand Insects of Japan. Tokyo. Numerous parts. [In Japanese] (1905–30).

Six Thousand Illustrated Insects of Japanese Empire. [In Japanese] viii + 1688 pp. Tokyo (1931). (Some parts are listed separately.)

MAXWELL-LEFROY, H. and HOWLETT, F. M. Indian Insect Life. 798 pp. Calcutta (1909).

METCALF, C. L., and FLINT, W. P. Destructive and Useful Insects. McGraw-Hill Book Co., New York. 981 pp. (1939). Third Edition. 1054 pp. McGraw-Hill. New York. (1951).

MICKEL, C. E. Classification of Insects. Ann. Ent. Soc. America, **42**, pp. 1–6 (1949).

MUSGRAVE, A. Bibliography of Australian Entomology. 380 pp. Royal Soc. New South Wales, Sydney. (1932.)

NEEDHAM, J. G., FROST, S. W., and TOTHILL, B. H. Leaf-mining Insects. 351 pp., 91 figs. Williams & Wilkins, Baltimore. (1928.)

OGILVIE, L. The Insects of Bermuda. 52 pp. (1928). Supplement, 10 pp. (1940).

OMER-COOPER, J. Classification of the Recent Hexapod Insects. Journ. Ent. Soc. Southern Africa, 1, pp. 137–148 (1939).

PETERSON, ALVAH. Keys to the Orders of Immature Stages of North American Insects. Ann. Ent. Soc. America, 32, pp. 267–268 (1939).
Larvæ of Insects, Pt. I, 315 pp., 84 pls. (1949); Pt. II, 415 pp., 104 pls. Columbus, Ohio (1951).

PINTO, C. Arthrópodes parasitos e transmissores de doenças. Vols. 1–2, 845 pp., 36 pls., 356 figs. Pimento de Mello, Rio de Janeiro (1930).

PORTEVIN, G. Histoire naturelle des Coléoptères de France. Encyc. Ent., Ser. A, 13, vii + 542 pp., 5 pls., 553 figs. (1931).

PROCTER, W. Insects of Mount Desert, Maine. Biological Surv. Mt. Desert, pt. VII. Wistar Inst., Philadelphia. 566 pp., 12 figs. (1946).

RILEY, C. V. Enumeration of the Published Synopses, Catalogues and Lists of North American Insects (1888).

RILEY, W. A. Medical Entomology. 483 pp. McGraw-Hill, New York. (1938).

ROSS, H. H. Textbook of Entomology. 532 pp. Wiley & Sons, New York and Chapman & Hall, London (1948).

ROUSSEAU, E. Les larves et nymphes aquatiques des Insectes d'Europe. 1, 967 pp. (1921).

SCHULZE, F. E., Editor. Das Tierreich. Berlin (1897–). (The parts are listed separately.)

SHARP, D. Insects. Cambridge Natural History, vols. 5 and 6, Macmillan & Co., New York and London (1895–99).

SHARP, D., Editor. Fauna Hawaiiensis. 3 vols. Honolulu (1899–1913).

SMART, J. Handbook for Identification of Insects of Medical Importance. Second Edition. British Mus. Nat. Hist. 295 pp. (1948).

SMITH, J. B. Catalogue of the Insects of New Jersey. Ann. Rept. New Jersey State Mus., 1909, 888 pp. (1910).

SNODGRASS, R. E. Studies on the Head of Mandibulate Insects. Comstock Pub. Co., Ithaca, N. Y. 125 pp., 37 figs. (1950).

SWAIN, R. B. Orders and Major Families of North American Insects. 261 pp., 56 figs. Doubleday, Garden City, N. Y. (1948).

TASCHENBERG, O. Bibliotheca Zoologica. Vol. 1 (1863); vols. 2 and 3 (1889–90). (Literature of Entomology to the year 1880.)

THOMPSON, M. T. Illustrated Catalogue of American Insect Galls. 116 pp. Nassau, N. Y. (1916).

TILLYARD, R. J. The Insects of Australia and New Zealand. 560 pp. Angus and Robertson, Sydney (1926).

TULLGREN, A. and WAHLGREN, E. Svenska Insekter. Stockholm, 812 pp. (1920–1922).

WEISS, H. B. Some Old Classifications of Insects. Canadian Ent., 47, pp. 369–376 (1915).

WILSON, H. F., and DONER, M. H. Historical Development of Insect Classification. Madison, Wisconsin, 133 pp., 28 figs. (1937).

WOLCOTT, G. N. An Economic Entomology of the West Indies. Ent. Soc. Porto Rico, San Juan. xviii + 688 pp., 111 figs. (1933).

WOLF, B. Insects. In Animalium cavernorum catalogus, pp. 225–544. W. Junk, Lochem (1935–36).

WU, C. F. Catalogus insectorum Sinensium. Vols. 1–6, 4168 pp. Peking Nat. Hist. Bull. (1935–41).

WYTSMAN, P., Editor. Genera Insectorum. Brussels (1902–). (The many fascicles of this work are listed separately under the families and subfamilies; each contains a synoptic key to genera and a catalogue of species of the family or subfamily treated.)

ZIMMERMAN, E. C. Insects of Hawaii. 5 vols. 1650 pp. Univ. Hawaii Press, Honolulu (1948–). (The parts are listed separately.)

ZOÖLOGICAL RECORD. Zoölogical Society of London (1865–). (Complete review of all literature in Zoölogy, year by year. The most complete and useful bibliographic index extant.)

ORDER PROTÙRA

(MIRIENTÓMATA)

Minute, slender, delicate, wingless, terrestrial, colorless or yellowish, blind species. Body bare; head pear-shaped, eyes and ocelli both absent; antennæ absent or reduced to a tubercle; abdomen comprising eleven segments, the last three very short, the basal three segments furnished with styles, no cerci; mouthparts formed for sucking, but retracted within the head, the mandibles long and styliform; legs short, tarsi one-jointed, with a single claw. Younger stages with only nine abdominal segments.

1. Tracheæ present, opening through two pairs of spiracles, one on mesothorax and one on metathorax; all vestigial abdominal appendages two-jointed; eighth segment of abdomen without pectines. (Eoséntomon, widespr.). . . . . EOSENTÓMIDÆ
   Tracheæ and spiracles absent; vestigial appendage on third abdominal segment one-jointed; eighth segment of abdomen usually with a pair of pectines. 2

2. Abdominal tergites without transverse sutures and laterotergites; each typical abdominal segment with a single complete transverse row of dorsal setæ; pectines of eighth abdominal segment reduced or absent. . . . . .PROTENTÓMIDÆ

a. Vestigial appendage on second abdominal segment two-jointed; eighth abdominal segment with pectines; front tarsi with sensory setæ. (Proturéntomon, Proténtomon, widespr.)
   PROTENTOMÌNÆ

Vestigial appendage on second abdominal segment one-jointed; eighth segment without pectines. (Microéntomon, widespr.)

MICROENTOMÎNÆ

Typical abdominal terga each with one to three transverse sutures and a pair of laterotergites; each typical abdominal segment with two complete rows of dorsal setæ; pectines on eighth segment not reduced. (Aceréntomon, Acerentulòides, widespr.). (Figs. 4, 12).

ACERENTÓMIDÆ

LITERATURE ON PROTURA

BERLESE, A. Monografia dei Myrientomata. Redia, 6 (1909).

CONDE, B. Protoures de l'Afrique orientale brittanique. Proc. Zool. Soc. London, 118, pp. 748–751 (1948).

EWING, H. E. New Genera and Species of Protura. Proc. Biol. Soc. Washington, 23, pp. 193–202 (1921).
Synonymy and Synopsis of the Genera of the Order Protura. Proc. Biol. Soc. Washington, 49, pp. 159–166 (1936).
Protura of North America. Ann. Ent. Soc. America, 33, pp. 495–551, 4 pls., 5 figs. (1940).

GISIN, H. Protoures de la Suisse. Rev. suisse Zool., 52, pp. 513–534, 7 figs. (1945).

LAMEERE, A. Protura. In Précis de Zoologie. Publ. Inst. zool. Torley-Rousseau, 4, pp. 154–158 (1934).

MILLS, H. B. Catalogue of the Protura. Bull. Brooklyn Ent. Soc., 27, pp. 125–130 (1932).

SILVESTRI, F. Descrizione di un nuovo genere di insetti apterigoti rappresentanti di un nuovo ordine. Boll. Lab. Zool. Gen. Agrar. Portici., 1, (1907).

STACH, J. Eosentomon armatum. (With list of known Protura.) Spraw. Kom. fizyogr., Krakow, 61, pp. 205–215 (1927).

STRENZKE, K. Norddeutsche Proturen. Zool. Jb., Syst., 75, pp. 73–102, 25 figs. (1942).

TUXEN, S. L. Monographie der Proturen (Morphologie). Zeitschr. f. Morph. u. Oekol., 22, pp. 671–720 (1931).
Danske Protura. Ent. Meddel., 17, pp. 306–311, 3 figs. (1931).
Lebenszyklus und Entwicklung zweier Proturen-gattungen. K. Dansk. Videns. Selskab., Biol., 6, 49 pp., 74 figs. (1949).

WOMERSLEY, H. Notes on the British Species of Protura. Ent. Monthly Mag., 63, pp. 140–148 (1927).
Further Notes on the British Species of Protura. Ent. Monthly Mag., 64, pp. 113–115 (1928).
A Preliminary Account of the Protura of Australia. Proc. Linn. Soc. New South Wales, 57, pp. 69–76 (1932).
On Two New Species of Protura from Iowa, U. S. A. Bull. Brooklyn Ent. Soc., 33, pp. 219–223 (1938).

ZIMMERMAN, E. C. Protura. In Insects of Hawaii, 2, pp. 42–43 (1948).

LITERATURE ON APTERYGOTA, GENERAL

DÉNIS, R. Diploures, Protoures, Thysanoures. In Grassé, Traité de Zoologie, **9**, pp. 112–276, 114 figs. (1949).

ZIMMERMAN, E. C. Thysanura and Entotrophi. Insects of Hawaii, **2**, pp. 29–42 (1948).

ORDER **THYSANÙRA**

(*ÁPTERA, ECTÓTROPHI, ECTÓGNATHA*)

Moderate-sized or small, wingless, terrestrial insects of active habits. Body usually elongate, tapering behind, clothed with scales except in the earliest instars and in adults of a few subterranean forms. Antennæ usually long, slender, with numerous joints. Head closely articulated with thorax. Compound eyes large and occupying most of the head capsule or small and lateral with a few large units (absent in a few subterranean forms). Three large ocelli or none. Mouthparts external, generalized; mandibles with one or two articulation points; maxillæ and labium large; palpi conspicuous, maxillary palpus with 5 or 7 segments, labial palpus with 3 segments. Thorax composed of three broad segments with rather large paranotal lobes, which may be closely appressed to the sides. Legs all similar; coxa large, sometimes bearing stylus; trochanter small but free; femur and tibia rather long; tarsus long, divided into 2 or 3 segments. Two tarsal claws, often with large median dactylopodite. Abdomen with ten similar segments visible dorsally; the minute eleventh bears a pair of long filamentous cerci and is developed as a long cerciform median structure which gives the abdomen the appearance of having three long, similar caudal filaments. Abdomen ventrally with simple segmental plates (fusion of coxopodites and sternite) or three closely fitted plates (median sternite and lateral diagonal coxopodites). Large paired styli present ventrally on two to eight abdominal segments; paired ventral sacs, visible when everted, often present. Ovipositor with only two pairs of valves. Penis well developed, rigid, never withdrawn into abdomen, as in higher insects. Metamorphosis slight. Silverfish, Bristle-tails, Rock-jumpers.

   1. Body strongly convex dorsally; coxa not greatly flattened, not much larger than femur; in living families eyes very large, many faceted, contiguous; paired lateral ocelli and single median ocellus present; many species with two pairs of eversible sacs on several segments; most species with styli (exites) on at least metathoracic legs (Superfamily MACHILÒIDEA) 2

      Body strongly flattened dorso-ventrally; coxa greatly flattened, much larger than any other leg segment; eyes widely separated (rarely absent); no lateral or median ocelli; never with more than one

pair of ventral eversible sacs on any segment; never with styli
(exites) on any coxæ (Superfamily LEPISMATÒIDEA)......3

2. Abdominal true sterna well developed, triangular, reaching at least
   one-half length of coxites on anterior segments; abdominal segment V always with exsertile vesicles; many genera with two
   pairs of vesicles on some segments; with antennal scape and pedicel
   scaled or with two pairs of vesicles on some segments or both.
   Cosmopol. (Máchilis, Pedetóntus, Petròbius, Mesomáchilis, Lepis-
   máchilis). (Fig. 10) ....MACHÍLIDÆ
   Abdominal true sterna weakly developed, reaching less than one-
   fourth length of coxites on all segments; abdominal segment V

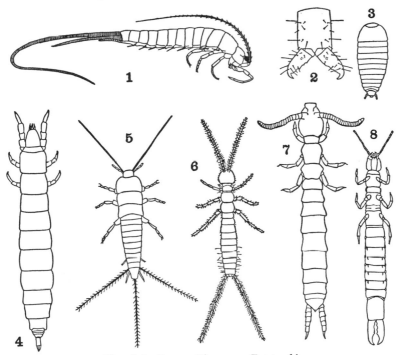

Figs. 1–8. Protura, Thysanura, Entotrophi

1. **Nesomachilis** (Tillyard) Meinertellidæ.
2. **Parajapyx,** apex of abdomen (Silvestri) Japygidæ.
3. **Gastrotheus** (Silvestri) Nicoletiidæ.
4. **Acerentomon** (Silvestri) Acerentomidæ.
5. **Lepisma** (Butler) Lepismatidæ.
6. **Campodea** (Maxwell-Lefroy) Campodeidæ.
7. **Anajapyx** (Silvestri) Projapygidæ.
8. **Japyx,** from below (Berlese) Japygidæ.

sometimes without exsertile vesicles; never more than one pair of vesicles on any segment; entire antenna scaleless. Cosmopol. (**Meinertéllus, Machilìnus, Hypomachilòdes, Machilòides, Nesomáchilis**). (Fig. 1) .... **MEINERTÉLLIDÆ**

3. Eyes always absent; scales usually absent; coxopodites of segments VIII and IX narrow, not covering base of ovipositor or parameres; most species ant or termite guests or living in a subterranean habitat, never domestic .... **NICOLETÌIDÆ**

a. Body form long, sub-cylindrical; usually scaleless; caudal filaments usually much longer than one-half body length; antenna usually more than two-thirds body length; width of head nearly as great as mesothorax. Subterranean or cavernicolous. Never ant or termite commensals. Widespr. (**Nicolètia, Lepidóspora, Trinemóphora, Prosthecina**). .... **NICOLETÌINÆ**

Body form oblong-oval or rapidly tapering toward rear; always with scales; caudal filaments usually less than one-half body length; antenna usually less than two-thirds body length; width of head hardly one-half width of mesothorax. Ant or termite commensals. Widespr. (**Atelùra, Grassiélla, Atopatelùra, Attatelùra**).

ATELURÌNÆ

Eyes always present; scales usually present; coxopodites of segments VIII and IX broad, covering base of ovipositor or parameres; most species free-living or domestic. (Fig. 9) ... **LEPISMÁTIDÆ**

a. Head distinctly longer than prothorax; inner edge of lacinia smooth; scales always absent; antenna and caudal filaments each at least as long as body. Arabia, Sahara Des., S. America (**Maindrònia**).

MAINDRONIÌNÆ

Head distinctly shorter than prothorax; inner edge of lacinia with teeth and setae; scales always present after second or third instar; antenna and caudal filaments either shorter or longer than body. Domestic or free-living. Cosmopol. (**Lepísma, Thermòbia, Ctenolepísma, Isolepísma, Panlepísma, Heterolepísma, Acrotélsa**). (Fig. 5) .... **LEPISMATÌNÆ**

ᶦLITERATURE ON THYSANURA

BAER, H. Beiträge zur Kenntnis der Thysanuren. Jenaische Zeitschr. Naturwiss., **48**, pp. 1–92 (1912).

CARPENTER, G. H. The Apterygota of the Seychelles. Proc. Roy. Irish Acad., **33**, B, pp. 1–70 (1916).

DENIS, J. R. Ordre des Thysanoures. In Grassé, P. P., Traité de Zoologie, **9**, pp. 209–275 (1949).

ESCHERICH, K. Das System der Lepismatiden. Zoologica, Heft 43, 164 pp. (1905).

HANDSCHIN, E. Urinsekten oder Apterygota. Tierwelt Deutschlands, Lief. 16 (1929).

LUBBOCK, J. Monograph of the Collembola and Thysanura. Ray Society, 276 pp. (1873).

SILVESTRI, F. Contributo alla conoscenza dei Machilidæ dell' America settentrionale. Boll. Lab. Zool. Gen. Agr. Portici, 5, pp. 324–350 (1911).

Tisanuri finora noti del Messico. Boll. Lab. Zool. Gen. Agr. Portici, 6, pp. 204–221 (1912).

Contributo alla conoscenza dei Machilidæ del Giappone. Boll. Lab. Zool. Gen. Agr. Portici, 32, pp. 283–306 (1943).

SLABAUGH, R. E. A New Thysanuran, and a Key to the Domestic Species of Lepismatidæ (Thysanura) found in the United States. Ent. News, 51, pp. 95–98 (1940).

STACH, J. Die Lepismatiden-Fauna Ägyptens. Ann. Musei Zool. Polonici, 11, pp. 27–111 (1935).

VERHOEFF, K. W. Über Felsenspringer, Machiloidea, 4. Aufsatz: Systematik und Orthomorphose. Zool. Anz., 36, pp. 425–438 (1910).

WOMERSLEY, H. Studies in Australian Thysanura. Trans. Roy. Soc. South Australia, 61, pp. 96–101; 166–172, 4 figs. (1937).

Primitive Insects of South Australia. Handb. Flora Fauna South Australia (1939).

WYGODZINSKY, P. W. Beiträge zur Kenntnis der Dipluren und Thysanuren der Schweiz. Denkschr. Schweiz. Naturf. Gesell., 74, pp. 107–227 (1941).

Contribução ao conhecimento da familia Machilidæ do Mexico, do Brasil e da Argentina. Rev. Entomologia, 15, pp. 54–96 (1944).

Sobre Nicoletia (Anelpistina) Silvestri, 1905 e Prosthecina Silvestri, 1933. Ciencia, 7, pp. 15–23 (1946).

Contribución al conocimiento de las Lepismatinæ americanas. Acta Zool. Lilloana, 6, pp. 215–227 (1948).

ORDER ENTÓTROPHI

(ENTÓGNATHA, DIPLÙRA, ÁPTERA, DICELLÙRA)

Small to medium-sized, slender, unpigmented; always wingless. Subterranean or cavernicolous, very active insects. Body without scaly covering (rarely with a few scales). Head large, prognathous, freely articulated with the thorax. Antennæ long, moniliform with numerous true segments. Eyes and ocelli absent. Mouthparts deeply retracted into the head, only the tips being visible; mandible with a single point of articulation; maxilla generalized, with 3-jointed palpus; labium reduced, palpi tiny or lost. Thorax with three subequal segments; no prominent paranotal lobes. Legs all similar; tarsus undivided; two claws; never with coxal stylus. Abdomen with ten conspicuous segments, terminated by a pair of well-developed cerci either long, many-jointed, and filamentous or short, unjointed and forceps-like or short, few-jointed, and straight; no median caudal filament. Abdomen ventrally with paired styli and exsertile sacs on some segments. Ovipositor, penis, and prominent gonopophyses always absent. Metamorphosis slight.

1. Abdomen terminated by strong, heavily sclerotized, undivided forceps; antennal joints broader than long; styli on first abdominal segment; tenth abdominal segment at least twice as long as ninth. Subterranean. Cosmopolitan. (Jápyx, Parajápyx, Heterojápyx, Evalljápyx, Dinjápyx) (Figs. 2, 8).............JAPÝGIDÆ
   Abdomen terminated by delicate cerci having few or many joints; tenth abdominal segment little longer than ninth.............2

2. Cerci usually as long as abdomen, with many pseudosegments, not bearing glandular duct with opening at tip; antennæ usually longer than head and thorax combined. Usually more than 4 mm. long when mature. Subterranean or cavernicolous. Cosmopolitan. (Campòdea, Eutrichocámpa, Lepidocámpa, Haplocámpa, Hemicámpa, Metriocámpa, Plusiocámpa, Parallocámpa) (Fig. 6, 13).
   ....CAMPODÈIDÆ
   Cerci less than half as long as abdomen, with less than ten joints, each with an internal duct leading from glands in the abdomen to the tip of the cercus; antennæ shorter than head and thorax combined. Always minute (under 4 mm. exclusive of antennæ and cerci). Subterranean. (Projápyx, Afr., S.Am.; Anajápyx, S. Europe, Afr., Mexico; Symphylurìnus, S.Am., Asia; Procampòdea, Italy, Sardinia) (Fig. 7).............PROJAPÝGIDÆ

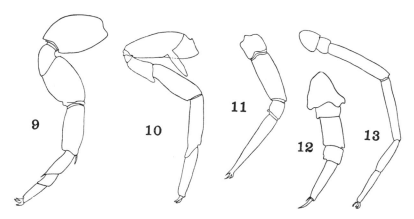

Figs. 9–13. Protura, Thysanura, Entotrophi, Symphyla

9. **Thermobia**, middle leg. Lepismatidæ.
10. **Machilis**, hind leg. Machilidæ.
11. **Hanseniella**, front leg. Scutigerellidæ.
12. **Acerentulus**, middle leg. Acerentomidæ.
13. **Campodea**, middle leg. Campodeidæ.

LITERATURE ON ENTOTROPHI

CARPENTER, G. H. The Apterygota of the Seychelles. Proc. Roy. Irish Acad., 33, B, pp. 1–70 (1916).

COOK, O. F. New Dicellura. Proc. Ent. Soc. Washington, 4, pp. 222–229 (1899).

DENIS, J. R. Sur la faune française des Aptérygotes. XIe note: Diplures, avec tableau de détermination des espèces françaises. Bull. Soc. Zool. France, 55 (1930).

Ordre des Diploures. In Grassé, P. P., Traité de Zoologie, 9, pp. 160–185 (1949).

HANDSCHIN, E. Urinsekten oder Apterygota. Tierwelt Deutschlands, Lief. 16 (1929).

LUBBOCK, J. Monograph of the Collembola and Thysanura. Ray Society. (1873).

SILVESTRI, F. Nuova contribuzione alla conoscenza dell' Anajapyx vesiculosus Silv. Boll. Lab. Zool. Gen. Agr. Portici, 1, pp. 3–15 (1905).

Nuovi Generi e Nuovi Specie de Campodeidæ (Thysanura) dell' America settentrionale. Boll. Lab. Zool. Gen. Agr. Portici, 6, pp. 5–25 (1912).

Contribuzione alla conoscenza dei Campodeidæ (Thysanura) d'Europa. Boll. Lab. Zool. Gen. Agr. Portici, 6, pp. 110–147 (1912).

Japygidæ dell' Estremo Oriente. Boll. Lab. Zool. Gen. Agr. Portici, 22, pp. 49–80 (1928).

Contribuzione alla conoscenza degli Japygidæ (Thysanura) dell' Africa occidentale. Boll. Lab. Zool. Gen. Agr., Portici, 23, pp. 149–196 (1929).

Contributions to a knowledge of the Indo-Malayan Japygidæ. Rec. Indian Mus., 32, pp. 439–489 (1930).

Japygidæ della regione australiana. Boll. Lab. Zool. Portici, 23, pp. 210–226, 13 figs. (1930).

Campodeidæ dell' Estremo Oriente. Boll. Lab. Zool. Gen. Agr., Portici, 25, pp. 286–320 (1931).

Nuovi contributi alla conoscenza della Fauna delle Isole italiane dell' Egeo. II. Thysanura-Entotropha. Boll. Lab. Zool. Gen. Agr., Portici, 27, pp. 61–111 (1932).

Quarto contributo alla conoscenza dei Campodeidæ del Nord America. Boll. Lab. Zool. Gen. Agr., Portici, 27, pp. 156–204 (1933).

Contribuzione alla conoscenza dei Projapygidæ. Boll. Lab. Zool. Gen. Agr., Portici, 30, pp. 41–74 (1936).

Some Japygidæ in the Museum of Comparative Zoology. Psyche, 54, pp. 209–229 (1947).

Sur les Japygidæ de Belgique. Bull. Ann. Soc. Ent. Belg., 84, pp. 211–217 (1948).

Contribuzione alla conoscenza degli Japygidæ. Rend. Accademia XL, (3), 27, pp. 1–115 (1948).

Descrizioni di alcuni Japyginæ del Nord America. Boll. Lab. Ent. Agr., Portici, 8, pp. 118–136 (1948).

Japyginæ della faune italiana finora note. Boll. Lab. Ent. Agr., Portici, 8, pp. 236–296 (1948).

Specie di Japygidæ finora raccolti nel Messico. Boll. Lab. Ent. Agr., Portici, **8**, pp. 297–320 (1948).

Distribuzione geografica di alcuni piccoli Arthropodi. I. *Procampodea brevicauda* Silv. Boll. Zool., **15**, pp. 19–24 (1948).

WOMERSLEY, H. Primitive Insects of South Australia. Handb. Flora Fauna South Australia, 322 pp. (1939).

WYGODZINSKY, P. W. Beiträge zur Kenntnis der Dipluren und Thysanuren der Schweiz. Denkschr. Schweiz. Naturf. Gesell., **74**, pp. 107–227 (1941).

Uma especie nova de Symphylurinus do Brasil. Rev. Entomologia, **12**, pp. 531–534 (1941).

Contribução ao conhecimento da familia Campodeidæ do Mexico. An. Esc. Nac. Cienc. Biol., **3**, pp. 367–404 (1944).

ORDER COLLÉMBOLA

Small to minute, soft-bodied wingless species, entotrophic, possessing four antennal segments, each with segmental musculature. Body globular — or subcylindrical to fusiform — rarely dorsoventrally compressed. Thorax of three segments, prothorax often reduced. Abdomen of six segments, frequently more or less ankylosed, with specialized ventral appendages on the first and third, and on either the fourth or fifth segments, and an unpaired gonopore located on the fifth segment. A median ventral projection, the ventral tube, apically bilobate and frequently possessing two extrusible tubes, always present on the first segment. Furcula or springing apparatus typically present on the fourth, or apparently the fifth, segment, with a catch or tenaculum for holding this structure on the third segment. Furcula composed of three portions: a large single basal piece, the manubrium; a pair of median segments, the dentes; and a pair of sclerotized apical mucrones. Legs similar in shape, typically possessing two subcoxal joints and a fused tibiotarsal segment. Tarsal claw single, usually with an empodial appendage. Eyes simple, discrete, typically sixteen in number, situated in dark pigmented fields directly behind the antennæ. Often with a pair of lobate or papillate postantennal organs. No metamorphosis and having postmaturation moults. Head prognathous to hypognathous. Tracheæ usually absent; when present opening by a single pair of simple apertures in the cervical region. Spring tails.

1. Head prognathous or hypognathous, body more or less elongate, never sub-spherical, segmentation distinct. (Suborder ARTHRO-PLÈONA) 2

   Head hypognathous, body sub-spherical, segmentation indistinct or obsolete. (Suborder SYMPHYPLÈONA) 8

2. Pronotum well developed, with setæ; imbrication of segments indistinct or wanting; furcula, when present, located on the fourth abdominal segment and lacking setæ on the ventral surface of the manubrium. (Section PODUROMÓRPHA) 3

Pronotum reduced, lacking setæ, united with the mesonotum, imbrication of body segments usually distinct; furcula when present tends to be displaced to the fifth abdominal segment. (Section ENTOMOBRYOMÓRPHA) 4
3. Head distinctly hypognathous. (Podùra) .... PODÙRIDÆ
   Head more or less prognathous .... HYPOGASTRÙRIDÆ

a. Lacking apertures in body wall (pseudocelli); sensory organ of third antennal segment simple, consisting of two small, variously modified, central sensory pegs, and two or more, more or less setiform, lateral sensory hairs, and without protecting papillæ; fourth antennal segment with a large apical bulb .... b
   Pseudocelli present (except *Pachytullbérgia*); sense organ of the third antennal segment complex (see fig. 15) consisting of two central sensory rods, plus other spherical, tubular, or variously club-shaped organs, usually situated behind several large protecting papillæ. Apical bulb of fourth antennal segment very small or lacking. (Onychiurus) .... ONYCHIURÌNÆ
b. Mandibles with well-developed molar plate or, if lacking, with quadrangular (fig. 14a) or short, claw-like (fig. 14b) head on maxillæ; maxillæ never elongate, lamellate, or needle-like. (Hypogastrùra, Ceratophysélla, Willèmia, Friesea, Brachystomélla). HYPOGASTRURÌNÆ
   Mandible often reduced or absent; when present, without well-developed molar plate (fig. 15a); maxillæ variously elongate, needle-like, or lamellate (fig. 15b), never short claw-like or quadrangular. (Neanùra, Anùrida, Paranùra, Pseudachorùtes). NEANURÌNÆ

4. Lacking differentiated short, erect, smooth setæ on the trochanter (trochanteral organ); ventral border of the claw simple, empodial appendage with no more than three lamellæ 5
   Differentiated trochanteral organ present; ventral edge of the claw split at its basal region; empodial appendage with four lamellæ or with a modification of four lamellæ. (Fig. 16). (Orchesélla, Entomòbrya, Lepidocýrtus, Paronélla, Cyphóderus). ENTOMOBRYÌDÆ
5. Head hypognathous, tracheæ present. (Actalètes). ACTALÉTIDÆ
   Head semi-prognathous, tracheæ absent 6
6. Postantennal organ typically present, furcula-bearing segment subequal to, or slightly smaller than, preceding segment 7
   Postantennal organ typically absent, furcula-bearing segment much shorter than preceding segment. (Tomócerus) (Fig. 17). TOMOCÉRIDÆ

7. Without scales and without long uniformly feathered setæ (bothro-trichia) on the thorax. (Isótoma, Proisótoma, Folsòmia, Tetra-canthélla, Isotomùris) . . . . ISOTÓMIDÆ
   With scales and/or bothrotrichia on the thorax. (Oncopodùra).
   ONCOPODÙRIDÆ
8. Thorax nearly as large or larger than abdomen; dorsum of first thoracic segment at approximately the same level as vertex of head; antennæ much shorter than head, inserted near or below its middle; lacking bothrotrichia and eyes. (Neèlus, Neélides, Megalothòrax) . . . . NEÉLIDÆ
   Thorax much smaller than abdomen; first thoracic segment con-siderably below level of vertex; antennæ at most only slightly shorter than head and inserted above the middle; eyes and bothro-trichia typically present 9
9. Antennal segment four longer than segment three. (Fig. 19).
   (Sminthùrus, Allácama, Sminthùrides, Arrhopalìtes, Bourletiélla).
   SMINTHÙRIDÆ
   Antennal segment four much shorter than segment three. (Dicýr-toma, Ptenòthrix) . . . . DICYRTÓMIDÆ

LITERATURE ON COLLEMBOLA

ABSOLON, K. and M. KSENEMANN. Ueber höhlenbewohnende Kollembola. Stud. Geb. allgem. Karstforsch. Brünn, 16, pp. 11–16 (1942).

BAGNALL, R. S. On the Classification of Onychiuridæ (Collembola), with particular reference to the genus *Tullbergia* Lubbock. Ann. Mag. Nat. Hist., (10)15, pp. 236–242, 10 figs. (1935).
   Contributions toward a Knowledge of the Tullbergiidæ. I–III. Ann. Mag. Nat. Hist., (11) 14, pp. 435–444 (1947).
   Contributions toward a Knowledge of the Onychiuridæ. I–IV. Ann. Mag. Nat. Hist., (11)14, pp. 631–642 (1948).

BONET, F. Colémbolos de la Republica Argentina. Eos, 9, pp. 123–194, 5 pls., 23 figs. (1934).
   Sobre la clasificación de los Oncopoduridæ (Collembola), con descripcion de especies nuevas. An. Esc. nac. Cienc. biol., 3, pp. 127–153, 22 figs. (1943).
   Monografia de la familia Neelidæ. Rev. Soc. mexicana Hist. Nat., 8, pp. 133–192, 69 figs. (1947).

BONET, F. and C. TELLEZ. Un nuevo genero de Esminturidos. Rev. Soc. mexicana Hist. Nat., 8, pp. 193–203, 19 figs. (1947).

BUITENDIJK, A. M. Fauna van Nederland. Collembola. Leiden Afl., 11, 99 pp., 24 figs. (1941).

DELAMARE-DEBOUTTEVILLE, C. Les Collemboles. Caractères généraux. Tableaux des principales familles européennes. L'Entomologiste, 3, pp. 34–37, 15 figs. (1947).
   Recherches sur les collemboles termitophiles et myrmecophiles. Arch. Zool. Expt. Gen., 85, pp. 261–425, 214 figs. (1948).

DENIS, J. R. Collemboles de Costa Rica. Boll. Lab. Zool. Portici, 25, pp. 69–170, 211 figs. (1931); *ibid.*, 27, pp. 222–322, 156 figs. (1933).

Sur la faune française des Apterygotes, XII. Arch. Zool. Expt. Gen., 74, pp. 357–383, 9 figs. (1932).

EDINGER, O. H., JR. Sminthuridæ of Southern California. Journ. Ent. Zool., 29, pp. 1–17, 3 pls. (1937).

FOLSOM, J. W. Tomocerinæ of North America. Proc. U. S. Nat. Mus., 46, pp. 451–472 (1914).

North American Collembolous Insects of the Subfamilies Achoreutinæ, Neanurinæ and Podurinæ. Proc. U. S. Nat. Mus., 50, pp. 477–525 (1916).

Subfamily Onychiurinæ. Proc. U. S. Nat. Mus., 53, pp. 637–659 (1917).

Nearctic Isotomidæ. Bull. U. S. Nat. Mus., 168, 144 pp., 39 pls. (1937).

GISIN, H. Hilfstabellen zum Bestimmen der holarktischen Collembolen. Verh. naturf. Ges. Basel, 55, pp. 1–130 (1943).

Materialien zur Revision der holarktischen Collembolen. Mitt. schweiz. ent. Ges., 19, pp. 121–156, 21 figs. (1944).

GUTHRIE, J. E. The Collembola of Minnesota. Geol. Nat. Hist. Surv. Minnesota, ser. 4, 110 pp. (1903).

HANDSCHIN, E. Die Onychiurinen der Schweiz. Verh. naturf. Ges. Basel, 32, pp. 1–37 (1920).

Collembolen aus Palästina, nebst einem Beitrag zur Revision der Gattung Cyphoderus. Rev. suisse Zool., 49, pp. 401–450, 11 figs. (1942).

LAMEERE, A. Collembola. In Précis de Zoologie. Publ. Inst. zool. Torley-Rousseau, 4, pp. 158–173 (1934).

LINNANIEMI, W. M. Die Apterygotenfauna Finlands. I. Allgemeiner Teil. Acta Soc. Scient. Fennicæ, 34, 130+XII pp.; II. Spezieller Teil. 40, 357 pp., 16 pls. (1907–12).

LUBBOCK, J. Monograph of the Collembola and Thysanura. Ray. Soc. London (1873).

MAYNARD, E. A. Monograph of Collembola of New York State. Comstock Pub. Co., Ithaca, N. Y. 362 pp., 671 figs. (1951).

MILLS, H. B. Monograph of the Collembola of Iowa. College Press, Ames, Iowa. vii+143 pp., 12 pls. (1934).

PERRIER, R. Collemboles de la France. Faune de France, 3, pp. 30–40, 44 figs. (1934).

SALMON, J. T. The Collembolan Fauna of New Zealand. Trans. Royal Soc. New Zealand, 70, pp. 282–431 (1941).

Keys and Bibliography to the Collembola. Zool. Publ. Victoria Univ. College, No. 8, 82 pp. (1951).

STACH, J. Species of Isotomurus occurring in European Caves. Acta Mus. Hist. Nat. Krakow, No. 2, 14 pp. (1946).

The Apterygotan Fauna of Poland in Relation to the World Fauna of this Group of Insect. Family Isotomidæ. Acta Monographica Musei Historiæ Naturalis, Krakow, 1947, pp. 1–485; Families Neogastruridæ and Brachystomellidæ. 1949, 341 pp., 35 pls.; Families Anuridæ and Pseudachorutidæ. 1949, 119 pp., 15 pls. (1947–1949).

WOMERSLEY, H. Collembola of Ireland. Proc. Roy. Irish Acad., 39B, pp. 160–202 (1930).

Preliminary Account of the Collembola — Symphypleona of Australia.

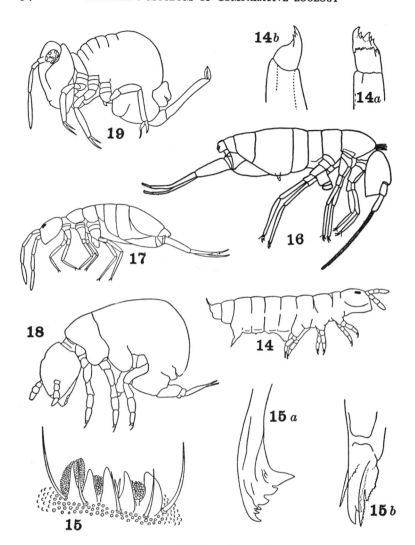

Figs. 14–19.   Collembola

14. **Hypogastrura** (Stach) Hypogastrurinæ.
14a. **Brachystomella**, maxilla (Stach) Hypogastrurinæ.
14b. **Xenyllodes**, maxilla (Stach) Hypogastrurinæ.
15. **Onychiurus**, sensory organ on third antennal segment (Folsom) Onychiurinæ.
15a. **Anurida**, mandibles (Stach) Neanurinæ.
15b. **Anurida**, maxilla (Stach) Neanurinæ.
16. **Entomobrya** (Folsom) Entomobryidæ.
17. **Tomocerus** (Folsom) Tomoceridæ.
18. **Oncopodura** (Bonet) Neelidæ.
19. **Sminthurides** (Folsom and Mills) Sminthuridæ.

Pamph. Counc. Sci. Ind. Res. Australia, No. 34, 47 pp., 19 figs. (1932).
Preliminary Account of the Collembola — Arthropleona of Australia. Trans. Roy. Soc. South Australia, **57**, pp. 48–77 (1933); **58**, pp. 37–47, 27 figs. (1934).
On the Collembolan Fauna of New Zealand. Trans. Roy. Soc. New Zealand, **66**, pp. 316–328, 2 figs. (1936).
Primitive Insects of South Australia. Silverfish, Springtails, and their Allies. Adelaide. 322 pp., 1 pl., 84 figs. (1939).
YOSII, R. Isotomid Collembola of Japan. Tenthredo, **2**, pp. 348–392, 23 figs. (1939).
ZIMMERMAN, E. C. Collembola. Insects of Hawaii, **2**, pp. 43–71 (1948).

ORDER PLECTÓPTERA

(*EPHEMERÓPTERA, EPHEMÉRIDA, AGNÁTHA*)

Delicate insects with short, filiform antennæ and vestigial mouthparts; abdomen slender, bearing two or three long, many-jointed caudal filaments; four wings, usually with very complex venation. Head not very freely movable, with the compound eyes and three ocelli present; antennæ with two large basal joints and a bristle-like, indistinctly jointed terminal portion. Prothorax more or less free, small or very small; mesothorax large. Fore wings much larger than the hind ones, usually with many longitudinal veins and a great number of cross-veins; commonly with numerous short longitudinal veins near the margin that are not attached at the base; media more complex than in other living orders, its anterior, convex branch preserved; hind wings often very small or even absent. Abdomen slender, usually cylindrical or tapering, with ten segments. Legs weak; tarsi usually with five or four joints. Metamorphosis incomplete, the nymph aquatic and provided with abdominal gills and three caudal filaments. Aerial form emerging from the nymph as a subimago which is similar to the imago, but which molts when it transforms to the imago. Imaginal life very short. Mayflies.

Adults

1. Base of media (M_{1+2}) in fore wing strongly divergent from Cu_1 at base; hind tarsi with four movable joints, or less; if a fifth joint is indicated it is immovably united to the tibia. (Superfamily EPHEMERÒIDEA) 2

   Base of media and Cu_1 parallel at base or very weakly divergent; tarsi with four or five freely movable joints 5

2. Subcosta in fore wing concealed in a fold of the wing membrane, visible only at the base; branches of the radius and media approximated in pairs; wings dull, translucent; legs of female short and weak; tibiæ and tarsi of male transversely striated; only

two caudal filaments. (**Palingènia, Anagenèsia,** Palæarc.; **Plethogenèsia,** Indoaustr.) . . . . **PALINGENÌIDÆ**
Subcosta completely developed, visible for its entire length 3

3. Wings translucent, subopaque in the male, entirely opaque in the female; hind margin of wings without unattached veinlets; legs weak, the front pair sometimes long in the male; hind legs almost always short and weak. (**Euthyplòcia,** Neotrop., Ethiop.; **Exeuthyplòcia, Povílla,** Ethiop.; **Campsùrus,** Am.; **Polymitárcys,** widespr.) (*EPHORÓNIDÆ*) . . . . **POLYMITÁRCIDÆ**
Wings transparent, shining; margin of wings, especially the hind pair, with numerous short unattached veinlets; legs strong, functional 4

4. First branch of cubitus in fore wing simple, not branched, but connected with the wing margin by numerous crossveins; fork of R_2 and R_4 in hind wing much longer than its stalk. (**Ephémera,** Holarc., Indoaustr.; **Hexagènia,** Am., Ethiop.; **Eatónica,** Ethiop.; **Pentagènia,** Nearc.) . . . . **EPHEMÉRIDÆ**
First branch of cubitus in fore wing forked; not connected to the wing margin by crossveins; fork of R_2 and R_4 in hind wing shorter or no longer than its stalk. (**Potamánthus, Neoephémera,** Holarc.; **Rhœnánthus,** Palæarc., Indoaustr.; **Potamanthòdes,** Indomal.) . . . . **POTAMÁNTHIDÆ**

5. Hind tarsi with four freely movable joints; if with the indication of a fifth joint, this is immovably attached to the tibia. (Superfamily BAETÒIDEA) 6
Hind tarsus with five freely movable joints 10

6. Subcosta in fore wing fused with the radius or wanting, at most visible at the base; wings milky or grayish, with very simple venation, the fore wing with only four to seven longitudinal veins, with crossveins in only from two to five of the anterior spaces; hind wing without or with very few crossveins which are restricted to the anterior part; large or medium sized species. (Fig. 22). (**Oligoneùria,** Palæarc., Neotrop., Ethiop.; **Homoneùria, Lachlania,** Holarc.; **Spaniophlèbia, Nòya,** Neotrop.; **Elassoneùria,** Ethiop.) . . . . **OLIGONEURÌIDÆ**
Subcosta in fore wing free, well developed and visible for its entire length 7

7. Anterior median vein in fore wing (MA) clearly forked 8
Anterior median vein in fore wing, simple, not forked, although behind it are two free veins which are not attached at the base (Fig. 21); fore wing usually with few crossveins; hind wings very small and narrow, sometimes absent, with at most two or three longitudinal veins. (**Clòeon,** cosmop.; **Baètis,** widespr.; **Centróptilum,** Holarc., Ethiop.; **Callibaètis,** Am.) . . . . **BAÉTIDÆ**

8. Wings milky or infuscated, ciliate on the hind margin; hind wings absent, although sometimes present in the subimago; no unattached intercalated veins; frequently with only a few crossveins; small species. (Fig. 24). (Caènis, widespr.; Tricoryphòdes, Leptòhyphes, Am.; Leptohyphòdes, Neotrop.; Tricórythus, Ethiop.). (Including *PROSOPISTOMÁTIDÆ?*). (*BRACHY-CÉRCIDÆ*) .... **CAÉNIDÆ**
Wings hyaline; hind wings almost always present; wings with numerous crossveins 9

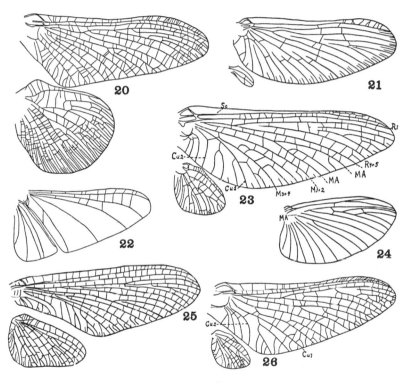

Figs. 20–26. **Plectoptera**

20. **Baetisca**, wings (Eaton) Baetiscidæ.
21. **Baetis**, wings (Eaton) Baetidæ.
22. **Oligoneuria**, wings (Eaton) Oligoneuriidæ.
23. **Ephemerella**, wings (Eaton) Ephemerellidæ.
24. **Caenis**, wing (Eaton) Caenidæ.
25. **Chirotenetes**, wings (Needham) Siphluridæ.
26. **Atalophlebia**, wings (Eaton) Leptophlebiidæ.

9. Second branch of cubitus in the fore wing usually widely separated
    at base from the first branch, but lying close to the first anal
    vein; no unattached intercalated veins between the media and
    cubitus and none in front of the posterior branch of the media.
    (Fig. 26). (Thraùlus, Palæarc., Neotrop., Indoaustr.; Atalo-
    phlèbia, Neotrop., Indoaustr.; Habrophlèbia, Leptophlèbia, Hol-
    arc.; Adenophlèbia, Ethiop.) ....LEPTOPHLEBÌIDÆ
    Second branch of cubitus in fore wing approximate at base to the
    first branch, but widely separated from the first anal vein; several
    (usually two) unattached intercalated veins between the media
    and cubitus and also in front of the posterior branch of the media.
    (Fig. 23). (Ephemerélla, Chitonóphora, Holarc.; Drunélla,
    Nearc.; Melanomerélla, Neotrop.; Teloganòdes, Indoaustr.).
    EPHEMERÉLLIDÆ

10. First and second branches of the cubitus running more or less
    parallel to the first anal vein; Cu$_1$ and Cu$_2$ connected by cross-
    veins, but the cubital area without paired crossveins or sinuous
    veins extending to the wing margin; hind wings rounded, with
    numerous long intercalated veins extending to the posterior part
    of the wing margin; prothorax very small. (Fig. 20). (Baetísca,
    Nearc.) ....BAETÍSCIDÆ
    First and second branches of the cubitus very close together at
    base and strongly divergent apically, the second branch much
    shorter than the first and strongly curved backwards towards apex,
    hind wings oval; pronotum well developed................11

11. Cubital area of fore wing with a number of more or less sinuous
    veins extending from the first branch of the cubitus to the wing
    margin. (Fig. 25). (Amelètus, Holarc., Austr.; Chirotónetes,
    Siphlùrus (= Siphlonùrus), Holarc.; Siphlonísca, Nearc.; Onis-
    cigáster, Indoaustr.). (SIPHLONÙRIDÆ).....SIPHLÙRIDÆ
    Cubital area of fore wing without oblique sinuous veins extending
    from the first branch of the cubitus to the wing margin, but
    with from two to four straight unattached veins more or less
    parallel to the branches of the cubitus.....................12

12. Only two unattached intercalated veins in the cubital area of the
    fore wing; if sometimes with a second pair indicated, these are
    short and lie close to the second branch of the cubitus; two or
    three caudal filaments. (Amétropus, Métropus, Palæarc.).
    AMETROPÓDIDÆ
    Four unattached intercalated veins in the cubital area of the fore
    wing, the longer pair lying close to the second branch of the
    cubitus; two caudal filaments. (Heptagènia, Epeòrus, Arthróplea,
    Holarc.; Ìron, Nearc., Ecdyùrus, Palæarc., Am.; Rhithrógena,
    Palæarc.; Atópopus, Indoaustr.). (Including ARTHROPLÈI-
    DÆ). (ECDYONÙRIDÆ). ....HEPTAGENÌIDÆ

Nymphs

1. Abdominal gills visible at their insertion above or on the sides of the abdomen 2

   Gills entirely concealed by a large shield-like prolongation of the thorax behind, which covers most of the abdomen. (Fig. 27). Imago unknown. (**Prosopístoma**, Palæarc., Ethiop.).

   PROSOPISTOMÁTIDÆ

2. Mandibles usually very long and extended anteriorly; six or seven pairs of plumose gills, the first sometimes much reduced; legs stout 3

   Mandibles very short, not extended anteriorly; gills not plumose; legs slender 6

3. Mandibles extremely large and projecting far beyond the head in front; gills extended dorsally over the abdomen 4

   Mandibles much shorter, but slightly projecting in front of the head; gills extended laterally, away from the abdomen. (Fig. 29).

   POTAMÁNTHIDÆ

4. Front with two tubercles anteriorly; mandibles curved outwards at tips; antennæ with long cilia . . . . EPHEMÉRIDÆ

   Front without tubercles; mandibles curved downwards at tips; antennæ without or with short cilia 5

5. Body short and stout; six pairs of similar gills; caudal filaments short, the median one shorter than the lateral ones. (Fig. 33).

   PALINGENÌIDÆ

   Body long and slender; seven pairs of gills, the first pair much reduced in size; anal filaments long, of equal length. (Fig. 28.)

   POLYMITÁRCIDÆ

6. Body strongly flattened, the head orbicular, or more or less transverse, the eyes placed on its dorsal surface .7

   Body more or less cylindrical, not or very slightly flattened, the eyes placed at the sides of the head 8

7. Gills uniform, extending from the sides of the abdomen; anal filaments at least as long as the body . . . . HEPTAGENÌIDÆ

   First pair of gills inserted on the under side of the first abdominal segment, the six following pairs extended from the sides of the abdomen . . . . OLIGONEURÌIDÆ

8. Lateral caudal filaments (cerci) fringed on both edges 9

   Lateral caudal filaments ciliated on the inner border only 11

9. Seven pairs of gills, inserted laterally at the sides of the abdomen; sometimes all are filamentous or the first is much reduced and the others leaf-like. (Fig. 32) . . . . LEPTOPHLEBÌIDÆ

   Five or six pairs of gills, inserted dorsally at the sides of the abdomen 10

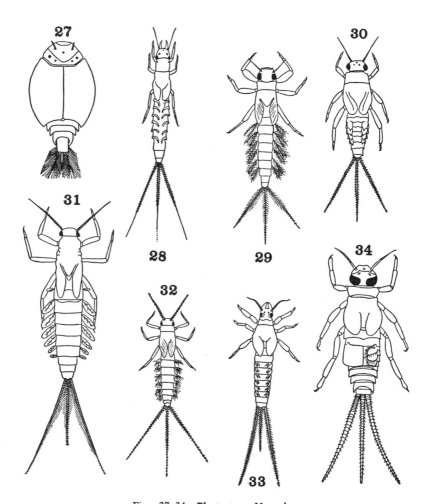

Figs. 27–34. **Plectoptera,** *Nymphs*

27. **Prosopistoma,** nymph (Rousseau) Prosopistomatidæ.
28. **Polymitarcys,** nymph (Rousseau) Polymitarcidæ.
29. **Potamanthus,** nymph (Rousseau) Potamanthidæ.
30. **Ephemerella,** nymph (Rousseau) Ephemerellidæ.
31. **Baetis,** nymph (Rousseau) Baetidæ.
32. **Habrophlebia,** nymph (Rousseau) Leptophlebiidæ.
33. **Palingenia,** nymph (Rousseau) Palingeniidæ.
34. **Tricorythus,** nymph (Rousseau) Caenidæ.

10. Six pairs of gills, the first very small, the second greatly enlarged and covering the following pairs which bear a long fringe. (Fig. 34) ....CAÉNIDÆ
Five pairs of gills, the last or the last two pairs not visible. (Fig. 30) EPHEMERÉLLIDÆ
11. Body cylindrical; head bent downwards; hind corners of abdominal segments not produced. (Fig. 31).................BAÉTIDÆ
Body more or less flattened; head horizontal or nearly so; hind corners of abdominal segments produced backwards to form a tooth-like projection 12
12. Claws not longer than the tibiæ ....SIPHLÙRIDÆ
Claws of four posterior legs stout, as long as their tibiæ, those of the front legs bifid at tips................AMETROPÓDIDÆ

LITERATURE ON PLECTOPTERA

BALTHASAR, V. Arthropleidæ, eine neue Familie der Ephemeropteren. Zool. Anz., 120, pp. 204–230, 15 figs. (1937).
BARNARD, K. H. South African May-flies. Trans. Roy. Soc. South Africa, 20, pp. 201–259, 48 figs. (1932).
BERNER, L. Mayflies of Florida. Univ. Florida Sci. Ser., 4, No. 4, xii+267 pp., 24 pls., 88 figs. (1950).
CHOPRA, B. Indian Ephemeroptera: Ephemeroidea. Rec. Indian Mus., 29, pp. 91–138 (1927).
DESPAX, R. Éphéméroptères. In Grassé, Traité de Zoologie, 9, pp. 277–309, 20 figs. (1949).
EATON, A. E. Revisional monograph of recent Ephemeridæ. Trans. Linn. Soc. London, (2), 3, (1883–85).
    Ephemeridæ. In Biologia centrali-Americana, pp. 1–16 (1892).
GROS, A. J. and J. A. LESTAGE. Contribution à l'étude des larves des Éphéméroptères. Ann. Biol. Lacust., 15, pp. 123, 133, 136, 161 (1927).
HSU, YIN-CHI. The Mayflies of China. Peking Nat. Hist. Bull., 11, pp. 129–148, 11 figs. (1936).
KIMMINS, D. E. Key to British Species of Ephemeroptera and Genera of Nymphs. Sci. Publ. Freshwater Biol. Assoc. British Empire, No. 7, 64 pp., 36 figs. (1942).
KLAPÁLEK, F. Ephemerida: Süsswasserfauna Deutschlands, Lief. 8 (1909).
LAMEERE, A. Ephemeroptera. In Précis de Zoologie. Publ. Inst. zool. Torley-Rousseau, 4, pp. 174–212 (1935).
LESTAGE, J. A. Notes sur les Éphémères de la "Monographical Revision" de Eaton. Ann. Soc. Ent. Belgique, 64, pp. 33–60 (1924).
    Les Éphéméroptères de la Belgique. Bull. Ann. Soc. Ent. Belgique, 68–69 (several parts).
    Contribution à l'étude des larves des Éphémères paléarctiques. Ann. Biol. Lacust., 8, pp. 213–457 (1918).
    La famille des Leptophlebiidæ. Miss. Biol. Belge Brésil, Brussels, 2, pp. 249–258 (1930).
NEEDHAM, J. G. Ephemeridæ of New York. Bull. New York State Mus., No. 86, pp. 17–62 (1905).

NEEDHAM, J. G., J. R. TRAVER and YIN-CHI HSU. The Biology of Mayflies. xiv + 759 pp., 40 pls., 168 figs. Comstock Publ. Co., Ithaca, New York (1935).

PERRIER, R. Ephémères de la France. Faune de France, **3**, pp. 41–50, 35 figs. (1934).

PHILLIPS, J. S. Revision of New Zealand Ephemeroptera. Trans. New Zealand Inst., **61**, pp. 271–390, 18 pls., 125 figs. (1930).

Studies of New Zealand Mayfly Nymphs. Trans. Ent. Soc. London, **79**, pp. 399–422, 8 pls. (1931).

ROUSSEAU, E. Les larves et nymphes aquatiques des insectes d'Europe, Vol. 1, pp. 162–273 (1921).

SCHOENEMUND, E. Plectoptera. Tierwelt Deutschlands, **19**, 110 pp., 186 figs. (1930).

SEEMAN, T. M. Dragonflies, Mayflies and Stoneflies of southern California. Pomona Journ. Ent. and Zool., **19**, pp. 1–69 (1927).

SPIETH, H. T. The Genus Stenonema. Ann. Ent. Soc. America, **40**, pp. 87–122 (1947).

TILLYARD, R. J. The Trout-food Insects of Tasmania. Part II. — A Monograph of the Mayflies of Tasmania. Pap. Proc. Roy. Soc. Tasmania, **1935**, pp. 23–59, 1 pl., 33 figs. (1935).

TRAVER, J. R. Heptageninæ of North America. Journ. New York Ent. Soc., **41**, pp. 105–125 (1933).

Mayflies of North Carolina. Journ. Elisha Mitchell Sci. Soc., **47**, pp. 85–236, 13 pls. (1932); **48**, pp. 141–206, 1 pl. (1933).

Notes on Brazilian Mayflies. Bol. Mus. Nac. Rio de Janeiro, (N.S.) Zool., **22**, 53 pp., 8 figs. (1944).

Notes on Neotropical Mayflies. Parts I–III. Rev. Ent., Rio de Janeiro, **17**, pp. 418–436, 18 figs.; **18**, pp. 149–160, 22 figs.; 370–395, 39 figs. (1947).

TÜMPEL, R. Die Geradeflügler Mitteleuropas. (Plectoptera, pp. 73–108) (1901).

ULMER, G. Übersicht über die Gattungen der Ephemeropteren. Stettiner Ent. Zeit., **81**, pp. 97–144 (1920).

Verzeichnis der deutschen Ephemeropteren. Konowia, **6**, pp. 234–262 (1927).

Ephemeroptera. In Tierwelt Mitteleuropas, **4**, Lief. 1b, pp. III, 1–43 (1929).

Die Trichopteren, Ephemeropteren und Plecopteren des arktischen Gebietes. Fauna arctica, **6**, pp. 219–222 (1932).

Revised Key to Genera of Plectoptera. Peking Nat. Hist. Bull., **7**, pp. 195–218, 2 pls. (1933).

ORDER ODONÀTA

(LIBELLULÒIDEA, PARANEURÓPTERA)

Slender predatory insects, usually of large or very large size and usually strong fliers; head mobile, eyes large, three ocelli; antennæ minute, four- to seven-jointed; mouth inferior, mandibles strong, maxillary palpi one-jointed, labial palpi two-jointed; prothorax small but free, meso- and metathorax fused, oblique; cerci one-jointed; legs not large, similar, usually armed with spines, placed far forward, tarsi three-jointed; wings four, nearly alike, elongate, membranous, net-veined, not folded, with characteristic nodus, arculus and triangle (see Figs. 41, 42). Abdomen long and narrow, cylindrical or flattened, sometimes clubbed at apex; ovipositor sometimes complete; male sexual apparatus attached to the second sternite. Metamorphosis considerable, the nymphs aquatic, no resting pupal stage. Damsel flies, Dragon flies.

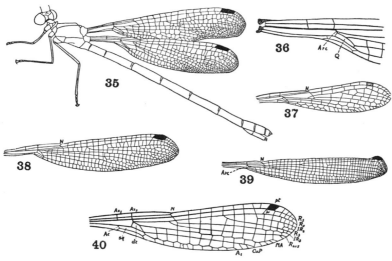

Figs. 35–40. **Odonata**

35. **Lestes** (Garman) Lestidæ.
36. **Chromagrion**, base of fore wing (Garman) Cœnagrionidæ.
37. **Hemiphlebia**, wing (Needham) Hemiphlebiidæ.
38. **Megalestes**, wing (Needham) Synlestidæ.
39. **Mecistogaster**, wing (Needham) Pseudostigmatidæ.
40. **Pseudagrion**, wing (Tillyard) Cœnagrionidæ.

Adults

1. Disoidal cell in fore wing never divided by a vein, although it is rarely divided in the hind wing; wings petiolate, sub-petiolate or without stalked base; nodus almost always before the middle of the wing; fore and hind wings essentially alike in form and venation; slender species, nearly always resting with the wings closed above the body 2

   Discoidal cell of both wings divided into two parts by an oblique vein into a triangle and supratriangle; wings never petiolate, nor with a distinctly narrowed stalklike portion at the base; hind wings noticeably different from the fore wings in shape and venation; nodus at or beyond the middle of the wings, at least in the fore pair; stouter-bodied forms that rest with the wings held extended horizontally from the sides of the body. (Suborder ANISÓPTERA) 18

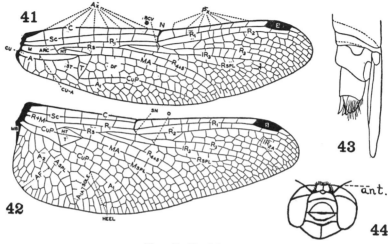

Figs. 41–44. Odonata

41. **Libellula,** fore wing (Borror) Libellulidæ.
42. **Libellula,** hind wing (Borror) Libellulidæ.
43. **Cordulegaster,** tip of abdomen of female (Tillyard) Cordulegastridæ.
44. **Libellula,** head; *ant.,* antenna (Hyatt and Arms) Libellulidæ.

2. Discoidal cell of similar form in both fore and hind wings; eyes strongly projecting from the sides of the head, often almost stalked and always separated by more than their width in dorsal view; mesothorax longer than wide; abdomen long and slender, cylindrical. (Fig. 35.) (Suborder ZYGÓPTERA)................3
Discoidal cell differing in form in the fore and hind wing; eyes less noticeably projecting laterally, separated by less than their width (female), or almost contiguous above (male); mesothorax wider than long; abdomen distinctly swollen apically. (**Epiophlèbia,** Ind., Japan.) (Suborder ANISOZYGÓPTERA).

EPIOPHLEBÏIDÆ

3. Only two, rarely three, complete antenodal crossveins (Fig. 38); arculus at least as near to the nodus as to the base of the wing; wings strongly petiolate; mesopleura not divided by an oblique suture 4

Five or more antenodal crossveins; arculus farther from the nodus than from the base of the wing, equidistant in some Chlorocyphidæ); wings less strongly petiolate; frequently with metallic coloration; mesopleura with a distinct oblique suture extending from the root of the wing toward the middle coxa. (Superfamily AGRIONÒIDEA (*AGRIÒIDEA*)) 13

4. Postnodal crossveins not at all in line with the crossveins beneath them; discoidal cell open basally; small, slender, metallic green species, with short wings. (Fig. 37.) (Hemiphlèbia, Austr.). (Superfamily HEMIPHLEBIÒIDEA) ... HEMIPHLEBÌIDÆ

   Postnodal crossveins more or less completely in line with the crossveins below them (*i.e.*, extending as straight lines from the costa to the first branch of the radius. (Superfamily COENAGRIONÒIDEA (*COENAGRIÒIDEA*)) 5

5. CuP arching strongly upwards on leaving the discoidal cell. (Synléstes, Chorismágrion, Austr.; Chloroléstes, Ethiop.; Periléstes, Neotrop.) ....SYNLÉSTIDÆ

   CuP not arched strongly at this point........................6

6. R4+5 and IR3 (intercalary) both arising far proximal to the level of subnodus, IR3 usually at least half-way between arculus and subnodus and usually nearer the arculus.....................7

   R4+5 and IR3 arising nearer the subnodus than arculus; at the most R4+5 arising half-way between arculus and subnodus...8

7. Veins CuP and 1A complete; supplementary sectors present between IR3, R4+5 and MA. (Léstes, cosmop.; Cryptoléstes, Am.; Sympýcna, Holarc.; Australéstes, Austr.)...............LÉSTIDÆ

   Vein CuP greatly reduced, vein 1A entirely absent; two straight supplementary sectors present, one between R2 and IR2 and another between IR2 and R3. (Lestòidea, Austr.).

   LESTOIDÈIDÆ

8. Nodus situated very close to base of wing, at from one-sixth to one-fourth the wing-length; pterostigma absent, or if present, abnormal, not fully chitinized, or made up of several cells, never braced. (Pseudostígma, Mecistogáster, Megalóprepus, Microstígma, Anomísma, Neotrop.) ....PSEUDOSTIGMÁTIDÆ

   Nodus lying more distal, usually more than one-fourth the wing-length from base (if nearer, then the pterostigma normal); pterostigma present, strongly chitinized (rarely hypertrophied), braced or unbraced 9

9. Supplementary sectors present distally and extending proximal as far as the level of pterostigma or further. (Megapodágrion, Neotrop.; Argioléstes, Podoléstes, Austromal.). (*MEGAPODAGRÌIDÆ*) ....MEGAPODAGRIÓNIDÆ

   Supplementary sectors absent or at most a few distal cellules aligned and not extending proximal as far as pterostigma...........10

10. Vein 1A absent or greatly reduced; vein CuP normal or reduced. .11
 Veins CuP and 1A normal 12
11. An extra crossvein present in the postcostal space, very close to base
 of wing and in addition to that of the anal-crossing (Ac); number
 of postnodals comparatively large. (Platystícta, Protostícta, Oriental; Palæmnema, Neotrop.) . . . . .PLATYSTÍCTIDÆ
 No additional crossvein in the postcostal space; number of postnodals comparatively small. (Protoneùra, Neoneùra, Neotrop.;
 Nosostícta, Neostícta, Austr.; Caconeùra, Ind.).
                                             PROTONEÙRIDÆ
12. Discoidal cell subrectangular; no marked zigzagging of any of the
 main veins (only distal portion of MA slightly zig-zagged).
 (Platycnèmis, Indocnèmis, Calicnèmia, Metacnèmis, Old World).
                                             PLATYCNEMÍDIDÆ
 Discoidal cell with distal angle markedly acute; veins IR3; MA
 and 1A strongly zig-zagged distally. (Cœnágrion (*Agrion*, auctt.),
 Ischnùra, Enallágma, widespr.; Pseudágrion, Indoaustr.; Árgia,
 Am.; Nehallènia, Holarc., Neotrop.). (*CŒNAGRIIDÆ*).
                                             CŒNAGRIÓNIDÆ
13. Arculus present 14
 Arculus absent, usually only the distal primary antenodal vein
 present. (Polythóre, Euthóre, Còra, Chalcópteryx, Neotrop.).
                                             POLYTHÓRIDÆ
14. Both primary antenodal veins present; discoidal cell well separated
 from R1 15
 Both primary antenodal veins absent 17
15. R2+3 more or less arched towards R1, shortly after its origin;
 secondary antenodals numerous 16
 R2+3 not arched towards R1; secondary antenodals few in number.
 (Amphípteryx, Neotrop.; Diphlèbia, Austr.; Devadátta, Indomal.;
 Pentaphlèbia, Ethiop.) . . . . .AMPHIPTERÝGIDÆ
16. Clypeus produced in the form of a prominent snout; no basal
 antenodals ever present. (Chlorocỳpha, Ethiop.; Neocỳpha, Libel-
 làgo, Indocỳpha, Indomal.) (*LIBELLAGÍNIDÆ*).
                                             CHLOROCÝPHIDÆ
 Clypeus not produced; nearly always basal; antenodals present.
 (Heliócharis, Dictèrias, Cyanócharis, Neotrop.).
                                             HELIOCHARÍTIDÆ
17. R2+3 not usually fused with R1, shortly after its origin; anal vein
 without a recurrent branch; discoidal cell short, usually shorter
 than basal space and either untraversed or traversed by very few
 crossveins. (Anisopleùra, Indophæa, Ind.; Epállaga).
                                             EPALLÁGIDÆ
 R2+3 nearly always fused with R1 for a short distance after its
 origin; anal vein with a recurrent branch or itself recurrent;

discoidal cell elongate, usually as long as basal space and traversed by numerous crossveins. (**Ágrion** (*Calópteryx*), Holarc.; **Sàpho**, Ethiop.; **Vestàlis**, Indomal.; **Neuróbasis**, Indoaustr.). (*CALOP-TERÝGIDÆ, AGRÌIDÆ*) .... AGRIÓNIDÆ [1]

18. Antenodal crossveins of the first and second series (*i.e.* above and below the subcostal vein) not corresponding or continuous, except for two greatly thickened ones that extend straight across from the costa to the radius; triangles in fore and hind wings alike or closely similar in shape and occupying the same position with reference to the arculus in both wings; labial palpi two-jointed. (Superfamily ÆSHNÒIDEA) 19
   Antenodal crossveins of the first and second series corresponding, extending as straight continuous veins from the costa to the radius, except sometimes the last one or two; none of these crossveins greatly thickened; triangles of fore and hind wings markedly different in form and position, placed much nearer to the arculus in the hind wing than in the fore wing. (Superfamily LIBEL-LULÒIDEA) 22

19. Eyes broadly contiguous above; anal loop in hind wing clearly formed. (**Æshna** (*Æschna*), widespr.; **Ànax**, cosmop.; **Austrophlèbia**, Austr.). (*ÆSCHNIDÆ*) .... ÆSHNIDÆ
   Eyes more or less separated above 20

20. Middle lobe of labium with a deep median fissure; eyes only moderately separated above 21
   Middle lobe of labium entire, not divided by a median fissure; eyes widely separated above; ovipositor reduced to a pair of valves attached to the eighth segment. (**Gómphus**, **Ophiogómphus**, Holarc.; **Lindènia**, Palæarc.; **Erpetogómphus**, Am.; **Ictìnus**, Indoaustr.) .... GÓMPHIDÆ

21. Pterostigma moderately long, emitting four or five crossveins from its lower edge; superior anal appendages of male narrow and acute at apex. (**Cordulegáster**, widespr.; **Anotogáster**, Holarc.; **Chlorogómphus**, Indomal.) .... CORDULEGÁSTRIDÆ
   Pterostigma very long and slender, emitting six or seven crossveins; superior anal appendages of male broadly triangular, obtuse at apex. (**Petalùra**, **Uropétala**, Austr.; **Phènes**, Neotrop.; **Tachópteryx**, Nearc.) .... PETALÙRIDÆ

22. Tibiæ of males with a long laminate keel on the flexor surface; base of hind wing of male usually strongly angulate; second abdominal segment with a flattened tubercle (auricle) at each side; body almost always metallic in color. (**Cordùlia**, **Somatochlòra**, Holarc.; **Macromìa**, widespr.; **Tetragoneùria**, Nearc.; **Phyllomacromìa**, Ethiop.) .... CORDULÌIDÆ

[1] The name Agrionidæ is used instead of Agriidæ on the basis of evidence submitted by Professor B. Elwood Montgomery.

Tibiæ of males not keeled; base of hind wing rounded in both sexes; second abdominal segment without tubercles; body rarely of metallic color. (Fig. 42). (Libéllula, Leucorrhínia, Holarc.; Sympètrum, Pántala, Orthètrum, cosmop.; Erythrodìplax, Neotrop.; Trapezostígma (Tràmea), Celíthemis, Nearc.).

LIBELLÙLIDÆ

Nymphs [1]

1. Body slender, bearing three long tracheal gills attached to the tip of the abdomen; these are usually leaf-like in shape and traversed by conspicuous tracheal tubes (rarely much reduced in some Cœnagrionidæ); lateral abdominal gills usually absent. (Suborder ZYGÓPTERA)... 3
   Body stout, the abdomen not narrow; without tracheal gills attached to the tip of the abdomen; the caudal gills concealed in an enlargement of the rectum; tip of abdomen bearing three spine-like or triangular processes...2
2. Gizzard with four to eight dental folds. (Suborder ANISÓPTERA)... 12
   Gizzard with sixteen dental folds; very rare Indian and Japanese species. (Suborder ANISOZYGÓPTERA) . . EPIOPHLEBÌIDÆ
3. Mask bearing at least two pairs, and usually with numerous stiff bristles or setæ... 4
   Mask destitute of setæ both on the mentum and the lateral lobes . . 6
4. Median lobe of mask incised; lateral lobes deeply cleft; caudal gills with the secondary tracheæ lying at right angles to the gill axis; legs long.. LÉSTIDÆ
   Median lobe of mask projecting, not incised; legs short or moderate in length...5
5. Caudal gills stalked, with pointed, leaf-like apical portion.
   PSEUDÓSTIGMÁTIDÆ
   Caudal gills usually slender, lamellate, held in a vertical plane, not clearly stalked, often distinctly constricted . . CŒNAGRIÓNIDÆ
6. Second joint of antennæ greatly lengthened, as long as or longer than the following together. (Fig. 45)....................7
   Second joint of antennæ not noticeably lengthened 8
7. Median caudal gill flat, much shorter than the lateral ones which are triangular in section...................... AGRIÓNIDÆ
   All three caudal gills of approximately the same size and shape.
   SYNLÉSTIDÆ
8. Caudal gills strongly constricted at the middle. (Fig. 46).
   PROTONEÙRIDÆ
   Caudal gills not constricted at the middle.....................9

---

[1] The following key will serve as an aid in determining the families, but must not be relied on as infallible.

9. Abdomen with six or seven pairs of lateral gills; caudal gills swollen, sac-like. 10
Abdomen without lateral gills 11
10. Caudal gills swollen, oblong, with sharply pointed tips. **EPALLÁGIDÆ**
Caudal gills with the apex broad, not pointed...**POLYTHÓRIDÆ**
11. Caudal gills broad and flat, leaf-like....**MEGAPODAGRIÓNIDÆ**
Caudal gills not flat; rounded in cross-section and tapering to a point..............................**AMPHIPTERÝGIDÆ**

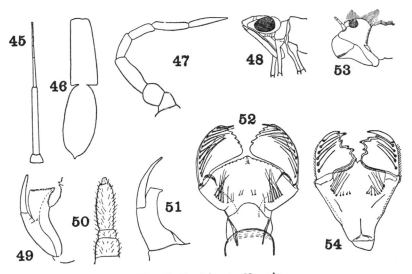

Figs. 45–54. Odonata, *Nymphs*

45. **Synlestes,** antenna of nymph (Tillyard) Synlestidæ.
46. **Isosticta,** caudal gill of nymph (Tillyard) Protoneuridæ.
47. **Æshnid,** antenna of nymph (Howe) Æshnidæ.
48. **Æshnid,** lateral view of head, with labium closed (Howe) Æshnidæ.
49. **Tachopteryx,** lateral lobe of labium (Howe) Petaluridæ.
50. **Gomphid,** antenna (Howe) Gomphidæ.
51. **Æshna,** lateral lobe of labium (Tillyard) Æshnidæ.
52. **Plathemis,** labium, open (Garman) Libellulidæ.
53. **Libellulid,** lateral view of head, with labium closed (Howe) Libellulidæ.
54. **Cordulegaster,** labium, open (Garman) Cordulegastridæ.

12. Antennæ seven-jointed; tarsi of all legs three-jointed 13
Antennæ four-jointed (Fig. 50); tarsi of front and middle legs two-jointed; mask with flat median lobe; distal margin of mentum not cleft.......................................**GÓMPHIDÆ**
13. Labium forming a more or less spoon-shaped mask which covers

the ventral and sometimes also the front surface of the head as
far as the antennæ (Fig. 53); setæ usually numerous.........14
Labium flat, not forming a spoon-shaped mask for the lower surface
of the head (Fig. 48), almost always without setæ............16

14. Lateral lobes of labium provided with a few large and irregular
teeth on the inner margin that interlock from the two sides when
closed; the median lobe divided at the tip by a median emargination (Fig. 54); mask extending to the base of the antennæ.

CORDULEGÁSTRIDÆ

Lateral lobes of labium variable in form, smooth, serrate, regularly
dentate or sometimes with a few long teeth, but in the last case
these do not interlock with those of the other side; median lobe
triangular, projecting, not bifid or emarginate. (Fig. 52)......15

15. Teeth along inner margin of lateral lobes of labium deep or moderate, the dentition always clearly marked; legs usually long, with
the hind femora longer than the width of the head; generally
large species...............................CORDULÌIDÆ

Teeth on inner margin of lateral lobes of labium usually reduced
to crenulations or obsolete (in a few forms with long teeth the
mask is either greatly enlarged (*Pantala*) or the species are very
small (Tetratheminæ))......................LIBELLÙLIDÆ

16. Antennæ long and slender, the segments longer than wide (Fig.
47); lateral lobes of labium with a long movable hook (Fig. 51).

ÆSHNIDÆ

Antennæ short and stout, the segments wider than long; lateral lobes
of labium with a short movable hook (Fig. 49).

PETALÙRIDÆ

LITERATURE ON ODONATA

ANDRES, A. The Dragonflies of Egypt. Mem. Soc. Ent. Egypte, 3, pp. 1–43
(1928).

BARTENEV, A. N. Libellulidæ II. Faune Russ. Pseudoneuroptera, 1, pp. 353–
576 (1919).

Bestimmungstabelle der Gattungen der Libellulinæ. Zool. Jahrb., Abt.
Syst., 56, pp. 357–424 (1929).

BORROR, D. J. Key to American Genera of Libellulidæ. Ann. Ent. Soc. America,
38, pp. 168–194 (1945).

BYERS, C. F. Odonata of Florida. Univ. Florida Publ. Biol. Sci. Ser., 1, No. 1,
327 pp., 11 pls., 19 figs. (1930).

CALVERT, P. P. Odonata. In Biologia Centrali-Americana, Neuroptera, 1,
pp. 17–420 (1901–08).

Odonata of Cuba. Trans. American Ent. Soc., 45, pp. 335–396 (1919).

CHOPARD, L. Atlas des libellules de France, Belgique, Suisse. Nouv. Atlas,
Ent., No. 3, 137 pp., 12 pls., 47 figs. (1948).

Odonaptères. In Grassé, Traité de Zoologie, 9, pp. 311–354, 30 figs.
(1949).

Costa Lima, A. da. Odonata. In Insetos do Brasil, **1** (1938).

Fraser, F. C. Indian Dragonflies. Journ. Bombay Nat. Hist. Soc., **25–36** (numerous parts) (1918–1933).

Revision of Petalidæ and Petaluridæ. Mem. Indian Mus., **9**, pp. 205–260, 31 figs. (1933).

Fauna of British India, Odonata. xiii + 423 pp., 180 figs. (1933); xxiii + 398 pp., 4 pls., 128 figs. (1934); xi + 461 pp., 2 pls., 125 figs. (1936). Taylor and Francis, London.

A Reclassification of the Order Odonata. Part III. Australian Zool., **9**, pp. 359–396, 15 figs. (1940). (See Tillyard and Fraser for Parts I and II).

The Odonata of the Argentine Republic. I–II. Acta zool. lilloana, **4**, pp. 427–461, 16 figs.; **5**, pp. 47–67 (1947–48).

Garman, P. The Zygoptera of Illinois. Bull. Illinois State Lab. Nat. Hist., **12**, pp. 411–587 (1917).

Odonata of Connecticut. Bull. State Geol. Nat. Hist. Surv., Connecticut, No. 39, 331 pp. (1927).

Howe, R. H. Manual of Odonata of New England. Mem. Thoreau Mus., Concord, Mass., **2**, 7 parts, 138 pp. and supplement (1917–23).

Kellicott, D. S. Odonata of Ohio. Ohio Acad. Sci., Special Paper, No. 2, 114 pp. (1899).

Kennedy, C. H. Classification of Zygoptera. Ohio Journ. Sci., **21**, pp. 83–88 (1920).

Klots, E. B. Odonata of Porto Rico and Virgin Islands. 107 pp. (1932).

Krüger, L. Einführung in das Studium der Libellen. Abh. Ber. pommers. naturf. Ges., **6**, pp. 53–106 (1925).

Lameere, A. Odonata. In Précis de Zoologie. Rec. Inst. zool. Torley-Rousseau, **4**, pp. 212–249 (1934).

Lieftinck, M. A. Annotated List of the Odonata of Java. Treubia, **14**, pp. 377–462 (1934).

The Dragonflies of New Guinea and Neighboring Islands. Nova Guinea, **15**, pp. 485–602, 67 figs. (1932); **17**, pp. 1–67, 35 figs. (1933); **17**, pp. 203–300, 50 figs. (1935); Treubia, **18**, pp. 441–608, 19 pls., 2 figs. (1942).

Key to Gynacantha from Celebes and the Moluccas. Treubia, **19**, pp. 417–428 (1948).

Longfield, C. Dragonflies of the British Isles. 220 pp., 38 pls. F. Warne & Co., New York and London (1937).

The Dragonflies of Scotland. Scottish Natural., **60**, pp. 65–74 (1948).

Lucas, W. J. British Dragonflies. London (1900).

The Aquatic (Naiad) Stage of British Dragonflies. xii + 132 pp., 35 pls., 30 figs. Ray Soc., London (1930).

Martin, R. Corduliidæ. Collection Zoologiques, Selys-Longchamps, fasc. 17 (1909).

Æschnidæ. Coll. Zool. Selys-Longchamps, fasc. 18–19 (1909).

Æschnidæ, Æschninæ. Gen. Insectorum, fasc. 115, 33 pp. (1911).

Corduliidæ. Gen. Insectorum, fasc. 155, 32 pp. (1914).

May, E. Die Odonaten des arktischen Gebietes. Fauna arctica, **6**, pp. 175–182 (1932).

Odonata oder Wasserjungfern. Tierwelt Deutschlands, **27**, pp. 1–124, 134 figs. (1933).

MUNZ, P. A. Keys for Identification of Genera of Zygoptera. Mem. American Ent. Soc., No. 3, 78 pp. (1919).

MUTTKOWSKI, R. A. Odonata of Wisconsin. Bull. Wisconsin Nat. Hist. Soc., 6, pp. 57–123 (1908).

Catalogue of Odonata of North America. Bull. Pub. Mus. Milwaukee, 1, Art. 1 (1910).

NEEDHAM, J. G. Manual of Dragonflies of China. Zoologica Sinica, Series A, 11, 344 pp. Peiping, China (1930).

Key to the Dragonflies of India. Rec. Indian Mus., 34, pp. 198–228, 7 figs. (1932).

North American Species of the Genus Gomphus. Trans. American Ent. Soc., 73, pp. 307–339, 1 pl. (1948).

NEEDHAM, J. G. and D. S. BULLOCK. Odonata of Chile. Field Mus. Publ., Zool., 24, pp. 357–373 (1943).

NEEDHAM, J. G. and E. FISHER. Nymphs of North America Libellulinæ. Trans. American Ent. Soc., 62, pp. 107–116 (1936).

NEEDHAM, J. G. and M. K. GYGER. Odonata of the Philippines. Philippine Journ. Sci., 63, pp. 21–101, 10 pls., 2 figs. (1937).

NEEDHAM, J. G. and H. B. HEYWOOD. Handbook of Dragonflies of North America. 378 pp., Springfield, Illinois (1929).

OGUMA, K. The Japanese Æschnidæ. Insecta Matsumurana, 1, pp. 78–100 (1926).

PERRIER, R. Libellules de la France. Faune de France, 3, pp. 57–71, 60 figs. (1934).

RIS, F. Odonata. Süsswasserfauna Deutschlands, Heft 9, 67 pp. (1909).

Libellulidæ. Coll. Zool. Selys-Longchamps, fasc. 9–16 (1909–14).

Neuer Beitrag zur Kenntnis der Odonatenfauna der Neu-Guinea Region. Nova Guinea, 13, pt. 2, pp. 81–131 (1913).

Die Odonatenfauna von Argentina. Mem. Soc. Ent. Belgique, 22, pp. 55–102 (1913).

Odonata of South Africa. Ann. South African Mus., 18, pp. 247–452 (1921).

SCHMIDT, E. Odonata. In Tierwelt Mitteleuropas, 4, Lief. 1b, pp. IV 1–66 (1929).

Bibliographia Odontologica, Lief. 1, pp. 1–116, 1 pl. Wagner, Vienna (1933).

Odonata der deutschen Limnologischen Sunda-Expedition. Arch. Hydrobiol., Suppl. 13, pp. 316–397, 4 pls., 93 figs. (1934).

SCHOUTEDEN, H. Catalogue de la faune du Congo Belge. Odonata. Ann. Mus. Congo Belge, Zool. (3) Sect. II, 3, pp. 1–83, 1 pl., 83 figs. (1934).

SEEMAN, T. M. Dragonflies, Mayflies and Stoneflies of Southern California. Pomona Journ. Ent. Zool., 19, pp. 1–69 (1927).

SJÖSTEDT, Y. Odonata der nordwestlichen Provinzen Chinas. Ark. Zool., 25A, No. 5, 22 pp., 3 pls. (1933).

TILLYARD, R. J. The Biology of Dragonflies. University Press, Cambridge, England (1917).

TILLYARD, R. J. and F. C. FRASER. Reclassification of the Odonata. Austr. Zool., 9, pp. 125–169; 195–221; 359–396, 15 figs. (1938–40).

WALKER, E. M. North American Species of Æschna. Univ. Toronto Stud. Biol. Ser., No. 11, pp. 1–213 (1912).

North American Somatochlora. Univ. Toronto Stud. Biol. Ser., No. 26, 202 pp. (1925).

WHITEHOUSE, F. C. Guide to Study of Dragonflies of Jamaica. Bull. Inst. Jamaica, Sci. Ser., No. 3, 69 pp., 7 figs. (1943).

Catalogue of Odonata of Canada, Newfoundland and Alaska. Trans. Roy. Canad. Inst., 27, pp. 3–56 (1948).

WILLIAMSON, E. B. Dragonflies of Indiana. Rept. Dept. Geol. Ind., No. 24, pp. 229–333 (1901).

North American Species of Macromia. Proc. U. S. Nat. Mus., 37, pp. 369–398 (1909).

WRIGHT, M. and A. PETERSON. Key to Genera of Anisopterous Dragonfly Nymphs of North America. Ohio Journ. Sci., 44, pp. 151–166 (1944).

ZIMMERMAN, E. C. Odonata. Insects of Hawaii, 2, pp. 321–385 (1948).

ORDER PLECÓPTERA

(PERLÁRIA)

Body soft, of moderate or large size; four membranous wings, usually with many veins and numerous crossveins, rarely reduced in size; anal area of hind wing large and pleated, usually separated by a notch from the rest of the wing. Head broad and flattened; mandibles either well developed or much reduced; antennæ long, thread-like; three ocelli; cerci usually long and many-jointed. Prothorax large, free; legs strong, tarsi three-jointed. Nymphs aquatic, commonly with tracheal gills; antennæ long, much like those of the adults; eyes well developed; ocelli present; cerci usually long, many-jointed. Metamorphosis slight. Stone-flies, Salmon-flies.

Adults

1. Hind wing with an anal lobe (Figs. 55, 58) which is separated by a notch or indentation on the outer margin just behind the cubital vein (Cu_2); no meshwork of delicate crossveins on anal lobe 2
   Hind wing with the outer margin entire, not notched; anal lobe with meshwork of fine veins. (Fig. 59). (Stenopérla, Eusthènia, Austr., Neotrop.). Including *GRIPOPTERÝGIDÆ*, part)
   EUSTHENÏIDÆ

2. Anterior coxæ closely approximated; mandibles very weakly developed; wings with crossveins except in the anal lobe of the hind pair, the anal area of the fore pair with two or more full rows of crossveins (Pteronárcys) ....**PTERONÁRCIDÆ**
   Anterior coxæ widely separated 3

3. Three ocelli present, the median one sometimes reduced in size 4
   Only two ocelli, the median one absent. (Peltopérla, Nearc.).
   PELTOPÉRLIDÆ

4. Mandibles reduced to a weak blade; clypeus and labrum concealed under a frontal shelf; third joint of tarsi much longer than the other two together. (Figs. 55, 56, 60). (**Pérla, Acroneùria, Hydropérla, Allopérla Isópteryx** (= *Chloropérla*)). (Including *CHLOROPÉRLIDÆ, ISOPÉRLIDÆ, PERLÓDIDÆ*).

PÉRLIDÆ

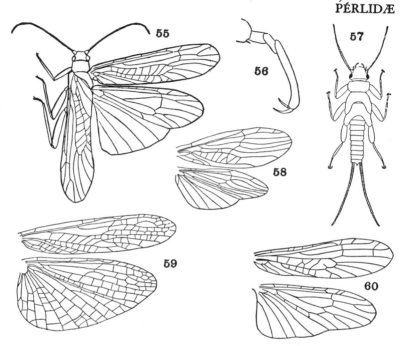

Figs. 55–60. Plecoptera

55. **Isopteryx** Perlidæ.
56. **Perla,** tarsus. Perlidæ.
57. **Perla,** nymph (Pictet) Perlidæ.
58. **Notonemoura,** wings. Nemouridæ.
59. **Stenoperla,** wings (Tillyard) Eustheniidæ.
60. **Perla,** wings. Perlidæ.

Mandibles well developed, clypeus and labrum not covered by a frontal shelf; third joint of tarsi shorter than the other two together 5

5. Fore wing with three anal veins, the first one lying very close to the second branch of the cubitus. Australian. (**Tasmanopérla, Austropérla**). (Including *GRIPOPTERÝGIDÆ*, part).

AUSTROPÉRLIDÆ

Fore wing with only two anal veins, the posterior one sometimes forked. 6
6. Both wings with the radius, media and cubitus connected near the middle of the wing by a transverse cord or continuous series of transverse veins; usually no crossveins present distal to this. (Fig. 58) 7
No such transverse cord near the middle of the wing; distal portion of wing with crossveins. Australian, Neotropical. (Leptopérla, Dinotopérla). (Including *GRIPOPTERÝGIDÆ*, part). LEPTOPÉRLIDÆ
7. Cerci very short, sometimes reduced to a single joint, never with more than ten joints; last anal vein in fore wing forked beyond the anal cell. 8
Cerci long, many-jointed; both anal veins simple 9
8. Apical marginal space beyond tip of subcosta in front wing with an oblique crossvein present. (Nemoùra, Holarc.). NEMOÙRIDÆ
Apical marginal space without such a crossvein. (Leùctra, Holarc.) LEÙCTRIDÆ
9. Second joint of tarsi about as long as the other joints. (Tæniópteryx, Brachýptera, Holarc.) ....TÆNIOPTERÝGIDÆ
Second joint of tarsi much shorter than the other joints. (Cápnia, Capnélla, Capnùra, Allocápnia, Nearc.) ....CAPNÌIDÆ

Nymphs

1. Visible gills present 2
No visible gills 7
2. Gills present on the thorax 3
Gills on the abdomen, but none on the thorax. 6
3. Gills on the thorax and also on the underside of abdominal segments 1 and 2, or 1 to 3 ....PTERONÁRCIDÆ
Gills present on thorax only 4
4. Gills on the underside of the prothorax only; small, robust; second joint of tarsi shorter than first..................NEMOÙRIDÆ
Gills on all three thoracic segments 5
5. Three pairs of gills in the form of filamentous tufts on the pleuræ; legs densely fringed with long hairs. ....Some PÉRLIDÆ
A pair of tubular gills at the base of each coxa; second joint of tarsi as long, or longer than the first. ....TÆNIOPTERÝGIDÆ
6. Gills a series of paired latero-ventral abdominal appendages on segments 1 to 5 or 1 to 6; large species. ......EUSTHENÌIDÆ
Gills a rosette of small filaments surrounding the anus. LEPTOPÉRLIDÆ
7. Underside of thorax covered with large overlapping shield-like plates; body resembling a cockroach in form. PELTOPÉRLIDÆ
Thorax without such ventral plates; body not cockroach-like 8

8. Palpi with the apical joints more slender than the basal ones
   (Fig. 57) .... PÉRLIDÆ
   Palpi with the apical joints as stout as the basal ones. 9
9. Small and robust nymphs, hairy; hind wing pads extending considerably outward from the body at an angle; gills present or
   absent in ventral cervical region. .... NEMOÙRIDÆ
   Small and slender nymphs; hairs few, fine or lacking; hind wing
   pads lying about parallel to longitudinal axis of body; no branched
   cervical gills. 10
10. Lateral margins of abdominal segments somewhat rounded, segments
    widest at posterior margin and narrower toward base; hind wing
    pads with anal lobe or area extending far beyond middle of wing
    pad; fore wing pads of males sometimes entirely lacking; last
    abdominal segment in males sometimes with a conical projection.
    CÁPNÏIDÆ
    Lateral margins of abdominal segments almost straight, abdomen
    appearing more cylindrical; each hind wing pad with anal lobe
    or area small and not extending much beyond middle of wing
    pad; fore wing pads of males always present; last abdominal
    segment in males without a conical projection. LEÙCTRIDÆ

LITERATURE ON PLECOPTERA

BANKS, N. Some Characters in the Perlidæ. Psyche, 54, pp. 266–291, 3
pls. (1947).
BARNARD, K. H. South African Perlaria. Ann. South African Mus., 30, pp.
511–548 (1934).
BENGTSSON, S. Beitrag zur Kenntnis der Plecopteren Schwedens. Acta Univ.
Lund, 29, pp. 1–50, 33 figs. (1934).
CLAASSEN, P. W. Plecoptera Nymphs of North America. Thomas Say Foundn.,
3, 199 pp., 36 pls. (1931).
A Catalogue of the Plecoptera of the World. Mem. Cornell Agric.
Exp. Sta., No. 232, 235 pp. (1940).
DESPAX, R. Plecoptères. In Grassé, Traité de Zoologie, 9, pp. 557–586 (1949).
ENDERLEIN, G. Klassifikation der Plecopteren. Zool. Anz., 34, pp. 385–419
(1911).
FRISON, T. H. Fall and Winter Stoneflies or Plecoptera of Illinois. Bull. Illi-
nois Nat. Hist. Surv., 18, pp. 345–409 (1929).
Studies on North American Plecoptera, Particularly Illinois. Bull. Ill.
Nat. Hist. Surv., 22, pp. 235–355, 1 pl., 126 figs. (1942).
HANSON, J. F. Records and Descriptions of North American Plecoptera. Parts
I–III. American Midl. Nat., 26, pp. 174–178, 13 figs.; 28, pp. 389–407,
27 figs., 29, pp. 657–669, 26 figs. (1940–43).
HYNES, H. B. N. Key to British Species of Plecoptera. Sci. Publ. Freshwater
Biol. Assoc. British Empire, 2, 39 pp., 14 figs. (1940).
KIMMINS, D. E. Synopsis of British Nemouridæ. Trans. Soc. British Ent., 7,
pp. 65–83, 8 figs. (1940).

KLAPÁLEK, F. Die Plecoptera. Coll. Zool. Selys-Longchamps, fasc. 4 and 4A, 266 pp., Brussels (1912–23).

KÜHTREIBER, J. Die Plecopterenfauna Nordtirols. Ber. naturw.-med. Ver. Innsbruck, 43–44, pp. 1–219, 6 pls., 138 figs. (1934).

LAMEERE, A. Plecoptera. In Précis de Zoologie. Rec. Inst. zool. Torley-Rousseau, 4, pp. 265–275 (1935).

LEROI, O. Zur Plecopteren von Rheinland-Westfalen. Ver. bot. zool. Ver. Rheinl.-Westf. 1912, pp. 25–51 (1912) (Extensive bibliography).

NEEDHAM, J. G. and BROUGHTON, E. Central American Stoneflies. Journ. New York Ent. Soc., 35, pp. 109–120 (1927).

NEEDHAM, J. G. and CLAASSEN, P. W. A Monograph of the Plecoptera or Stoneflies of America North of Mexico. 397 pp., Lafayette, Indiana (1925).

OKAMOTO, H. Japanische Plecopteren. Trans. Sapporo Nat. Hist. Soc., 4, pp. 105–170 (1913).

RICKER, W. E. Stoneflies of Southwestern British Columbia. Indiana Univ. Publ. Sci. Ser., No. 12, 145 pp., 129 figs. (1943).

SCHOENEMUND, E. Plecoptera. In Tierwelt Mitteleuropas, 4, Lief. 2, pp. V 1–18 (1928).

Die Larven der deutschen Perla-Arten. Ent. Mitt., 14, pp. 113–121 (1925).

SEEMAN, T. M. Dragonflies, Mayflies and Stoneflies of Southern California. Pomona Journ. Ent. Zool., 19, pp. 1–69 (1927).

SMITH, L. W. Studies in North American Plecoptera. (Pteronarcinæ and Perlodini). Trans. American Ent. Soc., 43, pp. 433–489 (1917).

TILLYARD, R. J. A new classification of the Order Perlaria. Canadian Ent., 53, pp. 35–43 (1921).

Revision of the Family Eustheniidæ. Proc. Linn. Soc. New South Wales, 46, pp. 221–226 (1921).

The Stone-flies of New Zealand. Trans. New Zealand Inst., 54, pp. 197–217 (1923).

ULMER, G. Die Trichopteren, Ephemeropteren und Plecopteren des arktischen Gebietes. Fauna arctica, 6, pp. 223–226 (1932).

WU, C. F. The Stoneflies of China. Peking Nat. Hist. Bull., 11, pp. 49–82, 163–189, 47 figs. (1936).

ORDER BLATTÀRIA

(OOTHECÀRIA, CURSÒRIA, BLATTÒIDEA)

Moderate-sized or large, sometimes very large, rarely very small, broadly oval, flattened, quick-running insects. Head free but inflexed so as to be nearly or quite concealed beneath the pronotum, the mouth posterior or nearly so. Mandibles strong, toothed; maxillæ well developed, bilobed, with five-jointed palpi; labial palpi three-jointed; eyes usually well developed, usually two ocelli; antennæ long, filamentous, many-jointed. Prothorax large, movable, usually transverse; meso- and metathorax subequal, not freely movable. Wings often absent or much reduced in size; when present, overlapped on the abdomen; fore wings parchment-like, containing many veins; hind wings with a large anal lobe, clearly separated from the rest of the wing and radially folded. Legs strong, similar, coxæ large; tibiæ usually strongly spinose; tarsi five-jointed. Abdomen with ten tergites of nearly equal size, broadly attached at the base and not very freely movable; cerci prominent and jointed. Metamorphosis slight. Roaches.

1. Middle and hind femora, or at least the hind femora, with several evident marginal spines beneath 2
   Middle and hind femora unarmed beneath, or furnished only with hairs and bristles, or with one or two apical or subapical spines ..9
2. Females with the seventh ventral segment divided posteriorly to form a valvular apparatus 3
   Seventh ventral segment of female large, undivided, and rounded ..5

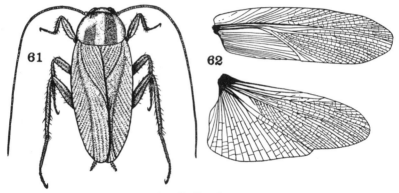

Figs. 61–62. Blattaria

61. **Blatella.** Phyllodromiidæ.
62. **Periplaneta,** wings. Blattidæ.

3. Apical portion of wings with at least some distinct venation, folded ⁰ or crumpled in repose, never coiled into a spiral 4
   Apical portion of wings entirely without venation, coiled in a spiral in repose. (**Oulópteryx,** Neotrop.).......**OULOPTERÝGIDÆ**
4. Moderate to large, heavily pigmented species, with eyes; tenth dorsal segment of the male more or less quadrangular, often impressed, or emarginate behind. Mainly tropical. (**Blátta,** cosmop. (*B. orientàlis,* Oriental cockroach); **Eurýcotis,** Neotrop.; **Polyzostèria,** Austr.; **Méthana,** Ethiop., Indoaustr.; **Deropéltis,** Ethiop.; **Periplanèta** (Fig. 62) cosmop. (*P. americàna,* American cockroach, *P. australàsiæ,* Australian cockroach)). (*PERIPLAN-ETÌNÆ*) ....**BLÁTTIDÆ**

Small, colorless, cave-inhabiting species, with the eyes vestigial or absent; wings reduced or absent; tenth dorsal segment of the male elongate triangular and emarginate behind. (Noctícola, Spelæoblátta, Indomal.) ....NOCTICÓLIDÆ

5. Moderate to large species, not living in ant nests; antennal joints short 6
Very small, wingless or subapterous species, 2 to 5 mm. in length, living in ant nests; entire body covered with loose hairs; legs stout, the tibiæ heavily spined; antennal joints much longer than wide. Neotropical. Ant guests. (Attáphila (Figs. 68, 69)). ATTAPHÍLIDÆ

6. Tenth dorsal segment of both sexes usually transverse and narrow; hind wings when present with an apical field; fore wings with the branches of M and Cu strongly oblique and leading toward the hind margin; hind femora usually sparsely armed with spines beneath. (Ectòbia, cosmop.; Anaplécta, Pseudectòbia, Neotrop., Ethiop., Indomal.; Hololámpra, Holarc., Ethiop.). ECTOBÍIDÆ
Tenth dorsal segment of both sexes more or less produced, triangular or emarginate; hind femora usually strongly spined beneath 7

7. Tenth dorsal segment of both sexes triangular and entire, the cerci distinctly projecting 8
Tenth dorsal segment of the male more or less quadrate, with obtuse angles, that of the female broadly rounded or lobate, the cerci not projecting; tarsi with distinct pulvilli. (Calolámpra, widespr.; Epilámpra, Leuroléstes, Phlebonòtus, Phoráspis, Hyporhicnòda (Fig. 67), Neotrop.; Homalópterus, Indomal., Neotrop.; Heterolámpra, Ethiop., Indoaustr.). (PHORASPÍDIDÆ) EPILÁMPRIDÆ

8. Pronotum and fore wings smooth; hind wings with the radial vein usually emitting several parallel costal veins; pulvilli absent. (Caloblátta, Pseùdomops, Neotrop.; Blatélla (B. germánica, Crotonbug) (Figs. 61, 65), Ischnóptera, Lobóptera, Phyllodròmia, Temnópteryx, cosmop.; Ellipsídion, Austr.). (PSEUDOMÓPIDÆ) ....PHYLLODROMÌIDÆ
Pronotum and fore wings covered with a silky pile; hind wings with the radial vein emitting irregular costal veins; pulvilli present; usually large species. Neotropical. (Megaloblátta, Nyctíbora, Heminyctíbora) ....NYCTIBÓRIDÆ

9. Abdomen with the seventh segment normal, not enclosing the terminal segments, the cerci and at least the tenth dorsal segment free 10
Abdomen with the seventh segment of both sexes broadly rounded, triangular and enclosing the terminal segments and also the cerci;

tibiæ short and strongly bristly; wingless and greatly convex species. (**Cryptocércus** (Fig. 64), Nearc., China)

CRYPTOCÉRCIDÆ

10. Hind wings twice as long as the fore wings, with a transverse fold at the middle through which the veins continue to the apex, folded in repose; fore wings elytra-like, with weak venation; insects resembling dytiscid beetles. (**Diplóptera** (Fig. 63) Austromal., Hawaii) ....DIPLOPTÉRIDÆ

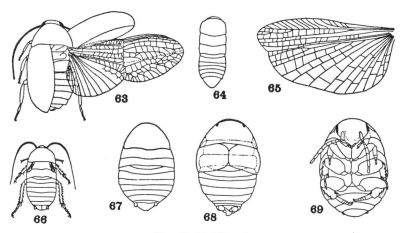

Figs. 63–69. Blattaria

63. **Diploptera** (Tillyard) Diplopteridæ.
64. **Cryptoceicus**, dorsal outline (Hebard) Cryptocercidæ.
65. **Blatella**, hind wing, Phyllodromiidæ.
66. **Cacoblatta** (Saussure) Blaberidæ.
67. **Hyporhicnoda** (Hebard) Epilampridæ.
68. **Attaphila**, dorsal view (Wheeler) Attaphilidæ.
69. **Attaphila**, ventral view (Wheeler) Attaphilidæ.

Hind wings without a middle transverse fold through which the veins continue to the apex, sometimes with an apical triangular field 11

11. Tenth dorsal segment semicircular, broadly produced, its hind margin more or less strongly dentate; last ventral segment of the male very small, without styles; legs robust, the front pair fossorial, tibiæ strongly spinose, tarsi relatively short, without arolia; costal margin of the fore wings split, wings often reduced. (**Panésthia, Salgànea**, Indoaustr.; **Geoscápheus**, Austr.).

PANESTHÌIDÆ

Last dorsal segment without produced and dentate hind margin. 12

12. Hind wings with an area between Cu and A capable of being folded, the anal fold large; small species 13
Hind wings without a cubital fold or at most with an indication of one, or the wings reduced 14

13. Fore wings with the branches of M and Cu directed toward the hind margin, anal area small, with few veins extending to the margin, costal area short. (Chorisoneùra, Am.; Chorístima, Austr.; Anáptycha, Hemiptérota, Neotrop.)
CHORISONEÙRIDÆ
Fore wings with the branches of M and Cu directed toward the apical margin, costal area usually long and narrow. (Areolària, Malay.; Hypnórna, Plectóptera, Neotrop.) . . . . . AREOLARÌIDÆ

14. Very small species, 5 to 7 mm. in length, living in nests of ants . . . 15
Larger species, not myrmecophilous 16

15. Flattened, narrow, winged species; fore wings pubescent, with weak venation, the branches of M and Cu parallel; tibiæ with long bristles; cerci long and jointed. Neotropical. (Nothoblátta).
NOTHOBLÁTTIDÆ
Rather convex insects with abbreviated fore wings and no hind wings; tibial spines weak; cerci short and broad. Ant guests. Neotropical. (Attícola) . . . . ATTICÓLIDÆ

16. Female with the seventh ventral segment divided behind to form a pair of valves 17
Female with the seventh ventral segment not forming a pair of valves 20

17. Large species; prothorax elongate-trapezoidal, not tomentose; legs very long, the tibial bristles weak; anal areas of the hind wings of the fully winged forms large and plaited several times in repose; fore wings with the costal cell narrow and without crossveins, subcosta long, reaching the middle of the wings. (Archiblátta, Cátara, Malay.) . . . . ARCHIBLÁTTIDÆ
Insects not conforming to the preceding description; anal area of the fully winged forms smaller, folded only once or twice 18

18. Small species with pubescent thorax; hind wings with a pronounced thickening surrounding the ends of the shortened subcosta. Widespread, tropical. (Compsòdes, Euthýrrhapha, Holocómpsa).
EUTHYRRHÁPHIDÆ
Hind wings without nodal thickening at the end of the subcosta . . 19

19. Small, delicate species; tibial bristles weak; cerci long; veins simple or few-branched (Latíndia, Neotrop.) . . . . LATINDÌIDÆ
Large species; tibial bristles strong; cerci short; veins many-branched. (Homœogàmia, Am.) . . . . HOMŒOGAMÌIDÆ

20. Tarsal claws without arolia, or with a minute arolium; tenth dorsal segment of the male abdomen more or less deeply notched 21
Tarsal claws with a distinct arolium between them 23

21. Prothorax smooth; anal field of the hind wings of the fully winged forms large and folded fan-like, with the anal area plaited; large, robust, but not greatly convex species. (**Archimandrìta, Blàterus, Cacoblàtta** (Fig. 66), **Blàptica,** Neotrop.)........**BLABÉRIDÆ**

Prothorax hairy; anal field of the hind wings of the fully winged forms smaller, folded only once or twice...................22

22. Tenth dorsal segment of the male abdomen transverse, often constricted at the middle; large, broadly convex species. (**Polýphaga,** Palæarc., Indomal., Ethiop.)...............**POLYPHÁGIDÆ**

Tenth dorsal segment more or less produced, its hind margin notched; broad beetle-like, showy insects. (**Corýdia,** Indomal.).
CORYDÌIDÆ

23. Dorsal segments of the abdomen with protruding lateral angles; tenth dorsal segment quadrangular and medially notched behind. (**Panchlòra, Nauphœta,** Neotrop., Ethiop.; **Gỳna,** Ethiop.; **Leucophæa, Pucnoscéllus,** Ind.; **Oniscosòma,** Austr.)
PANCHLÓRIDÆ

Abdominal segments without projecting lateral angles; tenth dorsal segment transverse, its hind margins straight or rounded......24

24. Hind wings more or less pointed or with a much produced apical field into which the cubital branches do not enter. (**Oxyháloa,** Ethiop., Neotrop.) ....**OXYHALÒIDÆ**

Hind wings with rounded tip and no specialized apical field. (**Elliptoblátta, Stenopilèma,** Ethiop.; **Hormética,** Am.; **Perisphæria,** Indomal.; **Parasphæria,** Neotrop.).......**PERISPHÆRÌIDÆ**

LITERATURE ON BLATTARIA

See also Orthoptera (*sens. lat.* p. 105)

BRUIJNING, C. F. A. An Account of the Blattidæ from Celebes, the Moluccas, and New Guinea. Zool. Meded., **27,** pp. 205–252, 8 figs. (1947).
Studies on Malayan Blattidæ. Zool. Meded., **29,** pp. 1–174, 56 figs. (1948).

BRUNNER, C. Nouveau Système des Blattaires. 426 pp. Vienna (1865).

CHOPARD, L. Orthoptères et Dermaptères. Faune de France (1922).
Blattidæ de la Nouvelle-Caledonie. Nova Caledònia, Berlin, A, Zool., **3,** pp. 301–336 (1924).

HANITSCH, R. Malayan Blattidæ. Journ. Roy. Asiatic Soc., Straits Branch, **69,** pp. 17–178 (1915).
Blattid Fauna of Celebes. Verh. naturf. Ges. Basel., **44,** pp. 119–150, 9 figs. (1933).

HEBARD, M. The Blattidæ of North America North of the Mexican Boundary. Mem. American Ent. Soc., **2** (1917).
The Blattidæ of Panama. Mem. American Ent. Soc., **4,** pp. 1–148 (1919).
The Blattidæ of French Guiana. Proc. Acad. Nat. Sci. Philadelphia, **78,** pp. 135–244 (1926).

Studies in Malayan Blattidæ. Proc. Acad. Nat. Sci., Philadelphia, **81**, pp. 1–109 (1929).

Australian Blattidæ of the Subfamilies Chorisoneurinæ and Ectobiinæ. Monogr. Acad. Nat. Sci. Philadelphia, No. 4, 129 pp., 14 pls. (1943).

KARNY, H. H. Monographie der Phyllophorinen. Treubia, **5**, suppl. 142 pp. (1924).

KIRBY, W. F. A Synonymic Catalogue of the Orthoptera. Vol. 1, British Mus. Nat. Hist. London (1904).

MORSE, A. P. Manual of the Orthoptera of New England. Proc. Boston Soc. Nat. Hist., **35**, No. 6 (1920).

RAMME, W. Monographie des Blattiden-Genus Ectobius. Arch. Naturg. **89**, pp. 97–145 (1923).

REHN, J. A. G. Dermaptera and Orthoptera of Chile. Trans. American Ent. Soc., **59**, pp. 159–190, 1 pl. (1933).

African and Malagasy Blattidæ. Proc. Acad. Nat. Sci. Philadelphia, **84**, pp. 405–511, 4 pls., 13 figs. (1933); ibid, **89**, pp. 17–123, 4 pls. (1937).

REHN, J. A. G. and HEBARD, M. The Orthoptera of the West Indies: Blattidæ. Bull. American Mus. Nat. Hist., **54**, pp. 1–320 (1927).

REHN, J. W. H. Classification of Blattaria. Mem. American Ent. Soc., **14**, 134 pp., 13 pls. (1950).

SAUSSURE, H. Mélanges Orthoptérologiques, fasc. 2, Blattidæ, 460 pp., Geneva (1865).

Revision de la tribu des Hétérogamiens. Rev. Suisse Zool., **1**, pp. 289–318 (1890).

Revision de la tribu des Périsphériens. Rev. Suisse Zool., **3**, pp. 1–59, (1895).

Revision de la tribu des Panesthiens et Épilampriens. Rev. Suisse Zool., **3**, pp. 299–361 (1895).

SHELFORD, R. Studies of the Blattidæ. Trans. Ent. Soc. London (1906–07) (several parts).

Blattidæ, Ectobiinæ. Gen. Insectorum, fasc. 55, 15 pp. (1907).

Blattidæ, Phyllodrominæ. Gen. Insectorum, fasc. 73, 29 pp. (1908).

Blattidæ, Nyctiborinæ. Gen. Insectorum, fasc. 74, 5 pp. (1908).

Blattidæ, Epilamprinæ. Gen. Insectorum, fasc. 101, 21 pp. (1910).

Blattidæ, Blattinæ. Gen. Insectorum, fasc. 109, 27 pp. (1910).

TEPPER, J. G. O. The Blattariæ of Australia and Polynesia. Trans. Roy. Soc. South Australia, **17**, pp. 25–130; **18**, pp. 169–189 (1893–94).

ORDER **ORTHÓPTERA**

The Orthoptera include a great variety of insects and the suborders given in the following key are frequently given the rank of orders. Characters for each of these four groups are given on pages 84, 92, 93, and 102 respectively, and the families of each suborder are keyed separately.

1. Front legs fitted for grasping, the tibiæ folding back, pincers-like on the femora; femora and tibiæ usually heavily spined; prothorax much elongated and freely movable.

    Suborder MANTEODEA (Page 84)

Front legs not fitted for grasping, rarely spinose; front coxæ never conspicuously lengthened; prothorax usually short, if long not so conspicuously freely movable 2

2. Hind femora almost always much larger and thicker than the tibiæ; jumping species, if not, the front or other tibiæ are broadened for burrowing; species usually capable of chirping or stridulation; body more or less cylindrical with the wings held sloping against the side of the body when at rest; tergites of abdomen usually larger than the sternites ..... Suborder SALTATORIA (Page 93)

Hind femora not larger than the fore femora; mute species; all three pairs of legs fitted for walking; wings, when present, superposed at rest; tergites and sternites subequal 3

3. Cerci long, many-jointed, at least half the length of the abdomen; wingless species with the prothorax longer than the mesothorax.

Suborder GRYLLOBLATTODEA (Page 92)

Cerci short, unjointed; prothorax short or very short, although the body is commonly much elongated; when wings are present the front wings are usually much larger than the hind ones.

Suborder PHASMATODEA (Page 102)

SUBORDER MANTEÒDEA

(MANTÒIDEA, MANTÒDEA)

Moderate-sized or large insects of predatory habits; the front legs very long, with the femora and tibiæ usually heavily spined and capable of being folded closely together to grasp the prey. Body elongate, sometimes very slender and usually flattened. Head freely movable, not inserted in the prothorax; eyes prominent, usually three ocelli; mandibles strong, the mouthparts inferior, rarely turned forwards; antennæ long and filamentous, many-jointed, rarely pectinate in certain males. Prothorax long or very long, freely movable, sometimes with the sides expanded; meso- and metathorax shorter, of about equal length, not freely movable. Four wings, overlapping on the abdomen, sometimes much reduced or absent, especially in the female; venation complex, fore wings usually considerably smaller than the hind pair and of stouter consistency. Tarsi almost always five-jointed, terminating in two claws; femora and tibiæ sometimes with expanded margins. Abdomen elongate oval or long and cylindrical, the terminal segments not abbreviated, tenth tergite forming a supra-anal plate; cerci usually jointed, never very long. Metamorphosis incomplete; habits similar throughout development. Praying mantids, Soothsayers.

A single family (MÁNTIDÆ) .... MANTÈIDÆ [1]

---

[1] The Manteidæ include an extensive series of very diverse forms and have been grouped into a large number of subfamilies by Giglio-Tos whose divisions have been

1. Front tibiæ without an apical hook, with two rows of spines below; cerci very long, many-jointed; small, winged species with freely movable head and simple posterior legs. (Fig. 79). (Chæteéssa, Neotrop.) ....CHÆTEESSÌNÆ
   Front tibiæ with apical hook...............................2

2. Front tibiæ with one or two long teeth on the dorsal side before the apical hook, otherwise with only very few spines; cerci simple; small slender species. (Fig. 75). (Bántia, Pseudomusònia (= Mìonyx), Bactromántis, Olígonyx, Neotrop.; Haania, Malay.)
   OLIGONYCHÌNÆ
   Front tibiæ without teeth above............................3

3. Front tibiæ without rows of strong spines below, or with only the inner row distinctly developed............................4
   Front tibiæ with the two rows of well developed spines below....5

4. Head with the mandibles directed forwards, the part behind the eyes well developed, usually long; slender, elongate species. (Fig. 77). (Compsothéspis, Ethiop., Austr.; Cliomántis, Austr.)
   COMPSOTHESPÌNÆ
   Head of normal form, with protuberant eyes; jaws not directed forwards; stouter species with the thorax comparatively short. (Perlamántis, Palæarc.; Amorphóscelis, Ethiop., As., Austr.). (AMORPHOSCÉLIDÆ) ....PERLAMANTEÌNÆ

5. Front femora with the spines of the internal row equal or alternately long and short..6
   Front femora with the spines of the internal row arranged so that the long spines are separated from one another by a series of three short ones. Usually large species, with the antennæ bipectinate in the male and the vertex prolonged into a more or less conical protuberance. (Fig. 76). (Empùsa, Palæarc.; Idolomórpha, Ethiop.; Blepharópsis, Ethiop. As.; Blepharòdes, Idòlum, Ethiop.) (EMPÙSIDÆ) ....EMPUSÌNÆ

6. Hind tibiæ carinate above, or bearing several ridges.............7
   Hind tibiæ smooth, not carinate or ridged....................8

7. Hind tibiæ bearing three ridges; body brilliantly metallic; front femora short and broad, with a very stout basal spine; stout species with short prothorax. (Fig. 78). (Metallýticus, Indomal.) (METALLYTÍCIDÆ) ....METALLYTICÌNÆ
   Hind and middle tibiæ with one or two carinæ above, except rarely in the male; prothorax long. (Fig. 81). (Oxyópsis, Pseudóxyops, Vàtes, Stagmatóptera, Neotrop.; Stenovàtes, Pòpa, Ethiop.; Æthalóchroa, Ceratocrània, Indomal.) (VÁTIDÆ) . VATÌNÆ

generally accepted. These together with several others of equal importance may be distinguished by the following key which follows the arrangement of Giglio-Tos. Several groups are regarded as of family rank by some recent workers. These changes are noted parenthetically in the key.

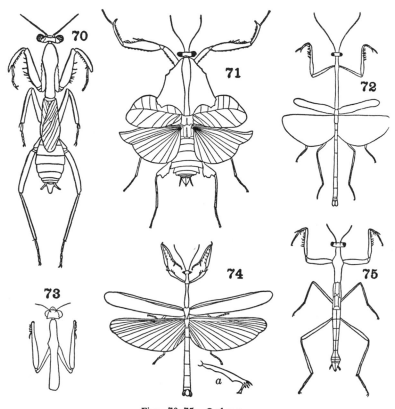

Figs. 70–75. Orthoptera

70. **Stagmomantis** (Rehn and Hebard) Manteidæ.
71. **Deroplatys** (Westwood) Manteidæ.
72. **Angela** (Saussure and Pictet) Manteidæ.
73. **Hoplocorypha** (Rehn) Manteidæ.
74. **Toxodera.** *a*, hind femur of same (Westwood) Manteidæ.
75. **Oligonyx** (Saussure and Pictet) Manteidæ.

8. Front femora externally with a series of five to seven spines......9
    Front femora with four spines in the external row..............19
9. Front femora with the first discoidal spine longer than the second;
    very long bodied, slender species. (**Schizocéphala**, Indomal.;
    Euchomenélla, Ind.; **Agrionópsis**, Ethiop.; **Ángela** (Fig. 72),
    Neotrop.). (*ANGELÍNÆ*) ...........SCHIZOCEPHALÍNÆ
    Front femora with the first discoidal spine shorter than the
    second. 10

10. Cerci flattened, dilated apically and more or less leaf-like; very elongate, slender species, with the front femora thin. (Fig. 74). (Toxódera, Eùthyphleps, Loxomántis, Indomal.; Calamothéspis, Belomántis, Ethiop.; Stenophýlla, Neotrop.). (*TOXODÉRIDÆ*).
 TOXODERÌNÆ
 Cerci conical or compressed, not leaf-like.....................11
11. Front femora with three discoidal spines.....................12
 Front femora with four discoidal spines.......................14
12. Front tibiæ with more than eleven spines in the outer row; front femora with five external and three discoidal spines; small species. (Acontísta, Tithròne, Astóllia, Callíbia, Neotrop.).
 ACONTISTÌNÆ
 Front tibiæ with from eight to eleven spines in the outer row....13
13. Frontal shield transverse; pronotum at least as long as the front coxæ, ovally dilated or sometimes with the sides more or less parallel. (Brunnèria, Macromántis, Photìna, Orthoderélla, Neotrop.; Ìris, widespr.).........................PHOTINÌNÆ
 Frontal shield subquadrate. (See couplet 23).
 EREMIAPHILÌNÆ, part
14. Supra-anal plate very long, lanceolate; hind femora and tibiæ with a few small spines beneath; body slender; pronotum as long as the front coxæ. (Bolivària, Geomántis, Rivetìna (= *Fischeria*), Palæarc.; Deíphobe, Indoaustr.; Ischnomántis, Omomántis, Ethiop.). (*FISCHERIÌNÆ*) ....RIVETÌNÆ
 Supra-anal plate short.......................................15
15. Front tibiæ with six to eleven spines in the outer row..........16
 Front tibiæ with more than eleven spines in the outer row 17
16. Front femora very broad, elliptical, with the upper margin strongly arcuate; vertex conically elevated with a tubercle on each side next to the eye; pronotum shorter than the front coxæ or barely as long, with conical tubercles on the disk; small species. (Oxypìlus, Euoxypìlus, Ethiop.; Pachymántis, Ceratomántis, Pseudoxypìlus, Indomal.) ....OXYPILÌNÆ
 Front femora narrower, more or less triangular; pronotum with rounded lateral dilations that give it a trifoliate appearance; small species. (Dystácta, Gonypetélla, Achlæna, Telomántis, Ethiop.)
 DYSTACTÌNÆ
17. Eyes acuminate, or the hind femora lobate; moderate-sized species colored like dry leaves. (Metília, Decímia, Acánthops, Epaphrodìta, Neotrop.; Phyllocránia, Ethiop.; Parablépharis, Mal.)
 EPAPHRODITÌNÆ
 Eyes rounded, or the hind femora simple.....................18
18. Frontal shield transverse (see couplet 13)....PHOTINÌNÆ, part
 Frontal shield subquadrate (see couplet 23).
 EREMIAPHILÌNÆ, part

19. Front coxæ with a minute apical lobe at the front margin......20
     Front coxæ without apical lobe...........................21
20. Front femora triangular, broad, not more than three times as long
     as wide; small species, the female often wingless. (Pseudomi-
     ópteryx, Mantíllica, Diabántia, Miobántia, Neotrop.).

                              PSEUDOMIOPTERYGÌNÆ

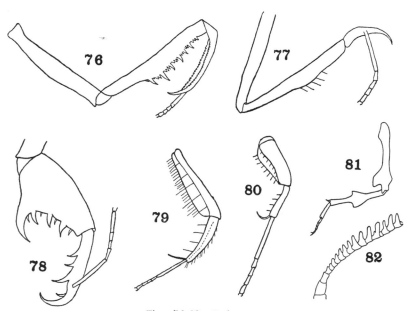

Figs. 76–82. Orthoptera

76. **Empusa,** front leg (Westwood) Manteidæ.
77. **Compsothespis,** front leg (Westwood) Manteidæ.
78. **Metallyticus,** front leg (Westwood) Manteidæ.
79. **Chæteessa,** front leg (Westwood) Manteidæ.
80. **Mantoida,** front leg (Westwood) Manteidæ.
81. **Vates,** hind leg (Saussure and Pictet) Manteidæ.
82. **Vates,** base of antenna of male (Saussure and Pictet) Manteidæ.

     Front femora slender, more than three times as long as broad; pro-
     notum long and narrow, not noticeably dilated; small slender
     species. (Fig. 73). (Musoniélla, Musònia, Diamusònia, Théspis,
     Neotrop.; Hoplocórypha, Ethiop.) ....THESPÌNÆ
21. Front femora with the two intermediate spines of the outer row
     longer than the others; pronotum longer than the front coxæ;
     fore wings long in the male, short in the female; body usually
     very slender. (See couplet 9)......SCHIZOCEPHALÌNÆ, part

Front femora with the two intermediate spines of the outer row not longer than the others...............................22
22. Front tibiæ with four or five spines in the outer row...........23
Front tibiæ with more than five spines in the outer row.......25
23. Front femora with the groove that receives the tibial claw remote from the base...24
Front femora with the claw groove close to the base. (Eremiáphila, Palæarc.; Tarachòdes, Galépsus, Tarachódula, Ethiop.; Parepiscòpus, Didymocórypha, Indomal.). (*ORTHODERÌNÆ, TARACHODÌNÆ, EREMIAPHÍLIDÆ*) ......ERÆMIAPHILÌNÆ
24. Vertex not produced (see couplet 20)..........THESPÌNÆ, part
Vertex produced into an elongate, triangular process. (Pyrgomántis, Ethiop.) (see couplet 23)...........EREMIAPHILÌNÆ, part
25. Lateral margins of pronotum parallel or divergent in front (see couplet 23). (Humbertiélla, Theopómpula, Indomal.; Elæa, Theopómpa, Ethiop.) ....EREMIAPHILÌNÆ, part
Lateral margins of pronotum more or less convergent in front....26
26. Front tibiæ with the spines in the outer row erect and remote from one another 27
Front tibiæ with the spines in the outer row decumbent and very close together 50
27. Front femora with from one to three discoidal spines..........28
Front femora with four discoidal spines......................29
28. Internal apical lobes of the front coxæ divergent, not dilated into a small lobe at the tip; small species. (Tarachìna, Bólbula, Enicophlæbia, Ethiop.; Bólbe, Ciulfìna, Austr.; Haplopèza, Iridópteryx, Fulciniélla, Eomántis, Indomal.)....IRIDOPTERYGÌNÆ
Internal apical lobes of the front coxæ contiguous. (See couplet 14) RIVETÌNÆ, part
29. Front femora with a well marked fovea or pit between the first and second spines of the outer row......................30
Front femora without such a fovea.........................34
30. Front femora with the discoidal spines forming a sinuous line; species of moderate size, with short, stout body, the pronotum broad and depressed. (Gonatísta, Liturgùsa, Neotrop.; Dactylópteryx, Ethiop.; Gonatistélla, Austr.)........LITURGUSÌNÆ
Front femora with the discoidal spines placed in a straight line...31
31. Spines of outer row on front femora very long and curved......32
Spines of outer row on front femora shorter, straight; slender-bodied species, with the wings well developed in both sexes. (Árria, Malay.; Sibýlla, Presibýlla, Ethiop.).............SIBYLLÌNÆ
32. Pronotum with two tubercles near the base of its posterior portion 33
Pronotum simple, without tubercles; slender or very slender species,

with well developed wings in both sexes. (Calìris, Ind.; Lepto-
mántis, Malay.; Deromántis, Ethiop.)..........CALIRIDÌNÆ

33. Hind femora with a small lobe or tooth below near tip; more or
less stout and short-bodied species with strongly prominent eyes.
(Majánga, Ethiop.; Majangélla, Malay.).......MAJANGÌNÆ
Hind femora simple, without such projection; body slender, flattened, the eyes moderately prominent. (Mellìera, Neotrop.; Mel-
lieriélla, Austr.) ....MELLIERÌNÆ

34. Vertex produced into an elongate process (see couplet 6).
OXYPILÌNÆ, part
Vertex not elongated or produced..........................35

35. Four posterior tibiæ or their femora minutely spinulose below....36
Four posterior tibiæ and femora with the lower edge smooth....37

36. Frontal shield transverse; discoidal portion of hind wings not
banded. (See couplet 14) ....RIVETÌNÆ, part
Frontal shield scarcely broader than high; discoidal portion of hind
wings with black cross-bands; pronotum at least as long as the
front coxæ. A cosmopolitan group. (Fig. 70). (Mántis, Palæarc.,
Austr.; Stagmomántis, Am. (S. carolìna, Carolina mantis); Auro-
mántis, Uromántis, Neotrop.; Calidomántis, Sphodromántis,
Ethiop.; Tenódera (T. sinénsis, Chinese mantis), Polyspolòta,
widespr.; Sphodrópoda, Austr.). (MANTÌNÆ)...MANTEÌNÆ

37. Lateral margins of pronotum strongly expanded, leaf-like......38
Lateral margins of pronotum not expanded..................40

38. Posterior femora simple.......................................39
Posterior femora lobed; large, brown, leaf-like species with con-
spicuous foliaceous expansions at the sides of the pronotum and
at the tips of the four posterior femora. (Fig. 71). (Deróplatys,
E. As.; Brancsíkia, Madagascar). (DEROPLATŸIDÆ).
DEROPLATYÌNÆ

39. Hind metatarsi simple, not carinate; large species with the pronotum
bearing leaf-like expansions at the sides. (Chœradòdis, Neotrop.,
Indomal.). (CHŒRADÓDIDÆ) ....CHŒRADODÌNÆ
Hind metatarsi carinate. (See couplet 36)....MANTEÌNÆ, part

40. Eyes produced laterally to form a conical, spiniform process; body
very slender, filiform. (Oxyothéspis, Ethiop., As.; Heterochætula,
Malay.) ....OXYOTHESPÌNÆ
Eyes rounded laterally 41

41. Fore wings and antennæ of the male ciliate..................42
Fore wings and antennæ of the male not ciliate..............44

42. Pronotum linear or extremely slender; small species; the female
apterous. (Miópteryx, Promiópteryx, Chloromiópteryx, Neotrop.)
MIOPTERYGÌNÆ
Pronotum more or less expanded............................43

43. Pronotum almost trilobed, the angulations of the expansions somewhat acuminate; fore wings of male broad (see couplet 16).

DYSTACTÌNÆ, part

Pronotum more or less elliptical, the angulations of the expansions rounded; elytra narrow. (See couplet 45)......AMELÌNÆ, part

44. Pronotum shorter than the front coxæ......................45
Pronotum as long as or longer than the front coxæ.............46

45. Hind wings not colored; small species. (Ámeles, Pseudoyersínia Palæarc.; Yersínia, Litaneùtria, Neotrop.; Amántis, Myrcìnus, Gonýpeta, Indomal.; Mententélla, Ligària, Ethiop.)...AMELÌNÆ
Hind wings brightly colored, otherwise similar to the Amelinæ. (Compsomántis, Opsomántis, Malay.). (COMPSOMANTÌNÆ).

COMPSOMANTEÌNÆ

46. Front tibia with the sixth spine from the apex in the outer row longer than the fifth. (See couplet 32) .. CALIRIDÌNÆ, part
Front tibia with the sixth spine not longer than the fifth.......47

47. Eyes produced laterally to form a conical, spiniform process. (See couplet 40) ....OXYOTHESPÌNÆ, part
Eyes not thus spined.......................................48

48. Front femora with the first spine in the discoidal row not shorter than the second; large species of elongate form; wings large in male, short in female. (Archimántis, Rheomántis, Pseudomántis, Austr.). (ARCHIMANTÌNÆ) ....ARCHIMANTEÌNÆ
Front femora with the first discoidal spine shorter than the second 49

49. Supra-anal plate very long, lanceolate; large species with the pronotum much longer than the front coxæ. (Solýgia, Ethiop.).

SOLYGIÌNÆ

Supra-anal plate short. (See couplet 36).....MANTEÌNÆ, part

50. Pronotum slender, as long as the front coxæ.................51
Pronotum more or less broadened, shorter than the front coxæ; body more or less short and stout; wings well developed in both sexes. (Odontomántis, Hestiásula, Creobròter, Ind.; Otomántis, Panúrgica, Harpagomántis, Ethiop.). (CREOBROTÌNÆ).

HYMENOPODÌNÆ

51. Margins of pronotum broadly laminate (see couplet 17).

EPAPHRODITÌNÆ, part

Margins of pronotum not broadly laminate; species of moderate size, with slender pronotum which is at least as long as the front coxæ. (Anaxárcha, Acromántis, Citharomántis, Indomal.; Theomántis, Sigérpes, Anasigérpes, Ethiop.). (ACROMANTÌNÆ).

ACROMANTEÌNÆ

SUBORDER GRYLLOBLATTÒDEA

(GRYLLOBLATTÒIDEA, NOTÓPTERA)

Elongate, more or less depressed, wingless insects, measuring about an inch in length. Head rather large, free, horizontal or slightly inclined; eyes small or absent, no ocelli; antennæ long, filiform, with about 30 to 40 joints, inserted at the sides of the front of the head near the

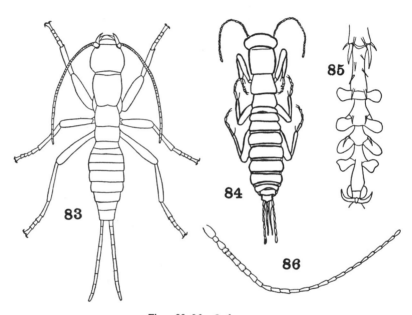

Figs. 83–86. Orthoptera

83. **Galloisiana** (Silvestri) Grylloblattidæ.
84. **Grylloblatta** (Walker) Grylloblattidæ.
85. **Grylloblatta,** tarsus of male (Walker) Grylloblattidæ.
86. **Galloisiana,** antenna (Crampton) Grylloblattidæ.

mandibles; mandibles large and strong. Prothorax quadrate or somewhat longer than wide, not expanded laterally; free and larger than the meso- or metathorax. Legs similar, formed for running, the coxæ close together; tarsi five-jointed, with two claws, those of the adult male with a pair of membranous lobes beneath each joint. Abdomen elongated, tergites more or less equal, transverse, extending down at the sides of the abdomen; cerci long, eight- or nine-jointed; ovipositor exserted, sword-shaped, composed of six paired pieces. Metamorphosis very slight, the nymphs very much like the adults and apparently of slow growth; terrestrial in all stages. (Figs. 83–86).

A single family. (Grylloblátta, western Canada, northwestern United States; Galloisiàna, Japan) ....GRYLLOBLÁTTIDÆ

SUBORDER SALTATÓRIA

Small to large, nearly always jumping species, often possessing a device on the wings for making a creaking or chirping sound; hind femora almost always very much stouter basally, or longer, or both, than the middle femora; wings of adults reposing over the abdomen, the fore wings toughened, narrower and thicker than the membranous,

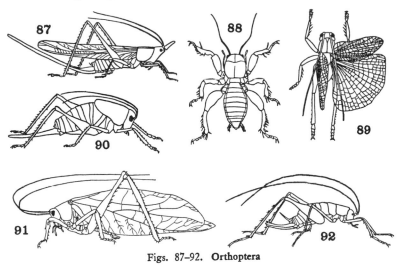

Figs. 87–92. Orthoptera

87. **Conocephalus** (Blatchley) Tettigoniidæ.
88. **Stenopelmatus** (Saussure) Stenopelmatidæ.
89. **Gryllacris** (Karny) Gryllacridæ.
90. **Anabrus** (Caudell) Tettigoniidæ.
91. **Stilpnochlora** (Saussure) Tettigoniidæ.
92. **Ceuthophilus** (Blatchley) Stenopelmatidæ.

plaited hind pair; sometimes the wings vestigial or completely absent; head usually vertical, sometimes conically produced forward; ovipositor almost always free, often long, sword- or needle-shaped; mouthparts conspicuous, mandibulate; antennæ long and many-jointed or short with few joints; tarsi usually four- or three-jointed; prothorax large, free, often much enlarged; cerci short. Metamorphosis gradual, the young resembling the adults, but with the small wings in a reversed postion in the last two nymphal stages, the hind wings then overlapping the fore wings.

1. Antennae usually long and many-jointed, delicately tapering and exceeding the body in length, rarely very short, with twelve segments or less; auditory organs if present, near the base of the front tibia; ovipositor of female almost always long and well developed; tarsi usually four-jointed. (TETTIGONIÒIDEA ($=LOCUSTÒIDEA$)) 2

Antennæ shorter, with less than 30 joints, filiform, rarely clubbed or serrate, but not delicately tapering; auditory organ if present, near the base of the abdomen; ovipositor of female never elongated; tarsi three-jointed, rarely with the front and middle ones two-jointed. (ACRIDÒIDEA) 14

2. Tarsi four-jointed, at least on the four posterior legs; antennæ always very long and tapering; ovipositor usually long and sword-shaped 3

Tarsi with three joints or less; ovipositor when present, needle-shaped 6

3. Tarsi more or less depressed 4

Tarsi distinctly compressed; almost always apterous forms, usually dull-colored .... STENOPELMÁTIDÆ

This family comprises six subfamilies, separable as follows:

a. Front tibiæ with an auditory organ .... b

Front tibiæ without an auditory organ .... d

b. Cerci very distinctly jointed apically. (Lezìna, Old World).
LEZINÌNÆ

Cerci simple c

c. Cerci short; first and second joints of tarsi indistinctly separated; wings large, with a chirping organ. (Prophalangópsis ($=Tárraga$), Ind.). (Including ABOILÌNÆ, HAGLÌNÆ, PAMPHAGOPSÌNÆ, ISFAROPTERÌNÆ, GEINITZIÌNÆ).
PROPHALANGOPSÌNÆ

Cerci long; first and second tarsal joints distinctly separated; usually wingless. (Anostóstoma, Ethiop., Austr.; Demácrida, Austr.; Magréttia, Ethiop., As.) .... ANOSTOSTOMATÌNÆ

d. Hind femora at base more sharply produced below than above; legs rather long and slender. Cave crickets. (Ceuthóphilus, Am. (Fig. 92); Dolichópoda, Palæarc.; Troglóphilus, Palæarc.; Rhaphidóphora, Indoaustr.). (CEUTHOPHILÌNÆ).
RHAPHIDOPHORÌNÆ

Hind femora at base more sharply produced above than below; legs stouter .... e

e. Front coxæ armed in front with a tooth-like projection. (Mimnérmus, Ethiop.; Cratomèlus, Neotrop.) ..... MIMNERMÌNÆ

Front coxæ simple, unarmed. (Fig. 88). (Stenopelmàtus, Am.).
STENOPELMATÎNÆ

4. Front tibiæ without an auditory organ........................5
Front tibiæ with an auditory organ. Long-horned locusts, Katydids.
(*PHASGONÙRIDÆ, LOCÙSTIDÆ*)......TETTIGONÎIDÆ

This very extensive family includes a number of subfamilies many of which are often given family rank. They may be separated as follows:

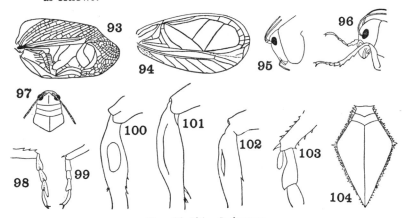

Figs. 93–104. Orthoptera

93. **Gryllus,** fore wing (Handlirsch) Gryllidæ.
94. **Œcanthus,** fore wing (Handlirsch) Gryllidæ.
95, 96. Superior and inferior insertion of antennæ (Caudell) Tettigoniidæ
97. **Mecopcda,** dorsal view of head and pronotum (Caudell) Tettigoniidæ.
98. Tarsus with sulcate segments (Caudell) Tettigoniidæ.
99. Tarsus with smooth segments (Caudell) Tettigoniidæ.
100. Open auditory pit (Caudell) Tettigoniidæ.
101. Linear auditory pit (Caudell) Tettigoniidæ.
102. Ear-like or shell-shaped auditory pit (Caudell) Tettigoniidæ.
103. Tarsus with free plantula (Caudell) Tettigoniidæ.
104. **Phyllophora,** hooded form of pronotum (Caudell) Tettigoniidæ.

a. Antennæ inserted between the eyes, nearer to the top of the occiput than to the clypeal suture. (Fig. 95)....................b
Antennæ inserted below the eyes, or between their lower margins, nearer to the clypeal suture than to the top of the occiput. (Fig. 96) ....o
b. First and second joints of tarsi longitudinally sulcate laterally. (Fig. 98) c
First and second tarsal joints smooth (Fig. 99); hind tibiæ with an apical spine on each side above. A large cosmopolitan group,

including many leaf-like species. (**Phaneróptera**, widespr.; **Isopsèra**, Ind.; **Scuddèria**, Am.; **Tylópsis**, Palæarc., Ethiop.; **Isóphya**, Palæarc., Am.) ....PHANEROPTERÌNÆ

c. Auditory pits on front tibiæ open. (Fig. 100).................d
Auditory pits covered partly by an ear-like or shell-shaped extension of the chitinous rim which partly covers them and narrows the aperture or reduces it to a linear slit. (Figs. 101, 102).....g

d. Posterior tibiæ with an apical spine on each side above..........e
Posterior tibiæ without apical spines above; body winged, very slender with slender legs. (**Zaprochìlus** (= *Prochìlus*), Austr.). (*PROCHÍLIDÆ*) ....ZAPROCHILÌNÆ

e. Prosternum armed with a pair of spines or tubercles.............f
Prosternum simple, unarmed. (**Meconèma**, **Cyrtáspis**, Palæarc.; **Amýtta**, **Anepitácta**, Ethiop.; **Thaumáspis**, Ind.).
MECONEMÌNÆ

f. Pronotum hood-like, strongly and acuminately produced behind; lateral carinæ of pronotum dentate or crenulate. (Fig. 104). (**Phyllóphora**, Indoaustr.; **Hyperhómala**, Austromal.).
PHYLLOPHORÌNÆ
Pronotum not hood-like, nor much produced behind. (Fig. 97). (**Mecópoda**, Austromal.; **Acridóxena**, **Apteroscírtus**, Ethiop.; **Tabària**, **Rhammatópoda**, Neotrop.)...........MECOPODÌNÆ

g. Front tibiæ without terminal spines above.....................h
Front tibiæ with a terminal spine above on the outer side (except *Arytropteris*) ....n

h. Antennal scrobes (*i.e.* the grooves in which the antennæ lie) with the margins produced. (**Pseudophýllus**, Palæarc., Indomal.; **Cleándrus**, **Phyllomìmus**, Indomal.; **Zabàlius**, Ethiop.).
PSEUDOPHYLLÌNÆ
Antennal scrobes with the margins hardly produced...........i

i. Hind tibiæ without apical spines above. (**Sàga**, Palæarc., **Clònia**, **Hemiclònia**, Ethiop.; **Hemisàga**, Austr.)............SAGÌNÆ
Hind tibiæ with an apical spine above on one or both sides.......j

j. Hind tibiæ with an apical spine only on the outer side above. (**Tympanóphora**, Austr.; **Mortoniéllus**, Malay.).
TYMPANOPHORÌNÆ
Hind tibiæ with an apical spine on both sides above, or only on the inner side..k

k. Front and middle tibiæ armed with short or medium sized spines...l
Front tibiæ, or both front and middle tibiæ, armed with long spines decreasing in length apically. (**Litróscelis**, **Phlùgis**, Neotrop.; **Hexacéntrus**, Indomal.; **Phìsis**, Ethiop., Indoaustr.).
LITROSCELÌNÆ

l. All the femora unarmed beneath, rarely the hind ones armed on the outer or on both sides; usually smaller species. (**Conocéphalus**

(= *Xiphídion*) cosmop.; **Orchélimum**, widespr.; **Odontoxiphí-dium**, Nearc.). (*XIPHIDIÌNÆ*)........CONOCEPHALÌNÆ
All femora usually spined below; rarely the hind ones armed only on the outer side, in which case the fastigium of the vertex is either forked or extended considerably beyond the basal joint of the antennæ; usually larger species......................m

m. Fastigium of the vertex usually noticeably narrower than the first joint of the antennæ, sometimes dorsally sulcate. (**Agrœcia,** Neotrop., Ethiop., Austromal.; **Eschatócerus,** Neotrop.; **Nícsara,** Austr.; **Salomòna,** Indoaustr.).................AGRŒCIÌNÆ
Fastigium of the vertex usually distinctly broader than the first joint of the antennæ, never sulcate. (**Neoconocéphalus,** Am.; **Euconocéphalus,** Ethiop., Indoaustr.; **Homorocóryphus,** cosmop.; **Copíphora,** Neotrop.). (*CONOCEPHALÌNÆ*).
COPIPHORÌNÆ

n. First joint of hind tarsi with a free plantula beneath (Fig. 103). (**Ánabrus,** Nearc.; **Metrióptera,** Holarc., Ethiop.; **Décticus,** Palæarc., Ethiop.). (*DECTICÌNÆ*).......TETTIGONIÌNÆ
First joint of hind tarsi without a free plantula, or with a very short one. (**Phasgonùra** (= *Locústa*), Palæarc.; **Onconòtus,** Palæarc.). (*LOCUSTÌNÆ*) ....PHASGONURÌNÆ

o. Third joint of hind tarsi longer than the second; front tibiæ with an apical spine on the inner side; hind tibiæ without an apical spine above on the outer side............................p
Third joint of hind tarsi shorter than the second; front and hind tibiæ with an apical spine above on both sides. (**Bradýporus,** Palæarc.; **Derállimus, Callímenus,** Palæarc.)...BRADYPORÌNÆ

p. Antennæ inserted between the lower margins of the eyes; pronotum unarmed; both sexes winged; front tibiæ with an apical spine above on the outer side; hind tibiæ with four apical spurs below. (**Pycnogáster, Ephíppiger, Urómenus, Steropleùrus,** Palæarc.) ....EPHIPPIGERÌNÆ
Antennæ inserted distinctly below the eyes; pronotum spined; female wingless; front tibiæ without apical spines above; hind tibiæ without apical spurs below, or with only two. (**Hetròdes, Acánthoplus, Eugáster, Anepiscéptus,** Ethiop.)......HETRODÌNÆ

5. Head vertical, body stout; usually brownish in color, with or without wings. (**Grýllacris,** tropicopol. (Fig. 89); **Camptonòtus,** Am.; **Paragrýllacris,** Austr.; **Erèmus,** As., Ethiop., Indoaustr.).
GRYLLÁCRIDÆ
Head horizontal; body long and slender, the legs all very thin and long; wingless species resembling walking sticks. (**Phasmòdes,** Austr.) ....PHASMÓDIDÆ

6. Antennæ very short, with twelve joints or less, not tapering at tip. (TRIDACTYLOIDEA) 7
   Antennæ many jointed, long and tapering...................8
7. Tarsi two-jointed; hind legs very short, body long, cylindrical; front tibiæ strongly dilated and digitate; large, entirely wingless species boring in the stems of plants. (Cylindrácheta, Austr., Chile) (Figs. 107, 111)...............CYLINDRACHÉTIDÆ
   Hind tarsi one-jointed; hind legs greatly enlarged, saltatorial; three small ocelli; small species not boring in plants. (Tridáctylus, cosmop.; Rhipípteryx, Am.) ....TRIDACTÝLIDÆ

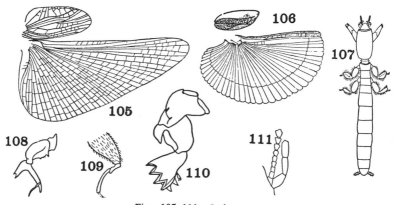

Figs. 105–111. Orthoptera

105. **Gryllotalpa,** wings (Handlirsch) Gryllotalpidæ.
106. **Tridactylus,** wings (Handlirsch) Tridactylidæ.
107. **Cylindracheta** (Giglio-Tos) Cylindrachetidæ.
108. **Tridactylus,** front leg (Saussure) Tridactylidæ.
109. **Tridactylus,** middle leg (Saussure) Tridactylidæ.
110. **Gryllotalpa,** front leg (Berlese) Gryllotalpidæ.
111. **Cylindracheta,** antenna and palpus (Giglio-Tos) Cylindrachetidæ.

8. Front tibiæ strongly dilated, digitate; ovipositor short, not protruded; large species with very large, elongate prothorax, burrowing in the soil. (Gryllotálpa (Figs. 105, 119), cosmop.; Scapteríscus, Am.) ....GRYLLOTÁLPIDÆ
   Front tibiæ not dilated and digitate; ovipositor projecting, usually long; antennæ always with more than thirty joints 9
9. Tarsi compressed, the second joint minute, compressed 10
   Tarsi with the second joint cordate, depressed 13
10. Hind tibiæ greatly widened, furnished with a few strong movable spines; hind femora very broad, oval; antennæ relatively blunt at tips; eyes minute; small, wingless species living in ants' nests. (Myrmecóphila, widespr.) ....MYRMECOPHÍLIDÆ

Hind tibiæ slender or only slightly widened, serrulate, or serrulate and spinose; femora more slender; antennæ finely tapered at tips; usually large, free living species 11

11. Hind tibiæ spinose, but not serrulate; stout-bodied, usually dark colored species. (Fig. 93). (Grýlus, Palæarc., Nemòbius, cosmop.; Gryllòdes, widespr.; Ácheta, Nearc.). (*ACHÉTIDÆ*)
GRÝLLIDÆ

a. Spines of hind tibiæ long, movable by an articulation at the base .... NEMOBIÌNÆ
Spines of hind tibiæ shorter, fixed and not movable at the base.
GRYLLÌNÆ

Hind tibiæ serrulate, sometimes spinose also 12

12. Hind tibiæ spinose, serrulate between the spines; body and legs slender; moderate or large species. Tree crickets. (Œcánthus, cosmop. (Fig. 94); Amphiacústa, Phalangópsis, Am.; Endacústa, Austr., Neotrop.; Phæophýllacris, Ethiop.). (Including *PHALAN-GÓPSIDÆ*) .... ŒCÁNTHIDÆ
Hind tibiæ with two rows of fine serrulations, but without spines or thorns. (Mogoplístes, Palæarc., Ethiop., Neotrop.; Ornèbius, widespr.; Cyclóptilum, Am.; Ectadóderus, widespr.).
MOGOPLÍSTIDÆ

13. Hind tibiæ not serrate, biseriately spinose and with five apical spurs. (Trigonídium, Palæarc., Ethiop., Indomal.; Cyrtóxiphus, widespr.; Homœóxiphus, Indomal.; Anáxiphus, Neotrop.)
TRIGONIDIÌDÆ
Hind tibiæ serrate, bearing more or less numerous spines and six apical spurs. (Eneóptera, Neotrop.; Nísitra, Malay.; Cardiodáctylus, Austromal.; Orócharis, Am.) .... ENEOPTÉRIDÆ

14. Tarsal claws without a pad (arolium) between them; pronotum greatly lengthened, extending backwards to cover the entire abdomen, fore wings vestigial, consisting of small scales at the base of the usually large hind wings; antennæ longer than the front femora; no tympanal organs at base of abdomen. Grouse locusts. (Tètrix (Figs. 114, 116), Paratéttix, widespr.; Neotéttix, Nearc.; Mazarrèdia, Indoaustr.; Tettigídea (Fig. 118), Am.). (*TETTÍGIDÆ, ACRYDIÌDÆ*, part). .... TETRÍGIDÆ
Tarsal claws almost always with an arolium between them; pronotum small, not extending backwards over more than a small basal part of the abdomen; if exceptionally enlarged, the wings and antennæ not as above 15

15. Body greatly lengthened and very slender, stick-like, with very long thin legs; wings absent or vestigial; head conical and greatly lengthened; prothorax tubular, not overlapping the mesonotum; antennæ eight-jointed; arolia sometimes small or indistinct. (Fig.

113). (Proscòpia, Prosárthria, Apióscelis, Corynorhýnchus, Astrò-
ma, Neotrop.) ....PROSCOPÌIDÆ
Of a different conformation 16

16. Hind legs similar to the middle ones; their femora scarcely lengthened and not strongly thickened; body, especially the abdomen
swollen or inflated; pronotum very large; green or brightly
colored species. (Pneùmora, Búlla, Cystocœlia, S. Afr.).

PNEUMÓRIDÆ

Hind legs very different from the middle ones, their femora large,
greatly thickened at the base and lengthened; abdomen not
noticeably swollen. Grasshoppers, Locusts, Short-horned locusts.
(*LOCÚSTIDÆ, ACRIDÌIDÆ, ACRYDÌIDÆ*, part).

ACRÍDIDÆ

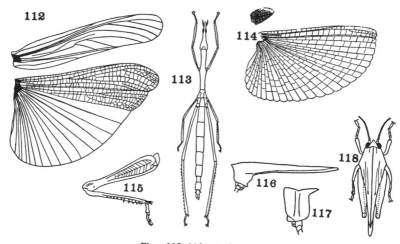

Figs. 112–118. Orthoptera

112. **Dissosteira**, wings (accessory veins in part omitted) (Snodgrass) Acrididæ.
113. **Prosarthria** (Brunner) Proscopiidæ.
114. **Tetrix**, wings (Handlirsch) Tetrigidæ.
115. **Acrida**, hind leg (Lugger) Acrididæ.
116. **Tetrix**, side view of pronotum (Packard) Tetrigidæ.
117. **Caloptenus**, side view of pronotum (Packard) Acrididæ.
118. **Tettigidea** (Blatchley) Tetrigidæ.

This family includes the following subfamilies:

a. Prosternum simple, flat ....b
   Prosternum with a spine, swelling, or lamellate elevation anteriorly..g
b. Antennæ longer than the front femora c
   Antennæ shorter than the front femora ....f

c. Vertex and front forming together a rounded surface, the front
vertical ....d
Vertex and front meeting at an angle, the surfaces of the two forming an angle when seen in profile ....e
d. Antennæ clavate, as long as the body; apterous species. (Gom-
phomástax, Palæarc., Ind.) ..........GOMPHOMASTACÌNÆ
Antennæ not clavate, shorter; usually winged species. A large
cosmopolitan group. (Œdípoda, widespr.; Árphia, Hippíscus,
Am.; Locústa, Pachýtylus, widespr.; Dissosteìra (Fig. 112),
Trimerótropis, Nearc.; Acrótylus, Œdàleus, Old World).
CEDIPODÌNÆ
e. Impressions of vertex wanting; head horizontal, the front nearly
horizontal; margins of antennæ serrate; apterous species.
(Psednùra, Austr.) ....PSEDNURÌNÆ
Impressions of vertex present, or if rarely wanting, the head is
conical, with the front more sloping, and wings are present.
(Truxàlis, Am.; Stenóbothrus, widespr.; Gomphócerus, palæarc.,
Am., Stauronòtus. Palæarc., Ind.; Mecostèthus, Palæarc.).
(*TRYXALÌNÆ, TRUXALÌNÆ*) ....ACRIDÌNÆ
f. Pronotum greatly flattened at the sides, roof-shaped and frequently
with a median ridge; posterior femora dilated and compressed.
(Scirtótypus, Ethiop., Indomal.; Chorœtypus, Indomal.; Brachýty-
pus, Ethiop.) ....CHORŒTYPÌNÆ
Pronotum not greatly flattened at the sides, and not ridged above;
posterior femora slender. (Eriánthus, Indoaustr.; Teìchophrys,
Eumástax, Masýntes, Neotrop.) ....EUMASTACÌNÆ
g. Impressions of the vertex large and shallow, forming the anterior
end of the vertex where they are separated by a very narrow
groove; front very strongly oblique and forming an angle with
the vertex. (Maùra, Chortógonus, Ethiop.; Pyrgomórpha, widespr.;
Monístria, Austr.; Desmóptera, Austromal.; Calámacris, Am.)
PYRGOMORPHÌNÆ
Impressions of vertex not forming the anterior end of the vertex,
placed above, at the sides or below, or obsolete ....h
h. Impressions of vertex dorsal in position and open behind; prosternum with a swelling, but rarely with a distinct thorn or
tubercle. (Pámphagus, Eurypóryphes, Acínipe, Palæarc.;
Lamarckiàna, Ethiop.) ....PAMPHAGÌNÆ
Impressions of vertex lateral or inferior in position or obsolete;
prosternum with a distinct sharply raised tubercle or spine.
(Melánoplus, Schistocérca, Am.; Acrýdium, Afr.; Indoaustr.; Podísma, Holarc., Cyrtacánthacris). (*ACRIDIÌNÆ.*
PODISMÌNÆ) ..................CYRTACANTHACRÌNÆ

SUBORDER PHASMATÒDEA

(PHÁSMIDA, PHASMÒIDEA, PHASMÒDEA, GRESSÒRIA, CHELEUTÓPTERA)

Large or very large insects, generally with very slender body of cylindrical, stick- or twig-like form; rarely greatly flattened and leaf-like. Head more or less freely movable, usually with long slender antennæ; eyes well developed; ocelli often absent. Prothorax short or very short, even in the very elongate forms; mesothorax short or elongate; metathorax frequently long, very closely united with the first abdominal segment (median segment), the suture between them often obscured or effaced. Abdomen usually long, cylindrical or tapering, the segments similar; cerci unjointed. Legs nearly always long or very long, similar, the tarsi five-jointed; rarely three-jointed. Wings very frequently entirely absent; when present the fore wings are usually very much smaller than the hind ones, of stouter consistency; hind wings when well developed with a narrow, stouter anterior portion and a very large delicate anal expansion or fan. Metamorphosis very slight and gradual; terrestrial and vegetarian in all stages. Mainly tropical species. Walking sticks, Stick insects, Leaf insects.

1. Tarsi five-jointed 2
   Tarsi three-jointed. (Tímema, Am.) ....TIMÉMIDÆ
2. Four posterior tibiæ each with a triangular area on the underside at apex (Fig. 119), usually marked off by grooves, rarely ending in a spine. (AREOLÁTÆ). (Superfamily PHASMATÒIDEA). 3
   Four posterior tibiæ simple, without a triangular area below at tip (Fig. 120). (ANAREOLÁTÆ). (Superfamily BACTERIÒIDEA) 5
3. Median segment (first abdominal segment) as long as or longer than the metanotum; often winged, with the fore wings reduced in size 4
   Median segment distinct from the metanotum, but often much shorter; always wingless; species with extremely long, slender body ....BACÍLLIDÆ

This family includes three groups, conveniently regarded as subfamilies, separable as follows:

a. Prosternum with two roughened tubercles between the front coxæ; antennæ often as long as or longer than the front legs, always much longer than the front femora. (Fig. 121). (Óbrimus, Heterocòpus, Tisámenus, Hoploclònia, Dátames, Dòres, Malay.).
   OBRIMÌNÆ
   Prosternum without roughened tubercles (except Pseudodatames which has short antennæ) ....b

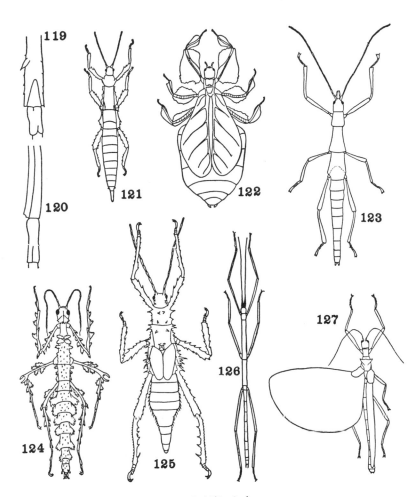

Figs. 119–127. Orthoptera

119. **Heteropteryx,** tip of hind tibia (Brunner) Phasmatidæ.
120. **Bacteria,** tip of hind tibia (Brunner) Bacteriidæ.
121. **Heterocopus** (Brunner) Bacillidæ.
122. **Phyllium** (Brunner) Phyllidæ.
123. **Anisomorpha** (Caudell) Phasmatidæ.
124. **Trychopeplus** (Hebard) Bacteriidæ.
125. **Heteropteryx** (Brunner) Phasmatidæ.
126. **Pseudomeryle** (Caudell) Phasmatidæ.
127. **Pomposa** (Brunner) Bacteriidæ.

b. Antennæ much shorter than the front legs, rarely (*Xylica*) as long; Old World species. (**Pseudodátames, Círsia, Antongília,** Madagascar; **Xýlica,** Ethiop.; **Bacíllus,** Palæarc.). . .BACILLÍNÆ
Antennæ as long as or longer than the front legs; mainly new world species. (**Pygirhýnchus, Céroys, Acanthocolònia, Mirophásma, Canulèius,** Neotrop.; **Oròbia,** Madagascar). PYGIRHYNCHÍNÆ

4. Antennae long in the male, many jointed, very short in the female, with few joints; mesonotum quadrate or transverse; fore wings of female covering the greater part of the abdomen, entire sides of abdomen broadly dilated into leaf-like extensions. (Fig 122). Leaf insects. (**Phýllium,** Ethiop., Indomal.; **Chitoníscus,** Polynes.; **Nanophýllium,** New Guinea) . . . . .PHYLLÍIDÆ
Antennæ long in both sexes; mesonotum longer than wide; abdomen simple, or at most not with the entire sides thus expanded. (Fig. 126) (*PSEUDOPHÁSMIDÆ*) . . . . . . .PHASMÁTIDÆ

Four subfamilies are recognized, separable by the following key:

a. Tarsal claws simple; fore wings, when present, lobate, very rarely filiform . . . . .b
Tarsal claws pectinate; fore wings when present filiform or stalked. (**Aschiphásma** (= *Ascepásma*), **Dìna,** Malay.; **Prebístus, Abrosòma,** Indomal.). (*ASCEPASMÌNÆ*).
ASCHIPHASMATÌNÆ

b. Body and legs armed with numerous spines (rarely the male not spiny); femora quadrate, not compressed, above with an apical spine; apical area of tibia produced into a spine. (Fig. 119). (**Anisacántha, Parectatosòma,** Madagascar; **Leócrates,** Malay.; **Heterópteryx,** Indoaustr.). . . . . .HETEROPTERYGÌNÆ
Body and legs armed with sparse teeth or spines; femora above without apical spine; apical area of tibia unarmed c

c. Sixth abdominal segment quadrate (male), or transverse (female), rarely elongate; legs unarmed; femora not compressed nor with leaf-like dilations; almost always wingless (Fig. 123). (**Anisomórpha,** Nearc., Neotrop.; **Agathomèra, Autólyca, Decídia,** Neotrop.) . . . . .ANISOMORPHÌNÆ
Sixth abdominal segment more elongate, much longer than wide (male) or quadrate (female); front femora either compressed or with leaf-like dilations. (**Donùsa, Eùcles, Strátocles, Brizòides, Phásma, Prexáspes, Prísopus,** Neotrop.; **Phæophásma,** Malay.; **Damasippòides,** Madagascar) . . . . .PHASMATÌNÆ

5. Median segment short, transverse or but little longer than wide, much shorter than the metanotum; wingless species.
BACUNCÙLIDÆ

This family is divisible into the following subfamilies:

a. Antennæ distinctly shorter than the front legs; old world species. (Clitúmnus, Cuniculìna, Indomal.; Pachymórpha, Indoaustr.; Gratídia, Ethiop., Ind.; Árphax) ....CLITUMNÌNÆ
   Antennæ as long as or longer than the front legs ....b
b. Last dorsal segment of male more or less bilobed; operculum (eight sternite of female) usually compressed, boat-shaped. (Menóxemus, Prómachus, Lonchòdes, Caraùsius, Indoaustr.; Dixíppus, Indomal.; Prosomèra, Malay.) .....LONCHODÌNÆ
   Last dorsal segment of male truncate; operculum vaulted, lanceolate. (Bacúnculus, Am.; Diapheromèra, N. Am.; Libèthra, Ocnóphila, Dỳme, Neotrop.) ....BACUNCULÌNÆ

Median segment as long as or longer than the metanotum, or at least much longer than wide; body frequently winged.
                                                    BACTERÌIDÆ

This family may be divided into three subfamilies as follows:

a. Antennæ shorter than or about equal in length to the front legs..b
   Antennæ much longer than the front legs, very thin and indistinctly jointed. (Fig. 127). (Necróscia, Diárdia, Pompòsa, Ásceles, Marmessòidea, Malay.; Aruanòidea, Indomal.; Sipylòidea, Indoaustr.) ....NECROSCIÌNÆ
b. Front femora unarmed above or similarly dentate on both sides, or not three-sided. (Fig. 124). (Bactrídium, Cleonístria, Bóstra, Bactèria, Neotrop.; Palòphus, Ethiop.; Dimorphòdes, Malay.; Eurycántha, Austr.). (PHIBALOSOMÌNÆ). ..BACTERIÌNÆ
   Front femora three-sided, spinose-dentate on the inner side above; cerci frequently large, leaf-like. (Hermárchus, Acrophýlla, Vetíllia, Austr.; Pharnàcia, Indomal.; Eurycnèma, Malay., Austr.)
                                                    ACROPHYLLÌNÆ

LITERATURE ON ORTHOPTERA (sens. lat.), INCLUDING PHASMATODEA, DERMAPTERA, BLATTARIA, AND MANTEODEA

BLATCHLEY, W. S. Orthoptera of Illinois. 27th Ann. Rept. Dept. Geol. Nat. Res. Indiana, 1902, pp. 123–471 (1903).
    The Orthoptera of Northeastern America. Nature Pub. Co. (1920).
BRUNER, L. Preliminary Catalogue of the Orthopteroid Insects of the Philippines. Univ. Nebraska Studies, 15, pp. 195–281 (1916).
BRUNNER, C. v. W. Prodromus der europäischen Orthopteren. Leipzig (1882).
    Revision du Système des Orthoptères. Ann. Mus. Civ. Stor. Nat. Genova, 13, pp. 1–230 (1893).
BURR, M. A Synopsis of the Orthoptera of Western Europe. London (1910).
CHAGNON, G. Orthoptères et Dermaptères du Québec. Nat. Canadien, 71, pp. 15–34; 54–74; 127–148, 36 figs. (1944).

CHOPARD, L. Orthoptères et Dermaptères. Faune de France, pt. 3, 212 pp. (1922).

Orthoptéroides de l'Afrique du Nord. Faun. Afr. Nord, 450 pp., 658 figs. (1943).

Atlas des Aptérygotes et Orthoptéroides de France. Nouv. Atlas, No. 2, 111 pp., 12 pls. (1947).

Orthoptères. In Grassé, Traité de Zoologie, 9, pp. 587–722, 135 figs. (1949).

FOX, N. List of Dermaptera and Orthoptera of New Jersey. Circ. N. J. Dept. Agric., No. 138, 58 pp. (1928).

FRÖHLICH, C. Die Odonaten und Orthopteren Deutschlands. Jena (1903).

FRUHSTORFER, H. Die Orthopteren der Schweiz. Arch. Naturg., Jahrg., 87A, Heft 5, pp. 1–262 (1921).

HEBARD, M. Studies on the Dermaptera and Orthoptera of Ecuador. Proc. Acad. Nat. Sci. Philadelphia, 76, pp. 109–248 (1924).

Studies on the Dermaptera and Orthoptera of Colombia. Trans. American Ent. Soc., 52, pp. 275–354 (1927).

The Orthoptera of Colorado. Proc. Acad. Nat. Sci., Philadelphia, 81, pp. 303–425 (1929).

Orthoptera of Minnesota. Tech. Bull. Minnesota Agric. Expt. Sta., No. 85, 61 pp. (1933).

Orthoptera [s. lat.] of Illinois. Bull. Illinois Nat. Hist. Survey, 20, pp. 125–279, 6 pls., 167 figs. (1934).

HOULBERT, C. Thysanoures, Dermaptères et Orthoptères. In Encycl. Sci. (1924).

HUBBELL, T. H. Dermaptera and Orthoptera of Berrien Co., Michigan. Pap. Mus. Zoöl., Univ. Michigan, No. 116, 77 pp. (1922).

INNES, W. Revision des Orthoptères de l'Egypt. Mém. Soc. Ent. Egypte, 3, pp. 5–176 (1929).

KARNY, H. Zur Systematik der Orthopteroiden Insekten. Treubia, 3, p. 236 (1923).

KIRBY, W. F. A Synonymic Catalogue of the Orthoptera. Vols. 2 and 3. British Mus. Nat. Hist., London (1907–10).

LAMEERE, A. Orthoptera. In Précis de Zoologie. Publ. Inst. zool. Torley-Rousseau, 4, pp. 287–305; 328–352 (1935).

LA RIVERS, I. A Synopsis of Nevada Orthoptera. American Midl. Nat., 39, pp. 652–720 (1948).

LUCAS, W. J. Monograph of the British Orthoptera. London, Ray Soc., 264 pp. (1920).

MORALES AGACINO, E. Notas sobre Ortopteroides· de Ifni y Sahara Español. Eos, 23, pp. 241–277, 4 figs. (1947).

MORSE, A. P. Manual of the Orthoptera of New England. Proc. Boston Soc. Nat. Hist., 35, no. 6 (1920).

Orthoptera of Maine. Bull. Maine Agric. Sta., No. 296, 36 pp. (1921).

PERRIER, R. Orthoptères de la France. Faune de France, 3, pp. 81–112, 108 figs. (1934).

PIERS, H. The Orthoptera of Nova Scotia. Proc. Nova Scotia Inst., Halifax, 14, pp. 201–351 (1918).

RAMME, W. Orthoptera, In Tierwelt Mitteleuropas, 4, Lief. 2, pp. VI, 1–22 (1928).

SAUSSURE, H. and others. Orthoptera. In Biologia Centrali-Americana, 1, 458 pp. (1893–99).

SCUDDER, S. H. Guide to the Genera and Classification of North American Orthoptera. Cambridge, Mass. (1897).
  Catalogue of Orthoptera of the United States. Proc. Davenport Acad. Nat. Sci., 8, pp. 1–101 (1900).
  Index to North American Orthoptera. Occas. Pap. Boston Soc. Nat. Hist., No. 6, pp. 1–436 (1901).

TÜMPEL, L. Die Geradeflügler Mitteleuropas, 2d edit. Gotha. 327 pp. (1907).

WALDEN, B. H. Orthoptera of Connecticut. Bull. State Geol. Nat. Hist. Surv. Connecticut, No. 16, pp. 48–169 (1911).

ZIMMERMAN, E. C. Orthoptera s. lat. Insects of Hawaii, 2, pp. 73–158 (1948).

SUBORDER MANTEODEA

BEIER, M. Die Mantodeen Chinas. Mitt. zool. Mus., Berlin, 18, pp. 332–337 (1933).
  Mantidæ. Gen. Insectorum, fasc. 196–198, 200–201, 203, 248 pp., 15 pls. (1934–37).

GIGLIO-TOS, E. Mantidi Esotici, I–XII. Boll. Soc. Ent. Italiana (1911–17). (Various parts.)
  Saggio di una nuova classificazione dei Mantidi. Boll. Soc. Ent. Italiana, 49, pp. 50–87 (1919).
  Mantidæ, Perlamantinæ. Gen. Insectorum, fasc. 144, 13 pp. (1913).
  Mantidæ, Eremiaphilinæ. Gen. Insectorum, fasc. 177, 36 pp. (1921).
  Mantidæ. Das Tierreich, Lief. 50, 707 pp. (1927).

KIRBY, W. F. A Synonymic Catalogue of the Orthoptera. Vol. 1. British Mus. Nat. Hist., London (1904).

MORALES AGACINO, E. Mantidos de la fauna iberica. Bol. Pat. veg. Ent. agric., Madrid, 15, pp. 149–164, 44 figs. (1947).

REHN, J. A. G. Mantidæ, Vatinæ. Gen. Insectorum, fasc. 119, 28 pp. (1911).
  The Orthoptera of Costa Rica, Part I — Mantidæ. Proc. Acad. Nat. Sci., Philadelphia, 87, pp. 167–272, 4 pls. (1935).

SAUSSURE, H. Essai d'un Système des Mantides. Mitt. schweiz. Ent. Ges., 3, pp. 49–73 (1869).

TINDALE, N. B. Review of Australian Mantidæ. Rec. South Australian Mus., 2, pp. 425–457 (1923).

TINKHAM, E. R. Studies in Chinese Mantoidea. Lingnan Sci. Journ., 16, pp. 481–499, 551–572, 2 pls. (1937).

TRAVASSOS, FILHO, L. Sobre a familia Acanthopidæ (Mantodea). Arq. Zool. S. Paulo, 4, pp. 157–231, 3 pls. (1945).

WESTWOOD, J. O. Revisio Mantidarum. London (1889).

SUBORDER GRYLLOBLATTODEA

CAUDELL, A. N. Grylloblatta in California. Canadian Ent., 53, pp. 148–150 (1923).
  Notes on Grylloblatta. Journ. Washington Acad. Sci., 14, pp. 369–371 (1924).

CAUDELL, A. N. and KING, J. L. A New Genus of Grylloblattidæ from Japan. Proc. Ent. Soc. Washington, 26, pp. 53–60 (1924).
GURNEY, A. B. Synopsis of Grylloblattidæ. Pan-Pacific Ent., 13, pp. 159–170 (1937).
    Taxonomy and Distribution of Grylloblattidæ. Proc. Ent. Soc. Washington, 50, pp. 86–102, 16 figs. (1948).
SILVESTRI, F. Grylloblattidæ. Boll. Zool. Gen. Agrar. Portici, 20, pp. 107–121 (1928).
WALKER, E. M. A New Species of Orthoptera Forming a New Genus and Family. Canadian Ent., 46, pp. 93–97 (1914).
    The Male and Immature Stages of Grylloblatta. Canadian Ent., 51, pp. 131–139 (1919).

SUBORDER SALTATORIA
TETTIGONOIDEA

BOLIVAR, J. Orthoptera palæarctica. Pycnogastrinæ. Eos, 2, pp. 423–463 (1926).
BRUNER, L. Revision of Tropical American Tettigonoidea. Ann. Carnegie Mus., 9, pp. 284–404 (1912).
BRUNNER, C. v. W. Monographie der Phaneropteriden. 399 pp., Vienna (1878).
    Monographie der Stenopelmatiden und Gryllacriden. Verh. zool.-bot. Ges., Wien, 38, pp. 247–394 (1888).
    Additamenta zur Monographie der Phaneropteriden. Verh. zool.-bot. Ges., Wien, 41, pp. 1–196 (1891).
    Monographie der Pseudophylliden. 282 pp., Vienna (1895).
CAUDELL, A. N. Cyrtophili of the United States. Journ. New York Ent. Soc., 14, pp. 32–45 (1906).
    The Decticinæ of North America. Proc. U. S. Nat. Mus., 32, pp. 285–410 (1907).
    Locustidæ, Decticinæ. Gen. Insectorum, fasc. 72, 43 pp. (1908).
    Locustidæ, Prophalangopsinæ. Gen. Insectorum, fasc. 120, 7 pp. (1911).
    Locustidæ, Ephippigerinæ. Gen. Insectorum, fasc. 140, 10 pp. (1913).
    Locustidæ; Meconeminæ, Phyllophorinæ, Tympanophorinæ, Phasgonurinæ, Phasmodinæ, Bradyporinæ. Gen. Insectorum, fasc. 138, 25 pp. (1913).
    Locustidæ, Mecopodinæ. Gen. Insectorum, fasc. 171, 32 pp. (1916).
    Locustidæ, Hetrodinæ. Gen. Insectorum, fasc. 168, 13 pp. (1916).
    Locustidæ, Saginæ. Gen. Insectorum, fasc. 167, 8 pp. (1916).
    The Genera of Rhaphidophorinæ of America North of Mexico. Proc. U. S. Nat. Mus., 49, pp. 655–690 (1916).
CHANG, K. S. F. Index of Chinese Tettigoniidæ. Notes Ent. chinoise, Mus. Heude, 2, pp. 25–77 (1935).
CHOPARD, L. Revision of the Indian Gryllidæ. Rec. Indian Mus., 30, pp. 1–36 (1928).
CHOPARD, L. Catalogue de la faune du Congo Belge. Gryllides. Ann. Mus. Congo Belge, (3)4, pp. 1–88, 37 figs. (1934).
    Contribution à l'étude des Gryllides du Congo belge. Rev. Zool. Bot. Afr., 41, pp. 109–121 (1948).
COUSIN, G. Systématique et méthodes biométriques à propos des grillons de France. Bull. Biol. France Belg., 80, pp. 389–465, 6 figs. (1947).

DE JONG, C. On Indo-Malayan Pterophyllinæ. Zool. Meded., 21, 109 pp., 18 figs. (1939).

FULTON, B. B. Tree Crickets of New York. Tech. Bull. No. 42, New York Agric. Exp. Sta. (1915).

GIGLIO-TOS, F. Sulla posizione systematica del genere Cylindracheta. Ann. Mus. Civ. Genoa (3), 6, pp. 81–101 (1914).

HEBARD, M. Review of North American Species of Myrmecophila. Trans. American Ent. Soc., 46, pp. 91–111 (1920).

Studies on the Gryllidæ of Panama. Trans. American Ent. Soc., 54, pp. 233–294 (1928).

Mogoplistinæ [Gryllidæ] of the United States. Trans. American Ent. Soc., 57, pp. 135–160 (1931).

HUBBELL, T. H. Revision of the Genus Ceuthophilus. Univ. Florida Sci. Ser., 2, 551 pp., 39 pls., 2 figs. (1936).

KARNY, H. Revisio Conocephalidarum. Abh. zool.-bot. Ges., Wien, 4, Heft 3, pp. 1–114 (1907).

Locustidæ, Listroscelinæ. Gen. Insectorum, fasc. 131, 20 pp. (1912).

Locustidæ, Conocephalinæ. Gen. Insectorum. fasc. 135, 17 pp. (1913).

Locustidæ, Copophorinæ. Gen. Insectorum, fasc. 139, 50 pp. (1913).

Locustidæ, Agrœciinæ. Gen. Insectorum, fasc. 141, 47 pp. (1913).

Fauna Buruana, Orthoptera, Fam. Gryllacridæ. Treubia, 7, pp. 41–84 (1925).

Revision of the South African Gryllacridæ. Ann. South African Mus., 29, pp. 77–151 (1929).

Gryllacridi dei Musei di Genova. Mem. Soc. Ent. Italiana, 7, pp. 5–154, 55 figs. (1929).

Gryllacriden des Wiener Museums. Ann. naturh. Mus. Wien, 44, pp. 49–198, 77 figs. (1930).

Gryllacridæ celebicæ. Treubia, 12, Suppl., pp. 141–184, 18 figs. (1931).

Tettigoniidæ celebicæ. Treubia, 12, Suppl., pp. 4–140, 70 figs. (1931).

Gryllacrididæ. Gen. Insectorum, fasc. 206, 317 pp., 7 pls. (1938).

KARSCH, F. Über die Hetrodiden. Berliner ent. Zeits., 31, pp. 43–72 (1887).

Über die Orthopterenfamilie der Prochiliden. Ent. Nachr., 17, pp. 97–107 (1891).

REDTENBACHER, J. Monographie der Conocephaliden. Verh. zool.-bot. Ges. Wien, 41, pp. 315–562 (1891).

REHN, J. A. G. and HEBARD, M. Revision of the Orthopterous Group Insaræ (Phaneropterinæ). Trans. American Ent. Soc., 40, pp. 37–184 (1914).

SAUSSURE, H. Mélanges Orthoptérologiques. Gryllides. 2 pts., Geneva (1877–78).

Revision du genre Tridactylus. Rev. Suisse Zool., 4, pp. 407–419 (1897).

SAUSSURE, H. and ZEHNTER L. Monographie des Gryllotalpiens. Rev. Suisse Zool., 2, pp. 403–430 (1894).

SCHIMMER, F. Monographie der Gryllodengattung Myrmecophila. Zeits. wiss. Zool., 93, pp. 409–534 (1909).

SCUDDER, S. H. The North American Ceuthophili. Proc. American Acad. Arts Sci., 30, pp. 17–113 (1894).

Stenopelmatinæ of the Western United States. Canadian Ent., 31, pp. 113–121 (1899).

SHIRAKI, T. Monographie der Grylliden von Formosa und Japan. 129 pp.
(1911).
    Gryllotalpidæ and Gryllidæ of Japan. Ins. Matsumurana, 4, pp. 181–252
(1930).
TEPPER, J. G. O. The Phanopterinæ of Australia. Trans. Roy. Soc. South
Australia, 15, pp. 77–113 (1892).
TINDALE, N. B. Australasian Mole Crickets of the Family Gryllotalpidæ.
Rec. South Australian Mus., 4, pp. 1–42 (1928).
TINKHAM, E. R. New species and records of Chinese Tettigoniidæ. Notes
Ent. chinoise, 10, pp. 33–66, 12 figs. (1943).
UVAROV, B. P. Revision of the Old World Cyrtacanthacrini. Ann. Mag. Nat.
Hist. (9), 11 and 12 (several parts) (1923).
VIGNON, P. Les sauterelles-feuilles de l'Amérique tropicale. Arch. Mus. Paris,
(6)5, pp. 57–214, 25 pls., 95 figs. (1930).
ZEUNER, F. The subfamilies of Tettigoniidæ. Proc. Roy. Ent. Soc. London,
(B)5, pp. 103–109 (1936).

ACRIDOIDEA

BOLIVAR, J. Acrididæ, Pyrgomorphinæ. Gen. Insectorum, fasc. 90, 58 pp
(1909).
    Acridiidæ, Pamphaginæ. Gen. Insectorum, fasc. 170, 40 pp. (1916).
BOLIVAR Y PIELTAIN, C. Monografia de los Eumastacidos. Trab. Mus. Nac.
Madrid, Ser. Zool., 46, xxxii+380 pp., 186 figs. (1930).
BRUNER, L. Orthoptera, Acridiidæ. Biologia Centrali-Americana, 2, 342 pp.
(1900–09).
    Synoptic List of the Paraguayan Acrididæ. Proc. U. S. Nat. Mus., 30,
pp. 613–694 (1906).
    South American Tetrigidæ. Ann. Carnegie Mus., 7, pp. 89–143 (1910).
BRUNNER, C. v. W. Monographie der Proscopiden. Verh. zool.-bot. Ges.,
Wien, 40, pp. 87–124 (1890).
BURR, M. Eumastacidæ. Gen. Insectorum, fasc. 15, 23 pp. (1904).
    Essai sur les Eumastacides. Ann. Soc. España Hist. Nat., 28, pp. 75–
112; 253–304 (1899).
    Monograph of the genus Acrida (= Truxalis). Trans. Ent. Soc.
London, 1902, pp. 149–187 (1902).
CLAASSEN, P. W. The Grasshoppers of Kansas, Pts. 1 and 2. Bull. Dept.
Ent. Univ. Kansas, No. 11, 126 pp. (1917).
FINOT, A. Sur le genre Acridium. Ann. Soc. Ent. France, 76, pp. 247–354
(1907).
FLETCHER, T. B. Acrydidæ. Cat. Indian Ins. Govt. India, Centr. Pub. Branch,
Calcutta, pt. 1 (1921).
GOLDING, F. D. The Acrididæ of Nigeria. Trans. Roy. Ent. Soc. London, 99,
pp. 517–587 (1948).
GUENTHER, K. Acrydiinenausbeute von Formosa. Stettin. ent. Zeitg., 102,
pp. 145–165, 2 pls. (1941).
HANCOCK, J. L. The Tettigidæ of North America. Chicago, 188 pp. (1902).
    Acridiidæ, Tetriginæ. Gen. Insectorum, fasc. 79, 4 pp. (1906).
HEBARD, M. Key to the North American genera of Acridinæ. Trans. American
Ent. Soc. 52, pp. 47–59 (1926).

Studies in the Tettigoniidæ of Panama. Trans. American Ent. Soc., **53**, pp. 79–156 (1927).

KEVAN, D. K. McE. Parasphena from East Africa. Journ. East African Nat. Hist. Soc., **19**, pp. 110–130 (1946).

KIRBY, W. F. Acrididæ. Fauna British India (1914).

LIEBERMANN, J. Catalogo sistematico y biogeografico de Acridoideos Argentinos. Rev. Soc. ent. Argent., **10**, pp. 125–230 (1939).

Generos y especies nuevos de Acridoideos chilenos. Rev. Soc. ent. Argent., **11**, pp. 400–410, 1 pl. (1943).

Los Acridios de Santa Fe. Rev. Soc. ent. Argent., **14**, pp. 55–114 (1948).

MacNEILL, J. Revision of the Truxalidæ of North America. Proc. Davenport Acad. Sci., **6**, pp. 179–274 (1897).

MELLO-LEITÃO, C. DE. Estudio monografico de los Proscopidos. Rev. Mus. La Plata, (N.S.), **1**, pp. 279–448, 13 pls., 100 figs. (1939).

RAMME, W. Die Acrididen-Fauna des indomalayischen und benachbarter Gebiete. Mitt. zool. Mus., Berlin, **25**, 243 pp., 21 pls., 55 figs. (1941).

REHN, J. A. G. North American Œdipodinæ. Trans. American Ent. Soc., **45**, pp. 229–255 (1919).

On New and Previously-known Species of Pneumoridæ. Trans. American Ent. Soc., **67**, pp. 137–159, 9 figs. (1941).

Review of Old World Euthyminæ (Cyrtacanthacridinæ). Proc. Acad. Nat. Sci. Philadelphia, **96**, pp. 1–135 (1944).

Revision of the Group Hyalopteryges (Acridinæ). Trans. American Ent. Soc., **70**, pp. 181–234 (1944).

The Acridoid Family Eumastacidæ. Proc. Acad. Nat. Sci. Philadelphia, **100**, pp. 77–139 (1948).

REHN, J. A. G. and J. W. H. Review of New World Eumastacinæ. Proc. Acad. Nat. Sci. Philadelphia, **91**, pp. 165–206, 3 pls., 6 figs. (1939); **94**, pp. 1–88, 2 pls., 60 figs. (1942).

A Contribution to our Knowledge of the Eumastacidæ of Africa and Madagascar. Proc. Acad. Nat. Sci. Philadelphia, **97**, pp. 197–248, 5 pls. (1945).

REHN, J. A. G. and HEBARD, M. Study of North American Eumastacinæ. Trans. American Ent. Soc., **44**, pp. 203–250 (1918).

SAUSSURE. H. Prodrome des Œdipodiens. Mem. Soc. Phys. Hist. Nat., Geneva, **28**, No. 9, 254 pp. (1884).

SCUDDER, S. H. Revision of the Melanopli. Proc. U. S. Nat. Mus., **20**, pp. 1–421 (1897) and Proc. Davenport Acad. Sci., **7**, pp. 155–205 (1899).

SHIRAKI, T. Acrididen Japans. Tokio, 90 pp. (1910).

SJOESTEDT, Y. Revision der Australischen Acridiodeen. K. Svenska Vetensk. Akad. Handl., (3)**15**, 191 pp., 2 pls. (1935).

SOMES, M. P. The Acrididæ of Minnesota. Bull. Minnesota Agric. Expt. Sta., No. 141, pp. 1–100 (1914).

THOMAS, C. Synopsis of the Acrididæ of North America. Rept. U. S. Geol. Surv. Terr., Washington Govt. Printing Office, 262 pp. (1873).

TINKHAM, E. R. Taxonomic Studies on the Cyrtacanthinæ of South China. Lingnan Sci. Journ., **19**, pp. 269–382. 7 pls. (1940).

TRINCHIERI, G. Secondo contributo alla bibliografia delle cavalette [Acrididæ]. Minist. Colon., Rome. 86 pp. (1933).

UVAROV, B. P. Revision of the Genus Locusta (= Pachytylus). Bull. Ent. Res., 12, pp. 135–163 (1921).

The Tribe Thrinchini of the Subfamily Pamphiginæ, and the Interrelations of the Acridid Subfamilies. Trans. Roy. Ent. Soc. London, 93, pp. 1–72, 73 figs. (1943).

WILLEMSE, C. Revision of Acrididæ of Sumatra. Tijdschr. v. Ent., 73, pp. 1–206 (1930).

Acrididæ celebicæ. Treubia, 12, Suppl., pp. 189–270, 24 figs. (1931).

SUBORDER PHASMATODEA

BRUNNER, C. v. W. and REDTENBACHER, J. Die Insekten-familie der Phasmiden. Parts I–III., 589 pp. Leipzig. (1906–08).

CAUDELL, A. N. The Phasmidæ or Walking Sticks of the United States. Proc. U.S. Nat. Mus., 26, pp. 863–885 (1903).

GÜNTHER, K. Die Phasmoiden Neuguineas. Mitt. zool. Mus. Berlin, 14, pp. 599–746 (1928).

Phasmoiden und Acrydiinen von Holländisch Neu Guinea. Nova Guinea, 17, Zool., pp. 323–344, 17 figs. (1935).

Phasmoiden aus Centralborneo. Ark. Zool., 28A, 29 pp., 9 figs. (1935).

Celebische Phasmoiden. Mitt. zool. Mus. Berlin, 21, 29 pp., 2 pls. (1936).

GURNEY, A. B. Australian Walking Sticks of the Genus Extatosoma. Ann. Ent. Soc. America, 40, pp. 373–396 (1947).

KIRBY, W. F. A Synonymic Catalogue of the Orthoptera, Vol. 1. British Mus., Nat. Hist., London (1904).

REHN, J. A. G. and J. W. H. Species of Phyllium. Proc. Acad. Nat. Sci. Philadelphia, 85, pp. 411–427, 2 pls. (1933).

Orthoptera of the Philippines, Pt. 1. Phasmatidæ; Obriminæ. Proc. Acad. Nat. Sci. Philadelphia, 90, pp. 389–487, 7 pls. (1939).

SHELFORD, R. Phasmidæ, in Biologia Centrali-Americana, 2, pp. 343–376 (1909).

SHIRAKI, T. Orthoptera of the Japanese Empire (Part IV). Phasmidæ. Mem. Fac. Sci. Agric. Taihoku, 14, pp. 23–88, 7 pls., 9 figs. (1935).

WESTWOOD, J. O. Catalogue of the Insects in the British Museum. Phasmidæ. London, British Mus., 195 pp., 48 pls. (1859).

ORDER DERMÁPTERA

Moderate-sized or small, more or less depressed insects, of elongate form, with the abdomen terminating in a pair of strong, movable forceps. Head free; antennæ filiform, with from 10 to 30, rarely more, joints; mandibles large, always (except *Arixenia*) fitted for biting. Prothorax free, more or less quadrate. Meso- and metathorax clearly separated; fore wings (elytra) short, leaving the abdomen exposed, heavily chitinized; hind wings, when present (Fig. 142), large, orbicular or broadly oval, at base with two or three cells surrounded by heavy veins; anal fan very large, with a number of radiating veins; radially folded from near the center, and when at rest almost entirely covered by the elytra; sometimes one or both sexes apterous. Abdomen long, very flexible, with from eight to ten exposed segments; cerci nearly always forming an anal forceps, one-jointed, except in the nymphs of a few genera, where they are multiarticulate. Legs rather short; tarsi three-jointed, with claws. Metamorphosis slight and gradual; terrestrial in all stages. Earwigs.

1. Cerci weakly sclerotized and not opposable; eyes much reduced or wanting; apterous species; ectoparasites of mammals 2
   Cerci heavily sclerotized and opposable like the blades of a pair of forceps; eyes well developed; usually winged when adult; body shining, rarely pubescent; mandibles usually fitted for chewing; not ectoparasitic. (Suborder FORFICULÌNA) 3
2. Antennæ as long as the body; mandibles not fitted for chewing, toothed at tips and fringed with bristles along the margin; body strongly pubescent; eyes present, but much reduced in size; living as ectoparasites on bats. (Suborder ARIXENÌNA). (Arixènia, Malay.) . . . . .ARIXENÌIDÆ
   Antennæ shorter, the basal joint greatly elongated; mandibles strong, dentate; eyes entirely wanting; ectoparasites of rodents. (Suborder DIPLOGLOSSÀTA (*DERMODERMÁPTERA*)). (Hemímerus, S. Afr.) . . . . .HEMIMÉRIDÆ
3. Metapygidium and telson present as two small plates behind the pygidium, or else all three are fused together with the tenth tergite to form a large horizontal plate (squamopygidium); pygidium simple, never with complex processes; ædeagus of male double . .4
   Metapygidium and telson not developed or vestigial; pygidium well developed, often with complex processes: ædeagus of male a single median piece. (*EUDERMÁPTERA*) 17
4. Squamopygidium absent, the pygidium, metapygidium and telson all present as separate plates; body not strongly flattened (except Platylabiidæ). 5
   Squamopygidium developed; hind wing with an oblique branch in the large basal cell; body very strongly flattened; a large scutellum visible between the elytra at base. (If elytra and scutellum are absent, see *Gonólabis*, couplet 14). (Apáchyus (Figs. 131, 137) Indomal., Austr.; Dendròiketes, Ind.). (Superfamily APACHY-ÒIDEA) (*PARADERMÁPTERA*) . . . . .APACHŶIDÆ
5. Metapygidium and telson not reduced, nearly as large as the relatively small pygidium; head depressed, truncate or concave and not emarginate behind; femora compressed and generally keeled. (PROTODERMAPTERA) (Superfamily PŸGIDICRANÒI-DEA) (*PYGIDICRANÁLES*). 6
   Metapygidium and telson much reduced in size, greatly smaller than the pygidium which is relatively very large; femora not com-

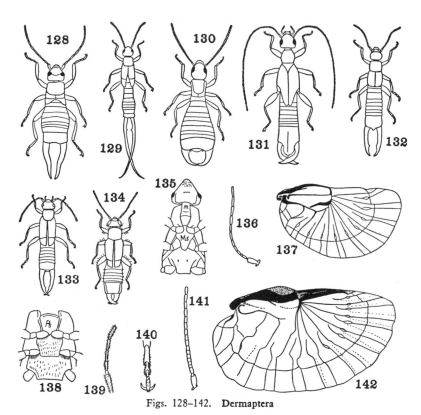

Figs. 128–142.   Dermaptera

128. **Burriola** (Burr) Cheliduridæ.
129. **Timomenus** (Burr) Opisthocosmiidæ.
130. **Esphalmenus** (Burr) Esphalmenidæ.
131. **Apachyus** (Burr) Apachyidæ.
132. **Labidura** (Burr) Labiduridæ.
133. **Doru** (Burr) Forficulidæ.
134. **Propyragra** (Burr) Pyragridæ.
135. **Allostethus**, underside of head and thorax (Burr) Allostethidæ.
136. **Anatælia**, antenna (Burr) Anatæliidæ.
137. **Apachyus**, wing (Tillyard) Apachyidæ.
138. **Esphalmenus**, underside of thorax (Burr) Esphalmenidæ.
139. **Ancistrogaster**, base of antenna (Burr) Ancistrogastridæ.
140. **Mesasiobia**, tarsus (Burr) Anechuridæ.
141. **Karschiella**, antenna (Burr) Karschiellidæ.
142. **Forficula**, wing, Forficulidæ.

pressed or keeled. (Superfamily LABIDURÒIDEA) (*LAB-IDURÁLES*) 11
6. Femora keeled 7
   Femora not keeled 10
7. Antennæ with from 15 to 25 joints, the fifth and sixth joints elongate (Fig. 136) 8
   Antennæ with 25 to 35 joints, the fifth and sixth short, transverse or quadrate (Fig. 141) 9
8. Both elytra and hind wings absent; metasternum truncate behind; nymphs with forceps-like cerci. (**Anatælia** (Fig. 136), Canary Isl.; **Chállia**, North China) ....ANATÆLÌIDÆ
   Elytra always, and hind wings usually perfect; metasternum sinuate or excavated behind; nymphs with long, many-jointed cerci, not forceps-like. (**Díplatys**, tropicopol.) ....DIPLATÝIDÆ
9. Antennæ unusually thick; fourth to sixth joints transverse (Fig. 141); nymphs with jointed cerci. (**Karschiélla, Bormánsia,** Ethiop.) ....KARSCHIÉLLIDÆ
   Antennæ not very thick; fourth to sixth segments short, but not transverse; cerci of nymphs forceps-like, not jointed. (**Pygidicràna**, Neotrop.; **Kalocrània**, Malay.; **Dicràna**, Ethiop., Indoaustr.; **Cranopýgia**, Ind.) ....PYGIDICRÁNIDÆ
10. Prosternum convex, more or less acute anteriorly; New World species, the body pubescent. (Fig. 134). (**Pyràgra, Pyragrópsis, Echinopsàlis, Propyràgra**, Neotrop.) ....PYRÁGRIDÆ
    Prosternum not acute anteriorly; Old World species, the body clothed with short, stiff bristles. (**Echinosòma**, Ethiop., Indoaustr.) ....ECHINOSOMÁTIDÆ
11. Body not very strongly flattened; forceps (cerci) not flattened nor sickle-shaped 12
    Body very strongly flattened; forceps strongly flattened and sickle-shaped; elytra perfectly developed, the hind wings short; antennæ 19–20 jointed. (**Platylàbia**, Indomal.). (*PALÍCIDÆ*)
    PLATYLABÌIDÆ
12. Mesosternum strongly narrowed behind (Fig. 135); stout species, sometimes without elytra and wings. (**Allostèthus, Gonolabidùra, Allostethélla**, Malay.) ....ALLOSTÉTHIDÆ
    Mesosternum not strongly narrowed behind 13
13. Prosternum not narrowed behind 14
    Prosternum narrowed behind (Fig. 138); without wings or elytra; abdomen of male much widened apically (Fig. 130). (**Esphálmenus**, Neotrop., Ethiop.; **Gonolabìna**, Neotrop.)
    ESPHALMÉNIDÆ
14. Mesosternum rounded behind; rather stout species, winged or apterous. (**Anisólabis**, cosmop.; **Psàlis, Gonólabis, Euboréllia,**

Neotrop., Ethiop., Ind.). (*PSÁLIDÆ, ANISOLÁBIDÆ*)

PSALÍDIDÆ

Mesosternum truncate behind 15

15. Antennæ with more than twenty-five joints; elytra always and wings usually present. (Fig. 132). (**Labidùra**, cosmop.; **Nàla**, Old World; **Forcípula**, widespr.; **Tomopýgia**, Indomal.).

LABIDÙRIDÆ

Antennæ with ten to fifteen joints; without elytra or wings 16

16. Last dorsal segment truncate. (**Idolopsàlis**, Neotrop.; **Pseudisólabis**, Indoaustr.; **Parisólabis**, Austr.) ....**PARISOLÁBIDÆ**

Last dorsal segment bifid; slender species with long legs. (**Ctenisólabis, Brachýlabis, Antisólabis,** Ethiop., Austr.; **Nannisólabis,** Ind.; **Metisólabis,** Ethiop., Ind.; **Leptisólabis,** widespr.)

BRACHYLÁBIDÆ

17. Second joint of tarsi simple, not lobed nor dilated. (Superfamily LABIÒIDEA) (*LABIÁLES*) 18

Second joint of tarsi lobed or dilated. (Superfamily FORFICU-LÒIDEA) (*FORFICULÁLES*) 24

18. Elytra with a sharp keel or a row of minute tubercles near the lateral margin 19

Elytra not thus keeled 22

19. Tarsi long and very slender; elytra granulose, the keel formed by a row of minute tubercles. (**Pericòmus**, Neotrop.).

PERICÓMIDÆ

Tarsi short and relatively thick; elytra smooth, with a sharp keel ..20

20. Antennæ with the joints cylindrical 21

Antennæ with the joints enlarged apically or clavate. (**Nesogáster**, Malay., Austr.) ....**NESOGÁSTRIDÆ**

21. Abdomen of male with the sides parallel; elytra entire, not abbreviated; antennæ 16- to 20-jointed; old world species of slender form. (**Vándex**, Ethiop.) ....**VANDÍCIDÆ**

Abdomen of male broadened at the middle; antennæ with 12–15 joints; elytra abbreviated; new world species of stout form. (**Strongylopsàlis**, Neotrop.) ....**STRONGYLOPSALÍDIDÆ**

22. Body not strongly flattened 23

Body strongly flattened. (**Sparátta, Parasparátta, Prosparátta,** Neotrop.; **Auchénomus,** Ethiop., Malay.) .....**SPARÁTTIDÆ**

23. Head transverse, the median and frontal sutures strong and deep; eyes large and prominent. (**Spongíphora, Pùrex,** Neotrop.; **Vóstox,** Am.; **Spongovóstox,** tropicopol.; **Márava,** Austromal.)

SPONGIPHÓRIDÆ

Head narrow, the sutures weak or obsolete; eyes small, no longer than the first joint of the antennæ. (**Làbia,** cosmop.; **Prolàbia,** tropicopol.; **Làrex,** Neotrop.; **Chætospània,** Ethiop., Indoaustr.; **Ándex,** Austr.) ....**LABÌIDÆ**

24. Second joint of tarsi with a narrow lobe produced beneath the third joint; moderately stout or robust species. (**Chelísoches**, Ethiop., Indoaustr.; **Énkrates, Pròreus**, Indomal.; **Solenosòma** Ind.; **Kleidùchus**, Austr.) ....CHELISÓCHIDÆ
   Second joint of tarsi with a dilated lobe on each side (Fig. 140) ...25
25. Sternal plates strongly transverse; elytra much reduced in size; abdomen depressed and dilated; pygidium transverse. (Fig. 128). (**Chelidùra, Burrìola**, Palæarc., **Mesochelidùra**, Palæarc., Ethiop.)
   CHELIDÙRIDÆ
   Sternal plates not very decidedly transverse 26
26. Antennal joints not very long and slender, the fourth often much shorter than the third and the first much shorter.than the head ..27
   Antennal joints all long and slender; fourth not shorter than the third; first longer and thicker than the others (Fig. 139) 30
27. Meso- and metasternum and pygidium broad; forceps remote, not depressed; elytra entire or abbreviated. (Fig. 140). (**Anechùra, Mesasiòbia**, Palæarc., Neotrop.; **Pseudochelidùra**, Palæarc.; **Pterýgida, Allodáhlia**, Indomal.) ....ANECHÙRIDÆ
   Meso- and metasternum quadrate or narrow; pygidium narrow ..28
28. Abdomen cylindrical, not depressed 29
   Abdomen depressed; forceps flattened or cylindrical; mesosternum rounded posteriorly; antennæ with 12–15 joints; elytra rarely shortened. (Fig. 133). (**Forfícula**, Holarc., Ethiop., Indomal. (*F. auriculària*, European earwig); **Chelidurélla, Apterýgida**, Palæarc., Ethiop.; **Dòru**, Amer., Austr.; **Skalístes**, Neotrop.; **Hypúrgus**, Indomal.) ....FORFICÙLIDÆ
29. Elytra entire, not shortened; mesosternum rounded posteriorly; Old World species. (**Eudóhrnia**, Ind.; **Kosmètor**, Indomal.)
   EUDOHRNÌIDÆ
   Elytra abbreviated; mesosternum truncate. (**Neolobóphora**, Neotrop.; **Árchidux**, Ethiop.) ....NEOLOBOPHÓRIDÆ
30. Sternal plates generally transverse, at least relatively broad; metasternum truncate; abdomen and forceps depressed; New World species. (Fig. 139). (**Ancistrogáster, Vláx, Pràos, Tristanélla, Paracósmia**, Neotrop.) ....ANCISTROGÁSTRIDÆ
   Sternal plates narrow; metasternum narrow, excavated posteriorly. 31
31. Abdomen but little depressed, surface rather convex; legs long and slender; pygidium narrow; forceps remote, slender. (Fig. 129). (**Dìnex**, Neotrop.; **Timómenus, Epárchus, Córdax**, Indomal.; **Opisthocósmia**, Ethiop., Malay.; **Thalpèrus**, Ethiop.).
   OPISTHOCOSMÌIDÆ
   Abdomen depressed and rather dilated; legs short; pygidium strongly transverse. (**Diaperásticus**, Ethiop.)
   DIAPERASTÍCIDÆ

LITERATURE ON DERMAPTERA

FORFICULINA AND ARIXENINA

See also Orthoptera (*s. l.*), p. 105

BEI-BIENKO, M. Faune de l'URSS. Insectes, Dermaptères. Inst. zool. Acad. Sci. URSS, (N.S.), No. 5, viii + 239 pp., 67 figs. (1936).

BORELLI, A. Dermaptères de Madagascar. Bull. Soc. Nat. Luxembourg, **42**, pp. 56–58 (1932).

Dermaptera de la Presqu'île Malaise. Bull. Raffles Mus., No. 7, pp. 80–95, 10 figs. (1932).

BORMANS, A. and KRAUSS, H. Dermaptera. Das Tierreich, Lief. 11 (1900).

BURR, M. Revision of Forficulidæ and Chelisochidæ. Trans. Ent. Soc. London, 1907, pp. 91–134 (1907).

Dermaptera. Fauna of British India. London (1910).

Revision of the Labiduridæ. Trans. Ent. Soc. London, 1910, pp. 161–203 (1910).

Dermaptera. Gen. Insectorum, fasc. 122, 112 pp. (1911).

Revision of the Genus Diplatys. Trans. Ent. Soc. London, 1911, pp. 21–47 (1911).

BURR, M. and JORDAN, K. On Arixenia, a Suborder of Dermaptera. Trans. 2d Ent. Congr. (1913).

CHOPARD, L. Orthoptères et Dermaptères. Faune de France, pt. **3**, 212 pp. (1922).

Dermaptères. In Grassé, Traité de Zoologie, **9**, pp. 745–770, 26 figs. (1949).

GÜNTHER, K. Die Dermapteren der deutschen Kaiserin-Augusta-Flusse-Expedition. Mitt. zool. Mus. Berlin, **15**, pp. 55–83 (1929).

Dermaptera der deutschen limnologischen Sunda-Expedition. SB. Ges. naturf. Freunde Berlin, 1932, pp. 471–491, 8 figs.; Arch. Hydrobiol., Suppl. 12, pp 503–517, 11 figs. (1933).

HINCKS, W. D. Dermaptera of Burma and British India. Ark. Zool., **39A**, 43 pp., 23 figs. (1947).

Notes on Mauritian Earwigs. Ann. Mag. Nat. Hist., (11)**14**, pp. 517–540 (1947).

KIRBY, W. F. A Synonymic Catalogue of the Orthoptera, vol. 1. British Mus. Nat. Hist., London (1904).

KRAUSS, H. Forficulidæ. Das Tierreich, Lief. 11, pp. 1–129. (1900).

LAMEERE, A. Dermaptera. Précis de Zoologie. Rec. Inst. zool. Torley-Rousseau, 4, pp. 279–287 (1935).

MACCAGNO, T. Dermatteri. Il genere Cylindrogaster Stål. Boll. Mus. Zool. Anat. Comp. Torino, (3)**41**, 15 pp., 5 figs. (1926–31).

REHN, J. A. G. The Dermaptera of the American Museum Congo Expedition with a Catalogue of the Belgian Congo Species. Bull. Am. Mus. Nat. Hist., **49**, pp. 349–413 (1924).

TOWNES, H. List of Generic and Subgeneric Names of Dermaptera. Ann. Ent. Soc. America, **38**, pp. 343–356 (1945).

WALDEN, B. H. Dermaptera of Connecticut. Bull. State Geol. Nat. Hist. Surv. Connecticut, No. 16, pp. 44–47 (1911).

ZACHER, F. Studien über das System der Protodermapteren. Zool. Jahrb. Abth. f. Syst., **30**, pp. 303–400 (1911).
ZIMMERMAN, E. C. Dermaptera. Insects of Hawaii, **2**, pp. 197–212 (1948).

DIPLOGLOSSATA

HANSEN, H. J. On the Structure and Habits of Hemimerus talpoides. Ent. Tidskr., **15**, pp. 65–93 (1894).
JORDAN, K. Anatomy of Hemimerus. Novitat. Zool., **16**, pp. 327–330 (1909).
KRAUSS, H. Forficulidæ. Das Tierreich, Lief. 11, pp. 130–132 (1900).
REHN, J. A. G. and J. W. H. Study of the Genus Hemimerus. Proc. Philadelphia Acad. Sci., **87**, pp. 457–508 (1925).

ORDER EMBIÒDEA

(EMBIIDÌNA, EMBIÒIDEA, EMBIÓPTERA, OLIGONEÙRA, ÆTIÓPTERA)

Elongate, slender, feeble insects of small or moderate size. Head large, elongate; eyes small or of moderate size; ocelli absent; antennæ slender, many-jointed (16–32). Thorax elongate; prothorax large, free; meso- and metathorax each about as large as the prothorax; males usually winged, females always wingless. Wings similar, pubescent, elongate, the media and cubitus much reduced; no anal fan or lobe. Wings lying flat on the abdomen when at rest. Abdomen ten-segmented; long, narrow and with parallel sides; tip of abdomen and cerci usually strongly asymmetrical in the male; cerci two-jointed. Tarsi three-jointed; first joint of front tarsi swollen, containing glands for spinning a silken web in which the insects live.

Metamorphosis gradual, incomplete. A small group, restricted to the tropics and subtropics.

1. Mandibles with two or three small, but distinct dentations at tip . . 2
   Mandibles sharply pointed at tip, but without dentations. (Anisémbia, Chelicérca, Am.) . . . . ANISEMBÌIDÆ
2. Either the anterior or posterior branch of the radial sector forked in both wings, or at least in the hind wing 3
   Both branches of the radial sector simple, unbranched. (Oligótoma, widespr.; Gynémbia, Nearc.) (Fig. 147). . . . OLIGOTÓMIDÆ
3. Anterior branch of the radial sector simple; the posterior sector branched 4
   Anterior branch of the radial sector branched; the posterior sector simple. (Teratémbia, Neotrop.) . . . . TERATEMBÌIDÆ
4. Left cercus smooth on its inner side 5
   Left cercus with minute denticulations on at least a part of its inner side, these usually located on a lobe or expansion (Fig. 146). (Émbia, Haploémbia, widespr.; Rhagádochir, Donaconèthis, Ethiop.; Pararhagádochir, Neotrop.) . . . . EMBÌIDÆ

Left cercus one-jointed in adult male, with no distinct second joint. (**Notoligótoma**, Austr.; **Ptilocerémbia**, Mal.)

NOTOLIGOTÓMIDÆ

5. Wings with well developed venation; anterior branch of the cubitus forked; abdominal terminalia nearly symmetrical; comparatively large species (15–18 mm. in length). (**Clothòda**, Neotrop.)

CLOTHÓDIDÆ

Wings with poorly developed venation, only the first three branches of the radius and one cubital vein distinct; abdominal terminalia strongly asymmetrical; small species (5–8 mm. in length). (**Oligémbia**, Neotrop.) ....**OLIGEMBÌIDÆ**

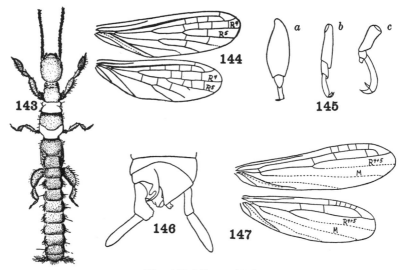

Figs. 143–147. **Embiodea**

143. **Oligotoma**, female (Melander) Oligotomidæ.
144. **Donaconethis**, wings (Enderlein) Embiidæ.
145. **Rhagadochir.** *a*, front tarsus; *b*, middle tarsus; *c*, hind tarsus (Silvestri) Embiidæ.
146. **Rhagadochir**, apex of abdomen of male (Enderlein) Embiidæ.
147. **Oligotoma**, wings (Enderlein) Oligotomidæ.

LITERATURE ON EMBIODEA

Davis, C. Studies in Australian Embioptera. Proc. Linn. Soc. New South Wales, 61, pp. 229–253, 43 figs.; pp. 254–258, 7 figs. (1936).

    Family Classification of the Order Embioptera. Ann. Ent. Soc. America, 33, pp. 677–682 (1940).

    Taxonomic Notes on the Order Embioptera, I–XX. Proc. Linn. Soc. New South Wales, 64, pp. 181–190, 5 figs.; pp. 217–222, 21 figs.; pp. 369–

384, 36 figs.; pp. 474–495, 83 figs.; pp. 559–575, 51 figs.; pp. **65**, pp. 171–191, 83 figs.; pp. 323–352, 41 figs.; pp. 362–387, 83 figs.; 525–542, 27 figs. (1939–40).
Revision of Embioptera of Western Australia. Journ. Roy. Soc. West Australia, **28**, pp. 139–147 (1944).
DENIS, R. Embioptères. In Grassé, Traité de Zoologie, **9**, pp. 723–743 (1949).
ENDERLEIN, G. Embiidinen. Coll. Zool. Selys-Longchamps, fasc. 3 (1912).
FRIEDRICHS, K. Das Gemeinschaftsleben der Embiiden, und Kenntnis der Arten. Arch. Naturg., N. F., **3**, pp. 405–444, 13 figs. (1934).
HAGEN, H. A Monograph of the Embidina. Canadian Ent., **17**, pp. 142–155 (1885).
KRAUSS, H. A. Monographie der Embien. Zoologica, Heft 60, 78 pp. (1911).
LAMEERE, A. Embioptera. In Précis de Zoologie. Publ. Inst. zool. Torley-Rousseau, **4**, pp. 275–279 (1935).
NAVÁS, L. Embiópteros de la America meridional. Brotéria, **16**, pp. 85–110 (1919).
ROSS, E. S. Revision of the Embioptera of North America. Ann. Ent. Soc. America, **33**, pp. 629–676 (1940).
Revision of the Embioptera of the New World. Proc. U. S. Nat. Mus., **94**, pp. 401–504 (1944).
The Embioptera of New Guinea. Pan-Pacific Ent., **24**, pp. 97–116 (1948).
TABORSKY, K. Monographische Studien ueber die Bulgarischen Embidinen. Sborn. Nár. Mus. Praze, **1B**, pp. 241–251 (1937).
TILLYARD, R. J. The Embioptera or Web-spinners of Western Australia. Journ. Roy. Soc. West Australia, **9**, pp. 61–68 (1923).
VERHOEFF, K. W. Zur vergleichende Morphologie und Systematik der Embiiden. Act. Acad. Leopold. Carol., **82**, pp. 145–204 (1904).
ZIMMERMAN, E. C. Embioptera. Insects of Hawaii, **2**, pp. 191–196 (1948).

ORDER ISÓPTERA

Small or medium sized, elongate, feeble insects living in large colonies and occurring as winged sexual individuals and wingless workers and soldiers; usually with weak chitinization, especially in the sterile castes which are soft-bodied and white, except for the heavily chitinized head. Head large, free, rather vertical; eyes and two ocelli usually present in the winged forms, or absent in the workers. Mandibles strong, often very large; antennæ filamentous, more or less moniliform. Prothorax free, but much smaller than the head. Legs similar, formed for running or walking; tarsi four- or rarely five-jointed, with well developed claws. Wings similar, long and narrow, deciduous soon after maturity at a preformed transverse suture near the base; long and narrow, superimposed over the abdomen, the hind pair very rarely with an anal area; venation almost always much reduced and without crossveins. Cerci short, one- to three-, rarely eight-jointed. Metamorphosis very incomplete. White ants, Termites.

Males and Females (Sexual Forms)

1. Tarsi four-jointed in all castes, sometimes with the indication of a fifth joint; fore and hind wings similar, narrow, the hind pair without anal lobe; transverse basal suture present on all four wings 2
   Tarsi five-jointed; hind wing with a well developed anal area which is capable of being folded beneath the remainder of the wing; transverse basal suture present only on fore wing. (**Mastotérmes,** Austr.) „(Fig. 154). .... MASTOTERMÍTIDÆ

2. Fontanel (the opening of the frontal gland on the face) wanting; radius usually with one or more superior branches forming a costal field; clypeus usually not divided by a median line 3
   Fontanel always present in the adult; radius simple, not or indistinctly forming any superior branches; clypeus with a median sutural line. Species usually living in populous colonies, often in large and elaborately constructed nests 5

3. Ocelli absent 4
   Ocelli present; basal stub of fore wing short; cerci two-jointed; no true worker caste. (**Kalotérmes, Neotérmes,** all warm regions; **Cryptotérmes,** widespr.; **Calcaritérmes,** Am.). (*PROTERMÍTI-DÆ, CALOTERMÍTIDÆ*). .... KALOTERMÍTIDÆ

4. Worker caste wanting, living in small colonies in wood; basal stub of fore wing longer than that of hind wing ....**TERMÓPSIDÆ**

a. Tarsi with pulvilli, a fifth joint separated from the fourth on the upper side; cerci long, four- to eight-jointed. (**Archotermópsis,** Ind., also fossil in Baltic amber; **Hodotermópsis,** Indomal.) **TERMOPSÌNÆ**
   Tarsi without pulvilli, only four tarsal joints visible ....b

b. Eyes of the soldier caste well developed, clearly composed of facets around the periphery; cerci four- or five-jointed. (**Stolotérmes,** Austr., S. Afr.) .... STOLOTERMITÌNÆ
   Eyes of the soldier caste poorly developed; cerci five-jointed. Species nesting in the trunks of trees. (**Porotérmes,** Austr., Chile; **Planitérmes,** S. Afr.) ....POROTERMITÌNÆ

   Worker caste present, living in populous underground colonies; integument of soldiers and workers strongly pigmented; basal stub of fore wing not reaching to the base of the stub of hind wing. (**Hodotérmes,** Ethiop.; **Anacanthotérmes,** Holarc.). **HODOTERMÍTIDÆ**

5. Stubs of fore wings longer than those of the hind wings (except the African *Psammotermes*); cerci two-jointed; wing surface often reticulated; radial sector present, simple; wings usually more or less transparent. (**Rhinotérmes, Serritérmes,** Neotrop.; **Reticuli-**

térmes, Holarc.; **Arrhinotérmes, Coptotérmes, Schedorhinotérmes,** widespr.; **Termitogèton,** Indomal.).   (*MESOTERMÍTIDÆ*)
RHINOTERMÍTIDÆ

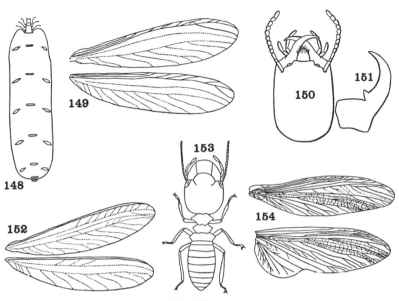

Figs. 148–154.   **Isoptera**

148. **Termes,** queen (Hegh) Termitidæ.
149. **Kalotermes,** wings (Kalotermitidæ).
150. **Nasutitermes,** head of worker. Termitidæ.
151. **Nasutitermes,** mandible of worker. Termitidæ.
152. **Reticulitermes,** wings (Banks) Rhinotermitidæ.
153. **Termes,** worker (Hegh) Termitidæ.
154. **Mastotermes,** wings (Desneux) Mastotermitidæ.

Stubs of fore wings short, not reaching the base of the hind wings; cerci one- or two-jointed; wing surface never completely reticulated; radius strongly reduced or absent; wings more or less opaque. (**Microtérmes, Amitérmes, Microcerotérmes, Nasutitérmes,** widespr.; **Térmes, Macrotérmes,** Ethiop., Indomal.; **Cubitérmes,** Ethiop.; **Capritérmes,** Indomal.; **Neocapritérmes,** Neotrop., Ethiop.; **Microcapritérmes,** Austr.).   (*METATERMÍTIDÆ*)
TERMÍTIDÆ

Soldiers

1. Tarsi distinctly five-jointed ....**MASTOTERMÍTIDÆ**
   Tarsi four-jointed, rarely with an indistinct fifth joint 2

2. Fontanel absent; eyes present; mandibles often with very strong teeth 3

Fontanel present; eyes entirely absent or rarely slightly indicated . . 4

3. Compound eyes usually very distinct, black, rarely not pigmented; antennæ with 23 to 31 joints; legs rather long and weak, extending well beyond body; cerci prominent, usually with three or more joints ....HODOTERMÍTIDÆ

Compound eyes present as white, rarely pigmented, finely faceted spots; antennæ with 10 to 20 joints; cerci very short, with two or, rarely, three joints ....KALOTERMÍTIDÆ

4. Pronotum flat, without separated lobes in front; head not nasute; mandibles not toothed ....RHINOTERMÍTIDÆ

Pronotum saddle-shaped, with distinct lobes in front; head either nasute or with toothed mandibles ....TERMÍTIDÆ

LITERATURE ON ISOPTERA

Banks, N. Antillean Isoptera. Bull. Mus. Comp. Zoöl., Harvard, **62**, pp. 475–489 (1919).

A Revision of the Nearctic Termites. Bull. U. S. Nat. Mus., No. 108 (1920).

Desneux, J. Termitidæ. Gen. Insectorum, fasc. 25, 52 pp. (1905).

Emerson, A. E. Termites of Kartabo, British Guiana. Zoölogica, New York, **6**, pp. 291–459 (1925).

Termites of the Belgian Congo and Cameroon. Bull. American Mus. Nat. Hist., **57**, pp. 401–574, 19 pls., 79 figs. (1928).

Revision of the Genera of Fossil and Recent Termopsinæ. Univ. California Publ. Ent., **6**, pp. 165–196, 40 figs. (1933).

Revision of Syntermes (Termitidæ). Bull. American Mus. Nat. Hist., **83**, pp. 427–472, 12 figs. (1945).

Emerson, A. E. and E. M. Miller. Key to the Termites of Florida. Ent. News, **55**, pp. 184–187 (1943).

Froggatt, W. W. Australian Termitidæ. Proc. Linn. Soc. New South Wales, **10–12** (1895–97) (several parts).

Fuller, C. The Termites of South Africa. South African Journ. Nat. Hist., **3**, pp. 14–52; 70–130 (1921–22).

Grassé, P. P. Systématique et biologie des Termites de l'Afrique occidentale française. Ann. Soc. Ent. France, **106**, pp. 1–100 (1937).

Isoptères. Traité de Zoologie, **9**, pp. 408–540, 101 figs. (1949).

Harris, W. V. Termites of Uganda. Proc. Roy. Ent. Soc., B, **17**, pp. 73–83 (1948).

Hegh, E. Les Termites. Brussels, 756 pp. (1922). Republished with additions in Bull. Agric. Congo Belge, Brussels. **11–14** (1920–23).

Hill, G. F. Isoptera from the Australian Region. Melbourne Counc. Sci. Industr. Res. Commonw. Australia, 479 pp., 24 pls., 353 figs. (1942).

Holmgren, N. Termitenstudien. I–IV. König. Svensk. Vet. Akad. Handl., **44, 46, 48, 50** (1909–13).

Hozawa, S. Revision of the Japanese Termites. Journ. Coll. Agric. Tokyo, **35**, pt. 7, 161 pp. (1915).

Kemner, N. A. Termitidæ. Fauna Sumatrensis. Tijdschr. Ent., **73**, pp. 298–324, 24 figs. (1930).

Die Termitenfauna von Amboina. Lunds Univ. Arsskr., N. F., **27**, pp. 1–53, 2 pls., 15 figs. (1931).

Studien über die Termiten Javas und Celebes. K. Svenska Vetensk. Akad. Handl., (3)**13**, 241 pp., 22 pls., 53 figs. (1934).

Lameere, A. Isoptera. In Précis de Zoologie. Publ. Inst. zool. Torley-Rousseau, **4**, pp. 305–328 (1935).

Light, S. F. Notes on Philippine Termites. Philippine Journ. Sci., **42**, pp. 13–58, 8 pls., 1 fig. (1930). (Other notes in vols. 18, 19, 40 [1921–29].)

Termites of Western Mexico. Univ. California Publ. Ent., **6**, pp. 79–164, 5 pls., 33 figs. (1933).

Pendlebury, H. M. List of Malayan Termites. Malayan Forest Rec., No. 8, pp. 45–56 (1931).

Silvestri, F. Termiti e termitofili dell' America meridionale. Redia, **1**, pp. 1–234 (1903).

Termiti e termitofili dell' Eritrea. Redia, **3**, pp. 341–359 (1906).

Termitidi e termitofili dell' Africa occidentale. Boll. Lab. Zool. Agrar. Portici, **9, 12** and **14** (1914–20).

Sjöstedt, Y. Monographie der Termiten Afrikas. Svensk. Vet. Akad. Handl., **34** and **38** (1900–04).

Revision der Termiten Afrikas. K. Svenska Vet. Akad. Handl., (3), **3**, 419 pp. (1926).

Snyder, T. E. Our Enemy the Termite. Second Edition. 257 pp. Comstock Pub. Co., Ithaca, N. Y. (1948).

Catalogue of the Termites of the World. Smithsonian Misc. Coll., **112**, 490 pp. (1949).

Zimmerman, E. C. Isoptera. Insects of Hawaii, **2**, pp. 159–189 (1948).

ORDER CORRODÉNTIA

(PSOCÓPTERA, COPEÓGNATHA)

Usually small or minute insects, rarely of moderate size, with short, soft body and usually winged. Head large, free, vertical, with a strong Y-shaped suture above; eyes large and prominent, except in a few wingless forms; three ocelli generally present; antennæ long and slender, filiform or bristle-like, many (13–50) jointed; mandibles strong, toothed and with a grinding surface. Prothorax almost always very small; mesothorax and metathorax usually separated, although rarely completely fused. Wings usually ample, sometimes much reduced or entirely absent; when at rest generally held in a sloping position, folded backwards over the body; fore pair larger than the hind pair, sometimes scaly or hairy; venation reduced, with few or no crossveins; one or several of the veins frequently strongly curved. Abdomen usually short, with nine or ten segments; cerci absent. Legs similar, fitted for running, the coxæ close together; tarsi two- or three-jointed, the first joint very long; two tarsal claws. Metamorphosis incomplete, the nymph similar to the adult form; terrestrial in all stages. Psocids, Book lice, Bark lice.

1. Tarsi three-jointed. (Fig. 165). 2
   Tarsi two-jointed. (Fig. 156). 10

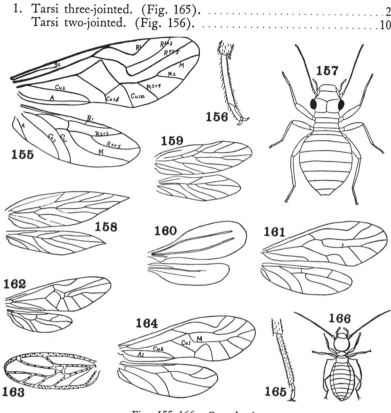

Figs. 155–166.   Corrodentia

155. **Psocus**, wings (Comstock and Needham) Psocidæ.
156. **Cæcilius**, tarsus (Tillyard) Cæciliidæ.
157. **Lepinotus** (Tillyard) Atropidæ.
158. **Oxypsocus**, wings (Tillyard) Lepidopsocidæ.
159. **Perientomum**, wings (Enderlein) Perientomidæ.
160. **Embidotroctes**, wings (Kolbe) Liposcelidæ.
161. **Cæcilius**, wings (Tillyard) Cæciliidæ.
162. **Thyrsophorus**, wings (Enderlein) Thyrsophoridæ.
163. **Vulturops**, wings (Corbett and Hargreaves) Psoquillidæ.
164. **Mesopsocus**, wings (Tillyard) Mesopsocidæ.
165. **Myopsocus**, tarsus (Tillyard) Myopsocidæ.
166. **Liposcelis** (Marlatt) Liposcelidæ.

2. Thorax composed of three distinct parts, the mesothorax separated from the metathorax by a suture; usually winged, rarely with the wings reduced or absent 3
   Thorax composed of two parts, the meso- and metathorax fused and without suture between them; wings usually entirely absent, if present without forked veins; second joint of palpi without clubbed sense organs. (Figs. 160, 166). (Lipóscelis (= Tróctes) (*L. divinatòria*, Book louse, Cereal psocid), cosmop.; Tropùsia, widespr.; Pachytróctes, Palæarc.; Embidopsòcus, Neotrop.; Embidotróctes, Ethiop.) (*TRÓCTIDÆ*) (Including *PACHY-TRÓCTIDÆ*) . . . . LIPOSCÉLIDÆ
3. Wings present; prothorax much smaller than the mesothorax 4
   Fore wings absent or very small and without venation; hind wings entirely absent; prothorax larger than the mesothorax. (Átropos (= Trògium) (*A. pulsatòria*, Death watch), widespr.; Lepinòtus (Fig. 157), Leprólepis, Hypéretes). (Including *TRO-GÌIDÆ*) . . . . ATRÓPIDÆ
4. Wings fully formed, with complete venation 5
   Venation of wings incomplete, the fore wings oval or rounded and much thickened; the veins usually very broad; hind wings reduced or absent; without scales. (Psoquílla, Holarc.; Psocinélla, Vúlturops, Am.) (Fig. 163) . . . . PSOQUÍLLIDÆ
5. Second branch of cubitus and first anal vein in fore wing meeting or closely approaching each other at apex (Fig. 164) 7
   Second branch of cubitus and first anal vein in fore wing divergent toward apex, or at least not approaching each other; body and wings clothed with hairs or scales; wings more or less pointed; antennæ with more than thirteen joints (Fig. 158) 6
6. Hind wings with a very narrow closed cell at the base between the media and cubitus; wing scales of symmetrical form, similarly curved on their two sides; antennæ with 20 to 25 joints. (Fig. 159). (Periéntomum, Ind.) . . . . PERIENTÓMIDÆ
   Hind wings without a closed cell; wing scales usually asymmetrical; antennæ with 26 to 47 joints. (Fig. 158). (Lepidopsòcus, Lepidílla, Echinopsòcus, Echmépteryx, Oxypsòcus). (*EMPHERÍ-IDÆ, LEPIDÍLLIDÆ*) . . . . LEPIDOPSÓCIDÆ
7. Antennæ 13-jointed 8
   Antennæ with 22 to 25 joints; body and wings not scaled; media two- or three-branched; prothorax visible from above. (Phyllipsòcus, Psylloneùra, Deipnopsòcus, Rhyopsòcus). (Including *PSOCATRÓPIDÆ*) . . . . PHYLLIPSÓCIDÆ
8. No scales on body or wings; only one anal vein in the fore wing . . .9
   Body and wings scaled; two anal veins in the fore wing. (Amphiéntomum, Ethiop., Ind.; Tineomórpha, Ind.; Stigmatópathus, Cymatopsòcus, Indomal.) . . . . AMPHIENTÓMIDÆ

9. Apex of cubitus in fore wing bent forward into a loop toward the media, but not touching it (Fig. 164); very small species. (Hemineùra, Elipsòcus, Philotársus, Mesopsòcus, Psilopsòcus, Actenotársus). (Including *ELIPSÓCIDÆ, PHILOTÁRSIDÆ*).
   .... MESOPSÓCIDÆ
   Cubital loop in fore wing either just touching the media, or fusing with it for a short distance (Fig. 165); larger species. (Myopsòcus, Propsòcus, Pentácladus, Photòdes, Lichenomìma, Tricladéllus)
   .... MYOPSÓCIDÆ
10. Prothorax well developed, visible from above; wings reduced in the female; of full size in the male, but with the venation incomplete. (Archipsòcus, Ind.) .... ARCHIPSÓCIDÆ
   Prothorax very small, not visible from above 11
11. Apex of cubitus in fore wing not bent forward into a loop, or if thus bent the loop does not meet the media. (Figs. 156, 161). A cosmopolitan group. (Cæcílius, Amphipsòcus, Callistóptera, Epipsòcus, Pterodèla). (Including *EPIPSÓCIDÆ, AMPHIPSÓCIDÆ, PTERODÉLIDÆ, STENOPSÓCIDÆ*). (*PERIPSÓCIDÆ, LACHESÍLLIDÆ*) .... CÆCILÌIDÆ
   Apical part of cubitus bent forward into a loop that touches the media or fuses with it for a short distance 12
12. Second branch of radial sector (R_{4+5}) fused with the media or connected with it by a crossvein (Fig. 162); third and fourth antennal joints lengthened, thicker and more densely hairy than the joints beyond; large species. (Thyrsóphorus, Dictyopsòcus, Ischnópteryx, Neotrop.) .... THYRSOPHÓRIDÆ
   Second branch of the radial sector free from the media; third and fourth antennal joints similar to the apical ones; moderate-sized or rather large species. An extensive and cosmopolitan group. (Ceratipsòcus, Amphigeróntia, Eremopsòcus, Hemipsòcus, Lasiopsòcus, Psòcus, Tæniostígma) (Fig. 155). (Including *HEMIPSÓCIDÆ*) .... PSÓCIDÆ

LITERATURE ON CORRODENTIA

BADONNEL, A. Contribution à l'étude des Psocoptères à Madagascar. Bull. Acad. Malgache (N. S.), **18**, pp. 97–120, 4 pls. (1935).
   Psocoptères. Faune de France, **42**, 164 figs., 375 figs. (1943).
   Psocoptères du Congo belge. Rev. Zool. Bot. Afric., **39**, pp. 137–196 (1946).
BANKS, N. Classification of the Psocidæ. Psyche, **36**, pp. 321–325 (1929).
CHAPMAN, P. J. Corrodentia of the United States. Journ. New York Ent. Soc., **38**, pp. 219–280; 319–402, 10 pls. (1930).
ENDERLEIN, G. Die Psocidenfauna Perus. Zool. Jahrb., Abth. f. Syst., **14**, pp. 133–160 (1900).
   Morphologie, Gruppierung und systematische Stellung der Corrodentien. Zool. Anz., **26** (1903).

Die Copeognathen des indoaustralischen Faunengebietes. Ann. Mus. Hist. Nat. Hungarici, **1**, pp. 179–344 (1903).

Morphologisches System und Biologie der Atropinen und Troctinen. Jægerskiöld Zool. Exped. Egypt. No. 18, 58 pp. (1905).

Die australischen Copeognathen. Zool. Jahrb., Abth. f. Syst., **23**, pp. 401–412 (1906).

Die Copeognathenfauna Japans. Zool. Jahrb., Abth. f. Syst., **23**, pp. 243–256 (1906).

The Scaly-winged Copeognatha. Spolia Zeylandica, **4**, pp. 39–122 (1906).

Copeognatha. In Tierwelt Mitteleuropas, **4**, Lief. 2, pp. VII, 1–16 (1928).

Die Copeognathen-Fauna der Seychellen. Trans. Linn. Soc. London (2) Zool., **19**, pp. 207–240, 3 pls., 52 figs. (1932).

GURNEY, A. B. A Synopsis of the Psocids of the Tribe Psyllipsocini. Ann. Ent. Soc. America, **36**, pp. 195–220, 6 pls. (1943).

HICKMAN, V. V. On Tasmanian Copeognatha [Corrodentia]. Occ. Pap. Roy. Soc. Tasmania, **1933**, pp. 77–89, 6 figs. (1933).

JENTSCH, S. Psocopterenfauna in Nordwestdeutschland. Verh. Ver. naturw. Heimatsforsch., **27**, pp. 114–121 (1938).

KARNY, H. Systematik der Orthopteroiden Insekten. Treubia, **12**, pp. 431–461 (1930).

KOLBE, H. Monographie der deutschen Psociden. Jahresber. zool. Sect. Westf. Ver., **8**, 1879–80, pp. 74–142 (1880).

LAMEERE, A. Psocoptera. In Précis de Zoologie. Rec. Inst. zool. Torley-Rousseau, **4**, pp. 352–359 (1935).

MENON, R. Studies on Indian Copeognatha. Indian Journ. Ent., **3**, pp. 13–23; **4**, pp. 23–42, 48 figs. (1941–42).

OKAMOTO, H. Die Psociden Japans. Trans. Sapporo Nat. Hist. Soc., **2**, pp. 113–147 (1907).

PEARMAN, J. V. The Taxonomy of the Psocoptera. Proc. Roy. Ent. Soc. London, (B) **5**, pp. 58–62 (1936).

PERRIER, R. Psocoptères de la France. Faune de France, **3**, pp. 72–76, 8 figs. (1934).

ROESLER, R. Neue und wenig bekannte Copeognathengattungen. Zool. Anz., **129**, pp. 225–243; ibid., **130**, pp. 1–25 (1940).

Ueber einige Copeognathengenera. Stettin. ent. Zeitg., **104**, pp. 1–14 (1943).

Die Gattungen der Copeognathen. Stettin. ent. Zeitg., **105**, pp. 118–161 (1944).

SOMMERMAN, K. M. Revision of North American Lachesilla. Ann. Ent. Soc. America, **39**, pp. 627–657, 4 pls. (1946).

TILLYARD, R. J. Monograph of Psocoptera or Copeognatha of New Zealand. Trans. New Zealand Inst., **54**, pp. 170–196 (1923).

ZIMMERMAN, E. C. Corrodentia. Insects of Hawaii, **2**, pp. 217–252 (1948).

ORDER ZORÁPTERA

Minute, terrestrial species of social habits, living in colonies; dimorphic, both sexes represented by winged and wingless individuals. Body depressed. Head free, somewhat inclined. Antennæ moniliform or filiform, nine-jointed, the second and often also the third joint smaller than the others; in the nymph eight-jointed. Mandibles well developed, toothed and fitted for biting. Eyes and ocelli present in the winged form; absent, or the eyes present as vestiges, in the wingless one. Thorax large, but

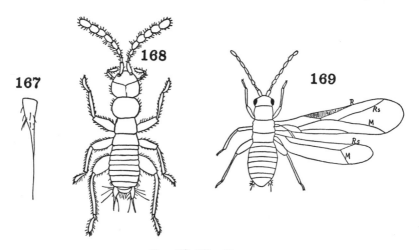

Figs. 167–169. Zoraptera

167. **Zorotypus**, cercus (Karny) Zorotypidæ.
168. **Zorotypus** (Silvestri) Zorotypidæ.
169. **Zorotypus**, winged form (Caudell) Zorotypidæ.

no wider than the head; prothorax free, not concealing the head nor expanded laterally; meso- and metathorax distinctly separated. Abdomen elongate-oval, never much longer than the thorax, with ten strongly transverse segments; cerci short, oval, one-jointed, with a bristle-like appendage at tip. Legs similar, formed for running; hind femora stout, sometimes armed beneath with spiny bristles; tarsi two-jointed, the first joint short, the second with two claws at tip. Metamorphosis gradual, the nymph similar to the adult, especially to the wingless form. Winged form with narrow, membranous wings, the fore pair larger; venation greatly reduced; wings commonly falling off after maturity, leaving a stub attached to the body, but not separating at a preformed suture; body of winged form more heavily chitinized than in the wingless one.

Both the alate and apterous forms of both sexes are fertile and there is no worker caste.

One family. (**Zorótypus**, Nearc., Neotrop., Indomal., Ethiop., Hawaii, Samoa, Fiji). (Figs. 167, 168, 169). . . . . ZOROTÝPIDÆ

LITERATURE ON ZORAPTERA

BOLIVAR Y PIELTAIN, C. Estudio de un nuevo Zoráptero de Mexico. An. Escuela Nac. Cien. Biol., **1**, pp. 515–522 (1940).

CAUDELL, A. N. Zoraptera not an Apterous Order. Proc. Ent. Soc. Washington, **22**, pp. 84–97 (1920).

DÉNIS, R. Zoraptères. In Grassé, Traité de Zoologie, **9**, pp. 545–555, 10 figs. (1949).

GURNEY, A. B. Synopsis of the Order Zoraptera. Proc. Ent. Soc. Washington, **40**, pp. 57–87 (1938).

     Zoraptera from Fiji. Occ. Papers Bishop Mus., **15**, pp. 161–165 (1939).

LAMEERE, A. Zoraptera. In Précis de Zoologie. Publ. Inst. zool. Torley-Rousseau, **4**, pp, 366–368 (1935).

SILVESTRI, F. Descrizione di un nuova ordine di insetti. Boll. Zool. Gen. Agrar. Portici, **7**, pp. 193–209 (1913).

ZIMMERMAN, E. C. Zoraptera. Insects of Hawaii, **2**, pp. 213–216 (1948).

ORDER MALLÓPHAGA

(*LIPÓPTERA*)

Small wingless insects averaging two mm. and very rarely over five mm. in length. Body oval, or elongate, very strongly flattened; usually strongly chitinized and generally with a conspicuous color pattern of pale or yellowish markings contrasting with spots or bands of dark brown or black. Mouth inferior, mandibles strong; antennæ three- to five-jointed; prothorax free, rarely fused with the mesothorax; legs short, no cerci. Metamorphosis very incomplete. External parasites of birds, more rarely of mammals, during entire life, feeding on feathers, fur or skin. Bird lice, Biting lice.

1. Abdomen consisting of more than seven segments; basal pair of abdominal spiracles usually on the second segment 2
   Abdomen with only seven visible segments; basal pair of abdominal spiracles on the first segment. Parasites of mammals. (**Heptapsogáster**, Neotrop.). . . . . HEPTAPSOGÁSTRIDÆ
2. Palpi present, two- to four-jointed; antennæ usually four-jointed and generally more or less distinctly clavate or capitate (Fig. 170), concealed in a groove on the underside of the head; mandibles horizontal; meso- and metathorax usually separated by a suture. (Suborder AMBLÝCERA) 3
   Palpi absent; antennæ three- or five-jointed, filiform, not con-

cealed; mandibles vertical; meso- and metathorax fused. (Suborder ISCHNÓCERA) 8
3. Tarsi with two claws; species usually infesting birds 4
   Tarsi with at most a single claw on the middle and hind legs, and
   usually on the front pair also, although these rarely bear two
   claws; claw rarely wanting (Fig. 174); some of the legs almost
   always modified to form hair claspers. (Gỳropus, Protogỳropus,
   Monogỳropus, Glirícola, on guinea pigs and other rodents, mainly
   Neotropical) ....GYRÓPIDÆ

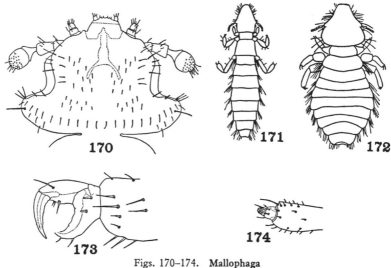

Figs. 170–174. Mallophaga

170. **Gyropus**, head (Ewing) Gyropidæ.
171. **Lipeurus** (Paine) Philopteridæ.
172. **Philopterus** (Paine) Philopteridæ.
173. **Gyropus**, tip of front leg (Ewing) Gyropidæ.
174. **Gliricola**, tip of front leg (Ewing) Gyropidæ.

4. Antennæ strongly clubbed, five-jointed; legs long and slender;
   body clothed with stiff, slender spines; species infesting Australian kangaroos and wallabies. (Boòpia, Heterodóxus, Latumcépha-
   lum) .... BOOPÏIDÆ
   Antennæ not strongly clubbed, four-jointed 5
5. Prothorax appearing like the metathorax inverted, usually fused
   with the mesothorax; only five abdominal segments with spiracles. (Triménopon, Philandèsia, Cummíngsia; Neotropical on
   rodents) ....TRIMENOPÓNIDÆ
   Prothorax not appearing like the metathorax inverted 6

6. Head evenly expanded behind, broadly triangular and strongly enlarged on the temples. (**Ménopon**, widespr. (*M. gallìnæ*, Chicken louse); **Colpocéphalum, Myrsídea, Trinòton**, widespr.; on birds) .... MENOPÓNIDÆ
Head not evenly expanded and broadly triangular, not enlarged on the temples 7
7. Sides of head with a strong lateral swelling in front of the eye; spiracles on abdominal segments three to eight. (**Læmobóthrion**, Holarc., Ethiop., Neotrop.; on birds). LÆMOBOTHRÌIDÆ
Head with the sides straight or concave; spiracles on abdominal segments two to seven. (**Rìcinus** (= *Leiótheum*), widespr.; **Trochilœcètes**, Am.; on birds). (*LEIOTHÈIDÆ*). . RICÍNIDÆ
8. Tarsi with one claw; antennæ three-jointed; species infesting mammals 9
Tarsi with two claws; antennæ five-jointed 10
9. Tarsal claws simple, not dentate. (**Trichodéctes, Eutrichóphilus, Bovícola**, widespr.). (Including *BOVICÓLIDÆ*).
TRICHODÉCTIDÆ
Tarsal claws of middle and hind legs dentate or serrate. (**Dasyonyx**).
DASYONÝGIDÆ
10. Species infesting birds 11
Species infesting mammals; head heavily chitinized at the sides and armed with strong hooks; last joint of antennæ somewhat swollen or clubbed. (**Trichophilópterus**, Ethiop.)
TRICHOPHILOPTÉRIDÆ
11. Meso- and metathorax clearly separated by a suture; eyes deeply constricted. (**Nesiotìnus**, Kerguelen Is., on penguins).
NESIOTÍNIDÆ
Meso- and metathorax not separated by a distinct suture. (**Goniòdes, Goniocòtes, Lipeùrus** (Fig. 171), **Philóoterus** (Fig. 172), **Degeeriélla, Esthiópterum**, widespr.; **Aptericola**, N. Zeal.; on birds). (Including *MEINERTZHAGENIÉLLIDÆ*) . *(GONIÓDIDÆ)* .... PHILOPTÉRIDÆ

LITERATURE ON MALLOPHAGA

BEDFORD, G. A. H. A New Genus (Neolignathus) from an Elephant Shrew. Ent. Monthly Mag., 56, pp. 87–90 (1920).
Trichodectidæ Parasitic on Procaviidæ. Proc. Zool. Soc. London, 1932, pp. 709–730 (1932).
Trichodectidæ of African Carnivora. Parasitology, 24, pp. 350–364 (1932).
CARRIKER, M. A. Studies in Neotropical Mallophaga. Pt. I. Proc. Acad. Nat. Sci. Philadelphia, 88, pp. 45–218, 32 pls. (1936); Pt. II. Lloydia, 3, pp. 281–350 (1940); Pt. III. Proc. U. S. Nat. Mus., 95, pp. 81–233, 29 figs. (1944).

DENNY, H. Monographia Anoplurorum Brittanniæ. London (1842).

EICHLER, W. Notulæ Mallophagologicæ, IV. Neue Gattungen und höhre Einheiten von Kletterfederlingen. Zool. Anz., **130**, pp. 97–103, 1 fig. (1940).

Dr. E. Mjöberg's Zoological Collections from Sumatra. 15. Mallophaga. Ark. Zool., **39A**, 21 pp., 40 figs. (1947).

ENDERLEIN, G. Mallophaga. In Tierwelt Mitteleuropas, **4**, Lief. 2, pp. VII 17–24 (1928).

EWING, H. E. Taxonomy, Biology and Distribution of Gyropidæ. Proc. U. S. Nat. Mus., **63**, art. 20, pp. 1–42 (1924).

Manual of External Parasites. xiv+225 pp., 96 figs. Bailliere, Tendall and Cox. London (1929).

New World Trichodectidæ. Journ. Parasitol., **22**, pp. 233–246. (1936).

FERRIS, G. F. The Mallophagan Family Trimenoponidæ. Parasitology, **14**, pp. 75–86 (1922).

The Mallophagan Family Menoponidæ. I. Parasitology, **16**, pp. 55–66 (1924).

FULMEK, L. Die Mallophagen. Mitt. naturw. Ver. Univ. Wien, **5**, pp. 1–50 (1907).

GIEBEL, C. G. A. Insecta Epizoa. 308 pp. Leipzig (1874).

GUIMARÃES, L. R. Espécies da familia Philopteridæ. Arq. Zool., **5**, pp. 243–309 (1947).

HARRISON, L. The Genera and Species of Mallophaga. Parasitology, **9**, pp. 1–156 (1916).

KÉLER, S. Monographie der Ueberfamilie Trichodectoidea. Nova Acta Leop. Carol. Halle, (N.F.) **5**, pp. 393–467, 40 figs. (1938).

Ueberfamilie der Nirmoidea. Nova Acta Leop. Carol., (N. F.) **8**, pp. 1–254, 4 pls., 114 figs. (1939).

Ueber brasilianische Mallophagen. 2. Beitrag. Arb. morph. taxon. Ent. Biol., **6**, pp. 222–253, 23 figs.; **10**, pp. 177–204, 22 figs. (1939–43).

Bestimmungstabelle der Ueberfamilie Trichodectoidea (Mallophaga). Stettin. ent. Zeitg., **105**, pp. 167–191; 3 figs. (1944).

KELLOGG, V. L. Mallophaga. Gen. Insectorum, fasc. 66, 87 pp. (1908).

KELLOGG, V. L. and FERRIS, G. F. Anoplura and Mallophaga of North American Mammals. Leland Stanford Jr. Univ. Pub. (1915).

LAMEERE, A. Mallophaga. In Précis de Zoologie. Publ. Inst. zool. Torley-Rousseau, **4**, pp. 359–366 (1935).

MJÖBERG, E. Studien über Mallophagen und Anopluren. Ark. f. Zool., **6**, No. 13, 297 pp. (1910).

A New Family and Three New Genera of Mallophaga. Ent. Tidskr., **40**, pp. 93–96 (1919).

PERRIER, R. Mallophages de la France. Faune de France, **4**, pp. 127–134, 32 figs. (1935).

SÉGUY, E. Insectes ectoparasites (Mallophages, Anoploures, Siphonaptera). Faune de France, **43**, pp. 23–407, (1944).

TASCHENBERG, O. Die Mallophagen. Halle (1882).

THOMPSON, G. B. A List of the Type-hosts of Mallophaga and the Lice described from them. Ann. Mag. Nat. Hist., (11)**14**, pp. 373–388; 737–767; (12)**1**, pp. 335–368 (1947–48).

UCHIDA, S. Studies on the Biting Lice (Mallophaga) of Japan and Adjacent

Territories (Suborder Ischnocera, Pt. 1). Japan. Med. Journ., **1**, pp. 303–326, 8 figs. (1948).

WERNECK, F. L. Os Malófagos de Mamíferos. Pt. 1. Amblycera e Ischnocera. Rev. Brasil. Biol., 243 pp., 431 figs. (1948); Pt. 2 (1950).

ZIMMERMAN, E. C. Mallophaga. Insects of Hawaii, **2**, pp. 253–294 (1948).

ZUNKER, M. Die Mallophagen des arktischen Gebietes. Fauna arctica, **6**, pp. 283–294, 14 figs. (1932).

ORDER THYSANÓPTERA

(PHYSÓPODA)

Small or minute, usually depressed, slender insects with the wings often reduced in size, and frequently capable of jumping, feeding generally on plant sap, or more rarely on animal juices. Head vertical, free; eyes well developed; usually three ocelli; mouthparts fitted for

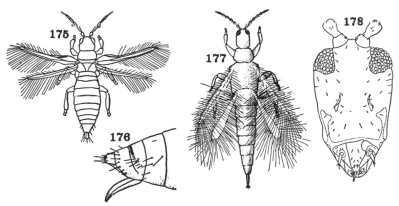

Figs. 175–178. Thysanoptera

175. **Heliothrips** (Russell) Thripidæ.
176. **Euthrips,** apex of abdomen of female, showing ovipositor (Russell).
177. **Thrips** Thripidæ.
178. **Cephalothrips,** head. (Peterson).

sucking, inferior, asymmetrical, consisting of a triangular clypeus fused with the bases of the maxillæ to form a sheath that encloses the mandibular and maxillary setæ. Prothorax free; wings four, similar, narrow, with few or no veins, closely fringed with long bristles, often vestigial or absent. Legs similar; tarsi one- or two-jointed, with one or two claws, and with a bladder-like or hoof-like enlargement at tip. Abdomen with ten visible segments; terminal one frequently tubular; basal one often closely attached to the thorax. Ovipositor present or absent, when present consisting of four more or less parallel, often strongly curved pieces. Metamorphosis gradual, the nymphs very similar to the adult; wings developing externally; penultimate instar often quiescent.

1. Wing surface microscopically hairy; wings usually present, fore wing with a marginal vein and at least one longitudinal vein attaining the wing tip; last abdominal segment rarely tubular, in the female usually conical and longitudinally divided beneath, in the male usually rounded at tip; ovipositor present, saw-like, composed of four pieces. (Suborder TEREBRÁNTIA). 2
   Wing surface bare, without pubescence; fore wing veinless, or at most with a single, abbreviated median vein, wings often absent; last abdominal segment tubular in both sexes and not divided beneath; no ovipositor. (Suborder TUBULÍFERA). 11
2. Ovipositor curved upwards; wings usually broad, with the tips rounded; body not flattened; antennæ nine-jointed. 3
   Ovipositor curved downwards; wings when present narrower and almost always pointed at tips; body more or less flattened; antennæ six- to nine-jointed. (THRIPÒIDEA). 7
3. Labial palpi with fewer joints than the maxillary palpi; all joints of antennæ usually freely movable 4
   Labial palpi with the same number of joints as the maxillary palpi, or with one more joint; last three to five joints of antennæ closely united, not freely movable. 6
4. Maxillary palpi with seven or eight joints. 5
   Maxillary palpi with three joints; labial palpi with two joints. (Melánothrips, Palæarc.; Ánkothrips, widespr.; Cránothrips, Austr.) (Including DACTULIOTHRÍPIDÆ).
                                              MELANOTHRÍPIDÆ
5. Labial palpi with four joints; wings greatly narrowed at the base, expanding broadly and rounded at apex. (Mymárothrips)
                                              MYMAROTHRÍPIDÆ
   Labial palpi with three to five joints; wings not thus clavate. (Désmothrips, Austr.; Órothrips, Nearc.; Stomátothrips).
                                              OROTHRÍPIDÆ
6. Antennæ extremely long and slender, the third joint at least ten times as long as thick and as long as the head (Fig. 179), joints three and four without elongated sensory areas; fore wing slender, without crossveins; anterior ocellus absent or very small. (Franklínothrips, Nearc., Ethiop.; Corynothripòides, Ethiop.).
                                              FRANKLINOTHRÍPIDÆ
   Antennæ much shorter; joints three and four with elongated sensory areas; wings broader, the fore wing with distinct crossveins; three well developed ocelli. (Æólothrips, Archæólothrips, Rhipídothrips). (COLEOPTRÁTIDÆ) .. ÆOLOTHRÍPIDÆ

7. Antennæ nine-jointed, sometimes apparently ten-jointed, without an apical stylus; front tarsus with a claw-like projection at the base of the second joint; third and fourth joints of antennæ enlarged, conical. (Hetérothrips, Am.). HETEROTHRÍPIDÆ
Antennæ six- to eight-jointed, rarely with the second joint divided by a suture so that the antennæ appear to be nine-jointed; antennæ usually with a one- or two-jointed style at apex (Fig. 183); front tarsus simple, without appendage on second joint; third and fourth joints of antennæ not conical. 8

8. Antennæ not moniliform, six- to eight-jointed, always with apical style; pronotum simple above, without longitudinal sutures; front and hind femora slender; ovipositor almost always well developed. 9
Antennæ moniliform (Fig. 180), eight-jointed, without apical style; pronotum with a longitudinal suture at each side; front and hind femora greatly thickened (Fig. 182); ovipositor much reduced. (Mèrothrips, Nearc., Neotrop.) .... MEROTHRÍPIDÆ

9. Sixth joint of antennæ well developed, usually as large as or larger than the fifth (Fig. 183) 10
Sixth or sixth and seventh joints of antennæ very small, style-like, very much smaller than the fifth. (Cerátothrips, Palæarc.).
CERATOTHRÍPIDÆ

10. Last abdominal segment in female cylindrical, very heavily chitinized, ninth and tenth segments with extremely long, stout, thorn-like bristles. (Panchætothrips, India; Dinùrothrips, Macrùrothrips).
PANCHÆTOTHRÍPIDÆ
Last abdominal segment in female conical, weakly chitinized, rarely more heavily chitinized than the preceding segments; ninth and tenth segments never with large thorn-like bristles. (Figs. 175, 183, 185). (Heliothrips, Thrips, Frankliniélla, Anáphothrips, Phỳsothrips and many other genera). (STENOPTÉRIDÆ).
THRÍPIDÆ

11. Maxillary palpi two-jointed; antennæ with seven or eight, usually eight joints; middle coxæ further apart than the other pairs. 12
Maxillary palpi one-jointed; antennæ with four to seven joints; hind coxæ further apart than the other pairs. (Fig. 181). (Ùrothrips, Ethiop.; Stephánothrips, Ethiop., Neotrop.; Brádythrips, Neotrop.; Bebélothrips, Palæarc.). (UROTHRIPÒIDEA).
UROTHRÍPIDÆ

12. Eighth segment of abdomen without peg-shaped projections on the posterior edge. 13
Eighth abdominal segment with long, posteriorly directed, peg-shaped projections along the posterior edge; last segment of abdomen extremely short and stout. (Chirothripòides).
CHIROTHRIPÒIDIDÆ

13. Head not produced anteriorly in front of eyes; vertex not sharply conical, rarely prominently overhanging the base of the antennæ. 14
Head more or less produced in front of the eyes; vertex conical, usually prominently overhanging the base of the antennæ and bearing the front ocellus at its extremity; usually with a strong bristle in front of the eye. (Idólothrips, Gigántothrips, Actínothrips). ....IDOLOTHRÍPIDÆ

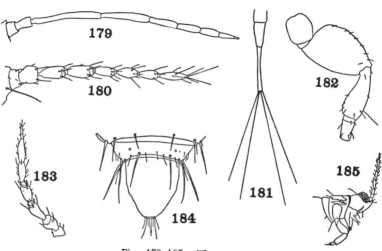

Figs. 179–185.   Thysanoptera

179. **Franklinothrips**, antenna (Hood) Franklinothripidæ.
180. **Merothrips**, antenna (Hood) Merothripidæ.
181. **Bradythrips**, apex of abdomen of female (Hood) Urothripidæ.
182. **Merothrips**, leg (Hood) Merothripidæ.
183. **Frankliniella**, antenna (Karny) Thripidæ.
184. **Pygothrips**, apex of abdomen of female (Hood) Pygothripidæ.
185. **Thrips**, head and anterior part of thorax (Shaw) Thripidæ.

14. Male with a stout tubular projection at each side of the sixth abdominal segment. (Mégathrips, Bacíllothrips, Megálothrips).
MEGATHRÍPIDÆ
Sixth abdominal segment of male simple, without a tubular projection laterally. 15
15. Last abdominal segment greatly elongated, about as long as the remainder of the abdomen and three or four times as long as the head. (Hystríchothrips, Holùrothrips).
HYSTRICHOTHRÍPIDÆ

Last abdominal segment much shorter, never greatly lengthened . . 16
16. Last abdominal segment short, swollen, rounded on the sides; preceding segments very much shorter than wide (Fig. 184). (Pýgothrips, Austr.). . . . . PYGOTHRÍPIDÆ
Last abdominal segment tubular, slightly narrowed apically, preceding segments not transversely linear, the ninth usually but little wider than long. 17
17. Third joint of antennæ with a strong crest-like ring of large sense cones at apex. (Ecacánthothrips, Indomal.; Órmothrips).
ECACANTHOTHRÍPIDÆ
Sense organs of third joint no more strongly developed than those of the other joints. 18
18. Sensory cones of antennæ unusually long and acute, each with an accessory cone or a long, slender bristle, the joints which bear the cones much swollen; eyes very much enlarged, contiguous. (Eupátithrips, Sedùlothrips). . . . . EUPATITHRÍPIDÆ
Sensory cones not remarkably developed; eyes much smaller. (Phlœothrips, Tríchothrips, Lìothrips, Acánthothrips, Zỳgothrips, and many others). . . . . PHLŒOTHRÍPIDÆ

LITERATURE ON THYSANOPTERA

BAGNALL, R. S. Synopsis of Æolothripidæ. Trans. 2d Congress Ent., **2,** pp. 394–397 (1913).
The Genus Melanothrips. Ent. Monthly Mag., **60,** pp. 9–11. (1924).
Classification of Thysanoptera. Ann. Mag. Nat. Hist., (10)**5,** pp. 571–575 (1930).
On the Æolothripid-complex and the Classification of the Sub-order Terebrantia (Thysanoptera). Bull. Soc. Nat. Luxembourg, **41,** pp. 115–118 (1931).
CAPPELLETO, A. I Tisanotteri italiani. Boll. Mus. Zool. Anat. comp. Torino, **44,** pp. 335–585, 14 pls., 2 figs. (1934).
COSTA LIMA, A. DA. Tisanópteros do Brasil. In vol. 1, Insetos do Brasil. (1939).
DOEKSEN, J. Bijdrage tot de vergelijkende morphologie der Thysanoptera. Meded. Landb. Hoogesch., **45,** 114 pp., 24 pls. (1941).
HINDS, W. E. Monograph of Thysanoptera of North America. Proc. U. S. Nat. Mus., **26,** pp. 79–242 (1902).
HOOD, J. D. Subfamilies of Thysanoptera. Proc. Biol. Soc. Washington, **28,** pp. 53–60 (1915).
Keys to Genera and North American Species of Urothripidæ. Bull. Brooklyn Ent. Soc., **24,** pp. 314–321 (1929).
Studies in Neotropical Thysanoptera. I, II. Rev. Ent., **6,** pp. 248–279, 4 figs.; pp. 424–460, 5 figs. (1936). Pts. III–VIII, ibid. (1938).
HOOD, J. D. and WILLIAMS, C. B. Synopsis of Urothripidæ. Ann. Ent. Soc. America, **20,** pp. 1–9 (1927).
KARNY, H. Synopsis der Megathripidæ. Neue Beiträge zur systematischen Insektenkunde, Berlin, **1,** pp. 105–110; 113–118 (1919).

Beiträge zur Malayischen Orthopteren-fauna, III. Thysanoptera. Treubia, 1, pp. 163–269 (1921).
   Studies on Indian Thysanoptera. Mem. Dept. Agric. India, 9, pp. 187–239 (1926).
KNECHTEL, W. K. Thysanoptere din Romania. Studin Monografic. Bulet. Agric., Bucarest, 2–3, pp. 1–235 (1923).
LAMEERE, A. Thysanoptera. In Précis de Zoologie. Rec. Inst. Zool. Torley-Rousseau, 4, pp. 368–380 (1935).
MOULTON, D. Synopsis, Catalogue and Bibliography of North American Thysanoptera. Bull. Bur. Ent. U. S. Dept. Agric., Tech. Ser. No. 21 (1911).
   The Thysanoptera of South America. Rev. Ent., Rio de Janeiro, 2, pp. 451–484, 3 figs. (1932).
   Thysanoptera of South America. Rev. Ent., Rio de Janeiro, 3, pp. 96–122; 227–262; 385–419; 447–458, 1 pl., 5 figs. (1933).
   The Genus Franklinella, with Key to Species. Rev. Ent., Rio de Janeiro, 19, pp. 55–114, 43 figs. (1948).
PERRIER, R. Thysanoptères de la France. Faune de France, 3, pp. 151–156 (1934).
PRIESNER, H. Die Thysanopteren Europas. Four parts. Vienna, Fritz Wagner (1926–28).
   Thysanoptera. In Tierwelt Mitteleuropas, 4, Lief. 2, pp. VIII, 1–18 (1928).
   Indomalayische Thysanopteren. Treubia, 11, pp. 357–371, 10 figs. (1930).
   Thysanopteren aus dem Belgischen Congo. Rev. Zool. Bot. afr., 32, pp. 154–175, 7 figs.; 33, pp. 49–66, 4 figs. (1939).
RAMAKRISHNA AYYAR, T. V. and MARGABANDHU, V. Thysanoptera. Cat. Indian Insects, Pt. 25, 64 pp. (1940).
SHUMSHER SINGH. Systematics of Indian Thysanoptera Terebrantia. Indian Journ. Ent., 7, pp. 147–188 (1946).
UZEL, H. Monographie der Thysanopteren. 472 pp. Königgrätz (1895).
WATSON, J. R. Synopsis and Catalogue of North American Thysanoptera. Florida Agric. Expt. Sta., Tech. Bull. No. 168, 100 pp. (1923).
ZIMMERMAN, E. C. Thysanoptera. Insects of Hawaii, 2, pp. 387–454 (1948).

ORDER HEMÍPTERA
SUBORDER HOMÓPTERA

(*RHYNCHÒTA*, part)

An assemblage of very diverse insects, difficult to define in a general way; usually of moderate or small size, rarely large; in the active forms four wings are present in both sexes; in the scale insects only the males are winged, and they have the hind wings absent; wings usually sloping over the sides of the body; fore wings never modified into a heavy basal and thinner apical portion; mouthparts forming a jointed beak, inserted at hind edge of the head and extending between the front coxæ, the basal joints very short, rarely the beak is absent in the males. Beak formed of the stylet-shaped mandibles and maxillæ which are enclosed in the labium. Cerci wanting. Metamorphosis usually incomplete, sometimes complete in the male or at least with a pupal stage in the male scale insects, rarely so in the female; all the species vegetarian.

1. Beak plainly arising from the base of the head; tarsi, at least of middle and hind legs, three-jointed, antennæ very short, with a small terminal bristle; active, free-living species. (AUCHENOR-RHŶNCHA) 2

   Beak appearing to arise between the front coxæ, rarely absent in male coccids and some aphids; tarsi two- or one-jointed; antennæ usually well developed and thread-like, sometimes atrophied or absent, without conspicuous terminal bristle; species often incapable of moving, or inactive in the female sex. (STERNORRHŶNCHA). (*GULARÓSTRIA*) 45

   Beak arising from the prothorax, sheathed at base by propleural structures; antennæ very short. (*COLEORRHŶNCHA*).....63

2. Ocelli (rarely absent) placed between the eyes on the vertex, on the front margin of the head, or on the front; middle coxæ short and close together, hind coxæ movable; tegulæ absent; fore wings with the two anal veins more or less parallel, or the second absent 3

   Ocelli (rarely absent) placed beneath or near the eyes, usually in cavities of the cheeks; middle coxæ elongate, widely separate, hind coxæ immovable, fused externally with the metathorax; tegulæ present as a scale between the base of the fore wing and the side angle of the pronotum; fore wings usually with the two anal veins joining apically to form a Y-vein. (Superfamily FULGORÒIDEA. Classification from F. Muir, 1930).....28

3. Three ocelli, placed close together on the disk of the vertex; antennæ with short basal joint, terminated by a hair-like process which is divided into about five joints; front femora thickened and generally spined beneath, hind legs not fitted for jumping; empodia absent; male almost always with a sound-producing structure on each side at the base of the abdomen; comparatively large species with entirely membranous wings; nymphs subterranean. Cicadas, "Locusts," Harvest-flies. (Figs. 186, 191, 192, 198). (**Cicàda** (*C. septéndecim*, Periodical Cicada or Seventeen-year locust), **Tibìcen, Platypèdia**) ....CICÁDIDÆ

   Two ocelli, rarely absent; empodia large; jumping species 4

4. Pronotum not prolonged over the base of the abdomen 5

   Pronotum prolonged backward into a hood or process of variable form, usually much elevated and more or less concealing the scutellum and extending over the abdomen, often the prothorax is grotesquely enlarged and ornamented; head vertical, cheeks not dilated, ocelli located between the eyes, antennæ inserted between and in front of the eyes. Tree hoppers.

MEMBRÁCIDÆ

a. Scutellum absent or vestigial, entirely concealed beneath the pronotum ....b

Scutellum present, usually exposed. (**Tropidáspus, Nicòmia, Tolània, Lycodères,** Neotrop.; **Centròtus, Tricéntrus,** Palæarc., Indomal.; **Tylocéntrus, Microcéntrus,** Am.) ....**CENTROTÍNÆ**

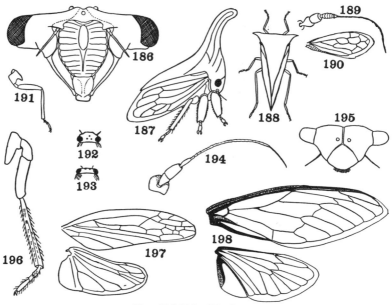

Figs. 186–198.   **Hemiptera**

186. **Cicada,** front view of head (Berlese) Cicadidæ.
187. **Entylia** (Branch) Membracidæ.
188. **Ceresa** (Marlatt) Membracidæ.
189. **Ceresa,** antenna (Marlatt) Membracidæ.
190. **Ceresa,** fore wing (Marlatt) Membracidæ.
191. **Cicada,** hind leg (Kolbe) Cicadidæ.
192. **Cicada,** dorsal view of head (Maxwell-Lefroy) Cicadidæ.
193. Leaf hopper, dorsal view of head (Maxwell-Lefroy) Jassidæ.
194. **Entylia,** antenna (Branch) Membracidæ.
195. **Entylia,** front view of head (Branch) Membracidæ.
196. **Entylia,** hind leg (Branch) Membracidæ.
197. **Gypona,** wings (Metcalf) Gyponidæ.
198. **Cicada,** wings. Cicadidæ.

b. Front tibiæ flattened, foliaceous. (**Membràcis, Enchenòpa, Spongó-phorus, Notócera,** Neotrop.; **Campylénchia, Leiocỳta,** Am.).
            MEMBRACÎNÆ
Anterior tibiæ simple, not flattened or leaf-like c
c. Hind tarsi very short, much shorter than the front or middle tibiæ. (**Alchísme, Metcalfiélla,** Neotrop.; **Platycòtis, Umbònia,** Am.).
            PLATYCOTÎNÆ
Hind tarsi as long or longer than the front or middle tibiæ. ......d
d. Third apical cell of corium petiolate. ....e
Third apical cell of corium truncate, never petiolate. (**Dárnis, Rhéxia, Aconóphora, Hyphínöe,** Neotrop.; **Stictopélta,** Am.).
            DARNÎNÆ
e. Tegmina coriaceous, opaque; apical veinless border very broad; small flattened beetle-like species. (**Tragòpa, Stilbóphora, Harìola,** Neotrop.). ....**TRAGOPÎNÆ**
Tegmina entirely or almost entirely membranous, the apical veinless border narrow. (**Cerèsa** (*C. bùbalus,* Buffalo tree hopper, Figs. 188, 189, 190); **Stictocéphala, Entỳlia** (Figs. 194, 195, 196), **Telamòna,** Am.; **Smìlia, Cyrtólobus,** N. Am.; **Xanthólobus,** Nearc.). ....**SMILIÎNÆ**

5. Hind coxæ short, conical, not laterally dilated; tibiæ cylindrical, smooth, the hind pair usually armed with one or two stout solid spines and with a cluster of spinules at apex; ocelli placed on the vertex, rarely absent; flagellum composed of a large pear-shaped base and a very slender seta; nymphs usually producing a mass of froth in which they live on the stems of various plants. Spittle insects, Frog hoppers. (Superfamily CERCOPÒIDEA. Classification from C. F. Baker) 6
Hind coxæ transverse, reaching the side margins of the sternum; hind tibiæ ridged, with a double series of articulated spines or seriately bristly (hairy in Æthalionidæ); cheeks dilated. Leaf hoppers, Sharp shooters. (Superfamily JASSÒIDEA) 9
6. Scutellum comparatively small and short (longer than pronotum only in Clastopteridæ); hind wings with outer fork of radius always present (sometimes broken at apex), thus forming a supernumerary (first) apical cell, the cubitus apically forked or simple; fore wings with claval veins when present usually distant and without connecting crossvein 7
Scutellum as long as or longer than pronotum, either simply long acuminate, or greatly elevated posteriorly and with a strongly curved, free, apical spine projecting backward; hind wings with outer fork of radius always absent, therefore no supernumerary (first) apical cell; fore wings with both claval veins when present fused at middle or before, or with a connecting crossvein.

Tube-forming spittle insects. Austr., Indomal., Ethiop. (Figs. 200, 204) . . . . MACHÆRÓTIDÆ

a. Scutellum not raised apically or with free apical spinous appendage; anterior margin of pronotum strongly extended between eyes; head usually obtuse-angulate; cubitus of hind wing apically forked. (Conmachæròta; Híndola, Enderleinia, Malay; Neuromachæròta, Ethiop.). (*ENDERLEINIÍNÆ*). . HINDOLÌNÆ
Scutellum usually greatly raised apically, always with a free apical spinous appendage extended backward; anterior margin of pronotum but very slightly extended between eyes; head strongly swollen and extended in front of eyes; cubitus of hind wing not forked. . . . . b

b. Form slender, body of scutellum high, arched posteriorly, with strong dorsal furrow; pronotum without laminately extended lateral angles, the anterior margin somewhat angulate between eyes. (Machæròta). MACHÆROTÌNÆ
Form very thick and stout; body of scutellum nearly flat and with dorsal furrow subobsolete; pronotum with lateral angles produced into high, thin, spreading laminæ; anterior margin of pronotum broadly, gently arcuate between eyes.

MAXUDEÌNÆ

7. Pronotal margin between eyes usually straight or slightly arcuate, pronotum commonly strongly enlarged and much broader than the head and with the anterolateral margins usually as long as or longer than the posterolateral; front commonly more or less swollen apically; head with thickened and lobate ridges above the antennæ. (Tomáspis) . . . . TOMASPÍDIDÆ
Pronotal margin between the eyes usually strongly arcuate or subangulate, the pronotum never greatly enlarged and rarely much wider than head, the anterolateral margins usually much shorter than the posterolateral; front usually swollen basally, if at all; supra-antennal ridges not lobate nor greatly thickened 8

8. Fore wings with clavus obliquely truncate at apex; corial appendix, the apical portion of the wing, divided into two very broad subequal portions, these at rest infolded at end of the stout and broad body to overlap; fork of radius in hind wings forming a very short first apical cell considerably before apex; cubitus of hind wings not forked apically; corium with three apical cells and two or less subapicals; scutellum longer than pronotum. (Clastóptera (Fig. 201)) . . . . CLASTOPTÉRIDÆ
Fore wings with the clavus narrowly acute or subacute apically; corial appendix either a narrow continuous membranous margin, or wanting, never bent inward beyond the clavus to overlap

at end of body; corial venation various but never as in the Clastopteridæ. (Cercòpa, Ptỳelus, Aphróphora, cosmop.; Monécphora, widespr.; Phymatostètha, Indomal.; Cosmoscárta, Palæarc., Indomal. (Figs. 199, 203))............CERCÓPIDÆ

9. Pronotum enlarged, swollen and with a median ridge, almost concealing the head and roundly produced over the base of the acute scutellum. (Æthiàlion, Neotrop.; Dárthula, India).

ÆTHIALIÓNIDÆ

Pronotum not thus modified to cover the head, although sometimes with lateral protuberances. (JASSIDÆ, in the broad sense. Classification from C. F. Baker, Philippine Jour. Sci., 1923.)......10

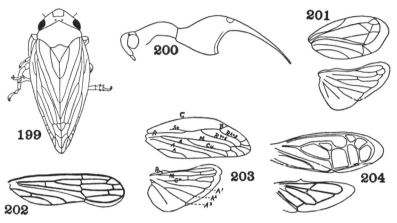

Figs. 199–204.   Hemiptera

199. Spittle insect (Stearns) Cercopidæ.
200. Machærota, profile of head, pronotum and scutellum (Baker) Machærotidæ.
201. Clastoptera, wings (Metcalf) Clastopteridæ.
202. Oncometopia, fore wing (Ball) Tettigellidæ.
203. Aphrophora, wings (Metcalf) Cercopidæ.
204. Machærota, wings (Baker) Machærotidæ.

10. Upper part of front strongly raised and produced, its posterior portion forming a large part of the superior surface of the head (crown); the true vertex confined to basal portion of crown, the ocelli thus on posterior disk of crown, usually remote from eyes and not visible in facial view.........................11
Upper part of front confined entirely to face, except sometimes for a narrow border; ocelli visible in facial view................15

11. Lateral sutures of front distinctly continued over the obtuse anterior margin of the crown to near the position of the ocelli, as in the Cercopidæ; antennæ between and near the eyes; body

usually elongate, cylindrical, head often angulate, face large, strongly convex, the cheeks rather long and narrow. (Tettigélla, Cicadélla, Dræculacéphala, Graphocéphala, Kólba, Oncometòpia (=Procònia) (Fig. 202), Tylozỳgus). (*PROCONÌIDÆ, TET-TIGONIÉLLIDÆ, TETTIGONÌIDÆ, CICADÉLLIDÆ*).
                                                              TETTIGÉLLIDÆ
 Lateral sutures of front obsolete beyond antennæ or beyond anterior border of crown...................................12

12. Antennæ not far removed from eyes and near but never above level of eyes; lateral margins of front obsolete beyond scrobes.......13
 Antennæ situated entirely above and far removed from eyes; head anteriorly transversely thin and leaf-like, often concave beneath 14

13. Head acutely angled between crown and face, the face of narrow proportions; lateral sutures of front entering and terminating in antennal scrobes, the face shallowly concave or weakly convex, the cheeks moderately swollen; body long, ovate, usually flattened. (Gýpona (Fig. 197), Xerophlœa)...............GYPÓNIDÆ
 Head obtusely rounded between the strongly declivous crown and face, strongly overhanging the latter, which is deeply concave; lateral sutures of front passing mesad of antennæ; face very short, far broader than long....................PENTHIMÌIDÆ

14. Outlined lower part of front short and broad.
                                                    THAUMASTOSCÓPIDÆ
 Outlined lower portion of front long and narrow; large, brownish species. Principally Indo-Australian. (Lèdra, Ledrópsis).
                                                              LÉDRIDÆ

15. Vertex entirely superior, occupying nearly all or all of crown, the junction with the front occurring on anterior border of crown, the ocelli on or near anterior border of head, rarely, in some Jassidæ and Ulopidæ, the ocelli indistinguishable 20
 Head very short, sometimes very broad, the vertex more or less roundly curved on to face and broadly visible in facial view; ocelli facial and between or above the eyes; basal suture of front, when present, far anterior to base of face; that portion of vertex visible from above usually very short and broad.............16

16. Anterior margin of pronotum extending beyond a line through the anterior margin of the eyes.............................17
 Anterior margin of pronotum not extending beyond the anterior margin of the eyes.......................................18

17. Vertex obtusely angulate; anterior margin of pronotum produced from one-third to nearly half its length beyond the anterior margin of the eyes; head and pronotum punctate or with irregular carinate lines. (Macrópsis, Oncópsis, Holarc.)......MACRÓPSIDÆ

Vertex broadly rounded; anterior margin of pronotum produced not more than one-fifth or one-sixth its length beyond the anterior margins of the eyes; head and pronotum finely granulate. (Agállia, Agalliópsis) ....AGALLÌIDÆ

18. Frontal suture extending beyond the antennal pit nearly to the ocellus; head wider than the pronotum; front wings bare between the veins. (Eurýmela, Idiócerus). (*IDIOCÉRIDÆ*). EURYMÉLIDÆ

Frontal suture not extending beyond the antennal pit..........19

19. Head narrower than the pronotum; front wings hirsute between the veins. (Bythoscòpus, Stragània)............BYTHOSCÓPIDÆ

Head wider than pronotum; front wings bare. (Aceratogállia) (see couplet 17) ....AGALLÌIDÆ, part

20. Basal suture of front distinct and entire, centrally at least, approaching more or less closely the anterior margin of vertex; when subobsolete above, its position always marked by a fold or carina; in the latter case, the remaining portion of frontal suture is always directed toward the base of front and not toward ocellus; anterior border of vertex usually marked by a sharp margin or carina 21

Basal suture of front usually obsolete, the basal lateral sutures running to and terminating at or near ocelli; vertex usually clearly connate with the front, only in highly specialized groups with a sharp edge or with transverse carinæ on anterior border; ocelli on anterior border of head or above it. (Fig. 193).....JÁSSIDÆ

a. Fore wings with well developed veins; head variously formed but not excessively long and narrow...........................b

Fore wings leathery, with obliterated venation; head very long and gradually tapering in front, body slender; tibiæ weakly spinose; Australian. (Cephalèlus (Fig. 212), Paradorýdium). CEPHALELÌNÆ

b. Fore wings with veins branching on the disk so that they form a series of preapical cells; ocelli present.......................c

Fore wings with veins, often weak at base, not branching on the disk, branching only near apex to form the apical cells; ocelli vestigial or wanting. (Typhlócyba (Fig. 205) (*T. austràlis*, Australian apple leaf-hopper), Dicraneùra, Empòa (*E. ròsæ*, Rose leaf-hopper), Empoásca (*E. màli*, Apple leaf-hopper), Erythroneùra (*E. còmes*, Grape leaf-hopper)). (*EUPTERÝGIDÆ*) TYPHLOCYBÌNÆ

c. Ocelli on vertex near margin, or between vertex and front, and remote from eyes. (Acucéphalus, Niònia, Strongylocéphalus, Xestocéphalus) ....ACUCEPHALÌNÆ

Ocelli on margin between vertex and front, usually very close to eyes. (Jássus (= *Cœlídia*), Chlorotéttix, Cicádula, Deltocéphalus (Fig. 210), Eùscelis, Eutéttix, Phlépsius, Platymetòpius, Scaphòideus, Thamnotéttix). (*CŒLÍDIDÆ*)..........JASSÏNÆ

21. Anterior border of vertex sharply laminately expanded, distinctly overhanging upper part of front; antennæ situated far mesad of eyes; ocelli, when distinguishable, lying between extended margin of vertex and basal margin of front in a transversely triangular (rarely linear) ocellar area and very remote from eyes 22

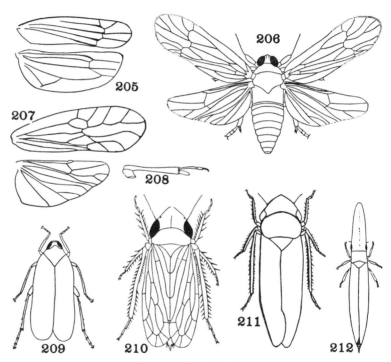

Figs. 205–212.   Hemiptera

205. **Typhlocyba,** wings. Jassidæ.
206. **Sogata** (Misra) Fulgoridæ.
207. **Liburnia,** wings (Metcalf) Areopodidæ.
208. **Liburniella,** hind leg (Garman) Areopodidæ.
209. **Cixius** (Metcalf) Cixiidæ.
210. **Deltocephalus** (DeLong) Jassidæ.
211. **Tettigoniella** (Ball) Tettigellidæ.
212. **Cephalelus** (Tillyard) Jassidæ.

Anterior border of vertex sharply marked (head may be laminately extended between eyes) but never with this margin extended beyond and overhanging upper part of front; usually with clearly marked subtriangular ocellar areas at sides between vertex and front; these areas are commonly occupied by the ocelli, though the latter may occur near by on upper surface of crown, then usually on or outside the carinate or raised lateral margin of vertex; antennæ situated close to interior line of eyes..........25

22. Pronotum extended between and in front of eyes; vertex very short, transverse and deeply concave.............................23

    Pronotum not abnormally extended between eyes; vertex not very short and widely transverse, the width of the vertex not more than twice the length; ocelli a little nearer to eyes than to median line, or indistinguishable.................................24

23. Tegmina normally veined; genæ narrower than front; front strongly excavate, with high raised margins; clypeus little exserted; ocellar area very broad; hind tibiæ with very few small spines and hairs on apical half; sculpture characterized by a deep thimble pitting. (**Paròpia** (= *Megophthálmus*) (Figs. 224, 225), **Mesoparòpia,** Malay.). (*MEGOPHTHÁLMIDÆ*) ....**PAROPÏIDÆ**

    Tegmina with numerous supernumerary veins; genæ wider than front; front convex; clypeus long exserted; ocellar area narrow, bounded beneath by a shallow fold; hind tibiæ with stout spinose teeth, few in number but distributed along entire length; sculpture characterized by coarse striations and wrinkles. (**Stenocòtis**).
    STENOCÓTIDÆ

24. Genæ longer than broad, flat or concave, outwardly emarginate, normally bordering the loræ to the clypeus; scrobes very shallow and lacking strong supra-antennal ledges (as in Stenocotidæ); pronotum with very short lateral margins, converging anteriorly, ocelli distinct. (**Koebèlea,** Nearc.). (Fig. 213)...**KOEBELÈIDÆ**

    Genæ broader than long, strongly convex, not passing loræ (at level of face), their apical margins roundly curved inward to meet the front above the loræ, leaving outer margin of latter fully exposed in facial view; scrobes very deep, under strongly overhanging and curved supra-antennal ledges; head wider than prothorax; pronotum with very long lateral margins, usually converging posteriorly; ocelli sometimes indistinguishable; all tibiæ ridged and feebly spined. (**Ulòpa** (Figs. 214, 215), **Mesárgus, Moonia**) ....**ULÓPIDÆ**

25. Upper margin of front a little extended beyond margin of vertex and plainly visible in dorsal view at least at sides, the lateral and anterior submarginal carinæ of vertex usually distinct, often very strong 26

Upper margin of face not at all extended beyond margin of vertex and not visible in dorsal view, or only a little so just in front of eyes; ocelli on anterolateral border of head or just above or below it; loræ very small and narrow; tegmina usually without anteapical cells and venation usually indistinct; antennæ situated above the eyes in facial view, rarely on upper line of or between eyes, in which case the head is long-produced....**NIRVÁNIDÆ**

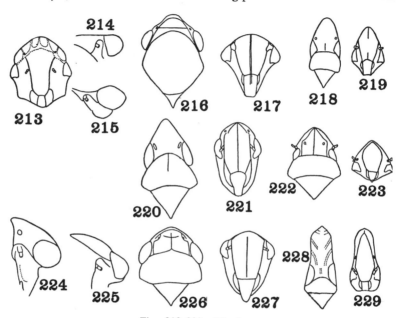

Figs. 213–229.   Hemiptera

213. **Koebelea,** face (Baker) Koebeleidæ.
214. **Ulopa,** face in frontal view (Baker) Ulopidæ.
215. **Ulopa,** face in lateral view (Baker) Ulopidæ.
216. **Signoretia,** head and pronotum, dorsal view (Baker) Signoretiidæ.
217. **Signoretia,** face (Baker) Signoretiidæ.
218. **Nirvana,** head and pronotum, dorsal view (Baker) Nirvanidæ.
219. **Nirvana,** face (Baker) Nirvanidæ.
220. **Pythamus,** head and pronotum, dorsal view (Baker) Pythamidæ.
221. **Pythamus,** face (Baker) Pythamidæ.
222. **Stenotortor,** head and pronotum, dorsal view (Baker) Nirvanidæ.
223. **Stenotortor,** face (Baker) Nirvanidæ.
224. **Paropia,** face, lateral view (Baker) Paropiidæ.
225. **Paropia,** face, frontal view (Baker) Paropiidæ.
226. **Euacanthus,** head and pronotum, dorsal view (Baker) Euacanthidæ.
227. **Euacanthus,** face (Baker), Euacanthidæ.
228. **Stenometopius,** head and pronotum, dorsal view (Baker) Nirvanidæ.
229. **Stenometopius,** face (Baker) Nirvanidæ.

a. Antennæ situated at upper angle of eyes (in facial view) or above this; lateral carinæ of vertex more or less distinct; ocelli always visible from above, on upper portion of lateral border, or on anterolateral portion of crown; eyes prominent; posterior border of pronotum more or less distinctly incurved:..............b

Antennæ situated at middle of eye margin (in facial view); lateral carinæ of vertex wanting; ocelli below anterior border of crown and not visible from above; head (from above) long spatulate, but not thin dorsoventrally; eyes not prominent, deeply set in vertex; pronotum subtruncate posteriorly; tegmina with two sub-apical cells. (Stenometòpius (Figs. 228, 229)).

STENOMETOPIÎNÆ

b. Antennæ situated in deep transverse, sharp-margined scrobes; face about as broad as long or broader; eyes small; vertex short, half-ovate. (Macroceratogònia, Balbíllus, Stenotórtor (Figs. 222, 223)).

MACROCERATOGONIÎNÆ

Antennæ in shallow scrobes of ordinary type; face usually much longer than broad; vertex long; eyes large; tegmina without subapical cells, the veins of corium usually indistinguishable except by transmitted light. (Nirvàna (Figs. 218, 219), Kàna, Ophiùchus, Pseudonirvàna) ....NIRVANÎNÆ

26. Pronotum very long, strongly produced and outcurved behind, largely covering the scutellum; head with eyes broader than pronotum; vertex with a very strong, thickened, basal transverse ridge; supra-antennal ledge callously thickened and lobed over frontal margin; clypeus truncate or notched apically and little or not exserted; sides of front not sinuate at scrobes; ocelli in marginal areas and visible from above and below; loræ very small and short. (Signorètia, Indoaustr. (Figs. 216, 217); Prèta).

SIGNORETIÎDÆ

Pronotum not produced behind over the very large scutellum, the hind border truncate or concave; head more or less distinctly narrower than pronotum; vertex without strongly thickened basal ridge; supra-antennal ledge neither strongly callous nor lobed over frontal margin; antennæ between the eyes near middle of their inner margins..27

27. Pronotum short, broad, broadly rounded anteriorly, the head but slightly narrower; vertex very broad, nearly twice as broad as long; width of head greater than length of head and pronotum together; ocelli situated a little within anterior margin of crown, but outside the anterolateral carina of vertex, and invisible in facial view. (Euacánthus (Figs. 226, 227); Búndera, India).

EUACÁNTHIDÆ

Pronotum more or less narrowly rounded anteriorly, the head very distinctly narrower, vertex always much less than twice as broad

as long; width of head always much less than length of head
and pronotum together; ocelli in or very near lateral areas, and
usually visible both in dorsal and facial views. (Pýthamus (Figs.
220, 221), Oniélla, Onùkia) .... PYTHÁMIDÆ
28. Flagellum of antennæ segmented; hind tibiæ without mobile spur;
lateral ocelli on the front, the front reaching from eye to eye
without lateral ridges dividing off a small area around the eyes;
sides of face (loræ) plainly visible in front view and forming a
continuous curve with the clypeus. (Tettigomètra, Egròpa, Hílda,
Euphyonártex) .... TETTIGOMÉTRIDÆ
Flagellum of antennæ not segmented; lateral ocelli outside the
lateral ridges of the front, generally beneath the eyes; sides of

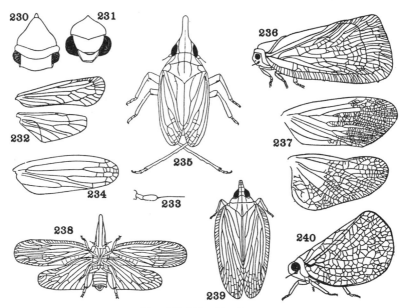

Figs. 230–240. Hemiptera

230. **Acanalonia**, head (Metcalf) Acanaloniidæ.
231. **Aphelonema**, head (Metcalf) Issidæ.
232. **Otiocerus**, wings (Metcalf) Derbidæ.
233. **Liburniella**, antenna (Garman) Areopodidæ.
234. **Scolops**, fore wing (Metcalf) Dictyopharidæ.
235. **Scolops** (Garman) Dictyopharidæ.
236. **Acanalonia** (Swezey) Acanaloniidæ.
237. **Poiocera**, wings (Metcalf).
238. **Pyrilla** (Misra) Lophopidæ.
239. Tropiduchid.
240. **Ormenis** (Swezey) Flatidæ.

face (loræ) not visible in front view, or forming an angle with the clypeus 29

29. Second joint of hind tarsi not very small, the apex truncate or emarginate and with a row of small spines; fore wing without costal area, or with only a small one without crossveins 30
Second joint of hind tarsus small or very small, the apex generally rounded or pointed and without spines or with only one at each side; costal area present or absent 38

30. Claval veins not granulate; or if so, the last joint of the labium short, not longer than wide 31
One or both claval veins granulate; apical joint of labium much longer than wide. Abdomen compressed, the sixth to eighth tergites with wax secreting pores; median ocellus usually present. (Meénoplus, Ánigrus, Sùva, Kermèsia) .... MEENÓPLIDÆ

31. Sixth, seventh and eighth abdominal tergites without wax pores.. 32
Sixth, seventh and eighth tergites with wax-secreting pores; ovipositor reduced, incomplete. (Kínnara, Eparmène, Prosótropis, Œclídius, Atopocíxius) ˜ .... KINNÁRIDÆ

32. Anal area of hind wings reticulate, with many crossveins; clypeus with lateral carinæ; head often greatly prolonged. (Fúlgora, Indomal.; Lanternària, Neotrop.; Ámycle, Cyrpóptus, Pỳrops). FULGÓRIDÆ
Anal area of hind wing not reticulate 33

33. Last joint of labium distinctly longer than wide 34
Last joint of labium about as long as wide. (Dérbe, Anòtia, Lamènia, Otiócerus (Fig. 232), Rhotàna, Venàta, Zoràida). DÉRBIDÆ

34. Claval vein entering the apex of the clavus 35
Claval vein not reaching the apex of the clavus, entering commissure before apex 36

35. Base of abdomen on each side with one or two short processes bearing three pits or depressions; body compressed, wing membranes not overlapping. (Achilíxia, Malay.; Bebaiòtes, Neotrop.). ACHILIXÌIDÆ
Base of abdomen without lateral processes; body usually flattened, the wing membranes overlapping. (Achìlus, Agandécca, Catònia, Elidóptera, Favéntia) .... ACHÍLIDÆ

36. Hind tibiæ with a strong, movable spur at the apex; fore wings without costal area; ovipositor well developed; often brachypterous. (Arèopus (Délphax), Libúrnia (Fig. 207), Perkinsiélla (P. saccharicìda, Sugarcane hopper), Pissonòtus, Stenócranus). (DELPHÁCIDÆ) .... AREOPÓDIDÆ
Hind tibiæ without apical movable spur 37

37. Head prolonged in front, sometimes greatly so, or if not the front bears two or three carinæ, or the tegulæ are absent and the claval

suture obscure; no median ocellus. (Dictyóphara, Cládypha, Dichóptera, Orgámara, Orgèrius, Scòlops (Figs. 234, 235)).

                                     DICTYOPHÁRIDÆ

Head not prolonged in front, or only moderately so, the front with only a median carina, in addition to the lateral margins; tegulæ present; median ocellus often present. (Cíxius (Fig. 209), Bothriócera, Koroàna, Mýndus, Oliàrus) . . . . CIXÌIDÆ

38. Second joint of hind tarsi with a spine on each side; claval vein nearly always extending to and ending in the apex of the clavus 39

Second joint of hind tarsus small, without spines 43

39. Mesonotum with the hind angles marked off by a groove or fine line; fore wings with the costal area absent, or very small and without crossveins, or with crossveins; basal joint of hind tarsi usually long, rarely padded below. (Tropidùchus, Alcéstis, Monópsis, Tambínia, Neurómeta) . . . . TROPIDÙCHIDÆ

Mesonotum with the hind angles not marked off by a groove or line; first joint of hind tarsus usually short or very short 40

40. Fore wings with a crossveined costal area; without granules on the clavus; clypeus nearly always with lateral carinæ. (Nogodìna).

                                     NOGODÍNIDÆ

Fore wings without a crossveined costal area, or if with such the clavus is granulate or the clypeus is without lateral carinæ 41

41. Clavus not granulate; base of costa not strongly curved 42

Fore wings with a crossveined costal area and with the clavus granulate, or the base of the costa strongly curved. (Flàta, Cerýnia, Flatòides, Nephèsa, Órmenis (Fig. 240), Phántia, Phỳma).

                                     FLÁTIDÆ

42. Fore wings large, held steeply against the sides of the body; head about as wide as thorax; pronotum with hind edge slightly roundly emarginate, sometimes straight; mesonotum large, long; hind tibiæ without spines; ovipositor incomplete. (Acanalònia (= Amphiscèpa) (Figs. 230, 236), Chloróchara). (AMPHI-SCÉPIDÆ) . . . . ACANALONÌIDÆ

Fore wings generally smaller, in Caliscelinæ very short, or very narrow, parchment-like; head usually as wide as thorax or wider; pronotum with hind margin straight, sometimes slightly concave or convex; mesonotum short, not more than twice the length of the pronotum, with a transverse ridge parallel to the pronotal suture dividing it into two parts of differing sculpturing, the anterior covered by the pronotum; hind tibiæ spined; claval suture present (Issinæ) or absent and fore wings thick, convex, and venation obscured (Hemisphæriinæ). (Bruchomórpha, Aphelónema (Fig. 231), Calíscelis, Hemisphærius, Íssus) . . . . . . ÍSSIDÆ

43. Fore wings wide on apical margin, steeply held against the sides of the body, with a crossveined costal area; clavus long; head as wide or nearly as wide as the thorax; hind trochanter directed downward; first joint of hind tarsi at least moderately short. (Ricània, Armàcia, Euricània, Privèsa) ....RICANÌIDÆ
   Fore wings not so wide on the apical margin and not held so steeply, or the head is distinctly narrower than the thorax; clavus shorter; hind trochanter directed backward; first joint of hind tarsi at least moderately long.............................44

44. Front wider than long, the sides angulate; clypeus without lateral carinæ and front without longitudinal carinæ or with only a very obscure one. (Eurýbrachys, Messèna, Platýbrachys, Théssitus)
   EURYBRÁCHIDÆ
   Front rarely as wide as long and often without angular margins, nearly always with one or three longitudinal carinæ. (Lòphops, Indomal.; Pyrilla (Fig. 238), Malay.; Elasmóscelis, Ethiop., Indomal.; Kasseròta, Indoaustr.)................LOPHÓPIDÆ

45. Tarsi two-jointed, the basal joint sometimes reduced, the outer joint with two claws; wings, when present, four in number, with few veins, at rest usually held in a sloping position over the abdomen; sutures between body segments distinct; mouthparts usually well developed in both sexes, labium usually long......46
   Tarsi one-jointed (in some Monoplebidæ and in the male cochineal insect there is an additional minute basal joint) and with a single claw; female stout-bodied, always wingless, often without legs so that they rarely move after maturity, remaining sessile on the host plant, rarely without mouthparts; males delicate, usually with mesothoracic wings alone developed, which are gauzy and almost veinless and lie flat, overlapping on the abdomen when at rest; antennæ of female absent or with as many as eleven joints, of male with ten to twenty-five joints; body of female and nymphal males scale-like, gall-like, or covered with waxy powder, tufts or scales, the sutures between the segments often indistinct. (Superfamily COCCÒIDEA).............51

46. Non-jumping insects, legs long and slender; both pairs of wings membranous or opaque whitish; antennæ three- to six-jointed...47
   Jumping insects, the femora thickened; antennæ long, five- to ten-jointed, usually ten-jointed, the last joint with two fine apical bristles; fore wings somewhat thicker, often more or less leathery; pad between the tarsal claws (empodium) present, bilobed. Jumping plant-lice. (PSÝLLIDÆ).................CHÉRMIDÆ

   a. Head deeply cleft, with the antennæ attached to the truncate anterior ends on each side of the cleft (Fig. 241); cheeks seldom produced into conical processes; media not dichotomously forked

(Fig. 243); hind tibiæ often without a spur at base. Indomalayan and Neotropical. (**Carsídara, Epicársa, Nesiòpe, Rhinopsýlla**).

CARSIDARÌNÆ

Head of a different form; if apparently cleft, this is due to the genal cones, which do not bear the antennæ...................b

b. Front not covered by the genæ (Fig. 244), which are not produced into conical processes (except *Calophya*); anterior ocellus at the upper extremity of the front..c

Front covered by the genæ (Fig. 253) which are usually produced below into conical processes; front ocellus at the junction of the front and genæ...d

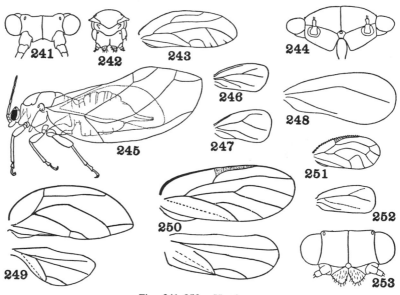

Figs. 241–253.   Hemiptera

241. **Freysiula,** head (Crawford) Chermidæ.
242. **Trioza,** head (Crawford) Chermidæ.
243. **Carsidara,** fore wing (Crawford) Chermidæ.
244. **Paurocephala,** head (Crawford) Chermidæ.
245. **Trioza** (Peterson) Chermidæ.
246. **Udamoselis,** fore wing (Quaintance and Baker) Aleyrodidæ.
247. **Aleurodicus,** wing (Quaintance and Baker) Aleyrodidæ.
248. **Aleurocanthus,** wing (Quaintance and Baker) Aleyrodidæ.
249. **Trioza,** wings (Patch) Chermidæ.
250. **Pachypsylla,** wings (Patch) Chermidæ.
251. **Ceriacremum,** fore wing (Crawford) Chermidæ.
252. **Aleyrodes,** fore wing (Quaintance and Baker) Aleyrodidæ.
253. **Pachypsylla,** head (Crawford) Chermidæ.

c. Vertex flat, horizontal; the front beneath it in the form of a narrow, usually elongate piece that extends from the clypeus to the anterior ocellus; wings often more or less thickened and spotted. (Aphálara, Aphalaròida, Lívia, Rhinócola)..........LIVIÌNÆ
Vertex not horizontal, its surface curved downwards anteriorly; front forming a small sclerite level with the vertex and genæ; wings usually membranous. (Calóphya, Am.; Leptynóptera, Indomal.; Heteropsýlla, Paurocéphala, Pauropsýlla, widespr.).
                              PÁUROPSYLLÌNÆ

d. Fore wing with more than two marginal cells, the radial sector branched or connected to the media by a crossvein near the tip of the wing (Fig. 251). (Ceriacrèmum, Neotrop.)
                              CERIACREMÌNÆ
Fore wing with only two marginal cells, formed by the furcation of the media and cubitus (Fig. 249), the radial sector not branched and not connected with the media by a crossvein......e

e. First joint of hind tarsi with two black, claw-like spines at tip; radius, media and cubitus not arising at the same point from the basal vein, the media and cubitus stalked; wings rarely angulate at apex. (Arytàina, Euphálarus, widespr.; Epipsýlla, Euphyllùra, Pachypsýlla (Figs. 250, 253); Chérmes (= Psylla) cosmop. (C. pyrícola, Pear psylla)). (PSYLLÌNÆ).
                              CHERMÌNÆ
First joint of hind tarsi simple, without such spines at tip; radius, media and cubitus usually arising at a common point, the media and cubitus not stalked; wings usually angulate at apex. (Ceropsýlla, Neotrop.; Megatriòza, widespr.; Paratriòza, Neotrop.; Triòza, cosmop.). (Figs. 242, 245, 249)...........TRIOZÌNÆ

47. Wings transparent, though sometimes colored, the hind wings smaller than the fore pair; tarsi with the basal joint sometimes much reduced, empodium greatly reduced or absent; body not mealy but sometimes with waxy wool; life cycle very complicated, including agamic and sexual generations, of dissimilar appearance. Plant lice, Aphids. (Superfamily APHIDÒIDEA).....48
Wings usually opaque, whitish, clouded, or mottled with spots or bands, the two pairs of wings subequal in size; the two tarsal joints subequal, usually a pad-like or spine-like process (empodium) between the tarsal claws; body of adult more or less mealy with fine, white, powdery wax, body of the scale-like legless nymphs not covered with powder, but often with marginal plates of wax. White flies.................ALEYRÓDIDÆ

a. Empodium spine-like; fore wings with vein Cu undeveloped. (Aleuródicus (Fig. 247), Dialeuródicus, Leonárdius, Paraleyròdes, Udamóselis, Neotrop.). (*ALEURODICÌNÆ*).

UDAMOSELÌNÆ

Empodium blade-like; fore wings with vein M undeveloped. (**Aleyròdes** (Figs. 252, 256, 257), **Aleurochìton, Aleurocánthus** (Fig. 248), **Neomaskiélla**).................ALEYRODÌNÆ

48. Fore wings with outer part of stigma bounded behind by vein R_1, the radial sector separate (Fig. 259); sexual females oviparous, summer parthenogenetic females viviparous; new-born with anterior pronotal pleural bristles absent.......................49

Fore wings with outer part of stigma bounded behind by the fused vein $R_1 + Rs$ (Figs. 254, 255), both the sexual and agamic females oviparous; first tarsal joint with two bristles; cornicles wanting; newly born with three-jointed antennæ and with anterior pronotal pleural bristle present.............................50

49. Parthenogenetic and oviparous females and usually males also with functional rostrum, able to suck sap and to defecate; oviparous females producing two or more eggs, rarely one; cornicles rarely absent .... APHÍDIDÆ

a. New-born individuals with four bristles on basal tarsal joint; head free, not fused with prothorax, adults with vertex margined; labium five-jointed; cornicles broadly conical to pore-like, rarely absent. (**Láchnus** (Pine aphids), **Cínara, Euláchnus, Tràma**).

LACHNÌNÆ

New-born individuals with two bristles on basal joint of tarsus; labium four-jointed; cornicles pore-like to elongate cylindrical, rarely absent; head of adult with vertex not margined.........b

b. Head free; newly born with faceted eyes; hind tibiæ of oviparous female thickened. (**Àphis** (Fig. 258), (*A. gossýpii*, Cotton aphis, *A. màidis*, Corn aphis, *A. pòmi*, Green apple aphis), **Rhopalosìphum, Toxóptera** (*T. gráminum*, Green bug of wheat); **Chaitóphorus; Saltusàphis; Callípterus; Pterocómma; Anuràphis** (*A. bàkeri*, Clover aphis, *A. màidi-rádicis*, Corn root aphis, *A. pérsicænìger*, Black peach aphis); **Cryptosìphum; Brachýcolus** (= *Brevicorýne*) **Hyalópterus; Liosomàphis; Amphoróphora** (= *Illinoia*); **Macrosìphum** (= *Siphonóphora*) (Fig. 259) (*M. solanifòlii*, Potato aphis); **Mỳzus** (*M. pérsicæ*, Green peach aphis); **Phòrodon** (*P. hùmuli*, Hop aphis))........................APHIDÌNÆ

Head fused with prothorax, the eyes located midway on the head, eyes of new-born with three facets; hind tibiæ of oviparous females not thickened c

c. Underside of antennæ with oval or rounded secondary sensoria; radial sector of fore wings arising at the base of the elongate stigma, cell R_1 therefore long; sexual forms small, the female laying a number of eggs. (Míndarus (Fig. 260), Anomalàphis, Theláxes). (*MINDARÌNÆ*) .... THELAXÌNÆ

Antennæ with narrow transverse sensoria; radial sector of fore wings arising from the stigma; wing veins much reduced so that the media is usually simple; cornicles usually absent or much reduced; sexual forms usually apterous and of small size; species usually producing galls; wax glands usually present. (Hormàphis, Ceratàphis, Hamamelístes) .... HORMAPHIDÌNÆ

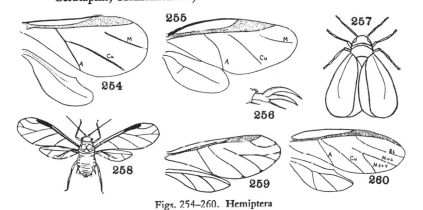

Figs. 254–260. Hemiptera

254. **Phylloxera**, wings (Patch) Phylloxeridæ.
255. **Adelges**, wings (Patch) Adelgidæ.
256. **Aleyrodes**, tarsus (Quaintance) Aleyrodidæ.
257. **Aleyrodes** (Bemis) Aleyrodidæ.
258. **Aphis** (Chittenden) Aphididæ.
259. **Macrosiphum**, wings (Patch) Aphididæ.
260. **Mindarus**, wings (Patch) Aphididæ.

Parthenogenetic females with functional rostrum, sexual forms greatly reduced and with no mouth parts; oviparous females producing only one egg; cornicles much reduced or absent; wax glands abundantly developed; wing venation usually reduced; antennal sensoria prominent .... ERIOSOMÁTIDÆ

a. Anal tergite of new-born with four bristles, new-born agamic individuals with four bristles on other tergites also; sexual individuals produced in the spring. (Fórda, Aploneùra, Melàphis, Pemphigélla) .... FORDÌNÆ

Anal tergite of new-born with four bristles, the other tergites with bristles forming six rows; sexual individuals produced after midsummer. (Eriosòma (*E. lanígerum*, Woolly aphis of apple), Asìphum, Pemphìgus, Procíphilus, Schizoneùra (*S. úlmi*, Elm aphis)) .... ERIOSOMATÌNÆ

50. Wings when at rest held roof-like, vein Cu of fore wing distant from first anal vein; antennæ of wingless agamic females three-jointed, of sexual forms four-jointed, of winged forms five-jointed; sexual as well as parthenogenetic females with beak; wingless agamic females secrete a waxy flocculence. Infesting only conifers; formerly known as *Chermes* .... ADÉLGIDÆ

   a. Abdomen with five pairs of spiracles, the first not evident; new-born fundatrix with ring-like dorsal wax glands. (Pinèus, Pineòdes, Dreyfùsia.) .... PINEÌNÆ

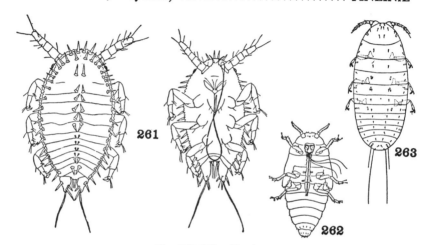

Figs. 261–263.   Hemiptera

261. **Phylloxera,** dorsal and ventral views. (Doten) Phylloxeridæ.
262. **Phylloxera,** nymph, ventral view (Simanton) Phylloxeridæ.
263. **Phœnicococcus,** larva (Morrison) Cylindrococcidæ.

   Abdomen with six pairs of spiracles, the first not evident; agamic young of two kinds, either (a) delicate summer forms, the first generation usually winged, with short rostrum, moulting four times, and not overwintering, or (b) chitinized, wingless, winter form, with long rostrum, moulting three times, which rest over summer and are active in fall. (**Adélges** (Fig. 255) (= *Cnapha-lòdes*), **Gilletteélla, Sacchiphántes**) .... ADELGÌNÆ

   Wings when at rest laid flat upon the abdomen, veins Cu and 1A fused at base forming a Y-vein; antennæ three-jointed; parthenogenetic females with beak, sucking but not defecating; sexual forms without beak; wingless agamic females not secreting a waxy flocculence, but in *Phylloxera* they secrete a waxy powder.

(**Phylloxèra** (*P. vastàtrix*, Grape phylloxera) (Figs. 254, 261, 262), Acanthochérmes, Moritziélla, Xerophýlla (*X. caryæcaulis*, Hickory phylloxeran)) . . . . **PHYLLOXÉRIDÆ**

51. Abdominal spiracles present in all stages; adult male usually with compound eyes 52
    Abdominal spiracles wanting in all stages; adult male without definite compound eyes, *i.e.* without clusters of facets in hemispherical or other shape. 53

52. Larva and all female stages with a distinctly developed flat anal ring bearing pores and six setæ; adult male with simple nine-jointed antennæ, with a rather conspicuous seta at extreme tip of apical joint; penis sheath of adult male appearing strongly bivalved. (Orthèzia, tropicopolitan). . . . . **ORTHEZÌIDÆ**
    None of the stages with a flat anal ring bearing pores and setæ; adult male nearly always with simple ten-jointed antennæ, rarely with pectinate antennæ or with more than ten joints; penis sheath of adult male mostly entire, or merely cleft at apex, at most with short bilobate tip, in which case the compound eyes are poorly developed. (*MARGARÓDIDÆ*). . . . .**MONOPHLÉBIDÆ**

a. Adult female with tarsi two-jointed (Fig. 278), rarely the legs reduced to a small unsegmented protuberance; disk-like simple pores present; intermediate female legless; halteres of male with four to six long curved apical bristles (Fig. 279). Widespread. (**Matsucóccus**, Palæarc. (Figs. 279, 282); **Stigmacóccus**, Neotrop. (Figs. 278, 285, 286); **Xylocóccus**, Nearc.) . . . .**XYLOCOCCÌNÆ**
    Adult female with tarsi one-jointed, legs, if reduced, with some segmentation; disk-like simple pores wanting. . . . . .b

b. Adult female with six to twelve large knobbed bristles surrounding and surpassing the tarsal claw (Fig. 283); antennæ contiguous at base; intermediate females legless; male with eyes reduced to a row of facets or even to a single facet. Holarctic. (**Stein-gèlia**, Palæarc.; **Stomacóccus**, Nearc.) . . . .**STEINGELIÌNÆ**
    Adult female usually with two bristles on tarsal claw, if more than two the bristles are short and acute; antennæ often close together but not contiguous at base; male with well developed compound eyes c

c. Adult female with dorsal anus, anal tube relatively well developed and provided with a simple proximal ring; intermediate female with antennæ and legs fully developed, anal tube with ring and anal opening distinctly dorsal; male tibiæ, tarsi and front femora with bifurcate setæ, middorsal area of thorax with an unchitinized area, and abdomen with one or more pairs of fleshy marginal tassels. (**Drósicha**, widespr.; **Icèrya**, tropicopol. (Figs. 267, 280); **Llavèia**, Neotrop., Indomal.; **Monóphlebus**, Indomal.; **Palæocóccus** (Fig. 268), widespr.; **Steatocóccus**) . . . .**MONOPHLEBÌNÆ**

Adult female with the anal tube, if well developed and with proximal ring, apical in position, if the anal opening is subapical the tube is poorly developed or wanting........................d

d. Adult female usually with disk pores in a band or plate within the thoracic spiracles, if without these the front legs enlarged and fitted for digging; intermediate female legless; male legs without bifurcate bristles, middorsal area of thorax chitinized. (Callipáppus, Austr.; Kuwània, Palæarc.; Margaròdes, widespr.).
MARGARODÌNÆ

Adult female usually with disk pores or pore plate external to, but never within the thoracic spiracle; intermediate female with antennæ and legs usually reduced but still segmented; male tibiæ, tarsi and front femora with bifurcate bristles; middorsal area of thorax unchitinized. Principally Neotropical and Australian. (Cœlostomídia, Austr.; Cryptokérmes, Neotrop.; Marchalìna).
CŒLOSTOMIDIÌNÆ

53. Abdomen of female and of nymphs terminating in a compound pygidium; anal opening simple; body covered by a secreted thin shield-like scale. Scale insects............................54

Abdomen of female and of nymphs not having the posterior segments fused to form a definite pygidium contrasting with the anterior segments; anal orifice often setiferous; body not covered by a thin shield-like scale.................................55

54. Scale covering constructed around the first moulted skin; pygidium of the covered insect definitely formed of the fused terminal segments contrasting with the anterior segments of the abdomen, pygidium of the first instar larva bearing two long anal setæ; legs and six-jointed antennæ present during the crawling stage but atrophied after the insect becomes sessile; beak one-jointed.
DIASPÍDIDÆ

a. Scale of adult female or second nymphal female more or less elongate or sometimes rounded, with exuviæ at one end, if nearly circular the exuviæ near margin or when central not concentrically superposed; exuvia of first nymphal female with the remains of antennæ showing as porrect appendages.....................b

Scale of adult and second nymphal female nearly circular, the exuviæ central, if elongate the exuviæ concentrically superposed, not projecting beyond margin of scale or attached at margin; exuvia of first nymphal female never showing remains of antennæ. (Aspidiòtus, widespr. (Fig. 266) (A. (Comstockáspis) perniciòsus, San José scale); Chrysómphalus, widespr.; Targiònia, widespr.) .... ASPIDIOTÌNÆ

b. Scale of female nearly circular, with nipple central or excentric, rarely projecting beyond margin of scale; male scale elongate, with almost parallel sides. (Aulacáspis, widespr. (Figs. 270, 271)

(*A. ròsæ*, Rose scale); **Diáspis**, widespr. (*D. bromèliæ*, Pineapple scale; *D. piricola*, Pear scale); **Howárdia**, widespr.).

DIASPIDÌNÆ

Scale of female not circular, but pyriform to linear, at least twice as long as wide, rarely, in certain gall-making species, the scale is reduced to a lining of the gall...........................c

c. Male scale elongate, very unlike the broader female, usually tricarinate and white or pale-colored...........................d

Male scale essentially similar in form and structure to that of the female ....e

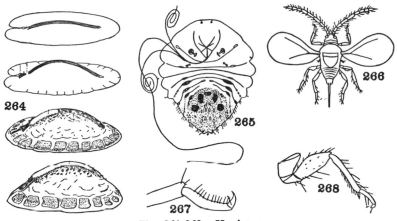

Figs. 264–268. Hemiptera

264. **Lecanium**, growth stages of female scale. Lecaniidæ.
265. **Diaspis**, female (Howard) Diaspididæ.
266. **Aspidiotus**, male (Howard) Diaspididæ.
267. **Icerya**, tarsus of female (Riley) Monophlebidæ.
268. **Palæococcus**, hind leg. Monophlebidæ.

d. Female scale with exuviæ small, not forming the greater part of the scale. (**Chionáspis**, widespr. (Figs. 272, 273, 274) (*C. fúrfura*, Scurfy scale; *C. pinifòliæ*, Pine leaf scale); **Hemichionáspis**, widespr., mainly Indomal., **Phenacáspis**, widespr.; **Poliáspis**, Ethiop., Indomal.) ....**CHIONASPIDÌNÆ**
Female scale elongate (Fig. 269), formed in greater part by the puparium (nymphal exuvia which encloses the adult); secreted part of scale thin. (**Adiscofiorínia**, Ethiop., Indoaustr.; **Fiorínia**, Indoaustr. (Fig. 269); **Trullifiorínia**, Indoaustr.)..**FIORINIÌNÆ**
e. Pygidium usually edged with a continuous series of lobes and wide fringed processes (pectinæ), rarely with pointed narrow plates;

preanal median group of wax glands often wanting, when present rarely with more than eight glands; scale white or whitish...f
Pygidium of adult female or of second nymphal stage usually with
   pointed narrow plates, and pectinæ at most with narrow shafts;
   scale of adult female with second exuvia small, rarely covering
   half of scale; usually more than eight preanal wax glands; scale

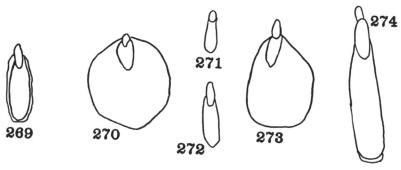

Figs. 269–274.   Hemiptera

269. Fiorinia, female, outline of scale. Diaspididæ.
270. Aulacaspis, female, outline of scale. Diaspididæ.
271. Aulacaspis, male, outline of scale. Diaspididæ.
272. Chionaspis, male, outline of scale. Diaspididæ.
273. Chionaspis, broad female scale. Diaspididæ.
274. Chionaspis, narrow female scale. Diaspididæ.

dark colored. Oyster-shell scales. (**Coccomýtilus**, widespr.; **Lepi-
dósaphes** (=*Mytiláspis*), widespr. (Fig. 277) (*L. bécki*, Citrus
purple scale; *L. úlmi*, Oyster-shell scale); **Pinnáspis**, Am., Indomal.; **Scrupuláspis**, Palæarc., Indoaustr.)..**LEPIDOSAPHÌNÆ**
f. Scale of adult female elongate, often pyriform, sometimes with
   parallel sides, formed mainly of the large puparium or nymphal
   exuvia which encloses the adult; male scale not carinate; basal
   segments of abdomen without lateral projections. (**Leucáspis**,
   widespr.; **Suturáspis**, widespr.).............**LEUCASPIDÌNÆ**
Scale of adult female round with small marginal exuviæ, or sub-
   quadrangular with large exuviæ, or elongate with terminal
   exuviæ; puparium usually converted into the second exuvia;
   basal segments of abdomen with lateral projections. (**Crypto-
   parlatòria**, Palæarc., Austromal.; **Gymnáspis**, widespr.; **Parlatòria**,
   widespr. (*P. blánchardi*, Date palm scale); **Syngenáspis**, widespr.
                                                     PARLATORIÌNÆ
Scale covering not containing the exuviæ of the early moults, pygidial
   segments less completely fused; legs present, even in adult female,
   tibio-tarsal suture obsolete; antennæ of adult female three-jointed;

beak two-jointed. (**Concháspis**, Neotrop., Ceylon (Fig. 276); **Fasisùga**, Chile; **Scutàre**, Neotrop.) . . . . CONCHASPÍDIDÆ

55. Female with posterior end cleft; anus closed by a pair of dorsal plates; larvæ also with the anal cleft bounded on each side by a prominent seta-bearing lobe or plate; beak one-jointed; wax glands very rarely paired to resemble the figure 8; body of adult female sometimes greatly convex, bare or encased in waxy or cottony secretion. (**Ceroplástes**, cosmop. (*C. ceríferus*, Indian wax scale); **Lecànium**, cosmop. (Fig. 264) (*L. córni*, Brown scale; *L. hespéridum*, Soft brown scale; *L. pérsicæ*, Peach scale); **Lecaniópsis**, **Neolecànium**, Am.; **Physokérmes**, Nearc.; **Pulvinària**, widespr. (*P. vìtis*, Cottony maple scale); **Saissètia**, widespr. (*S. òleæ*, Black scale); **Toumeyélla**) . . . . LECANÌIDÆ
Anal end of abdomen not medially cleft, if apparently cleft and provided with lobes some of the microscopic wax glands are paired to resemble the figure 8 56

56. End of abdomen more or less narrowed or prolonged into a tubular anal projection; beak two-jointed. Species inhabiting galls, or enclosed in wax 57
Abdomen not narrowed at tip or prolonged into an anal protuberance 58

57. Insects enclosed in a mass of resinous cells, each cell with three adjacent openings; adult female legless, body globular or subconical, with mouthparts at one end and three tubular processes at the opposite end, one of the projections bearing the anus and the other two the mesothoracic spiracles. Lac insects. (**Láccifer** (= *Tachárdia*), Ind.; **Tachardiélla**, widespr.; **Tachardìna**, Ethiop.). (*TACHARDÌIDÆ*) . . . . LACCIFÉRIDÆ
Insects forming galls. Usually on Eucalyptus trees; adult female segmented, top-shaped, with at least one pair of legs, or segmentation obsolete, head and thorax globular, abdomen reduced to a tubercle, and legs and antennæ wanting. Australian. Peg-top Coccids. (**Apiomórpha**, **Áscelis**, **Cystocóccus**, **Opisthóscelis**). (*BRACHYSCÉLIDÆ*) . . . . APIOMÓRPHIDÆ

58. Wax glands distributed largely in pairs resembling the figure 8, generally arranged in rows; beak one-jointed; anal ring provided with setæ; legs of adult female vestigial or wanting. (**Asterolecànium**, **Cerocóccus** (Fig. 281), **Lecaniodiáspis**, widespr.; **Ollíffia**, Austr.) . . . . ASTEROLECANÌIDÆ
Wax glands not seriately arranged in pairs resembling the figure 8 59

59. Antennæ of adult female eleven-jointed; male eyes consisting of eight units arranged in a circle; anal ring distinct and provided with six prominent anal ring setæ, no anal lobes or anal setæ. (**Phenacoleachia**, Austr.) . . . . PHENACOLEACHÌIDÆ

Antennæ of adult female with at most nine joints, often reduced or wanting; male eyes consisting of fewer parts, not arranged in a circle 60

60. Adult female and all nymphs with no anal ring and corresponding setæ 61
Adult female and intermediate nymphs with anal ring developed, with or without setæ, first stage nymphs with anal ring setæ . . . 62

61. Adult female with all legs present and subequal in length, their antennæ normally seven-jointed, and body deep carmine red. Cochineal insects. (**Cóccus,** widespr. (orig. Am.); **Epicóccus,** Austr.) . . . . **CÓCCIDÆ**

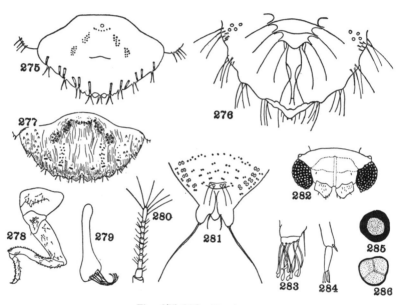

Figs. 275–286.   **Hemiptera**

275. **Lepidosaphes,** pygidium of adult female (Green) Diaspididæ.
276. **Conchaspis,** pygidium of adult female (Green) Conchaspididæ.
277. **Lepidosaphes,** pygidium of adult female (Quayle) Diaspididæ.
278. **Stigmacoccus,** leg of adult female (Morrison) Monophlebidæ.
279. **Matsucoccus,** halter of male (Morrison) Monophlebidæ.
280. **Icerya,** antenna of female (Riley) Monophlebidæ.
281. **Cerococcus,** pygidium of adult female (Green) Asterolecaniidæ.
282. **Matsucoccus,** male, dorsal view of head (Morrison) Monophlebidæ.
283. **Steingelia,** tip of tarsus of female (Morrison) Monophlebidæ.
284. **Rhizococcus,** tip of tibia and tarsus (Packard) Diaspididæ.
285. **Stigmacoccus,** simple disk pore (Morrison) Monophlebidæ.
286. **Stigmacoccus,** trilobate disk pore (Morrison) Monophlebidæ.

Adult female with some or all legs wanting, or when all legs present the hind pair are two or three times as long as the others; antennæ, if present, with less than seven joints, often vestigial or wanting. Southern hemisphere. (Apiocóccus, Neotrop.; Cylindrocóccus, Austr.; Halimocóccus, Ethiop.; Ourocóccus, Austr.). (*IDIOCÓCCIDÆ*) ....CYLINDROCÓCCIDÆ

62. Anal ring and distinct anal ring setæ present in young and adult females, anal lobes present. (Antònia, Eriocóccus, Phenacóccus, widespr.; Gossypària, Holarc., Austr. (*G. spùria*, Elm bark louse); Pseudocóccus (=*Dactylòpius*), cosmop. Mealy bugs; Triónymus, Holarc.). (*PSEUDOCÓCCIDÆ, DÁCTYLOPIÌNÆ*).
ERIOCÓCCIDÆ

Adult female rarely with anal ring, female nymphs with anal ring and anal ring setæ, anal lobes not formed; adult female berry-like or gall-like, living on oaks. (Kérmes (=*Kermocóccus*), Holarc., Austr.). (*HEMICOCCÌNÆ*).........KERMÉSIDÆ

63. Head freely articulated with the thorax; fore wings membranous, with veins and cross veins that enclose numerous cells. Terrestrial. (Pelorídium, Neotrop.; Xenophỳes, Hemiodœcus, Austr.).
PELORIDÌIDÆ

Head more or less completely fused with the thorax, not movable; upper wings very thick, covering the whole abdomen; scutellum short and broad; aquatic. (Plèa, widespr.)...........PLÈIDÆ

SUBORDER HETERÓPTERA
(*HEMÍPTERA, RHYNCHÒTA*, part)

Terrestrial or aquatic species ranging from minute to large size; usually more or less flattened or cylindrical; feeding on the juices of plants or animals. Head free, bearing a sucking, inflexed, jointed beak which is usually inserted toward the front end of the head; antennæ with few joints, those of the terrestrial species usually long; in the aquatic forms very short. Prothorax large, free; mesothorax and metathorax firmly united; scutellum very large. Wings overlapping on the abdomen, the fore pair (hemelytra) tough at the base and membranous apically, the hind pair with large anal field, the venation much reduced and irregular, wings sometimes reduced or absent; legs of variable form, tarsi usually three-jointed, rarely reduced to two, or one joint. Abdomen with ten visible segments, frequently the sternites are larger than the tergites; no cerci. Metamorphosis incomplete. True Bugs.

1. Antennæ as long as or longer than the head, usually free, rarely (Phymatidæ) fitting in a groove under the sides of the prothorax, if the antennæ are slightly shorter than the head the eyes and ocelli are absent; tarsal claws with or without arolia. (*GEO-CÓRISÆ*). GYMNOCÉRATA 2

Antennæ shorter than the head, usually (except Ochteridæ) hidden in cavities beneath the eyes; meso- and metasternum composite, metasternal gland openings absent; tarsal claws without arolia; aquatic or hygrophilous species. (*HYDROCÓRISÆ*). CRYPTO-CÉRATA 49

2. Eyes and generally also the ocelli present (eyes small in *Aepophilus*, Couplet 13) 3
   Both eyes and ocelli wanting; scutellum not formed...........58

3. Claws apical, the last tarsal joint with entire tip...............4

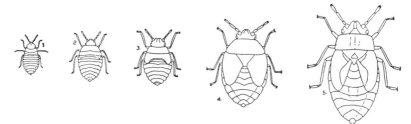

Fig. 287.   Hemiptera

Piesma, developmental stages. Five larval instars, 1–5. (Barber) Piesmidæ.

Claws of at least front tarsi distinctly anteapical, the apex of the last tarsal joint more or less cleft; hind coxæ distant; upper wings of uniform texture, the clavus, corium and membrane confluent; underside of body with silvery, velvety pubescence; aquatic, surface-living. Water striders, Jesus-bugs. (Superfamily GERRÓIDEA) 48

4. Head shorter than thorax including the scutellum; body rarely very narrow 5
   Body linear; head horizontal, as long as the entire thorax and widened toward the apex; legs slender; upper wings with corium and membrane not separate; wings often absent; antennæ four-jointed. Marsh-treaders. (**Hydrómetra** (=*Limnóbates*), cosmop.) (Figs. 288, 289). (*LIMNOBÁTIDÆ*).....**HYDROMÉTRIDÆ**

5. Antennæ four-jointed, disregarding minute intermediate ring-joints or antenniferous tubercles on the head which are sometimes present; head not shield-like, the antennæ visible from above....6
   Antennæ with five principal joints..........................42

6. Upper wings more or less lace-like in appearance, the small reticulate cells usually with membranous center; body with reticulate sculpturing; tarsi two-jointed; small, more or less flattened

bugs, less than five mm. in length. Lace-bugs. (Superfamily TINGÒIDEA) 7
Upper wings and body not so reticulate; ocelli usually present.....8

7. Middle lobe of head (tylus) not extending forward as much as the side lobes (juga), the head appearing bifid in front; ocelli present; upper wings with the membrane not reticulate but the remainder reticulately punctate; pronotum not covering the scutellum. (Piésma (Fig. 287))...................PIÉSMIDÆ
Side lobes of head not prominent; ocelli absent; upper wings entirely reticulate; pronotum with an angular process extending over the scutellum and often with an anterior hood more or less covering the head. (Phatnòma, Cantácader, widespr.; Acalýpta, Corýthucha (Fig. 291), Galeàtus, palæarc., Indomal.; Gargáphia, Gelchóssa). (TINGÍDIDÆ, TINGÍTIDÆ)........TÍNGIDÆ

8. Tarsal claws devoid of basal pads (arolia), if very rarely the arolia are present (Miridæ, Reduvioidea) the meso- and metasternum are composite or the front legs are raptorial.................9
Tarsal claws always provided with arolia; proboscis generally four-jointed; meso- and metasternum simple.....................33

9. Antennæ whip-like, the basal two joints very short, last two joints long and very slender, pilose, the third joint thickened at the base; ocelli present; proboscis three-jointed; tarsi three-jointed; veins of upper wings forming cells; small or minute species. (Superfamily DIPSOCORÒIDEA) 10
Third antennal joint not thickened at base, the second joint often longer than the third or equal to it, rarely shorter............11

10. Head more or less extended horizontally, or slightly bent down; proboscis long; eyes small; front coxal cavities not prominent. (Ceratocómbus, Crescéntius, Ind.). (CERATOCÓMBIDÆ, CRYPTOSTEMMÁTIDÆ) ....DIPSOCÓRIDÆ
Head transverse, inflexed between the prominent front coxæ; costa of fore wings not fractured. (Hypselosòma (= Glyptocómbus)). SCHIZOPTÉRIDÆ

11. Meso- and metasternum composite, formed of more than one piece, very rarely the sutures obsolete, in which case the clypeus is triangulate (Cimicidæ); cuneus of the fully winged forms more or less distinct; hind coxæ hinged (except in a few Miridæ) (Superfamily CIMICÒIDEA) 12
Meso- and metasternum simple, formed of a single piece; hind coxæ rotating with a ball and socket joint (except in Saldidæ)..19

12. Proboscis three-jointed; upper wings, when developed, with an embolium; when the wings are vestigial no ocelli are present. (Compare also Microphysidæ, couplet 18, some of which have three-jointed proboscis, but no embolium).......................13
Proboscis four-jointed 16

13. Metapleuræ without glands; body not broadly oval and thorax not flattened; occurring under stones along Atlantic coast of Europe. (Aepóphilus) ....AEPOPHÍLIDÆ
Metapleuræ with glands...................................14
14. Wings vestigial; clypeus triangular, broader apically; ocelli absent; parasitic on man, bats and birds. Bedbug family. (Cìmex (*C. lectulàrius*, Bedbug) (Figs. 292, 295), Primicìmex, Nearc., Hæmatosìphon). (*ACANTHÌIDÆ* of authors, *CLINOCÓRIDÆ*) ....CIMÍCIDÆ

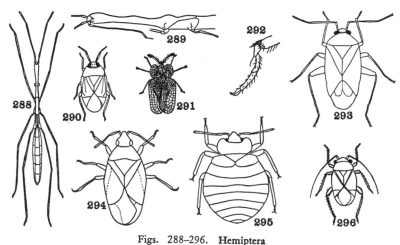

Figs. 288–296. Hemiptera

288. **Hydrometra** (Miall) Hydrometridæ.
289. **Hydrometra,** profile of anterior portion of body (Hungerford) Hydrometridæ.
290. **Isometopus** (Heidemann) Isometopidæ.
291. **Corythucha** Tingidæ.
292. **Cimex,** tip of tibia and tarsus (Eysell) Cimicidæ.
293. **Lygus** (MacGregor) Miridæ.
294. **Triphleps** (MacGregor) Anthocoridæ.
295. **Cimex** (Patton and Cragg) Cimicidæ.
296. **Halticus** (Distant) Miridæ.

Wings usually well developed; sides of clypeus parallel or sub-parallel; ocelli present; proboscis three-jointed................15
15. Membrane of fore wings with many distinct veins; antennæ long and thin; proboscis long; gland opening of metathorax small; legs long and thin, similar; eyes large and bulging; moderately large species. (Velocípeda, Indomal.).......VELOCIPÉDIDÆ
Membrane with few veins, legs not lengthened; small species. Minute pirate-bugs. (Anthócoris, Tríphleps, cosmop. (*T. insidiòsus*, Predatory flower-bug)). (Fig. 294)......ANTHOCÓRIDÆ

16. Ocelli of both sexes absent; tarsi three-jointed (exceptionally two-jointed in a few Miridæ)..................................17
Ocelli present; membrane of upper wings with one or two small basal cells 18

17. Proboscis with basal joint scarcely longer than wide, not extending backward beyond middle of eyes; membrane of upper wings with a single large quadrangular cell. (Hesperophỳlum, Termatophỳlum) .... TERMATOPHÝLIDÆ
Proboscis with basal joint longer than broad, usually reaching beyond hind margin of head; membrane with two, sometimes one, small cells near base, rarely with irregular free veins. Leaf-bugs, Plant-bugs. (Hálticus (Fig. 296), Psállus, Calócoris, Pœcilocápsus, Irbísia, widespr.; Lỳgus (Fig. 293), (L. praténsis, Tarnished plant-bug), Mìris, cosmop.; Cápsus, Camptóbrochis, Palæarc., Indomal.). (CÁPSIDÆ) ....MÍRIDÆ [1]

a. Tarsi with a pair of arolia present...........................b
Arolia absent, at most two thin bristly hairs present between the tarsal claws ....h

b. Arolia well separated at base, or arising next to the base of the claws c
Arolia closely approximate at base, usually narrow and ribbon-like..f

c. Pronotum anteriorly with a transverse collar, separated by an impressed groove, at least at the sides........................d
Pronotum simple, without a collar anteriorly..................e

d. Loræ distinctly separated from the genæ as a linear sclerite; last tarsal joint not widened; tibiæ finely spinulose
DICYPHÌNÆ, part
Loræ and genæ confluent; last tarsal joint swollen; tibiæ without spinules ....BRYOCORÌNÆ, part

e. Loræ distinctly separated from the genæ; tibiæ usually spinose.
PHYLÌNÆ, part
Loræ and genæ confluent; last tarsal joint swollen.
BRYOCORÌNÆ, part

f. Arolia bowed outward, then converging at tips..ORTHOTYLÌNÆ
Arolia divergent from base to tip..........................g

g. Tarsal claws sharply bent near the base; arolia broadened.
DICYPHÌNÆ, part
Tarsal claws more or less arcuate or bent at the middle or beyond,
MIRÌNÆ

h. Prothorax with a transverse impression anteriorly, at least at the sides, defining a collar......................................i
Prothorax simple ....PHYLÌNÆ, part

[1] A number of rather ill-defined subfamilies are generally recognized.

i. Tarsal claws stout, usually sharply curved or bent, with a tooth or internal swelling at the base..............................j
Tarsal claws simple, slender; usually porrect at tips....**CYLAPÌNÆ**

j. Pronotum with a distinct, complete collar....................k
Pronotum with a collar indicated only at the sides.
CLIVINEMÌNÆ

k. Fore wings in great part hyaline............**DICYPHÌNÆ**, part
Fore wings not hyaline; tarsal claws often with two bristles between them at base.............................**DERÆOCORÌNÆ**

18. Tarsi two-jointed; proboscis normally four-jointed, the third joint very small, or three-jointed. (**Mallochìola, Cyrtostérnum, Pachytársus,** Indomal.) ....**MICROPHÝSIDÆ**
Tarsi three-jointed. (**Cortícoris, Díphleps, Isometòpus,** Palæarc., Indomal. (Fig. 290), **Myiómma**)..............**ISOMETÓPIDÆ**

19. Front legs not raptorial; prosternum without medial stridulation groove; head rarely cylindrical...........................20
Front legs more or less raptorial; prosternum usually with a median transversely striated or granulated stridulation groove in front of the front coxæ; pronotum with a transverse groove; head cylindrical; proboscis three-jointed, fitted for piercing, rarely with an extra very short basal joint, the first joint stout and usually curved. (Superfamily REDUVIÒIDEA)...........28

20. Ocelli absent; proboscis three-jointed or apparently so when the basal joint is minute; body flat, adapted for living under bark. (Superfamily ARADÒIDEA) 21
Ocelli present, when rarely absent the proboscis is four-jointed and the head is not apically widened......................23

21. Proboscis arising before the end of the head and lying in a groove between the cheeks....................................22
Proboscis terminal, not lying in a ventral groove. (**Isodérmus,** Austr., Neotrop.; **Procympiùtus,** Austr.)......**ISODÉRMIDÆ**

22. Head not wide behind the eyes, which are prominent; proboscis longer than the head; trochanters very short, fusing with the femora; abdominal spiracles placed near the base of the segments. (**Áradus, Brachyrhýnchus,** cosmop.; **Eumenòtes,** Indomal. (Fig. 297), **Carvéntus,** Neotrop., Indoaustr.)............**ARÁDIDÆ**
Posterior part of head wide, enclosing the eyes, often spinose; proboscis rarely longer than the head; trochanters distinct; abdominal spiracles remote from the base of the segments. (**Aneùrus, Mezìra, Neuróctenus**). (*MEZÍRIDÆ*)........**DYSODÌIDÆ**

23. Membrane of upper wings destitute of veins, more or less confluent with the membranous clavus................................26
Membrane furnished with four or five long closed cells, the clavus more or less distinct.....................................24

24. Abdominal spiracles on the sternites.......................25

Abdominal spiracles on the tergites. (Léptopus, Vallerìola, Erianòtus, Old World) .... LEPTOPÓDIDÆ
25. Eyes contiguous with the pronotum. Shore bugs. (Sálda, cosmop.; Sáldula, Pentácora (Fig. 299)). (ACANTHIÌDÆ of some authors) .... SÁLDIDÆ
Eyes not reaching the margin of the pronotum. (Leótichus, Ind.).
LEOTÍCHIDÆ

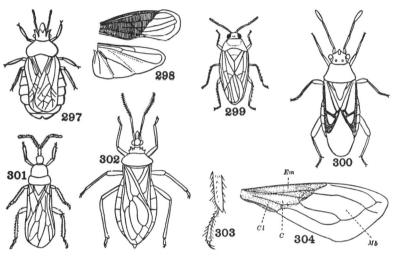

Figs. 297–304. Hemiptera
297. Aradus (Howard) Aradidæ.
298. Pentatomid bug, wings (Handlirsch) Pentatomidæ.
299. Pentacora (Torre Bueno) Saldidæ.
300. Corizus (Hambleton) Corizidæ.
301. Henicocephalus (Maxwell-Lefroy) Henicocephalidæ.
302. Triatoma (Chagas) Reduviidæ.
303. Reduvius, tip of tibia and tarsus (Eysell) Reduviidæ.
304. Triatoma, wing (Patton and Cragg). Em., embolium; Cl., C., corium; Mb., membranaceous area. Reduviidæ.

26. Ocelli approximated; semiaquatic bugs 27
Ocelli widely separated; flattened, oblong-oval bugs with large porrect head. (Fig. 310). (Xylastodòris (Royal-palm bug)). (THAUMASTOCÓRIDÆ) .... THAUMASTOTHERÌIDÆ
27. Antennæ long and slender; body narrow; tarsi three-jointed, the basal joint minute; corium submembranaceous with elevated veins. (Mesovèlia, widespr.) .... MESOVELÌIDÆ
Basal two joints of antennæ thicker than the others; body robust, not over 2.5 mm. in length; tarsi two-jointed; head and thorax grooved beneath; body densely clothed with velvety pile. (Mer-

ragàta; Hèbrus, widespr.) (*NÆOGEIDÆ*). (See couplet 42).

HÉBRIDÆ, part

28. Pronotum divided into three lobes; head constricted at the base and behind the eyes, swollen between; upper wings wholly membranous, with longitudinal veins and a few crossveins; front tibiæ swollen; front tarsi one-jointed, hind tarsi two-jointed; minute, delicate species. (**Henicocéphalus,** cosmop. (Fig. 301), **Systellóderes**). (*ENICOCEPHÁLIDÆ*) ....**HENICOCEPHÁLIDÆ**
    Pronotum simple, often large and broad, or long and narrow; head not constricted at the base behind the eyes...................29

29. Antennæ elbowed, slender, filiform or often very thin apically....30
    Antennæ short, with the last joint swollen or enlarged; membrane with the veins joined, frequently forked and uniting; tarsi two-jointed; front legs very stout, raptorial, the front femora greatly thickened. (**Phýmata** (Ambush-bug); **Macrocéphalus; Amblythỳreus,** Indomal.; **Carcinócoris,** Indoaustr.). (*MACROCEPHÁLIDÆ*) ....**PHYMÁTIDÆ**

   a. Scutellum large; rounded apically; sides of head and propleura not grooved for the reception of the antennæ.

MACROCEPHALÌNÆ

   Scutellum small, triangular; sides of head and propleura grooved for the reception of the antennæ..............**PHYMATÌNÆ**

30. Prosternum with a cross-striated median stridulation groove; proboscis three-jointed 31
    Prosternum without a stridulation groove; proboscis usually four-jointed, rarely three-jointed............................32

31. Front coxæ short; rather robust species, the body not linear; ocelli usually present; front legs raptorial, but not greatly modified. Assassin bugs. (**Acantháspis,** Ethiop., Indomal.; **Apiomèrus** (*A. cróssipes,* Bee assassin); **Arìlus** (*A. cristàtus,* Wheelbug); **Melanoléstes** (*M. pícipes,* Kissing-bug); **Redùvius,** Palæarc., Ethiop., Indoaustr. (Fig. 303); **Sìnea,** Holarc.; **Triátoma** (= *Conorhìnus*) widespr. (*T. sanguisùga,* Big bedbug) (Figs. 302, 304); **Oncocéphalus, Harpáctor, Piràtes,** widespr.)........**REDUVÌIDÆ**

   a. Membrane with three simple veins; hamus absent; body extremely flattened .... **ELASMOCORÌNÆ**
   Membrane with one or more closed cells.....................b

   b. Base of abdomen produced towards meta-sternum to form a trichome; last two antennal segments each inserted before apex of preceding segment; hamus absent.........**HOLOPTILÌNÆ**
   Base of abdomen without a trichome; last two antennal segments inserted at apices of preceding segments....................c

   c. Under surface of head moderately to strongly produced on either side throughout its length, forming a more or less distinct rostral groove ....d

Under surface of head without a buccal groove.................e

d. Ocelli absent; apical three antennal segments usually slender; body usually clothed with a dense tomentum.
TRIBELOCEPHALÌNÆ

Ocelli present; apical three antennal segments not long and slender; body without a dense vestiture of apically curved hairs.
PHIMOPHORÌNÆ

e. Anterior coxæ elongated, usually at least four times longer than wide and usually extending well beyond apex of head; long slender insects with hemelytra almost entirely membranous; front legs raptorial .... **BACTRODÌNÆ**

Anterior coxæ shorter, usually less than twice as long as broad and not extending beyond apex of head; usually broader insects with well differentiated clavus, corium, and membrane and without greatly modified front legs..............................f

f. Pronotum constricted behind the middle....................g

Pronotum constricted at or near the middle...................h

g. Ocelli present; front and middle tibiæ not curved apically, provided with spongy fossæ at their apices.................**PIRATÌNÆ**

Ocelli absent; front tibiæ curved apically and produced beyond insertion of tarsi as a stout spine; spongy fossæ absent..**VESCIÌNÆ**

h. Ocelli always absent...i

Ocelli present except in rare brachypterous forms...............j

i. Second rostral segment swollen at base; membrane with at least two closed cells .... **SAICÌNÆ**

Second rostral segment not swollen at base; membrane with only a single large cell........................... **CHRYXÌNÆ**

j. Cubitus branching to form an additional four- to six-angled cell between corium and membrane...........................k

Cubitus simple, not forming such an extra cell................m

k. Cubital cell usually hexagonal; first antennal segment stout, porrect; abdomen with only two scent glands........ **STENOPODÌNÆ**

Cubital cell usually quadrangular; first antennal segment usually relatively slender; abdomen with three scent glands...........l

l. First antennal segment short, but little longer than head; ocelli often farther apart than eyes; claws simple .... **APIOMERÌNÆ**

First antennal segment usually longer than head; ocelli usually closer together than eyes; claws dentate or appendiculate.
HARPACTOCORÌNÆ

m. Second antennal segment subdivided into from eight to thirty pseudo-segments; eyes located posteriorly, the ocelli placed between them ....**MICROTOMÌNÆ**

Second antennal segment not subdivided; ocelli located behind the
compound eyes ....n

n. Head rarely transversely constricted behind the eyes, the ocelli
usually located on oblique elevations at postero-lateral angles of
the long, cylindrical head; dorsal abdominal scent gland openings
absent .... TRIATOMÌNÆ
Head transversely constricted behind the eyes; abdominal scent
glands present ....o

o. Eyes strongly pedunculate.....................CETHERÌNÆ
Eyes not stalked or pedunculate...............................p

p. Antennæ inserted anteriorly or, more commonly, laterally but not
on long, anteriorly projecting tubercles.........REDUVIÌNÆ
Antennæ inserted on prominent, anteriorly projecting tubercles at
front of head..q

q. Front tarsi two-segmented; middle and hind tarsi three-segmented.
SALYAVATÌNÆ
All tarsi three-segmented...................SPHÆRIDOPÌNÆ

Front coxæ greatly elongated; body greatly elongated, the middle
and hind legs long and thin, the front legs highly raptorial;
ocelli absent. Thread-legged bugs. (Bárce, Ploiària (=Émesa),
widespr.; Myióphanes, Palæarc., Indoaustr.; Stenolæmus, Gárdena,
widespr.). (EMÉSIDÆ) ....PLOIARÌIDÆ

32. Legs slender, the front pair strongly raptorial; tarsi three-jointed;
membrane of upper wings with more or less distinctly branched
veins, or with two or three longitudinal cells emitting radiating
veins. Damsel-bugs. (Nàbis (= Coríscus, = Reduvìolus), cosmop., Págasa) .....:...........................NÁBIDÆ

a. Metathoracic scent gland ostioles not visible between middle and
hind coxæ ....PACHYNOMÌNÆ
Metathoracic scent gland ostioles distinct with well developed, transverse canals between middle and hind coxæ.................b

b. Abdomen narrowed at base; ovipositor reduced; hamus absent.
ARACHNOCORÌNÆ
Abdomen broad at base; ovipositor well developed, the seventh
sternite cleft; hamus present...............................c

c. Front coxal cavities closed behind....................GORPÌNÆ
Front coxal cavities open behind............................d

d. Pronotal collar reduced; clavus narrowed posteriorly, the commissure
shorter than scutellum....................PROSTEMMÌNÆ
Pronotal collar broad and distinct; clavus broadened posteriorly, the
commissure longer than scutellum.................NABÌNÆ

Legs short, tarsi two-jointed; membrane with four free veins.
(Joppèicus, Palæarc.) ....JOPPEÍCIDÆ

33. Membrane of upper wings with many longitudinal veins which often unite; antennæ inserted well up on the sides of the head; ocelli present. (Superfamily COREÒIDEA) 34

Membrane usually with a few veins, if many branching veins are present the ocelli are absent. (Superfamily LYGÆÒIDEA, et al.) 36

34. Fourth dorsal segment of the abdomen constricted medially; gland openings of the metathorax usually obsolete, if rarely visible, placed behind the hind coxal cavities and emitting two divergent grooves. (Córizus, cosmop. (Fig. 300); Harmóstes; Serinètha, Ethiop., Indomal.) . . . . CORÍZIDÆ

Basal margin of fourth and fifth dorsal segments of the abdomen usually sinuate in parallel manner; gland openings of metathorax almost always distinct 35

35. Head much narrower and shorter than the prothorax, cheeks usually reaching behind the insertion of the antennæ; exterior margin of hind coxal cavities nearly parallel with axis of the body. (Ánasa (Figs. 306, 307, 311, 312) (A. trístis, Squash-bug); Leptoglóssus, widespr. (Fig. 305) (L. phýllopus, leaf-footed bug); Acanthócoris, Stenocéphalus, widespr.; Homœócerus, Ethiop., Palæarc., Indomal.; Míctis, widespr.; Anoplocnèmis, Ethiop., Indomal.) . . . . COREÍDÆ

Head nearly as broad and long as the prothorax, wider than the front margin of the pronotum; cheeks scarcely extending behind the base of the antennæ; exterior margin of the hind coxal cavities more or less transverse. (Álydus, Leptocórisa (L. trivittàta, Boxelder bug), widespr.; Cùru, Neotrop., Indomal.; Pròtenor, Stachyocnèmus). (CORÍSCIDÆ) . . . . ALÝDIDÆ

36. Ocelli present 37
    Ocelli absent 41

37. Wing membrane without veins 38
    Wing membrane with veins 39

38. Wings when present long and narrow, without distinct veins; slender species with long, thin antennæ and abdomen narrowed at base. Indoaustr. and Neotrop. (Colobathrístes, Perùda, Phænacántha, Málcus) . . . . COLOBATHRÍSTIDÆ

Fore wings with a number of closed cells basally, but without veins on the membrane. (Macrovèlia, Nearc.) . . . . MACROVELÌIDÆ

39. Antennæ not elbowed; head not constricted in front of the eyes . . . 40
    Antennæ elbowed, the first joint long and clubbed, the last joint spindle-shaped; head constricted in front of the eyes; scutellum small; femora clubbed; body and legs extremely slender. Stilt bugs. (Jálysus, widespr.; Nèides, Metacánthus, Palæarc., Indomal.). (BERÝTIDÆ) . . . . NEÍDIDÆ

40. Veins of membrane usually four or five in number and not forming anteapical cells. (**Geócoris, Nýsius,** cosmop. (False chinch-bug); **Graptostèthus,** Palæarc., Ethiop., Indomal.; **Oncopéltus, Lygæus, Ligyrócoris** (Fig. 313), **Lygæosòma,** widespr.; **Blíssus** (*B. leucópterus,* Chinch-bug (Fig. 308))). (*GEOCÓRIDÆ, MYODÓCHIDÆ*) .... **LYGÆIDÆ**

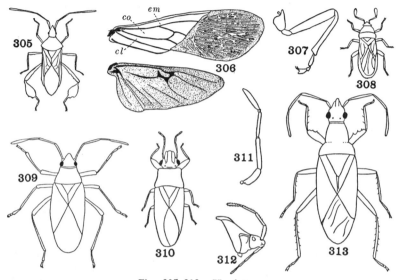

Figs. 305–313. Hemiptera

305. **Leptoglossus** (Chittenden) Coreidæ.
306. **Anasa,** wings (Tower) Corcidæ.
307. **Anasa,** leg (Tower) Coreidæ.
308. **Blissus** (Webster) Lygæidæ.
309. **Dysdercus** (Barber) Pyrrhocoridæ.
310. **Xylastodoris** (Barber) Thaumastocoridæ.
311. **Anasa,** antenna (Tower) Coreidæ.
312. **Anasa,** lateral view of prothorax and head (Hyatt and Arms) Coreidæ.
313. **Ligyrocoris** (Barber) Lygæidæ.

Veins of membrane four in number, arising distinctly from the corium, forming three large preapical cells and thence branching. (**Hyocéphalus,** Austr.) .... **HYOCEPHÁLIDÆ**

41. Membrane of upper wings with two large basal cells which emit seven or eight branching veins; stout bugs of moderate size. (**Dysdércus,** widespr. (Fig. 309) (Cotton stainers); **Physopélta,** widespr.; **Euryophthálmus; Pyrrhócoris,** Palæarc., Ind.; **Éctatops, Antílochus,** Ethiop., Indoaustr.)............ **PYRRHOCÓRIDÆ**

Membrane with few veins forming one or two basal cells. (See couplet 17) ....MÍRIDÆ, part

42. Upper wings with the clavus membranous and confluent with the membrane which is devoid of veins; head and thorax grooved beneath; antennæ with the two basal joints stouter than the others; tarsi two-jointed; small, semiaquatic bugs. (See couplet 27). (Hèbrus (=Næogeus), widespr.)................HÉBRIDÆ

Upper wings with the clavus noticeably heavier than the membrane; antennæ with the first joint thickened, the second joint slender; head more or less expanded, the side margins acute in front of the eyes and thickened above the base of the antennæ; ocelli present; scutellum large or very large; terrestrial. (Super-family SCUTELLERÒIDEA.) (PENTATOMÒIDEA) 43

43. Scutellum excessively large, U-shaped and convex, covering the greater part of the abdomen; opaque part of the corium much narrowed toward the apex....................................44

Scutellum nearly always narrowed behind, more or less triangular; opaque part of the corium subtriangular, broad apically. (If the scutellum is entirely hidden, not extending beyond metathorax, cf. Yang, 1935, the imperfectly known TAHÍTOCÓRIDÆ)...47

44. Tibiæ not armed with strong spines..........................45

Tibiæ with two or more rows of distinct spines. Negro-bugs. (Corimelæna (=Thyreócoris)). (THYREOCÓRIDÆ).
CORIMELÆNIDÆ

45. Fore wings about twice as long as the abdomen, folded at the middle and at rest tucked under the scutellum; tarsi two-jointed. (Brachýplatys, Ethiop., Indoaustr.; Coptosòma, Old World; Platáspis, Palæarc.). (COPTOSÒMIDÆ, PLATÁSPIDÆ).
PLATASPÍDIDÆ

Fore wings of normal length, not folded; tarsi nearly always three-jointed 46

46. Sides of the prothorax without a strong tooth or lobe in front of the humeral angles and another on the front angles; hind wings with a heavy, abrupt, spur-like vein (hamus). Shield-back bugs. (Eurygáster, Holarc.; Homæmus, widespr.; Scutéllera, Chrysócoris, Pœcilócoris, Indomal.)...............SCUTELLÉRIDÆ

Sides of the thorax with a prominent tooth or lobe in front of both the humeral and the front angles; eyes protuberant; hind wings with no hamus. (Arctócoris, Palæarc.; Oncozýgia, Pòdops, widespr.). (GRAPHOSOMÁTIDÆ) ....PODÓPIDÆ

47. Tibiæ strongly spinose, front legs fossorial; veins of the membrane radiating from the base. (Aèthus, widespr.; Geótomus, Cýdnus, cosmop.; Brachypélta, Palæarc., Ethiop., Indoaustr.; Cyrtómenus, Pangæus) .... CÝDNIDÆ

Tibiæ unarmed, or at most with weak spines, front legs not fossorial; veins of membrane extending from a vein which arises near the inner basal angle and lies nearly parallel with the edges of the corium. Stink-bugs. (Brochýmena, Cosmopépla, Euschístus (Fig. 315), Murgántia (*M. histriónica*, Harlequin cabbage-bug); Pentátoma, Períbalus, Podìsus, Catacántha (Fig. 314))

PENTATÓMIDÆ

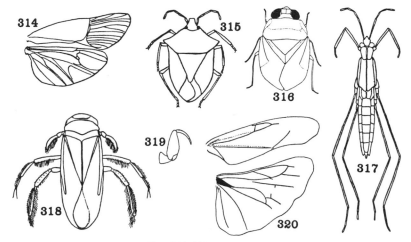

Figs. 314–320.   Hemiptera

314. **Catacantha**, wings (Kirkaldy) Pentatomidæ.
315. **Euschistus**. Pentatomidæ.
316. **Ochterus** (Garman) Ochteridæ.
317. **Gerris** (Miall) Gerridæ.
318. **Corixa** (Miall) Corixidæ.
319. **Corixa**, front leg (Kolbe) Corixidæ.
320. **Corixa**, wings (Handlirsch) Corixidæ.

48. Hind femora extending much beyond the apex of the abdomen, the posterior pairs of legs arising close together and very distant from the front pair; proboscis four-jointed, but the first joint short. (Gérris, cosmop. (Fig. 317); Halóbates, tropicopol.; Rheumatóbates; Onychótrechus, Chimarrhómetra, Indomal.). (*HYDROBÁTIDÆ*) .... GÉRRIDÆ
Hind femora not extending much beyond the apex of the abdomen (except *Rhagovelia*); middle legs about midway between the front and hind pairs (except *Rhagovelia*); proboscis three-jointed. Broad-shouldered water-striders. (Microvèlia, Rhagovèlia, cosmop.; Vèlia, Am., Palæarc.) .... VELÌIDÆ
49. Head articulated with the thorax as usual or at most partly fused with it; tarsi with more than a single joint 50

Head completely fused with the thorax, the boundary more or less indicated by a shallow impression; antennæ one- or two-jointed; eyes located rather dorsally; proboscis four-jointed; no distinct venation; all tarsi with two claws; male genitalia strongly asymmetrical. .... HELOTRÉPHIDÆ

Three subfamilies, probably deserving family rank, may be distinguished as follows:

a. All tarsi three-jointed. (Neótrephes, Parátrephes, Neotrop.).
NEOTREPHÌNÆ
Fore tarsi one-jointed; hind tarsi with two joints................b
b. Body flattened, suture between head and pronotum absent; antennæ one-jointed. (Idiócoris, Páskia, Ethiop.)........IDIOCORÌNÆ
Body strongly convex; suture between head and thorax visible; antennæ two-jointed. (Helótrephes, Hydrótrephes, Indomal.).
HELOTREPHÌNÆ

50. Front tarsi of the usual form...............................51
Front tarsi consisting of a single spatulate joint bearing a leaf-like claw; body flattened above; head overlapping the pronotum; proboscis very short, hidden, one- or two-jointed; middle legs long, hind legs formed for swimming; hind tarsi with indistinct bristle-like claws. Water boatmen.................CORÍXIDÆ

a. Scutellum visible from above, covered by pronotum only at anterior margin ....b
Scutellum covered by the pronotum entirely or with only the apex visible c
b. Two ocelli; antennæ four-jointed. (Diaprepócoris, Austr.).
DIAPREPOCORÌNÆ
Ocelli wanting; antennæ three-jointed. (Micronècta, Tenagòbia, widespr.) ....MICRONECTÌNÆ
c. Fore wings with an embolar groove (a deep groove next the front margin on basal half of wing)...........................d
Fore wings without embolar groove. (Stenocoríxa, Ethiop.).
STENOCORIXÌNÆ
d. Proboscis smooth, without transverse ridges; median vein in fore wing curving abruptly to the costal margin. (Cymàtia, widespr.).
CYMATIÌNÆ
Proboscis roughened by transverse ridges; median vein in fore wing usually curving posteriorly at tip to fuse with the cubitus.......e
e. Cheeks, below the eyes, very broad, lower margin of eye concave; median vein indistinct, parallel and very close to cubitus. (Heterocoríxa, widespr.) ....HETEROCORIXÌNÆ
Cheeks not broad below; median vein distinct, midway between cubital vein and costal margin, usually fused at apex with cubitus.

(Glenocórisa, Holarc.; Coríxa, cosmop. (Figs. 318, 319, 320); Graptocoríxa, Neotrop.; Agraptocoríxa, Old World). (Including *SIGÁRIDÆ* and *MICRONÉCTIDÆ*) ....**CORIXÌNÆ**

51. Upper wings of leathery consistency, with the clavus, corium and membrane developed; legs often modified for swimming or grasping 52
Upper wings transparent, the corium and membrane not separated, with longitudinal veins and crossveins that enclose numerous cells. Austr. and Neotrop. (**Pelorídium**). (See page 167).
PELORIDÌIDÆ

52. Ocelli present; proboscis four-jointed; shore-living species.......53
Ocelli absent; proboscis usually three-jointed; aquatic species.....54

53. Antennæ exposed; front legs as long as the middle pair, formed for running; small active bugs. (**Óchterus** (=*Pelógonus*), widespr., **Megóchterus**, Austr.) (Fig. 316). (*PELOGÓNIDÆ*)
OCHTÉRIDÆ
Antennæ hidden; front legs raptorial; short, broad species with prominent eyes. Toad-bugs. (**Mónonyx, Nérthra, Gelastócoris** (=*Gálgulus*)). (*GALGÚLIDÆ, GELASTOCÓRIDÆ, MONONÝCHIDÆ*) ....**NÉRTHRIDÆ**

54. Front coxæ inserted at or near the front margin of the prosternum; front legs formed for grasping; hind tarsi with distinct claws...56
Front coxæ inserted at the hind margin of the short prosternum; legs fitted for swimming, the hind tarsi without claws; upper wings strongly convex, the membrane without veins; body convex above. Back-swimmers 55

55. Hind tibiæ and tarsi ciliate; hind tarsi with only one claw; abdomen with a median carinate ridge below; beak four-jointed; eyes large. (**Notonécta**, cosmop.; **Ánisops**, widespr.; **Buénoa**, Am. (Fig. 321)).
NOTONÉCTIDÆ
Hind tibiæ and tarsi simple, not ciliate; hind tarsi with two claws; abdomen not carinate beneath; beak three-jointed; eyes small. (**Plèa**, widespr.). (See page 167) .... **PLÈIDÆ**

56. Upper wings with the membrane reticulately veined; beak with very small labial palpi..................................57
Membrane without veins; beak without labial palpi; hind coxæ hinged; hind tibiæ slender, with small spines. Water creepers. (**Heleócoris**, widespr.; **Cheirochèla**, Indomal.; **Ambrỳsus, Naucoris, Pelócoris**). (Including *APHELOCHÍRIDÆ*) ..**NAUCÓRIDÆ**

a. Proboscis as long as the front femora, slender; antennæ extending beyond the side margins of the head; front legs with the tibiæ straight, the tarsi movable..................................b
Proboscis much shorter than front femora, thickened at base; an-

tennæ completely concealed beneath margin of head; front femora much thickened, their tibiæ curved, and their tarsi not movable...c

b. Proboscis very long, reaching as far as middle coxæ, its last joint shorter than the preceding one; front tarsi three-jointed.
                                                                APHELOCHIRÌNÆ
   Proboscis reaching only to front coxæ, the last two joints subequal; front tarsi one-jointed....................**POTAMOCORÌNÆ**

c. Anterior margin of pronotum deeply emarginate medially........d
   Anterior margin of pronotum straight or scarcely concave.......f

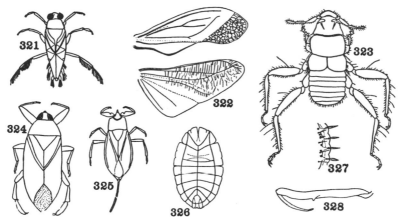

Figs. 321–328.   Hemiptera

321. **Notonecta** (Miall) Notonectidæ.
322. **Nepa,** wings (Handlirsch) Nepidæ.
323. **Polyctenes** (Westwood) Polyctenidæ.
324. **Lethocerus** (Smith) Belostomatidæ.
325. **Nepa** (Miall) Nepidæ.
326. **Termitaradus** (Myers) Termitaphididæ.
327. **Termitaradus,** marginal lobe (Myers) Termitaphididæ.
328. **Ranatra,** apical portion of front leg (Hungerford) Nepidæ.

d. Proboscis arising in a deep pit, well behind the anterior margin of the head............................... **CHEIROCHELÌNÆ**
   Proboscis arising at the anterior margin of the head.............e

e. Prosternum completely exposed, separated from the flattened pleuræ by simple sutures....................... **CRYPHOCRICÌNÆ**
   Prosternum covered behind by the propleuræ which are produced medially covering its hind part................ **AMBRYSÌNÆ**

f. Front tarsi two-jointed, with two, often vestigial claws.
                                                                LACCOCORÌNÆ
   Front tarsi one-jointed, without or with one vestigial claw.......g

g. Inner margin of eyes divergent anteriorly.....LIMNOCHORÌNÆ
Inner margin of eyes divergent posteriorly........NAUCORÌNÆ

57. Hind coxæ hinged, hind legs fitted for swimming, posterior tibiæ flattened and fringed, hind femora usually sulcate; tip of abdomen with two short, flat, retractile appendages. Giant waterbugs, Electric light bugs, Toe-biters. (Belóstoma, Benàcus, Ábedus, Lethócerus, widespr. (Fig. 324); Zàitha, Sphæródema).

BELOSTOMÁTIDÆ

Hind coxæ globular, rotating; hind legs formed for walking, not flattened; apical appendages of abdomen long and slender, not retractile, forming a respiratory siphon. Water-scorpions. (Laccótrephes, Palæarc., Indoaustr.; Cercomètus, Indomal. (Figs. 322–325); Nèpa, Ránatra, cosmop. (Fig. 328))..........NÉPIDÆ

58. Broadly oval, flat, completely wingless species; head in front with a deep median incision; clypeus without movable appendage; living in termite nests. (Termitàphis (= Termitócoris), Termitáradus (Figs. 326, 327) Neotrop.). (TERMITOCÓRIDÆ).

TERMITAPHÍDIDÆ

Body oblong, head broadly triangular with series of comb-like spines beneath; eyes and scutellum absent; upper wings vestigial; parasites of bats. (Eóctenes, Hesperóctenes, Polýctenes, widespr. (Fig. 323)) ....POLYCTÉNIDÆ

LITERATURE ON HEMIPTERA

BANKS, N. Catalogue of Nearctic Hemiptera-Heteroptera. Philadelphia, Am. Ent. Soc., 103 pp. (1910).

BERG, C. Hemiptera Argentina. Anal. Soc. Cient. Argentina, 5–34 (1878–1892) (numerous parts).

BRITTON, W. E. (Editor). Hemiptera and Homoptera of Connecticut. Connecticut Nat. Hist. Surv., Bull. No. 34, 783 pp. (1923). (Various authors).

BUTLER, E. A. A Biology of the British Hemiptera-Heteroptera. London, 695 pp. (1923).

CHAMPION, G. C. Hemiptera-Heteroptera. In Biologia Centrali-Americana, 2 (1897–1901).

DISTANT, W. L. Hemiptera-Heteroptera. In Biologia Centrali-Americana, 1 (1880–1893).

  Rhynchota in Fauna of British India, 5 vols., London (1902–10).

DOHRN, A. Catalogus Hemipterorum. Ent. Verein, Stettin, 112 pp. (1859).

GUÉRIN, J. and PENEAU, J. Faune entomologique armoricaine, Hémiptères. Trav. Sci. Univ. Rennes, 13, pp. 201–301 (1915).

HORVÁTH, G. Nomenclature des familles des Hémiptères. Ann. Mus. Nat. Hungarici, 9, pp. 1–34 (1911).

  Hemiptera. Fauna Regni Hungariæ, 1, pp. 5–64 (1918).

KIRKALDY, G. W. Hemiptera. Fauna Hawaiiensis, 3, Pt. 2 (1902); 2, Pt. 6 (1902).

LETHIERRY, L. and SEVERIN, G. Catalogue Générale des Hémiptères, 3 vols., Brussels (1893–96).

OSHANIN, B. Verzeichnis der paläarktischen Hemipteren. Ann. Mus. Zool. Acad. Imp. Sci. St. Petersbourg, 11–15 (1906–10).
Katalog der paläarktischen Hemipteren, 187 pp., Berlin (R. Friedländer und Sohn) (1912).
Vade mecum destiné a faciliter la détermination des Hémiptères. Hor. Soc. Ent. Rossicæ, 42, No. 2, pp. 1–106 (1916). (Very complete and classified list of literature.)

PENEAU, M. J. Hémiptères. In Houlbert, Encyclop. Sci., 2 yols. (1922).

STÅL, C. Bidrag till Rio Janeiro-traktens Hemipter-fauna. K. Svensk. Akad. Handl., 2 and 3 (1860–62).
Hemiptera africana, 1–4, Holmiæ (1864–66).
Hemiptera Fabriciana. Svensk. Vet. Akad. Handl., 7 and 8 (1868–69).
Enumeratio hemipterorum. Svensk. Vet. Akad. Handl., 9–15 (1870–76).

VAN DUZEE, E. P. Catalogue of the Hemiptera of America north of Mexico, except Aphididæ, Coccidæ and Aleurodidæ. Univ. California Pub. Ent., 2, 902 pp. (1917).

VILLIERS, A. Hémiptères de France. In Faune de France, fasc. 1–3, 206 pp., 24 pls. 316 figs. (1945–47).

LITERATURE ON SUBORDER HOMOPTERA
(GENERAL)

(See also General List on Hemiptera, p. 184)

COSTA LIMA, A. DA. Homopteros do Brasil. Ins. do Brasil, 3, 327 pp., 267 figs. (1942).

DISTANT, W. L. Fauna of British India, 6, 240 pp. (Homoptera appendix).

DISTANT, W. L. and W. W. FOWLER. Homoptera. In Biologia Centrali-Americana, 1 (1881–1905).

EDWARDS, J. The Hemiptera Homoptera of the British Isles. 271 pp., London (1894–96).

FOWLER, W. W. Homoptera. In Biologia Centrali-Americana, 2, pt. 1 (1894–1909).

JENSEN-HAARUP, A. C. The Danish Homoptera. Copenhagen (1920).

MELICHAR, L. Die Homopterenfauna von Ceylon. 248 pp., Berlin (1903).

METCALF, Z. P. Bibliography of the Homoptera (Auchenorrhyncha). (Authors' List and Journals). 2 vols., 1072 pp. Univ. North Carolina, Raleigh (1945).
Homoptera of Guam. Bull. Bishop Mus., 189, 58 pp. (1946).

OSBORN, H. Homoptera of Porto Rico and the Virgin Islands (Exclusive of Sternorrhyncha). Sci. Surv. Porto Rico, 14, pp. 111–260, 71 figs. (1935).

OSHANIN, B. Katalog der paläarktischen Hemipteren. 187 pp., Berlin (R. Friedländer und Sohn) (1912).
Vade mecum destiné a faciliter la determination des Hémiptères. Hor. Soc. Ent. Rossicæ, 42, No. 2, pp. 1–106 (1916). (Very complete and classified list of literature.)

VAN DUZEE, E. P. Catalogue of the Hemiptera of America north of Mexico, except Aphididæ, Coccidæ and Aleyrodidæ. Univ. California Publ. Tech. Bull. Ent., **2** (1917).

WALKER, F. List of Specimens of Homopterous Insects in the British Museum, 1–4 (1850–52); Supplement (1858) London, British Museum.

ZIMMERMAN, E. C. Homoptera. Insects of Hawaii, **4–5**, 732 pp. (1948).

CICADOIDEA

ASHTON, H. A Revision of the Australian Cicadidæ, Pt. 1. Proc. Roy. Soc Victoria, **33,** pp. 87–107 (1921).

BUCKTON, G. B. A Monograph of the British Cicadæ. 2 vols., London (1890–91).

DELETANG, L. F. Monográfia de los Cicádidos Argentinos. An. Mus. Nac. Buenos Aires, **31**, pp. 538–649 (1923).

DISTANT, W. L. Monograph of the Oriental Cicadidæ. London, 158 pp. (1889–92).

   A Synonymic Catalogue of the Cicadidæ. 207 pp., London, British Museum (1906).

   Cicadidæ, Cicadinæ. Gen. Insectorum, fasc. 142, 64 pp. (1913).

   Cicadidæ, Gæaninæ. Gen. Insectorum, fasc. 158, 38 pp. (1914).

HAUPT, H. Neueinteilung der Homoptera-Cicadina. Zool. Jahrb. Abth. f. Syst., **58**, pp. 173–286 (1929).

HORVÁTH, G. Cicadidarum genera palæarctica. Ann. Mus. Nat. Hungarici, **10**, pp. 599–609 (1912).

KATO, M. Catalogue of Japanese Cicadidæ. Trans. Nat. Hist. Soc. Formosa, **17**, pp. 19–41 (1927).

LAWSON, P. B. The Cicadidæ of Kansas. Kansas Univ. Sci. Bull., **12**, pp. 307–352 (1920).

MELICHAR, L. Die Cicadinen von Mitteleuropa. Berlin, 364 pp. (1896).

MOULTON, J. Cicadas of Malaysia. Journ. Fed. Malay States Mus., **11**, pp. 69–182 (1923).

MYERS, J. G. Insect Singers. A Natural History of the Cicadas. London, Geo. Routledge and Sons (1929). (Very complete bibliography).

OSSIANNILSSON, F. Catalogue of Cicadina of Sweden. Opusc. Ent., **13**, 25 pp. (1948).

MEMBRACOIDEA

BALL, E. D. A Monographic Revision of the Tree-hoppers of the Tribe Telamonini of North America. Ent. Americana, **12**, pp. 1–69, 4 pls., (1932).

BUCKTON, G. B. Monograph of Membracidæ. 296 pp., London (1901–03).

CALDWELL, J. S. Revision of North American Ceresini. Proc. U. S. Nat. Mus., **98**, No. 3234, pp. 491–521 (1949).

EVANS, J. W. On the Classification of Membracidæ. Trans. Roy. Ent. Soc. London, **99**, pp. 497–515 (1948).

FUNKHOUSER, W. D. Review of the Philippine Membracidæ. Philippine Journ. Sci., **10D**, pp. 365–405 (1915).

   Membracidæ. Gen. Cat. Hemip. fasc. 1 (1927) Smith College, Northampton, Mass.

Membracidæ of Guatemala. Ann. Ent. Soc. America, **36**, pp. 455–482, 2 pls. (1943).

Membracidæ. Gen. Insectorum, fasc. **208**, 383 pp., 14 pls. (1950).

GODING, F. W. Catalogue of Membracidæ of North America. Bull. Illinois State Lab. Nat. Hist., **3**, pp. 391–482 (1892).

A Monograph of the Australian Membracidæ. Proc. Linn. Soc. New South Wales, **38**, pp. 2–41 (1903).

Classification of the Membracidæ of America. Journ. New York Ent. Soc., **34**, pp. 295–317 (1926).

Revision of the Membracidæ of South America and the Antilles. Journ. New York Ent. Soc., **35**, pp. 183–191 (1927).

The Membracidæ of South America and the Antilles. Pt. 4, Trans. American Ent. Soc., **55**, pp. 197–330 (1929).

The Old World Membracidæ. Journ. New York Ent. Soc., **39**, pp. 299–313, 606 (1931); **42**, pp. 451–480 (1934); **47**, pp. 315–349 (1939).

LAWSON, P. B. Membracidæ of Kansas. Kansas Univ. Quarterly, **13**, pp. 29–110(1922).

RICHTER, O. Contribucion al conocimiento de los Membracidæ de Colombia. II–IV. Caldasia, **3**, pp. 41–48; **5**, pp. 41–49, 15 figs.; **6**, pp. 81–112 (1941–42).

VAN DUZEE, E. P. Review of North American Membracidæ. Bull. Buffalo Soc. Nat. Sci., **9**, pp. 29–129 (1908).

CERCOPOIDEA

BAKER. C. F. Some Philippine and Malaysian Machærotidæ. Philippine Journ. Sci., **32**, pp. 529–548 (1927).

DOERING, K. Synopsis of North American Cercopidæ. Journ. Kansas Ent. Soc., **3**, pp. 53–64; 81–108 (1930).

GODING, F. W. Synopsis of Genera of North American Cercopidæ. Bull. Illinois State Lab. Nat. Hist., **3**, pp. 483–501 (1895).

LALLEMAND, V. Cercopidæ. Gen. Insectorum, fasc. 143, 167 pp. (1913).

MATSUMURA, S. Monographie der Cercopiden Japans. Journ. Sapporo Agric. Coll., **2**, p. 15 (1903) and Annot. Zool. Japonenses, **5**, pp. 31–55 (1904).

METCALF, Z. P. and G. HORTON. The Cercopoidea of China. Lingnan Sci. Journ., **13**, pp. 307–429, 7 pls., 2 figs. (1934).

PENDLEBURY, H. M. Malaysian Cercopidæ. Journ. Fed. Malay States Mus., **16**, pp. 108–118 (1930).

SCHMIDT, E. Monographie der Macherotiden. Stettiner Ent. Zeitg., **68**, pp. 165–200 (1907).

JASSOIDEA

BUYS, J. L. Cicadellidæ of Ithaca, New York. Mem. Cornell Univ. Agric. Expt. Sta., No. 80, 115 pp. (1924).

CRUMB, S. E. Partial Key to Genera of North American Jassidæ. Trans. Kansas Acad. Sci., **25**, pp. 129–137 (1914).

DE LONG, D. M. A Monographic Study of the North American Species of the Subfamily Gyponinæ. xiv + 187 pp., 35 pls. Ohio State Univ., Columbus (1942).

Leaf-hoppers or Cicadellidæ of Illinois. Bull. Illinois Nat. Hist. Surv., **24**, pp. 97–376, 514 figs. (1948).

DE LONG, D. M. and J. CALDWELL. Check List of Cicadellidæ of North America. iv + 93 pp. Ohio State Univ., Columbus (1937).

EVANS, J. W. Revision of the Ipoinæ (Eurymelidæ). Trans. Roy. Soc. South Australia, **58**, pp. 149–167, 4 figs. (1934).

The Bythoscopidæ of Australia. Pap. Proc. Roy. Soc. Tasmania, **1935**, pp. 61–83, 3 pls. (1936).

A Contribution to the Study of the Jassoidea. Pap. Proc. Roy. Soc. Tasmania, **1938**, pp. 19–55, 8 pls., 3 figs. (1939).

A Natural Classification of Jassoidea. Trans. Roy. Ent. Soc. London, **96**, pp. 47–60; **97**, pp. 39–54 (1946).

HARTZELL, A. Empoasca in North America. Proc. Iowa Acad. Sci., **30**, pp. 87–133 (1923).

JOHNSON, D. M. Leafhoppers of Ohio. 86 pp., 5 pls. (1935).

LATHROP, F. H. The Cicadellidæ of South Carolina. Bull. South Carolina Agric. Expt. Sta., **199**, 119 pp. (1919).

LAWSON, P. B. The Cicadellidæ of Kansas. Kansas Univ. Sci. Bull., **12**, No. 1, Ent., 4, pp. 1–306 (1920).

MATSUMURA, S. Monographie der Jassinen Japans. Termes. Füzetek, **25**, pp. 353–404 (1902).

Revision of the Palæarctic and Oriental Typhlocybid-Genera with Descriptions of New Species and New Genera. Ins. Matsumurana, **6**, pp. 93–120 (1932).

McATEE, W. L. The Genera of the Eupterygidæ. Proc. Biol. Soc. Washington, **31**, pp. 109–124 (1918).

Genera and Subgenera of Eupteryginæ. Proc. Zool. Soc. London, **1934**, pp. 93–117, 5 pls. (1934).

MEDLER, J. T. Cicadellidæ. Tech. Bull. Minn. Agric. Exp. Sta. No. **155**, pp. 1–196, 9 pls. (1942).

MELICHAR, L. Monographie der Cicadelliden. I–IV. Ann. Hist.-nat. Mus. Hung., **21**, pp. 195–243 (1924); **22**, pp. 329–410 (1925); **23**, pp. 273–394 (1926); **27**, pp. 285–328 (1931).

MERINO, G. Philippine Cicadellidæ. Philippine Journ. Sci., **61**, pp. 307–400, 4 pls. (1937).

METCALF, Z. P. Tettigellidæ and Gyponidæ of British Guiana. Zoologica, New York, **34**, pp. 259–282 (1949).

METCALF, Z. P. and S. C. BRUNER. Gyponidæ of Cuba. Florida Ent., **32**, pp. 90–104 (1949).

NAUDÉ, T. J. Cicadellidæ of South Africa. Ent. Mem. Dept. Agric. Pretoria, No. 4, 106 pp. (1926).

OMAN, P. W. Classification of Agallian Leaf-hoppers. Bull. U. S. Dept. Agric., No. **372**, 93 pp., 4 pls., 18 figs. (1933).

Revision of American Bythoscopinæ and South American Jassinæ. Univ. Kansas Sci. Bull., **24**, pp. 343–420, 9 pls. (1936).

OSBORN, H. The Leafhoppers of Ohio. Ohio State Univ. Bull. **32**, pp. 199–374 (1928).

Neotropical Homoptera, Part 6. (Typhlocybinæ). Ann. Carnegie Mus., **18**, pp. 253–298 (1928).

Cicadellidæ. Insects of Samoa, fasc. **2**, pp. 163–192, 15 figs. (1932).

FULGOROIDEA

BAKER, C. F. Spolia Mentawiensia: Homoptera Fulgoroidea. Philippine Journ. Sci., 32, pp. 391–412 (1927).

CALDWELL, J. S. Issidæ from Mexico. Ann. Ent. Soc. America, 38, pp. 89–120 (1945).

CRAWFORD, D. L. Monograph of American Delphacidæ. Proc. U. S. Nat. Mus., 46, pp. 557–640 (1914).

DOERING, K. C. Taxonomy of Issinæ of North America. I–IV. Univ. Kansas Sci. Bull., 24, pp. 421–467, 7 pls. (1936); 25, pp. 447–575 (1938); 26, pp. 83–167, 10 pls. (1940); 27, pp. 185–233, 6 pls. (1941).

DOZIER, H. L. The Fulgoridæ of Mississippi. Tech. Bull. Mississippi Agric. Expt. Sta., No. 14, 152 pp. (1928).

FENNAH, R. G. The Tropiduchidæ of the Lesser Antilles. Proc. Ent. Soc. Washington, 47, pp. 137–167, 2 pls. (1945).

GIFFARD, W. M. A Review of the Hawaiian Cixiidæ, with Descriptions of Species (Homoptera). Proc. Hawaiian Ent. Soc., 6, pp. 51–156 (1925).

LINDBERG, H. Materialien zu einer Monographie der Gattung Tettigometra. Notul. Ent., 28, pp. 1–40, 4 pls., 23 figs. (1948).

MATSUMURA, S. Uebersicht der Fulgoriden Japans. Ent. Nachricht., 26, pp. 205–213; 257–270 (1900).
    Beitrag zur Kenntnis der Fulgoriden Japans. Ann. Mus. Nat. Hungarici, 12, pp. 261–305 (1914).
    Die Cixiinen Japans. Annot. Zool. Jap. Tokyo, 8, pp. 393–434 (1914).

MELICHAR, L. Monographie der Ricaniiden. Ann. Hofmus. Wien, 13, pp. 197–359 (1898).
    Monographie der Acanaloniden und Flatiden. Ann. Hofmus. Wien, 16, pp. 178–258 (1901); 17, pp. 1–253 (1902).
    Monographie der Issiden. Abh. zool.-bot. Ges. Wien, 3, pp. 1–327 (1906).
    Monographie der Dictyopharinen. Abh. zool.-bot. Ges. Wien, 7, pp. 1–221 (1912).
    Monographie der Tropiduchinen. Verh. naturh. Ver. Brünn, 53, pp. 82–225 (1914).
    Monographie der Lophopinen. Ann. Mus. Nat. Hungarici, 13, pp. 337–385 (1915).

METCALF, Z. P. Fulgoridæ of Eastern North America. Journ. Elisha Mitchell Sci. Soc., 38, pp. 139–230 (1923).
    Catalogue of Tettigometridæ. Fasc. IV, Cat. Hemiptera, Northampton, Mass., Part 1, 69 pp. (1932).
    Catalogue of Cixiidæ. Ibid, Part 2, 269 pp. (1936).
    Catalogue of Aræopidæ (Delphacidæ). Ibid, Part 3, 552 pp. (1943).
    Catalogue of Derbidæ. Ibid, Part 4, pp. 11–212 (1945).
    Catalogue of Achilixiidæ. Ibid, Part 5, pp. 213–218 (1945).
    Catalogue of Meenoplidæ. Ibid, Part 6, pp. 219–238 (1945).
    Catalogue of Kinnaridæ. Ibid, Part 7, pp. 239–252 (1945).
    Catalogue of Dictyopharidæ. Ibid, Part 8, 246 pp. (1946).
    Catalogue of Fulgoridæ. Ibid, Part 9, 276 pp. (1947).
    Catalogue of Achilidæ. Ibid, Part 10, 85 pp. (1948).

Fulgorina of Panama. Bull. Mus. Comp. Zool., **82**, pp. 277–423, 23 pls. (1938).

Bibliography of Homoptera Auchenorryncha. 2 vols. 1672 pp. Raleigh, North Carolina (1945).

METCALF, Z. P. and S. C. BRUNER. Acanaloniidæ and Tropiduchidæ of Cuba. Psyche, **37**, pp. 407–417 (1930).

Cuban Flatidæ. Ann. Ent. Soc. America, **41**, pp. 63–118 (1948).

MUIR, F. Derbidæ of the Philippine Islands. Philippine Journ. Sci., **12D**, pp. 49–104 (1917).

Classification of the Fulgoroidea. Proc. Hawaiian Entom. Soc., **5**, pp. 205–247 (1922).

South American Fulgoroidea, Pt. 1, Delphacidae. Bull. Hawaiian Sugar Planters' Exp. Sta., No. 18 (1926).

Classification of the Fulgoroidea. Ann. Mag. Nat. Hist. (10), **6**, pp. 461–478 (1930).

MUIR, F. and W. M. GIFFARD. Studies in North American Delphacidæ. Entom. Bull. Hawaiian Sugar Planters' Expt. Sta., No. 15, 53 pp. (1924).

OSBORN, H. Fulgoridæ of Ohio. Bull. Ohio Biol. Surv., **35**, pp. 283–349, 42 figs. (1938).

VAN DUZEE, E. P. Review of North American Delphacidæ. Bull. Buffalo Soc. Nat. Sci., **5**, pp. 225–261 (1897).

CHERMOIDEA

AULMANN, G. Psyllidarum catalogus. 92 pp. W. Junk, Berlin (1913).

BLÖTE, A. C. Overzicht der Nederlandsche Psyllidensoorten. Tijdschr. Entom., **69**, pp. 57–84 (1926).

CRAWFORD, D. L. Monograph of Psyllidæ of the New World. Bull. U. S. Nat. Mus., **85**, 186 pp. (1914).

The Psyllidæ of the Hawaiian Islands. Proc. Hawaiian Entom. Soc., **3**, pp. 430–457 (1918).

PFLUGFELDER, O. Psyllina (Chermoidea). In Bronn, Klass. u. Ordnungen des Tierreichs, **5**, Abt. 3, Buch VIII, pp. 1–95, 75 figs. (1941).

TUTHILL, L. D. The Psyllids of America North of Mexico. Iowa State Coll. Journ. Sci., **17**, pp. 443–667, 19 pls. (1943).

ALEYRODOIDEA

BAKER, A. C. and M. L. MOLES. Aleyrodidæ of South America. Rev. Chilena Hist. Nat., **25**, pp. 609–648 (1923).

BEMIS, F. E. Aleurodidæ of California. Proc. U. S. Nat. Mus., **27**, pp. 471–537 (1904).

CORBETT, G. H. Malayan Aleurodidæ. Journ. Fed. Malay States Mus., **17**, pp. 722–852, 105 figs. (1935).

DREWS, E. A. and W. W. SAMPSON. List of Genera of Aleyrodidæ. Bull. Brooklyn Ent. Soc., **35**, pp. 90–99 (1940).

MASKELL, W. M. Contributions toward a Monograph of the Aleurodidæ. Trans. New Zealand Inst., **28**, pp. 411–449 (1896).

QUAINTANCE, A. L. Aleyrodidæ. Gen. Insectorum, fasc. 87, 11 pp. (1908).

QUAINTANCE, A. L. and A. C. BAKER. Classification of the Aleyrodidæ. Bull. Bur. Entom., U. S. Dept. Agric. Tech. Ser., No. 27, 109 pp. (1913).
A Contribution to our Knowledge of the Aleyrodinæ. Proc. U. S. Nat. Mus., 51, pp. 335–445 (1917).

RUSSELL, L. M. North American Species of Trialeurodes. Misc. Publ. U. S. Dept. Agric., No. 635, 85 pp., 34 figs. (1948).

SAMPSON, W. W. A Generic Synopsis of the Aleyrodoidea. Ent. Americana, 23, pp. 173–223 (1943).

SAMPSON, W. W. and E. A. DREWS. Fauna Mexicana — IV. Review of Aleyrodidæ of Mexico. An. Esc. nac. Cienc. biol. Mexico, 2, pp. 143–189, 24 figs. (1940).

SINGH, K. Aleyrodidæ of India. Mem. Dept. Agric. India, 12, pp. 1–98, 37 pls. (1931).

TAKAHASHI, R. Aleyrodidæ of Formosa. Rept. Dept. Agric. Formosa, 4 parts, 59, 57 pp. (1932); 60, 24 pp., 15 figs. (1933); 63, pp. 39–71, 22 figs. (1934); 66, pp. 39–65 (1935).

APHIDOIDEA

ANNAND, P. N. A Contribution toward a Monograph of the Adelginæ (Phylloxeridæ) of North America. Stanford Univ. Publ. Biol. Sci., 6, pp. 1–146 (1928).

BAKER, A. C. A Generic Classification of the Hemipterous Family Aphididæ. Bull. U. S. Dept. Agric., 826, pp. 1–109 (1920).

BLANCHARD, E. E. Estudio sistematico de los Afidoideos argentinos. Physis, 17, pp. 857–1003 (1939).

BÖRNER, C. Das System der Phylloxerinen. Zool. Anz., 33, pp. 600–612 (1908).
Monographische Studie über die Chermiden. Arb. Kais. biol. Anst. Land. Forstwirtsch., 6, Pt. 2 (1908).
Beiträge zu einem neuen System der Blattläuse. Arch. Klass. Phylog. Ent., 1, pp. 115–194 (1930).

BUCKTON, G. B. A Monograph of the British Aphides. 4 vols. London, Ray Soc. (1875–82).

CHOLODKOWSKY, N. Die Koniferen-Läuse Chermes. 44 pp. Berlin, Friedländer (1907).

DAVIDSON, J. A List of British Aphides. 176 pp. London, Longmans, Green & Co. (1925).

ESSIG, E. O. The Aphididæ of California. Univ. California Publ. Ent., 1, pp. 301–346 (1917).

GILLETE, C. P. and M. A. PALMER. Aphididæ of Colorado. Ann. Ent. Soc. America, 24, pp. 827–934, 100 figs. (1931).

GOOT, P. van der. Zur Systematik der Aphididen. Tijdschr. Ent., 55, pp. 69–154 (1903).

HILLE RIS LAMBERS, D. On Palestine Aphids. Trans. Roy. Ent. Soc., 99, pp. 269–289 (1948).

HOTTES, F. C. and T. H. FRISON. Aphididæ of Illinois. Bull. Illinois Nat. Hist. Surv., 19, pp. 121–447, 10 pls., 50 figs. (1931).

KIRKALDY, G. W. Catalogue of the Genera of Aphidæ. Canadian Ent., 37, 38, 40 (1905–08) (various parts).

LOMBARDI, D. Contribuzione alla conoscenza della tribu Fordina. Bull. Lab.
Zool. Gen. Agrar. Portici, **7**, pp. 149–188 (1913).
LOU, HOAI-PAO. Recherches sur la faune aphidologique de la Chine. 124 pp.,
6 figs. Lyon, Bosc Frères. (1935).
MORDVILKO, A. K. Aphidoidea. Faune Russie, Hemiptera, **1**, pp. 237–508
(1919).
Die Blattläuse mit unvollständigem Generationszyklus und ihre Ent-
stehung. Ergebnis. Zool., **8**, pp. 36–328, 217 figs. (1935).
OESTLUND, O. W. Key to Aphididæ of Minnesota. 19th Rept. Minnesota State
Entomologist, pp. 114–151, St. Paul (1923).
Systema Aphididarum. v + 78 pp. Augustana Book Concern, Rock
Island, Illinois (1942).
ROBERTI, D. Afidi d'Italia. Boll. Lab. Zool., Portici, **30**, pp. 169–238, 51 figs.
(1938).
SCHOUTEDEN, H. Catalogue des Aphides de Belgique. Mém. Soc. Ent. Belgique,
12, pp. 189–246 (1906).
TAKAHASHI, R. Aphididæ of Formosa. Pt. 1, from Agric. Expt. Sta. Govt.
Formosa (1921); Pts. 2–5, Repts. 4, 10, 16, and 22 from Govt. Res. Sta.
Formosa (1923, '24, '25, and '27).
Aphididæ of Malay Peninsula. Ann. Ent. Soc. America, **43**, pp. 587–607
(1950).
THEOBALD, F. V. Aphididæ of Great Britain. I. 372 pp. London, Headley
Bros. (1926).
TSING, S. and CHIA-CHU TAO. List of the Aphididæ of China. Ent. and
Phytopath., **4**, pp. 120–176, 3 figs. (1936).
WILSON, H. F. A Synopsis of the Aphid tribe Pterocommini. Ann. Ent. Soc.
America, **8**, pp. 347–358 (1915).
WILSON, H. F. and R. A. VICKERY. Species List of Aphididæ of World and
Food Plants. Trans. Wisconsin Acad. Sci., Arts, Letters, **19**, Pt. 1, pp. 22–
355 (1918).

COCCOIDEA

CHAMBERLIN, J. C. Systematic Monograph of the Tachardiinæ. Bull. Ent. Re-
search, **14**, pp. 147–212 (1923).
COCKERELL, T. D. A. Coccoidea. In Biologia Centrali-Americana, Homoptera,
2, Pt. 2 (1899).
FERNALD, M. E. Catalogue of the Coccidæ of the World. Bull. Massachusetts
Agric. Expt. Sta., No. 88, 360 pp. (1903).
FERRIS, G. F. Contributions to Knowledge of Coccidæ. Microentomology, **2**,
pp. 1–122, 95 figs.(1937).
Atlas of Scale Insects of North America. Stanford Univ. Press, Califor-
nia. Series 1, Nos. 1–136 (1937); Series II, Nos. 137–268 (1938); Series
III, Nos. 269–384 (1941); Series IV, Nos. 385–448 (1942); Series V,
vii + 278 pp. (1950).
FROGGATT, W. W. A Descriptive Catalogue of the Scale Insects of Australia.
Agric. Gazette New South Wales, **25** (1914) (six parts).
GOMEZ-MENOR, J. Coccidos de España. xi + 432 pp., 136 figs. Est. fitopat.
Agric. Almeria, Madrid (1937).

GREEN, E. E. The Coccidæ of Ceylon. 5 vols. London (1896–1922).
Annotated List of the Coccidæ of Ceylon. Spolia Zeylandica, **20,** pp. 277–341 (1937).

HALL, W. J. Observations on the Coccidæ of Southern Rhodesia. Bull. Ent. Res., **20,** pp. 345–376 (1929).

HEMPEL, A. As Coccidas do Brazil. Cat. Fauna Brasiliera. Rev. Mus. São Paulo, **3,** pp. 1–77 (1912).

KUWANA, I. The Diaspine Coccidæ of Japan. Imp. Plant Serv. Tech. Bulls., Nos. 1–3, 80 pp. (1925); continued in Sci. Bull. Minist. Agric. For. Japan, No. 3, 51 pp., 11 pls. (1933).

LEONARDI, G. Monografia delle Cocciniglie Italiane. 555 pp. Portici (1920).

LEPÀGE, H. S. Catalogo dos Coccideos do Brasil. Rev. Mus. Paulista, **23,** pp. 327–491 (1938).

LINDINGER, L. Die Schildläuse (Coccidæ) Europas, Nordafrikas und Vorderasiens. Stuttgart (1912).
Beiträge zur Kenntnis der Schildläuse. Konowia, **11,** pp. 177–205 (1932).
Verzeichnis der Schildlaus-Gattungen (Coccoidea). Ent. Jahrb., **1937,** pp. 178–198 (1937).

LUPO, V. Revisione delle Cocciniglie italiane. Parts i, ii, Boll. Lab. Zool. Portici, **30,** pp. 121–162, 255–322, 63 figs. (1938); Part iii, ibid., **31,** pp. 69–136, 39 figs. (1939); Part iv, Boll. Lab. Ent. Portici, **5,** pp. 206–242, 20 figs. (1944); Part v, ibid., **8,** pp. 33–79 (1947); Part vi, ibid., **8,** pp. 137–208, 203 figs. (1948).

MACGILLIVRAY, A. D. The Coccidæ. Scarab Co., Urbana, Ill. (1921).

MORRISON, H. The Non-diaspine Coccidæ of the Philippines. Philippine Journ. Sci., **17,** pp. 147–202 (1920).
Classification of Ortheziinæ. Journ. Agric. Res., **30,** pp. 97–154 (1925).

NEWSTEAD, R. A Monograph of the Coccidæ of the British Isles. 2 vols. London, Ray Soc. (1901–03).

PFLUGFELDER, O. Coccina. In Bronn, Klass. u. Ordnungen des Tierreichs, **5,** Abt. iii, Buch 8, Teil b.e., pp. 1–121, 92 figs. (1939).

RAMAKRISHNA AYYAR, T. V. South Indian Coccidæ. Bull. Agric. Res. Inst. Pusa, **197,** 78 pp., 31 pls., 9 figs. (1930).

STEINWEDEN, J. B. Bases for the Generic Classification of the Coccidæ. Ann. Ent. Soc. America, **22,** pp. 197–243 (1929).

COLEORRHYNCHA

MYERS, J. G. and W. E. CHINA. The Systematic Position of the Peloridiidæ. Ann. Mag. Nat. Hist. (10)3, pp. 282–294 (1929).

LITERATURE ON SUBORDER HETEROPTERA
(GENERAL)

(See also General List on Hemiptera, p. 184)

BARBER, H. G. Heteroptera of Porto Rico and Virgin Islands. 178 pp. (1939).

BEIER, M. Hemiptera, oder Rhynchota. In Kükenthal, Handbuch der Zoologie, **4,** Heft 2, Lief 11, pp. 2040–2140, 110 figs. (Errata); Lief 13, pp. 2141–2456; Lief 14, pp. 2457–2490 (1938).

BLATCHLEY, W. S. Heteroptera of Eastern North America. Indianapolis, Nature Pub. Co., 1116 pp. (1926).

BÖRNER, C. Ueber System und Stammesgeschichte der Schnabelkerfe. Ent. Beihefte, Berlin, 1, pp. 138–144 (1934).

CHINA, W. E. Hemiptera-Heteroptera. Insects of Samoa, 2, pp. 81–162, 28 figs. (1930).

COSTA LIMA, A. DA. Hemipteros. In Insetos do Brasil, 2, 351 pp., figs. 219–446. Esc. nac. Agron., Rio de Janeiro (1940).

FROESCHNER, R. C. Hemiptera of Missouri. Amer. Midl. Nat., 26, pp. 122–146, 3 pls., 2 figs. (1941); 27, pp. 591–609 (1942); 31, pp. 638–683, 3 pls. (1944).

GULDE, J. Die Wanzen (Hemiptera-Heteroptera) der Umgebung von Frankfurt a. M. Abh. Senckenberg. naturf. Ges., 37, pp. 329–503 (1921).
    Die Wanzen Mitteleuropas. Hemiptera Heteroptera Mitteleuropas. Teil 2, pp. 1–76, 6 figs.; Teil 3, pp. 77–194, 58 figs.; Teil 4, pp. 195–316, 66 figs.; Teil 5, pp. 1–104, 39 figs.; Teil 6, pp. 105–377, 73 figs. Frankfurt a. M. (1933–38).

JORDAN, K. H. C. Die Wanzen Mitteleuropas. Hemiptera Heteroptera Mitteleuropas. Literaturteil 1934, pp. 1–34; Teil 12, pp. 1–105, 134 figs. Frankfurt a. M. (1934–35).

LAMEERE, A. Hemiptera. In Précis de Zoologie. Publ. Inst. zool. Torley-Rousseau, 4, pp. 383–458 (1935).

LUNDBLAD, O. Die aquatilen und semiaquatilen Hemipteren von Sumatra, Java und Bali. Arch. Hydrobiol., Suppl. 12, 1–195; 263–489, 21 pls., 142 figs. (1933).

MYERS, J. G. The Order Hemiptera in New Zealand with Special Reference to its Biological and Economic Aspects. New Zealand Journ. Sci. Tech., 5, pp. 1–12 (1922).

MYERS, J. G. and W. E. CHINA. A List of New Zealand Heteroptera. Ann. Mag. Nat. Hist. (10) 1, pp. 378–388 (1928).

PARSHLEY, H. M. List of Hemiptera of New England. Occ. Pap. Boston Soc. Nat. Hist., 7, pp. 1–125 (1920).
    Bibliography of North American Hemiptera-Heteroptera. 252 pp. Smith College, Northampton, Mass. (1925).

PERRIER, R., L. BERTIN and L. GAUMONT. Hémiptères de la France. Faune de France, 4, pp. 1–126 (1935).

PUTON, A. Synopsis des Hémiptères-Hétéroptères de France, 4 vols. (1878–81).

REUTER, O. M. Hemiptera Gymnocerata Europæ. 5 vols. (1878–96).

SAUNDERS, E. The Hemiptera-Heteroptera of the British Isles. 350 pp. London (1892).

SEABRA, A. F. Sinopse dos Hemípteros Heterópteros de Portugal. Mem. Estud. Mus. Zool. Univ. Coimbra (1), No. 1, pp. 1–67 (1924–25).
    Sinopse dos Hemípteros de Portugal. Piesmidæ, Tingitidæ, Phymatidæ, Hebridæ, Mesoveliidæ. Mem. Estud. Mus. Zool. Univ. Coimbra (1), No. 1, pp. 295–457, 111 figs. (1930–31).

STICHEL, W. Illustrierte Bestimmungstabellen der deutschen Wanzen. Berlin (1927).

TAEUBER, H. W. Beiträge zur Kenntnis der Heteropteren-Fauna der Philippinen. Konowia, 6, pp. 165–201 (1927); 8, pp. 194–233 (1929).

Torre-Bueno, J. R. de la. Synopsis of the Hemiptera Heteroptera of America. Ent. Americana, 19, pp. 141–304; 21, pp. 41–122; 26, pp. 1–141 (1939–46). (Incomplete.)

Usinger, R. L. Heteroptera of Guam. Bull. Bishop Mus., 237 pp., 58 figs. (1946).

Vidal, J. Hémiptères de l'Afrique du Nord. Mém. Sci. Nat. Maroc, 48, 238 pp. (1949).

Weber, H. Biologie der Hemiptera. vii + 543 pp., 329 figs. Berlin, Springer. (1930).

Zimmerman, E. C. Heteroptera. Insects of Hawaii, 3, 255 pp. (1948).

GYMNOCERATA

SCUTELLEROIDEA

Barber, H. G. Cydnidæ of Cuba. Journ. Dept. Agric. Porto Rico, 16, pp. 231–240, 1 pl. (1932).

  Pentatomidæ of Cuba. Journ. Dept. Agric. Porto Rico, 16, pp. 240–278, 2 pls., 10 figs. (1932).

Distant, W. L. Revision of Pentatomidæ in the Hope collection. Proc. Zoöl. Soc. London, 1900, pp. 807–825 (1900).

Hart, C. A. Pentatomoidea of Illinois with Keys to Nearctic Genera. Ill. Nat. Hist. Surv. Bull., 13, pp. 157–223 (1919).

Hoffman, W. E. First Supplement to Catalogue of Scutteleroidea. Lingnan Sci. Journ., 22, pp. 1–41 (1948).

Horvath, G. Revision of the American Cimicidae. Ann. Mus. Nat. Hungarici, 10, pp. 257–262 (1912).

  Analecta ad cognitionem Cydnidarum. Ann. Mus. Nat. Hungarici, 17, pp. 205–273 (1919).

Kirkaldy, G. W. Catalogue of Hemiptera. Pentatomidæ (Cimicidæ). 392 pp. Berlin (1909).

  Generic Key to Phyllocephalinæ, Phlocinæ and Dinidorinæ (Pentatomidæ). Canadian Ent., 45, pp. 81–84 (1913).

McAtee, W. L. and J. R. Malloch. Revision of the Subfamily Thyreocorinæ (Corimelænidæ). Ann. Carnegie Mus., 21, pp. 191–412, 12 pls. (1933).

Parshley, H. M. Synopsis of the Pentatomidæ of New England. Psyche, 22, pp. 170–177 (1915).

Schouteden, H. Pentatomidæ, Scutellarinæ. Gen. Insectorum, fasc. 24, 100 pp. (1904).

  Pentatomidæ, Graphosomatinæ. Gen. Insectorum, fasc. 30, 46 pp. (1905).

  Pentatomidæ, Aphylinæ. Gen. Insectorum, fasc. 47, 4 pp. (1906).

  Pentatomidæ, Asopinæ = Amyoteinæ. Gen. Insectorum, fasc. 52, 82 pp. (1907).

  Pentatomidæ, Dinidorinæ. Gen. Insectorum, fasc. 153, 19 pp. (1913).

Signoret, V. Revision du Groupe des Cydnides. Ann. Soc. Ent. France, 1–3 (various parts) (1881–83).

Stoner, D. The Scutelleroidea of Iowa. Univ. Iowa Studies Nat. Hist., 8, No. 4, pp. 1–140 (1920).

Van Duzee, E. P. List of Pentatomidæ of America North of Mexico. Trans. American Ent. Soc., 30, pp. 1–80 (1904).

YANG, W. I. Revision of Chinese Plataspidæ. Bull. Fan Mem. Inst. Biol., 5, pp. 137–235, 42 figs. (1934).
    A New Family (Tahitocoridæ) of Heteroptera. Ann. Mag. Nat. Hist., (10) 16, pp. 476–484 (1935).
ZIMMER, J. F. The Pentatomidæ of Nebraska. Univ. Nebraska, Contr. Dept. Ent., No. 4, pp. 1–33 (1912).

COREOIDEA

DEAY, H. O. The Coreidæ of Kansas. Kansas Univ. Sci. Bull., 18, pp. 371–415 (1928).
FRACKER, S. B. Alydinæ of the United States. Ann. Ent. Soc. America, 11, pp. 255–280 (1918).
    Review of North American Coreini. Ann. Ent. Soc. America, 16, pp. 165–173 (1923).
KIRITSCHENKO, A. Coreidæ, Coreinæ. Fauna Russie Hemiptera, 6, pt. 2, pp. 1–395 (1916) (In Russian).
PENNINGTON, M. S. Notas sobre Coréidos Argentinos. Physis, Buenos Aires, 5, pp. 125–170 (1922).
SCHOUTEDEN, H. Coreidæ. Explor. Parc Not. Albert, fasc. 56, 42 pp. (1948).

GERROIDEA

BERGROTH, E. Gerridæ, Subfamily Halobatinæ. Ohio Naturalist, 8, pp. 371–382 (1908).
DRAKE, C. and H. M. HARRIS. Gerrinæ of the Western Hemisphere. Ann. Carnegie Mus., 23, pp. 179–240, 6 pls. (1934).
ESAKI, T. The Halobatinæ in the Hungarian National Museum. Ann. Mus. Nat. Hungarici, 23, pp. 117–164 (1926).
    Marine Gerridæ from Korea. Ent. Monthly Mag., 66, pp. 158–161, 4 figs. (1930).
MCKINSTRY, A. P. A New Family of Hemiptera — Heteroptera. Pan-Pacific Ent., 18, pp. 90–96, 4 figs. (1942).
POISSON, R. Contribution à l'étude des Gerris de France et de l'Afrique du Nord. Bull. Soc. sci. Bretagne, 17, pp. 140–173, 29 figs. (1941).
WHITE, F. B. Report on the Pelagic Hemiptera. Challenger Exped., Zoöl., 7, pt. 19, p. 82 (1883).

ARADOIDEA

HARRIS, H. M. and C. J. DRAKE. New Apterous Aradidæ from the Western Hemisphere. Proc. Ent. Soc. Washington, 46, pp. 128–132 (1944).
HORVÁTH, G. Monographie des Mesovéliides. Ann. Mus. Nat. Hungarici, 13, pp. 535–556 (1915).
    Mesoveliidæ. Gen. Cat. Hemiptera, pt. 2, 24 pp., Northampton, Mass., Smith College (1929).
PARSHLEY, H. M. American Species of Aradus. Trans. American Ent. Soc., 47, pp. 1–106 (1921).
REUTER, O. M. and B. R. POPPIUS. Zur Kenntnis der Termatophyliden. Öfv. Finska Vet. Soc. Förh., 54A, pp. 1–17 (1912).

USINGER, R. L. A New Philippine Leptopodid and Classification of the Family. Bull. Brooklyn Ent. Soc., **37**, pp. 103–106 (1942).

LYGAEOIDEA

BARBER, H. G. Synoptic Keys to the Lygæidæ of the United States. Psyche, **24**, pp. 128–135 (1917); **25**, pp. 71–88 (1918).

Lygæidæ of Cuba. Mem. Soc. Cubana Hist. Nat. **19**, pp. 55–75 (1947).

BARBER, H. G. and S. C. BRUNER. A New Subfamily [Pamphantinæ] of Lygæidæ. Journ. New York Ent. Soc., **41**, pp. 531–542, 2 pls. (1933).

HORVÁTH, G. Monographia Colobathristidarum. Ann. Mus. Hist. Nat. Hungarici, **2**, pp. 117–172 (1904).

HUSSEY, R. F. Pyrrhocoridæ. Gen. Cat. Hemiptera, 144 pp. Northampton, Mass., Smith College (1929).

KNIGHT, H. H. A Revision of the Genus Lygus in America North of Mexico. Bull. Cornell Agr. Exp. Sta., No. 391, pp. 555–645 (1917).

McATEE, W. L. Key to Nearctic Geocorinæ (Lygæidæ). Proc. Biol. Soc. Washington, **14**, p. 102 (1914).

Key to Nearctic Berytidæ. Journ. New York Ent. Soc., **27**, pp. 79–92 (1919).

SCHMIDT, E. Zur Kenntnis der Familie Pyrrhocoridæ. Teil II. Wiener ent. Zeit., **49**, pp, 236–281, 328 (1932).

TORRE-BUENO, J. R. DE LA. North American Lygæidæ. Ent. Americana, **26**, pp. 1–141 (1946).

TINGOIDEA

BARBER, H. G. Tingitoidea of New Jersey. Circ. New Jersey Dept. Agric. Bur. Statistics, No. 54, 24 pp. (1922).

DRAKE, C. J. Australian Tingitidæ. Bull. South. Calif. Acad. Sci., **46**, pp. 111–121, 3 figs. (1947).

The Genus Compscuta. Proc. Ent. Soc. Washington, **50**, pp. 197–204 (1948).

American Tingitidæ. Rev. Ent. Rio de Janeiro, **19**, pp. 429–436 (1948).

DRAKE, C. J. and E. J. HAMBLETON. Brazilian Tingitidæ. Rev. Ent. Rio de Janeiro, **4**, pp. 435–451, 2 figs. (1934).

DRAKE, C. J. and M. E. POOR. The Genera and Genotypes of Tingitoidea of the Western Hemisphere. Iowa State Coll. Journ. Sci., **10**, pp. 381–390 (1936).

HORVÁTH, G. Synopsis Tingitidarum regionis Palæarcticæ. Ann. Mus. Nat. Hungarici, **4**, pp. 1–118 (1906)

McATEE, W. L. Key to Piesmidæ. Bull. Brooklyn Ent. Soc., **14**, pp. 80–93 (1919).

MONTE, O. Catálogo dos Tingitídeos do Brasil. Arq. Zool. São Paulo, **2**, pp. 65–174 (1941).

OSBORN, H. and C. J. DRAKE. The Tingitoidea of Ohio. Ohio State Univ. Bull., **20**, pp. 217–251 (1916).

POOR HURD, M. Generic Classification of North American Tingidæ. Iowa State Coll. Journ. Sci., **20**, pp. 429–489 (1946).

REDUVIOIDEA

BARBER, H. G. Stenopodinæ (Reduviidæ) of America. Ent. Americana, **10**, pp. 149–238 (1930).

BRUNER, S. C. Sinopsis de los Redúvidos de Cuba. Mem. Soc. Cubana Hist. Nat., **7**, pp. 65–82 (1926).

ESAKI, T. and T. ISHIHARA. Nabidæ of Micronesia. Mushi, **15**, pp. 69–75 (1943).

EVANS, J. H. Revision of North American Phymatidæ. Ann. Ent. Soc. America, **24**, pp. 711–736, 2 pls. (1931).

FRACKER, S. B. Reduviidæ of North America. Proc. Iowa Acad. Sci., **19**, pp. 217–247 (1912).

HANDLIRSCH, A. Monographie der Phymatiden. Ann. Hofmus. Wien, **12**, pp. 127–230 (1897).

HARRIS, H. M. A Monographic Study of the Hemipterous Family Nabidæ in North America. Ent. Americana, **9**, pp. 1–90 (1928).

HOFFMAN, W. E. Catalogue of Reduviidæ of China. Lingnan Univ. Sci. Bull., No. **10**, 80 pp. (1944).

JOHANNSEN, O. A. North American Henicocephalidæ. Psyche, **16**, pp. 1–4 (1909).

LENT, H. Genus Rhodnius. Rev. Brasil., Biol., **8**, pp. 297–339, 47 figs. (1948).

LENT, H. and P. WYGODZINSKY. Reduviinæ Americanos. Rev. Brasil., Biol., **7**, pp. 423–434 (1947).

Key and Notes on Reduviidæ. Ibid., **8**, pp. 43–55, 54 figs. (1948).

McATEE, W. L. and J. R. MALLOCH. Revision of the Ploiariinæ (Reduviidæ). Proc. U. S. Nat. Mus., **67**, Art. 1, 135 pp. (1925).

MILLER, N. C. E. New Genera and Species of Malaysian Reduviidæ. Journ. Fed. Malay States Mus., **18**, pp. 415–599, 126 figs.; 601–804, 175 figs. (1941).

New Genera and Species of Reduviidæ [Pacific Islands]. Trans. Roy. Ent. Soc. London, **99**, pp. 411–473 (1948).

NEIVA, A. and H. LENT. Notas e commentarios sobre Triatomideos. Lista de especies e sua distribução geográphica. Rev. Ent., Rio de Janeiro, **6**, pp. 153–190 (1936).

PINTO, C. Ensaio Monográphico dos Reduvideos hæmatóphagos o "Barbieros." 118 pp. Rio de Janeiro (1925).

Classification des genres de la famille Triatomidæ. Bol. Biol. São Paulo, fasc. 8, pp. 103–114 (1927).

READIO, P. A. Biology of the Reduviidæ of America North of Mexico. Sci. Bull. Univ. of Kansas, **17**, pp. 1–248 (1927).

REUTER, O. M. Monographia Nabidarum orbis terrestris. Acta Soc. Sci. Fennica, **37**, pp. 1–62 (1909).

USINGER, R. L. Miscellaneous Studies in the Henicocephalidæ (Hemiptera). Pan-Pacific Ent., **8**, pp. 145–156, 1 pl. (1932).

Classification of Reduvioidea, with a New Subfamily from South America. Ann. Ent. Soc. America, **36**, pp. 602–618 (1943).

The Triatominæ of North and Central America and West Indies. Public Health Bull., No. **288**, 83 pp., 12 pls. (1944).

Classification of the Enicocephalidæ. Ann. Ent. Soc. America, **38**, pp. 321–342 (1945).

VILLIERS, A. Morphologie et systematique des Tribelocephalitæ africains. Rev. française Ent., **10**, pp. 1–28, 53 figs. (1943).

WYGODZINSKY, P. Contribuçáo áo conhecimento do género Elasmodemia. Rev. brasil. Biol., **4**, pp. 193–213, 56 figs. (1944).

POLYCTENOIDEA

COSTA LIMA, A. Insectos da Familia Polyctenidæ. Arch. Esp. Agric. Med. Vet. Nictheroy, **4**, pp. 61–71 (1920).

FERRIS, F. F. and R. L. USINGER. The Family Polyctenidæ. Microentomology, **4**, pp. 1–50, 25 figs. (1939).

    Notes and Descriptions of American Polyctenidæ. Pan-Pacific Ent., **21**, pp. 121–124 (1945).

HORVÁTH, G. Description of a New Bat-Bug from India. Rec. Indian Mus., **27**, pp. 191–192 (1925).

JORDAN, K. Morphology and Systematics of the Polyctenidæ. Novit. Zool., **18**, pp. 555–579 (1912).

    The American Polyctenidæ. Ectoparasites, **1**, pp. 204–215 (1922).

CIMICOIDEA

ATKINSON, E. T. Catalogue of the Capsidæ. Suppl. Journ. Roy. Asiatic Soc., **58**, pt. 2, pp. 25–200 (1889).

    Isometopidæ of New Zealand. Notulæ Ent., **4**, pp. 3–9 (1924).

BRUNER, S. C. Notes on Cuban Dicyphinæ. Mem. Soc. Cubana Hist. Nat., **8**, pp. 35–49, 3 pls. (1934).

CARVALHO, J. C. M. Mirídeos neotropicais. Rev. Ent., Rio de Janeiro, **16**, pp. 158–187, 45 figs. (1945).

CHINA, W. E. and J. G. MYERS. Classification of the Cimicoid Families. Ann. Mag. Nat. Hist., (10) **3**, pp. 97–125 (1929).

GIBSON, E. H. Isometopidæ of North America. Bull. Brooklyn Ent. Soc., **12**, pp. 73–77 (1917).

HSIAO, T. Y. List of Chinese Miridæ with Keys to Subfamilies, etc. Iowa State Coll. Journ. Sci., **16**, pp. 241–269 (1942).

KNIGHT, H. H. Key to Subfamilies of Miridæ. Journ. New York Ent. Soc., **26**, pp. 40–44 (1918).

    Monograph of the North American Species of Deræocoris (Miridæ). 18th Rept. State Ent. Minnesota for 1920, pp. 76–210. Reprinted as Tech. Bull. **1**, Univ. Minnesota Agr. Exp. Sta. (1921).

    The plant bugs, or Miridæ, of Illinois. Bull. Ill. Nat. Hist. Surv., **22**, pp. 1–234, 1 pl., 181 figs. (1941).

    Hyaliodinæ, New Subfamily of Miridæ. Ent. News, **54**, pp. 119–121 (1943).

KNIGHT, H. H. and W. L. McATEE. Miridæ of the District of Columbia. Proc. U. S. Nat. Mus., **75**, Art. 13, 27 pp. (1929).

McATEE, W. L. Key to the Nearctic Species of Paracalocoris (Miridæ). Ann. Ent. Soc. America, **9**, pp. 366–390 (1916).

POPPIUS, B. R. Beiträge zur Kenntnis der Anthocoriden. Acta Soc. Sci. Fennica, **37**, No. 9, pp. 1–43 (1909).

    Zur Kenntnis der Cylapinæ. Acta Soc. Sci. Fennica, **37**, No. 4, pp. 1–45 (1909).

Beiträge zur Miridenfauna Australiens. Öfv. vet. Soc. Förh., **53**, No. 3, pp. 1–16 (1911).

Beiträge zur Kenntnis der Miriden von Ceylon. Öfv. vet. Soc. Helsingfors, **53**, No. 2, pp. 1–36 (1911).

Miriden der æthiopischen Region. Part I, Acta Soc. Sci. Fennica, **41**, pp. 1–203 (1912); Part II, ibid., **44**, pp. 1–138 (1914).

REUTER, O. M. Monographia anthocoridarum orbis terrestris. Acta Soc. Sci. Fennica, **14**, pp. 555–758. Also published separately (1885).

Neue Beiträge zur Phylogenie und System der Miriden. Acta Soc. Sci. Flor. Faun. Fennica, **37**, No. 3, pp. 1–167 (1910).

Die Familie der Bettwanzen. Zeits. wiss. Insektenbiol., **9**, p. 251 etc. (several parts) (1913).

STICHEL, H. Miridæ. Illustrierte Tabellen der deutschen Wanzen, Lief. **6,7**, pp. 147–210, 167 figs.; **8, 9**, pp. 211–274, 111 figs. (1932–33).

VAN DUZEE, E. P. Keys to Genera of North America Miridæ. Univ. California Pubs., Ent., **1**, pp. 199–216 (1916).

WATSON, S. A. The Miridæ of Ohio. Ohio State Univ. Bull., **33**, 44 pp. (1928).

DIPSOCOROIDEA

McATEE, W. L. and J. R. MALLOCH. Revision of Cryptostemmatidæ in the United States National Museum. Proc. U. S. Nat. Mus., **67**, Art. 13, 42 pp. (1925).

REUTER, O. M. Monographia Ceratocombidarum orbis terrestris. Acta Soc. Sci. Fennica, **19**, pp. 1–28 (1891).

HELOTREPHOIDEA

CHINA, W. E. New and Little Known Helotrephidæ. Ann. Mag. Nat. Hist., (10) **15**, pp. 593–614, 11 figs. (1935).

New South American Helotrephidæ. Ann. Mag. Nat. Hist., (11) **5**, pp. 106–126, 11 figs. (1940).

ESAKI, T. and W. E. CHINA. A New Family (Helotrephidæ) of Hemiptera. Trans. London Ent. Soc., **75**, pp. 279–295 (1927).

Monograph of the Helotrephinæ. Eos, **4**, pp. 129–172 (1928).

TERMITAPHIDOIDEA

MORRISON, H. On three apparently new species of Termitaphis. Zoologica, New York, **3**, pp. 403–408 (1923).

MYERS, J. G. On the Systematic Position of the Family Termitaphididæ. Psyche, **31**, pp. 259–278 (1924).

USINGER, R. L. Revision of Termitaphididæ. Pan-Pacific Ent., **8**, pp. 155–159. (1942).

CRYPTOCERATA

CARLO, J. A. DE. Los Belostomátidos Americanos. An. Mus. Argentina Cien. Nat., **39**, pp. 189–260, 8 pls. (1938).

Los Ranatridæ de Sud America. An. Mus. Argentina Cien. Nat., **42**, pp. 1–38 (1946).

Revisión del género Abedus. Commun. Mus. Argentina Cien. Nat., No. **5**, 24 pp., 3 pls. (1948).

CHAGNON, G. and O. FOURNIER. Aquatic Hemiptera of Quebec. Natural. Canad., **75**, pp. 49–69; 97–138, 18 figs. (1948).

CUMMINGS, C. The Giant Water Bugs (Belostomatidæ). Sci. Bull. Univ. Kansas, **21**, pp. 197–219, 2 pls. (1934).

FERRARI, E. Die Hemipterengattung Nepa. Ann. Hofmus. Wien, **3**, pp. 161–194 (1888).

HALE, H. M. Two New Hemiptera from New South Wales. Proc. Linn. Soc. New South Wales, **49**, p. 462 (1924).

Studies in Australian Aquatic Hemiptera. Rec. South Australian Mus., **3**, pp. 195–217 (1926).

HOFFMANN, W. E. Catalogue of Aquatic Hemiptera of China, Indo-China, Formosa and Korea. Lingnan Sci. Journ., **20**, pp. 1–78E (1941).

HUEBER, T. Deutsche Wasserwanzen. Jahrb. Ver. Vaterl. Naturk. Würtemburg, **61**, pp. 91–176 (1905).

HUNGERFORD, H. B. The Biology and Ecology of Aquatic and Semiaquatic Hemiptera. Univ. Kansas Sci. Bull., **11**, pp. 3–265 (1919).

The Nepidæ of North America North of Mexico. Kansas Univ. Sci. Bull., **14**, pp. 425–469 (1922).

Revision of the Notonectidæ and Corixidæ of South Africa. Ann. South African Mus., **25**, pp. 375–474 (1929).

Corixidæ of Western Hemisphere. Sci. Bull. Univ. Kansas, **32**, 827 pp., 112 pls. (1948).

HUTCHINSON, G. E. Review of the Notonectidæ and Corixidæ of South Africa. Ann. South African Mus., **25**, pp. 359–474, 15 pls. (1929).

Review of the Corixidæ of India and Surrounding Regions. 138 pp., 36 pls. (1940).

KARNY, W. H. Biologie der Wasserinsekten. xv + 311 pp. Wagner, Berlin. (1934).

KIRKALDY, G. W. A Guide to the Study of British Waterbugs (Aquatic Rhynchota). Ent., **31**, pp. 177–180 (1898); continued in vols. 32, 33, 38, 39, 41 (1899–1908).

Revision of Notonectidæ. Trans. Ent. Soc. London, 1897, pp. 393–426 (1897) and Wiener Entom. Zeitg., **23**, pp. 111–135 (1904).

Notes on Corixidæ. No. 1. Canadian Ent., **50**, pp. 117–120 (1908).

MAYR, G. L. Die Belostomiden. Verh. zool.-bot. Ges. Wien, **21**, pp. 399–440 (1871).

MELIN, D. Neotropical Gelastocoridæ (partial revision). Zool. Bidrag., **12**, pp. 151–198 (1930).

POISSON, R. Les Hémiptères aquatiques de la faune française. Arch. Zool. exp. gen., **77**, pp. 455–563, 78 figs. (1935).

SCHELL, D. V. The Ochteridæ (Hemiptera) of the Western Hemisphere. Journ. Kansas Ent. Soc., **16**, pp. 29–47 (1943).

TORRE-BUENO, J. R. The Genus Notonecta in North America. Journ. New York Ent. Soc., **13**, pp. 143–167 (1905).

USINGER, R. L. Naucoridæ of the Philippine Islands. Philadelphia Journ. Sci., **64**, pp. 299–311 (1938).

Key to Subfamilies of Naucoridæ, with Generic Synopsis of Ambrysinæ. Ann. Ent. Soc. America, **34**, pp. 5–16 (1941).

Classification of the Cryphocricinæ. Ann. Ent. Soc. America, **40**, pp. 329–343, 3 figs. (1947).

PELORIDOIDEA

Myers, J. G. and W. E. China. The Systematic Position of the Peloridiidæ. Ann. Mag. Nat. Hist. (10), 3, pp. 282–294 (1930).

ORDER ANOPLÙRA

(SIPHUNCULÂTA, PSEUDORHYNCHÒTA, PARASÌTA, PHTHIRÁPTERA, ELLIPÓPTERA)

Small, more or less flattened, wingless ectoparasites of mammals. Head free, horizontal; eyes reduced or absent; mouth anterior, comprising an unjointed, fleshy beak; antennæ short, simple. Thoracic segments fused. Legs very stout; tarsi single-jointed, forming a claw at the end of the tibia. No cerci. Metamorphosis very slight. True lice, Sucking lice, Cooties.

1. Body with spines or hairs arranged in definite rows, rarely also with scales; body flattened; spiracles only at each side of the mesothorax and on abdominal segments three to eight; antennæ three or five-jointed; living exclusively on terrestrial mammals...2
   Body thickly clothed with stout, thorn-like bristles or with spines and scales; body thick and stout; mesothorax and metathorax each with a pair of spiracles as well as abdominal segments two to eight; eyes absent; antennæ four- or five-jointed; living exclusively on marine mammals. (**Echinophthírius, Lepidophthírius, Antarctophthírius**) ....**ECHINOPHTHIRÌIDÆ**

2. Head rounded in front, not tubularly produced; tibiæ of at least one pair of legs below with a large tooth or thumb-like process opposing the claw-like tarsus...........................3
   Head tubularly produced anteriorly to form a beak longer than the remainder of the head; tibiæ without such a process opposing the tarsus. (**Hæmatomỳzus**, on elephants, Afr., E. Ind.). (This family is sometimes placed in the Mallophaga.).
   HÆMATOMÝZIDÆ

3. Eyes present, large, convex and almost always distinctly pigmented; proboscis short; tibia and tarsus without a distinct sclerite between them; pleural plates usually well developed.................4
   Eyes absent or very indistinct; proboscis very long; legs with a chitinized sclerite between the tibia and tarsus; parasitic on a great variety of mammals but not on man...................5

4. Segments three to five of abdomen fused as indicated by three pairs of spiracles on this apparent segment; sides of abdomen with segmentally placed lateral lobes; front legs much more slender than the others. (**Phthírius** (Fig. 330), on man and gorilla (*P. pùbis*, Pubic or Crab louse))........**PHTHIRÌIDÆ**

Abdominal segments all free, as indicated by the position of their spiracles; sides of abdominal segments without such lateral lobes; front legs similar to the others, and scarcely more slender. (**Pedículus** (Figs. 329, 331), on man and monkeys. Cooties. (*P. humanus*, Head louse, Body louse))...........**PEDICÙLIDÆ**

5. Antennæ five-jointed 6

    Antennæ three- or four-jointed. (**Hæmatopinòides**, on *Geomys*; **Hamophthírius**, on monkeys)........**HÆMATOPINÒIDIDÆ**

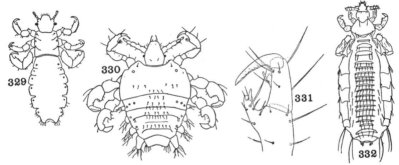

Figs. 329–332. Anoplura

329. **Pediculus** (Patton and Cragg) Pediculidæ.
330. **Phthirius** (Patton and Cragg) Phthiriidæ.
331. **Pediculus**, tip of leg (Ewing) Pediculidæ.
332. **Hoplopleura** (Ferris) Hæmatopinidæ.

6. Thorax and abdomen distinctly separated. (**Hæmatópinus**, on ungulates (*H. sùis*, Hog louse); **Hoplopleùra** (Fig. 332), on Rodentia; **Linógnathus**, on Artiodactyla and dogs; **Pólyplax**, on Rodentia and Insectivora). (Including *HOPLOPLEÙRIDÆ*).

                        HÆMATOPÍNIDÆ

Thorax and abdomen fused together; abdominal tergites and sternites not developed; very small slender species parasitic on elephant shrews. (**Neolinógnathus**, Ethiop.).....**NEOLINOGNÁTHIDÆ**

LITERATURE ON ANOPLURA

Bedford, G. A. H. A Synoptic Check List and Host List of the Ectoparasites found on South African Mammalia, Aves and Reptilia (Second Edition). Rep. Vet. Res. S. Africa, **18**, pp. 308–414, 4 figs. (1932).

Brinck, P. Catalogus insectorum sueciæ. IX. Anoplura. Opusc. Ent., **13**, pp. 129–133 (1948).

Buxton, P. A. The Louse. Anoplura of Man. viii + 164 pp., 47 figs. Arnold and Co., London (1947).

Dalla Torre, K. W. Anoplura. Gen. Insectorum, fasc. 81, 22 pp. (1908).

Denny, H. Monographia Anoplurorum Britanniæ. London (1842).

EICHLER, W. Zur Klassification der Lauskerfe. Arch. Naturg., B **10**, pp. 345–398 (1941).

ENDERLEIN, G. Läuse-Studien. Zool. Anz., **27**, pp. 220–223 (1904); **28**, pp. 626–638 (1905).

EWING, H. E. Revision of the American Lice of the Genus Pediculus. Proc. U. S. Nat. Mus., **68**, Art. 19, pp. 1–30 (1926).

FAHRENHOLZ, H. Zur Systematik der Anopluren. Z. Parasitenk., **9**, pp. 50–56 (1936).

FERRIS, G. F. A Catalogue and Host List of the Anoplura. Proc. California Acad. Sci. (4) **6**, pp. 129–213 (1916).

Sucking Lice, a Monograph. Leland Stanford Jr. Univ. Pub. Univ. Ser. **2**, 8 parts, 634 pp. (1919–1935).

The Sucking Lice. Mem. Pacific Coast Ent. Soc., **1**, 320 pp., 124 figs. (1951).

JANCKE, O. Anoplura. Tierwelt Deutschlands, **35**, pp. 43–78, 26 figs. (1938).

KELLOGG, V. L. and G. F. FERRIS. Anoplura and Mallophaga of North American Mammals. Leland Stanford Jr. Univ. Pub. Univ. Ser. **1915**, 74 pp. (1915).

NUTTALL, G. H. F. Classification of Anoplura. Parasitology, **11**, pp. 329–346 (1919).

PIAGET, E. Les Pédiculines. I., 714 pp. (1880); II., 162 pp. (1885) Leiden.

SÉGUY, E. Insectes ectoparasites (Mallophages, Anoploures, Siphonaptera). Faune de France, **43**, pp. 409–459 (1944).

ZIMMERMAN, E. C. Anoplura. Insects of Hawaii, **2**, pp. 295–314 (1948).

ORDER NEURÓPTERA
SUBORDER SIALÒDEA

(MEGALÓPTERA)

Soft-bodied species with large wings, long and sometimes pectinate antennæ and simple, similar legs. Costal cell with many transverse veins, subcosta and first radius simple, apically fused, the radial sector arising near the base; hind wings with the anal space normally large, folded fan-like when at rest. Prothorax quadrate. Metamorphosis complete; larvæ aquatic, living in freshwater streams; predatory, mandibulate, possessing lateral abdominal gill-filaments; wings appearing in the pupal stage; no cocoon.

Adults

1. Three ocelli present; fourth joint of the tarsi simple, not bilobed; venation regular, with the crossveins weakly formed, branches of the radial sector directed backward; large or medium sized species, 45 to 100 mm. in wing expanse. (Figs. 333, 335). (**Archichauliòdes**, Austr.; **Chauliòdes, Neohérmes, Corýdalis** (Dobson, Hellgrammite), Am.; **Neochauliòdes**, Indomal.; **Hérmes, Neùromus, Protohérmes, Neoneùromus**, Asia) ......**CORYDÁLIDÆ**

Ocelli absent; fourth joint of the tarsi prominently bilobed; some of the branches of the radial sector directed forward; medium sized species, 20 to 40 mm. in wing expanse. (Fig. 334). (Proto-sìalis, Am.; Austrosìalis, Stenosìalis, Austr.; Sìalis, Holarc.).

SIÁLIDÆ

Larvae

1. Eight pairs of lateral gills; a pair of hooked anal prolegs, but no terminal filament .... CORYDÁLIDÆ
Seven pairs of lateral gills; no anal prolegs; terminal filament present .... SIÁLIDÆ

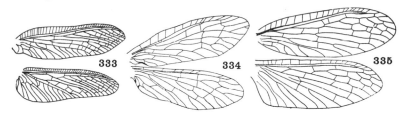

Figs. 333–335.   Neuroptera

333. **Corydalis**, wings. Corydalidæ.
334. **Austrosialis**, wings (Tillyard) Sialidæ.
335. **Chauliodes**, wings. Corydalidæ.

SUBORDER **RAPHIDIÒDEA**

(*RAPHIDIÒIDEA, EMMENÓGNATHA*, part.)

Moderate-sized, slender, predatory species with elongate cylindrical prothorax; head large, nearly horizontal, mandibles strong, antennæ long and thread-like; ovipositor long; cerci not developed; wings membranous, both pairs similar, with numerous forkings, the costal cell with crossveins, subcosta not fused with the first radial; legs similar, the first pair attached at the base of the prothorax, tarsi five-jointed. Metamorphosis complete; larvæ terrestrial. Snake-flies, Serpent-flies.

1. Ocelli present; pterostigma bordered proximally by a veinlet from R_1. (**Raphídia**, Palæarc.; **Agúlla**, Palæarc., Am. (Figs. 336, 338)).

RAPHIDìIDÆ

Ocelli absent; pterostigma not bordered proximally by a veinlet from R_1. (**Inocéllia**, Holarc. (Fig. 337); **Fíbla**, Eur.) . INOCELLìIDÆ

SUBORDER PLANIPÉNNIA

(*SYNISTÁTA*, part., *DICTYÓPTERA*, part.)

Small to rather large, slender, predaceous insects with large wings, but of slow flight. Head free, vertical, eyes prominent, mouth inferior, mandibles strong; prothorax more or less freely movable and prominent, meso- and metathorax not closely grown together; abdomen long and

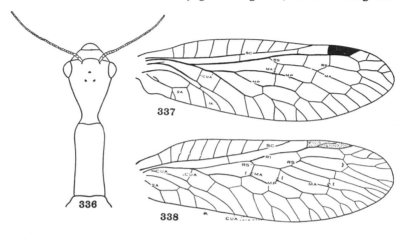

Figs. 336–338. **Neuroptera**

336. **Agulla**, head and prothorax of female, Raphidiidæ.
337. **Inocellia**, fore wing (Carpenter) Inocelliidæ.
338. **Agulla**, fore wing (Carpenter) Raphidiidæ.

narrow, the first sternite reduced, no cerci; wings similar, membranous, no large anal field; when at rest the wings usually lie roof-like over the abdomen, longitudinal veins almost always very numerous through repeated branching, costal cell almost always with crossveins. Metamorphosis complete, larvæ terrestrial, aquatic only in Sisyridæ, strongly mandibulate, the mandibles and maxillæ specialized for sucking the body juices of the insect prey; pupæ in cocoons.

1. Veins and usually crossveins abundant, radial sector with several
     branches or forkings; wings not covered with a whitish powder. . 2
   Veins and crossveins few in number, the radial sector at most only
     forked; wings covered with a whitish powder; very small, slender,
     pale-colored rare species, of 3 to 10 mm. wing expanse. (Super-
     family CONIOPTERYGÒIDEA) . . . .**CONIOPTERÝGIDÆ**

The following subfamilies are distinguished:

a. Outer lobe of maxilla three-jointed; abdomen with four to six pairs
     of everted ventral pouches; stem of media of fore wings usually

with two thickenings which bear bristles. (**Aleurópteryx,** Holarc.; **Coniocómpsa, Helicocònis,** Holarc., Austr., Neotrop.; **Heterocònis,** Austr.) ....**ALEUROPTERYGÌNÆ**
Outer lobe of maxilla with only one joint; abdomen without ventral pouches; stem of media of fore wings without thickenings bearing bristles. (**Coniópteryx, Parasemídalis,** widespr.; **Conwéntzia,** Holarc.; **Nìphas,** Neotrop.; **Semídalis,** Palæarc., Am., Ethiop.)
CONIOPTERYGÌNÆ

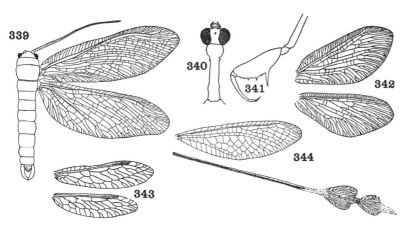

Figs. 339–344. Neuroptera

339. **Ithone,** Outline of body and wings (Tillyard) Ithonidæ.
340. **Mantispa,** head and thorax from above. Mantispidæ.
341. **Mantispa,** raptorial front leg. Mantispidæ.
342. **Dilar,** wings (Handlirsch) Dilaridæ.
343. **Mantispa,** wings (Handlirsch) Mantispidæ.
344. **Chasmoptera,** wings (Tillyard) Nemopteridæ.

2. Large, stout, showy, moth-like, cursorial species, of 30 to 79 mm. wing-expanse; costal area not broad, Sc, R and R_s not forming a distinct triple vein; head small and closely set on the prothorax; antennæ long and filiform, and tapering in both sexes, 40- to 50-jointed; abdomen of the male terminating in large forcipate appendages; ovipositor not exserted (Fig. 339). Superfamily ITHONÒIDEA). (**Ithòne, Várnia,** Austr.; **Oliárces,** Calif.; **Rapísma,** Asia). (Including *RAPÍSMIDÆ*)......**ITHÒNIDÆ**
Small to large, but not moth-like insects, except the showy Psychopsidæ which have a very broad costal area and distinctive triple vein; otherwise differing............................3
3. Antennæ never enlarged toward the end, moniliform or filiform, rarely pectinate; Cu usually ending near or before the middle

of the wing and without a straight longitudinal branch behind
Cu_1 4

Antennæ at least thickly cylindrical, variable in length, usually
gradually enlarged toward the end, or filiform with clavate end;
at least the discal portion of the wings densely reticulate, Sc
and R_1 apically fused, Cu ending in the apical part of the wing
and commonly with a long straight branch behind Cu_1 (Superfamily MYRMELEONTÒIDEA) 16

4. Hind wings not longer than the fore wings, the two pairs similar
in form and venation. (Superfamily HEMEROBIÒIDEA) 5

Hind wings greatly elongate and ribbon-like, often with widened,
spoon-like ends; head usually rostrate. (Fig. 344). (Superfamily
NEMOPTERÒIDEA). (Chasmóptera, Austr.; Cròce, Palæarc.,
Ethiop., Austr.; Nemóptera, Nìna, Palæarc.; Nemopístha, Nemop-
terélla, Ethiop.; Veurise, Argent.) ....NEMOPTÉRIDÆ

5. Front legs normal, not raptorial 6

Front legs strong, formed for seizing prey, their coxæ elongate;
femora robust and spined, and tibiæ curved to meet femora, prothorax usually greatly lengthened; antennæ short; wings rather
narrow. (Figs. 340, 341, 343). Mainly tropicopol. (Climaciélla,
Drepánicus, Sýmphrasis, Neotrop.; Ditáxis, Austr.; Mantíspa, cosmop.; Euclimàcia, Ethiop., Austro-mal.) ....MANTÍSPIDÆ

6. Fore wings with two or more branches of R_s arising from the
apparently fused stems of R_1 and R_s 7

Fore wings with all the branches of R_s arising from a single sector ..9

7. Antennæ moniliform in both sexes; ovipositor not projecting; cross-
veins few; ocelli absent 8

Antennæ of male coarsely pectinate; ovipositor exserted; vertex with
three prominent ocellus-like tubercles; crossveins numerous; rather
small species. Cosmopol. (Dìlar (Fig. 342), Lìdar, Eur.; Nallà-
chius, Am.; Nèpal, Asia) ....DILÁRIDÆ

8. Fore wings with three or more branches of the radial sector pres-
ent, veins R_4 and R_5 arising separately. (Fig. 345). Cosmopol.
(Boriomỳia, Drepanépteryx, Gayomỳia, Hemeròbius, Megalòmus,
Micròmus) (MICRÓMIDÆ) ....HEMEROBÌIDÆ

Fore wings with apparently two radial sectors, one of which is
R_{2+3} and the other R_{4+5}. Widespread. (Pséctra, Sympheròbius).
SYMPHEROBÌIDÆ

9. Rather large, moth-like species, with broad wings, the costal area
of the fore wings very wide, Sc, R_1 and R_s closely parallel, forming a chitinized triple midrib and fusing at the apical fourth
of the wing, antennæ short; rare, nocturnal species. (Fig. 346).
(Psychópsis, Megallànes, Austr.; Psychopsélla, Arteriópteryx, Psy-
chóphasis, Ethiop.; Megapsỳchops) ....PSYCHÓPSIDÆ

Not moth-like, wings not broadly rounded, with normal costal area
and without the above-described prominent triple vein........10

10. Ocelli present; discal area of the wings with many crossveins, marginal area with no crossveins but with many forked veinlets;
moderate to large, slender species. Widespr., but not North
American. (Euporísmus, Œdósmylus, Ósmylus, Porísmus, Spil-
ósmylus) ....OSMÝLIDÆ
Ocelli absent 11

11. Humeral crossvein forming a recurrent vein; discal area of the
wings with a simple graduate series of crossveins, and distinct
from the costal and marginal areas which have very many forked

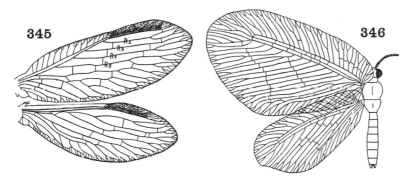

Figs. 345–346.   Neuroptera

345. **Micromus**, wings (Tillyard) Hemerobiidæ.
346. **Psychopsella**, outline of body and wings (Tillyard) Psychopsidæ.

veinlets; Sc and R_1 fused near wing-tip; vertex convex; antennæ
moderate in length; rather large, nocturnal species, wing-expanse
40 to 75 mm. (**Polystœchotes**, Am.).... POLYSTŒCHÓTIDÆ
No recurrent vein at the humeral angle of the wings; discal area
of the wings not differentiated from the marginal area; antennæ
longer than the head and thorax; smaller species.............12

12. Vertex convex; wing venation relatively simple, radial sector of
fore wings without definitive accessory veins, Sc and R_1 coalesced near tip of wing, costal crossveins not forked, r-m crossvein of hind wings in the axis of the wing; size small, 6 to 8 mm.
in length; larvæ aquatic, feeding on freshwater sponges. (Fig.
348). Spongilla-flies. (**Climàcia**, Nearc.; **Neurórthrus, Sisyrélla,**
Palæarc.; **Sísyra**, Holarc.)........................SISÝRIDÆ
Vertex flattened; the single radial sector in the fore wings with
definitive accessory veins; hind wings with the r-m crossvein
oblique or transverse; size larger.........................13

13. Costal crossveins not forked, Sc and R_1 free at the tip, R_s swinging away from R_1, the cell R_1 broad and containing many crossveins; wings rounded, not falcate.........................14

Costal crossveins forked, cell R_1 narrow and almost devoid of crossveins, apical portion of the hind margin of the fore wings sometimes widely notched, leaving the apex more or less acute (the falcate condition); wings and body hairy, especially the hind margin of the wings.................................15

14. Wings of nearly equal width, a crossvein placed near base of the subcostal cell, less than thirty crossveins in the costal cell before the stigma. (Fig. 351). Green lacewings, Stink-flies; the larvæ are Aphis-lions. Cosmopolitan. (**Allochrỳsa, Chrysòpa, Meleòma, Nothochrỳsa**) .... **CHRYSÓPIDÆ**

Fore wings distinctly wider than the hind pair, no crossveins near the base of the subcostal cell, more than forty costal crossveins before the stigma. (Fig. 349). Austr., Malay. (**Apochrỳsa, Oligochrỳsa**) .... **APOCHRÝSIDÆ**

15. Fore wings with Sc and R fused before the wing-tip; peculiar seed-like scales often present on some part of the wings. (Fig. 350). (**Acroberòtha**, Ethiop., Ind.; **Beròtha**, Indomal.; **Isoscelípteron**, Palæarc.; **Lomamỳia**, Am.; **Cycloberòtha**, Austr.). **BERÓTHIDÆ**

Fore wings with Sc and R not fused apically; hairs of body and wings conspicuously long. (Fig. 347). (**Stenobiélla, Trichòma**, Austr.) .... **TRICHOMÁTIDÆ**

16. Wings about one-third as wide as long, costal area wide, marginal veinlets forked, subcostal cell with many crossveins; antennæ long, cylindrical. (**Myiodáctylus, Ósmylops**, Austr.).

MYIODACTÝLIDÆ

Wings much narrower, the marginal area at least in large part closely reticulate 17

17. Antennæ elongate cylindrical; subcostal area with many crossveins. (**Austronýmphes, Nýmphes, Nymphídrion**, Austr.).

NÝMPHIDÆ

Antennæ more or less distinctly clavate, or apically swollen or flattened; subcostal cell without crossveins..................18

18. Antennæ about as long as the head and thorax; wings usually with an elongate narrow cell immediately behind the point of fusion of Sc and R_1...19

Antennæ long, slender, strongly clavate apically; eyes usually divided into two parts by a groove; no elongate hypostigmatic cell differentiated. Widespread, mainly tropical. (**Acmonòtus**, Austr.; **Ascálaphus**, Palæarc.; **Colobópterus**, Am.; **Hỳbris**, Indomal.; **Neuróptynx**, Nearc.; **Suhpalácsa**, Ethiop., Indoaustr.; **Ululòdes**, Am.; **Nephoneùra**, Ethiop.)................**ASCALÁPHIDÆ**

19. Antennæ weakly clubbed, or flattened at tip; hypostigmatic cell elongate; body and wings pubescent; weak fliers. Larvæ are called ant-lions or doodle-bugs. Widespread, mainly tropical. (Brachynemùrus, Creàgris, Dendròleon, Formicàleo, Hesperòleon, Myrmèleon, Palpàres, Protopléctron). (*MYRMELEÓNIDÆ*).

MYRMELEÓNTIDÆ

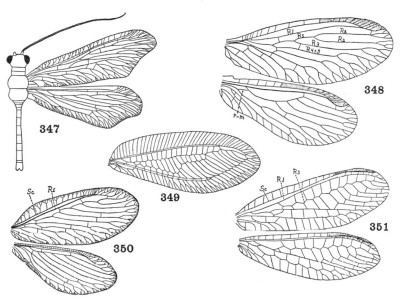

Figs. 347–351. Neuroptera

347. **Trichoma,** outline of body and wings (Tillyard) Trichomatidæ
348. **Sisyra,** wings (Tillyard) Sisyridæ.
349. **Oligochrysa,** fore wing (Tillyard) Apochrysidæ.
350. **Protobiella,** wings (Tillyard) Berothidæ.
351. **Chrysopa,** wings (Tillyard) Chrysopidæ.

Antennæ strongly clubbed; hypostigmatic cell variable; abdomen and wings shining; crepuscular, strong fliers, superficially resembling dragonflies. (**Stilbópteryx,** Austr.) **STILBOPTERÝGIDÆ**

LITERATURE ON NEUROPTERA

ALBARDA, H. Revision des Raphidides. Tijd. Ent., **34**, pp. 65–184 (1891).

ALEXANDROV-MARTYNOV, O. M. Nemopteriden Persiens und Mittelmeerländer. Zool. Anz., **90**, pp. 235–250, 18 figs. (1930).

BAGNALL, R. S. Review of British Coniopterygidæ. Ent. Rec., **27**, pp. 241–247 (1915).

BARNARD, K. H. Cape Megaloptera. Trans. Roy. Soc. South Africa, **19**, pp. 169–184 (1931).

BANKS, N. Revision of Nearctic Chrysopidæ. Trans. American Ent. Soc., **29**, pp. 137–162 (1903).

A Revision of the Nearctic Hemerobiidæ. Trans. American Ent. Soc., **32**, pp. 21–51 (1905).

Catalogue of the Neuropteroid Insects of the United States. American Ent. Soc., Philadelphia, 53 pp. (1907).

A Revision of the Nearctic Coniopterygidæ. Proc. Ent. Soc. Washington, **8**, pp. 77–86 (1907).

Revision of the Nearctic Myrmeleonidæ. Bull. Mus. Comp. Zool. Harvard, **68**, pp. 1–84 (1927).

Myrmeleonidæ of Lower California. Proc. California Acad. Sci., (4) **24**, pp. 133–152 (1942).

Neuroptera of Northern South America. Bol. Ent. venezolana, **2**, pp. 59–66, 161–173; **3**, pp. 1–34 (1943–44).

Review of the Chrysopidæ (Nothochrysidæ) of Central America. Psyche, **52**, pp. 139–174 (1946).

CARPENTER, F. M. Revision of the Nearctic Raphidiodea (Recent and Fossil). Proc. American Acad. Arts Sci., **71**, pp. 89–157, 2 pls., 13 figs. (1936).

Revision of Nearctic Hemerobiidæ, Berothidæ, Sisyridæ, Polystœchotidæ and Dilaridæ. Proc. American Acad. Arts Sci., **74**, pp. 193–280, 3 pls., 75 figs. (1940).

CHOPARD, L. Neuroptera. In Grassé, Traité de Zoologie, **9**, pp. 355–407, 40 figs. (1949).

COSTA LIMA, A. DA. Neurópteros. Insetos do Brasil, **4**, pp. 73–108, 34 figs. (1943).

DAVIS, K. C. Sialididæ of North and South America. Bull. New York State Mus., **68**, pp. 442–487 (1903).

ENDERLEIN, G. Monographie der Coniopterygiden. Zool. Jahrb. Abth. f. Syst., **23**, pp. 173–242 (1906).

Coniopterygidæ. Gen. Insectorum, fasc. 67, 18 pp. (1908).

Klassifikation der Mantispiden. Stettiner Ent. Zeit., **71**, pp. 341–379 (1910).

Die Klassifikation der Coniopterygiden. Arch. Klass. Phylog. Ent., **1**, pp. 98–114 (1930).

ESBEN-PETERSEN, E. Megaloptera. Gen. Insectorum, fasc. 154, 13 pp. (1913).

HAGEN, H. A. Neuroptera of North America. Smithsonian Misc. Coll., **4**, 347 pp. (1862).

KILLINGTON, F. J. Synopsis of British Neuroptera. Trans. Ent. Soc. Hampshire and South England, **1929**, pp. 1–36, 6 pls., 6 figs. (1929).

Monograph of British Neuroptera. I. 269 pp., 15 pls.; II. 307 pp., 15 pls. Ray Soc., London (1936–37).

Generic Names of British Nemoptera, with a Check-List of Species. Generic Names of British Insects, **4**, pp. 65–80 (1937).

KIMMINS, D. E. Revision of the Osmylid Subfamilies Stenosmylinæ and Kalosmylinæ. Nov. Zool., **42**, pp. 165–202, 8 pls., 28 figs. (1940).

KRÜGER, L. Beiträge zu einer Monographie der Osmyliden. Stettiner Ent. Zeitg., **75**, pp. 9–130 (1914); **76**, pp. 60–87 (1915).

Revision of Osmylidæ. Stettiner Ent. Zeitg., **75**, pp. 9–130 (1914); **76**, pp. 60–87 (1915).

Systematische Uebersicht der Neuropteren. Stettiner Ent. Zeitg., **78**, pp. 116–137 (1917).

Revision of Psychopsidæ. Stettiner Ent. Zeitg., **83**, pp. 17–48 (1922).

Revision of Berothidæ. Stettiner Ent. Zeitg., **83**, pp. 49–88 (1922).

Revision of Hemerobiidæ. Stettiner Ent. Zeitg., **83**, pp. 138–173 (1922).

KUWAYAMA, S. Studies on the Dilaridæ of Japan. Trans. Sapporo Nat. Hist. Soc., **8**, pp. 51–83 (1921).

LACROIX, J. L. Faune des Plannipennes de France. Ascalaphidæ. Bull. Soc. Étude Sci. Nat. Elbeuf., **41**, pp. 65–100 (1923).

LAMEERE, A. Neuroptera. In Précis de Zoologie. Rec. Inst. zool. Torley-Rousseau, **5**, pp. 25–49, 32 figs. (1936).

LESTAGE, J. A. Note sur les Sisyridés (Hémérobiiformes à larve aquatique). Bull. Ann. Soc. ent. Belg., **75**, pp. 385–394, 1 fig. (1935).

MOCSARY, A. Neuroptera. Fauna Regni Hungariæ, pp. 33–44 (1918).

NAKAHARA, W. Osmylinæ of Japan. Annot. Zool. Japonenses, Tokyo, **8**, pp, 489–518 (1914).

NAVÁS, L. Neurópteros (*s. lat.*) de España y Portugal. Brotéria, **5, 6, 7** (three parts) (1906–08).

Monográfia de la familia de los Diláridos. Mem. R. Acad. Barcelona, **7**, No. 17, pp. 619–671 (1909).

Monográfia de los Nemoptéridos. Mem. R. Acad. Barcelona, **8**, No. 18, pp. 1–70 (1910).

Nemopteridæ. Gen. Insectorum, fasc. 136, 23 pp. (1913).

Ascaláfidos sudamericanos. Revist. Chil. Santiago, **17**, pp. 41–74 (1914).

Dilaridæ. Gen. Insectorum, fasc. 156, 14 pp. (1914).

Les Myrméléonides d'Europe. Insecta, Rennes, **5**, pp. 57–62 (1915).

Crisopids d'Europe. Arixius Inst. Cien. Barcelona, **3**, No. 2, pp. 1–98 (1915).

Monografià de l'orde dels Rafidiopters. Arch. Inst. Catalans, Barcelona, 93 pp. (1918).

Monográfia de los Berotidos. Mem. Acad. Cien. Zaragoza, **2**, 107 pp., 44 figs. (1929).

Monográfia de la familia de los Sisíridos. Mem. Acad. Cienc. Zaragoza, **4**, 87 pp., 40 figs. (1935).

REHN, J. W. H. Studies in North American Mantispidæ. Trans. American Ent. Soc., **65**, pp. 237–263, 1 pl. (1939).

ROSS, H. H. and T. H. FRISON. Nearctic Species of Sialis. Bull. Illinois Nat. Hist. Surv., **21**, pp. 57–100 (1937).

STITZ, H. Neuroptera. In Tierwelt Mitteleuropas, **6**, Lief. 1, pp. XIV 1–19 (1928).

TILLYARD, R. J. Studies in Australian Neuroptera. Proc. Linn. Soc. New South Wales, **41**, pp. 269–332 (1916).

The Family Psychopsidæ (Australian). Proc. Linn. Soc. New South Wales, **43**, pp. 750–786 (1918).

Revision of the Family Ithonidæ. Proc. Linn. Soc. New South Wales, **44**, pp. 414–437 (1919).

TOWNSEND, L. H. Key to the Larvae of Certain Nearctic Neuroptera. Proc. Ent. Soc. Washington, **37**, pp. 25–30 (1935).

WEELE, H. W. Ascalaphiden. Coll. Zool. Selys-Longchamps. fasc. 8, Brussels (1908).

Megaloptera. Coll. Zool. Selys-Longchamps, fasc. 5, Brussels (1910).

WITHYCOMBE, C. L. A Contribution towards a Monograph of the Indian Coniopterygidæ. Mem. Dept. Agric. India, **9**, pp. 1–19 (1925).

ORDER MECÓPTERA

(*PANORPÀTÆ, PANORPÌNA, MECÁPTERA*)

Small or moderate-sized, rather slender, insects with the head nearly always prolonged downwards to form a sort of beak. Eyes large; ocelli present or absent; mandibles small. Wings usually present, almost always long and narrow, similar; radius extensively branched; media and cubitus with few branches; crossveins only rarely numerous; anal area almost always very small, not separated; wing surface without scales. Antennæ long, many-jointed, slender. Prothorax small, free; meso- and metathorax similar. Legs long, slender, similar, fitted for running; coxæ large, pendant and approximate; tarsi five-jointed. Abdomen usually slender; cerci small; genitalia of male usually greatly swollen, forming a reflexed bulb. Metamorphosis complete, the larvæ caterpillar-like. Scorpion flies.

1. Tarsi slender, filiform; the apical joint bearing two claws and not capable of folding back on the fourth.....................2

   Tarsi each with a single claw; the apical joint modified for grasping, the fifth joint folding back on the fourth; legs extremely long and slender, wings usually present. (**Bíttacus**, cosmop.; **Neobíttacus, Kalobíttacus, Pàzius**, Neotrop.; **Harpobíttacus**, Austr.) (*BITTACÙSIDÆ*) ....**BITTÁCIDÆ**

2. Female without an ovipositor, usually with normal wings; wings of male fully developed, rarely entirely absent (*i.e.* not vestigial) 3

   Female with an ovipositor, and wings reduced to scales; wings of male reduced to stout bristles. (**Bòreus** (Fig. 354), Holarc.).

   BORÉIDÆ

3. Wing always present; in the fore wings, radial sector and media both with more than four branches; radial sector arising close to the base of the wing; media branching much before the middle of the wing; wings short and broad, with rather dense venation; body depressed; male genitalia simple, not forming a bulb 4

   Wings usually present, rarely absent (*Apteropanorpa*), radial sector or media, or both with four branches or less; radial sector arising at or beyond the basal third of the wing; media branching at about the middle of the wing; wings long and slender, with rather open venation; body more or less cylindrical; male genitalia enlarged, forming a swollen bulb. (Figs. 353, 355).

PANÓRPIDÆ

This family is divisible into three well-defined subfamilies which are accorded family rank by some workers.

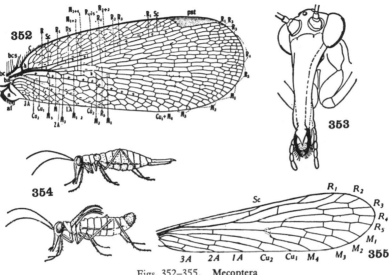

Figs. 352–355.   Mecoptera

352. **Notiothauma,** fore wing (Crampton) Notiothaumidæ.
353. **Panorpa,** head (Lameere) Panorpidæ.
354. **Boreus,** male (lower figure) and female (upper figure) (Lameere) Boreidæ.
355. **Panorpa,** fore wing (Tillyard) Panorpidæ.

a. First branch of cubitus in fore wing fused with the main stem of media for a greater or less distance........................b
   First branch of cubitus in fore wing entirely free from the main stem of the media; media four branched in both wings; radial sector usually with more than four branches. (**Panórpa,** Palæarc., Am.; **Panorpòdes,** Japan; **Neopanórpa, Leptopanórpa,** Indomal.; **Brachypanórpa,** Nearc.; **Apteropanórpa,** Tasmania).

PANORPÍNÆ

b. Radial sector three-branched; cubitus and main stem of media of fore wing coalescent for a considerable distance; small active species. (**Nannochorísta,** Neotrop., Austr.; **Choristélla,** Austr.).

NANNOCHORISTÍNÆ

   Radial sector four-branched; cubitus and main stem of media of fore wing touching only at a point or for a very short distance; larger species. (**Chorísta, Tæniochorísta**, Austr.)..**CHORISTÍNÆ**

4. Ocelli present; wings with very dense and irregular venation, the anal area well developed; radius and media coalescent on the basal fifth of the wing. (Fig. 352). (**Notiothauma**, Neotrop.).

NOTIOTHAUMIDÆ

Ocelli absent; venation of wings more open and regular, the anal area slightly developed; radius and media not coalescent at the base of the wing. (**Mérope**, Nearc.; **Austromérope**, Austr.) (*MERÓPIDÆ*)............................. **MEROPÈIDÆ**

LITERATURE ON MECOPTERA

CARPENTER, F. M. Revision of Nearctic Mecoptera. Bull. Mus. Comp. Zoöl. Harvard Univ., **72**, pp. 205–277 (1931).

COSTA LIMA, A. DA. Panorpatos. Insetos do Brasil, **4**, pp. 1–15, 6 figs. (1943).

ENDERLEIN, G. Ueber die Phylogenie und Klassifikation der Mecopteren. Zool. Anz., **35**, pp. 385–399 (1910).

ESBEN-PETERSEN, P. Tables for Determination of Danish Mecoptera and Megaloptera (in Danish). Kopenhagen, Flora og Fauna, pp. 129–144 (1914); pp. 1–16, 41–47 (1915).

A Synonymic List of the Mecoptera. Entom. Meddel., **10**, pp. 216–242 (1915).

Mecoptera. Coll. Zool. Selys-Longchamps, fasc. 5 (1921).

GRASSÉ, P.-P. Mecoptera. Traité de Zoologie, **10** (1), pp. 71–124, 64 figs. (1951).

JAFFUEL, R. F. Mecoptera of Chile. Rev. chilena Hist. Nat., **33**, pp. 537–549, 2 pls., 5 figs. (1930).

KILLINGTON, F. J. A New Genus and Species of Meropeidæ (Mecoptera) from Australia. Ent. Month. Mag., **69**, pp. 1–4 (1933).

LAMEERE, A. Mecoptera. In Précis de Zoologie. Rec. Inst. zool. Torley-Rousseau, **5**, pp. 5–16, 14 figs. (1936).

LESTAGE, J. A. Pour l'histoire des Boreus (Stégoptères — Mécoptères). Ann. Soc. zool. Belg., **72**, pp. 5–29, 105–125 (1941).

MIYAKE, T. Studies on the Mecoptera of Japan. Journ. Coll. Agric. Imp. Univ. Tokyo, **4**, pp. 265–400 (1913).

STITZ, H. Mecoptera. In Tierwelt Mitteleuropas, **6**, Lief. 1, pp. XIV 19–22 (1928).

TILLYARD, R. J. Nannochoristidæ. Proc. Linn. Soc. New South Wales, **17**, pp. 284–301 (1917).

ORDER **TRICHÓPTERA**

(*PHRYGANÒIDEA*)

Small to medium-sized, slender, flying insects; head freely movable, vertical, eyes prominent, ocelli three or none, mandibles vestigial or absent, palpi prominent, antennæ thread-like, often very long; prothorax small, free; meso- and metathorax similar; wings more or less clothed with hairs, with many veins and a few crossveins; the hind wings often with a folded anal area; wings rarely reduced in size; legs similar, coxæ pendant and approximate, tibiæ always with spurs, tarsi five-jointed. Metamorphosis complete. Larvæ aquatic; usually with tufted tracheal gills; more or less caterpillar-like and usually living in cases constructed of small objects spun together with silk. Caddis (or Caddice) flies; larvæ called Caddis worms.

Adults

1. Scutellum with its posterior portion forming a triangular, flat area with steep sides; mesonotum without warts; tibiæ with one spur or none; very small species (6 mm. or less), the front wings covered with projecting, clubbed hairs; wings, especially the hind pair, with very long marginal fringe. (Fig. 359). (**Hydróptila, Allotríchia,** Holarc.; **Oxyethìra,** widespr.; **Mortoniélla,** Neotrop.).
   HYDROPTÍLIDÆ
   Scutellum either evenly convex, without a posterior portion set off by sharp sides, or the mesonotum with warts; usually larger or much larger species; front wings without, or with solitary thickened and projecting hairs; marginal fringe of wings shorter than the width of the wings..................................2
2. Ocelli present 3
   Ocelli absent 9
3. Maxillary palpi strongly hairy or scaly; tibial spurs 1–3–4 or 2–4–4......................a few **SERICOSTOMÁTIDÆ**
   Maxillary palpi with only weak hairs, not scaly.................4
4. Last joint of maxillary palpi divided into false ring-joints, curved and as long as the third and fourth joints together; front tibiæ without or with two, three, or four spurs....................5
   Last joint of maxillary palpi not ringed, rarely curved, subequal to the other joints (palpi absent in some Hydropsychidæ).....6
5. Hind wings not dilated, in shape similar to the fore wings. (**Chimárrha,** cosmop.; **Philopótamus,** Holarc.)..**PHILOPOTÁMIDÆ**
   Hind wings with expanded anal angle, much wider than the fore wings. (**Stenopsỳche,** Indomal.; **Parastenopsỳche,** Palæarc.; **Pseudostenopsỳche,** Neotrop.)..........**STENOPSÝCHIDÆ,** part
6. Front tibiæ with one or no spur; middle tibiæ with three or two spurs 7
   Front tibiæ with two or three spurs, middle tibiæ with four spurs; maxillary palpi four- or five-jointed......................8
7. Middle tibiæ widened, their tarsi broadened and armed with stiff hairs (See couplet 8). (**Agrypnètes,** Holarc.).
   PHRYGANÈIDÆ, part
   Middle tibiæ simple with two or three spurs; normal front tibiæ

with not more than one spur; maxillary palpi of male three-jointed, of female five-jointed, but of similar structure in the two sexes. (Anabòlia, Stenóphylax, Limnéphilus, Hálesus, Apatània, Holarc.) (Figs. 357, 361)............LIMNEPHÍLIDÆ

8. Maxillary palpi five-jointed, the basal two joints very short and thick (Fig. 356). (Rhyacóphila, Glossosòma, Agapètus, Holarc.; Hydrobiòsis, Psilochorèma, Austr.).......RHYACOPHÍLIDÆ

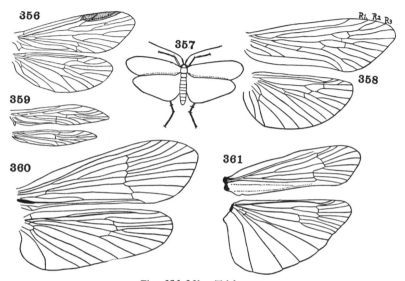

Figs. 356–361.   Trichoptera

356. **Hydrobiosis,** wings (Tillyard) Rhyacophilidæ.
357. **Limnephilus,** outline. Limnephilidæ.
358. **Hydropsyche,** wings. Hydropsychidæ.
359. **Allotrichia,** wings. Hydroptilidæ.
360. **Phyllorheithrus,** wings (Tillyard) Calamoceratidæ.
361. **Limnephilus,** wings. Limnephilidæ.

Maxillary palpi of male four-jointed, of female five-jointed, the joints cylindrical, the second joint not short, the palpi of the two sexes similar; front tibiæ with two or more spurs, middle tibiæ with four spurs. (Neurònia, Agrýpnia, Phrygànea, Holarc.). PHRYGANÈIDÆ

9. Hind wing distinctly concave on the apical half of its costal margin; basal half of the costal margin with a fringe of short hamuli. (Helicopsỳche, Holarc.) .... HELICOPSÝCHIDÆ

Hind wing without hamuli, the apical half of its costal margin straight or convex....................................10

10. Tibial spurs 3–4–4; maxillary palpi weakly hairy, five-jointed, the first and second joints very small, the last joint ringed and curved; antennæ thickened.............................11
    Usually two, very rarely one, but never three, spurs on front tibiæ...12
11. Mandibles robust; maxillary palpi with the second joint short. (Stenopsychòdes, Austr.) (See couplet 5).
                                    STENOPSÝCHIDÆ, part
    Mandibles slender and sinuous; maxillary palpi with the second joint bulbously enlarged internally. (Polycéntropus, Plectrocnèmia, Neureclípsis, Holarc.; Polypléctropus, Neotrop., Austr.).
                                    POLYCENTROPÓDIDÆ
12. Last joint of the five-jointed, scarcely hairy, maxillary palpi annulate and arcuate 13
    Last joint of the usually strongly hairy maxillary palpi neither ringed nor curved 15
13. Mesopræscutum set off by distinct sutures. (Xiphocéntron, widespr.) ....XIPHOCENTRÓNIDÆ
    Mesopræscutum fused with the scutum 14
14. First vein from the discal cell of the fore wing (anterior branch of the radial sector) forked; maxillary palpi long and thin. (Fig. 358). (Hydropsỳche, Macronèmum, cosmop.; Hydropsychòdes, widespr.; Arctopsỳche, Dipléctrona, Holarc.; Smícridea, Am.). (Including ARCTOPSÝCHIDÆ).......HYDROPSÝCHIDÆ
    First fork (R₂) wanting in both fore and hind wings; first joint of the maxillary palpi small. (Psychomỳia, Tinòdes, Holarc.; Lỳpe, Metalỳpe, Palæarc.).................PSYCHOMYÌIDÆ
15. Both median and discal cells of fore wings present and closed; maxillary palpi five-jointed (Fig. 360). (Heteropléctron, Am.; Ganonèma, Am., Ind.; Anisocéntropus, Holarc., Indoaustr.; Calamóceras, Palæarc.; Phyllòicus, Neotrop.; Phyllorheìthrus, Austr.).
                                    CALAMOCERÁTIDÆ
    Median cell of fore wings absent...........................16
16. Maxillary palpi of the male three-jointed, or very rarely one-jointed; of the female five-jointed...............................17
    Maxillary palpi five-jointed in both sexes....................19
17. Middle tibiæ with four apical spurs........................18
    Middle tibiæ with two or three apical spurs; discal cell always closed in the fore wings and open in the hind wing. (Brachycéntrus, Micrasèma) .... BRACHYCÉNTRIDÆ
18. Mesoscutellum with a single large, oval or rounded boss on wart-like elevation. (Gòera, Sìlo, Pseudogòera).............GOÉRIDÆ
    Mesoscutellum with a pair of smaller, separated bosses; middle tibiæ not spinose. (Lepidóstoma, Holarc.; Atomỳia, Atomyòides, Am.).
                                    LEPIDOSTOMÁTIDÆ

19. Discal cell absent in both fore and hind wings..................20
    Discal cell present in fore wing............................21
20. Tibial spurs 2,4,4; maxillary palpi with the basal two joints very
    short. (Molánna, Holarc., Indomal.; Molannòdes, Holarc.).
                                                    MOLÁNNIDÆ
    Tibial spurs 2,2,4; maxillary palpi with the first joint short, the
    second and third of about equal length. (Beræa, Holarc.;
    Beræòdes, Palæarc.) ....BERÆIDÆ
21. Middle tibiæ with two spurs; discal cell of hind wings almost
    always open or absent, only the upper branch of the radial sector
    forked, only the first apical fork present; joints of maxillary palpi
    uniform; antennæ long and slender. (Leptócerus, Œcetis, Setòdes,
    widespr.; Mystácides, Holarc.; Leptocélla, Am.; Notanatólica,
    Indoaustr.) .... LEPTOCÉRIDÆ
    Middle tibiæ usually with four spurs; discal cell of hind wings
    closed, both branches of radial sector of fore wings forked, at
    least the first and second apical forks present; basal joint of
    antennæ large. (Neróphilus, Nearc.; Psilotrèta, Holarc.; Odon-
    tócerum, Palæarc.; Marília, Am.; Barypénthus, Neotrop.).
                                                 ODONTOCÉRIDÆ

Larvæ

1. Abdomen greatly wider than the thorax; very minute species with
   all three thoracic segments heavily chitinized above, living in
   portable silken cases which are much larger than the larvæ;
   vegetarian .... HYDROPTÍLIDÆ
   Abdomen not much wider than the thorax, much larger species
   usually with only the prothorax heavily chitinized............2
2. Anal leg with an elongate sclerite; last abdominal segment with a
   chitinous shield above; predatory or vegetarian.
                                              RHYACOPHÍLIDÆ
   Anal leg not with an elongate sclerite; last abdominal segment without a chitinous shield...................................3
3. Mandible with numerous bristles on the outer edge; tracheal gills
   present along the sides of the abdomen; legs very unequal; predatory or vegetarian......................HYDROPSÝCHIDÆ
   Mandible with only two bristles on the outer edge; tracheal gills
   absent 4
4. Labrum soft, whitish, retractile under the edge of the clypeus.
   (Fig. 367) ....PHILOPOTÁMIDÆ
   Labrum sclerotized, yellowish or brownish....................5
5. Claws of hind legs very small, those of the front and middle legs
   large .... MOLÁNNIDÆ
   Claws of hind legs as long as those of middle legs..............6

6. Antennæ elongate, at least eight times as long as thick, inserted at the base of the mandibles; femur of hind leg divided into a short basal and long apical piece. Vegetarian species.

LEPTOCÉRIDÆ, part

Antennæ much shorter and stouter, never more than three or four times as long as thick and sometimes minute.................7

7. Mesonotum submembranous, with a pair of curved sclerotized bars whose convex sides lie toward the median line.

LEPTOCÉRIDÆ, part

Mesonotum without such thickened bars......................8

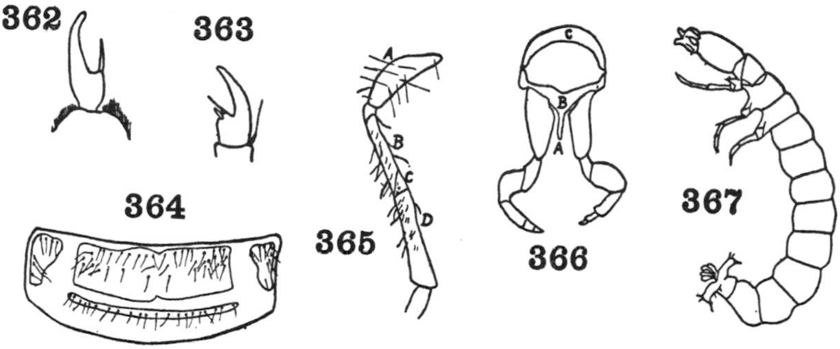

Figs. 362–367. Trichoptera, *Larvæ*

362. **Phylocentropus,** tarsal claw of front leg (Krafka) Polycentropodidæ.
363. **Timeodes,** tarsal claw (Rousseau) Psychomyiidæ.
364. **Psilotreta,** dorsal view of metathorax showing chitinous plates. (Krafka) Odontoceridæ.
365. **Leptocella,** front leg. *a,* coxa; *b,* trochanter; *c* and *d,* femur. (Krafka) Leptoceridæ.
366. **Limnephilus,** anterior view of prothorax in section showing prosternal horn (Krafka) Limnephilidæ.
367. **Philopotamus,** larva (Rousseau) Philopotamidæ.

8. Both meso- and metanotum entirely membranous, at most with only minute thickened spots. Larval case tubular, open at both ends, usually straight or but little bent, built on a spiral axis.

PHRYGANÈIDÆ

Mesonotum, and usually also the metanotum with some well developed thickened sclerites...............................9

9. Labrum with a complete transverse row of stout setæ extending across its disk.................... CALAMOCERÁTIDÆ

Labrum without such a row; usually bearing six to eight large setæ and small ones, irregularly placed....................10

10. Anal hooks with a deeply serrate edge of comb-like teeth; larva living in a spiral case strikingly similar in form to a snail shell.

HELICOPSÝCHIDÆ

Anal hooks without a comb-like edge; larval case not formed like
a snail shell..11

11. Metanotum with several well developed sclerites, a large transverse
one, a narrow longitudinal one on each side near the lateral margin and a less clearly defined narrow transverse one near the
posterior edge .... **ODONTOCÉRIDÆ**
Metanotum of a different conformation; with no large sclerites and
only a few very small poorly developed ones.................12

12. Anal hooks each bearing two or three subequal, large teeth.
SERICOSTOMÁTIDÆ
Anal hooks each bearing a single large tooth supplemented by one
or several small ones......................................13

13. Pronotum with a deep transverse furrow which is edged behind
by a raised, carinate ridge.............**BRACHYCÉNTRIDÆ**
Pronotum of a different conformation, at most with a weakly concave transverse impression...............................14

14. Claws of hind tarsi as long as the tibiæ, extremely slender.
BERÆIDÆ
Claws of hind tarsi not lengthened, very much shorter than the
tibiæ 15

15. Mesonotum not divided into plates, covered by a single rectangular
sclerite, with at most a line of fracture along the median line...16
Mesonotum covered by four sclerites, a large anterior pair and a
smaller posterior pair separated by a median and a transverse
suture .... **GOÉRIDÆ**

16. Antennæ inserted very close to the eyes; first abdominal tergite
smooth, without a hump.............**LEPIDOSTOMÁTIDÆ**
Antennæ inserted as near or nearer to the margin of the head than
to the eye; first abdominal tergite with a median tubercle. Vegetarian species .... **LIMNEPHÍLIDÆ**

Pupæ

1. Tip of abdomen simple, without sclerotized plates or projections,
at most with only ventral membranous lobes.................2
Tip of abdomen bearing paired sclerotized lobes, triangular plates
or finger-like, often pointed structures.....................4

2. Mandibles serrate or with distinct teeth internally before the apex..3
Mandibles falcate, without teeth or serrations internally.
HYDROPTÍLIDÆ

3. Teeth of mandibles near the middle, or the edge serrate.
RHYACOPHÍLIDÆ
Teeth of mandibles in a group near the tip....**PHILOPOTÁMIDÆ**

4. Fifth abdominal tergite with both an anterior and posterior pair
of small plates that bear small hooks......................5

Fifth tergite with only a single pair of hook-bearing plates.
HYDROPSÝCHIDÆ

5. Seventh tergite entirely membranous, without sclerotized plates...6
Seventh tergite with a pair of plates, bearing hooks.............9

6. Processes at tip of abdomen triangular in dorsal view, sharply curved downward in lateral view.................BERÆIDÆ
Processes at tip of abdomen much longer, or not curved downward 7

7. First abdominal tergite without a transverse ridge or carina on its disk before apex; at least some of the plates on fifth and sixth tergites bearing only 2–3 hooks.........................8
First abdominal tergite with an arcuate ridge near the center; plates on fifth and sixth tergites each bearing 4–8 hooks.
MOLÁNNIDÆ

8. Apical processes of abdomen narrow, finger-like, bearing long black hairs at their tips......................HELICOPSÝCHIDÆ
Apical processes of abdomen of a different conformation or without long hairs at tip...........................LEPTOCÉRIDÆ

9. Sides of abdomen conspicuously hairy......................10
Abdomen without lateral fringe of hair; tip of abdomen bilobed and emarginate medially...................PSYCHOMYÌIDÆ

10. Abdomen bearing hooks in a pair of transverse lines between the fifth and sixth tergites.................BRACHYCÉNTRIDÆ
Hooks between fifth and sixth tergites arranged in much broader bands or forming rounded groups.........................11

11. Processes at tip of abdomen triangular or plate-like in dorsal view.
PHRYGANÈIDÆ
Processes at tip of abdomen usually much longer, finger-like; if not, each bears a group of very long black hairs apically.....12

12. Processes at tip of abdomen short, widely separated, and bearing black spines several times as long as the processes.
LEPIDOSTOMÁTIDÆ
Processes either much longer or more narrowly separated.......13

13. Tip of mandibles pointed, but not produced into a styliform tip...14
Tip of mandibles produced at apex into a narrow, whip-like style.
ODONTOCÉRIDÆ

14. Abdomen bare above, with isolated setæ only.................15
Abdomen above bearing dense patches of fine hair, forming more or less complete transverse bands.......CALAMOCERÁTIDÆ

15. Apical processes of abdomen each with a slender terminal appendage.
SERICOSTOMÁTIDÆ
Apical processes without such an appendage..................16

16. Antennæ twice as long as the body, looped several times around the apical processes of the abdomen.........LEPTOCÉRIDÆ

Antennæ much shorter and not looped around the apical processes 17

17. Apical processes sharply narrowed toward the tip into a sinuate, thread-like extension ....**GOÉRIDÆ**
Apical processes not greatly narrowed at tip, not sinuate, bearing apical bristly hairs.......................**LIMNEPHÍLIDÆ**

LITERATURE ON TRICHOPTERA

BANKS, N. Genera of Nearctic Leptoceridæ. Trans. American Ent. Soc., **25,** pp. 199–218 (1898).
  Genera of Nearctic Hydropsychidæ. Trans. American Ent. Soc., **32,** pp. 1–20 (1906).
  Genera of Nearctic Sericostomatidæ. Proc. Ent. Soc. Washington, **8,** pp. 117–133 (1906).
  Classification of Nearctic Limnephilidæ. Canadian Ent., **48,** pp. 117–122 (1916).
BARNARD, K. H. South African Trichoptera. Trans. Roy. Soc. South Africa, **21,** pp. 291–394, 52 figs. (1934).
BERLAND, L. and M. E. MOSELY. Catalogue des Trichoptères de France. Ann. Soc. ent. France, **106,** pp. 133–168 (1937).
BETTEN, C., *et al.* Trichoptera of New York State. Bull. New York State Mus., No. 292, 576 pp., 67 pls., 61 figs. (1934).
COSTA LIMA, A. DA. Tricopteros. Insetos do Brasil, **4,** pp. 109–113, 14 figs. (1943).
DENNING, D. G. The Hydropsychidæ of Minnesota. Ent. Americana, (N.S.), **23,** pp. 101–170, 5 pls. (1943).
DÖHLER, W. Systematik und Biologie der Trichopteren. Sitzb. naturf. Ges. Leipzig, **41** (1915).
EATON, A. E. Review of Hydroptilidæ. Trans. Ent. Soc. London, 1873, pp. 125–151 (1873).
HAGEN, H. A. Phryganidarum synopsis. Verh. k. k. zool.-bot. Ges. Wien, **14,** pp. 799–890 (1864).
  Beiträge zur Kenntnis der Phryganiden. Verh. k. k. zool.-bot. Ges. Wien, **23,** pp. 377–452 (1873).
HANDLIRSCH, A. and M. BEIER. Zehnte Ueberordnung der Pterygogenea: Panorpoidea. In Kükenthal, Handb. Zool., **4,** Hälfte 2, Lief. 6, pp. 1491–1553, 69 figs. (1936).
HICKIN, N. E. Larvæ of the British Trichoptera. Trans. Roy. Ent. Soc. London, **97,** pp. 187–212 (1946).
  Pupæ of the British Trichoptera. Trans. Roy. Ent. Soc. London, **100,** pp. 275–289, 10 figs. (1949).
IWATA, M. Trichopterous larvæ from Japan. Annot. Zool. Japonenses, **11,** pp. 202–233 (1927).
KRAFKA, J. Key to the Families of Trichopterous Larvæ. Canadian Ent., **47,** pp. 217–225 (1915).
KUWAYAMA, S. The Stenopsychidæ of Japan. Ins. Matsumurana., **4,** pp. 109–119 (1930).

LAMEERE, A. Trichoptera. In Précis de Zoologie. Rec. Inst. zool. Torley-Rousseau, **5**, pp. 49–70, 29 figs. (1938).

LESTAGE, J. A. Trichoptera, in Rousseau, Larves et Nymphes aquatiques des Insectes d'Europe, pp. 343–964 (1921).

Catalogue des Trichoptères d'Afrique. Rev. Zool. Africaine, **6**, pp. 251–335 (1919) and Ann. Soc. Ent. Belgique, **59**, pp. 130–135 (1919).

Note Trichoptérologique. Bull. and Ann. Ent. Soc. Belgique, **65**, pp. 363–386 (1926).

LLOYD, J. T. Larvæ of North American Trichoptera. Bull. Lloyd Libr., Cincinnati, Ent. Ser., No. 1, 124 pp. (1921).

MARLIER, G. J. Trichoptères du Congo belge. Rev. Zool. Bot. afr., **37**, pp. 64–88, 13 figs. (1943).

MARTYNOV, A. V. Preliminary revision of Phryganeidæ. Ann. Mag. Nat. Hist. (9), **14**, pp. 209–224 (1924).

On the family Stenopsychidæ. Eos, **2**, pp. 281–308 (1926).

Trichoptera of China and Eastern Tibet. Proc. Zool. Soc. London, **1930**, pp. 65–112, 1 pl., 71 figs. (1930).

Trichoptera of the Amur Region. Trav. Inst. zool. Acad. Sci. URSS, **2**, pp. 205–395, 198 figs. (1935).

On a Collection of Trichoptera from the Indian Museum. Part 1. Rec. Indian Mus., **37**, pp. 93–209, 109 figs. (1935); Part 2, *ibid.*, **38**, pp. 239–366, 74 figs. (1936).

McLACHLAN, R. A monographic revision and synopsis of the Trichoptera of the European fauna. London. Van Voorst (1874–80).

MILNE, L. J. Studies in North American Trichoptera. Three parts. 128 pp. Cambridge, Mass., privately printed (1934–36).

MILNE, L. J. and M. J. Arctopsychidæ of Continental North America. Bull. Brooklyn Ent. Soc., **33**, pp. 97–110, 3 pls. (1938).

MILNE, M. J. Immature North American Trichoptera. Psyche, **46**, pp. 9–19 (1939).

MORTON, K. J. North American Hydroptilidæ. Bull. New York State Mus., No. 86, pp. 63–75 (1905).

MOSELY, M. E. Trichoptera of Corsica. Eos, **6**, pp. 147–184, 81 figs. (1930).

Revision of Beræinæ. Ann. Mag. Nat. Hist., (10)**6**, pp. 392–414 (1930).

Indian Trichoptera. Journ. Bombay Nat. Hist. Soc., **37**, pp. 620–629, 5 figs. (1934); **38**, pp. 123–133, 9 pls. (1935); **38**, pp. 447–478, 18 pls., 16 figs. (1936); **40**, pp. 486–496, 12 pls. (1938); **41**, pp. 39–47, 332–339, 19 pls. (1939); **42**, pp. 772–781, 12 pls. (1941).

Tasmanian Trichoptera. Proc. Zool. Soc. London, **1936**, pp. 395–424, 72 figs. (1936).

Revision of the Triplectidinæ, Subfamily of the Leptoceridæ. Trans. Roy. Ent. Soc. London, **85**, pp. 91–130, 98 figs. (1936).

Trichoptera. Ruwenzori Exped. 1934–35, **3**, 1–40, 3 pls., 123 figs. British Mus. (Nat. Hist.), London (1939).

British Caddis-flies. xiii + 320 pp., 631 figs., 3 pls. Geo. Routledge and Sons, Ltd., London (1939).

MOSELY, M. E. and D. E. KIMMINS. Trichoptera of Australia and New Zealand. 550 pp., 364 figs. British Mus. (Nat. Hist.), London (1953).

PERRIER, R. Trichoptères de la France. Faune de France, **3**, pp. 127–150 (1934).

Ross, H. H. Trichoptera of Illinois. Bull. Illinois Nat. Hist. Surv., **23**, pp. 1–326, 961 figs. (1944).

Review of Nearctic Lepidostomatidæ. Ann. Ent. Soc. America, **39**, pp. 265–291 (1946).

TSUDA, M. Untersuchungen über die japanischen Wasserinsekten. I. Annot. Zool. Japonenses, **15**, pp. 394–399, 1 pl. (1936).

ULMER, G. Trichoptera. Gen. Insectorum, fasc. 60, 289 pp. (1907).

Trichoptera. Süsswasserfauna Deutschlands, Lief. 5 and 6, 326 pp. (1909).

Literature on Trichoptera (1910–14). Zeits. wissensch. Insektenbiol., **15** (various parts) (1919–21).

Trichoptera. In Tierwelt Mitteleuropas, **6**, Lief. 1, pp. XV, 1–46 (1928).

Trichopteren von den Philippinen und Sunda Inseln. Treubia, **11**, pp. 373–498, 147 figs. (1930).

Die Trichopteren, Ephemeropteren und Plecopteren des arktischen Gebietes. Fauna arctica, **6**, pp. 219–222 (1932).

Trichopteren von den Sunda-Inseln. Arch. Hydrobiol., **19**, Suppl., 328 pp. (1951).

ORDER LEPIDÓPTERA [1]

(GLOSSÀTA)

Rather large, sometimes small, or very large insects; wings and body thickly clothed with scales that usually form a color pattern, the wings opaque, with the venation and membrane obscured by the scales; scaly covering rarely restricted to certain portions of the wings; wings very rarely absent. Antennæ long, many-jointed, variously modified, filiform, pectinate or clubbed; ocelli often present. Mouthparts suctorial, frequently vestigial, when not in use coiled under the head; the galea of the maxillæ modified into an unjointed sucking tube; mandibles absent, except in a few primitive forms; palpi usually well developed, the labial ones generally larger than the maxillary. Prothorax small; wings large, membranous, similar, the fore pair usually somewhat longer; venation complete, but not complex, few crossveins. Legs similar, tarsi ordinarily five-jointed. No cerci. Metamorphosis very great; larvæ with chewing mouthparts, usually caterpillar-like, and usually with paired false-legs on some of the abdominal segments in addition to three pairs of thoracic legs; the false-legs (prolegs) usually bear distally several minute hooks (crochets); larvæ almost always plant-feeders; pupæ with appendages free or soldered to body, usually enclosed in a cocoon or earthen cell. Moths, Butterflies and Skippers.

Adults

1. Wings absent or greatly reduced in size......................153
   Wings normally developed...................................2

[1] Revised by C. L. Remington.

2. Fore and hind wings with four or five radial veins, rarely with three, Sc and R_1 separate (Fig. 374); wings of similar shape, more or less pointed at tip, with ten or more veins, the membrane with minute spines (Fig. 369); fore wings with a thumb-like lobe (jugum) at basal angle (except *Neopseustis*); a coiled proboscis never developed. (Suborder HOMONEÙRA) (*MICRO-PTERYGÌNA, JUGÀTÆ, ARCHILEPIDÓPTERA, ISONEÙ-RIA*) 3

Fore and hind wings dissimilar in shape and venation, hind wings with Sc and R_1 fused at least at tip (not to be confused with R_s which is usually the only free radial vein (Fig. 368)), rarely two free radial veins present, at most six veins arising from the cell;

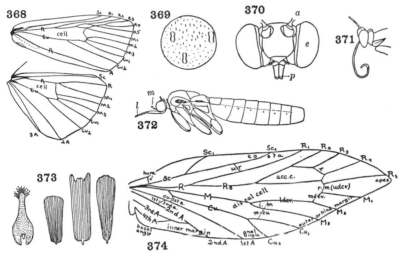

Figs. 368–374. **Lepidoptera**

368. **Noctua,** wings (Forbes): Sc, subcosta, R, radius, M, media, Cu, cubitus (their branches indicated by numbers), A, 2A, 3A, anal veins; cell, discal cell. Noctuidæ.
369. Portion of bleached wing membrane, showing attachments of three scales and numerous aculeæ.
370. **Danaus,** head in frontal view: a, base of antenna; e, eye; p, base of proboscis. Danaidæ.
371. **Nymphalis,** head, prothorax and part of mesothorax (Scudder) Nymphalidæ.
372. **Crambus,** lateral outline of body (Fernald): m, maxillary palpus; l, labial palpus.
373. Scales from the wings of various Lepidoptera (Scudder).
374. **Micropteryx** (Forbes): Sc, subcosta; R, radius; M, media; Cu, cubitus; A, anal (their branches indicated by numbers); hum, humeral crossvein; udcv, upper discocellular vein (radio-medial crossvein); ldcv, lower discocellular vein; i, intercalated cell; acc. c, accessory cell. Micropterygidæ.

jugum and mandibles not developed. (Suborder HETERO-
NEÙRA) (*FRENÀTÆ, ANISONEÙRIA*) 10
3. Wings usually hardly wider than the fringe of hairs on their hind
   margin; small species, wing-expanse up to one-half inch; jugum
   usually minute, frenulum present. (*MICROJUGÀTÆ, JUGO-
   FRENÀTÆ*) 4
   Wings ample, fringe narrower; larger species, wing expanse about
   one-half to nine inches; tibial spurs usually wanting; jugum
   usually underlapping the hind wing, no frenulum; mouthparts
   (except labial palpi) vestigial, functionless. (Superfamily HEP-
   IALÒIDEA). (*MACROJUGÀTÆ*) 7
4. Middle tibiæ without spurs, but with an apical group of bristles;
   functional, toothed mandibles present; maxillary galeæ short; Sc
   forked near middle. (**Epimartýria**, N. Am.; **Micrópteryx** (= *Erio-
   céphala*) (Fig. 374), Holarc.; **Sabatínca**, Austr.). (Superfamily
   MICROPTERYGÒIDEA) (*ZEUGLÓPTERA*). (*ERIOCEPHÁ-
   LIDÆ*) .... **MICROPTERÝGIDÆ**
   Middle tibiæ with one or two spurs; mandibles vestigial or wanting;
   maxillary galeæ long, forming a rudimentary proboscis; Sc simple
   or forked near tip. (Superfamily ERIOCRANIÒIDEA) (*DÁC-
   NÓNYPHA*) 5
5. Jugum absent; middle and hind tibiæ with spurs. (**Neopseùstis**,
   India, Formosa) .... **NEOPSEÙSTIDÆ**
   Jugal lobe present; hind tibiæ with or without spurs..........6
6. Middle tibiæ with one spur; hind tibiæ with four; Sc forked near
   tip, at least in fore wing; jugum large, overlapping the hind wing;
   scales not scalloped nor coarsely striated. (**Dyseriocrània**, Holarc.;
   Eriocrània, Palæarc.) .... **ERIOCRANÌIDÆ**
   Middle tibiæ with two spurs; hind tibiæ with none; Sc simple;
   jugum much reduced, underlapping the hind wing; scales with
   scalloped border and coarse striation. (**Mnesarchæa**, N. Zealand).
   MNESARCHÆIDÆ
7. Tibial spurs entirely absent or small and single, on middle and
   hind legs 8
   Two apical spurs on middle tibia, four on hind tibia; Sc forked in
   forewing; two or three discal cells, at least in hindwing, produced
   by persistence of veins M_{1+2} and M_{3+4}; antennal segments simple and hairy. (**Protótheòra**, **Metatheòra**, S. Afr.; **Anómoses**,
   Austr. (Fig. 377)). (*ANOMOSÉTIDÆ*).
   PROTOTHEÓRIDÆ
8. Tibial spurs absent 9
   Small single tibial spur present on middle and hind legs; Sc forked
   in forewing; two discal cells present; antennæ simple and hairy.
   (**Genùstes**, Assam)
   .... **PALÆOSÉTIDÆ**, part

9. Discal cell subdivided into three cells by veins M_{1+2} and M_{3+4} (Fig. 375); Sc usually simple (rarely forked); antennal segments usually angular and dentate or bipectinate; wing expanse one to nine inches. (**Hepìalus,** Cosmop.; **Korscheltéllus, Phimátopus,** Holarc.; **Sthenòpsis,** Nearc.; **Triódia,** Palæarc.; **Phássus,** widespr.; **Charàgia,** Austr.; **Porìna,** Austr., Patagonia; **Leto,** S. Afr.).
.... HEPIÁLIDÆ
Discal cell single or at most double, never subdivided by vein M_{1+2} (Fig. 376); Sc forked (*Palæoses*) or simple (*Ogygìoses*); antennal segments simple and hairy. (**Palæoses,** Austr.; **Ogygìoses,** Formosa) .... PALÆOSÉTIDÆ, part

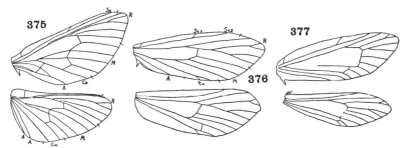

Figs. 375–377. Lepidoptera

375. **Phassus,** wings (Hampson) Hepialidæ.
376. **Palæoses,** wings (Turner) Palæosetidæ.
377. **Anomoses,** wings (Turner) Prototheoridæ.

10. Antennæ simple or variously modified (Figs. 378, 379, 380), only rarely swollen at the tip, and in such cases a frenulum and usually a tympanum are present or the subcosta of hind wing is not strongly arched; most forms with a frenulum; the subcosta of the hind wing either relatively little arched at the base or there is a large area between it and the fore margin of the wing; wings at rest usually overlapping the abdomen, sloping roof-like against the sides, or horizontally outspread; body often relatively stout; ocelli often present. Moths. (HETERÓCERA).......11
Antennæ knobbed at the tip, or thickened a little before the tip (Figs. 431, 432), without pectinations, projecting processes or conspicuous arrangements of hairs along the shaft; hind wings without a frenulum (except *Euschèmon*), but with the Sc strongly arched forward at the base; tympanum absent; proboscis well-developed; the wings usually erect when at rest; no ocelli; nearly all diurnal. Butterflies and Skippers. (RHOPALÓCERA)...143
11. Wings, especially the hind ones, usually deeply cleft, or divided

into plume-like divisions (Figs. 384, 385); legs very long. Plume
moths 12
Wings entire, not cleft nor divided into finger-like divisions, rarely
(Gelechiidæ) the fore wings moderately cleft 14
12. Wings divided into two to four divisions 13
Each wing divided into six plumes; small, silvery white moths.
(**Orneòdes,** widespr.) (Fig. 384) ....**ORNEÓDIDÆ**

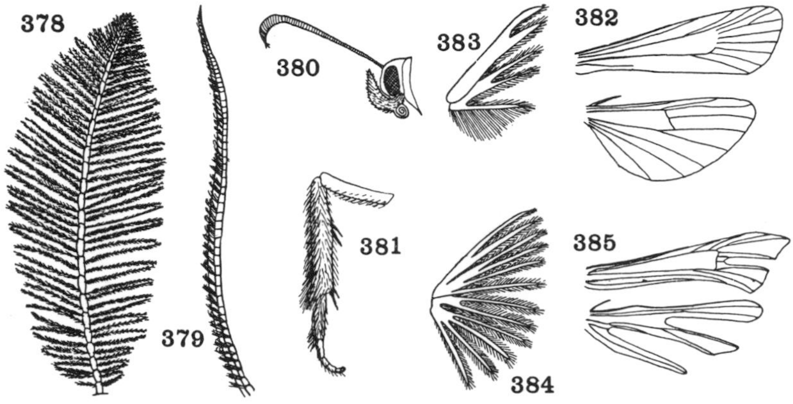

Figs. 378–385.　Lepidoptera

378. Plumose antenna of moth (Duncan).
379. Pectinate antenna of moth (Duncan).
380. **Melittia,** head, in lateral view (Beutenmüller) Ægeriidæ.
381. **Bembecia,** middle leg (Beutenmüller) Ægeriidæ.
382. **Melittia,** wings (Beutenmüller) Ægeriidæ.
383. **Pterophorus,** wings (Berlese) Pterophoridæ.
384. **Orneodes,** wings (Berlese) Orneodidæ.
385. **Platyptilia,** wings (Fernald) Pterophoridæ.

13. Fore wings divided into two plumes, rarely four, hind wings into
three; double series of large, divergent scales along underside of
cubital vein of hind wing; small, delicate moths, usually prettily
colored. (**Oxýptilus, Platyptília,** cosmop.; **Pteróphorus,** widespr.)
(Figs. 383, 385, 404). (*ALUCÍTIDÆ*).....**PTEROPHÓRIDÆ**
Each wing divided into two plumes. (**Cenóloba,** Indomal., Austr.)
(See couplet 39) ....**OXYCHIRÓTIDÆ,** part
14. Underside of hind wing with a double series of enlarged and divergent scales along the cubital vein; tibiæ exceptionally long,
thin and with long spurs. (**Agdístis,** Palæarc., Ethiop.).
PTEROPHÓRIDÆ, part
Underside of wings without such specialized scales 15

15. Hind wings usually in large part transparent and devoid of scales, except on margins and veins; fore wing narrow, at least four times as long as wide; inner margin of fore wing and costal margin of hind wing each with a row of recurved, interlocking spines; Sc of hind wings close to cell and to next vein, somewhat hidden in a fold and apparently absent; frenulum well developed; ocelli and proboscis present; antennæ usually dilated and tufted at tip; wasp-like, day-flying moths (Figs. 380, 381, 382). Clear-wing moths. (**Paranthrène**, widespr.; **Ramosia**, Nearc.; **Trochílium**, Holarc., Ethiop.; **Melíttia, Ægèria**, cosmop.). (*SESI-IDÆ*) .... ÆGERÏIDÆ

Wings scaled throughout, or if clear, the fore wings are triangular; wings not interlocking by series of spines on both fore and hind wings; Sc of hind wing present (except Euchromiidæ), usually noticeable, though sometimes close to or in part fused with R.. 16

16. Antennæ thin, swollen at tip to form a more or less distinct club, as in the butterflies, or even recurved at tip, as in the skippers; tympanum absent; frenulum present........................17

Antennæ variously modified, if swollen subapically or toward the middle they gradually taper on distal portion, or tympanum present 19

17. Fore wing with some branches of R stalked; frenulum well developed in both sexes 18

Fore wing with all veins arising from discal cell, medial stem reduced; both wings with first anal vein lacking; eyes not ciliated; male alone with frenulum. (See couplet 143). (**Euschèmon**, Austr.) ....HESPERÏIDÆ, part

18. Fore wings with M_2 arising midway between M_1 and M_3, or closer to M_1; hind wings with first A wanting; chætosema present; ocelli absent; proboscis present. African. (**Apoprógenes**). APOPROGÉNIDÆ

Fore wings with M_2 arising nearer M_3 than M_1 (if M_2 and M_3 are stalked, cf. Ctenuchidæ, couplet 75); chætosema absent; ocelli present .... CASTNÏIDÆ

a. Fore wings with first A present, discal cell closed; proboscis developed. (**Cástnia**, Neotrop.; **Synèmon**, Austr.).....CASTNÏINÆ

Both wings with first A reduced; discal cell open; proboscis vestigial. (**Táscina** (=*Neocástnia*), Indomal.). (*NEOCASTNÏIDÆ*). TASCINÏINÆ

19. Hind wings with three anal veins (if less than three anals, tiny species with narrow wings, the hind pair with reduced venation and bearing a long fringe of hairs on the hind margin almost as wide as, or wider than, the wing, and the tibial spurs more than twice the width of the tibiæ); fore wings usually with first

anal vein complete, *i.e.* usually two anal veins reaching the margin 20

Hind wings with two anal veins, rarely with one, in addition to a possible unthickened fold in the membrane, or in the Australian genus *Oxychirota* both wings lack all anals; wings almost never very narrow, the hind wing not more than half longer than wide, except rarely in large species when a tail-like projection is developed, and never with the fringe as wide as the wing; fore wings usually with but one complete anal vein, when accessory cell is present it is not completely contiguous with the discal cell (if accessory cell is completely contiguous refer to couplet 97, Cecidosetidæ) 38

20. Hind wings with veins $Sc+R_1$ and R_s widely separate beyond discal cell...21

Hind wings with veins $Sc+R_1$ and R_s fused or very closely parallel for a greater or less distance between the end of the discal cell and the tip of the wing, the base of R sometimes evanescent. (PYRALÍDIDÆ, *s.lat.*)..68

21. Hind wings ribbon-like, with a long apical tail (Fig. 386). (**Himantópterus, Semióptila,** African).

HIMANTOPTERÌNÆ; ZYGÆNIDÆ

Wings normal 22

22. Hind wings with veins $Sc+R_1$ and R_s fusing to near the end of the discal cell, or fusing beyond the middle of the cell, or these veins coincident throughout..23

Hind wings with veins $Sc+R_1$ and R_s separate from the base, or fusing only a short distance along the discal cell, the fusion located at the base or before the middle of the cell, or sometimes connected by a bar..24

23. Proboscis well developed; chætosema present; wings thinly scaled, translucent; hind wings with basal part of R represented as a spur in the cell, or entirely lost. (**Acolòithus, Pyromórpha,** Am.) (see couplet 41). (*ZYGÆNIDÆ*, of authors).

PYROMÓRPHIDÆ, part

Proboscis obsolete; chætosema present; hind wings with $Sc+R_1$ and R_s separate in part; wings heavily and loosely clothed with soft scales, mixed with curly hair in the northern species; hind wings (in American species) with R free at base. Flannel moths. (**Nòrape, Podàlia, Àides, Xenárchus, Somábrachys, Lagòa, Megalopỳge**). (*LAGÒIDÆ*) ....MEGALOPÝGIDÆ

Proboscis and palpi absent; chætosema absent; veins $Sc+R_1$ and R_s coincident throughout. (**Eulophónotus,** Ethiop.).

EULOPHONOTÌNÆ; CÓSSIDÆ

24. The fringe on the anal angle of the hind wings not or but slightly

longer than elsewhere; tibial spurs at most about as long as the
width of the tibiæ..25
The fringe on the anal angle of the hind wings distinctly longer
than elsewhere; tibial spurs more than twice the width of the
tibiæ; when the accessory cell is present its longest side is contiguous with the discal cell. (TINEÒIDEA)................85
25. Fore wings with accessory (radial) cell.......................26
Radial cell not formed......................................30
26. Proboscis vestigial...27
Mouthparts usually developed, with scaled proboscis; tibial spurs
long; female usually with an anal tuft; small to minute moths.
(TINEOIDEA) 85

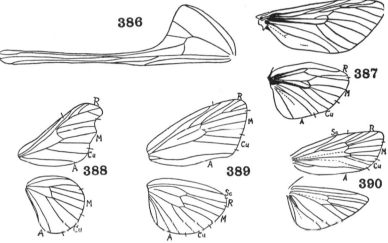

Figs. 386–390. Lepidoptera

386. **Himantopterus,** hind wing (Westwood) Zygænidæ.
387. **Prionoxystus,** wings (Comstock and Needham) Cossidæ.
388. **Bombyx,** wings. Bombycidæ.
389. **Metarbela,** wings (Hampson) Cossidæ.
390. **Simaethis,** wings (Spuler) Glyphipterygidæ.

27. Tibial spurs short or wanting; large moths, except Epipyropidæ....28
Hind tibiæ with two pairs of spurs; small species, 9–18 mm.;
R 4-branched; ♀ wingless. (**Talæpòria,** Old World, **Solenòbia,**
Holarc.; **Lúffia,** Palæarc.).....**TALÆPORIÌNÆ; PSÝCHIDÆ**
28. Fore wings with some branches of R stalked; accessory cell ex-
tending beyond the discal cell; body heavy, or wings ample....29
Fore wings with no stalked radial branches; accessory cell not ex-

tending beyond the discal cell; antennæ bipectinate in both sexes; small moths, larvæ living as external parasites on Fulgoridæ and Cicadidæ. (**Epipỳrops**, Indoaustr., Am., Japan) . .EPIPỲRÓPIDÆ

29. Wings strong and more or less lanceolate; body heavy and surpassing the hind wings; median cell and strong medial stem nearly always present in discal cell of each wing; larvæ borers. Carpenter moths . . . . CÓSSIDÆ

a. Fore wing with first anal vein well developed. . . . . .b
Fore wing with first anal vein reduced. c

b. Hind wing with Sc entirely fused with the cell and R. (See couplet 23) . . . . .EULOPHONOTÌNÆ
Hind wing with Sc entirely separate from the cell and R. (Fig. 387). (**Zeùzera**, Palæarc., Ind.; **Cóssus**, cosmop.; **Prionoxýstus**, Am.; **Phragmatœcia**, Palæarc.). (*ZEUZÉRIDÆ, HYPÓPTIDÆ*).
COSSÌNÆ

c. Frenulum present. Restricted to Madagascar. (**Chrysótypus, Argyrótypus**). (*CHRYSOTÝPIDÆ*) . . . . .ARGYROTYPÌNÆ
Frenulum usually absent; small, brightly colored species. Tropicopolitan. (**Metarbèla, Terágra, Selágena, Lepidarbèla**). (*ARBÉLIDÆ, HOLLÁNDIDÆ, TERÁGRIDÆ*). . . . . .METARBELÌNÆ

Wings ample, the subtriangular fore wings about half longer than wide and with the tip more or less acute, the hind pair with nearly straight end; abdomen not extending beyond the hind wings; mainly South American. (**Dálcera, Ácraga**, S. Am.; **Dalcérides**, Ariz.). (*ACRÁGIDÆ*).
DALCERÌNÆ; EUCLÈIDÆ

30. Frenulum absent or vestigial, humeral angle of hind wing more or less expanded; M_2 of fore wings arising midway between M_1 and M_3 or closer to M_1; chætosema absent; moderately large moths with broad hind wings. 31
Frenulum present (if absent in moths of small size with narrow and more or less oblong wings, refer to couplet 77). 33

31. Fore wings with radial branches $R_{2+3+4+5}$ united on a common stalk; hind wings with Sc and R connected by a bar (Fig. 388). (See couplet 56). . . . . .BOMBÝCIDÆ
Fore wing with radial branches R_{2+3}, R_{4+5} stalked independently of R_{1+2}; hind wings with Sc and R free beyond base. 32

32. The five branches of R very long, occupying more than one-third the apical edge of the wing, only R_3 and R_4 on a short stalk, the other radial branches free; wings large. (**Chrysopóloma, Éctropa**, Ethiop.). (*ECTRÓPIDÆ*) . . . . .CHRYSOPOLÓMIDÆ
Radial branches occupying one-fourth of the apical edge of the fore wings, R_{2+3}, or R_{4+5}, tip of fore wings extended and rather

pointed, the apical margin sinuate. American, mostly Neotropical. (See couplet 52) ....MIMALLÓNIDÆ

33. Fore wings with M_2 arising midway between M_1 and M_3, M_3 and Cu_1 united for a considerable distance beyond the discal cell, $R_{2,3,4,5}$ united, and first A absent; hind wings with Sc free from R_s from base, and first A evanescent on basal half. (See couplet 47). (Phryganídia, Cal.) ....DIÓPTIDÆ
Fore wings with M_2 arising closer to M_3 than to M_1, thus causing the cubitus to appear four-branched 34

34. Hind wings very small, with Sc and R separate beyond the base; hind tibiæ with strong middle and apical spurs; antennæ dilated apically; chætosema absent. African. (Charídea, Toòsa).
CHARIDÈIDÆ
Hind wings with Sc and R connected by a bar, or by fusion before the middle of the discal cell 35

35. Fore wings with first and second anals connected by a crossvein, or fusing before the tip. (Fig. 391). Bagworm moths. (See couplets 27, 42, 154). (Pachythèlia, Palæarc.; Fùmea, Palæarc.).
PSÝCHIDÆ, part
Fore wings with first and second anals not connected, nor apically fusing, or ıA absent 36

36. Proboscis well developed; chætosema present; antennæ dilated or pectinate in the male. (Cyclòsia; Gíngla; Campylòdes; Erásmia; Zygæna, Palæarc.; Pròcris, Palæarc., Indoaustr.; Chalcòsia; Aglàope). (Including CHALCOSÌIDÆ). ......ZYGÆNIDÆ
Proboscis and palpi much reduced 37

37. Fore wings with R_3, R_4 and R_5 stalked or united. (Sibìne, Phobè-tron, Prolimacòdcs, Am.; Eùclea, Am., tropicopol.; Heterogènea, Holarc.). (HETEROGENÈIDÆ, COCHLIDÌIDÆ, LIMA-CÓDIDÆ) ....EUCLÈIDÆ
Fore wings with only three simple branches of the radius, all aris-ing from the cell. (Heterógynis ♂, S. Eur.). (See couplet 153). (EPICNOPTERÝGIDÆ). ....HETEROGÝNIDÆ

38. Antennæ thickened, spindle-shaped, sometimes hooked or recurved at the tip, the joints usually carinated beneath, sometimes pectinated; hind wings with Sc and R_s connected by a strong crossvein near the middle of the discal cell, then extending closely parallel to the end of the cell or beyond; proboscis and palpi present; chætosema absent; stout, often large moths, with rather narrow wings, the hind pair much shorter than the fore wings. Hawk moths, Humming-bird moths. (Phlegethóntius (= Protopárce) Am.; Sphínx (= Hylòicus), cosmop.; Hémaris (= Hæmorrhàgia), Holarc.; Smerínthus, Celèrio (= Deilé-

phila), cosmop.; **Macroglóssa,** Palæarc.; **Acheróntia,** Old World
(*A. átropos,* Death's head moth)) . . . . .SPHÍNGIDÆ
Antennæ simple, thin, serrate, or pectinate, rarely swollen gradually near apex; wings proportionally larger; hind wings with
Sc and R_s rarely connected by a strong crossvein, and if so,
strongly divergent beyond it 39
39. Fore wings with one or two anal veins 40
Fore wings with no anal veins. (**Oxychiròta,** Austr.). (See couplet
13). . . . . .OXYCHIRÓTIDÆ

Figs. 391–393.   Lepidoptera

391. **Solenobia,** wings (Spuler) Psychidæ.
392. **Harrisina,** wings (Jones) Pyromorphidæ.
393. **Hemiceras,** wings (Hampson) Notodontidæ.

40. Fore wings with two distinct free anal veins 41
Fore wings with the anal veins more or less fused, or with but one
complete anal vein 42
41. Ocelli present; chætosema present; fore wing four times as long as
wide. (**Harrísina,** Am., Fig. 392). (See couplet 23).
                                        PYROMÓRPHIDÆ, part
Ocelli and chætosema absent; fore wing not more than twice as long
as wide; hind tibia with two pairs of spurs; antenna simple.
Tropical; Japan. (**Hyblæa, Erythròchrus**) . . . .**HYBLÆIDÆ**
42. Fore wings with the anal veins more or less fused or connected
by a crossvein so as to end as a single vein. (**Eurycýttarus,
Thyridópteryx**). (See couplets 27, 35, 154) . . . .**PSÝCHIDÆ,** part
Fore wings with a single complete anal vein, *i.e.* 2A, the first
anal always reduced, at most represented by a fold, and the third
anal short or wanting, generally connecting with the second
anal so that the latter appears to have a basal fork 43
43. Fore wings with M_2 arising from the middle of the end of the
discal cell, or in front of the middle, *i.e.* the cubitus apparently
three-branched 44

Fore wings with M_2 arising behind the middle of the discal cell, *i.e.* the cubitus apparently four-branched 62

44. Hind wings with Sc strongly angled, or rarely swollen and sinuous, at the base, usually with a strong humeral brace-vein at the bend, thence very close to or fusing with R_s for a greater or less distance along the cell; palpi and proboscis well developed; chætosema present 45

Hind wings with Sc and R_s fused from base to beyond the middle of the wing, swollen at base, then rapidly diverging; rather small, very slender species, with finely scaled wings, the fore pair narrow, the hind pair broad; the apparent three-branching of the cubitus of the fore wings due to the absence of M_2 and M_3. (See couplet 77) ....LITHOSÌIDÆ, part

Hind wings with Sc straight or gently curving at base, separate from R_s, no connecting bar present; proboscis often weak or undeveloped; chætosema weak or absent 46

45. Antennæ dilated toward tip; eyes hairy and ciliated. (**Sematùra, Coronídia, Lonchotùra,** Neotrop.; **Anurápteryx,** Am.). (*MANIDÌIDÆ*) ....SEMATÙRIDÆ

Antennæ slender or feathered, if dilated toward tip the eyes are bare; females of many species with minute or small, flightless wings. (See couplet 160). ....GEOMÉTRIDÆ

a. Radial areoles absent (rarely present in Ennominæ, which have vein M_2 of hind wing very weak or absent) c

One or two radial areoles present on fore wing (rarely absent); vein M_2 of hind wing strong, base usually midway M_1 and M_3; Sc of fore wing never anastomosed with R; small moths ....b

b. Hind wing with vein Sc anastomosed with R only near base; hind tibia of male either enlarged and with concealed hair-pencil or tibia much reduced. Cosmopolitan. (**Stèrrha, Scópula, Anisòdes, Cosýmbia, Timándra, Euacidàlia**). (*ACIDALÌINÆ*) STERRHÌNÆ

Hind wing with Sc anastomosed with R for long distance (rarely free and connected with R by cross-vein); hind tibia well developed and slender, hair-pencil external and slender when present. Cosmopolitan, but scarce in tropics. (**Dýsstroma, Lỳgris, Hydriómena, Hýdria, Xanthorhòe, Chloroclýstis, Notòreas, Dasyùris, Percnoptilòta, Operóphtera, Eupithècia, Horísme, Lýthria, Lobóphora**). (*HYDRIOMENÌNÆ*) ....LARENTÌINÆ

c. Hind wing with vein M_2 strong.........................d

Hind wing with vein M_2 very weak or absent (present in *Abraxas*), Sc entirely free from R or only shortly anastomosed at base and the two veins not bridged by a cross-vein; radial cell rarely present; hind tibia usually with a hair-pencil, lying in tibial groove; male antenna usually pectinate (rarely females); male hind wing often with blister-like "fovea" near anal vein, forming concavity on underside; often stout, hairy moths. Cosmopolitan. (Abráxas, Càbera, Ourápteryx, Énnomos, Bápta, Campæa, Selènia, Semiothìsa, Eránnis, Boármia, Gnóphos, Éctropis, Epímecis, Phigàlia, Paleácrita, Drepanulàtrix, Euchlæna, Carípeta, Metarránthis, Plagòdis, Pèro, Nacóphora, Azelìna, Declàna). (*GEOMET-RÌNÆ*, of authors; *BOARMIÌNÆ*) . . . . **ENNOMÌNÆ**

d. Hind wing with vein Sc free of R or diverging from R much below middle of cell (sometimes a crossvein between Sc and R); fore wing with Sc usually fused or connected with R; R_3 and R_4 distinct but on same stalk . . . . e

Hind wing with vein Sc fused with R to middle of cell, fore wing with Sc free; hind wing with base of M_2 midway between M_1 and M_3; fore wing with R_3 and R_4 fused or very long-stalked, always ending in costal margin; long-haired moths with very small labial palpi and small, oval eyes. Diurnal, early spring moths. (Bréphos, Leucobréphos, Holarc.) . . . . **BREPHÌNÆ**

e. Hind wing with vein M_2 at base midway between M_1 and M_3; fore wing with R_4 ending in outer margin. Cosmopolitan. (Alsóphila, Amètris, Aplásta, Neárcha, Taxeòtis, Dichromòdes, Œnochròma, Epidésma, Eumèlea, Celerena, Hedyle, Orthostíxis) **ŒNOCHROMATÌNÆ**

Hind wing with M_2 at base much nearer M_1 than M_3; fore wing with Sc and R always anastomosed, R_4 ending in costal margin (often near tip); tibial hair-pencil present but in groove; antennæ usually pectinate, pectinations on distal part of each joint; proboscis strong; primarily green moths with close scaling (*i.e.*, not hairy). Mainly tropical. (Térpna, Nemoùria, Chlorochlàmys, Agáthia, Racheóspila, Hippárchus, Chloríssa). (*HEMITHEÌNÆ*) **GEOMETRÌNÆ**

46. Frenulum well developed, more than one-fifteenth the length of the wing 47
Frenulum vestigial or absent; hind wings with Sc never fusing with R_s, but sometimes connected by a weak bar 52

47. M_3 and Cu_1 of both wings usually stalked for a considerable distance beyond the cell, stem of M indicated through the cell; fore wing with R_{2-5} or R_{3-5} stalked; proboscis present; thoracic tympanum small and subdorsal; hind tibiæ with both middle and apical spurs; slender, butterfly-like species. Neotropical, Calif. (Myònia, Tithraùstes, Actèa, Dióptis, Scèa, Jòsia, Dòa, Phryganídia). (See couplet 33) . . . . **DIÓPTIDÆ**, part
Of other conformation 48

48. Hind wings with Sc widely separated from R_s from near the base; fore wings with R_5 stalked with M_1 and well separated from R_4;

proboscis present. Widespread. (**Epiplèma, Calledápteryx, Nedùsia, Melèaba**) .... **EPIPLÉMIDÆ**
Hind wings with Sc close to R_s; fore wings with M_1 not stalked with R_s 49

49. Hind wings with Sc and R well separated, R_s and M_1 stalked beyond the cell; fore wings commonly with a radial areole. (If R_1 of fore wings is much shorter than discal cell, see couplet 68, Pyralididæ) 50

Hind wings with Sc and R close beyond the cell, M_1 free, R_s arising before or at the end of the discal cell 51

50. Proboscis present, often weak, sometimes absent; tympanum present in metathorax; fore wings fully scaled, usually with R_{2-5} stalked, often with a radial areole; frenulum with bristles; claws bifurcate. (Fig. 393). Principally Neotropical. (**Cerùra**, Palæarc., Am., Indoaustr.; **Notodónta, Drymònia**, Holarc.; **Stauròpus**, Palæarc., Indomal.; **Phalèra**, Palæarc., Indomal.; **Datàna** (*D. minístra*, Yellow necked apple worm); **Schizùra** (*S. concínna*, Red humped apple worm); **Heterocámpa**, Am.; **Tarsólepis; Thyrètes, Ápisa**, Afr.; **Thaumetopœa**, Palæarc., Ethiop.; **Ánaphe, Epánaphe**, Afr.). (*CERÙRIDÆ, THAUMETOPŒIDÆ, THYRÉTIDÆ*).

NOTODÓNTIDÆ

Proboscis wanting; tympanum absent; fore wings usually with $R_{2,3}$ and $R_{4,5}$ stalked together; wings of northern species with clear spots; frenulum usually without bristles; claws simple or serrate. Am., esp. Neotrop. (See couplet 56). (**Apatelòdes, Zánola, Colóbata, Olceclostera**).....**APATELODÌNÆ; EUPTERÓTIDÆ**

51. Fore wings with discal cell large, reaching much beyond the middle of the wing; hind wings with cubitus apparently three-branched; no abdominal tympanum. (**Áxia, Epicimèlia**, S. Eur.) ..**AXÌIDÆ**

Discal cell not or scarcely extending beyond the middle of the wing; hind wings with cubitus apparently four-branched; frenulum of male knobbed; abdominal typanum present. (Fig. 398). (See couplet 70). (**Polýploca, Palimpséstis**, Palæarc.; **Habrósyne**, Holarc.; **Cymatóphora**). (*CYMATOPHÓRIDÆ, PALIMPSÉSTIDÆ, TETHÈIDÆ, POLYPLÓCIDÆ*).....**THYATÍRIDÆ**

52. Base of M absent or very faint in cell; one or two distinct anal veins in hind wing; M_1 of hind wing not nearer M_3 than M_1 at base ..53

Base of vein M strong, dividing cell on fore and hind wings; three distinct anal veins in hind wing; shaft and pectinations on antenna scaled; proboscis absent; Sc of hind wing entirely free beyond base; frenulum only a simple thickening of costal margin of hind wing; M_1 of hind wing between M_1 and M_3 or nearer M_3 at base; stout, medium-sized moths. American. (**Mimállo, Lacosòma, Trogóptera, Cicínnus**). (*PROTOPSÝCHIDÆ,*

PEROPHÓRIDÆ, LACOSÓMIDÆ, LASCOSOMÁTIDÆ) (See couplet 32). . . . . MIMALLÓNIDÆ

53. Hind wing with vein Sc approaching R beyond end of cell; frenulum at most only a thickening of base of hind wing costal margin; claws simple 54
    Hind wing with Sc not nearer R beyond end of cell than before it, generally diverging steadily from base 55

54. Proboscis present; fore tibia without spurs; large moths, wings broad and with eye-like markings. (**Brahmæa**, Ethiop., Asia; **Spiramióp-sis**, S. Africa) . . . . BRAHMÆIDÆ
    Proboscis entirely atrophied; fore tibia with normal spurs; medium-sized, body robust, wings brown or yellow, without eye-like markings. Palæarctic only. One genus. (**Lemònia**) LEMONÌIDÆ

55. Shaft of antenna usually at most with scattered scales near base; hind wing with one or two anal veins; frenulum entirely absent, base of costal margin not even thickened; R branches on fore wing reduced to three or four, all on one stalk from cell 57
    Shaft of antenna closely scaled above; hind wing always with two anal veins; frenulum present, at least as thickening at base of costal margin 56

56. Fore wing with veins R_2 and R_3 completely fused; no crossvein connecting Sc of hind wing with anterior edge of cell (R); usually large, broad-winged moths. Mainly Old World tropics. (**Eupterote, Cotàna, Sabàlia, Jàna, Phyllàlia**). (See couplet 50)
    EUPTEROTÌNÆ; EUPTERÓTIDÆ
    Fore wing with veins R_1, R_2, and R_3 separate and successively arising from stem of R_{4+5}; crossvein connecting Sc of hind wing with anterior edge of cell (R); smaller moths with relatively short wings and heavy body (Fig. 388). Mainly Asia. (See couplet 31) (**Bómbyx**, with *B. mòri*, the cultivated silkworm; **Dalailàma,** Tibet; **Rondòtia, Oberthüria, Theóphila**, E. Asia) BOMBÝCIDÆ

57. Fore wings with $R_{4,5}$ stalked 58
    Fore wings with R_5 free, arising from the discal cell 60

58. Proboscis lacking or rudimentary 59
    Proboscis rather well developed, bearing numerous carinate papillæ; antennæ in both sexes quadripectinate; two apical spurs on hind tibia. Neotropical. (Fig. 396). (**Asthenídia, Oxýtenis, Homœóp-teryx**) . . . . OXYTENÍDIDÆ

59. Proboscis absent; antenna in both sexes with dorsal or, rarely, with lateral pectinations; two subapical spurs on hind tibia; hind wing with Sc and R connected by a bar. (Fig. 394). (**Cercóphana**, Chile; **Janiòdes**, Andes) . . . . CERCOPHÁNIDÆ
    Proboscis absent or rudimentary; antenna, if quadripectinate, with apical rami of one segment adjacent to basal rami of next segment or with multiple antennal cones; carinate papillæ absent on pro-

boscis unless the pilifers bear bristles; one, two, or no subapical spurs on hind tibia; hind wing with Sc and R not connected by a bar. (*ATTÁCIDÆ*) ....SATURNÌIDÆ

a. Carinate papillæ often present on proboscis; pilifer with bristles; one, two, or no subapical spurs on hind tibia; frontal protuberance present; labial palpus always long; anepisternum large; large, broad-winged moths. Neotropical. (**Copiópteryx; Rhescýntis** (incl. *Arsenùra, Dysdæmònia*); **Almeidàia**) (*ARSENÚRIDÆ*)
RHESCYNTIDÌNÆ

Carinate papillæ never present on proboscis; pilifer never with bristles; one or no subapical spurs on hind tibia (except *Adetómeris, Ormiscòdes*) ....b.

b. Frontal protuberance present; labial palpus usually reduced; hind tibia with two apical, but no subapical spurs; frons convex at sides; without multiple antennal cones; anepisternum large; rather heavy bodied moths with narrowed, powerful wings; mostly Neotropical. (**Èacles; Citherònia; Anisòta; Sýssphinx**). (*CERATOCÁMPIDÆ, SYSSPHÍNGIDÆ*) ......CITHERONÌINÆ

Frontal protuberance absent if frons convex at sides ....c.

c. Subapical spurs always absent on hind tibia; labial palpus always long; frons not convex at sides; frontal protuberance absent; antennal cones not multiple; vein M_2 arising in front of middle of apex of cell; anepisternum large. (Two species, **Áglia tau** L., Palæarc.; **A. japonica** Leech, Japan.)..............AGLIÌNÆ

If antennal cones not multiple, then frontal protuberance present . . d.

d. Anepisternum small; labial palpus usually long; frons not convex at sides; frontal protuberance present; few antennal cones; vein M_2 arising in front of middle of apex of cell; hind tibial subapical spurs either one or none (two in *Adetomeris, Ormiscodes*). American. (**Hemilcùca**, Am.; **Adetómeris**, Neotrop.; **Autómeris**, Am.; **Hylèsia, Dírphia, Lonòmia**, Neotrop.; **Polythỳsana**, Chile). (*LONOMÌIDÆ*). .... HEMILEUCÌNÆ

Anepisternum large or if small, frontal protuberance present. . . . .e.

e. Vein M_2 arising in front of middle of apex of cell; labial palpus greatly reduced; frons not convex at sides; frontal protuberance absent; anepisternum large; no subapical spurs on hind tibia; small saturniids. All Ethiopian. (**Lùdia, Orthogonióptilum, Goodia, Holócera**) ....LUDIÌNÆ

Vein M_2 not arising in front of middle of apex of cell; labial palpus usually long ....f

f. Frontal protuberance present; frons not convex at sides; labial palpus long, 3-segmented; antennal cones absent; anepisternum large; one subapical spur on hind tibia. (One genus, **Salássa**, S. Asia) ....SALASSÌNÆ

Frontal protuberance absent; frons often not convex at sides; labial palpus often much reduced, sometimes fused; antennal cones numerous; anepisternum small; no subapical spur on hind tibia. Including·many very large moths. Widespread. (Satúrnia (incl. *Agapèma, Calosatúrnia*), Holarc.; Copáxa, Neotrop.; Áctias, widespr.; Antheræa (incl. *Tèlea*), widespr.; Rothschíldia, Neotrop.; Grællsia, Palæarc.; Sàmia (*Philosàmia*), Asia; Hyalóphora (incl. *Platysàmia, Callosàmia, Eupackárdia*), Holarc.; Coscinóscera, Austr.; Áttacus, Indoaustr.) (Fig. 395) ....SATURNIÌNÆ

60. Fore wings with M₁ free, not stalked with R₅ 61
   Fore wings with M₁ stalked with R₅, or arising very close to R₅ at the apex of the discal cell (Fig. 399). (Urània, Chrysirídia, Alcìdis, Nyctálemon, Urapteròides) ....URANÌIDÆ

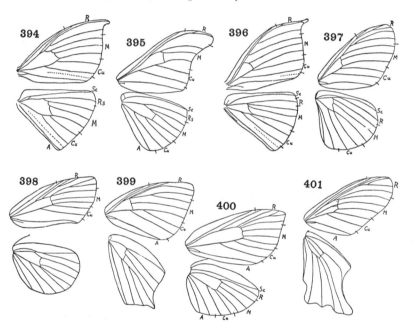

Figs. 394–401. Lepidoptera

394. Janiodes, wings (Jordan) Cercophanidæ.
395. Antheræa, wings (Hampson) Saturniidæ.
396. Oxytenis, wings (Jordan) Oxytenididæ.
397. Brahmæa, wings (Hampson) Brahmæidæ.
398. Thyatira, wings (Hampson) Thyatiridæ.
399. Urapteroides, wings (Hampson) Uraniidæ.
400. Addæa, wings (Hampson) Thyrididæ.
401. Epicopeia, wings (Hampson) Epicopeiidæ.

61. Fore wings with $R_{3,4}$ stalked. (See couplet 59d).
HEMILEUCÌNÆ; SATURNÌIDÆ
Fore wings with $R_{2,3,4}$ stalked. (Fig. 401). (Epicopèia, Indomal.).
EPICOPEÌIDÆ

62. All branches of R, M and Cu of both wings arising from the open or closed discal cell, rarely $R_{3,4}$ or $R_{4,5}$ short-stalked; maxillary palpi minute; wings often with unscaled spots. (Fig. 400). Mainly tropical. (Thỳris, Striglìna, Addæa, Rhodoneùra, Dysòdia, Risàma, Méskea) ....THYRÍDIDÆ
Veins variously fusing beyond the discal cell 63

63. Frenulum present, more than one-fifteenth the length of the wing 64
Frenulum vestigial or absent 79

64. Hind wings with Sc and R_s separate from near the base, or fused beyond the cell, when joined near the base the fusion not extending to the middle of the cell 65
Hind wings with Sc and R_s fused to near or beyond the middle of the cell, sometimes forming a small basal areole (in Euchromiidæ completely fused so that Sc appears to be absent) 75

65. Shaft of antennæ tapering evenly from base to tip 66
Antennæ thickened before tip, usually ending in a recurved hook ..78

66. Hind wings with Sc free from R_s along the cell, though sometimes approaching it, or briefly touching near the apex of the cell, sometimes fused for a greater or less distance beyond the cell 67
Hind wing with Sc fused with R_s for a short distance before the middle of the cell 73

67. Hind wings with Sc dipping toward R_s, sometimes fused with it beyond the cell, but not connected with it by a bar; proboscis present (if proboscis is vestigial, compare Lymantriidæ, couplets 72, 74) 68
Hind wings with Sc and R_s connected by a bar before the discal cell (Fig. 402) 71

68. Hind wing with one or two distinct anal veins; proboscis not scaled; radial areole often present 69
Hind wing usually with three strong anal veins; proboscis scaled at base; no radial areole. (Fig. 406). (See couplet 49). A very large, widespread group. ....PYRALÍDIDÆ, part

a. Fore wing with 1A present; proboscis weak or absent; hind wings with the fringe on Cu weak or absent; larvæ bore in aquatic or marsh plants. (Schœnòbius, Acéntropus, Ràmila). (SIGÍNÆ)
SCHŒNOBÌINÆ
Fore wings with 1A absent ....b

b. Fore wings with 3A curving forward to meet 2A and forming a small elongate cell near the base of the wing c

Fore wings with 3A free or curving into 2A toward the middle of
the wing to form a wide loop, often vestigial .... f
c. Proboscis and ocelli absent; male usually with third joint of the
palpi vestigial .... d
Proboscis and ocelli present; labial palpi normal .... e
d. Front with a conical tuft; general vestiture deep and mixed; larvæ
living as scavengers in nests of social Hymenoptera or in dried
foods. (Gallèria (G. melonélla, Bee moth), Paralíspa, Achròia).
(TINEÌNÆ, Hampson) .... GALLERIÌNÆ
Front and thorax smooth-scaled; larvæ feeding on scale insects.
(Macrothèca) .... MACROTHECÌNÆ
e. Maxillary palpi rather well developed; hind wings with Sc free.
(Pýralis (P. farinàlis, Meal moth)). (See couplet 1, below)
PYRALIDÌNÆ, part
Maxillary palpi absent; hind wings with Sc and R usually fusing.
(Árta, Chrysaùge, Clydonópteron, Bradypodícola, Gephỳra,
Náchaba). (SEMNIÌNÆ) .... CHRYSAUGÌNÆ
f. Hind wings with M_1 arising from the vein closing the cell, widely
separated from Sc, cell closed by a weak but distinct vein, R
more or less weakened; labial palpi beak-like, maxillary palpi
triangular; mainly Old World species. (Ancylolòmia, Prion-
ápteryx, Eufernáldia) .... ANCYLOLOMIÌNÆ
Hind wings with M_1 closely approximate to R .... g
g. Fore wings with R_5 stalked with R_{3+4}; only one free vein below
the forked vein which runs to the apex from the radial stem ....h
Fore wings with R_5 free; two free veins from the radial stem below
the forked one; hind wings with Sc and R almost always fusing .m
h. Fore wings with R_3 and R_4 completely fused; hind wing with
strong fringe on Cu i
Fore wings with R_3 and R_4 stalked, separating apically .... k
i. Cell in hind wing closed by a delicate but nearly complete vein;
frenulum of female consisting of a single spine .... j
Cell in hind wing widely open; frenulum of female multiple. (See
couplets k, m). (Raphíptera) .... CRAMBÌNÆ, part
j. Proboscis strong, separating the palpi toward the base: larvæ
usually leaf-rollers, a few feeding in stored foods. (Phỳcita,
Ephéstia (Fig. 406) (E. kuehniélla, Mediterranean flour moth),
Plòdia (P. interpunctélla, Indian-meal moth, world wide pest of
dried fruits, nuts, corn and other cereals), Acróbasis, Diorýctria,
Nephópteryx). (ANERASTIÌNÆ, Hampson). PHYCITÌNÆ
Proboscis weak or vestigial, not separating the palpi and concealed
by them when coiled. (Peòria, Poujàdia, Anerástia, Hypsó-
tropa). (HYPSOTROPÌNÆ) .... ANERASTIÌNÆ
k. Hind wings with a heavy fringe on the base of Cu; labial palpi
beak-like, the maxillary palpi triangular. (Argýria, Crámbus,

Diatræa (corn and sugar cane borers), Thaumatópsis). (See couplets i, m) ....CRAMBÌNÆ, part

Fringe on base of Cu very light or wanting; maxillary palpi plumose, or small and concealed 1

l. Fore wings with raised scale-tufts. (Epipáschia, Tetrálopha, Oneìda, Pocócera). (POCOCERÌNÆ) ....EPIPASCHIÌNÆ

Fore wings smooth, without raised scale-tufts. (Aglóssa, Hercùlia, Cleodòbia, Omphalócera) ....PYRALIDÌNÆ

m. Hind wings with fringe on Cu heavy; labial palpi beak-like, the maxillary palpi triangular. (See couplets i, k).
CRAMBÌNÆ, part

Fringe on Cu light or absent; labial palpi rarely beak-like, the maxillary palpi usually moderate or small, not triangular ......n

n. Hind wings without loose, spatulate hairs on the upper surface ..o

Some loose hair near the inner margin of the hind wing, part of it forming a weak fringe on Cu which runs into a group of spatulate hairs or scales below Cu. (Glaphýria, Dicymolòmia, Lipocósma) ....GLAPHYRIÌNÆ

o. Fore wings with R_2 stalked with R_3 and R_4. (Elóphila, Nýmphula (= Hydrocámpa), Eurrhýpara, Musotìma). (HYDROCAM-PÌNÆ) .... NYMPHULÌNÆ

Fore wings with R_2 free ....p

p. Labial palpi beak-like; maxillary palpi large and triangular; fore wing usually slightly rough-scaled, with M_1 well separated from R_5 at origin, about as far from base of R_{3+4} as from M_2. (Scopària, Xeróscopa) ....SCOPARIÌNÆ

Labial palpi often upturned; maxillary palpi very rarely large and triangular (Loxostegópsis) and in that case with R_{3+4} and M_1 closely approximate. (Loxóstege (Web-worms), Désmia, Phlyctænia, Agrótera, Sylépta, Margarònia, Héllula, Pantógrapha, Diaphània (Melon and Pickle worms), Pyraùsta (P. nubilàlis, European corn borer)). (AGROTERÌNÆ)
PYRAUSTÌNÆ

69. Tympanum developed in abdomen; chætosema reduced or wanting; dip in Sc of hind wings located beyond the discal cell and sometimes resulting in a fusion with R_s 70

Tympanum not developed; chætosema present; dip in Sc of hind wings opposite the middle of the discal cell, humeral vein present; cell of hind wings always open, of fore wings usually so; frenulum reduced; no radial areole; ocelli absent; day-flying, butterfly-like moths. (See couplet 84) ....CALLIDÙLIDÆ

70. Ocelli well developed; fore wings with vein Cu quadrifid; frenulum of male knobbed. (Thyatìra, Palæarc.). (See couplet 51).
THYATÌRIDÆ, part

Ocelli vestigial; frenulum normal, weak; fore wings with vein Cu trifid; fore wings commonly with recurved tip. (Fig. 405). (See couplet 83). (Euchèra, Edápteryx, Drépana, Cìlix, Palæarc.; Falcària, Holarc.). (*DREPANÙLIDÆ*). ......DREPÁNIDÆ

71. Proboscis present, palpi recurved above the vertex, with bare third joint; ocelli present, eyes bare; thorax and abdomen smoothly clothed with scales; day-flying, often brightly colored. (Fig. 402). (Aganàis, Perídrome, Neochèra, Ásota, Callimórpha, Nyctémera). (*HÝPSIDÆ, AGANÀIDÆ, CALLIMÓRPHIDÆ, ASÓTIDÆ*) (See couplet 73). ....NYCTEMÉRIDÆ

Proboscis absent (except in *Munichryia*); thorax and abdomen hairy 72

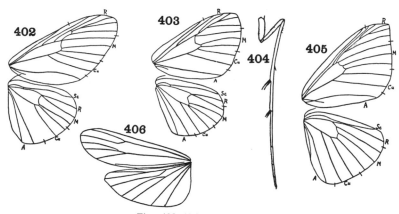

Figs. 402–406. Lepidoptera

402. **Asota**, wings (Hampson) Nyctemeridæ.
403. **Lymantria**, wings (Hampson) Lymantriidæ.
404. **Pterophorus**, hind leg of male (Fernald) Pterophoridæ.
405. **Euchera**, wings (Hampson) Drepanidæ.
406. **Ephestia**, wings (Chittenden) Pyralididæ.

72. Fore wings with a single radial areole, apex of wings rounded; tympanum conspicuous. (See couplets 67, 74)

LYMANTRÌIDÆ, part

Fore wings with two radial areoles, the basal one very long, apex of wing acute; female without frenulum. (See couplet 80). Australasian. (Anthèla, Chelépteryx) ....ANTHÉLIDÆ, males

73. Tympanal hoods large, consisting of two rounded bosses separated by about one-third the width of the abdomen; black moths with light marks on the wings and often with metallic tints. (See couplet 71). Mainly Neotropical. (Darìtis, Hyalúrga, Gnophæla, Perícopis). ....PERICOPIDÌNÆ; NYCTEMÉRIDÆ

Tympanal hoods less conspicuous and more lateral; fore wings with radial areole usually present 74

74. Ocelli absent; hind wings with M_2 as strong as the other veins, M_1 stalked with R_s, basal areole more than one-sixth the length of the discal cell. (Fig. 403). (See couplet 72). Principally Indomalayan and Ethiopian, but containing the following important species of Holarctic distribution: (**Lymántria** (= *Líparis*) (*L. mónacha*, Nun moth); **Porthètria** (= *Ocnèria*) (*P. díspar*, Gipsy moth); **Nýgmia** (= *Euproctis*) (*N. phæorrhœa*, = *chrysorrhœa*, Browntail moth); **Stilpnòtia** (*S. sálicis*, Satin moth); **Orgỳia** (= *Notólophus*); **Hemerocámpa** (Tussock moths). (*LIPARÍDIDÆ, LIPÁRIDÆ, OCNERIIDÆ*).

LYMANTRÌIDÆ

Ocelli usually present; hind wings with M_2 sometimes weak, or rarely absent, M_1 independent or very short-stalked with R_s, basal areole formed by Sc and R very small, less than one-sixth the length of the discal cell. (*PHALÆNIDÆ*) ....NOCTÙIDÆ

a. M_2 of hind wing very weak or present only as fold ("Trifids"); teeth of claw on inner side of claw when present ....b

M_2 of hind wing a more or less strong vein ("Quadrifids"); teeth of claws, when present, usually on ventral side ....e

b. Hind and middle tibiæ without spines c

Hind (and often middle) tibiæ with small spines. (**Heliothis**, **Euxòa**, **Nóctua** (= *Agròtis*), **Schinia**, **Tímora**, **Féltia**, **Graphíphora**, **Anomogỳna**). (*AGROTÌNÆ, HELIOTHIDÌNÆ*)

NOCTUÌNÆ

c. Eye hairless ....d

Eye with hairs on surface. (**Scotográmma**, **Pòlia**, **Misèlia** (= *Maméstra*), **Hadèna**, **Lacinipòlia**, **Orthòdes**, **Xylomỳges**, **Orthòsia**, **Pseudalètia**, **Leucània**). (*MAMESTRÌNÆ, CARADRININÆ*, part, *MELANCHRÌNÆ*) ....HADENÌNÆ

d. Eye with marginal row of long cilia curving over it. (**Cucúllia**, **Oncocnèmis**, **Graptolítha**, **Conístra**, **Cósmia**). (*POLIÌNÆ*, part, *GRAPTOLÍTHIDÆ*) ....CUCULLIÌNÆ

Eye not ciliated. (**Séptis**, **Amphipyra**, **Olígia**, **Papaipèma**, **Platysénta**, **Acronýcta**, **Áthetis**). (*AMPHIPYRÌNÆ, ZENOBIÌNÆ, CARADRINÌNÆ*, part) ....ACRONYCTÌNÆ

e. Hind wing with veins M_1 and M_2 close at base, diverging distally ..f

Hind wing with veins M_1 and M_2 parallel. (**Gábara**, **Bomólocha**, **Hypèna**, **Polypógon**, **Hermínia**). (*POLYPOGONÌNÆ*)

HYPENÌNÆ

f. Female with simple frenulum ....g

Female with frenulum a group of bristles ....h

g. End of abdomen with lateral hair tufts. (Eutèlia, Marathýssa, Pǽctes) ....EUTELIÌNÆ
   End of abdomen lacking lateral hair tufts; fore wing usually with erect scales in cell. Entirely tropical. (Stictóptera, Lophóptera, Gýrtona) ....STICTOPTERÌNÆ
h. Retinaculum of male usually in form of an erect tongue i
   Retinaculum in form of group of bristles ....j
i. Fore wing with erect scales in cell; length of labial palpus at least three times diameter of eye. (Sarróthripus, Casándria, Baileya, Iscàdia, Rísoba). (HYLOPHÍLIDÆ) ....SARROTHRIPÌNÆ
   Fore wing without erect scales in cell; length of labial palpus less than three times diameter of eye. Entirely Old World. (Eàrias, Hylóphila, Càrea, Westermánnia, Arcyóphora). (CAR-EÌNÆ, CHLOËOPHÓRIDÆ) ....WESTERMANNIÌNÆ
j. Middle tibia spineless ....k
   Middle tibia with small spines. (Catocàla, Parallèlia, Cænúrgina, Zàle, Grámmodes, Drásteria, Alabàma) .....CATOCALÌNÆ
k. Surface of eye hairy l
   Surface of eye bare ....m
l. Antenna thickened before tip, simple. (See couplet 78). All Papuan. (Cocýtia, Eucocýtia). (COCYTÌIDÆ, EUCOCYTÌIDÆ) COCÝTIÌNÆ
   Antenna not thickened, often pectinate. (Colocàsia, Pánthea, Mòma, Charàdra, Ràphia). (PANTHEÌNÆ, DIPHTERÌNÆ). MOMÌNÆ
m. Eye not ciliated ....n
   Eye with marginal row of long cilia curling over it. (Sýngrapha, Autógrapha, Plùsia, Abróstola, Omórphina). .....PLUSIÌNÆ
n. Hind wing with vein M_2 as strong as M_1 and M_3, arising near M_3. (Polydésma, Serícia, Thysània, Érebus, Ophiùsa, Rívula, Ophíderes, Cálpe, Pángrapta). (NOCTUÌNÆ, of authors; RIVULÌNÆ, part) ....OPHIDERÌNÆ
   Hind wing with vein M_2 distinctly weaker than M_1 and M_3, arising near M_1. (Eublémma, Eustròtia, Erástria, Tarachídia, Acóntia). (ERASTRIÌNÆ) ....ACONTIÌNÆ
75. Hind wings small, with Sc apparently wanting; tympanal hoods very large (lost in Amata), the abdomen sometimes constricted behind them; antennæ swollen into a club at tips; day-flying, usually brightly colored moths. (Fig. 407). Mainly Neotrop. (Euchròmia, Ctenùcha, Amàta (= Sýntomis), Císseps, Cosmosòma). (SYNTÓMIDÆ, AMÁTIDÆ, EUCHROMÌIDÆ, SYNTOMÍDIDÆ) ....CTENÙCHIDÆ
    Hind wings with Sc well developed; tympanal hoods not exceptionally large 76

76. Ocelli present. Large, widespread group. (Phægóptera (= Ophàrus), Parasèmia (= Hyphoràia), Nemeóphila (= Parasèmia, pt.), Árctia, Háploa, Utetheìsa, Apántesis, Hyphántria (Webworms), Euprèpia, Autómolis, Halisidòta, Estígmene, Diacrísia) ....ARCTÌIDÆ
Ocelli absent (rudimentary in Hypoprepia) 77
77. Fore wings smoothly scaled, rarely M_2 or M_3 wanting. (See couplet 44). (Eudésmia (= Císthene, auct.), Císthene (= Íllice), Lithòsia, widespr.; Hypoprèpia, Am.; Chionæ̀ma, Old World)
LITHOSÌIDÆ
Fore wings with tufts of raised scales (Fig. 411). (Nòla, Rœsèlia, Ùraba, Célama) ....NÓLIDÆ
78. Hind wings with Sc entirely free from R. Indomalayan. (See couplet 74, 1) ....COCYTÌINÆ; NOCTÙIDÆ
Hind wings with Sc and R connected (closely parallel in Alýpia) for a short distance at base, sometimes forming a very small basal areolet; rather small or medium-sized day-flying moths of brilliant colors, often dark, ornamented with large pale spots. (Fig. 409). Forester moths. Principally Ethiopian and Indoaustralian. (Agarísta, Pemphigóstola, Alýpia, Andrulòma, Eusèmia, Phalænòides). (PHALÆNÒIDIDÆ). ....AGARÍSTIDÆ
79. Hind wings with the straight Sc connected with the cell by a bar near or before the middle of the discal cell 80
Hind wings with Sc free from R or fusing for a greater or less distance, but not joined to the cell by a bar near the base of the cell 82
80. Fore wing with two radial areoles; stem of M in hind wing very faint, simple; rather large, showy moths with apex of fore wing usually acute. Australian and Papuan only. (Male with frenulum, see couplet 72). ....ANTHÉLIDÆ, females
Fore wings without radial sector 81
81. Base of vein M clearly present in cell of hind wing; fore and hind wings similar in shape; body slender. Indomalayan only. (Ratárda, Callosìope) ....RATÁRDIDÆ
Base of M present in cell of hind wing, but indistinct and forked; fore and hind wings very dissimilar in shape; body stout. (One species only, Éndromis versicólora, Eur.). (ENDRÓMIDÆ)
ENDROMÍDIDÆ
82. Fore wings with Cu_2 arising basad of middle of cell, R_4 long and free, or arising from base of the stalked $R_{2,3}$; R_5 and M_1 short-stalked; hind wings with Sc and R_s fused for a greater or lesser extent near the middle of the discal cell, humeral angle wide and strengthened by one or more humeral veins; tympanum, proboscis, chætosema all absent. (Fig. 412). Widespread, mainly tropical. (Tólype, Epicnáptera (= Gastrópacha), Lasiocámpa,

Eriogáster, Malacosòma (= *Clisiocámpa*) Tent caterpillars)).
(*LACHNÈIDÆ*) ....LASIOCÁMPIDÆ
Fore wings with Cu_2 arising beyond middle of cell, R_4 short and
arising apically from R_3 or from R_{2+3}; proboscis present 83

83. Fore wings with R_5 free, R_4 remote from R_3 and ending beyond
tip of the wing, outer margin not sinuate; hind wings with Sc
dipping toward R_8 in front of cell 84

Fore wings with R_{2-5} stalked, R_4 very close to R_3 and entering the
costal margin; hind wings with Sc dipping toward or fusing with
R_8 beyond the cell; tympanum present in abdomen. (See couplet
70). (Orèta) ....DREPÁNIDÆ, part

84. Fore wings with R_2 free, only R_{3+4} stalked; hind wings with lower
margin usually bearing a double fringe of long woolly hairs;
tympanum present in metathorax. (Fig. 408). Indian and
African. (Pterothýsanus, Caloschèmia, Hibríldes).

PTEROTHYSÁNIDÆ

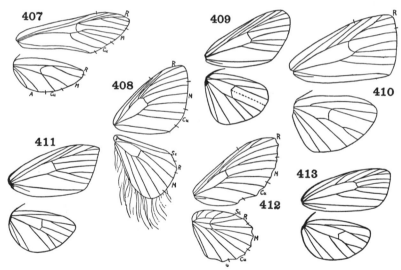

Figs. 407–413. Lepidoptera

407. **Euchromia**, wings (Hampson) Ctenuchidæ.
408. **Pterothysanus**, wings (Hampson) Pterothysanidæ.
409. **Alypiodes**, wings (Hampson) Agaristidæ.
410. **Earias**, wings (Hampson) Noctuidæ, Westermanniinæ.
411. **Nigetia**, wings (Holland) Nolidæ.
412. **Epicnaptera**, wings (Hampson) Lasiocampidæ.
413. **Hypoprepia**, wings (Hampson) Lithosiidæ.

Fore wings with R_{2-4} stalked; hind wings without long fringe; tympanum absent; chætosema present. Indomalayan, Asia. (See couplet 69). (**Callídula, Ágonis, Comélla, Clèis**)

CALLIDÙLIDÆ

85. Maxillary palpi conspicuous, folded in resting position 86
Maxillary palpi straight and porrect, or vestigial (if of folded type, inconspicuous or invisible) 92

86. Basal segment of antennæ enlarged and concave beneath, forming an eye-cap, larger than the eye; wing-membrane aculeate 87
Eye-cap small or undeveloped; fore wings usually with large cell and branched veins 88

87. Fore wings with branched veins, normally with short trapezoidal cell; aculeæ distributed over entire membrane; cell sometimes absent; media usually dipping deeply into wing; extremely small moths, the wing expanse as little as 3 mm. (Fig. 414). Leaf miners. (**Neptícula,** cosmop.; **Scoliaùla,** Eur.; **Glaucólepis; Ectœdèmia; Obrússa; Trifúrcula**). (*STIGMÉLLIDÆ*).

NEPTICÙLIDÆ

Fore wings with three or four simple veins only, aculeæ pointing forward, in rows and confined to a small area at the base of the wing; hind wings linear. Mostly oriental, three North American species. Larvæ legless miners in bark or rind. (**Opóstcga**) .... **OPOSTÉGIDÆ**

88. Fore wings with R_5 extending to outer margin, wing-membrane not aculeate; head with a few erect hairs behind. (**Acrolèpia,** cosmop.) .... **ACROLEPÌIDÆ**
Fore wings with R_5 extending to the costa, sometimes absent ... 89

89. Head usually entirely smooth; strongly flattened species, coxæ flat and appressed, fore wings curved down at apex, hind wings narrow-lanceolate; venation sometimes reduced. Mostly Oriental. (**Opógona,** Ethiop.; **Phæoses,** Nearc.; **Œnóphila,** Ethiop., Indomal.). (*OINOPHÍLIDÆ, ERECTHÌIDÆ*)

ŒNOPHÍLIDÆ

Head tufted, at least on the vertex, sometimes with a naked area above the eyes behind the antennæ, in which case the hind wings are ample; venation complete, accessory cell commonly present, four or five branches of R extending to the costal margin 90

90. Wing-membrane aculeate (Fig. 369); hind wings with Sc having a strong basal fork (the lower branch being R_1) or considerably swollen at the base, R and Sc usually sharply divergent from the base; vertex roughly hairy 91
Wing-membrane not aculeate; hind wings with R_1 rarely as strong as the other veins and when distinct placed well out from the base of the wing, connecting Sc and R which are closely parallel

toward the base. Widespread. (See couplet 100) (**Isocórypha, Diachorísia, Leucómele, Œnoe**). ....TINÈIDÆ

91. Folded part of maxillary palpi half as long as the width of the head. (**Incurvària**, Holarc.; **Phyllopòria**, Palæarc.; **Lamprònia**, Holarc., Ethiop.; **Nemóphora, Paracleménsia**). (*LAMPRO-NÌIDÆ*) ....INCURVARÌIDÆ
    Folded part of maxillary palpi two-thirds as long as the width of the head. (Fig. 415). Yucca moths; larvæ boring in seed pods of Yucca. (**Prodóxus, Tegetícula** (= *Pronùba*), Am.).
    PRODÓXIDÆ

92. Basal joint of the antennæ enlarged and concave beneath, forming an eye-cap 93
    Basal joint of the antennæ not forming an eye-cap, sometimes provided with tufts of scales or a pecten of bristles 95

93. Venation complete and nearly parallel, hind wings with Sc ending at apical fourth and discal cell reaching the middle of the wing. (**Calósima**, Am.). (See couplet 135) ....BLASTOBÁSIDÆ
    Venation reduced, wings linear-lanceolate with sharply pointed apex, fore wings with the veins at the apex of the discal cell radially diverging; hind wings without discal cell, the principal vein axial. (Fig. 417) 94

94. Labial palpi minute and drooping, or absent; fore wings typically with a closed anal cell, or the vertex rough. (Fig. 417). (**Bucculàtrix** (Ribbed cocoon makers), **Lyonètia**, cosmop.; **Bedéllia, Leucóptera** (= *Cemióstoma*), widespr.; **Phyllobróstis**). (*BEDEL-LÌIDÆ, CEMIOSTOMÁTIDÆ, HIEROXÉSTIDÆ*). (Including *BUCCULATRÍGIDÆ*). ....LYONETÌIDÆ
    Labial palpi moderate, upcurved; no anal cell; vertex smooth; eye-cap small, no pecten; hind tibiæ spined. (**Phyllocnístis**, part). (See couplet 128) ....PHYLLOCNÍSTIDÆ

95. Vertex and upper face at least tufted with dense bristly hairs (with flattened short hair in Amydriidæ, which have strongly bristly palpi) 96
    At least the face smooth and with short scales even though the vertex may be rough-crowned 97

96. Labial palpi with the first joint short, and the second joint bristly on the outer side and equal to the fusiform third joint 98
    Mouthparts wholly vestigial. South American gall-making species, with very indistinct venation. (**Ridiáschina**). RIDIASCHÍNIDÆ

97. Labial palpi scaled or with short-hairs, the third joint usually long and pointed, or very short in the species with roughest vesti-ture 101
    Mouthparts wholly undeveloped; front and hind wings each with a single anal vein, fringe short; larvæ gall-makers. (Fig. 418). South American. (**Cecidòses, Olièra**) ....CECIDOSÈTIDÆ

98. Wing-membrane aculeate over all; female with piercing ovipositor; antennæ often longer than the wings. (**Adèla**, Palæarc., Neotrop.; **Nemotòis**, Old World; **Chalcèopla**, Nearc.) ....**ADÉLIDÆ**

Wing-membrane not generally aculeate; ovipositor membranous, retractile 99

99. Fore wings with R₃ free, arising from the accessory cell (Fig. 419) 100

Fore wings with a hyaline aculeate fovea in the accessory cell distorting the venation, R₃,₄,₅ seriately stalked. (Fig. 416). (**Setomórpha**, widespr.) ....**SETOMÓRPHIDÆ**

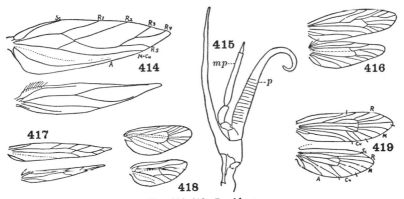

Figs. 414–419. **Lepidoptera**

414. Ecœdemia, wings (Braun) Nepticulidæ.
415. Tegeticula, mouthparts of female (Packard): m p, maxillary palpus; p, palpifer.
416. Setomorpha, wings (Busck) Setomorphidæ.
417. Bedellia, wings (Clemens) Lyonetiidæ.
418. Cecidoses, wings (Brethes) Cecidosetidæ.
419. Tinea, wings (Spuler) Tineidæ.

100. Vertex with high, rough, bristling vestiture. (Fig. 419). (**Tínea** (Clothes moths), **Monòpis, Scárdia**, cosmop.; **Tinèola** (*T. biselliélla*, Clothes moth), **Trichóphaga** (*T. tapetzélla*, Case-bearing clothes moth), **Ténaga**, widespr.; **Elatòbia**, Holarc.). (See couplet 90). (Including *MONÓPIDÆ*) ....**TINÈIDÆ**

Vertex with short, flattened hair. (**Amýdria**, Nearc.)

AMYDRÌIDÆ

101. Labial palpi elongate, deeply scaled, but not bristly, with the first joint at least subequal to the second joint, or much longer, of female typically porrect, of male upturned; eyes sometimes hairy or scaly 102

Labial palpi with the first joint small; eyes bare 105

102. Proboscis absent or obsolete; neuration complete; moderate-sized
     species; no ocelli 103
     Proboscis well developed 104
103. Slender, long-legged ægeriid-like moths; vesniture not spatulate or
     tufted; antennæ exteriorly ciliated on apical half; third joint of
     labial palpi minute and bare. (**Ashinàga**, Formosa).

     ASHINÁGIDÆ
     Vesniture deep and spatulate on the thorax, with well marked an-
     terior and posterior tufts; eyes more or less distinctly hairy; stout,
     noctuid-like moths. American, mostly tropical. (**Acrólophus**,
     Burrowing webworms) ....**ACROLÓPHIDÆ**
104. Hind wings trapezoidal, apex pointed, outer margin strongly
     sinuate, veins R_s, M_1 and M_2 nearly parallel; fore wings with
     R_4 and R_5 stalked or coincident; hind tibiæ thinly clothed with
     long hairs above, densely rough-haired between spurs beneath.
     Indomalayan. (**Amphithèra, Agriothèra, Telethèra**).

     AMPHITHÉRIDÆ
     Hind wings with greatly reduced venation, frenulum of female
     simple; ocelli posterior; larvæ on cocoanut. Austromal. (**Ago-
     nóxena, Hæmolytis**). (See couplet 142) ....**AGONOXÉNIDÆ**
105. Hind wings relatively ample, with well developed anal region,
     rounded at apex or trapezoidal, or more or less deeply notched
     below the apex, often wider than their fringe; venation more or
     less complete 106
     Hind wings narrow-lanceolate and pointed, or linear, never much
     wider than their fringe; sometimes without closed cell, venation
     often much reduced 123
106. Hind wings with M_1 and sometimes also M_2 absent 107
     Hind wings with M_1 present, associated with R_s (if M_1 of the hind
     wings absent (rarely, in Gelechiidæ) the outer margin of the
     hind wings is more or less emarginate) 108
107. Hind wings with the cell closed, M_1 and M_2 both wanting, R_s
     extending alone, the outer margin not concave; fore wings
     heavily tufted, all the branches of R free, R_5 ending beyond the
     wing tip, Cu_2 from near end of cell, 1A absent. Mostly Australian
     and Hawaiian. (**Carposìna, Bóndia**) ....**CARPOSÍNIDÆ**
     Hind wings trapezoidal-ovate, with cell open and M_1 and some-
     times also M_2 absent; fore wings with R_5 absent. (**Metachánda,
     Ancylomètis, Chanýstis**, Ethiop., Ind.) ....**METACHÁNDIDÆ**
108. Hind wings with 3A distally forked; venation complete, acces-
     sory cell present, all veins separate; front wings with two medial
     stems in cell. (Larvæ at first parasitic in Homoptera, later
     myrmecophilous). (**Cyclotórna**, Austr.) ....**CYCLOTÓRNIDÆ**
     Anal vein not distally forked 109
109. Hind wings with radial vein shortly furcate at apex; labial palpi

with second joint thickened and with rather appressed scales, last joint very short, filiform, obtuse; front tarsi much longer than their tibiæ. (Anomóloga, Ethiop.) .... ANOMOLÓGIDÆ
Hind wings with radial vein not furcate at apex 110

110. Fore wings with Cu$_2$ arising before the last fourth of the cell; labial palpi beak-like, with the third joint short and blunt and the second joint closely or roughly scaled and usually porrect or oblique (short and nearly smooth in *Laspeyresia*, which usually has a strong fringe on the base of Cu of the hind wings) 111
Fore wings with Cu$_2$ arising further out on the cell (except Glyphipterygidæ, part, which have no fringe on the base of Cu) 113

111. Upper side of the hind wings with a fringe of long hairs on the basal part of Cu (if rarely absent in some species of *Laspeyresia* the fore wings have M$_1$ and M$_2$ rather close together at the tip); fore wings with R$_4$ and R$_5$ separate, or with veins M$_2$, M$_3$ and Cu$_1$ converging strongly toward the margin. (Fig. 420). A cosmopolitan group. (Áncylis (*A. comptàna*, Strawberry leaf-roller), **Carpocapsa** (= *Cydia*, auct.) (*C. pomonella*, Codling moth); **Rhyacionia** (= *Evetria*, auct., = *Retinia*) (Pine twig moths); **Epinotia** (= *Enarmonia*, auct.), **Laspeyresia** (*L. prunivora*, Lesser apple worm; *L. interstinctana*, Clover-seed worm; *L. saltitans*, Mexican jumping bean moth), **Spilonota** (= *Tmetocera*) (*S. ocellàna*, Budmoth), **Olethreùtes, Melíssopus, Polychròsis** (*P. viteàna* Grape-berry moth), **Gypsónoma, Eucósma, Argyróploce, Hemímene, Pámmene**). (*EUCÓSMIDÆ, EPIBLÉMIDÆ*) .... OLETHREÙTIDÆ
Hind wings without a fringe of long hairs on the basal part of Cu (if rarely present the fore wings have R$_4$ and R$_5$ stalked or united); fore wings with veins M$_2$, M$_3$ and Cu$_1$ divergent or parallel 112

112. Fore wings with R$_3$ and R$_4$ stalked or coincident; hind wings with M$_2$ and M$_3$ parallel, R$_8$ and M$_1$ stalked. (Chlidanòta, Ceylon; **Trymáltis**, Austr.) .... CHLIDANÓTIDÆ
Fore wings with R$_3$ and R$_4$ separate or rarely stalked, if stalked then hind wings with M$_2$ and M$_3$ arising close together from the cell; distal end of 1A usually present (if wings are close-scaled, 1A absent, and 2A simple, and the second joint of labial palpi is broad, refer to Thyrididæ, couplet 62). A large widespread family. (Cacœcia (= *Árchips*) (*C. argyrospìla*, Fruit tree leaf-roller; *C. rosaceàna*, Oblique-banded leaf-roller), **Eùlia, Christoneùra** (*C. fumiferàna*, Spruce bud-worm), **Peronèa, Rhopóbota** (*R. nævàna*, Cranberry fireworm), **Pándemis, Tórtrix** (*T. citràna*, Orange tortrix; *T. franciscàna*, Apple-skin worm),

Cnephàsia, Argyrotóxa, Sparganòthis). (*SPARGANÓTHIDÆ*)
TORTRÍCIDÆ

113. Labial palpi beak-like, with the second joint rough-scaled on the upper side and smooth within, and the third joint porrect and inconspicuous; fore wings with 1A lost, all veins independently arising from the discal cell, rarely R_4 and R_5 stalked; hind wings with R and M_1 approximate or stalked and widely distant from M_2. (If the second joint of the palpus is bristly on the outer side and third joint is well set off refer to couplet 89; if R_{4+5} are stalked and both terminate in the costa and M_2 of the hind wings is not widely separate from M_1 see *Anarsia* ♂ of the Gelechiidæ, couplet 114). Mainly Holarctic and Neotropical. (**Commó-**

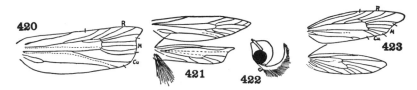

Figs. 420–423. Lepidoptera

420. **Hystrichophora,** fore wing (Heinrich) Olethreutidæ.
421. **Agnippe,** wings (Busck) Gelechiidæ.
422. **Gnorimoschema,** head from side (Busck) Gelechiidæ.
423. **Glyphipteryx,** wings (Spuler) Glyphipterygidæ.

phila, **Hysteròsia, Phalònia** (= *Cónchylis*), **Phármacis, Chlidònia, Phtheóchroa, Euxánthis**). (*COMMOPHÍLIDÆ, CONCHÝ-LIDÆ*) .... **PHALONÌIDÆ**
Palpus upturned to the middle of the front or beyond, the third joint long and slender, usually tapering. (If the palpi and proboscis are obsolete, see couplets 27, 35, 42, Psýchidæ).......114

114. Both wings with 1A lost (extreme tip present in *Symmoca*, spp.); outer margin of hind wing usually concave, sometimes quite emarginate and the apex produced; fore wings with R_5 running into the costa, stalked with R_4. (Figs. 421, 422). The largest family of Microfrenatæ, with about 400 genera and 3,700 species including many destructive species. (**Anacámpsis** (Leaf-rollers), **Anársia** (*A. lineatélla*, Peach twig-borer), **Aristotélia** (*A. fragàriæ,* Strawberry crown-miner), **Dùvita, Dichómeris, Glyphidócera, Recurvària, Sitotròga** (*S. cerealélla,* Angoumois grain-moth), **Pectinóphora** (*P. gossypiélla,* Pink boll-worm), **Phthorimæa** (*P. operculélla,* Potato tuber moth), **Telphùsa, Thiótricha, Gnorimoschèma** (Goldenrod gall moth), **Geléchia, Sophrònia, Sýmmoca, Trichótaphe**). (*DICHOMÉRIDÆ*). Most **GELECHÌIDÆ**
1A preserved, at least at margin 115

115. Hind wings with R and M_1 close together, connate, or stalked . .116
Hind wings with R and M_1 well separated at origin, at least half
as far apart as at the margin 119

116. Fore wings elongate triangular, costa slightly bent near middle
where R_5 terminates, Sc, R_1 and R_2 short, ending before middle
of wing, M_1 absent, M_2 and M_3 both ending in costal margin;
maxillary palpi vestigial. (**Strepsímana**, India).
STREPSIMÁNIDÆ
Fore wings with anterior veins longer, M_3 at least ending beyond
wing tip 117

117. Wings relatively ample, fore wings blunt; maxillary palpi of
the folded type 118
Wings rather narrow, fore wings sometimes falcate; maxillary
palpi porrect. (**Ceróstoma**, Holarc., Neotrop.). (See couplet
122) .... PLUTÉLLIDÆ, part

118. Fore wings with R_5 long-stalked and extending to the outer
margin, Cu_1 and Cu_2 widely separated; mainly Old World.
(**Ptochorýctis**, **Cryptóphasa**, **Xyloríctes**). (*CRYPTOPHÁSIDÆ,
UZÚCHIDÆ*) .... XYLORÍCTIDÆ
Fore wings with R_5 usually free and usually extending to the
costa, Cu_1 and Cu_2 usually connate or stalked; mostly New
World species. (**Stenòma**, **Menésta**, **Setióstoma**). (*STENO-
MÁTIDÆ*) .... STENÓMIDÆ

119. Ocelli small or absent 120
Ocelli usually very large and conspicuous; fore wings with R_5
ending beyond the wing-tip (Fig. 423). Largely oriental.
(*CHOREÙTIDÆ, HEMEROPHÍLIDÆ, SIMAÉTHIDÆ*).
GLYPHIPTERÝGIDÆ

Two well-marked subfamilies may be distinguished:

a. Wings relatively narrow, the apex of the fore wings more or less
extended as a lobe-like prolongation. (**Glyphípteryx**, cosmop.,
mainly Austr.) .... GLYPHIPTERYGÍNÆ
Wings broad and triangular, the apex not lobed. (**Choreùtis**,
widespr., **Simaèthis** (= *Allonónyma*), cosmop., mainly tropical) .... CHOREUTÍNÆ

120. Fore wings with R_4 and R_5 stalked 122
Fore wings with R_4 and R_5 separate, R_5 ending beyond the wing-
tip 121

121. Hind wings with M_2 arising nearer M_1 than to M_3. (**Éthmia**,
cosmop.) .... ETHMIÍNÆ; ŒCOPHÓRIDÆ
Hind wings with M_2 arising nearer M_3 than to M_1; palpi long,
reaching or surpassing the vertex. (**Œcóphora**, Palæarc.;
Depressària, widespr.; **Agonópteryx**, **Dasýcera**, **Pleùrota**). (See

couplet 138). (*DEPRESSARÌIDÆ*). (Including *THALA-MÁRCHIDÆ*) ....Most other **ŒCÓPHÓRIDÆ**

122. Hind wings with M_1 and M_2 stalked; antennæ extending forward in repose; small ocelli present; labial palpus tufted on second segment. (**Plutélla** (*P. maculipénnis* (= *cruciferàrum*), Diamond-back cabbage moth), cosmop.). (See couplet 117).

PLUTÉLLIDÆ

Hind wings with M_1 and M_2 separate; ocelli absent; labial palpi smooth. (**Yponomeùta**, widespr.; **Átteva**, tropicopol.; **Orthotælia**, Palæarc.; **Uròdus**). (*ATTÉVIDÆ*, based on pupal characters only, *HYPONÓTIDÆ*, misprint, *HYPSELÓPHIDÆ*, *HYPO-NOMEÙTIDÆ*, *ORTHOTÆLÌIDÆ*) ....**YPONOMEÙTIDÆ**

123. Fore wings without closed cell 124
Fore wings with discal cell formed 125

124. Hind tibiæ heavily spined; tarsi spinose at apex of joints; fore and hind wings linear, with three or four unbranched veins only; middle or hind legs commonly displayed when at rest. (See couplet 130) ....**HELIODÍNIDÆ**, part
Hind tibiæ hairy; fore wings lanceolate, with seven veins reach-ing the margin. (**Coptodísca**, "Shield-bearers"). (See couplet 128) ....**HELIOZÉLIDÆ**, part

125. Hind wings lanceolate, sometimes very small, at least one-sixth as wide as long, with the R-stem axial, widely separated from Sc 126
Hind wings with the R-stem closely associated with Sc at the base, or lost; or wing linear and the veins crowded or much reduced, the R-stem not prominently axial 129

126. Hind wings without discal cell, Cu-stem often simple; palpi drooping 127
Hind wings usually lanceolate, with a discal cell, the Cu-stem at least two-branched; fore wings with R_1 arising before the middle of the cell; palpi usually upturned beyond the middle of the front, often strongly divergent. (Fig. 425). (**Elachísta**, cosmop.; **Cycnòdia**, **Chrysopelèia**, Nearc.; **Períttia**, Palæarc.). (*APHELOSETÌIDÆ*, *CYCNODÌIDÆ*, *CHRYSOPELEÌIDÆ*)

ELACHÍSTIDÆ

127. Hind wings with an oblique branch from the R-stem to the costa near the middle of the wing, and sometimes another nearer the tip. (**Tinágma**, Holarc.; **Douglasia**, Palæarc.).

DOUGLASÌIDÆ

Hind wings with R-stem not sending a branch to the costa near the middle of the wing-length, but sometimes with a branch near the tip 128

128. Discal cell two-thirds the wing-length, lanceolate; hind tibiæ hairy.

(Fig. 429). (**Antispìla, Heliozèla,** widespr.). (See couplet 124)
Most **HELIOZÉLIDÆ**
Discal cell reaching almost to the end of the wing, its posterior
edge straight, the branches of R, M and Cu very short; hind
tibiæ with a row of strong bristles. (Some species of *Phyllo-
cnistis*). (See couplet 96) .... **PHYLLOCNÍSTIDÆ**

129. Accessory cell unusually large, extending halfway to the base of
the wing and hind wing without closed cell and with reduced
venation; hind tibiæ very hairy; antennæ long, those of the male
heavily ciliate; vertex often with a large loose semi-erectile tuft.
(Fig. 427). (**Tischèria,** widespr. (*T. malifoliélla,* Apple leaf-
miner)) .... **TISCHERÍIDÆ**

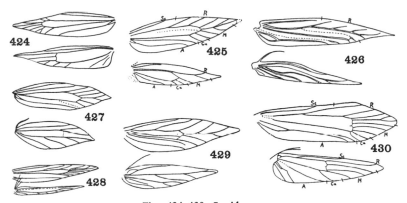

Figs. 424–430. Lepidoptera

424. **Scythris,** wings (Walsingham) Scythrididæ.
425. **Elachista,** wings (Spuler) Elachistidæ.
426. **Coleophora,** wings (Forbes) Coleophoridæ.
427. **Coptotriche,** wings (Walsingham) Tischeriidæ.
428. **Mompha,** wings (Busck) Cosmopterygidæ.
429. **Antispila,** wings (Spuler) Heliozelidæ.
430. **Holcocera,** wings (Forbes) Blastobasidæ.

Accessory cell smaller, or more often absent (if long, hind wing
with closed cell and complete venation); otherwise of different
conformation 130

130. Hind tarsi with more or less distinct groups of bristles near the
ends of the several joints, the hind tibiæ smooth-scaled or with
stiff bristles; middle or hind legs displayed when in resting
position, either raised or held out sideways. (**Heliodìnes,** Holarc.,
Austr.; **Schreckensteìnia,** Holarc.; **Pancàlia, Augásma,** Palæarc.;
Stathmópoda, Indoaustr., Ethiop., Palæarc.; **Idioglóssa**). (*TINÆ-*

GERìIDÆ). (See couplet 124). . . . . Most **HELIODÍNIDÆ**

Hind tarsi without evident groups of bristles 131

131. Fore wings with four veins or less, either free or stalked, extending from the cell to the costa, and five or six from the cell to the inner margin, the last branch of R ending beyond the tip of the wing; hind wings with R and M usually widely separated at the margin 132

Fore wings with five veins extending from the cell to the costa, or with only three or four to the inner margin, the last branch of R ending before the tip of the wing (except Epimarptidæ) . . 134

132. Fore wings with R_1 arising beyond the middle of the cell, about as long as R_2. (Fig. 424). (**Scỳthris** (= *Butàlis*), cosmop.; **Paralogístis**, Ethiop.). (*SCÝTHRIDÆ, BUTÁLIDÆ*).

SCYTHRÍDIDÆ

Fore wings with R_1 arising before the middle of the cell, longer than R_2 133

133. Hind tibiæ stiffly bristled, normally in tufts at the spurs; hind wings with M_1 and M_2 separate. (**Epermènia** (= *Chauliòdus*), widespr.; **Acanthèdra**, Nearc.; **Catapléctica**, Palæarc.)

EPERMENìIDÆ

Hind tibiæ with long loose hair; palpi small and drooping; hind wings with M_1 and M_2 united or long-stalked. (**Argyrésthia** (*A. conjugélla*, Apple fruit-miner), widespr.; **Zellèria**, cosmop.; **Hofmánnia**) . . . . **ARGYRESTHÌIDÆ**

134. Fore wings with the discal cell set obliquely, the end distinctly closer to the hind margin than to the costa, Cu_2 very short and usually extending directly back to the margin 135

Fore wings with the discal cell axial and central, Cu_2 normally longer and continuing parallel with the medial veins, rarely obsolete 137

135. Fore wings with blunt discal cell, R_1 arising from the middle of the wing, veins R_2 to Cu arising from the end of the discal cell, with a long stigmal thickening between the costa and R_1; hind wings with Sc and R normally fused for a short distance near the base; antennæ with a heavy pecten on the basal joint. (Fig. 430). Mainly Nearctic species. (**Blastóbasis**, widespr.; **Auximóbasis**, Am.; **Dryopèria, Holcócera, Pigrítia, Valentínia**). (See couplet 93) . . . . Most **BLASTOBÁSIDÆ**

Fore wings without stigma, R_2 arising distinctly before the end of the discal cell; hind wings with R not fused with Sc, sometimes vestigial. (Fig. 426) 136

136. Front tibiæ slender, with the epiphysis small and apical or wanting, the hind tibiæ with the upper spurs above the middle; antennæ porrect in repose. (Fig. 426). (**Coleóphora** (= *Haploptília*), cosmop. (*C. fletcherélla*, Cigar case-bearer; *C. malivor-*

élla, Pistol case-bearer); **Goniodòma, Metriòtes,** Palæarc.).
(EUPÍSTIDÆ, HAPLOPTILÌIDÆ) ..... COLEOPHÓRIDÆ
Front tibiæ stouter, with the epiphysis at the middle; antennæ
turned back in repose. (**Batráchedra, Blastodácna, Pyrodérces**).
(See couplet 142) .... COSMOPTERÝGIDÆ, part

137. Labial palpi with the third joint normally blunt, fusiform and
more or less angulate with the second, the joints not curving;
maxillary palpi porrect but not folded across the proboscis, or
reduced, sometimes absent; 2A not forked at the base. (**Acro-
cércops, Gracilària** (*G. syringélla,* Lilac leaf-miner); **Lithocollètis**
(= *Phyllonorýcter*) (Leaf blotch-miners); **Mármara** (*M. pomonélla,* Apple-skin miner); **Paréctopa, Parórnix, Órnix**).
*(EUCÉSTÍDÆ, LITHOCOLLÉTIDÆ, PHYLLONORYCTÉR-
IDÆ)* .... GRACILARÌIDÆ
Labial palpi with the third joint long, tapering, pointed, the
second joint curving up; maxillary palpi small, but of folded
type, curving over the base of the proboscis; 2A commonly
formed at the base 138

138. Both wings with 1A preserved at the margin and 2A forked at the
base; basal joint of the antennæ with a strong pecten of bristles.
(**Borkhausènia, Éndrosis**). (See couplet 121).
                                   ŒCOPHÓRIDÆ, part
Hind wings and usually also the fore wings lacking A1; antennæ
often without a pecten 139

139. Fore wings with no veins emerging from the end of the discal cell
between the continuations of the R and Cu + M stems. (**Hèlice,
Theísoa**). (See couplet 114) ....GELECHÌIDÆ, part
The oblique end of the discal cell of the fore wings emitting
several veins between the R and Cu stems 140

140. Labial palpi with appressed scales, the second joint with a projecting pencil of scales above; antennæ with the basal joint
elongate, a notch near the base of the stalk covered by an
oblique tooth beneath it; hind tibiæ rough-haired above; fore
wings with R_5 ending beyond the wing-tip. (**Epimárptis,** India)
                                   EPIMÁRPTIDÆ
Labial palpi without dorsal tuft; base of antennæ not toothed;
R_5 ending in costal margin before wing-tip 141

141. Hind wings elongate-ovate or ovate-lanceolate with the costal margin simple, evenly arched. Hawaiian. (**Hyposmócoma, Diplósara,
Aphthonètus**). *(DIPLOSÁRIDÆ)* ....HYPOSMOCÓMIDÆ
Hind wings lanceolate or linear, with a slightly developed costal
lobe toward the base, accentuated by a tuft of stiff bristles beyond
which the costa is straight or slightly concave, the apex always
acute 142

142. Hind wings with reduced neuration, R, M and Cu apparently

simple veins, no crossveins, subcosta very short, frenulum simple; ocelli present; labial palpi strongly flattened and rather rough-scaled on anterior edge throughout. Austromalayan. (Agonóxena, Hæmólytis). (See couplet 104) ....AGONOXÉNIDÆ
Hind wings, except when linear, with several branches of Cu, M

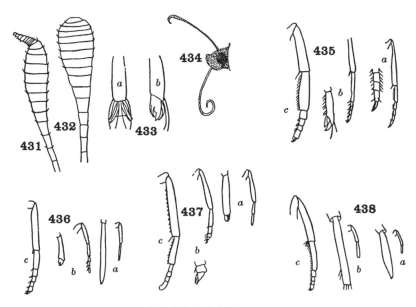

Figs. 431–438. **Lepidoptera**

431. Antenna of skipper, apical portion (Duncan) Hesperiidæ.
432. Antenna of butterfly, apical portion (Duncan).
433. **Epargyreus**, last joint of tarsus of male (Scudder): *a*, dorsal view; *b*, lateral view. Hesperiidæ.
434. **Epargyreus**, side view of head (Scudder) Hesperiidæ.
435. **Lycæna**, details of legs (Scudder): *a*, front leg of male with tarsal joints at left more enlarged; *b*, front leg of male with last tarsal joint at left more enlarged; *c*, middle leg of male. Lycænidæ.
436. **Nymphidia**, details of legs (Scudder): *a*, tibia and tarsus of front legs of male, with tarsus at left more enlarged; b, tibia and tarsus of front leg of female, with last joint at left more enlarged; *c*, tibia and tarsus of middle leg of male. Riodinidæ.
437. **Euphydryas**, details of legs (Scudder): *a*, tibia and tarsus of front leg of male, with last joints of tarsus on left more enlarged; *b*, tibia and tarsus of front leg of female with last joints of tarsus below more enlarged; *c*, tibia and tarsus of middle leg of male. Nymphalidæ.
438. **Megisto**, details of legs (Scudder): *a*, tibia and tarsus of front leg of male, with tarsus at left more enlarged; *b*, tibia and tarsus of front leg of female, with tarsus at left more enlarged; *c*, tibia and tarsus of middle leg of male. Satyridæ.

and the crossvein preserved, cell often closed, frenulum usually multiple; ocelli often absent; palpi with the second joint smooth or tufted below. (Fig. 428). A large cosmopolitan group. (**Cosmópteryx, Chrysoclísta, Homalèdra, Synallágma, Wálshia, Stagmatóphora, Lavérna, Lophóptilus, Mómpha, Perimède, Psacáphora, Limnœcia** (*L. fragmitélla,* Cat-tail moth)). (Compare couplet 136). (*LAVÈRNIDÆ*) .... Most **COSMOPTERÝGIDÆ**

143. All veins arising from cell of fore wing simple; eyes strongly "lashed" in front; head very broad; antennæ separated at base by two to four times their width; antennæ usually with narrowed, pointed, or hooked tip beyond club (apiculus); body very stout, wings relatively small; flight rapid, erratic. Skippers. (HESPERIÒIDEA) ....**HESPERÌIDÆ**

a. Head distinctly narrower than thorax; only one pair of spurs on hind tibia; labial palpus porrect, unusually small; antennal club large, blunt, not recurved, lacking apiculus; expanse over 40 mm.; fore wing with base of vein M_2 nearer M_3 than M_1; powerful fliers. Restricted to southern U.S.A. and northern Mexico. (**Megathỳmus, Ægiàle**) ....**MEGATHYMÌNÆ**
Head about as wide as thorax or distinctly wider; usually with two pairs of hind tibial spurs; antennal club always recurved or with tapered distal portion (apiculus); expanse under 50 mm. ......b

b. Labial palpus peculiar: second segment erect, third segment porrect, long, slender; two pairs of hind tibial spurs, one spur of each pair longer than its mate; spines absent on middle tibia except in *Állora*; fore wing with vein M_2 at origin usually equally distant from M_1 and M_3; abdomen shorter than thoracic dorsum; small tuft of hairs (eyelash) absent alongside base of antenna; bare portion of antenna club (nudum) with 25–36 divisions; tibial hair-pencils and discal stigma or brand often present in males; club of antenna slender and long, apiculus long, curved, and pointed. Large skippers. Confined to Africa, Asia, and Indoaustralian region. (**Bìbasis,** China, Indomal.; **Hásora,** Indoaustr.; **Choáspes,** China to New Guinea; **Cœlìades,** Ethiop.). (*ISMENÌNÆ, RHOPALOCAMPTÌNÆ*) ....**CŒLIADÌNÆ**
Labial palpus otherwise; eyelash present c

c. Antennal club large and blunt, always recurved before enlarged part; cell of fore wing very long. All of South America, north to Arizona. (**Pyrrhopỳge, Mysòria, Mýscelus, Yanguna, Jemàdia, Apýrrhothrix**). (*THAMYRÍDIDÆ*) ....**PYRRHOPYGÌNÆ**
Antennal club never wholly recurved, reflexed portion when present always beyond widest part ....d

d. Median vein in cell of hind wing with the lower branch down to base of M_3; end of cell (discocellular) slanted toward outer costal point of hind wing; fore wing cell not very long; fore wing with

M_2 at origin usually nearer M_1 than M_3, often decurved at base; labial palpus with third segment short, bluntly pointed, always bent downward and protruding; abdomen equal to or longer than thoracic dorsum; nudum of antennal club with 12 to 36 divisions; male often with discal stigma on fore wing, but never with hair-pencils on hind tibia. Confined to Australia and New Guinea. (Trapezìtes, Anisýnta, Toxídia, Hesperílla)

TRAPEZITÌNÆ

Median vein of hind wing cell, if forked, with lower branch meeting discocellular well above base of M_3; discocellular pointing toward costa much basad of outer point; abdominal length equal to or shorter than dorsum of thorax ....e

e. Vein M_2 not curved at base, at origin either median between M_1 and M_3 or nearer M_1; no row of spines on the middle tibia (except in *Euschèmon* and *Muschámpia*); males rarely with a tuft of hairs on the hind tibia, often with a costal fold on the fore wing; male of *Euschèmon* with a frenulum. Cosmopolitan. (Pýrgus, Holarc.; Chætocneme, Austr., Papuan; Muschámpia, Ethiop., Oriental; Thórybes, Nearc.; Urbànus, Neotrop.; Pholisòra, Am.). (*ACHYLÓDIDÆ, EUDÁMIDÆ, ERYNNÌNÆ, TELE-GÓNIDÆ, THYMÉLIDÆ, URBANÌNÆ, HESPERIÌNÆ* of authors). (Incl. *EUSCHEMÓNIDÆ*). (Figs. 433, 434)

PÝRGÌNÆ

Vein M_2 usually curved at base, at origin usually nearer M_3 than M_1; a row of spines usually present on middle tibia; males never with a costal fold but commonly with a brand or stigma on the fore wing and hind tibial hair-pencils. Cosmopolitan. (Hespèria, Holarc., N. Afr.; Carterocèphalus, Ochlòdes, Holarc.; Aerómachus, Thoréssa, Hálpe, Plastíngia, Potánthus, Oriental; Kobròna, Mimène, Papuan; Taractrócera, Telícota, Indoaustr.; Gorgỳra, Metisélla, Platylésches, Ethiop.; Pánara, Palæarc., Ethiop.; Polìtes, Poànes, Atrýtone, Amblyscírtes, Leròdea, Nearc.). (*PAMPHILÌNÆ, CYCLOPÍDIDÆ*) ....HESPERIÌNÆ

At least one vein arising from discal cell forked; eye rarely "lashed"; head narrower; antennæ closer, separated by about their width or less; antennal club not narrowed to point or hook at tip; wings much larger in relation to body. Butterflies. (PAPILIONOIDEA) 144

144. Fore leg of male greatly shortened, tarsus generally unsegmented, clawless; if claw present, eye is emarginated and "lashed" (hairy); two distinct anal veins on hind wing 146

Fore leg of both sexes normal; cell of fore and hind wings closed; no strong bladder-like expansions at bases of veins of fore wing; eye entire and bare; labial palpus much less than one half length of antennæ (except *Teinopálpus,* which has two long tails on hind wing 145

145. Claws large, not toothed or bifid (except in one *Leptocírcus*); fore tibia with a process (epiphysis) on underside; only one prominent anal vein in hind wing (except *Barònia*); anal (inner) margin of hind wing concave. Often large species with prominent tails on anal angle of hind wing ....**PAPILIÓNIDÆ**

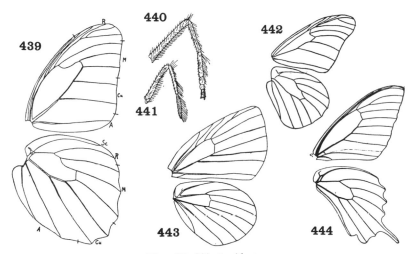

Figs. 439–444. Lepidoptera

439. **Caligo,** wings (Stichel) Amathusiidæ.
440. **Caligo,** tibia and tarsus of front leg of female (Stichel) Amathusiidæ.
441. **Caligo,** tibia and tarsus of front leg of male (Stichel) Amathusiidæ.
442. **Danaus,** wings (Scudder) Danaidæ.
443. **Nymphidia,** wings (Stichel) Riodinidæ.
444. **Papilio,** wings (Comstock) Papilionidæ.

a. Radial vein of fore wing 4-branched (if 5-branched, labial palpi twice length of head); M_2 arises nearer M_3 than M_1; no supernumerary vein between Cu and anal vein ....b
Radial vein of fore wing 5-branched; M_2 arises midway between M_1 and M_3; supernumerary vein present between Cu and anal vein; one anal vein present; R_3 present; labial palpus very short (except *Teinopálpus*); antenna unscaled (except *Gràphium* and *Lampróptera*); tails often present on hind wings. Cosmopolitan. (**Papílio, Gràphium,** cosmop.; **Atrophaneùra,** cosmop., exc. Palæarc.; **Lampróptera, Teinopálpus,** oriental; **Báttus,** Am.; **Tròides** (= *Ornithóptera*), Indoaustr.; **Créssida,** Austr.; **Euryades,** Neotrop.). (Fig. 444) ....**PAPILIONÍNÆ**

b. Radial vein of fore wing 4-branched; if antenna unscaled, then two anal veins present; tails never present c
Radial vein of fore wing 5-branched; one anal vein; all twelve veins of fore wing present, free; tails always at least slightly developed on hind wing; labial palpus twice length of head, porrect; antenna unscaled. Palæarctic and Oriental. (Zerýnthia (= Thais), Palæarc.; Lühdorfia, Serícinus, Bhutanìtis, Orient.)
ZERYNTHIÌNÆ

c. One anal vein present; antenna scaled; labial palpus short. Holarctic. (Parnássius, Holarc.; Árchon, Near East; Hypermnéstra, centr. Palæarc.) ....PARNASSIÌNÆ
Two anal veins present; antenna unscaled, very short, club broad, straight; R_3 absent; R_1 and Sc fused. Mexico only. (One species, Barònia brevicórnis) ....BARONIÌNÆ

Claws bifid or strongly toothed; fore tibia lacking epiphysis; two distinct anal veins in hind wing; anal margin of hind wing normal (at least slightly convex). Small and medium-sized species, usually white or yellow except in tropics. (ASCÌIDÆ, PIÉRIDÆ) ....PIERÍDIDÆ

a. Fore wing with vein M_2 arising from cell; antenna strongly clubbed ....b
Fore wing with vein M_2 stalked with R_{3-5}, radius 3-branched; male valves fused ventrally; antenna only slightly clubbed. (One genus, Pseudopóntia, W. Equ. Afr.) ....PSEUDOPONTIÌNÆ

b. Fore wing with vein M_2 nearer M_1 than M_3 at base, radius 3- to 5-branched, R_1 arising from cell; male valves never fused very far. (Pìeris, Eurèma, cosmop.; Catastícta, Neotrop.; Dèlias, Indomalay.; Anápheis, Orient., Afr.; Áppias, tropicopol., except Austromal.; Áscia, Phœbis, Am.; Euchlòe, Anthócaris, Holarc.; Còlias, Holarc., Ethiop., S. Am.; Colotis, Ethiop., Indomal.)
PIERIDÌNÆ
Fore wing with vein M_2 not nearer M_1 than M_3 at base, radius 5-branched, R_1 arising beside the cell; male valves connected ventrally by strong sclerotization. (Dismórphia, Enantia, Pseudopìeris, Neotrop.; Leptídea, Palæarc.). . .DISMORPHIÌNÆ

146. Fore leg of female normal, claws fully developed; generally small butterflies (less than 75 mm. expanse) 147
Fore leg of female degenerate, clawless; male usually with terminal tuft of hairs on fore leg; precostal spur usually present on hind wing; usually large or medium-sized species. 149

147. Labial palpus much shorter than thorax, third segment hairy; eye emarginate (invaded by antennal sockets), and usually "lashed" (hairy) 148

Labial palpus about as long as thorax, protruding spout-like in front, third segment very hairy; eye entire; hind wing with precostal spur (humeral vein); fore wing rather falcate. (Libýthea, Palæarc., Indoaustr., Ethiop.; Libythèana, Am.).

LIBYTHÈIDÆ

148. Fore tarsus of male functional for walking, but shortened to one segment, one or both claws lost (except African *Arrùgia*, with joints and two claws); fore wing venation reduced to 10 or 11 veins (R_4 and R_5 fused); usually without precostal spur on hind wing; claws bifid or toothed; small species, often blue or with slender tails on hind wings. Cosmopolitan. (Lycæna (= *Chrysóphanus*), Holarc., N. Zeal.; Plebèius, Philòtes, Callòphrys, Thécla, Lycæides, Holarc.; Nacadùba, Lámpides, Rápala, Liphỳra, Indomal.; Polyómmatus, Palæarc.; Ogỳris, Austr.; Thysónotis, Gérydus, Amblypòdia, Indoaustr.; Strỳmon, Holarc., Neotrop.; Feníseca, Nearc.; Líptena, Mimacræa, Lachnócnema, Ethiop.). (Subfamily classification in confused state.) ....LYCÆNIDÆ
Fore tarsus of male degenerate, reduced to one segment (rarely four), not functional for walking, clawless; precostal spur present on hind wing; usually tailless and rarely blue. ....RIODÍNIDÆ

a. Costal margin of hind wing with basal vein-like thickening; many mimics, colors often brilliant. Am., but mainly Neotrop. (Nymphídia (= *Caléphelis* of authors), Apodèmia, Am.; Eurýbia, Neotrop.). (*ERYCÍNIDÆ, LEMONÌIDÆ* auctt.)

RIODINÌNÆ

Costal margin of hind wing lacking basal false vein. Tropicopolitan, few Palæarctic. (Nemeòbius, Eur.; Taxília, Dòdona, Indomal.; Abísara, Indoaustr., Ethiop.; Euselàsia, Helícopis, Neotrop.) ....NEMEOBIÌNÆ

149. Veins of fore wing not greatly dilated at base (partly so in a few tropical Nymphalidæ) 150
One to three veins of fore wing greatly dilated at base (rarely veins generally thickened); cell of hind wing closed; labial palpus slender, flattened, with fringe of long hairs; fore leg terminating in thick tuft of hairs in both sexes, that of female not knobbed or clubbed; usually medium-sized or rather small species with brownish ground color and at least one eye-like spot on underside of hind wing. (Fig. 438). (Sátyrus, Palæarc.; Cercyònis, Nearc.; Erèbia, Œnèis, Cœnonýmpha, Holarc.; Lèthe, Holarc., Indomal.; Megísto, Am.; Taýgetis, Pierélla, Lymanópoda, Pedaliòides, Neotrop.; Melanìtis, Ethiop., Indoaustr., Palæarc.; Ýpthima, Asia, Indoaustr., Afr.; Mycálesis, Indomal., Ethiop.; Élymnias, Indomal.). (*AGAPÉTIDÆ*) ....SATÝRIDÆ
150. Large tropical species with eye-like markings on underside of hind

wing; wing huge in relation to body, abdomen very short; fore wing often shorter than hind wing, never much longer; vein R_4 of fore wing ending in costal margin or wing-tip; fore tarsus of female smoothly scaled, not hairy (some with spines) 151

Size various; eye-like markings rarely present on underside of hind wing (then hind wing cell open or closed by thin veinlet); cell of hind wing and often fore wing open in many forms with short abdomen 152

151. Cell of hind wing closed and eye hairy in Neotropical species; fore tarsus of male unsegmented with long hairs; fore tarsus of female 5-jointed, bearing spines but not hairs, not clubbed; large crepuscular or shade-loving species; brownish, with rather subdued colors aside from eye-spots on underside. (Amathùsia, Faunis, Tænaris, Discóphora, Indomal.; Brássolis, Opsíphanes, Erýphanis, Calìgo, Naròpe, Neotrop.) (*BRASSÓLIDÆ, CALIGÍNIDÆ*)
AMATHUSÌIDÆ

Cell of hind wing open; fore tarsus of male with rather sparse, short hairs; fore leg of female weakly clubbed; eye bare; large sun-loving species, the males either brilliantly metallic blue above, or whitish. (One genus, Mórpho, Neotrop.) ..MORPHÒIDÆ

152. Cell of hind wing open or closed by thin veinlet; fore wing cell rarely open; tarsus of female with small knob; anal vein (2A) of fore wing single throughout ....NYMPHÁLIDÆ

a. Cell of hind wing usually closed (all exceptions Neotropical); fore wing narrow, much longer than hind wing; no bared hollow on inner margin to accommodate abdomen; eye naked; fore wing with vein R_4 usually ending in costal margin or at wing-tip; wings lacking "tails" and other projections ....b

Cell of hind wing commonly open; fore wing usually little longer than hind wing; hollow present on inner margin of hind wings to accommodate abdomen when wings closed, bare of most scales and hairs; eyes hairy or naked; fore wing with vein R_4 usually ending in outer margin well beyond wing-tip; wings often with "tails" or other projections (angled); labial palpus stout, cylindrical, with short fringe of hairs. (Apatùra, Argýnnis, Palæarc.; Calinaga, Ind.; Chloríppe, Athèna, Adélpha, Ágrias, Prépona, Catagrámma, Neotrop.; Anæ̀a, Phyciòdes, Am.; Bolòria, Polygònia, Nýmphalis, Limenìtis, Melitæ̀a, Euphýdryas, Holarc.; Vanéssa, cosmop.; Speyeria, Asterocámpa, Nearc.; Prècis, Indoaustr., Am., Ethiop.; Hypolímnas, tropicopol.; Érgolis, Cethòsia, Kállima, Cyréstis, Indomal.; Néptis, Palæarc., Ethiop., Indoaustr.; Euthàlia, Palæarc., Indomal.; Charáxes, Afr., Indomal.; Pseudacræa, Euphæ̀dra, Ethiop.) ....NYMPHALÌNÆ

b. Humeral vein (precostal spur) of hind wing curving inward toward base of wing; cell of hind wing open except in *Heliconius;* male

with claws of each pair on middle and hind legs equal; labial palpus compressed, scales at sides, hairs at front; often brilliantly colored, not mottled. (Helicònius, Diòne, Drỳas, Neotrop.; Agràulis, Am.) (*EUEÍDIDÆ*) .... HELICONIÌNÆ
Humeral vein curving outward toward tip of wing; cell of hind wing always closed; male with claws of each pair on middle and hind legs usually very unequal; labial palpus cylindrical, sparsely hairy; wings rather thinly scaled, translucent, mottled toward base with dark spots. (Acræa, Indomal., Ethiop.; Planèma, Pardópsis, Ethiop.; Actínote, Neotrop.) .... ACRÆIÌNÆ

Cell of fore wing closed; fore tarsus of female heavily clubbed; anal vein of fore wing bifurcate at base; fore wing with vein R_4 usually ending in costal margin or wing-tip; rather large, long-winged species with disagreeable odors .... DANÀIDÆ

a. Labial palpus with first segment distinctly shorter than second; fore tarsus of male discrete, long, slender, shaggy; androconial scales present on hind wing of male .... b
Labial palpus with first segment scarcely shorter than second; fore tarsus of male fused with tibia, unsegmented, clubbed; fore tarsus of female long, slender; androconial scales absent on hind wing of male; no hair-pencils near end of abdomen of male; wings long and narrow. Entirely Neotropical. (Ithòmia, Melinæa, Thyrídia, Mechanìtis, Dircénna, Hymenìtis). (*NEOTROPÌNÆ*) ITHOMIÌNÆ
b. Fore tarsus of female four-segmented, spiny, club-shaped; hair-pencils present near end of abdomen of male; wings usually relatively broad. Cosmopolitan, mainly tropical. (Dánaus, Indomal., Asia, Am.; Euplœa, Ethiop., Indomal.; Lycorélla, Ituna, Neotrop.; Ideópsis, Héstia, Indomal.; Amàuris, Ethiop.). (*LYMNÁDIDÆ*). (Fig. 442) .... DANAÌNÆ
Fore tarsus of female five-segmented, less spiny; hair-pencils absent near end of abdomen of male; wings usually relatively narrow. Papuan only. (One genus, Tellérvo) .. TELLERVÌNÆ

153. Head of female moth of the usual form and structure 154
Head of female of abnormal form and structure, resembling that of the caterpillar. (See couplet 37).
Females of some HETEROGÝNIDÆ
154. Moth developing in and frequently never leaving a sack or case constructed by the larva and carried about by the latter during growth. (See couplets 27, 35, 37, 42).
Females of PSÝCHIDÆ and some HETEROGÝNIDÆ
Moth not developing in such a sack constructed by the larva, the latter entirely free-living 155

155. Proboscis absent or vestigial; females only 156
     Proboscis not absent or vestigial; if maxillary palpus vestigial, then
     labial palpus also reduced or absent 160
156. Maxillary palpus large; ocelli present; wings very small; moth
     aquatic, never emerging from water. (Acéntropus, Europe,
     Canada). (See couplet 68) .... PYRALÍDIDÆ, part
     Maxillary palpus absent or vestigial; not aquatic 157
157. Chætosema absent; ocelli absent 158
     Chætosema present; wings absent; head densely hairy, body softly
     woolly; fore femur with conspicuous curved spine. (Somábrachys,
     N. Afr., Palestine). (See couplet 23) .. MEGALOPÝGIDÆ, part
158. Mandible minute but present; brachypterous, fore wing 6 to 11 mm.
     long; alpine females. (Korscheltéllus, Europe). (See couplet 9)
                                                    HEPIÁLIDÆ, part
     Mandible absent; micropterous, fore wing less than 6 mm. long. 159
159. Labial palpus well developed. (Chondróstega, Palæarc.). (See
     couplet 82) ....LASIOCÁMPIDÆ, part
     Labial palpus rudimentary or absent; body stout, densely woolly.
     Many species. (See couplet 74). .... LYMANTRÌIDÆ, part
160. Labial and maxillary palpi clearly present 161
     Labial and maxillary palpi vestigial or absent; ocelli absent;
     chætosema present; abdomen closely scaled, not woolly; females
     only. Several genera, especially in late fall or early spring. (See
     couplet 45) ....GEOMÉTRIDÆ, part
161. Chætosema absent 162
     Chætosema present; ocelli present; palpi short, almost concealed.
     (See couplet 112) ....Females of some TORTRÍCIDÆ
162. Maxillary palpus short, four-jointed; labial palpus long, last joint
     tapered to tip; ocelli present or absent; females only. (Dasystròma,
     Cheimábache, Eur.). (See couplet 121) .. ŒCOPHÓRIDÆ, part
     Maxillary palpus short, with less than three joints, or very long,
     with more than three joints; if long, then ocelli absent 163
163. Ocelli absent; both pairs of palpi long, conspicuous; antenna very
     long, filiform; short-winged species (both sexes) less then 10 mm.
     long; fore wings hairy; hind wings one-fifth body length and
     veinless 164
     Ocelli present; maxillary palpus short, one- to three-segmented;
     females only; body length more than 10 mm. 165
164. Maxillary palpus 5-jointed, longer than proboscis; forewing with
     11 veins (R_5 and M_1 fused distally); antenna long, with about
     100 joints; length slightly less than 6 mm. (Embryonópsis,
     Kerguelen Is. and Marion Is., S. Pacific). (See couplet 122)
                                                  YPONOMEÙTIDÆ, part
     Maxillary palpus 4-jointed, much shorter than proboscis; fore wing
     with six visible veins, all reaching margin; antenna long, with

about 40 joints; length slightly more than 9 mm. (**Pringleóphaga,** Kerguelen Is. and Crozet Is., S. Pacific). (See couplet 100)

TÌNÈIDÆ, part

165. Hood of tympanic organ enclosing spiracle. (**Euxòa,** Eur.) (See couplet 74b) ....NOCTÙIDÆ, part

Hood above spiracle. (**Ocnogỳna,** Eur.). (See couplet 76).

ARCTÌIDÆ, part

Lepidoptera, Larvæ

The key given below follows in most sections that used by Forbes in his *Lepidoptera of New York and Neighboring States,* which is based on the system elaborated by Fracker. The sections dealing with the butterflies and Bombycoidea are new. It includes the more important families as they may be distinguished on the basis of those genera whose larvæ have been carefully and systematically studied. Wherever possible other families have been added, but at present a knowledge of even the European and North American forms other than butterflies is so incomplete that the present key must be used only as a guide in identification, and must in no way be relied upon as presenting characters of definite and final accuracy. Many families are necessarily omitted.

1. Thoracic legs present, formed of distinct segments; abdominal prolegs usually present or indicated by crochets 2

 Thoracic legs wanting or reduced to fleshy swellings without sclerotized segments; prolegs frequently vestigial or absent 7

2. Eyes present as five closely grouped facets; antennæ usually longer than head, which is retractile; prolegs present as fleshy processes on abdominal segments one to eight; no crochets; setæ modified as thick three-dimensional scales; very small, slug-like larvæ on mosses and liverworts ....MICROPTERŶGIDÆ

 Eyes present as dissociated single units, usually six in number, on each side, never with five-faceted eye; prolegs with crochets usually present but never on abdominal segments one and two; no such modified setæ 3

3. Prolegs vestigial or absent, entirely without crochets 4

 Prolegs present, or at least indicated by crochets which may be reduced but never entirely absent 14

4. Front not extending upwards to the vertex, except in cases where the vertex forms a very narrow slit 5

 Front extending upwards to the vertex; small species, the larvæ living in portable cases from which they protrude the anterior part of the body to feed externally or eat into the tissues of leaves, fruits, etc. (See couplet 25). Case-bearers.

COLEOPHÓRIDÆ

5. Head free, exposed in front of the thorax; no mid-ventral suckers on abdomen; body segments separated by strong incisures; only the primary body setæ present, these usually distinct 6
Head concealed within the prothorax partly protruded for feeding; body almost always with spines or secondary hair, the primary setæ obsolete; abdomen with seven mid-ventral suckers; body with obscure incisures, but usually with pits. Slug-caterpillars.

EUCLÈIDÆ

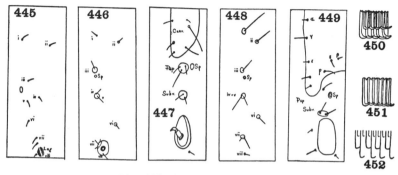

Figs. 445–452.   Lepidoptera, *Larvæ*

445. **Adela,** setal map of third abdominal segment (Forbes) Adelidæ.
446. **Dichomerus,** setal map of sixth abdominal segment (Forbes) Gelechiidæ.
447. **Dichomerus,** setal map of prothorax (Forbes) Gelechiidæ.
448. **Dicymolomia,** setal map of third abdominal segment (Forbes).
449. **Sthenopis,** setal map of prothorax (Fracker).
450. Biordinal or double-rowed arrangement of crochets on abdominal **proleg** (Forbes).
451. Uniordinal or single-rowed arrangement of crochets on abdominal **proleg** (Forbes).
452. Triordinal or triple-rowed arrangement of crochets of abdominal **proleg** (Forbes).

6. Setæ iv. and v. distant on the abdominal segments; prolegs present, but without hooks; living in the pods of Yucca.

Tegetícula of the **PRODÓXIDÆ**

Setæ iv. and v. adjacent (Fig. 446); prolegs absent. (See couplets 23, 43). ....A few **GELECHÌIDÆ**

7. Body fusiform, thickest at the middle; head small, the front reaching only about two-thirds of the way to the vertex, closed above and separated from the vertex by the epicrania; living in the pods of Yucca. (**Prodóxus**). (See couplet 6). .... **PRODÓXIDÆ**
Body cylindrical or flattened; if somewhat fusiform, the front extends upwards to the vertex 8

8. Head with two ocelli on each side, or with one large one or with the ocelli obsolete 9
Head with six small ocelli on each side 13
9. Two ocelli on each side of the head; front not extending to the vertex; larvæ leaf-miners, forming blotch mines .. HELIOZÉLIDÆ
One large ocellus on each side of head or ocelli obsolete 10
10. Front triangular, the ocellus frontal; larva making a large blotch mine from which it drops to spin a cocoon in the ground.
ERIOCRANÏIDÆ
Front quadrangular; ocellus lateral in position 11
11. Front narrowed behind, wider in front; body cylindrical; prolegs, if present, vestigial and borne on the second to seventh abdominal segments 12
Front widest behind; body usually depressed; prolegs, if present, borne on the third to fifth segments of abdomen. (See couplets 13, 15) .... GRACILARÏIDÆ
12. Body not greatly lengthened, about five times as long as thick; prolegs usually present; larvae mining in leaves, bark or fruits, or forming galls in twigs or petioles .... NEPTICÙLIDÆ
Body very slender, about ten times as long as thick; prolegs absent; larvæ mining near the surface of the stems of herbaceous or other plants .... OPOSTÉGIDÆ
13. Vestigial prolegs, bearing hooks, present on the third to sixth abdominal segments; larvæ mining in leaves, usually making a blotch mine .... TISCHERÏIDÆ
Abdomen without prolegs on the sixth segment; larvæ leaf miners, at least in the early stages, the older larvæ sometimes spinning a shelter on the surface of the leaf. (See couplets 11, 15).
GRACILARÏIDÆ
14. Body without secondary or tufted setæ; tubercle vi. with a single seta; vii. with at most three setæ, unless the proleg has a multiserial circle of hooks when it may bear four setæ 15
Body bearing tufted or secondary hairs; at least two setæ on tubercle vi. on the sixth abdominal segment, or with additional setæ on the proleg 51
15. Sixth abdominal segment bearing prolegs, although prolegs may be absent on the more anterior segments 16
Sixth abdominal segment without prolegs. (See couplets 11, 13).
GRACILARÏIDÆ
16. Hooks (crochets) of the prolegs arranged in a circle or ellipse, which may be incomplete, or in transverse band 17
Crochets forming a single band, sometimes with a few vestigial ones in addition 45
17. Prespiracular wart of prothorax with two setæ 18
Prespiracular wart of prothorax bearing three setæ 19

18. Hooks on prolegs uniordinal, *i.e.* with their tips forming a single line (Fig. 451); body cylindrical; tubercle vii. of mesothorax bearing a single seta; surface of body rough and granular.
                                                                    ORNEÓDIDÆ
    Hooks on prolegs biordinal or triordinal, *i.e.* with their tips forming two or three parallel lines (Figs. 450, 452), or (Chrysauginæ) uniordinal in larvæ with stout body and bisetose tubercle vii. of mesothorax. ....PYRALÍDIDÆ

19. Hooks on prolegs forming two transverse bands, rarely reduced to one 20
    Hooks on prolegs forming a circle or ellipse which is sometimes broadly interrupted 26

20. Prolegs with the hooks either in a single transverse row, or in two multiserial bands 21
    Prolegs with the hooks arranged in two simple (uniordinal) series 22

21. Prolegs represented by one uniserial band of very small hooks, the prolegs practically absent; leaf-miners or case-bearers.
                                                                    INCURVARÌIDÆ
    Prolegs with many, short, vestigial hooks arranged in two transverse multiserial bands (Fig. 458); case-bearers living in a portable lenticular case made of a piece of leaf ......ADÉLIDÆ

22. Setæ iv. and v. of abdomen remote; young larvæ living in serpentine mines in leaves, later feeding externally. (See couplet 28).
                                              Bucculatrix of the LYONETÌIDÆ
    Setæ iv. and v. of abdomen adjacent (Fig. 448) 23

23. Hooks on the anal prolegs disposed in two groups; habits various. (See couplets 6, 43). ....GELECHÌIDÆ
    Hooks on the anal prolegs in a single series 24

24. Front long, extending upwards at least two-thirds of the way to the vertex 25
    Front short extending about one-third the way to the vertex. (See couplet 41). ....*Cossula* of the CÓSSIDÆ

25. Spiracles elliptical, normal in size, those of the eighth abdominal segment placed higher up than the others; body white, without markings; boring in woody, or more rarely in the stems of herbaceous plants ....ÆGERÌIDÆ
    Spiracles very small, circular, the last pair about in line with the others; larvæ usually living in portable cases and feeding externally or sometimes mining, but never boring into the stems of plants. (See couplet 4). ....COLEOPHÓRIDÆ

26. Setæ iv. and v. on abdomen remote, or very rarely absent in minute species 27
    Setæ iv. and v. adjacent, often on a common tubercle; no small hooks at the base of the principal series on the prolegs 32

27. Hooks on prolegs arranged in a single, complete ellipse 28
    Hooks on prolegs forming an incomplete ellipse, or with additional
    minute series at the base of the large ones 30

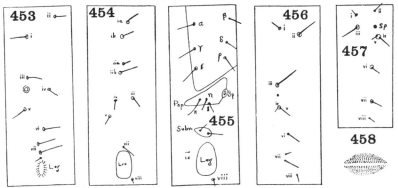

Figs. 453–458. Lepidoptera, *Larvæ*

453. **Scardia,** setal map of third abdominal segments (Forbes) Tineidæ.
454. **Acrolophus,** setal map of mesothorax (Fracker) Acrolophidæ.
455. **Acrolophus,** setal map of prothorax (Fracker) Acrolophidæ.
456. **Carposina,** setal map of first abdominal segment (Forbes) Carposinidæ.
457. **Carposina,** setal map of eighth abdominal segment (Forbes) Carposinidæ.
458. **Adela,** arrangement of crochets on proleg (Forbes) Adelidæ.

28. Setæ of prespiracular group on prothorax about as far from the
    spiracle as from one another; seta i. of abdomen placed at a
    higher level than ii. (See couplet 22). ....LYONETÏIDÆ
    Setæ of prespiracular group on prothorax about twice as far from
    the spiracle as from one another. (Fig. 449) 29
29. Seta i. of abdomen much lower than ii. (Fig. 453); larvæ generally
    case-bearers; the case usually ending in a triangular valve, more
    rarely lenticular; often living on animal matter, fungi, etc.
    TINÈIDÆ
    Seta i. of abdomen not lower than ii.; habits varied. (See couplet 39).
    HELIODÍNIDÆ
30. Meso- and metathorax with setæ i.a and i.b close together (Fig.
    454); abdomen with seta iv. below the level of the spiracle 31
    Meso- and metathorax with seta i.a in front of i.b and well sepa-
    rated from it; larvæ boring in herbs and woody plants, commonly
    in the roots ....HEPIÁLIDÆ
31. Prothorax with seta *beta* at a higher level than *alpha* (Fig. 455).
    ACROLÓPHIDÆ
    Prothorax with seta *beta* at a lower level than *alpha*. The Argy-

resthiidæ and Acrolepiidæ will also run out here. (See couplet 46).
PLUTELLIDÆ and YPONOMEÛTIDÆ

32. Last pair of spiracles placed very high up, nearer to the mid-dorsal line than setæ i. of the anterior abdominal segments; larvæ internal feeders in the fruits of various plants. (Figs. 456, 457) ....**CARPOSÍNIDÆ**
Last pair of spiracles placed lower down, in the normal position . . 33

33. Mesothorax with two setæ on tubercle vii., above base of leg. 34
Mesothorax with only a single seta on tubercle vii. (Fig. 459); seta ii. on ninth abdominal segment placed higher up than i. (Fig. 463) 36

34. Prothoracic spiracle higher than wide, *i.e.* with its longer axis vertical; seta i. of ninth abdominal segment placed higher up than ii.; larvæ boring in the tissues of plants, or leaf-rollers.
THYRÍDIDÆ
Prothoracic spiracle with its longer axis horizontal; larvæ living in a portable case, from the anterior end of which they protrude the anterior end of the body when feeding 35

35. Thoracic legs with the last two segments stout; seta i. on abdominal segments below the level of seta ii. (Fig. 460).
Most **PSÝCHIDÆ**
Thoracic legs with the last two segments very slender; seta i. on abdominal segments above the level of seta ii. (as in Fig. 461) ....**TALÆPORIÏNÆ; PSÝCHIDÆ**

36. Setæ ii. of ninth segment nearer together across the dorsum than these setæ are on the preceding segments, frequently on the same plate 37
These setæ as far apart across the dorsum on the ninth segment as on any of the preceding segments, very rarely on the same plate 38

37. Setæ iv. and v. on abdomen placed at almost the same level (Fig. 461); prolegs with the hooks forming a uniordinal row (Fig. 451); larvæ boring in herbaceous plants or feeding in the seeds.
PHALONÏIDÆ
Setæ iv. and v. on abdomen not at the same level, a line connecting them diagonal or vertical; hooks on prolegs usually multiordinal (Fig. 452). (Including the Olethreutidæ and several other related families) ....**TORTRÍCIDÆ**

38. Coxæ of the metathoracic legs separated by less than twice their own width 39
Coxæ of the metathoracic legs separated by twice their own width; prolegs small; small species; larvæ with varied habits, mining in leaves, boring in stems, rolling leaves or feeding in seeds.
COSMOPTERÝGIDÆ

39. Setæ i. and ii. on abdomen widely separated 40
    Setæ i. and ii. on abdomen close together. (See couplet 29).
    HELIODÍNIDÆ, part
40. Front short, not extending more than half way to the vertex,
    usually much less than half way 41
    Front longer, extending almost or fully two-thirds of the distance
    to the vertex, narrowly pointed above; small species with uni-
    ordinal or biordinal hooks on the prolegs 42
41. Species boring in plants, usually in wood; setæ iv. and v. placed
    on separate tubercles on the ninth abdominal segment; body
    white. (See couplet 24). ....COSSIDÆ

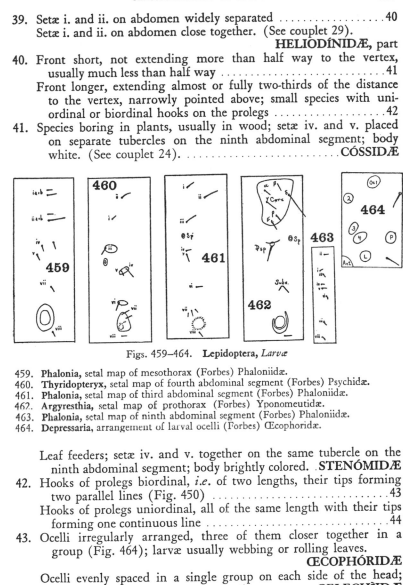

Figs. 459–464.   Lepidoptera, *Larvæ*

459. **Phalonia**, setal map of mesothorax (Forbes) Phaloniidæ.
460. **Thyridopteryx**, setal map of fourth abdominal segment (Forbes) Psychidæ.
461. **Phalonia**, setal map of third abdominal segment (Forbes) Phaloniidæ.
462. **Argyresthia**, setal map of prothorax (Forbes) Yponomeutidæ.
463. **Phalonia**, setal map of ninth abdominal segment (Forbes) Phaloniidæ.
464. **Depressaria**, arrangement of larval ocelli (Forbes) Œcophoridæ.

Leaf feeders; setæ iv. and v. together on the same tubercle on the
    ninth abdominal segment; body brightly colored. STENÓMIDÆ
42. Hooks of prolegs biordinal, *i.e.* of two lengths, their tips forming
    two parallel lines (Fig. 450) 43
    Hooks of prolegs uniordinal, all of the same length with their tips
    forming one continuous line 44
43. Ocelli irregularly arranged, three of them closer together in a
    group (Fig. 464); larvæ usually webbing or rolling leaves.
    ŒCOPHÓRIDÆ
    Ocelli evenly spaced in a single group on each side of the head;
    habits various. (See couplets 6, 23). .... GELECHÏIDÆ
44. Seta iii. on the eighth segment of the abdomen usually placed above
    and behind the spiracle; habits varied, often scavengers, feeding

in nuts, or predaceous on scale insects ...... BLASTOBÁSIDÆ

Seta iii. on eighth segment of abdomen usually placed just above or slightly before the spiracle; larvæ leaf-rollers or feeding generally on foliage .... GLYPHIPTERÝGIDÆ

45. Prespiracular wart of prothorax bearing three setæ 46

Prespiracular wart of prothorax bearing two setæ 47

46. Setæ iv. and v. of abdomen remote, or if approximate the setæ *beta* of the two sides of the body much closer together than the setæ *alpha* of the two sides of the body on the prothorax (Fig. 462); prolegs long and slender. (See couplet 31).

YPONOMEÙTIDÆ

Setæ iv. and v. of abdomen placed close together; *beta* about as far apart as *alpha;* prolegs usually short. (See couplet 74).

ETHMIÌNÆ; ŒCOPHÓRIDÆ

47. Tubercle vii. on meso- and metathorax with two setæ 48

Tubercle vii. on meso- and metathorax with a single seta 50

48. Body setæ minute, the tubercles placed in obscure rings; head unusually wide; prolegs reduced; larvæ forming nests in loosely rolled leaves .... THYATÍRIDÆ

Body setæ heavy, almost always spinulose, on conspicuous tubercles 49

49. Tubercle iii. of abdomen bearing two setæ; larvæ usually feeding on lichens .... LITHOSÌIDÆ

Tubercle iii. of abdomen with a single seta. (See couplet 68).

Utetheisa of the ARCTÌIDÆ

50. Body usually with enlarged contrasting tubercles; eighth abdominal segment with a conspicuous hump; banded or spotted with black; larvæ feeding externally on foliage. .... AGARÍSTIDÆ

Body not as above; usually dully colored and not with conspicuous transverse bands of black; usually external feeders on the leaves of plants, sometimes boring into fruits, or cutworms.

Most NOCTÙIDÆ

51. Less than four pairs of ventral prolegs or with the first pair greatly reduced 52

Four pairs of ventral prolegs bearing hooks, and sometimes with additional ones not bearing hooks 53

52. Body hairs tufted; hooks on prolegs uniordinal (Fig. 451); three pairs of ventral prolegs; larvæ feeding externally on foliage.

NÓLIDÆ

With only a few accessory hairs or sometimes with fine secondary hair; usually only one pair of ventral prolegs (on the sixth abdominal segment) in addition to the anal pair (on the eighth segment) .... GEOMÉTRIDÆ

53. Four pairs of abdominal prolegs; and prolegs sometimes reduced or absent 54

Four pairs of abdominal prolegs on segments three to six and in addition a pair without hooks on segments two and seven; body bearing stinging hairs mixed with tufts of dense, soft hair. **MEGALOPÝGIDÆ**

54. Anal prolegs entirely absent; body with secondary hair below, but none above except on the few enlarged tubercles. **DREPÁNIDÆ**

Anal prolegs present as a pair of large tubercles, or flagella at least normally fully developed 55

55. Hooks on the prolegs uniordinal, all of equal length, their tips forming a single continuous line (Fig. 451) 56

Hooks on the prolegs biordinal or triordinal, of two or three lengths, their tips forming two or three parallel lines 70

56. Setigerous tubercles vestigial or absent, or obscured by secondary hair 57

At least tubercle vi. many haired and distinct; secondary hairs sparse or absent above the prolegs 64

57. Anal plate bifurcated; head roughly papillose; third ocellus very large. (See couplet 96). ....**SATÝRIDÆ**

Anal plate simple; head smoother; third ocellus rarely much enlarged 58

58. Body caterpillar-like in form; vegetarian species, not parasitic on other insects 59

Body hemispherical, with a complete circle of uniordinal hooks; living as external parasites of Homoptera (Jassidæ and Fulgoroidea) ....**EPIPYRÓPIDÆ**

59. Spiracles small, circular; ventral prolegs slender, more or less petiolate, with expanded walking surface; usually leaf-rollers, more rarely boring in the stems of plants. (See couplet 66). **PTEROPHÓRIDÆ**

Spiracles elliptical, larger; ventral prolegs short 60

60. Body bearing dense secondary setæ 61

Secondary setæ very sparse or absent above the prolegs; with simple setæ or a few accessory ones 62

61. Notch of labrum deep, with parallel sides; anal prolegs as well developed as the ventral ones. (See couplet 50). A few **NOCTÙIDÆ**

Notch of labrum acute, with convergent sides; anal prolegs much reduced, not functional; body often with spines, long fleshy tubercles or humps, frequently brightly colored. (See couplet 63). **NOTODÓNTIDÆ**

62. Tubercle iv. much lower on the seventh abdominal segment than on the other segments; anal prolegs more or less reduced or modified 63

Tubercle iv. at about the same level on abdominal segments six, seven and eight. (See couplet 64) ....A few **LYMANTRÌIDÆ**

63. Skin shagreened ....DIÓPTIDÆ
    Skin smooth, not shagreened. (See couplet 61) NOTODÓNTIDÆ
64. Sixth and seventh abdominal segments bearing eversible glands
    in the middle above; body hairy, usually with conspicuous tufts
    of brightly colored hairs; feeding externally on foliage. (See
    couplet 62). ....LYMANTRÏIDÆ
    No dorsal eversible glands 65
65. Spiracles small, circular 66
    Spiracles of the usual size, elliptical 67
66. Ventral prolegs short, with a straight band of heavy hooks.
                                            PYROMÓRPHIDÆ
    Ventral prolegs slender, more or less petiolate, with expanded
    walking surface sometimes bearing a circle of hooks. (See
    couplet 59) ....PTEROPHÓRIDÆ
67. Mesothorax with two or three setigerous tubercles above the level
    of the spiracles 68
    Mesothorax with only one such tubercle above the level of the
    spiracles; externally feeding species, commonly on grasses and
    low plants, also some on lichens ....CTENUCHIDÆ
68. Tubercle, or seta iv. placed much lower on the seventh abdominal
    segment than on the sixth or eighth segment, or absent 69
    Tubercle, or seta iv. placed at the same level on the seventh as
    on the adjacent abdominal segments; body clothed with dense
    clusters of hairs and often with long, brightly colored tufts;
    feeders on a great variety of plants. (See couplet 49).
                                              ARCTÏIDÆ
69. Hooks on prolegs of even length, or gradually decreasing in size
    toward the ends of the row. (See couplet 50).
                                            A few NOCTÙIDÆ
    Hooks on prolegs abruptly decreasing in size toward each end of
    the row; feeding externally on leaves, often brightly colored.
                                            NYCTEMÉRIDÆ
70. Body without noticeable accessory or secondary hair; with not
    more than eight hairs on the prolegs 71
    Body with numerous secondary setæ, at least on the prolegs; anal
    prolegs well developed 76
71. Prolegs with the hooks arranged to form a complete circle 72
    Prolegs bearing a band of hooks on the inner side, and sometimes
    also a much weaker band on the outer side 74
72. Subdorsal setæ of abdomen simple 73
    Subdorsal setæ of abdomen represented by warts; body with tufted
    hair from small warts; often webbing leaves.
                                            SCYTHRÍDIDÆ
73. Surface of head rugose; body widest on the segments that bear

the prolegs; larva spinning leaves together for a nest when young, later making a portable case of silk and pieces of leaf.
MIMALLÓNIDÆ

Surface of head smooth; body widest on the first segment of the abdomen; larva constructing a portable case. . .**XYLORÝCTIDÆ**

74. Prespiracular wart of prothorax bearing two setæ; setæ iv. and v. of abdomen usually distant from each other 75

Prespiracular wart of prothorax bearing three setæ; setæ iv. and v. of abdomen approximate; anal prolegs well developed, with hooks; larva spinning a light web. (See couplet 46).
ETHMIÎNÆ; ŒCOPHÓRIDÆ

75. Spiracles subequal in size (See couplet 48) ....**THYATÍRIDÆ**

First and last spiracles twice as large as the other; young caterpillars living in a communal web, later feeding more or less exposed.
EPIPLÉMIDÆ

76. Setæ very irregular in length, some ten times as long as others; head very conspicuously setose; body usually with numerous long setæ above prolegs, but lacking long tubercles and stout, branched spines 77

Setæ subequal (sometimes accompanied by prominent tubercles and branching spines) 80

77. Head rather evenly rounded, without strong spines; abdomen without pair of prominent wart-like or spinose dorsal anal processes; crochets biordinal 79

Head with strong spines (up to four pairs), or conical processes; abdomen with pair of dorsal anal processes; restricted to tropics 78

78. Head much larger than prothorax, rough, with pair of close postero-dorsal conical processes partly veiled by long, dense head-hair; prothorax with large eversible mid-ventral gland in front of legs; body very hairy; abdominal tail-processes coriaceous, rather short; crochets multiordinal; often brightly colored; larvæ in clusters; food-plants all dicotyledonous; Neotropical only.
MORPHÒIDÆ

Head smaller, usually smooth and shining, but with numerous fine, long, stiff setæ; head with crest of two to eight strong spines (rarely short cones as in Morphoidæ, or none in *Discophora*); prothorax lacking large mid-ventral eversible gland; abdominal tail-processes may be like Morphoidæ, often much longer; many with soft dorsal warts on some segments; body very hairy in Old World genera, almost naked in Neotropical; cryptically colored, usually with longitudinal stripes; larvæ in clusters or pairs; foodplant always monocotyledonous ....**AMATHUSÌIDÆ**

79. Labrum with a notch that extends for two-thirds of its length, or with the notch somewhat shallower and continued as a groove to

the base of the labrum; body hairy, strongly depressed, often with
slender dorsal hair-pencils. **APATELODÍNÆ; EUPTERÓTIDÆ**
Labrum with a shallower notch which is not continued as a groove;
no dorsal hair-pencils; larva very hairy, with dense secondary
hair; usually feeding on the foliage of trees, sometimes in a
communal web .... **LASIOCÁMPIDÆ**

80. Eighth abdominal segment bearing a median horn, high hump,
plate, or tubercle 81
Eighth abdominal segment not thus armed on the mid-dorsal line . 88

81. Body bearing several branching spines or enlarged tubercles 82
Body not thus ornamented, at most with two pairs of small spines
on the thorax (then dorsal spine of abdominal segment VIII is
large, pointed) 84

82. Head evenly rounded; crochets or prolegs biordinal (Fig. 450) . . 83
Head angulated or spined above, or the abdomen with several mid-
dorsal spines; crochets of prolegs usually triordinal (Fig. 452).
(See couplets 98, 99)...................... **NYMPHÁLIDÆ**

83. Long, paired dorsal spines on mesothorax, metathorax, and abdominal
segment IX; Asiatic only .... **BRAHMÆIDÆ**
If long, paired dorsal spines present on meso- and metathorax, then
abdominal segment IX with single major mid-dorsal spine.
SATURNÍIDÆ

a. Abdominal segment IX with rather stout median dorsal spine ....b
Abdominal segment IX not bearing median dorsal spine.
SATURNIÍNÆ

b. Spines delicate, never profusely branched; body not covered with
numerous rather long, urticating hairs; mesothorax humped
(**Aglia**, Palæarc.). .... **AGLIÍNÆ**
Spines often profusely branched or very stout and long or with
numerous rather long urticating hairs c

c. Spines on mesothorax (and often metathorax) at least twice as
long as those on abdominal segments I to VI; spines never pro-
fusely branched or very numerous and urticating. American
CITHERONIÍNÆ
Spines on mesothorax scarcely longer than on abdominal segments
I to VI; latter often profusely branched, often urticating ......d

d. African only .... **LUDIÍNÆ**
American only .... **HEMILEUCÍNÆ**

84. Metathorax greatly enlarged laterally or produced forward into
high peak; preanal process a short backward peak or S-shaped
horn; Neotropical only 85
Metathorax of different form; preanal process a strong, rather
straight or evenly arched horn or erect, high tubercle 86

85. Preanal process a conspicuous S-shaped horn with tip bifid; meta-thorax with lateral extensions bearing an eye-spot on each side dorsally; Neotropical .... OXYTENÍDIDÆ

Preanal process a short backward peak; metathorax widest, pro-duced forward into high peak; raised lateral line from metathorax to anal segment; Chile .... CERCOPHÁNIDÆ

86. Preanal process a rather short, blunt, upward process; green with several bright white, oblique lateral stripes slanting upwards toward the head end; one species (*Endromis*), Europe only
ENDROMÍDIDÆ

Preanal process a rather long, pointed, backward directed horn; color and pattern various 87

87. Abdominal segments each divided into six or eight annulets; prolegs normal, not widely separated; body more or less cylindrical, usually with oblique stripes or bands of color. Sphinx caterpillars
SPHÍNGIDÆ

Abdominal segments with two or three obscure annulets; prolegs unusually widely separated; strongly humped on thorax; body without oblique color marking. Cultivated silkworm
BOMBÝCIDÆ

88. Head rounded, of the usual form 89

Head higher than wide, triangular in outline.
Lapara of SPHÍNGIDÆ

89. Ninth abdominal segment without a median dorsal spine 90

Ninth abdominal segment bearing a small median dorsal spine. (See couplet 83c) .... *Anisota* of CITHERONIÍNÆ

90. Large dorsal hump on metathorax; head small; green with eight lateral whitish oblique stripes; not noticeably covered with short body-hairs; Palæarctic (**Aglia**). (See couplet 83b).
AGLIÍNÆ; SATURNIÍDÆ

Metathorax without large hump; body with very many short hairs 91

91. Crochets arranged in broken circle or single row, parallel to mid-line of body; long or branched setæ or fleshy filaments may be present, or head may be retractile and body onisciform 92

Crochets arranged in broken circle or double row, perpendicular to mid-line of body; body never onisciform, never with fleshy fila-ments or long or branched setæ; vesture of fine, short hairs only .... HESPERIÍDÆ

a. Head smaller than prothorax; crochets always biordinal, often arranged as two transverse rows; borers in Yucca or Agave; southwestern U.S.A. and Mexico only ...... MEGATHYMIÍNÆ

Head much larger than prothorax; crochets either biordinal or triordinal, arranged as complete or broken transverse circle
HESPERIÍNÆ and PYRGIÍNÆ

92. Band of hooks on the prolegs reduced or interrupted at the middle
and with a narrow, spatulate, fleshy lobe arising near the interrup-
tion; head small 93
Prolegs without a fleshy lobe near the middle of the band of
hooks 94
93. Head about half as wide as the body; commonly with hard anterior
processes on prothorax; body often bearing a considerable amount
of secondary hair ....RIODÍNIDÆ
Head smaller, rarely more than one-third as wide as the body;
secondary hair less prominent; body short and broad, more or
less slug-like, with the legs and prolegs very short ..LYCÆNIDÆ
94. Prothorax without a dorsal scent gland 95
Prothorax bearing a dorsal eversible, forked scent gland (osmater-
ium); gland when retracted showing as a groove; body without
long hairs or spines, but sometimes bearing fleshy filaments
PAPILIÓNIDÆ

a. Body with numerous short hairs; fleshy processes not longer than
width of body ....b
Body glabrous; often with long, soft, fleshy filaments, or paired
short spines on thorax; thorax often enlarged; foodplants usually
Aristolochiaceæ, Lauraceæ, Rutaceæ, or Umbelliferæ
PAPILIONÌNÆ
b. Body clothed with dense, velvety vestiture; fleshy tubercles absent;
foodplants usually *Sedum, Saxifraga,* or *Aristolochia*
PARNASSIÌNÆ
Body hairs not dense; short fleshy tubercles bearing hairs present
(except *Lühdorfia*); foodplants Aristolochiaceæ; Palæarctic only.
ZERYNTHIÌNÆ

95. Head and body entirely without spines, high tubercles or fleshy
filaments 96
Spines, high tubercles or fleshy filaments well developed on the
body; when reduced, large spines or tubercles are present on the
head 99
96. Anal plate rounded, entire 97
Anal plate bifurcate at tip, bearing two distinct processes. (See
couplet 57). ....SATÝRIDÆ
97. Prolegs with only a single row of hooks (crochets), forming a
curved band 98
Prolegs with reduced crochets on the outer side in addition to the
well developed band; head small; setæ never borne on prominent
warts; foodplant *Celtis* ....LIBYTHÈIDÆ
98. Head noticeably larger than the prothorax. (See couplets 82, 99).
NYMPHÁLIDÆ
Head smaller than the prothorax; setæ usually borne on very numer-

ous prominent warts; foodplants commonly Leguminosæ, Cruciferæ, or Capparidaceæ ....PIERÍDIDÆ
99. Mesothorax and sometimes several other segments bearing long fleshy filaments (rarely warts); secondary setæ short and confined to the prolegs ....DANÀIDÆ
Body without fleshy filaments. (See couplets 82, 98).

NYMPHÁLIDÆ

a. Body spines slender, at least ten times as long as wide; those on the abdomen as long as the width of the metathorax; each abdominal segment with three lateral spines but no median ones above.

HELICONIÌNÆ and ACRAEÌNÆ

Body spines, if present, not so slender; those on the abdomen shorter than the width of the metathorax; median spines usually present on the dorsum ....NYMPHALÌNÆ

LITERATURE ON LEPIDOPTERA, GENERAL

AURIVILLIUS, C. and H. WAGNER. Lepidopterorum Catalogus. Parts 1–94. W. Junk, Berlin (1911–39). (The parts so far as they have appeared are listed separately.)

BANG-HAAS, O. Katalog der im Seitz nicht enthaltenen paläarktische Macrolepidopteren. Novitates Macrolep., Dresden, 1, pp. 1–238 (1926).

BARNES, W. and J. H. McDUNNOUGH. Check list of the Lepidoptera of Boreal America. 392 pp. Decatur, Ill. (1917).

BARRETT, C. G. The Lepidoptera of the British Isles. 11 vols. London (1893–1907).

BÖRNER, C. Die Grundlagen meines Lepidopterensystems. Verhandl. VII. internat. Kongr. Ent., Berlin, 2, pp. 1372–1424 (1939).

BOURGOGNE, J. Lépidoptères. In Grassé, Traité de Zoologie, 10, pp. 174–448, 3 pls. (1951).

BUCKLER, W. (edited by H. T. Stainton and G. T. Porritt). Larvæ of British Butterflies and Moths. 9 vols., London (1886–1901).

CAMPOS, F. Catálogo preliminar de los Lepidópteros del Ecuador. Rev. Col. Rocafuerte, Guayaquil, 9, pp. 3–106 (1927); 45, pp. 3–162 (1931).

CANDÈZE, L. Lépidoptères Hétérocères de l'Indochine Française. (Catalogue) Encycl. Ent. Lépidop. II, fasc. 2, pp. 73–133 (1927).

COSTA LIMA, A. DA. Lepidópteros, 1a parte. Insetos do Brasil, 5, pp. 1–379, 235 figs. (1945).

CORBET, A. S., and W. H. T. TAMS. Keys for the Identification of the Lepidoptera Infecting Stored Food Products. Proc. Zool. Soc. London (B), 113, pp. 55–148, 5 pls., 287 figs. (1943).

COTES, E. C. and C. SWINHOE. Catalogue of the Moths of India. 7 parts. Calcutta (1887–89).

DRUCE, H. Heterocera. In Biologia Centrali-Americana, 3 vols. 1112 pp., 101 pls. (1881–1900).

DYAR, H. G. A List of North American Lepidoptera and Key to the Literature. Bull. U. S. Nat. Mus., No. 52, 723 pp. (1902).

EECKE, R. VAN. De Heterocera van Sumatra. I. Zool. Meded., 8, pp. 153–217 (1925).

FORBES, W. T. M. Field Tables of Lepidoptera. 141 pp. Worcester, Mass. (1906).
Lepidoptera of New York and Neighboring States (Primitive Forms, Microlepidoptera, Pyraloids, Bombyces). Mem. Cornell Univ. Agric. Expt. Sta., 68, 729 pp. (1923); (Geometridæ, Sphingidæ, Notodontidæ, Lymantriidæ). Ibid., 274, 263 pp. (1948).
Lepidoptera. In Leonard, A List of the Insects of New York, Mem. Cornell Univ. Agric. Expt. Sta., 101, pp. 532–687 (1928).
Heterocera (except Noctuidæ, Geometridæ and Pyralidæ) of Porto Rico and Virgin Islands. Sci. Surv. Porto Rico and Virgin Isl., 12, pp. 1–172, 2 pls., 17 figs. (1930).
FRACKER, S. B. The Classification of Lepidopterous Larvæ. Illinois Biol. Monog., 2, No. 1, 161 pp., 10 pls. (1915).
FRIONNET, C. Les premiers États des Lépidoptères français. Mém. Soc. Lettres St.-Dizier, 10, fasc. 2; 12 (1906, 1910).
GAEDE, M. Lepidoptera Heterocera. Tierwelt Deutschlands, 14, pp. 1–334, 197 figs. (1929).
GERASIMOV, A. M. Bestimmungstabelle der Familien von Schmetterlingsraupen. Stettiner Ent. Zeitg., 98, pp. 281–300 (1937).
HAMPSON, G. F. The Moths of India. Fauna of British India, 4 vols. (1892–96).
The Moths of South Africa. Ann. South African Mus., 2, pp. 33–255; 3, p. 389 (1900–05). (In three parts.)
HAMPSON, G. F. and J. H. DURRANT. List of the Families and Subfamilies of the Lepidoptera. Novitat. Zool., 25, pp. 383–394 (1918).
HERBULOT, C. Atlas des Lépidoptères de France, fasc. 2, 145 pp., 16 pls. (1948); fasc. 3, 145 pp., 12 pls. (1949). N. Boubée et Cie., Paris.
HERING, M. Lepidoptera. In Tierwelt Mitteleuropas, 6, Lief. 3, pp. XVIII, 1–94 (1928).
Die Schmetterlinge nach ihren Arten dargestellt. Tierwelt Mitteleuropas Ergänzungsbd., 1, 545 pp., 813 figs. (1932).
HOLLAND, W. J. The Moth Book. Doubleday, Page & Co., New York (1903); 2nd Ed. (1937).
HUDSON, G. V. The Butterflies and Moths of New Zealand. 481 pp., 72 pls. Ferguson and Osborn, Wellington (1928, 1939).
JANSE, A. J. T. Check-List of South African Lepidoptera Heterocera. Transvaal Mus. Pretoria, 219 pp. (1917).
A Key to the Families, Subfamilies and Tribes of the Order Lepidoptera with Special Reference to the South African Species. South African Journ. Sci., 22, pp. 318–345, 3 pls. (1925).
The Moths of South Africa. Vols. 1–4. Parts listed separately (1933–).
KIRIAKOFF, S. G. A Classification of the Lepidoptera and Related Groups with Some Remarks on Taxonomy. Biol. Jaarb., Antwerp, 15, pp. 118–143 (1948).
KISHIDA, K., and Y. NAKAMURA. A Catalogue of Japanese Insects. Fasc. 9. Lepidoptera. Ent. World, 4, pp. 433–673 (1936).
KITSCHELT, R. Grossschmetterlinge von Südtirol. 421 pp., publ. by author. Vienna (1925).
LAMEERE, A. Lépidoptères. Précis de Zoologie, Publ. Inst. Zool. Torley-Rousseau, 5, pp. 162–272, 110 figs. (1938).

LEDERER, G. Handbuch für den praktischen Entomologen., **2**, Rhopalocera, 172 pp., **3**, Heterocera, 172 pp. Frankfurt a. M. (1921–23).

LHOMME, L. Catalogue des Lépidoptères de France et de Belgique. **1** (Macrolépidoptères), 800 pp. (1923–35); **2** (Microlépidoptères), fasc. 1–6, incomplete (1936–). Le Carriol, publ. by author.

McDUNNOUGH, J. H. Check List of the Lepidoptera of Canada and the United States of America. Part I, Macrolepidoptera; Part II, Microlepidoptera. Mem. Southern California Acad. Sci., **1**, pp. 1–271 (1938); **2**, pp. 1–171 (1939).

MARIANI, M. Catalogo ragionato dei Lepidotteri d'Italia. Giorn. Sci. Nat. Econ. Palermo, **42**, no. 3, pp. 1–237 (1941–43).

MATSUMURA, S. Illustrated Common Insects of Japan. Butterflies, **1**, 45 + 66 + 37 + [4] pp., 16 pls.; Moths, **2**, 96 + 132 + [8] pp., 15 pls. (1929–30).

MEYRICK, E. A Revised Handbook of British Lepidoptera. 914 pp. Watkins and Doncaster, London (1928).

MEYRICK, E. and T. DE G. WALSINGHAM. Lepidoptera. In Fauna Hawaiiensis, 2 vols. (1899–1907).

MOORE, F. Lepidoptera of Ceylon. 3 vols. 930 pp., 215 pls. London (1880–87).

MOSHER, EDNA. A Classification of Lepidoptera Based on Characters of the Pupa. Bull. Illinois State Lab. Nat. Hist., **12**, pp. 12–159 (1916).

NORDSTRÖM, F., et al. Svenska Fjärilar. Macrolepidoptera. 86 + 354 pp., 50 pls. Stockholm (1941).

PERRIER, R., L. BERTIN and L. GAUMONT. Lépidoptères de la France. Faune Ent. France, **4**, pp. 135–243 (1935).

PETERSON, A. Larvæ of Insects. An Introduction to Nearctic Species. Pt. 1, Lepidoptera and Plant-Infesting Hymenoptera. 315 pp., 84 pls. Columbus, Ohio, publ. by author (1948).

REBEL, H. Schmetterlingsbuch. Stuttgart. (1910).

RONDOU, J. P. Catalogue des Lépidoptères des Pyrénées. Ann. Soc. Ent. France, **101**, pp. 165–244; **102**, pp. 237–316; **103**, pp. 257–320; **104**, pp. 189–258 (1932–35).

SEITZ, A. Macrolepidoptera of the World (1906–   ). (Issued in a large number of parts containing many illustrations and much valuable material, but not yet indexed. Many families have so far been very completely treated. See also Closs, A. The Systematic Arrangement of Families in Seitz's "Macrolepidoptera." Ent. Mitteil., **9**, pp. 22–30 (1920).)

SOUTH, R. The Moths of the British Isles. Edited and revised by H. M. Edelsten. First Series, Sphingidæ to Agrotidæ, 360 pp., 159 pls., 16 figs.; Second Series, Agrotidæ to Hepialidæ, 399 pp., 159 pls., 19 figs. London and New York, Frederick K. Warne + Co., Ltd. (1939).

SPULER, A. Die Schmetterlinge Europas. 3 vols. and vol. 4 on Caterpillars. Stuttgart (1901–10).

STANDFUSS, M. Handbuch der paläarktischen Grossschmetterlinge. Jena (1896).

STAUDINGER, O. and H. REBEL. Catalog der Lepidopteren des palæarktischen Faunengebietes, 3rd ed. Berlin (1901).

STOKOE, W. J., and G. H. T. STOVIN. The Caterpillars of British Moths. First Series, Sphingidæ to Brephidæ, 408 pp., 90 pls.; Second Series, Geometridæ to Hepialidæ, 381 pp., 51 pls. London and New York, Frederick Warne + Co. (1948).

SWINHOE, C. Catalogue of Eastern and Australian Lepidoptera Heterocera. 2 vols. Oxford (1895–1900).

TILLYARD, R. J. Order Lepidoptera. In Insects of Australia and New Zealand, pp. 396–467, 18 pls., 70 figs. Angus and Robertson, Ltd., Sydney (1926).

TURNER, A. J. Revision of the Lepidoptera of Tasmania. Pap. Proc. Roy. Soc. Tasmania, **1925,** pp. 118–151 (1925); **1927,** pp. 29–65 (1928).

A Second Revision of the Lepidoptera of Tasmania. Pap. Proc. Roy. Soc. Tasmania, **1938,** pp. 57–115 (1939).

A Review of the Phylogeny and Classification of the Lepidoptera. Proc. Linn. Soc. New South Wales, **71,** pp. 303–338, 96 figs. (1947).

TUTT, J. W. A Natural History of the British Lepidoptera. 9 vols. London (1899–1914).

ZERNY, H., and M. BEIER. Ordnung der Pterygogenea: Lepidoptera-Schmetterlinge. In Kükenthal, Handb. Zool., **4,** Hälfte. 2, Lief. 7, 8, pp. 1554–1728, 195 figs. (1936).

SUBORDER HOMONEURA

ISSIKI, S. T. Morphology and Systematics of Micropterygidæ. Proc. Zool. Soc. London, **1931,** pp. 999–1039, 39 figs. (1931).

JANSE, A. J. T. Jugatæ. Moths of South Africa, **4,** xxv + 78 pp., 16 pls., (1942).

MEYRICK, E. Micropterygidæ. Gen. Insectorum, fasc. 132, 9 pp., 1 pl. (1913). Micropterygidæ. Lepid. Cat., **6,** pp. 17–24 (1912).

PFITZNER, R., and M. GAEDE. Hepialidæ. Seitz, Macrolepidoptera of World, **10,** pp. 825–847, 2 pls. (1933).

TINDALE, N. B. Revision of the Australian Ghost Moths (Lepidoptera, Homoneura, family Hepialidæ). Parts I, II, III. Rec. South Australian Mus., **4,** pp. 497–536, 64 figs. (1932); **5,** pp. 14–43, 92 figs. (1933); **5,** pp. 275–332, 129 figs. (1935).

TURNER, A. J. Australian Lepidoptera Homoneura. Trans. Ent. Soc. London, **1921,** pp. 592–604 (1922).

VIETTE, P. Lépidoptères Homoneures. Faune de France, **49,** pp. 1–83 (1948).

WAGNER, H., and R. PFITZNER. Hepialidæ. Lepid. Cat., **4,** 26 pp. (1911).

SUBORDER HETERONEURA
NEPTICULOIDEA

BRAUN, A. F. The Nepticulidæ of North America. Trans. American Ent. Soc., **43,** pp. 155–209 (1917).

JANSE, A. J. T. Nepticulidæ. Moths of South Africa, **4,** pt. 3, pp. 151–185 (1948).

INCURVAROIDEA

BUSCK, A. Family Prodoxidæ, Synoptic Table of Genera. In McKelvey, S. D., Yuccas of the Southwestern United States, pt. 2, 192 pp. Arnold Arboretum, Jamaica Plain (1947).

DYAR, H. G. A Review of the North American Species of Pronuba and Prodoxus. Journ. New York Ent. Soc., **11,** pp. 102–104 (1903).

JANSE, A. J. T. Adelidæ. Moths of South Africa, **4**, pt. 2, pp. 79–150, 19 pls. Pretoria, Transvaal Museum (1945).

MEYRICK, E. Adelidæ. Gen. Insectorum, fasc. 133, 12 pp., 1 pl. (1913). Adelidæ. Lepid. Cat., **6**, pp. 3–16 (1912).

COSSOIDEA

BARNES, W. and J. H. McDUNNOUGH. Revision of the Cossidæ of North America. Contrib. Nat. Hist. Lepidoptera N. Am. **1**, No. 1, 35 pp., 7 pls. Decatur, Ill. (1911).

BRYK, F. Cossidæ, II. Lepid. Cat., **81**, 4 pp. (1937).

DALLA TORRE, K. W. Cossidæ. Lepid. Cat., **29**, 63 pp. (1923).

DALLA TORRE, K. W. and E. STRAND. Lepidarbelidæ. Lepid. Cat., **28**, 10 pp. (1923).

DYAR, H. G., and W. SCHAUS. Cossidæ (American). Seitz, Macrolepidoptera of World, **6**, pp. 1264–1272 (1937).

GAEDE, M. Indarbelidæ. Seitz, Macrolepidoptera of World, **10**, pp. 803–806 (1933).
Cossidæ. Seitz, Macrolepidoptera of World, **10**, pp. 807–824; Suppl. **2**, pp. 241–245 (1933).

JANSE, A. J. T. Revision of the South African Metarbelinæ. South African Jour. Nat. Hist., **5**, pp. 61–100, 5 pls. (1925).

TURNER, A. J. Observations on Cossidæ and the Classification of the Lepidoptera. Trans. Ent. Soc. London, **1918**, pp. 155–190 (1918).
A Revision of the Australian Cossidæ. Proc. Roy. Soc. Queensland, **56**, pp. 47–70 (1945).

TINEOIDEA

BENANDER, P. Gelechiidæ of Sweden. Svensk Insektfauna, **10**, 97 pp., 7 pls. (1928).

BEUTENMÜLLER, W. The Sesiidæ of North America. Mem. American Mus. Nat. Hist., **1**, pp. 217–352, 8 pls. (1901).

BRADLEY, J. D. Notes on the Family Arrhenophanidæ. Entomologist, **84**, pp. 178–185 (1951).

BRAUN, A. F. Revision of North American Species of Lithocolletis. Trans. American Ent. Soc., **34**, pp. 269–357 (1908).
Elachistidæ of North America. Mem. American Ent. Soc., **13**, 110 pp., 26 pls. (1948).

BRÈTHES, J. Lepidópteros argentinos productores de agallas. An. Soc. Sci., Argentina, **82**, pp. 113–140 (1916). (Cecidosetidæ and Ridiaschinidæ).

BUSCK, A. Revision of American Gelechiidæ. Proc. U. S. Nat. Mus., **25**, pp. 767–938 (1903).
Generic Revision of American Œcophoridæ. Proc. U. S. Nat. Mus., **35**, pp. 187–207 (1909).
Microlepidoptera of Cuba. Entomologica Americana, **13**, pp. 151–203, 7 pls. (1933).
Stenomidæ. Lepid. Cat., **67**, 73 pp. (1935).

CLARKE, J. F. G. Revision of the North American Moths of the Family Œcophoridæ. Proc. U. S. Nat. Mus., **90**, pp. 33–286, 48 pls. (1941).

CLEMENS, B. Tineina of North America. 282 pp., London (1872).

DALLA TORRE, K. W. and E. STRAND. Ægeriidæ. Lepid. Cat., 31, 202 pp. (1925). Psychidæ. Lepid. Cat., 34, 211 pp. (1929).

DIETZ, W. G. Revision of Amydriinæ and Tineinæ of North America. Trans. American Ent. Soc., 31, pp. 1–96 (1905). Revision of Blastobasidæ of North America. Trans. American Ent. Soc., 36, pp. 1–72 (1910).

ELY, C. R. Revision of North American Gracilariidæ. Proc. Ent. Soc. Washington, 19, pp. 29–77 (1917).

ENGLEHARDT, G. P. North American Ægeriidæ. Bull. U. S. Nat. Mus., No. 190, 222 pp., 32 pls. (1946).

FLETCHER, T. B. Cosmopterygidæ. Cat. Indian Ins. 16, 33 pp. Govt. India, Centr. Pub. Branch, Calcutta, (1928). Yponomeutidæ. Cat. Indian Ins. 17, 26 pp. Govt. India, Centr. Pub. Branch, Calcutta, (1928).

GAEDE, M. Ægeriidæ. Seitz, Macrolepidoptera of World, 10, pp. 775–802, 3 pls., Suppl. 2, pp. 229–240 (1933). Psychidæ (American). Seitz, Macrolepidoptera of World, 6, pp. 1177–1186, 1 pl. (1936). Gelechiidæ. Lepid. Cat., 79, 630 pp. (1937). Œcophoridæ. Lepid. Cat., 88, 92, 476 pp. (1938–39).

HACKMANN, W. Die Coleophoriden Finnlands. Notul. ent., 25, pp. 1–63, 17 pls. (1945).

HEYLAERTS, F. J. M. Monographie des Psychides paléarctiques. Ann. Soc. Ent. Belgique, 25, pp. 29–73 (1881).

JONES, F. M., and H. B. PARKS. The Bagworms of Texas. Bull. Texas Agric. Exp. Sta., 382, 36 pp. (1928).

MEYRICK, E. Orneodidæ. Gen. Insectorum, fasc. 108, 4 pp., 1 pl. (1910). Gracilariidæ. Gen. Insectorum, fasc. 128, 36 pp. 1 pl. (1912). Gracilariidæ. Lepid. Cat., 6, pp. 25–68 (1912). Carposinidæ, Heliodinidæ, Glyphipterygidæ. Lepid. Cat., 13, 53 pp. (1913). Orneodidæ. Lepid. Cat., 17, pp. 40–44 (1913). Hyponomeutidæ, Plutellidæ, Amphitheridæ. Lepid. Cat., 19, 64 pp. (1914). Glyphipterygidæ. Gen. Insectorum, fasc. 164, 39 pp. 2 pls. (1914). Heliodinidæ. Gen. Insectorum, fasc. 165, 29 pp. (1914). Revision of New Zealand Tineina. Trans. New Zealand Inst., 47, pp. 205–244 (1915). Carposinidæ. Gen. Insectorum, fasc. 179, 10 pp., 1 pl. (1922). Œcophoridæ. Gen. Insectorum, fasc. 180, 224 pp., 6 pls. (1922). Gelechiidæ. Gen. Insectorum, fasc. 184, 290 pp., 5 pls. (1925).

STAINTON, H. The Natural History of the Tineina. Vols. 1–13, London (1855–1873).

TURNER, A. J. Studies in Australian Ægeriidæ. Proc. Roy. Soc. Victoria, 35, pp. 26–62 (1922). Revision of Australian Lepidoptera. Œcophoridæ. I–XIV. Proc. Linn. Soc. New South Wales, 57, pp. 261–279 (1932); 58, pp. 80–98 (1933); 60, pp. 1–15, 315–339 (1935); 61, pp. 298–317 (1936); 62, pp. 85–106 (1938); 63, pp. 27–54 (1938); 64, pp. 54–72 (1939); 65, pp.

421–446 (1940); **66,** pp. 401–424 (1941); **69,** pp. 49–61, 253–273 (1944); **72,** pp. 143–158 (1947).

A New Family of Lepidoptera. Proc. Linn. Soc. New South Wales, **64,** pp. 335–337 (1939).

Revision of Australian Gracilariidæ. Trans. Roy. Soc. South Australia, **64,** pp. 50–69 (1940).

Revision of the Australian Heliodinidæ. Trans. Roy. Soc. South Australia, **65,** pp. 14–27 (1941).

Revision of the Australian Psychidæ. Proc. Roy. Soc. Queensland, **57,** pp. 57–64 (1947).

VAZQUEZ, L. Estudio monográphico de las Psychidæ de México. Pt. 1. An. Inst. Biol. México, **12,** pp. 295–310, 3 pls., 18 figs. (1941); **13,** pp. 257–300 (1942).

WALSINGHAM, T. DE G. Heterocera 4, [Tineoidea]. In Biologia Centrali-Americana, 482 pp., 10 pls. (1909–15).

WEHRLI, E. Psychidæ. Seitz, Macrolepidoptera of World, Suppl. **2,** pp. 211–226, 286–287 (1933–34).

ZUKOWSKY, B. Ægeriidæ. [American]. Seitz, Macrolepidoptera of World, **6,** pp. 1215–1240, 1 pl. (1936).

TORTRICOIDEA

BUSCK, A. Review of Tortricid Subfamily Phaloniinæ. Journ. New York Ent. Soc., **15,** pp. 19–36 (1907).

DIAKONOFF, A. The Genera of Indo-Malayan and Papuan Tortricidæ. Zool. Meded., **21,** pp. 111–240, 19 figs. (1939).

Revision of the Family Ceracidæ. Bull. Brit. Mus. (Nat. Hist.), Ent., **1,** pp. 173–219 (1950).

FERNALD, C. H. The Genera of Tortricidæ. Amherst, Mass. 69 pp. (1908).

HEINRICH, CARL. Revision of North American Moths of Subfamily Eucosminæ of the Family Olethreutidæ. Bull. U. S. Nat. Mus., No. **123,** 298 pp. (1923).

Revision of North American Laspeyresiinæ and Olethreutinæ. Bull. U. S. Nat. Mus., No. **132,** 216 pp. (1926).

KENNEL, J. Die paläarktischen Tortriciden. Zoologica, Heft 54, 5 parts, 742 pp. (1908–21).

MEYRICK, E. Tortricidæ. Gen. Insectorum, fasc. 149, 81 pp. (1913).

Tortricidæ. Lepid. Cat., **10,** 86 pp. (1912).

ZYGÆNOIDEA

AURIVILLIUS, C. Chrysopolomidæ. Lepid. Cat., **1,** 4 pp. (1911).

BRYK, F. Zygænidæ II. Lepid. Cat., **71,** pp. 95–332 (1936).

BURGEFF, H. Zygænidæ. Lepid. Cat., **33,** 91 pp. (1926).

DYAR, H. G., and W. SCHAUS. Limacodidæ [American]. Seitz, Macrolepidoptera of World, **6,** pp. 1113–1136 (1937).

DYAR, H. G., and E. STRAND. Megalopygidæ, Dalceridæ, Epipyropidæ. Lepid. Cat., **16,** pp. 7–35 (1913).

EECKE, R. VAN. Cochlidionidæ (Limacodidæ). Lepid. Cat., **32,** 79 pp. (1925).

FLETCHER, T. B. Zygænidæ. Cat. Indian Ins., **9,** 92 pp. Govt. India, Centr. Pub. Branch, Calcutta (1925).

HERING, M. Revision der orientalischen Chalcosiinen. Arch. f. Naturg., Jahrg. 88A, Heft 11, pp. 1–93 (1922).

  Limacodidæ. Seitz, Macrolepidoptera of World, 10, pp. 665–720, 4 pls. (1931).

  Megalopygidæ and Limacodidæ. Seitz, Macrolepidoptera of World, Suppl. 2, pp. 197–209 (1933).

  Synopsis der Himantopterinæ, Anomosetinæ. Rev. Zool. Bot. Africaines, 29, pp. 237–265 (1937).

HOPP, W. Megalopygidæ. Seitz, Macrolepidoptera of World, 6, pp. 1071–1080 (1934).

KATO, M. Monograph of the Epipyropidæ. Ent. World, 8, pp. 67–94, 4 pls. (1940).

STRAND, E. Catalogus Heterogynidarum. Arch. Naturg., Jahrb. 82A, Heft 3, pp. 47–50 (1922).

  Heterogynidæ. Lepid. Cat., 28, pp. 11–14 (1923).

TURNER, A. J. Revision of Australian Drepanidæ, Limacodidæ and Zygænidæ. Proc. Linn. Soc. New South Wales, 51, pp. 411–445 (1926).

CASTNIOIDEA

DALLA TORRE, K. W. Castniidæ. Lepid. Cat., 15, 28 pp. (1913).

HOULBERT, C. Révision monographique des Castniinæ. In Oberthür, Études Lépidop. Comp., fasc. 15, 736 pp. (1918).

PYRALIDOIDEA

BARNES, W., and A. W. LINDSEY. The Pterophoridæ of North America. Contrib. Nat. Hist. Lepid. N. Am., Decatur, Illinois, 4, pp. 281–452 (1921).

BEIRNE, B. P. British Pyralid and Plume Moths. 208 pp., 16 pls. F. Warne and Co., London (1952).

DALLA TORRE, K. W. Thyrididæ. Lepid. Cat., 20, 55 pp. (1914).

DYAR, H. G. North American Nymphulinæ and Scopariinæ. Journ. New York Ent. Soc., 14, pp. 77–107 (1906).

  North American Chrysauginæ. Proc. Ent. Soc. Washington, 10, pp. 92–96 (1908).

  North American Pyralinæ. Proc. Ent. Soc. Washington, 10, pp. 96–102 (1908).

FERNALD, C. H. Crambidæ of North America. Bull. Massachusetts Agric. Coll., Amherst, Mass., 93 pp. (1896).

  Pterophoridæ of North America. Mass. Agric. Coll. Spec. Bull. 84 pp. (1898).

FLETCHER, T. B. Catalogue of Indian Pterophoridæ. Cat. Indian Ins., 20, iv + 61 pp. Govt. India, Centr. Publ. Branch (1931).

GAEDE, M. Thyrididæ. Seitz, Macrolepidoptera of World, 10, pp. 743–774 (1932).

  Thyrididæ (American). Seitz, Macrolepidoptera of World, pp. 1187–1213, 2 pls. (1936).

HAMPSON, G. F. Classification of Schœnobiinæ and Crambinæ. Proc. Zool. Soc. London, 1895, pp. 897–974 (1895).

Classification of the Thyridïdæ. Proc. Zool. Soc. London, **1897**, pp. 603–633 (1897).

Classification of the Chrysauginæ. Proc. Zool. Soc. London, **1897**, pp. 633–692 (1897).

Classification of some Subfamilies of Pyralididæ, Epipaschiinæ, Endotrichinæ and Pyralidinæ. Trans. Ent. Soc. London, **1896**, pp. 451–550.

Hydrocampinæ, Scopariinæ, ibid., **1897**, pp. 127–240 (1897).

Revision of the Pyraustinæ. Proc. Zool. Soc. London, **1898**, pp. 590–761 (1898) and **1899**, pp. 172–291 (1899).

Classification of the Pyralidæ, Subfamily Galleriinae. Novitat. Zool., **24**, pp. 17–58 (1917).

Classification of Pyralidæ, Subfamily Hypsotropinæ. Proc. Zool. Soc. London, **1918**, pp. 55–131 (1918).

HEINRICH, C. The Cactus-feeding Phycitinæ: A Contribution Toward a Revision of the American Pyralidoid Moths of the Family Phycitidæ. Proc. U. S. Nat. Mus., **86**, pp. 331–413, 29 pls. (1939).

HERING, E. Uebersicht der Sumatra-Pyraliden. Stettiner Ent. Zeitg., **62–64** (1901–03). (Three parts.)

HOLLAND, W. J. and W. SCHAUS. The Epipaschiinæ of the Western Hemisphere. Ann. Carnegie Mus., Pittsburgh, **16**, pp. 49–130 (1925).

HULST, G. D. Epipaschiinæ of North America. Entomologica Americana, **5**, pp. 41–52; 61–76 (1889).

The Phycitidæ of North America. Trans. American Ent. Soc., **17**, pp. 93–228 (1890).

KLIMA, A. Scopariinæ and Nymphulinæ (Pyralidæ). Lepid. Cat., **84**, 226 pp. (1937).

Pyralididæ: Subfamily Pyraustinæ. Lepid. Cat., **89, 94**, 384 pp. (1939).

MEYRICK, E. Pterophoridæ, Orneodidæ. Lepid. Cat., **17**, 44 pp. (1913).

Pterophoridæ. Gen. Insectorum, fasc. 100, 21 pp. (1910).

SCHAUS, W. Moths of the Families Geometridæ and Pyralidæ of Porto Rico. Sci. Surv. Porto Rico, **12**, pp. 291–417 (1940).

SHIBUYA, J. The Japanese Crambinæ and Pyralidinæ. Journ. Fac. Agric. Sapporo Univ., **21**, pp. 121–176 (1928).

Systematic Study of Formosan Pyralididæ. Journ. Fac. Agric., Sapporo Univ., **22**, pp. 1–300 (1928).

SYLVÉN, E. Systematic Studies of the Swedish Species of Pyralinæ, Nymphulinæ and Pyraustinæ. Ark. Zool., **38A**, pp. 1–37, 131 figs. (1947).

TURNER, A. J. Studies in Australian Tineodidæ. Proc. Roy. Soc. Victoria, **35**, pp. 26–62 (1922).

A Revision of the Australian Anerastriinæ. Proc. Linn. Soc. New South Wales, **48**, pp. 451–461 (1923).

A Revision of Australian Phycitidæ. Pt. 1. Trans. Roy. Soc. South Australia, **71**, pp. 28–53 (1947).

GEOMETROIDEA

CULOT, J. Noctuelles et Géomètres d'Europe. 4 vols., Geneva (1909–20).

DALLA TORRE, K. W. Cymatophoridæ. Lepid. Cat., **25**, 38 pp. (1921).

Epiplemidæ, Uraniidæ. Lepid. Cat., **30**, 55 pp. (1924).

FORBES, W. T. M. The Genera of Hydriomeninæ of the United States. Journ. New York Ent. Soc., **25**, pp. 44–67 (1917).

Thyatiridæ. Ann. Ent. Soc. America, **29**, pp. 779–803 (1936).

GAEDE, M. American Uraniidæ. Seitz, Macrolepidoptera of World, **6**, pp. 829–837, 3 pls. (1930).

Drepanidæ. Lepid. Cat., **49**, 60 pp. (1931).

Epiplemidæ (American). Seitz, Macrolepidoptera of World, **6**, pp. 1141–1170, 5 pls. (1936).

GOLDFINCH, G. M. Revision of Australian Geometridæ. Proc. Linn. Soc. New South Wales, **54**, pp. 378–407 (1929).

HOULBERT, C. Révision monographique de la famille des Cymatophoridæ, Etudes Lépid. Comp., **18**, pt. 2, pp. 23–252 (1921).

HULST, G. D. Classification of Geometrina of North America. Trans. American Ent. Soc., **23**, pp. 235–386 (1896).

INOUE, H. Catalogue of Geometridæ of Corea. Bull. Lepid. Soc. Japan, **1**, pp. 19–59 (1946).

JANET, A., and P. WYTSMAN. Epicopiidæ. Gen. Insectorum, fasc. 16, 5 pp. (1904).

JANSE, A. J. T. Sematuridæ and Geometridæ. Moths of South Africa, **1**, xi + 376 pp., 15 pls., 130 figs. (1932).

Cymatophoridæ, Callidulidæ, and Noctuidæ (partim). Moths of South Africa, **3**, xv + 435 pp., 47 pls., 102 figs. (1937–39).

MATSUMURA, S. Cymatophoridæ of Japan. Insecta Matsum., **8**, pp. 89–103 (1933).

McDUNNOUGH, J. H. Studies on North American Cleorini. Bull. Canada Dept. Agric. Ent., No. 18, 64 pp. (1920).

Revision of the North American Species of the Genus Eupithecia. Bull. American Mus. Nat. Hist., **93**, pp. 533–728, pls. 26–32 (1949).

MEYRICK, E. Classification of the Geometridæ of Europe. Trans. Ent. Soc. London, **1892**, pp. 53–140 (1892).

OZORSKI, E. Tableau de détermination des espèces françaises des genres Scopula et Sterrha. Bull. Soc. ent. Mulhouse, **1948**, pp. 1–6, 9–12, 17–22 (1948).

PACKARD, A. S. Monograph of the Geometrid moths or Phalænidæ of the United States. Rept. U. S. Geol. Survey, **10**, 607 pp. (1876).

PROUT, L. B. Geometridæ, Brephinæ. Gen. Insectorum, fasc. 103, 16 pp. (1910).

Œnochromatinæ. Gen. Insectorum, fasc. 104, 120 pp. (1910).

Hemitheinæ. Gen. Insectorum, fasc. 129, 274 pp. (1912).

Palæarctic Geometræ. Seitz, Macrolepidoptera of World, **4**, 479 pp., 25 pls. (1912–16).

Hemitheinæ. Lepid. Cat., **14**, 192 pp. (1913).

Geometridæ. Seitz, Macrolepidoptera of World, **12**, pp. 69–116, 1 pl. (1932).

Geometridæ. Seitz, Macrolepidoptera of World, **16**, pp. 49–160, 7 pls.; Suppl. **4**, pp. 1–112, 4 pls. (1933–35).

Geometridæ, Subfamily Sterrhinæ. Lepid. Cat., **61**, **63**, **68**, 486 pp. (1934–35).

Geometridæ [Palæarctic]. Seitz, Macrolepidoptera of World, Suppl. **4**, pp. 57–248 (1936–38).

American Geometridæ. Seitz, Macrolepidoptera of World, **8**, pp. 1–104, 12 pls. (1938).

RINDGE, F. H. A Revision of the Geometrid Moths Formerly Assigned to the Genus Drepanulatrix. Bull. American Mus. Nat. Hist., **94**, pp. 231–298 (1949).

SCHAUS, W. Moths of the Families Geometridæ and Pyralidæ of Porto Rico. Sci. Surv. of Porto Rico, **12**, pp. 291–417 (1940).

SUZUKI, M. Cymatophoridæ of Japan. [In Japanese]. Ent. Mag., Kyoto, **2**, pp. 67–84 (1916).

TURNER, A. J. Revision of Australian Geometridæ. Proc. Linn. Soc. New South Wales, **44**, pp. 258–310; 383–413 (1919).

Australian Geometrites. Proc. Roy. Soc. South Australia, **46**, pp. 225–294 (1922).

Revision of Australian Drepanidæ, Limacodidæ, Zygænidæ. Proc. Linn. Soc. New South Wales, **51**, pp. 411–445 (1926).

Revision of Australian Œnochromatidæ. Proc. Linn. Soc. New South Wales, **54**, pp. 463–504 (1929); **55**, pp. 1–40; 191–220 (1930).

New Australian Species of Boarmiadæ. Proc. Roy. Soc. Queensland, **58**, pp. 71–112 (1947).

CALLIDULOIDEA

JANSE, A. J. T. Cymatophoridæ, Callidulidæ, and Noctuidæ (partim). Moths of South Africa, **3**, xv + 435 pp., 47 pls., 102 figs. (1937–39).

PAGENSTECHER, A. Callidulidæ. Das Tierreich, Lief. 17, 27 pp. (1901).

Callidulidæ. Lepid. Cat., **2**, 14 pp. (1911).

BOMBYCOIDEA

BOUVIER, E. L. Les Saturnioides de l'Afrique tropicale française. Faune colon. franç., fasc. 2, pp. 449–708 (1928).

Étude des Saturnioides normaux. Famille des Syssphingidés. Mém. Acad. Sci. France, (2) **60**, 290 pp., 5 pls., 92 figs. (1931).

Étude des Saturnioides. Famille des Hémileucidés. Ann. Sci. nat. Paris, (10) **15**, pp. 363–426, 1 pl., 22 figs. (1932); (10) **18**, pp. 217–418, 6 pls., 39 figs. (1935); (10) **19**, pp. 31–293, 4 pls., 41 figs. (1936).

Étude des Saturnioides normaux. Famille des Saturniidés. Mém. Mus. Nat. Hist. Nat. Paris (n.s.), **3**, pp. 1–350, 12 pls., 82 figs. (1936).

Les papillons de la tribu Lonomiicæ. C. R. Acad. Sci. France, **198**, pp. 1941–1944 (1933).

COLLIER, W. A. Lasiocampidæ. Lepid. Cat., **73**, 484 pp. (1936).

DRAUDT, M. Palæarctic Saturniidæ. Seitz, Macrolepidoptera of World, **6**, pp. 769–827, 3 pls. (1930).

FLETCHER, T. B. Lasiocampidæ. Cat. Indian Ins., **7**, 29 pp. Govt. India, Centr. Pub. Branch, Calcutta (1925).

GAEDE, M. Mimallonidæ. Lepid. Cat., **50**, 21 pp. (1931).

Lasiocampidæ. Seitz, Macrolepidoptera of World, Suppl. 2, pp. 109–125 (1932).

HERING, M. Ratardidæ. Lepid. Cat., **81**, 3 pp. (1937).

HOFFMANN, C. C. Catálogo sistemático de los Lepidópteros Mexicanos, Pt. 3. An. Inst. Biol., México, **13**, pp. 213–256 (1942).

HULSTAERT, P. G. Anthelidæ. Gen. Insectorum, **191**, 13 pp., 1 pl. (1928).

JORDAN, K. Monograph of the Ludiinæ. Nov. Zool., **29**, pp. 249–326 (1922).
On the Saturnoidean Families Oxytenidæ and Cercophanidæ. Nov. Zool., **31**, pp. 135–193 (1924).

MATSUMURA, S. Generic Revision of Palæarctic Notodontidæ. Insecta Matsum., Sapporo, **4**, pp. 78–93 (1929).
Lasiocampidæ of Japan. Insecta Matsum., **7**, pp. 33–54, 1 fig. (1933).

MELL, R. Die Brahmæiden und Eupterotiden Chinas. Deutsche Ent. Zeits., **1929**, pp. 337–494 (1930).

MICHENER, C. D. The Saturniidæ of the Western Hemisphere: Morphology, Phylogeny, and Classification. Bull. American Mus. Nat. Hist., **98**, pp. 335–502, pl. 5 (1952).

OITICICA, J. FILHO. Sôbre a nomenclatura dos lepidópteros da família Adelocephalidæ. Arq. Zool. São Paulo, **2**, pp. 325–339 (1941).

PACKARD, A. S. Monograph of the Bombycine Moths of America North of Mexico. Notodontidæ. Mem. Nat. Acad. Sci., Washington, **7**, 390 pp., 49 pls. (1895).
Monograph of the Bombycine Moths of America. Family Ceratocampidæ, subfamily Ceratocampinæ. Mem. Nat. Acad. Sci., Washington, **9**, 272 pp., 61 pls. (1905).
Monograph of the Bombycine Moths of North America. Pt. 3, Mem. Nat. Acad. Sci. Washington, **12**, 516 pp. (1914). (Edited by T. D. A. Cockerell).

SCHÜSSLER, H. Saturniidæ. Lepid. Cat., **55, 56, 58, 65**, 769 pp. (1933–34).
Syssphingidæ (Citheroniidæ). Lepid. Cat., **70**, 230 pp. (1936).
Oxytenidæ. Lepid. Cat., **75**, 20 pp. (1936).
Cercophanidæ. Lepid. Cat., **76**, 12 pp. (1936).

STRAND, E. Brahmæidæ. Lepid. Cat., **16**, pp. 3–6 (1913).
Catalogus Ratardidarum. Arch. f. Naturg., Jahrg. **82A**, Heft 4, pp. 53–54 (1917).

TURNER, A. J. Revision of Australian Saturniidæ, Bombycidæ, Eupterotidæ, Notodontidæ. Proc. Linn. Soc. New South Wales, **47**, pp. 348–390 (1922).
Revision of Australian Lasiocampidæ. Proc. Linn. Soc. New South Wales, **49**, pp. 397–428 (1924).

URETA R., E. Saturniidæ in Chile, pt. 3. Bol. Mus. Nac. Hist. Nat. Chile, **22**, pp. 49–64 (1944).

SPHINGOIDEA

BELL, T. R. D., and F. B. SCOTT. Sphingidæ of British India. Fauna of British India, Moths, Pt. V, xiv + 537 pp., 15 pls., 124 figs. (1937).

DRAUDT, M. American Sphingidæ. Seitz, Macrolepidoptera of World, **6**, pp. 841–896, 22 pls. (1931).
Sphingidæ. Seitz, Macrolepidoptera of World, Suppl. **6**, pp. 897–900, 6 pls. (1932).

HOFFMANN, C. C. Catálogo sistemático de los Lepidópteros Mexicanos, Pt. 3. An. Inst. Biol. México, **13**, pp. 213–256 (1942).

KIRBY, W. F. A Synonymic Catalogue of the Lepidoptera Heterocera. Vol. I. Sphinges and Bombyces. 951 pp. London (1892).

ORFILA, R. N. Catálogo de los Sphingidæ Argentinos. Rev. Soc. Ent. Argentina, **5**, pp. 189–206 (1933).

ROTHSCHILD, W. and K. JORDAN. Sphingidæ. Gen. Insectorum, fasc. 57, 157 pp. (1907).
　Revision of the Lepidopterous family Sphingidæ. 2 vols., Suppl. to Nov. Zool., 9, 972 pp., 67 pls. London (1903).
SMITH, J. B. Monograph of Sphingidæ of North America. Trans. American Ent. Soc., 15, pp. 49–242 (1888).
WAGNER, H. Sphingidæ, Subfamilies Philampelinæ, Acherontiinæ, Chœrocampinæ, Ambulicinæ, Sesiinæ. Lepid. Cat., 12, 18, 21, and 23, 440 pp. (1913–19).

NOCTUOIDEA

BARNES, W. and J. McDUNNOUGH. Illustrations of North American Species of the Genus Catocala. Mem. American Mus. Nat. Hist., 3, 47 pp. (1918).
BEUTENMÜLLER, W. Descriptive Catalogue of Noctuidæ within 50 miles of New York City. Bull. American Mus. Nat. Hist., 14, pp. 229–312 (1901); 16, pp. 413–458 (1902).
BRYK, F. Dioptidæ. Lepid. Cat., 42, 65 pp. (1930).
　Pericopidæ. Lepid. Cat., 45, 57 pp. (1931).
　Lymantriidæ. Lepid. Cat., 62, 441 pp. (1934).
　Callimorphinæ, Nyctemerinæ. Lepid. Cat., 82, 105 pp. (1937).
COLLENETTE, C. L. The Lymantriidæ of Celebes. Ann. Mag. Nat. Hist., (11) 14, pp. 1–60, 5 pls. (1947).
　The Lymantriidæ of Bali. Entomologist, 82, pp. 169–175, 1 pl. (1949).
　The Lymantriidæ of Java. Ann. Mag. Nat. Hist., (12) 1, pp. 685–744, 3 pls. (1949).
CORTI, A., and M. DRAUDT. Agrotinæ. Seitz, Macrolepidoptera of World, Suppl. 3, pp. 22–333, 11 pls. (1933–38).
CULOT, J. Noctuidæ of Europe. Vols. 1 and 2 (1910–12).
DANIEL, F. Beiträge zur Kenntnis der Arctiidæ Ostasiens. Mitt. münchn. ent. Ges., 33, pp. 247–269, 1 pl.; pp. 673–759, 9 pls., 33 figs. (1943).
DRAUDT, M. Noctuidæ. Seitz, Macrolepidoptera of World, 7, pp. 365–380, 1 pl. (1930).
　Syntomidæ. Seitz, Macrolepidoptera of World, 6, pp. 53–60, 1 pl. (1931).
　Arctiidæ. Seitz, Macrolepidoptera of World, Suppl. 2, pp. 61–94 (1931–32).
　Notodontidæ. Seitz, Macrolepidoptera of World, 6, pp. 901–1040, 20 pls. (1932–33).
FLETCHER, T. B. Amatidæ (Syntomidæ). Cat. Indian Ins. 8, 35 pp. Govt. India Centr. Pub. Branch, Calcutta (1925).
FORBES, W. T. M. Genera of Noctuidæ of Northeastern North America. Journ. New York Ent. Soc., 22, pp. 1–33 (1914).
GAEDE, M. Epiplemidæ, Notodontidæ. Seitz, Macrolepidoptera of World, 10, pp. 605–655 (1910).
　Aganaidæ (Hypsidæ). Lepid. Cat., 52, 39 pp. (1932).
　Notodontidæ. Seitz, Macrolepidoptera of World, Suppl. 2, pp. 173–186, 1 pl. (1933).
　Notodontidæ. Lepid. Cat., 59, 351 pp. (1934).

Agaristidæ and Noctuidæ. Seitz, Macrolepidoptera of World, **15**, pp. 23–29; 30–158 (1935).

Noctuidæ. Seitz, Macrolepidoptera of World, **11**, pp. 352–496, 19 pls. (1937–38).

GROTE, A. R. Die Apateliden. Mitt. Römer. Mus. Hildesheim, No. 3, 18 pp. (1896).

HAMPSON, G. F. Catologue of the Lepidoptera Phalænæ in the British Museum [Syntomidæ, Arctiidæ, Noctuidæ]. 15 vols., 9767 pp., 308 pls. British Mus. Nat. Hist., London (1898–1920).

HULSTAERT, P. G. Anthelidæ. Gen. Insectorum, fasc. 191, 13 pp. (1929).

JANSE, A. J. T. Cymatophoridæ, Callidulidæ, Noctuidæ (part) of South Africa. Moths of South Africa, **3**, xv + 435 pp., 47 pls., 102 figs. (1937–39).

JORDAN, K. Agaristidæ [Palæarctic]. Seitz, Macrolepidoptera of World, **3**, pp. 5–8 (1909–13).

KÖHLER, P. Agaristidæ de la república Argentina. Rev. Soc. Ent. Argentina, **2**, pp. 235–245 (1929).

Los Noctuidæ argentinos. Subfamilia Agrotinæ. Acta zool. lilloana, **3**, pp. 59–134, 2 pls., 13 figs. (1945).

Los Noctuidæ argentinos. Subfamilia Hadeninæ. Acta zool. lilloana, **4**, pp. 69–105 (1947).

MATSUMURA, S. Catalogue of Japanese Arctiidæ. Insecta Matsum., Sapporo, **5**, pp. 58–94 (1930).

Lymantriidæ of Japan. Insecta Matsum., **7**, pp. 111–152 (1933).

McDUNNOUGH, J. H. Generic Revision of North American Agrotid Moths. Bull. Canada Dept. Mines, No. **55**, Biol. ser. 16, 78 pp. (1928).

Revision of North American Plusiinæ. Mem. Southern California Acad. Sci., **2**, pp. 175–232, 6 pls. (1944).

MELL, R. Beiträge zur Fauna sinica. X. Die Agaristiden Chinas. Stettin. ent. Zeitg., **97**, pp. 1–43, 161–188, 1 pl., 18 figs. (1936).

MEYRICK, E. Monograph of the Noctuidæ of New Zealand. Trans. New Zealand Inst., **19**, pp. 3–40 (1886); **20**, pp. 44–106 (1887).

PIERCE, F. N. The Genitalia of the Group Noctuidæ of the Lepidoptera of the British Islands, 2nd ed. 64 pp., 15 pls. (1952).

PROUT, L. B. Provisional Arrangement of the Dioptidæ. Nov. Zool., **25**, pp. 395–429 (1918).

SCHAUS, W. Revision of American Notodontidæ. Trans. Ent. Soc. London, 1901, pp. 257–344 (1901).

Revision of Noctuidæ of Porto Rico and Virgin Islands. Sci. Surv. Porto Rico, **12**, pp. 177–290 (1940).

SMITH, J. B. Catalogue of the Lepidopterous Superfamily Noctuidæ found in Boreal America. Bull. U. S. Nat. Mus., **44**, 424 pp. (1893).

Revision of the Deltoid Moths. Bull. U. S. Nat. Mus., **48**, 120 pp. (1895).

STRAND, E. Agaristidæ. Lepid. Cat., **5**, 82 pp. (1912).

Arctiidæ. Lepid. Cat., **22, 24, 26**, 899 pp. (1919–22).

SWINHOE, C. A Revision of the Genera of the Family Liparidæ. Ann. Mag. Nat. Hist., (9) **10**, pp. 449–484; **11**, pp. 47–97, 289–304, 400–442 (1922–23).

TIETZ, H. M. Manual of the Noctuidæ of Pennsylvania. Bull. Pennsylvania Agric. Expt. Sta., No. **335**, 164 pp., 2 figs. (1936).

Toxopeus, L. J. Notes on Lymantriidæ, with Partial Revision of Redoa. Treubia, **19**, pp. 429–481 (1948).

Turner, A. J. A New Family of Lepidoptera (Anthelidæ). Trans. Ent. Soc. London, 1919, p. 415 (1919).

    Revision of the Australian Noctuidæ. Trans. Roy. Soc. South Australia, **44**, pp. 120–189 (1920).

    Revision of Australian Lepidoptera. Liparidæ. Proc. Linn. Soc. New South Wales, **45**, pp. 474–499 (1921).

    Revision of Anthelidæ. Proc. Linn. Soc. New South Wales, **46**, pp. 164–191 (1921).

    Revision of Australian Arctiidæ. Proc. Roy. Soc. Queensland, **51**, pp. 51–131 (1940).

    Revision of Australian Nolidæ. Proc. Roy. Soc. Queensland, **55**, pp. 13–50 (1944).

Viette, P. Les Ophideres du Pacifique. Rev. franç. Ent., **15**, pp. 209–220 (1948).

Warren, W. Noctuidæ [Palæarctic]. Seitz, Macrolepidoptera of World, **3**, pp. 9–511, pls. 2–75 (1909–13); Suppl. (M. Draudt), pp. 5–333, 26 pls. (1938).

Zerny, H. Syntomidæ. Lepid. Cat., **7**, 179 pp. (1912).

SUBORDER RHOPALOCERA, GENERAL

Aurivillius, C. Rhopalocera Æthiopica. 561 pp. Stockholm (1898).

Barnes, W., and F. H. Benjamin. Check-list of the Diurnal Lepidoptera of Boreal America. Bull. Southern California Acad. Sci., **25**, pp. 3–27, 88–98 (1926).

Bates, M. Butterflies of Cuba. Bull. Mus. Comp. Zool. Harvard **78**, pp. 63–258, 24 figs. (1935).

Bingham, C. T. Butterflies. 2 vols., 511 + 480 pp. Fauna of British India, London (1905–07).

Bourquin, F. Mariposas argentinas. ⌊10⌋ + 212 pp., 192 figs. Publ. by author. Buenos Aires (1945).

Carpenter, G. D. H. The Rhopalocera of Abyssinia. Trans. Roy. Ent. Soc. London, **83**, pp. 313–447, 6 pls. (1935).

Clark, A. H. The Butterflies of the District of Columbia and Vicinity. Bull. U. S. Nat. Mus., **157**, 337 pp., 64 pls. (1932).

    Arctic Butterflies. Report Smithsonian Inst., **1934**, pp. 267–296, 7 pls. (1935).

    Classification of the Butterflies, with the Allocation of the Genera Occurring in North America North of Mexico. Proc. Biol. Soc. Washington, **61**, pp. 77–81 (1948).

Comstock, J. A. Butterflies of California. 334 pp., 63 pls. Publ. by author. Los Angeles (1927).

Comstock, J. H. and A. B. How to Know the Butterflies [Eastern U.S.A.]. xii + 311 pp., 45 pls. D. Appleton and Co., New York (1904).

Corbet, A. S., and H. M. Pendlebury. Butterflies of the Malay Peninsula. xxvi + 252 pp., 14 pls., 34 figs. Palmer and Co., Kuala Lumpur (1934).

DAVENPORT, D., and V. G. DETHIER. Bibliography of the Described Life-histories of the Rhopalocera of America North of Mexico, 1889–1937. Entomologica Americana, 17, pp. 155–194 (1938).

DISTANT, W. L. Rhopalocera malayana, 481 pp., London (1882–86).

EDWARDS, W. H. Butterflies of North America. 3 vols., Boston and New York. (1880–84–97).

EVANS, W. H. Identification of Indian Butterflies. Journ. Bombay Nat. Hist. Soc., 29, pp. 230–260; 519–537; 780–797 (1923).
    The Identification of Indian Butterflies. x + 454 pp., 32 pls. Bombay Nat. Hist. Soc. (1932).

FERRAR, M. L. Butterflies of the Andamans and Nicobars. Journ. Bombay Nat. Hist. Soc., 47, pp. 470–491 (1948).

FIELD, W. D. Manual of the Butterflies and Skippers of Kansas. Bull. Univ. Kansas, 39, 328 pp., 2 pls. (1938).

FORD, E. B. Butterflies. 368 pp., 48 pls. Collins, London (1945).

GODFREY, E. J. List of Butterflies of Siam. Journ. Siam. Nat. Hist. Soc., Suppl. 7, pp. 203–397 (1930).

GODMAN, F. D., and O. SALVIN. Rhopalocera. In Biologia Centrali-Americana, 2 vols., 1269 pp., 112 pls. (1879–1901).

HINTON, H. E. On the Homology and Nomenclature of the Setæ of Lepidopterous Larvæ, with some Notes on the Phylogeny of the Lepidoptera. Trans. Roy. Ent. Soc. London, 97, pp. 1–37 (1946).

HOFFMANN, C. C. Catálogo sistemático y zoogeográphico de los Lepidópteros Mexicanos. Parts 1, 2. An. Inst. Biol. México, 11, pp. 639–739; 12, pp. 237–294 (1940–41).

HOLLAND, W. J. The Butterfly Book. Doubleday and Co., New York (1899). Second Edition, 424 pp., 77 pls. (1931).

KALIS, J. P. A. Lepidoptera Rhopalocera van Nederlandsch-Indië. Tijdschr. Ent., 76, pp. 47–86 (1933).

KAYE, W. J. The Butterflies of Jamaica. Trans. Ent. Soc. London, 1925, pp. 455–504 (1925).

KIRBY, W. F. Synonymical Catalogue of Diurnal Lepidoptera. John van Voorst, London (1871–77). (Various parts.)

KLOTS, A. B. A Field Guide to the Butterflies. 349 pp., 40 pls. Houghton Mifflin Co., Boston (1951).

LANG, H. C. Rhopalocera Europæ. 2 vols., London (1884).

LE CERF, F. Rhopalocères. Atlas des Lépidoptères de France, fasc. 1, 115 pp., 12 pls. N. Boubée et Cie., Paris (1944).

MABILLE, P. Lépidoptères Rhopalocères de Madagascar. In Grandidier, Hist. Nat. Madagascar, 18, 364 pp. (1885–88).

MACY, R. W., and H. H. SHEPARD. Butterflies. 247 pp., 4 pls. Univ. Minnesota Press (1941).

MARSHALL, G. F. L. and L. DE NICEVILLE. The Butterflies of India. 3 vols., Central Press, Calcutta (1882–1890).

MOORE, F. Lepidoptera indica (Rhopalocera). 8 vols., London (1890–1911).

MOULTON, J. C. Butterflies of Borneo. Sarawak Mus. Journ., 2, pp. 197–266 (1915).

NORDSTRÖM, F. Laplands Fjärilar [Rhopalocera]. Ent. Tidskr., 54, pp. 145–214, 9 pls. (1933).

OBERTHÜR, C., and C. HOULEBERT. Rhopalocères. Faune Ent. Americaine, **3**, pp. 47–260 (1922).

PIERCE, F. N. and B. P. BEIRNE. The Genitalia of the British Rhopalocera and the Larger Moths. 66 pp., 21 pls. Oundle (1941).

REUTER, E. Über die Palpen der Rhopaloceren. Acta Soc. Sci. Fennicæ, **22**, 577 pp., 6 pls. (1896).

SCHATZ, E., and J. RÖBER. Die Familien und Gattungen der Tagfalter. Exot. Schmett., **2**, 284 pp., Furth (1885–92).

SCHWARZ, R. Motyli [of Czechoslovakia], 1 (Papilionidæ, Pieridæ, Satyridæ), 56 pp., 48 pls. (1948); 2 (other Rhopalocera), 79 pp., 48 pls. (1949). Prague.

SCUDDER, S. H. Butterflies of Eastern United States and Canada. 3 vols. 1958 pp., 89 pls. Cambridge (1888–89).

SOUTH, R. The Butterflies of the British Isles. 204 pp., 127 pls. F. Warne and Co., London (1906).

STOKOE, W. J., and G. H. T. STOVIN. The Caterpillars of the British Butterflies. 248 pp., 32 pls. Frederick Warne + Co., London and New York (1944).

TALBOT, G. Butterflies. Fauna of British India. **1**, xxix + 600 pp., 3 pls., 184 figs. (1939); **2**, xv + 506 pp., 2 pls. (1947). Taylor and Francis, London.

TRIMEN, R. and H. BOWKER. South African Butterflies. 3 vols., London (1887–1889).

URBAN, E., and H. Die Schmetterlinge Pommerns. Stettin. Ent. Zeitg., **100**, pp. 185–826, 19 figs. (1939).

VERITY, R. Le farfalle diurne d'Italia. xxxiv + 131 pp., 6 pls., Florence (1940).

VIETTE, P. Lépidoptères Rhopalocères de l'Océanie française. Faune Empire franç., **13**, 101 pp. Larose, Paris (1950).

WAGNER, W. H., JR., and D. F. GRETHER. Butterflies of the Admiralty Islands. Proc. U. S. Nat. Mus., **98**, pp. 163–186 (1948).

WATERHOUSE, G. A. and G. LYELL. The Butterflies of Australia, 239 pp., Sydney (1914).

WOODHOUSE, L. G. O. The Butterfly Fauna of Ceylon, 2nd ed. 231 pp., 55 pls. Colombo (1950).

WRIGHT, W. G. Butterflies of the West Coast of the United States. San Bernardino, California, 257 pp. (1906).

WRIGHT, W. S. Annotated List of Butterflies of San Diego County, California. Trans. San Diego Soc. Nat. Hist., **6**, pp. 1–40 (1930).

HESPERIOIDEA

BARNES, W. and J. H. McDUNNOUGH. Revision of the Megathymidæ. Contrib. Nat. Hist. Lepidoptera N. Am., **1**, No. 3, 43 pp., 6 pls. Decatur, Ill. (1912).

BELL, E. L. Studies in the Pyrrhopyginæ [Hesperiidæ]. Journ. New York Ent. Soc., **41**, pp. 265–295; 481–529, 9 pls. (1933).

A Catalogue of the Original Descriptions of the Rhopalocera Found North of the Mexican Border. Part I. The Hesperioidea. Bull. Cheyenne Mt. Mus., **1**, 35 pp. (1938).

Catalogue of the Hesperioidea of Venezuela. Bol. Ent. venezolana, **5**, pp. 65–203 (1946).

ELWES, H. J. and J. EDWARDS. Revision of Oriental Hesperiidæ. Trans. Zool.
Soc. London, **14,** pp. 101–324 (1897).

EVANS, W. H. Catalogue of the African Hesperiidæ. xii + 212 pp., 30 pls.
British Mus. Nat. Hist., London (1937).
    Catalogue of the Hesperiidæ from Europe, Asia, and Australia in the
British Museum. 502 pp., 53 pls. Brit. Mus., London (1949).

HAYWARD, K. J. Hesperiidarum Argentinæ Catalogus. Rev. Mus. La Plata,
(n.s.) Zool., **2,** pp. 227–340 (1941).
    Catalogus Hesperiidarum Rei Publicæ Colombianæ. Acta zool. lilloana,
4, pp. 201–392 (1947).
    Insecta, Lepidoptera (Rhopalocera), Familia Hesperiidarum. 2 vols.
Genera et Species Animalium Argentinorum, 389 pp., 27 pls. (1948); 388
pp., 26 pls. (1950). Buenos Aires.

HOLLAND, W. J. Revision and Catalogue of African Hesperiidæ. Proc. Zool.
Soc. London, **1896,** pp. 2–107 (1896).

LINDSEY, A. W., E. L. BELL and R. C. WILLIAMS. Hesperioidea of North
America. Journ. Sci. Labs. Denison Univ., **26,** pp. 1–142, 33 pls. (1931).

MABILLE, P. Hesperiidæ. Gen. Insectorum, fasc. 17, 210 pp. (1904).
    Hesperiidæ. Lepid. Cat. **9,** 18 pp. (1912).

McDUNNOUGH, J. Megathymidæ. Lepid. Cat., **9,** pp. 19–22 (1912).

MEYRICK, E. and O. B. LOWER. Revision of Australian Hesperiidæ. Trans.
Roy. Soc. South Australia, **26,** pp. 38–129 (1902) and **31,** pp. 192–208
(1907).

SHEPARD, H. H. Hesperiidæ, Pyrginæ. Lepid. Cat., **47, 64, 69, 74,** 679 pp.
(1931–36).
    Hesperiidæ, Ismeninæ. Lepid. Cat., **57,** 55 pp. (1933).
    Hesperiidæ, Euschemoninæ et Trapezitinæ. Lepid. Cat., **77,** 35 pp.
(1936).
    Hesperiidæ, Hesperiinæ I, II. Lepid. Cat., **83, 90,** 206 pp. (1937–39).

WARREN, B. C. S. Revision of Palæarctic Hesperiinæ. Trans. Ent. Soc. London,
74, pp. 1–170 (1926).

WATERHOUSE, G. A. Australian Hesperiidæ. II, III. Proc. Linn. Soc. New
South Wales, **57,** pp. 218–238;   409–410, 2 figs. (1932).

WATSON, E. Y. Classification of Hesperiidæ. Proc. Zool. Soc. London, **1893,**
pp. 3–132 (1893).

PAPILIONOIDEA

D'ALMEIDA, R. F. Revisão das especies americanas da superfamilia Danaoidea.
Parte 1. Familia Danaidæ, Danainæ. Mem. Inst. Oswaldo Cruz, **34,**
pp. 1–114, 30 pls. (1939).

AVINOFF, A., and W. R. SWEADNER. The Karanasa Butterflies, a Study in
Evolution. Ann. Carnegie Mus., **32,** 250 pp., 17 pls. (1951).

BAKKER, D. Revision of the Amathusiidæ in the Museums at Leiden and at
Amsterdam. Zool. Meded., **23,** pp. 171–216, 5 pls., 3 figs. (1942).

BERGER, L. A. Papilionidæ. In Cat. rais. faune ent. Congo Belge, Ann. Mus.
Congo Belge, Tervuren, (C) **8,** pp. 1–104 (1950).

BETHUNE-BAKER, G. T. Revision of the Amblypodia Group of Lycænidæ.
Trans. Zool. Soc. London, **17,** pp. 1–164 (1903).

Bollow, C. Pieridæ. Seitz, Macrolepidoptera of World, Suppl. 1, pp. 93–125, 3 pls. (1930).

Bollow, C., and M. Gaede. Palæarctic Nymphalidæ. Seitz, Macrolepidoptera of World, Suppl. 1, pp. 191–235 (1930).

Brown, F. M. Taxonomy and Distribution of Pierella. Ann. Carnegie Mus., 31, pp. 49–87, 11 figs. (1948).

Bryk, F. Papilionidæ. Lepid. Cat., 35, 37, 39, 676 pp. (1929–30).
    Baroniidæ, Teinopalpidæ, Parnasiidæ. Lepid. Cat., 27, 247 pp. (1923).
    Parnasiidæ, Baroniidæ, Teinopalpidæ. Das Tierreich, Lief. 64, xiii + 131 pp., 87 figs.; 65, li + 790 pp., 698 figs. (1934–35).
    Danaidæ. Lepid. Cat., 78, 80, 702 pp. (1937).

Chermock, R. L. Generic Revision of the Limenitini of the World. American Midl. Natural., 43, pp. 513–569 (1950).

Clark, A. H. The Interrelationships of the Several Groups Within the Butterfly Family Nymphaloidea. Proc. Ent. Soc. Washington, 49, pp. 148–149 (1947).

Dillon, L. S. Tribe Catagrammini. Pt. 1. Genus Catagramma and Allies. Sci. Publ. Reading Public Museum, No. 8, 113 pp. (1948).

Draeseke, J. Lycænidæ I. Lepid. Cat., 72, 48 pp. (1936).

Druce, H. H. Monograph of Bornean Lycænidæ. Proc. Zool. Soc. London, 1895, pp. 556–627 (1895) and 1896, pp. 650–683 (1896).

Eltringham, H. and K. Jordan. Acræidæ. Lepid. Cat., 11, 65 pp. (1913).

Forbes, W. T. M. Revisional Notes on the Danainæ. Entomologica Americana, 19, pp. 101–139 (1939).
    Review of Melinaea and Mechanitis. Journ. New York Ent. Soc., 56, pp. 1–24 (1948).

Ford, E. B. The Classification of the Papilionidæ. Trans. Roy. Ent. Soc. London, 94, pp. 201–223 (1944).

Forster, W. Beiträge zur Kenntnis der ostasiatischen Yphthima-Arten. Mitt. münchn. ent. Ges., 34, pp. 472–492 (1948).

Gaede, M. Satyridæ. Lepid. Cat., 43, 46, 48, 759 pp. (1931).

Gaede, M., and C. Bollow. Palæarctic Lycænidæ. Seitz, Macrolepidoptera of World, Suppl. 1, pp. 239–288, 3 pls. (1930).

Hayward, K. J. Contribución al conocimiento de las Riodinidae argentinas. Physis, 17, pp. 317–374 (1939).
    Lepidópteros argentinos, Familia Nymphalidæ. Rev. Soc. Ent. Argentina, 4, pp. 1–200, 21 pls., 6 figs. (1931).

Huang, S. M. Y. The Chinese Lycænidæ. Notes Ent. Chinoise, 10, pp. 67–213 (1943).

Hulstaert, P. G. Danaidæ [part]. Gen. Insectorum, fasc. 193, 215 pp., 6 pls. (1931).

Jordan, K., and H. Eltringham. Nymphalidæ, Acræinæ. Gen. Insectorum, fasc. 169, 81 pp. (1916).

Klots, A. B. Generic Revision of the Pieridæ. Entomologica Americana, 12, pp. 139–242, 4 pls. (1933).

Kusnezov, N. J. Insecta Lepidoptera. I. Danaidæ [Pieridæ]. dxcix + 64 pp., 23 figs. Faune de l'U. R. S. S. et des pays limitrophes. (Pub. by Mus. Zool. Acad. Sci., Leningrad) (1915, 1929).

MURRAY, D. P. South African Butterflies. A Monograph of the Family Lycænidæ. vi + 195 pp., 144 figs. J. Bale, Sons, and Danielsson, London (1935).

NEUSTETTER, H. Nymphalidæ, Heliconiinæ. Lepid. Cat., 36, 136 pp. (1929).

PAGENSTECHER, A. Libytheidæ. Das Tierreich, Lief. 14, 18 pp. (1901).
    Libytheidæ. Gen. Insectorum, fasc. 5, 4 pp. (1902).
    Libytheidæ. Lepid. Cat., 3, 12 pp. (1911).

DOS PASSOS, C. F. Catalogue of Satyridæ Found North of Mexico. Bull. Cheyenne Mt. Mus., 1, no. 2, 13 pp. (1939).

DOS PASSOS, C. F., and L. P. GREY. Systematic Catalogue of Speyeria. American Mus. Novitat., 1370, 30 pp. (1947).

RIPPON, R. H. E. Monograph of Ornithoptera. 2 vols., London (1898–1907).
    Papilionidæ, Sect. Troides. Gen. Insectorum, 6, 15 pp., 2 pls. (1902).

ROEPKE, W. Rhopalocera javanica, Papilionidæ en Pieridæ. Wageningen, Fonds Landbouv Export Bur. 1916–18, Publ. no. 12, pp. 1–102, 12 pls., 8 figs. (1935).

ROTHSCHILD, W. A Revision of the Papilios of the Eastern Hemisphere. Novitat. Zool., 2, pp. 167–463 (1895).

ROTHSCHILD, W. and K. JORDAN. A Revision of the American Papilios. Novitat. Zool., 13, pp. 411–752 (1906).

SEITZ, A. Das System der Schmetterlinge; III. Die Danaiden. Ent. Rundschau, 44, pp. 32, 35–36, 39–40, 44, 47–48 (1927).

SEITZ, A., M. GAEDE and H. GOLTZ. Palæarctic Satyridæ. Seitz, Macrolepidoptera of World, Suppl. 1, pp. 129–190 (1930).

STICHEL, H. Brassolidæ. Das Tierreich, Lief. 25, 258 pp. (1908).
    Nymphalidæ, Dioninæ. Gen. Insectorum, fasc. 63, 38 pp. (1908).
    Papilionidæ, Parnasiinæ. Gen. Insectorum, fasc. 58, 60 pp. (1907).
    Riodinidæ. Gen. Insectorum, fasc. 112, 452 pp. (1911).
    Papilionidæ, Zerynthiinæ. Gen. Insectorum, fasc. 59, 27 pp. (1907).
    Nymphalidæ, Brassolinæ. Gen. Insectorum, fasc. 20, 48 pp. (1904).
    Nymphalidæ, Discophorinæ. Gen. Insectorum, fasc. 31, 16 pp. (1905).
    Nymphalidæ, Hyantinæ. Gen. Insectorum, fasc. 39, 7 pp. (1906).
    Nymphalidæ, Amathusiinæ. Gen. Insectorum, fasc. 36, 67 pp. (1906).
    Nymphalidæ, Heliconiinæ. Gen. Insectorum, fasc. 37, 74 pp. (1906).
    Amathusiidæ. Das Tierreich, Lief. 34, 263 pp. (1912).
    Vorarbeiten zu einer Revision der Riodinidæ. Deutsch. Ent. Zeits., 1926, pp. 385–396 (1927).
    Nemeobiinæ. Das Tierreich, Lief. 51, 329 pp. (1928).
    Riodinidæ. Lepid. Cat., 38, pp. 1–112; 40, pp. 113–544; 41, pp. 545–720; 44, pp. 721–795 (1930–31).
    Brassolidæ. Lepid. Cat., 51, 115 pp. (1932).
    Amathusiidæ (Morphoidæ). Lepid. Cat., 54, 171 pp. (1933).
    Nymphalidæ, I, II, III. Lepid. Cat., 86, 91, 93, 794 pp. (1938–39).

STICHEL, H., and H. RIFFARTH. Heliconiidæ. Das Tierreich, Lief. 22, 305 pp. (1905).

TALBOT, G. Pieridæ. Lepid. Cat., 53, 60, 66, 697 pp. (1932–35).

TORRE Y CALLEJAS, S. L. DE LA. Revision de las especies cubanas de la familia Papilionidæ. Rev. Inst. Matanzas, 1, pp. 22–43, 4 pls., 3 figs. (1947).

VAN SON, G. Butterflies of Southern Africa. I. Papilionidæ and Pieridæ. Transvaal Mus. Mem. 3, 237 pp., 41 pls. (1949).

VERITY, R. Rhopalocera Palæarctica. Papilionidæ and Pieridæ. lxxxvi + 368 pp., 72 pls. Florence (1905–11).
Le farfalle diurne d'Italia, vol. 3. Papilionidæ and Pieridæ. 318 pp. Marzocco, Florence, Italy (1947).
WARREN, B. C. S. Monograph of the Genus Erebia. 407 pp., 104 pls. Brit. Mus. Nat. Hist., London (1936).
WYTSMAN, P. Papilionidæ, Leptocircinæ. Gen. Insectorum, fasc. 4, 3 pp. (1902).

ORDER DÍPTERA

(ANTLIÀTA, HALTERÀTA, HALTERÍPTERA, HAUSTELLÀTA)

Minute to moderate-sized, rarely large (over one inch) insects, usually with good powers of flight: head usually vertical, freely movable; antennæ variable, comprising either many similar joints or frequently only three, the last joint sometimes annulated, sometimes provided with a sensory style or arista as a phyletic adaptation of the original terminal joints; mouthparts suctorial, incapable of mastication, usually constructed for lapping, sometimes for piercing; both prothorax and metathorax small and fused with the prominent mesothorax; only the mesothoracic pair of wings developed, the veins and crossveins not numerous, hind wings replaced by small knobbed structures (halteres), rarely wings vestigial or even absent; legs usually alike, the tarsi regularly five-jointed. Metamorphosis complete, the larvæ wholly unlike the adults; larvæ almost always legless maggots or grubs, never with true jointed legs, frequently with indistinct head and retracted mouthparts; pupæ with the appendages more or less adherent, the body either free or entirely encased in a seed-like capsule (puparium) formed of the indurated last larval moult. Food habits highly variable. Flies, Mosquitoes, Gnats, Midges.

Adults

1. Winged, *i.e.* wings functionally developed, the insect capable of flight 2
   Wingless, or with vestigial or abortive wings, incapable of functioning for flight (Figs. 662–678) 149
2. Antennæ generally longer than the thorax, usually consisting of a flagellum of 6 to 16, rarely up to 39, nearly similar free joints in addition to the two basal joints (Fig. 465A), rarely with a differentiated style or bristle, sometimes (*e.g. Bibio*, Fig. 465D; *Simulium*, Fig. 465B; *Silvicola*, Fig. 465E) the flagellar joints are crowded together; anal cell (cell Cu) widely open, rarely narrowed in the margin of the wing, discal cell usually absent,

"second" vein (R_{2+3}) sometimes forked; calypters absent; palpi usually elongate, hanging downward and normally comprising 4 or 5 joints; body very rarely with bristles; pleural suture usually extending nearly straight between root of wing and middle coxæ. (Suborder NEMATÓCERA) * 3

Antennæ shorter, usually three-jointed, the third joint occasionally complex, with more or less distinct annulations (Fig. 518B-E), or bearing a differentiated style (Fig. 518F, G) or arista (Fig. 556), in Rhachicerinæ the third joint divided into about 25 segments (Fig. 518A); anal cell (Cu) distally narrowed or closed, sometimes retracted and very short, or even absent, discal cell usually

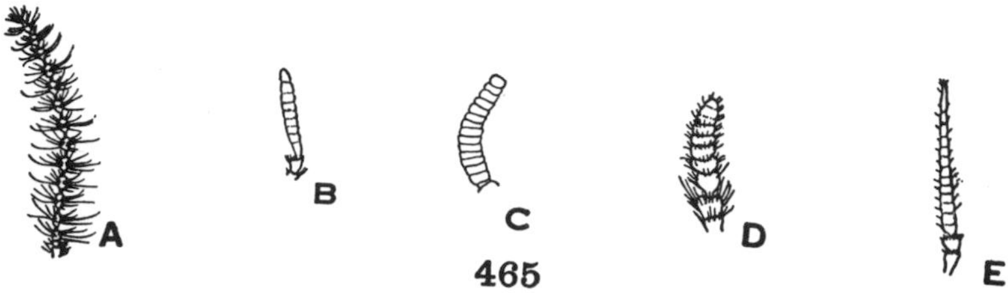

465

Fig. 465. Nematocerous Antennæ

A, **Perrisia** (Verrall) Cecidomyiidæ; B, **Simulium** (Lugger) Simuliidæ; C, **Ceroplatus** (Johannsen) Ceroplatidæ; D, **Bibio** (Verrall) Bibionidæ; E, **Silvicola** (Verrall) Silvicolidæ.

present, "second" vein (R_{2+3}) never furcate; palpi short, one- or two-jointed, projecting forward; pleural suture between root of wing and middle coxæ twice bent at sharp angles. (Suborder BRACHÝCERA) 36

3. Mesonotum with a more or less distinct V-shaped transverse suture beginning on each side in front of root of wings, the pointed middle part close to the scutellum (Fig. 472); postpronotum well developed; female with a conical, generally protruding, chitinized ovipostor; male genitalia usually enlarged; males dichoptic, eyes rounded, not excised at antennæ; legs very long and slender, easily breaking from the body at the trochanters; costa encompassing wing, nine or more veins terminating in wing-margin, subcosta long, ending beyond middle of wing. (Superfamily TIPULÒIDEA) 4

Mesonotum without such a transverse V-shaped suture, a distinct

* The Japanese family NYMPHOMYIIDÆ possesses brachycerous antennæ but is related to the Nematocera. It is an elongate minute insect with snout, atrophied mouthparts, tibial membranous sub-basal area, non-angulated mesopleural suture, non-differentiated abdominal segments, large cerci, no pulvilli, and the narrow heavily fringed wings have almost no veins. **Nymphomyia.**

but interrupted suture present only in Blepharoceridæ which have less than nine veins ending in the wing-margin; no discal cell 9

4. Radius with five branches all ending in the wing-margin, subcosta furcate at its extremity, Sc_2 appearing like a crossvein ending in R_1; first basal cell closed at middle of wing, second basal cell distinctly shorter; one anal vein. (**Tanydèrus**, Neotrop.; **Peringueyomyìna**, Ethiop.; **Protóplasa**, Nearc. (Fig. 466)).

TANYDÉRIDÆ

Radius with only three or four branches ending in wing-margin; basal cells long, nearly always ending distinctly beyond middle of wing and coextensive or nearly so, or the second longer than the first; an accessory or marginal cell commonly present in front of the end of the first basal cell, formed by the erect or reflexed shortened R_2 or R_{2+3} located near the end of R_1 5

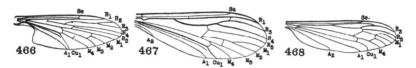

Figs. 466–468. Tanyderidæ, Petauristidæ, Cylindrotomidæ

466. Protoplasa, wing (Alexander) Tanyderidæ.
467. Paracladura, wing (Edwards) Petauristidæ.
468. Cylindrotoma, wing (Alexander) Cylindrotomidæ.

5. R_5 apparently simple (Fig. 467), R_4 in closer association with R_3 than with R_5; two distinct anal veins reaching hind margin of wing; discal cell usually present at end of first basal cell; empodium present, pulvilli absent 6

R_4 and R_5 stalked together (Fig. 474); one distinct anal vein reaching hind margin; no discal cell formed between the branches of media; a longitudinal fold in the wing-membrane crossing anterior crossvein; ocelli absent; mesonotal suture not deep; empodium minute, pulvilli present.

PTYCHOPTÉRIDÆ or LIRIOPÈIDÆ

a. Antennæ 16-jointed; fourth vein forked as M_1 and M_2; legs not banded. (**Ptychóptera** or **Lirìope** (Fig. 474), widespr.).

PTYCHOPTERÌNÆ or LIRIOPEÌNÆ

Antennæ 20-jointed; fourth vein simple as M_{1+2}; legs banded with black and white. (**Bittacomórpha** (Fig. 475), **Bittacomorphélla**, Nearc.) ..........................BITTACOMORPHÌNÆ

6. Two or three ocelli present; last anal vein typically short, abruptly curving into the anal angle; antennal segmentation indistinct except at base; one pair of male claspers. (**Petaurísta** (= *Trichócera*) Winter-gnats, **Diazósma, Nothotrichócera, Paracladùra** (Fig. 467), mostly Holarc.; **Íschnothrix,** Cape Horn). (*TRI-CHOCÉRIDÆ*) ....PETAURÍSTIDÆ
   Ocelli absent; last anal vein not retracted; two pairs of male claspers 7
7. Last joint of maxillary palpi lash-like, much longer than the three preceding together; Sc ending in R_1 by an abrupt curvature of the

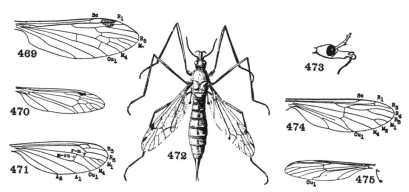

Figs. 469–475. Tipulidæ, Limoniidæ, Ptychopteridæ

469. **Limnophila,** wing (Alexander) Limoniidæ.
470. **Tipula,** wing. Tipulidæ.
471. **Dolichopeza,** wing (Alexander) Tipulidæ.
472. **Tipula,** female. Tipulidæ.
473. **Tipula,** profile of head, showing palpus (Alexander) Tipulidæ.
474. **Ptychoptera,** wing (Alexander) Ptychopteridæ.
475. **Bittacomorpha,** wing. Ptychopteridæ.

tip but almost never also in the costa (Fig. 470); nearly always two anal veins reaching margin; antennæ usually with 12 or 13 joints, rarely more; nasus usually distinct. Many species, widespread, but principally Holarctic ....TIPÙLIDÆ

a. Vein R_2 absent, or else the second anal vein not more than one-third as long as the first anal vein; legs excessively long and slender. (**Dolichopèza** (Fig. 471), **Brachyprémna, Megistócera, Tanyprémna**) ....DOLICHOPEZÌNÆ
   Vein R_2 present; second anal vein one-half as long as first anal vein; legs relatively shorter and stronger ....b
b. Antennæ verticillate, *i.e.* with whorls of hairs, flagellum of male

not pectinate. (**Típula** (Fig. 472), **Holorùsia, Longùrio, Pàles** (= *Nephrótoma,* = *Pachyrrhìna*)) ....TIPULÌNÆ
Antennæ not verticillate; flagellum of male antennæ pectinate. (**Flabellífera** (= *Ctenóphora*), **Xiphùra**). (*CTENOPHORÌNÆ*)
FLABELLIFERÌNÆ

Last joint of palpi shorter or not much longer than the two preceding together; Sc ending in costa and usually furcate at tip, the lower branch connecting as Sc_2 with R_1 (Fig. 468); antennæ 6- to 16-jointed, rarely more, usually with 14 to 16 joints; no distinct nasus 8

8. Tibiæ spurred; two branches of radius reaching margin, due to the apparent fusion of R_1 with R_{2+3}, rarely R_2 and R_3 separate, in which case three branches of radius reach margin, R_s long, arising near middle of wing; larvæ eruciform. Principally Holarctic. (**Cylindrótoma** (Fig. 468), **Lióʒma, Trióʒma, Phalacrócera; Stibadócera,** oriental) ....CYLINDROTÓMIDÆ
Four branches of radius reaching margin, if but three branches reach margin R_1 ends in costa and R_s usually arises beyond middle of wing. A large, cosmopolitan family. (*LIMNOBÌIDÆ*).
LIMONÌIDÆ

a. Tibiæ spurred at tip ....b
   Tibiæ not spurred at tip ....f
b. Antennæ with six to ten joints; all tibiæ with strong spurs c
   Antennæ with more than ten joints ....d
c. Discal cell closed. (**Penthóptera**) ....PENTHOPTERÌNÆ
   Discal cell open. (**Hexátoma, Anisomèra, Eriócera**). (*ANISOM-ERÌNÆ*) ....HEXATOMIÌNÆ
d. Antennæ twelve- or sixteen-jointed; at least hind tibiæ with spurs. (**Cryptèria, Adelphomỳia**) ....CRYPTERIÌNÆ
   Antennæ with at least sixteen joints; all tibiæ spurred; discal cell closed ....e
e. Sc_2 located beyond origin of R_s; eyes bare. (**Limnóphila** (Fig. 469), **Dactylòbius, Epiphrágma**) ....LIMNOPHILÌNÆ
   Sc_2 located before origin of R_s; wings mostly glabrous; discal cell usually closed; at least hind tibiæ with apical spurs; eyes hairy. (**Pedícia, Dicranòta, Rhaphiólabis, Tricyphòna, Ùla**)
PEDICIÌNÆ
f. Radius with four branches reaching margin; wing-membrane or at least veins and margin strongly hairy; antennæ sixteen-jointed. (**Polymèda** (= *Erióptera*); **Chiònea** (wingless); **Cladùra, Gnophomỳia, Gonomỳia, Helòbia, Molóphilus, Ormòsia, Trimìcra**). (*ERIOPTERÌNÆ*) ....POLYMIDÌNÆ
   Radius with three branches reaching margin ....g

g. Antennæ usually sixteen-jointed, rarely twelve-jointed (*Toxorhìna*) or fifteen-jointed (*Elephantomỳia*); tarsal claws usually without teeth beneath. (**Ántocha, Atárba, Dicranóptycha, Elephantomỳia, Megarhìna** (= *Hélius*, = *Rhamphídia*), **Teuchólabis**). (*MEGA-RHYNÌNÆ*) ....ANTOCHÌNÆ

Antennæ fourteen-jointed; claws with teeth beneath; Cu_2 not strongly bent. (**Limònia** (= *Limnòbia*), **Dicranomỳia, Discóbola, Geranomỳia, Rhipídia**). (*LIMNOBIÌNÆ*) ......LIMONIÌNÆ

9. Wing membrane with a secondary venation due to creases from the folding of the wing in the pupa; legs long and slender;

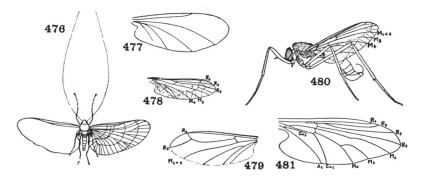

Figs. 476–481. Blepharoceridæ, Deuterophlebiidæ

476. **Deuterophlebia** (Edwards) Deuterophlebiidæ.
477. **Hammatorrhina,** wing (Bezzi) Blepharoceridæ.
478. **Blepharocera,** wing (Comstock) Blepharoceridæ.
479. **Paltostoma,** wing (Williston) Blepharoceridæ.
480. **Bibiocephala** (Cole) Blepharoceridæ.
481. **Edwardsina,** wing (Alexander) Blepharoceridæ.

hygrophilous species, frequenting swift-running streams, where their larvæ live 10

Wings without an extensive secondary venation 11

10. Wings large, densely covered with fine hairs, true veins almost absent but an elaborate fan-like development of secondary folds present; antennæ excessively long, six-jointed; ocelli and mouthparts absent. (**Deuterophlèbia,** India (Fig. 476)).

DEUTEROPHLEBÌIDÆ

Secondary venation forming a delicate network like spider webbing, in addition to the primary veins; mesonotum with a V-shaped suture; ocelli and mouthparts present; eyes usually divided horizontally into two parts by an unfaceted stripe; hind coxæ broadly attached to thorax. Widespread, mainly Holarctic and Neotropical. (*ASTHÉNIDÆ, LIPONEÙRIDÆ*).

BLEPHAROCÉRIDÆ

a. Wings with M_3 arising from middle of upper branch of cubital fork (M_4) (Fig. 481), m-cu crossvein present and almost in transverse alignment with r-m crossvein and the short angulate bases of R_{4+5} and R_s, a long spur from R_s projecting basal to the angulation, radius four-branched; front trochanters scarcely half as long as coxæ. (**Edwardsìna**, Neantarc. (Fig. 481)). EDWARDSÌNÆ Wing with M_3 free or absent, when present disconnected from the other veins; if m-cu crossvein is present it is not in alignment with the angulations of the branches of the radius, R_s without basal spur; front trochanters nearly as long as coxæ . . . . b

b. Fourth vein bifurcate, the lower branch (M_3) disconnected from the upper (M_{1+2}); second and third veins subequal in length, usually arising separately from the cell; eight veins reaching margin. (**Blepharócera** (Fig. 478), **Bibiocéphala** (Fig. 480), **Liponeùra, Philòrus**, Holarc.) . . . . BLEPHAROCERÌNÆ Fourth vein (M_{1+3}) simple; R_2 short or absent c

c. Labial palpi small, usually oval and pubescent, much shorter than basal part of labium, if somewhat longer the palpi are rigid and the whole labium is reduced; third vein forked, *i.e.* the second vein (R_{2+3}) short, arising from the third vein (R_{4+5}) near its tip; seven veins reaching margin . . . . d Labial palpi very long, slender, bare, usually curled outwardly; basal part of labium also long; maxillary palpi one-jointed; no macrotrichia on R_1; R_s forked near tip, or simple, or absent; only five or six veins reaching margin. (**Apistomỳia**, widespr.; **Hammatorrhìna** (Fig. 477), Ind.; **Neocurùpira, Perithèates,** Austr.) . . . . APISTOMYÌNÆ

d. Hind tibiæ spurred; claws of both sexes similar; female with strong mandibles. (**Paltóstoma** (Fig. 479), **Curùpira, Kelloggìna, Limonícola,** Neotrop.) . . . . PALTOSTOMATÌNÆ Hind tibiæ without spurs; male holoptic, claws wanting; female dichoptic, claws dentate, mouthparts atrophied. (**Hapálothrix,** Eur.) . . . . HAPALOTRICHÌNÆ

11. Costa continuing around the wing-margin, although often weaker along hind margin 12
    Costa disappearing beyond tip of wing 18
12. At least nine veins reaching wing-margin 13
    Less than nine veins terminating in the margin of the wing; often holoptic 17
13. Wing-veins, including hind margin, very hairy or scaly (Figs. 484, 490); body and legs hairy or scaly; ocelli absent 14

Veins not fringed with flat scales; body and legs not scaly; sub-costa ending in costa at or beyond middle of wing; dichoptic; legs long and slender 16

14. Wings short and broadly ovate or pointed (Fig. 484), held sloping roof-like against the body when at rest, no crossveins except sometimes near base, Sc very short, weak, ending free, radius usually five-branched; tibiæ without apical spurs; second an-tennal joint not enlarged; small, apparently robust species with densely hairy body, legs and wings; widespread, mostly in warm or temperate regions. Moth-flies .... PSYCHÓDIDÆ

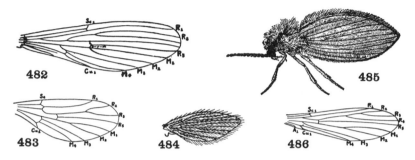

Figs. 482–486. Psychodidæ

482. **Bruchomyia**, wing (Alexander) Psychodidæ.
483. **Sycorax**, wing (Eaton) Psychodidæ.
484. **Pericoma**, wing. Psychodidæ.
485. **Psychoda** (Cole) Psychodidæ.
486. **Phlebotomus**, wing (Alexander) Psychodidæ.

a. Radial sector with four branches (Figs. 482, 486) .... b
   Radial sector with three branches, Sc short and apically erect;
   (**Trichomỳia, Lèpria, Sycòrax** (Fig. 483)) .. TRICHOMYIÌNÆ
   Radial sector with two branches, R_{2+3} one-branched. (**Horaiélla,** India) .... HORAIELLÌNÆ

b. Distal section of Cu_1 elongate, extending generally parallel to M_4, cell M_4 about equal to cell M_3 along the wing-margin, Sc re-duced. (**Psychòda** (Fig. 485), **Maruìna, Perícoma** (Fig. 484), **Telmatóscopus, Termitadélphus Ulomỳia**) ..... PSYCHODÌNÆ
   Distal section of Cu_1 short, bent toward the axilla, cell M_4 at wing-margin at least as wide as cell Cu, Sc long, Sc_2 and usually Sc_1 preserved c

c. Radial sector pectinately four-branched; mouthparts elongate, formed for sucking blood. Sand-flies. (**Phlebótomus** (Fig. 486))
   PHLEBOTOMÌNÆ
   Radial sector dichotomously four-branched; mouthparts not formed

for sucking blood. (**Bruchomỳia** (Fig. 482), **Nemopálpus,** Neotrop.). (*NEMOPALPÌNÆ*) . . . . **BRUCHOMYIÌNÆ**

Wings longer and narrow (Fig. 490), not held sloping against the sides of the body, wing-margin and veins scaly, Sc ending in costa beyond middle of wing, radius four-branched; antennæ of male usually feathered with long hairs; second antennal joint enlarged: slender species, usually with long, moderately hairy or scaly legs. In all regions, many species 15

15. Proboscis short, not fitted for piercing; wings hairy, scaled only at margin; mesosternum without ridge; sternopleura divided by transverse suture; lateral sclerite of metasternum much reduced, not triangular (Fig. 488). (**Corèthra** (= *Móchlonyx*), **Chaóborus** (= *Sayomyia*), **Corethrélla, Eucorèthra** (= *Pelorémpis*). (*CHAOBÓRÌDÆ*) . . . . **CORÉTHRÌDÆ**
Proboscis much longer than head, firm, of female adapted for piercing (except *Toxorhynchites*), palpi porrect; wings always fully scaled; mesosternum ridged; sternopleura not divided by transverse suture (except Uranotæniini, Fig. 487); lateral sclerite of metasternum forming a triangular piece between the bases of middle and hind coxæ . . . .**CULÍCIDÆ**

a. Palpi of female more than one-third as long as proboscis; abdomen sometimes without scales, first tergite without scales, sternites nearly always without scales; scutellum crescent-shaped, with marginal bristles evenly distributed; larva without respiratory siphon, resting horizontally at surface of water; eggs provided with lateral floats. (**Anópheles** (Malaria mosquitoes); **Bironella,** E. Ind.; **Chagasia,** Neotrop.) . . . .**ANOPHELÌNÆ**
Palpi of female less than one-third as long as proboscis; abdomen always scaled: larva with well developed respiratory siphon; eggs without lateral floats . . . . .b

b. Scutellum evenly rounded; clypeus much broader than long; proboscis rigid, apically curving back; calypteres not ciliated; bright-scaled, day-flying, not blood-sucking, feeding on nectar of flowers. (**Megarhìnus**). (*MEGARHINÌNÆ*). **TOXORHYNCHITÌNÆ**
Scutellum trilobed, with marginal bristles only on the lobes c

c. Base of hind coxa in line with upper margin of lateral metasternal sclerite which is a small triangular piece located between bases of middle and hind coxæ: day-fliers. (**Sabèthes, Goeldia, Isostomỳia, Joblotia, Limàtus, Menólepis, Miamỳia, Wyeomỳia**).
SABETHÌNÆ
Base of hind coxa, distinctly below upper margin of lateral metasternal sclerite; body scales usually sparse and rarely with metallic colors: disease-bearing or obnoxious mosquitoes . . . . .d

d. Anal vein extending well beyond fork of cubitus; wings villose;

upper calypter usually ciliated. (**Cùlex** (*C. quinquefasciàtus,* Filaria mosquito), **Aèdes** (*A. ægypti* (*cálopus*) (= *Stego-myia fasciàta*), Yellow-fever and Dengue-fever mosquito), **Deinocerìtes, Eretmapodìtes,** Afr.; **Hæmagògus,** Neotrop.; **Lùtzia, Ochlerótatus, Orthopodomỳia, Psoróphora, Tæniorhýnchus** (= *Mansonia*), **Theobáldia** (= *Culisèta*)) . . . . CULICÌNÆ Anal vein ending opposite or before fork of cubitus; wings not villose; calypteres not ciliate. (**Uranotænia** (Fig. 487)).

URANOTÆNIÌNÆ

16. Radius with four nearly parallel curving branches (Fig. 489), the second vein (R_{3+4}) strongly arched, R_5 ending beyond apex of wing; basal cells reaching distinctly beyond middle of wing, coextensive; ocelli absent; joints of flagellum of antennæ indistinctly separated. Few species, widespread, but mostly Holarctic. (**Díxa** (Fig. 489); **Microdíxa,** Eur.; **Neodíxa,** N. Zeal.) . . . . DÍXIDÆ

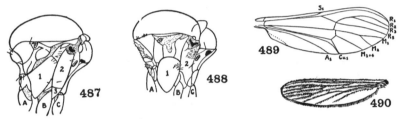

Figs. 487–490. Culicidæ, Corethridæ, Dixidæ

487. **Uranotænia,** side view of thorax (Dyar and Shannon) Culicidæ.
    1, sternopleura; 2, mesepimeron; 3, merite of middle coxa; A, front coxa; B, middle coxa; C, hind coxa.
488. **Eucorethra,** side view of thorax (Dyar and Shannon) Corethridæ. Explanation of parts same as for Fig. 487.
489. **Dixa,** wing. Dixidæ.
490. **Culex,** wing. Culicidæ.

Radius with three to five branches (Fig. 492), the second vein ending before apex of wing; basal cells usually not extending beyond middle of wing, the second basal cell always shorter than first; ocelli well developed; antennæ 8- to 18-jointed, the joints distinctly separated. Rare. (**Hesperìnus** (Fig. 492); **Cramptonomỳia,** western Nearc.) . . . . HESPERÍNIDÆ

17. Antennæ composed apparently of two thick basal joints and a terminal nine- or ten-jointed arista; wings with seven longitudinal veins (Fig. 493), media unbranched, both basal cells closed, second basal cell short; both sexes holoptic, ocelli absent. Small, rare, woodland species, occurring in Europe, North

America and the Canary Islands. (Thaumàlea (= *Orphnéphila*)
(Fig. 493), Androprosòpa). (*ORPHNEPHÍLIDÆ*)

THAUMALÈIDÆ

Antennæ long, composed of 10 to 36 cylindrical or bead-like joints;
wings with greatly reduced venation, second basal cell open. (Figs.
494–496) .... CECÍDOMYÌIDÆ or ITONÍDIDÆ

a. Wings broad, with three or at most six longitudinal veins, sometimes media and cubitus branches stalked, crossveins apparently
wanting; abdomen not swollen; eyes round or reniform, sometimes
with confluent projections above antennæ: delicate, often minute
species. Gall gnats; widespread, principally Holarctic .... b

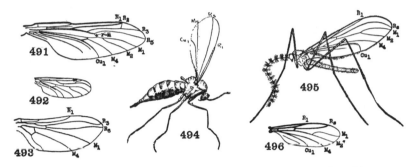

Figs. 491–496. Pachyneuridæ, Hesperinidæ, Thaumaleidæ, Cecidomyiidæ

491. Axymyia, wing (Edwards) Pachyneuridæ.
492. Hesperinus, wing (Johannsen) Hesperinidæ.
493. Thaumalea, wing (Williston) Thaumaleidæ.
494. Mayetiola. Cecidomyiidæ.
495. Hormosomyia (Cole) Cecidomyiidæ.
496. Lestremia, wing (Kieffer) Cecidomyiidæ.

Wings much atrophied (Fig. 670) crumpled, with two longitudinal
and two crossveins; first five segments of abdomen enormously
swollen, the apical four segments small and slender, forming a
post-abdomen; eyes confluent above, separated below antennæ:
adults found exclusively in nests of termites. (Termitomástus
(Fig. 670), South America). (See couplet 155)

TERMITOMASTÍNÆ

b. Wing-membrane peculiarly pubescent, the hairs (macrotrichia)
directed toward base of wing; eyes bridged above or nearly so;
tarsi five-jointed c
Wing-membrane with simple microscopic pubescence; metatarsus
longer than following joint, or the tarsi with less than five
joints; eyes usually without bridge above; ocelli absent; media

wanting or represented by a fold. (Heteropèza, Brachyneùra, Lasiópteryx, Leptósyna, Miástor, Oligárces) . . HETEROPEZÌNÆ

c. Media (M_{1+2}) forked or simple, radial sector present but sometimes crowded close to costa; ocelli present; metatarsus longer than following joint. (Lestrèmia (Fig. 496), Asynápta, Campylomỳza, Hormosomỳia (Fig. 495), Micromỳia, Monárdia, Prionéllus, Strobliélla, Winnertzia) (*CAMPYLOMYZÌNÆ*).

LESTREMIÌNÆ

Media with anterior branch (M_{1+2}) wanting, M_{3+4} absent or represented by a fold; ocelli absent; metatarsus much shorter than following joint; antennal joints with whorls of looped threads, or sometimes with horseshoe-like appendages. (Cecidomỳia or Itónida, Asphonodỳlia, Asteromỳia, Colpòdia, Contarínia (*C. jóhnsoni*, Grape blossom-midge; *C. pyrívora*, Pear midge), Dasyneùra (*D. rhodóphaga*, Rose midge; *D. trifolii*, Clover leaf midge), Diarthronomỳia (*D. hypogæa*, Chrysanthemum gallmidge), Diplòsis, Lasióptera, Oligótrophus, Phytóphaga (*P.* (*Mayetiòla*) *destructor*, Hessian fly, Fig. 494), Porricóndyla, Rhabdóphaga) . . . . CECIDOMYIÌNÆ or ITONIDÌNÆ

18. Discal cell present in middle of wing contiguous to end of basal cells (Fig. 500), media four-branched, eight veins reaching wing-margin; cells of wing with abundant macrotrichia; ocelli present; dichoptic; antennæ 12- to 16-jointed; pulvilli wanting, but empodium pulvilliform. Widespread, not many species. (Silvícola (= *Anìsopus*, = *Rhỳphus*, = *Phrỳne*) (Figs. 465E, 500), Lobogáster, Olbiogáster). (*ANISOPÓDIDÆ, PHRYNÈIDÆ, RHÝPHIDÆ*) . . . . SILVICÓLIDÆ
Wings without a discal cell formed between branches of the usually petiolate media . . . . : 19

19. Ocelli present, sometimes the lateral ocelli next to the eyes and the middle one vestigial or absent (PROTOPHTHALMIA) 20
Ocelli absent or at most vestigial; posterior spiracle placed high; coxæ not lengthened 34

20. Second basal cell present (Fig. 501), usually longer than the first basal and attaining middle of wing (shorter than first in *Plecia* (Fig. 499) which has third vein furcate), anterior veins strong; pulvilli present; antennæ usually shorter than thorax, rather stout, without constrictions between joints; male holoptic, eyes large and divided into upper and lower parts; palpi four-jointed. Widespread, mostly Holarctic. March flies . . . . . BIBIÓNIDÆ

a. Third vein furcate; front femora not thickened. (Plècia (Fig. 499), Penthètria) . . . . PLECIÌNÆ
Third vein simple; front femora thickened. (Bíbio (Fig. 501), Bibiòdes, Phília, Dílophus) . . . . BIBIONÌNÆ

Second basal cell imperfectly separated from first (*i.e.* base of media weak or undeveloped), or apically open, or very short, never longer than first basal cell; pulvilli absent or very minute 21

21. At least the four posterior tibiæ without apical spurs (Fig. 498); coxæ short, much less than half the length of femora; antennæ short and robust, 10- or 11-jointed, the middle joints shorter than broad; anterior veins strong, crowded close to costa, other veins weak and inconspicuous, m-cu crossvein absent; eyes contiguous or nearly so; palpi one-jointed. Minute species, mostly Holarctic 22

All tibiæ with apical spurs (compare Fig. 502); coxæ longer, usually about half the length of femora 23

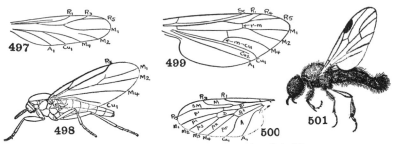

Figs. 497–501. Scatopsidæ, Bibionidæ, Silvicolidæ

497. **Canthyloscelis,** wing (Edwards) Scatopsidæ.
498. **Scatopse** (Cole) Scatopsidæ.
499. **Plecia,** wing. Bibionidæ.
500. **Silvicola,** wing. Silvicolidæ.
501. **Bibio,** male. Bibionidæ.

22. Third vein forked, *i.e.* R$_3$ arising from R$_5$, costa reaching much beyond R$_5$, anal vein reaching margin. (Corynóscelis, Synneùron, Holarc.; Canthylóscelis (Fig. 497), Austr.) CORYNOSCÉLIDÆ

Third vein (R$_s$) simple; costa scarcely continued beyond third vein, anal vein wanting ....SCATÓPSIDÆ

a. Holoptic, face narrow, eyes finely hairy; front tibiæ without apical spine; mesonotum not elevated in front. (Scatópse (Fig. 498), Aldrovandiélla, Anapaùsis, Reichertélla, Rhegmoclèma, Swammerdamélla) ....SCATOPSÌNÆ

Dichoptic, face rather broad, eyes bare; front tibiæ ending in a spine; mesonotum elevated in front. (Aspístes, Árthria) ASPISTÌNÆ

23. Radial sector with three branches, *i.e.* second longitudinal vein forked, the second vein (R$_{2+3}$) arising from the third (R$_5$) at

or before the anterior crossvein (r-m) (Fig. 491); antennæ 15-jointed, the joints longer than wide; male dichoptic; coxæ not lengthened. (**Pachyneùra**, Palæarc.; **Axymỳia** (Fig. 491), Nearc.)

PACHYNEÙRIDÆ

Radial sector with two branches 24

24. Second basal cell apically widely open, the posterior branch of the media when complete arising from the cubitus usually near the base, anal vein incomplete, not reaching margin of wing (see Fig. 504) 25

Second basal cell closed (see Fig. 506), the apparent crossvein (*i.e.* the angular origin of M_4) sometimes located close to base of wing (Fig. 507), or the media and cubitus coalescent where the crossvein usually is located, or when the basal section of M is wanting, the media appears to arise from Cu_1; anal vein reaching margin at least as a fold 29

25. Anterior branch (R_{2+3}) of radial sector abruptly extending to R_1, appearing like an extra crossvein closing the small rectangular or trapezoidal cell R_1 (Fig. 503); Sc usually reaching cell R_1; ocelli usually remote from eye-margin; microscopic hairs of wing-membrane typically irregularly scattered or the wings pubescent. Many genera; Europe, America, Australia.

SCIOPHÍLIDÆ

a. Wings pubescent; usually three ocelli. (**Scióphila** (Fig. 503), **Allocotócera, Diómonus, Leptomórphus, Monoclòna, Neurotèlia, Polylépta, Syntémna**) ....**SCIOPHILÌNÆ**

Wings only microscopically hairy ....b

b. Three ocelli; tibial bristles irregular c

Two ocelli close together; tibial bristles in rows. (**Mycomỳia, Neoemphèria**) ....**MYCOMYIÌNÆ**

c. Fork of M longer than its petiole, R_1 long. (**Gnoríste, Boletìna** (Fig. 505), **Coelòsia, Dziedzíckia, Sýnapha**) ....**GNORISTÌNÆ**

Fork of M subequal to its petiole, R_1 short. (**Lèia** (= *Neoglaphyróptera*), **Docòsia, Nováckia, Pnýxia** (male), **Rondaniélla, Tetragoneùra**) ....**LEIÌNÆ**

Radial sector not branched, the cell R_1 open to the wing-margin; Sc usually vestigial; microscopic hairs of wing-membrane seriately arranged 26

26. Coxæ much elongated, fully half the length of femora; r-m crossvein usually distinctly angulated from the second section of radial sector (Fig. 505); cubitus usually formed and long petiolate, rarely simple; eyes oval or reniform but without bridging projections above antennæ; palpi 4- or 5-jointed; prothorax with bristles 27

Coxæ not greatly elongated, somewhat less than half the length of the femora; r-m crossvein appearing like a continuation of the strong second section of the radial sector (Fig. 504), posterior veins weak, cubitus forked near base of wing, m-cu crossvein absent; eyes more or less completely connected by a narrow projection above base of antennæ; palpi 3-, 2-, or 1-jointed. Cosmopolitan .... SCIÁRIDÆ or LYCORÏIDÆ

a. Third vein forked. (Crátyna) .... CRATYNÎNÆ
Third vein simple .... b
b. Cubitus and M₄ forking beyond origin of M_{1+2}. (Megalósphys, Fungivórides, Phorodónta) .... MEGALOSPHYÎNÆ
Cubitus and M₄ forking before or opposite origin of M_{1+2} c

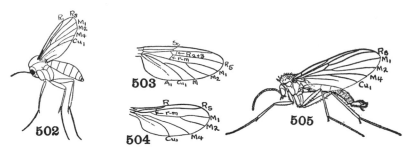

Figs. 502–505. Mycetophilidæ, Sciophilidæ, Sciaridæ

502. **Mycetophila** (Johannsen) Mycetophilidæ.
503. **Sciophila**, wing (Johannsen) Sciophilidæ.
504. **Sciara**, wing (Johannsen) Sciaridæ.
505. **Boletina**, male (Cole) Mycetophilidæ.

c. Medial cell (between M₁ and M₂) not wider than adjacent cells. (**Sciara** or **Lycória** (Fig. 504), **Epídapus** (wingless), **Plastoscíara, Psiloscíara**) .... SCIARÎNÆ or LYCORÏIÑÆ
Medial cell much wider than adjacent cells; male antennæ with flagellar joints cylindrical and long-stalked. (**Zygoneùra**, Eur.) ZYGONEURÎNÆ

27. R₁ and R₈ running separately to base of wing, traces of base of R₂₊₃ present; proboscis long. (**Lygistorrhìna**, Austr.) LYGISTORRHÍNIDÆ
R₈ arising from R₁ well beyond base of wing, or base of R₈ wanting; R₂₊₃ not present 28
28. Antennæ inserted plainly above middle of head; pronotum without bristles; occiput flattened, orbital bristles seriate; media with only apical disconnected parts present. (**Manòta**, Holarc.) MANÓTIDÆ

Antennæ inserted at middle of head; pronotal bristles developed; occiput convex, orbital bristles not seriate; base of media developed, at most the forward branch interrupted. The dominant family of Fungus-gnats. Widespread.

MYCETOPHÍLIDÆ or FUNGIVÓRIDÆ *

a. Mesopleuræ without bristles; empodium undeveloped or vestigial; tibial bristles short. (Exèchia, Allòdia, Anatélla, Brachypèza, Rhymòsia) ....EXECHIÌNÆ
Mesopleuræ with bristles; empodium usually well developed. (Mycetóphila or Fungívora (Fig. 502), Dynatosòma, Phrònia, Polyxèna (= Córdyla), Trichónta, Zygomỳia)

MYCETOPHILÍNÆ or FUNGIVORÌNÆ

29. Second basal cell minute, much shorter than first basal cell due to the proximal location of the apparent m-cu crossvein (Fig. 507), radius three-branched, the middle branch short and commonly ending in R₁ near its tip; Sc complete; basal and middle sections

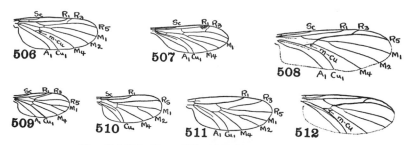

Figs. 506–512. Mycetobiidæ, Bolitophilidæ, Diadocidiidæ, Ditomyiidæ, Ceroplatidæ, Macroceridæ

506. **Palæoplatyura,** wing (Johannsen) Mycetobiidæ.
507. **Bolitophila,** wing (Johannsen) Bolitophilidæ.
508. **Macrocera,** wing. Macroceridæ.
509. **Mycetobia,** wing (Johannsen) Mycetobiidæ.
510. **Diadocidia,** wing (Johannsen) Diadocidiidæ.
511. **Ditomyia,** wing (Johannsen) Ditomyiidæ.
512. **Ceroplatus,** wing. Ceroplatidæ.

of media continuous; mesonotum without rows of bristles. (Bolitóphila (Fig. 507), Arachnocámpa, Austr., Bolitophilélla).

BOLITOPHÍLIDÆ

Second basal cell nearly or quite as long as first, sometimes confluent with it 30

---

* If subcosta is well-developed, r-m crossvein transverse, media once forked, M₃ and cubitus simple and complete, and the mesonotum is coated with white scales compare **ALLACTONEURIDÆ** (*Allactoneura*, Java).

30. Radius three-branched; if the basal cells are coextensive and the
crossveins transverse then the Sc meets the costa beyond the
basal fourth of the wing 31
Radius two-branched (Fig. 510); Sc short, evanescent; basal cells
coextensive and more or less fused, the two crossveins in the
same straight line perpendicular to the wing-axis; mesonotum
with rows of bristles. Holarctic. (Diadocídia (Fig. 510)).
                                        DIADOCIDÌIDÆ
31. Anterior crossvein (r-m) present though short (Fig. 509); middle
branch of radius (R_3) usually arising from the third vein (R_5)
before the middle of that vein and usually much longer than
half of R_5...32
Anterior crossvein (r-m) obliterated by the coalescence of the radial
sector and the media for a short distance where the crossvein
usually is; R_3 much shorter than half of R_5 (Fig. 508).......33
32. Subcosta short, evanescent, ending free; pronotum with bristles.
(Ditomỳia (Fig. 511), Sýmmerus)............DITOMYÌIDÆ
Subcosta relatively long, reaching at least one-fourth the wing-
length and usually ending in the costa; pronotum without bristles.
(Mycetòbia (Fig. 509), Palæoplatyùra (Fig. 506), Holarc.;
Mesòchria, Seychelles) ....MYCETOBÌIDÆ
33. Antennæ short, usually thick-set and often flattened; tibial bristles
present though usually small, posterior tibiæ with unequal apical
spurs; forks of cubitus evenly diverging from the beginning.
Europe, N. America, N. Africa, Australia. (Ceróplatus (Fig.
512), Asíndulum, Cerotèlion, Nervijúncta, Zelmìra (= Apèmon,
= Platyùra). (PLATYÙRIDÆ). ....CEROPLÁTIDÆ
Antennæ usually very slender, nearly as long as or even much longer
than the whole body; tibiæ without bristles, posterior tibiæ with
subequal apical spurs; forks of apparent cubitus (M_4 and Cu_1)
parallel for a short distance and then diverging. (Macrócera or
Euphrósyne (Fig. 508), widespr.; Chiasmoneùra, Indomal.)
                        MACROCÉRIDÆ or EUPHROSÝNIDÆ
34. Wings long and narrow; cubital vein commonly forked near middle
of wing (Fig. 513), radial branches not greatly thicker than the
other veins; antennæ of male often with very long plumes and of
female bead-like; eyes separated, sometimes males are holoptic; first
abdominal segment without fringed flap....................35
Wings broad, cubitus forked at base, not petiolate, second basal cell
open; anterior veins thick, others very weak (Fig. 517); antennæ
about as long as head, ten-jointed, the flagellar joints closely
united (Fig. 465B); male holoptic; first abdominal tergite with
a conspicuous fringed flap-like scale; male metatarsi usually
dilated. Widespread, mostly Holarctic and Neotropical. Blackflies, Buffalo-gnats ....SIMULÌIDÆ or MELUSÍNIDÆ

a. R₁ joining costa about middle of wing; microtrichia of anterior veins hair-like; male dichoptic. (**Parasimùlium,** Calif.)

PARASIMULIÌNÆ

R₁ joining costa well beyond middle of wing; microtrichia of anterior veins more bristle-like, sometimes spiniform at least on costa; male usually holoptic ....b

b. Radial sector forked, the two branches close together; second joint of hind tarsus without dorsal incision, the first joint apically truncate. (**Prosimùlium, Hélodon,** Holarc.; **Cnèphia,** Nearc.; **Tænioptérna,** Palæarc.) ....PROSIMULIÌNÆ

Radial sector not forked c

c. Hind metatarsi apically truncate, front metatarsi not broadened ...d

Hind metatarsi roundly projecting below at apex ....e

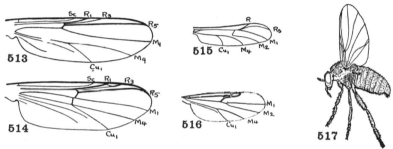

Figs. 513–517. Chironomidæ, Ceratopogonidæ, Simuliidæ

513. **Chironomus,** wing (Kieffer) Chironomidæ.
514. **Anatopynia,** wing (Kieffer) Chironomidæ.
515. **Stenoxenus,** wing (Kieffer) Ceratopogonidæ.
516. **Hartomyia,** wing (Cole) Ceratopogonidæ.
517. **Simulium** (Lugger) Simuliidæ.

d. Second joint of hind tarsi without dorsal incision. (**Hellíchia, Ástega,** Palæarc.) .... HELLICHIÌNÆ

Second joint of hind tarsi with a deep incision on dorsal side toward base. (**Ectémnia,** Nearc.; **Pternáspatha,** Neotrop.)

ECTEMNIÌNÆ

e. Second joint of hind tarsi without dorsal incision; front metatarsi normal. (**Stegoptérna,** Palæarc.; **Gigántodax,** Neotrop.; **Mallochélla,** Holarc.) ....STEGOPTERNÌNÆ

Second joint of hind tarsi with a dorsal sulcus ....f

f. Front metatarsi normal. (**Nevermánnia,** Holarc.; **Frièsia, Wilhélmia,** widespr.; **Cnètha, Schoenbaueria,** Palæarc.) NEVERMANNIÌNÆ

Front metatarsi of both sexes flattened and broadened. (**Simùlium** or **Melusìna** (Fig. 517), **Odágmia,** widespr.; **Boóphthora,** Holarc.; **Býssodon,** Nearc.; **Edwardséllum,** Ethiop.)

SIMULIÌNÆ or MELUSINÌNÆ

35. Anterior branch of media not forked; mouthparts not chitinized, not fitted for piercing; front legs lengthened, commonly raised up and vibrated when at rest; metanotum generally with median longitudinal furrow or keel

CHIRONÓMIDÆ or **TENDIPÉDIDÆ**

a. Crossvein between M_1 and cubitus present, *i.e.* second basal cell complete (Fig. 514) ....b
Crossvein between media and cubitus absent, no second basal cell (Fig. 513) ....d

b. R_{2+3} present and forked, *i.e.* connected with R_1 by a crossvein, or absent altogether; antennæ with 12 to 15 joints c
R_{2+3} present and simple, not connected with R_1 and always distinct; antennæ usually with 7 or 8 joints. (Diámesa) ..DIAMESÌNÆ

c. Wings superposed; R_{2+3} absent, R_1 and R_{4+5} well separated; metanotum without median furrow. (Podónomus, Lasiodiámesa)

PODONOMÌNÆ

Wings held roof-like over abdomen; R_{2+3} usually present. (Pelònia (= *Tánypus*), Ablabesmỳia (= *Pentaneùra*), Anatopỳnia (Fig. 514), Macropelòpia, Proclàdius, Proténthes, Psilotánypus). (*TANYPODÌNÆ*) ....PELOPIÌNÆ

d. Front metatarsus shorter than tibia, the latter with spur, hind tibia with one or two spurs, and usually with a terminal pecten of free spicules; last joint of male styles folded inward ....e
Front metatarsus nearly always longer than tibia, the latter rarely with spur, hind tibia with pecten, which often has an interrupted space devoid of spicules; last joint of male styles extending rigidly backward. (Chirónomus or Téndipes (Fig. 513), Micropséctra, Polypedìlum, Tanytársus)

CHIRONOMÌNÆ or **TENDIPEDÌNÆ**

e. Pronotal lobes broadly separated; anepisternal suture obsolete; male antennæ not plumose. Seashore species. (Clùnio, Telmatogèton, Thalassomỳia) ....CLUNIONÌNÆ
Pronotum scarcely divided; anepisternal suture well developed (*i.e.* an oblique slash-like cleft extending from base of wing nearly to front coxa, as in Fig. 487); male antennæ normally plumose ....f

f. R_1 wholly fused with R_{4+5} and forming a stigma with the costa at most at two-thirds the wing-length, a false vein extending close to costa from the stigma nearly to tip of wing. (Corynoneùra, Thienemanniélla) .... CORYNONEURÌNÆ
R_1 and R_{4+5} separated, not fused with the costa, the end of the costa surpassing two-thirds wing-length, no such false vein present. (Orthoclàdius, Chætoclàdius, Cricótopus, Limnophỳes, Metriocnèmis, Psectroclàdius, Smíttia, Spaniótoma (= *Camptoclà-dius*), Trichoclàdius) (*HYDROBÆNÌNÆ*).

ORTHOCLADÌNÆ

Media forked (Fig. 516); mouthparts chitinized, fitted for piercing; postnotum gently rounded, without median furrow; front legs not lengthened. Mainly Holarctic. Punkies, No-see-ums, Sand-flies. (**Ceratopògon** or **Hèlea, Bézzia, Culicòides, Dasyhèlea, Forcipomỳia, Hartomỳia, Palpomỳia**). (Including *JOHANNSENOMYÌIDÆ, STENOXÉNIDÆ*)

CERATOPOGÓNIDÆ or HELÈIDÆ

Suborder Brachycera, Section Orthorrhapha

36. Last tarsal joint furnished with three nearly equal pads under the tarsal claws, *i.e.* empodium developed pulvilliform (Fig. 534); head and thorax with no strong bristles; anal cell closed near margin, or even narrowly open; third vein almost always forked, *i.e.* R_4 and R_5 separate 37

Empodium wanting or replaced by a bristly hair, therefore only two tarsal pads (pulvilli) (Fig. 557) very rarely the pulvilli also absent; bristles often well developed; third antennal joint never truly annulated 47

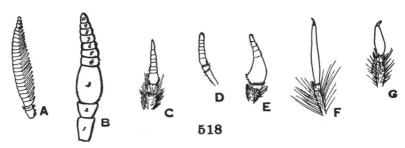

Fig. 518. Brachycerous Antennæ (Orthorrhapha)

A, **Rhachicerus** (Vollenhoven) Rhachiceridæ; B, **Subulonia** (Enderlein) Solvidæ; C, **Cœnomyia** (Verrall) Cœnomyiidæ; D, **Xylophagus** (Verrall) Xylophagidæ; E, **Tabanus** (Verrall) Tabanidæ; F, **Bombylius** (Verrall) Bombyliidæ; G. **Thereva** (Verrall) Therevidæ.

37. Third antennal joint complex, annulated into three to eight apparent segments (Fig. 518 B-E), or the antennæ more than three-jointed, rarely (some Stratiomyiidæ) the third complex-joint bearing an elongate arista (Fig. 520) 38

Antennæ three-jointed, the third joint compact, not composed of rings (Fig. 518 F, G), usually bearing an elongate arista or style, rarely the two basal joints fused 44

38. Prefurca (first section of R_8) short, *i.e.* R_8 arising opposite first fork of M which forms the base of the discal cell (Fig. 521);

tibial spurs wanting, at most middle tibiæ with a slight spur; proboscis short 39

Prefurca longer, *i.e.* R$_8$ arises distinctly before base of discal cell (Fig. 526); at least middle tibiæ with distinct spurs; costa continuing around hind margin of wing as the ambient vein 41

39. Second vein (R$_{2+3}$) arising at or beyond anterior crossvein (r-m), discal cell small, usually pentagonal and located closer to the costa than usual; submarginal cell or cells very small and narrow and located entirely before wing-tip, anterior veins usually crowded near costa, the other veins faint; four or five posterior cells present, all open; costa ending before wing-tip, no vein on hind margin of wing; scutellum often armed with marginal spines. Soldier flies. A large, widespread family with many tropical genera ........................STRATIOMYIIDÆ

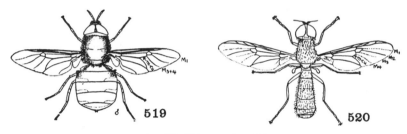

Figs. 519, 520. Stratiomyiidæ

519. **Eulalia,** male (Cole) Stratiomyiidæ.
520. **Geosargus,** male (Verrall) Stratiomyiidæ.

a. Abdomen with seven visible segments; middle tibiæ sometimes spurred; third antennal joint normally with eight annulations and without a style ....b

Abdomen with five or six visible segments; tibiæ not spurred; third antennal joint with not more than six annulations ....d

b. Scutellum with four or more spines c

Scutellum not spined, rarely with marginal row of small teeth. (**Metopònia,** Austr.; **Allognósta,** Holarc.; **Berismỳia, Hylòrus,** Neotrop.) ....METOPONIÏNÆ

c. Media three-branched; palpi often reduced. (**Bèris, Hoplacántha,** widespr.; **Béridops, Heteracánthia,** Neotrop.; **Eumécacis,** Austr.)
                                                    BERIDÌNÆ

Media four-branched; palpi three-jointed. (**Actìna,** widespr.; **Apospásma, Huttonélla, Neoexaìreta,** mostly Austr.)
                                                    ACTINÌNÆ

d. Media three-branched (Fig. 523), *i.e.* discal cell emitting two veins from its apex in addition to the vein forming its under side ....e

Media four-branched (Fig. 524), *i.e.* discal cell emitting three
veins from its apex or the third just below ....g

e. Anterior branch of cubital fork (M_{3+4}) joined to the discal cell by
an apparent crossvein, *i.e.* discal cell emitting only two veins;
apical antennal segment bristle-like, as long as remainder of
antenna. (**Prosopochrỳsa**, Java) .....**PROSOPOCHRYSÌNÆ**
M_{3+4} forming the lower side of the discal cell for a greater or less
distance, the discal cell emitting therefore three veins in all ....f

f. Antennæ with last, terminal or subterminal, segment (tenth) bristle-
like and tipped with an extra hair, segments three to nine usually

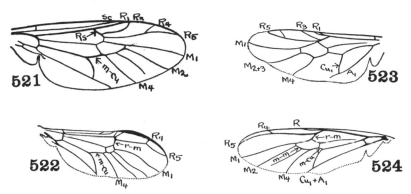

Figs. 521–524. Stratiomyiidæ

521. **Archistratiomys**, wing (Enderlein) Stratiomyiidæ.
522. **Analcocerus**, wing (Williston) Stratiomyiidæ.
523. **Cynipimorpha**, wing (Williston) Stratiomyiidæ.
524. **Chrysochlora**, wing. Stratiomyiidæ.

short and forming an oval or spherical complex third antennal
joint. (**Pachygáster**, Holarc.; **Cynipimórpha** (Fig. 523), **Zabráchia**,
Nearc.; **Panàcris, Psephiócera**, Neotrop.; **Evàsa**, Malay.; **Plátyna**,
Ethiop.) ....**PACHYGASTRÌNÆ**
Antennæ with tenth segment not bristle-like, usually flattened,
long, strap-shaped and fringed on edges, sometimes all ten
antennal segments are similar, suggesting the Nematocera.
(**Lophóteles, Artemìta, Psegmómma**, Neotrop.; **Isomerócera,
Ptilócera, Tínda**, Ethiop., Indomal.) ....**LOPHOTELÌNÆ**

g. All four medial branches arising from discal cell (Fig. 524) .....h
M_4 apparently connected with discal cell by a crossvein (Fig. 520) .k

h. Last antennal piece (tenth segment) ribbon-like; segments six to
eight with groove in front; scutellum without spines. (**Hermètia, Acrodésmia, Amphilécta**, mainly Neotrop.; **Eudmèta**,
Malay; **Patagiomỳia**) ....**HERMETIÌNÆ**

Last antennal part styliform or undifferentiated, not ribbon-like, segments six to eight without furrow i
i. Scutellum with marginal spines .... j
Scutellum without spines. (**Chrysochlòra** (Fig. 524), **Ábavus, Anacanthélla, Porpócera, Rùba**) ..... CHRYSOCHLORÌNÆ
j. Scutellum with four to twelve spines. (**Antíssa, Parantíssa,** Neotrop.; **Tetracanthìna,** Java) .... ANTISSÌNÆ
Scutellum with two spines. (**Potámida** (= *Clitellària,* = *Ephíppium*), **Euparỳphus, Nemótelus, Hermìone** (= *Oxýcera*) Holarc.; **Negritomỳia,** Ethiop., Malay.; **Euryneùra,** Nothomỳia). (*CLITELLARIÌNÆ*) .... POTAMIDÌNÆ
k. Antennæ with elongate terminal or dorsal arista l
Antennæ without a distinct arista .... m
l. Scutellum with two spines, or with vestiges of two spines. (**Rhaphiócera, Hoplístes, Lysòzum,** Neotrop.) RHAPHIOCERATÌNÆ
Scutellum without spines; metanotum prominently convex and with upturned hairs. (**Geosárgus** (= *Sárgus*) (Fig. 520), **Chrysochròma, Microchrỳsa, Ptécticus,** widespr.; **Gongròzus,** Malay.). (*SARGÌNÆ*) .... GEOSARGÌNÆ
m. Antennæ ending in an elongate and broadly flattened ribbon-like segment; scutellum with two spines. (**Analcócerus** (Fig. 522), Neotrop.) .... ANALCOCERÌNÆ
Antennæ with last segment of third joint usually short, never ribbon-like .... n
n. Scutellum with two spines. (**Stratiomỳia** (= *Stratìomys*), **Eulàlia** (= *Odontomỳia*) (Fig. 519), widespr. mostly in temperate zone; **Cyphomỳia,** widespr., mostly tropical; **Myxosárgus, Rhingiópsis,** Neotrop.; **Hírtea, Hoplodónta**). .... STRATIOMYIÌNÆ
Scutellum unarmed. (**Lasiòpa,** widespr.; **Chordonòta,** Neotrop.; **Udamacántha**) .... LASIOPÌNÆ

Second vein arising before anterior crossvein (r-m), veins not crowded anteriorly; mostly Neotropical species 40
40. Third vein simple, ending before wing-tip; all posterior cells open; third antennal joint usually three-segmented; abdomen slender, comprising seven segments; species under one inch in length. (**Chiromỳza, Clavimỳia** (Fig. 528), **Mesomỳza, Nonàcris, Xenomórpha,** Neotrop.; **Archimỳza,** Austr.) .. CHIROMÝZIDÆ
Third vein forked, its branches (R_4 and R_5) widely divergent and enclosing the tip of the wing (Fig. 525), fourth posterior cell (M_3) closed; abdomen broadly rounded; gigantic species, not common. (**Pantophthálmus, Acanthomèra, Atopomỳia, Rhaphiorrhýnchus,** Neotrop.). (*ACANTHOMÉRIDÆ*).
PANTOPHTHÁLMIDÆ
41. Calypteres conspicuous, but not concealing halteres, their margin fringed; head widely hemispherical (Fig. 527); third antennal

joint composed of four to eight annuli; branches of third vein (R_4 and R_5) widely diverging and enclosing tip of wing; females usually blood-sucking. A large family of conspicuous flies, occurring in all regions, most species tropical. Horse-flies, Gad-flies, Deer-flies ....TABÁNIDÆ

a. Anal vein sinuate, anal cell open; subepaulets bare, not inflated; four or five abdominal segments present, female with long slender retractile post-abdomen; face swollen, antennæ placed above middle of head. (**Pelecorhýnchus, Archeomỳia,** Austr.; **Bequaertomỳia,** N. Amer.; **Cœnula,** So. Amer.)........PELECORHÝNCHÍNÆ
   Anal vein straight or gently curved, usually meeting Cu_2 at or before margin; subepaulets bare or hairy; abdomen with seven normal segments, not with a specialized ovipositor ....b.

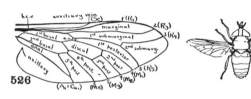

525

526

527

Figs. 525–527. Pantophthalmidæ, Tabanidæ

525. **Pantophthalmus,** photograph of specimen in O. S. Westcott collection. Pantophthalmidæ.
526. **Tabanus,** wing (Williston) Tabanidæ.
527. **Tabanus,** photographed specimen. Tabanidæ.

b. Hind tibiæ with two apical, usually strong, spines; subepaulets bare, not inflated; labella with shining chitinized parts; ocelli present. (OPISTHACÁNTHÆ) ....c.
   Hind tibiæ without apical spurs; subepaulets mostly hairy, sometimes bare, often inflated; subcosta generally hairy, or at least with some hairs beneath; ocelli usually absent. (OPISTANÒ-PLÆ) ....g.
c. Third antennal joint with at most five segments, rarely three or four, the basal plate large, or the segments fused to a single joint ....d.
   Third antennal joint with eight annuli, the basal ones not clearly differentiated ....f.
d. First posterior cell open ....e.
   First posterior cell closed. (**Scárphia, Metáphara,** So. Afr.)
                                                    SCARPHIÍNÆ
e. Third antennal joint with five divisions; usually rather slender flies

with pictured wings. (**Chrỳsops**, Deer-flies, cosmop., **Hemòrius, Sílvius**) (*SILVIÌNÆ*) .... CHRYSOPÌNÆ
Third antennal joint with three divisions; robust *Tabanus*-like flies. (**Merycomỳia**, Nearc.) .... MERYCOMYIÌNÆ

f. First posterior cell open, rarely closed at margin of wing. (**Mélpia, Ósca**, Neotrop.; **Apatoléstes, Gòniops**, Nearc.; **Corizoneùra** (= *Buplex*), widespr.) .... MELPIÌNÆ
First posterior cell closed and usually petiolate; proboscis often exceeding head-height. (**Pangònia**, Palaearc.; **Eisenbéckia, Fidèna, Sciòne**, Neotrop.; **Lilæa**, Austr. **Phàra**, Ethiop.) . PANGONIÌNÆ

g. Third antennal joint divided into four, rarely three, segments, scape longer then thick; eyes in life with irregular bands and spots. (**Chrysozòna** (= *Hæmatopotìna*), widespread; **Heptátoma**, Europe). (*HÆMATOPOTÌNÆ*) .... CHRYSOZONÌNÆ
Third antennal joint divided into five segments, antennæ therefore apparently seven-jointed, rarely indistinctly ten-jointed; eyes in life unicolorous or banded .... h.

h. Anal cell open, or rarely closed to a point; ocelli absent. (**Chásmia**, Malay.) .... CHASMIÌNÆ
Anal cell closed and petiolate .... i.

i. Palpi shining black with last joint flattened and greatly inflated; wings black on basal half, hyaline apically; largely black or violet shining species with shining facial callosities. (**Lepidosélaga, Selasòma**, Neotrop.) .... LEPIDOSELAGÌNÆ
Palpi with last joint normal .... j.

j. Labella fleshy, distorted and shrunken when dried; first antennal joint usually much longer than wide; first posterior cell open; ocelli absent; eyes with diagonal bands in life; relatively slender species. (**Diachlòrus, Acanthócera, Lutziélla, Stenotabànus**, Neotrop.) .... DIACHLORÌNÆ
Labella sclerotized, smooth and shining; first antennal joint about as long as wide .... k

k. Subepaulets usually bare and flat; eyes not banded .... l.
Subepaulets with as coarse hairs as those on costa, often inflated . . m.

l. At least fore tibiæ swollen; wings much infuscated, no spur-vein, R_4 curved abruptly forward apically; first antennal joint and face swollen; body mostly black. (**Bolbodimỳia**) BOLBODIMYIÌNÆ
Tibiæ normal; wings mostly hyaline and normally with spur at base of R_4; body unicolorous, dull greenish or yellowish. (**Chlorotabànus**) .... CHLOROTABANÌNÆ

m. First posterior cell closed; ocelli absent. (**Bellárdia, Chelotabànus, Psalídia**) .... BELLARDIÌNÆ
First posterior cell open; ocelli sometimes present. (**Tabànus** (Figs. 518 E, 526, 527), **Atylòtus, Chelómnia, Dichelácera, Hybomìtra** (= *Theriopléctes*), **Leucotabànus, Stibasòma**) ..... TABANÌNÆ

Calypteres small or vestigial; head not hemispherical, the occiput convex; abdomen oblong; second submarginal cell (R_4) not wide 42

42. Fourth posterior cell (M_3) almost or quite closed (Fig. 529); dichoptic. (*XYLOMYÌIDÆ*) . . . . SÓLVIDÆ

a. Third joint of antennæ divided into eight annulations. (**Sólva** (= *Xylomỳia*) (Fig. 529); **Nematocerópsis**, Manchuria; **Prísta**, Malay.; **Subulònia**, Nearc.). (*XYLOMYIÌNÆ*). . . . .SOLVÌNÆ
Flagellum of antenna divided into 20 to 36 usually pectinate divisions (Fig. 518a). (**Rhachícerus**, Holarc., Malay.). (*RHACHICÉRIDÆ*) . . . . .RHACHICERÌNÆ

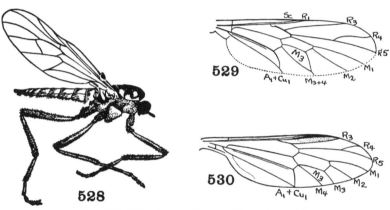

Figs. 528–530. Chiromyzidæ, Solvidæ, Xylophagidæ

528. **Clavimyia** (Enderlein) Chiromyzidæ.
529. **Solva**, wing. Solvidæ.
530. **Xylophagus**, wing. Xylophagidæ.

Fourth posterior cell (M_3) open (Fig. 530) 43

43. Face flat or produced, the facial orbits and cheeks not sutured; hind margin of wing thin before anal angle; male dichoptic. Very slender flies resembling ichneumon-flies. (**Xylóphagus** or **Erínna** (Fig. 530), Eur., Am., Austr.; **Archimỳia**)
XYLOPHÁGIDÆ or ERÍNNIDÆ
Facial orbits and cheeks separated from the central part; hind margin of wing veined throughout; male holoptic; scutellum of *Cœnomyia* spined. Mostly robust, yellowish or blackish flies; widespread, but rare . . . . CŒNOMYÌIDÆ

a. Proboscis short ....b
Proboscis as long as head and thorax, obliquely porrect; body robust.
(**Arthróteles,** Ethiop.) ....**ARTHROTELÌNÆ**
b. All tibiæ with apical spurs c
Front tibiæ without spurs. (**Arthróceras, Arthròpeas, Glùtops**).
ARTHROCERATÌNÆ
c. Abdomen broader than thorax; scutellum spined or not. (**Cœ-nomỳia** (Fig. 518C), **Anacantháspis,** Holarc.) ..**CŒNOMYIÌNÆ**
Abdomen elongate, narrower than thorax; scutellum armed with spines. (**Stratioléptis,** Siberia, Japan). ....**STRATIOLEPTÌNÆ**

44. Costa continuing around wing-margin, venation normal (Fig. 531), anterior crossvein (r-m) distinct, five posterior cells (*Hilarimorpha* with four); at least posterior tibiæ with spurs; calypteres vestigial; mostly Holarctic, inhabiting woodlands 45

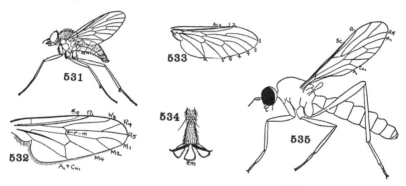

Figs. 531–535. Rhagionidæ, Hilarimorphidæ

531. **Rhagio,** male (Cole) Rhagionidæ.
532. **Hilarimorpha,** wing. Hilarimorphidæ.
533. **Chrysopilus,** wing. Rhagionidæ.
534. **Rhagio,** end of tarsus, showing broad empodium. Rhagionidæ.
535. **Vermileo** (Wheeler) Rhagionidæ.

Costa more or less thinned beyond tip of wing, venation usually eccentric (Figs. 537, 551), anterior crossvein (r-m) usually absent or located near base of discal cell; tibiæ with short or no spurs; proboscis sometimes excessively long 46
45. Empodium undeveloped; discal cell open, fourth vein (media) forked and long-petiolate; tibiæ without spurs. (**Hilarimórpha** (Fig. 532), Holarc.) ....**HILARIMÓRPHIDÆ**
Empodium pulvilliform (Fig. 534); discal cell present. Snipe-flies. (**LÉPTIDÆ**) ....**RHAGIÓNIDÆ**

a. Face flattened and projecting, nasiform; the antennæ inserted above middle of eyes; alula undeveloped, calypteres reduced; front tibiæ with strong apical spur. (Vermíleo (Fig. 535), Lampromỳia) .... VERMILEONÍNÆ
   Face socketed and not projecting, separated by a groove from the rather wide cheeks, antennæ inserted below middle of eyes; alula present, calypteres well developed .... b

b. Front tibiæ with one or two spurs, hind tibiæ with two spurs. (Bicálcar, Palæarc.; Bolbomỳia, Diálysis, Triptótricha, Nearc.)
   BICALCARÍNÆ
   Front tibiæ without spurs c

c. Hind tibiæ with two spurs; eyes not bisected. (Rhàgio (= Léptis) (Fig. 531), Athèrix, Átrichops). (LEPTÍNÆ) .RHAGIONÍNÆ

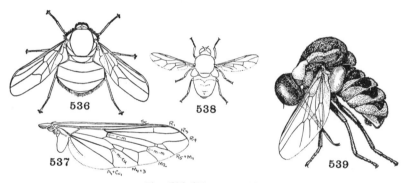

Figs. 536–539. Acroceridæ

536. **Pterodontia**, female (Cole) Acroceridæ.
537. **Ocnæa**, wing. Acroceridæ.
538. **Acrocera** (Verrall) Acroceridæ.
539. **Thyllis** (Cole) Acroceridæ.

Hind tibiæ with one spur which is sometimes reduced; eyes bisected, the lower facets smaller than the upper; second vein short, curving upward at end close to first (R_1) vein. (Chrysopìlus (Fig. 533), Omphalóphora, Ptiolìna, Spània, Symphoromỳia)
CHRYSOPILÍNÆ

46. Head as wide as the depressed thorax; calypteres vestigial; posterior veins parallel with hind margin (Fig. 551), sometimes forming a secondary network of small cells, first basal cell very long, its forward border continued obliquely across the wing as a "diagonal vein." Rare species, inhabiting arid regions, principally Asia Minor, S. Africa, Chile and Australia.....NEMESTRÍNIDÆ

a. Proboscis elongate, slender and hard, the labella usually narrow, palpi short. (Nemestrìnus, Trichophthálma, Fallénia, Megistorhýnchus, Neorhynchocéphalus (Fig. 551), Rhynchocéphalus)
                                        NEMESTRINÌNÆ
Proboscis short and broad, the labella fleshy, palpi long and upturned; ovipositor telescopic; alula broad. (Hirmoneùra, Hyrmophlæba) ....HIRMONEURÌNÆ
Mouthparts vestigial. (Trichopsídea, Atrìadops (= Còlax), Symmíctus) .... TRICHOPSIDEÌNÆ

Head placed low, very small as compared with the greatly humpbacked body, abdomen rounded, often inflated (Fig. 536); calypteres inflated, hiding the halteres; costa discontinued at wing-tip, posterior veins not parallel with hind margin of wing and not forming accessory cells; eyes of both sexes broadly contiguous. Spider parasites, rare species; widespread, but poorly represented in Indo-australia and tropical Africa. (CÝRTIDÆ, HENÓPIDÆ, ONCÓDIDÆ) ....ACROCÉRIDÆ

a. Third antennal joint small, with terminal style or hair-like rays; proboscis short ....b
Third antennal joint large, more or less compressed, without terminal style; proboscis often very long, sometimes vestigial. (Pánops, Astomélla, Eulónchus, Ocnæa (Fig. 537), Làsia, Pialeòidea)
                                        PANOPÌNÆ
b. Prothoracic lobes separated; abdomen usually inflated. (Acrócera (Fig. 538), Cýrtus, Nòthra, Oncódes, Opsèbius, Pterodóntia (Fig. 536)). (CYRTÌNÆ, ONCODÌNÆ) ....ACROCERÌNÆ
Lobes of prothorax very large and broadly fused in the middle to form a shield in front of the mesonotum; abdomen not inflated. Mainly Neotropical, some Ethiopian. (Philpota, Hélle, Melgálybus, Thýllis (Fig. 539)) ....PHILPOTÌNÆ

47. Anal cell distinctly longer than second basal cell, either open, or acutely closed in or near margin of wing, basal cells usually relatively large (see Fig. 545); [1] head bristles rarely evident 48

[1] The following forms having short acute anal cell slightly longer than the second basal cell will cause confusion at this point of the key. The strength of the head bristles is then the best guide.
Opetia, Clythiidæ, couplet 63, Fig. 581: head bristles weak, no discal cell, the third vein not forked.
Sciadoceridæ, couplet 57, Fig. 584: head bristles strong, subcosta ending in R1.
Empididæ, Brachystomatinæ, couplet 53, Fig. 559; and Noezinæ, couplet 62, Fig. 563: head bristles weak, anal and basal cells rather long. Remaining Empididæ, couplet 58, have the anal cell small and either perpendicularly or obtusely closed.
Musidoridæ, couplet 59, Fig. 572: head bristles strong, wings lancet-shaped, no discal cell. The female has a false anal cell.
Euribiidæ, couplet 133, Fig. 656, and the Otitid series, couplets 101 to 104: anal crossvein (Cu1) angulately broken, the anal cell therefore with a pointed apical lobe.
Tachiniscidæ, couplet 106, Fig. 633: body bristly.

Anal cell shorter, rarely acute, closed some distance from wing-margin, usually by a turning back of Cu_1, sometimes the anal cell completely absent; "small crossvein" (see couplet 50) never formed, *i.e.* never five posterior cells; some bristles commonly developed on head 55

48. Radial sector three-branched, *i.e.* third longitudinal vein (R_{4+5}) forked (see Fig. 543) 49
    Radial sector two-branched, *i.e.* third longitudinal vein simple (R_4 absent). (If the second vein is short and terminates in the first vein (Fig. 546), see Bombyliidæ, Mythicomyiinæ, couplet 53,j) 60

49. Vertex plane or convex, the eyes not bulging, eyes of male often meeting; legs not robust 50
    Vertex sunken, the eyes bulging above and never contiguous; wing-veins numerous; often large species with strong legs 54

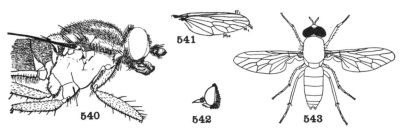

Figs. 540–543. Apioceridæ, Therevidæ

540. **Ripidosyrma**, head and thorax (Melander) Apioceridæ.
541. **Thereva**, wing. Therevidæ.
542. **Psilocephala**, profile of head (Cole) Therevidæ.
543. **Psilocephala**, male (Cole) Therevidæ.

50. Media four-branched, "small crossvein" present, *i.e.* the obtuse apex of the second basal cell touches two posterior cells in addition to the discal cell (Fig. 541), five posterior cells present, the fourth commonly closed; thorax with some bristles; abdomen long and tapering 51
    Media three- or two-branched, four or three posterior cells present, if rarely five posterior cells present the extra one is due to an extra vein bisecting the third, the fourth posterior cell not closed, "small crossvein" absent, *i.e.* the acute apex of the second basal cell touches but one posterior cell in addition to the discal cell (see Fig. 545); abdomen usually oval or oblong; thorax without true bristles 52

51. Apical veins curving forward, the third vein (R_5) and nearly always also the fourth (M_1) ending before apex of wing; at least the

scutellum bristly; antennæ with a very short style; eyes separated; palpi broadened at tip. A small family; occurring in arid places; South Africa, America, Australia, Borneo. ......**APIOCÉRIDÆ**

a. Palpi two-jointed, distally broadened; proboscis not lengthened, with broad labellæ. (Apiócera) ....**APIOCERÌNÆ**
Palpi one-jointed, not broadened distally; proboscis elongate, with narrow labellæ. (**Rhaphiomỳdas, Apomìdas, Ripidosýrma (Fig. 540)** ....**RHAPHIOMYDAÌNÆ**

Fourth vein ending beyond apex of wing (Fig. 541); body usually furry rather than bristly, sometimes nearly bare; palpi not broadened apically. Widespread, principally Holarctic. (**Théreva (Fig. 541), Anaborrhýnchus, Epomỳia, Dialineùra, Henicomỳia, Phỳcus, Psilocéphala (Figs. 542, 543), Tabùda, Xestomỳia)**
THERÉVIDÆ

52. Costa not continuing beyond apex of wing, fourth vein (M_1) ending at or before wing-tip, three posterior cells (Fig. 552); proboscis hidden; antennæ without a style; body bare. Holarctic, Neotropical and Oriental; about thirty species; some are found on windows. (**Scenópinus** or **Omphràle** (Fig. 552), **Lepidomphràle, Pseudatríchia**) ....**SCENOPÍNIDÆ** or **OMPHRÁLIDÆ**
Costa continuing around entire wing, fourth vein (M_1) ending beyond wing-tip, usually four posterior cells. (If the discal cell is open and the fourth vein is forked and long-petiolate (Fig. 532), see Hilarimorphidæ, couplet 45) 53

53. Antennæ usually ending in a small style, style-like process, or circlet of bristly hairs; tibiæ usually with spicules; proboscis usually long, thin and porrect; body usually furry and stout, rarely (Systropodinæ) extremely slender, bare and wasp-like; anal vein complete, anal cell (Cu) usually reaching margin, often open, alula usually distinct. Mostly occurring in sunny dry localities; alert, quick-flying species; many genera and species ....**BOMBYLÌIDÆ**

a. Second vein (R_3) arising almost perpendicularly from R_8 very close to the anterior crossvein (r-m) and forming a knee at its origin, only the third vein (R_{4+5}) continuous with the prefurca (Fig. 545); eyes with an indentation in the middle of the hind margin ....b
Second and third veins forking acutely or in an arch and at a greater distance before the anterior crossvein than the length of that crossvein (see Fig. 548) c

b. Calypteres margined with fringe of hairs; antennal style with a pencil of hairs at its tip; metapleuræ bare. (**Ánthrax** (Fig. 545), **Argyramœba, Chionamœba, Coquilléttia, Spongostỳlum**).
ANTHRACÌNÆ

Calypteres margined with scales; style without apical crown of hairs; metapleuræ hairy. (**Exoprosòpa, Dipálta, Hemipénthes, Hyperalònia, Lepidánthrax, Stónyx, Thyridánthrax, Vílla** (= *Hyalánthrax*)) ....**EXOPROSOPÌNÆ**

c. Antennæ widely separated; abdomen elongate, cylindrical; hind margin of eyes not indented. (**Cytherèa** (= *Mùlio*), **Callístoma, Gyrocráspedum, Pantárbes, Sericosòma**) ......**CYTHEREÌNÆ**
Antennæ approximated, if the antennæ are widely separated the abdomen is not slender ....d

d. Eyes with an indentation in the middle of the hind margin at which arises an impressed bisecting line in both sexes ....e
Eyes without posterior indentation and the bisecting line, at most with a rounded indentation ....g

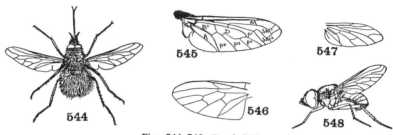

Figs. 544–548. Bombyliidæ

544. **Bombylius** (Verrall) Bombyliidæ.
545. **Anthrax**, wing. Bombyliidæ.
546. **Mythicomyia**, wing (Williston) Bombyliidæ.
547. **Geron**, wing (Williston) Bombyliidæ.
548. **Epacmus**, male (Cole) Bombyliidæ.

e. Face produced roof-like over the long and narrow mouth-opening, proboscis short; second vein arising in a curve. (**Tomomỳza, Antònia, Plesiócera**) ....**TOMOMYZÌNÆ**
Face convex, not projecting; second vein arising acutely ....f

f. Head no broader than thorax; abdomen at least as broad as thorax, flattened; anterior crossvein much beyond middle of discal cell. (**Lomàtia, Anisotàmia, Canària, Comptòsia, Oncodócera**). **LOMATIÌNÆ**
Head broader, but the hind edge narrower than the thorax; body more cylindrical than depressed; anterior crossvein near middle of discal cell. (**Aphœbántus, Desmatoneùra, Epácmus** (Fig. 548), **Eucéssia, Petroróssia**) ....**APHŒBANTÌNÆ**

g. Face vertical, much longer than the front; clypeus separated from cheeks by a deep groove; second vein arising in a curve. (**Mariobézzia**) ....**MARIOBEZZIÌNÆ**

Face at most as long as front; clypeus not separated from cheeks by a deep groove; second vein arising at an acute angle ....h

h. Abdomen very long and slender, pedunculate; metasternum very strongly developed; occiput concave; eyes united in both sexes or nearly so; body bare; wings narrowed at base, without alula and calypteres. (Sýstropus, Dolichomỳia) ..SYSTROPODÌNÆ
Abdomen not remarkably slender; wings with alula and calypter ..i

i. Third vein simple, therefore only one submarginal cell; small bare flies with humped thorax ....j
Third vein forked, two or three submarginal cells, second vein long, never ending in the first vein ....k

j. Second vein very short, ending in the first vein, or entirely absent. (Mythicomỳia (Fig. 546), Empidideìcus, Glabéllula (= Pachynères)). (GLABELLULÌNÆ) ....MYTHICOMYIÌNÆ
Second vein normal, ending independently in costa. (Cyrtòsia; Cyrtòides, Afr.; Cyrtomórpha, Platypỳgus)......CYRTOSIÌNÆ

k. Body more or less hunched, narrow, or at least not broad, thorax prominent, abdomen cylindrical or sometimes flattened; sometimes bare, or scaly, or with bristles; wings usually relatively short l
Body not narrow nor hunched, the abdomen rather flattened and usually hairy and without bristles ....m

l. Prothorax in shape of an anterior ring beset with strong curved bristles. (Toxóphora, Heniconeùra, Lepidóphora)
TOXOPHORÍNÆ
Prothorax smaller and not beset with curved bristles. (Cyllènia, Amíctus, Éclimus, Exepácmus, Epíbates, Hénica, Metacósmus Paracósmus, Thevenetimỳia) ....CYLLENIÌNÆ

m. First antennal joint thickened and long-hairy; wings short, with four open posterior cells. (Conóphorus (= Plòas), Aldríchia, Codiònus, Platamòdes) ....CONOPHORÍNÆ
First antennal joint not thickened; wings not short ....n

n. Face protruding as a very short muzzle, proboscis short, porrect, with fleshy tip; eyes of male bisected; discal cell broadened at end, much broader than second posterior cell; nearly bare species. (Heterótropus (= Malthacótricha), Apystomỳia, Cænòtus, Proràtes) ....HETEROTROPÌNÆ
Face, when developed, convex or somewhat conically projecting, but not beak-like, proboscis long, with small labella; rarely wholly bare ....o

o. Second vein and fork of third vein in line with wing-axis; body not broad but rather humped, vestiture fine and not abundant; leg bristles weak or absent. (Phthíria, Apólysis, Crocídium, Gèron (Fig. 547), Oligodrànes (= Rhabdopsélaphus), Semiràmis)
PHTHIRIÌNÆ

Second vein and fork of third vein curving forward, ending distinctly before tip of wing; body usually broad ....p
p. Vestiture short or undeveloped; no bristles on legs; head small. (Ùsia, Corsomỳza, Legnotomỳia, Psiathalássius) .....USIÌNÆ
Vestiture usually pronounced; tibiæ with three rows of evident bristles; lower occiput usually broadened. (Bombýlius (Fig. 544), Dischístus, Heterostỳlum, Lordòtus, Sparnapòlius, Systœchus, Triplàsius) ....BOMBÝLIÌNÆ

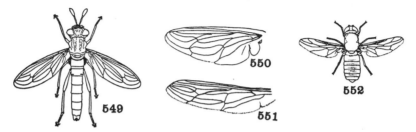

Figs. 549–552. Mydaidæ, Nemestrinidæ, Scenopinidæ

549. **Leptomydas,** male (Cole) Mydaidæ.
550. **Mydas,** wing. Mydaidæ.
551. **Neorhyncocephalus,** wing (Williston) Nemestrinidæ.
552. **Scenopinus** (Verrall) Scenopinidæ.

Antennal style longer than the third joint; tibiæ without spicules; proboscis short, sharp and incurved; body slender, nearly bare; anal cell closed within the wing, the anal vein not reaching margin. Delicate, shade-loving flies. (See couplet 58, g, Brachystomatinæ) ....EMPÍDIDÆ, part
54. Body without bristles; fourth vein (M_1) curving forward to end at or before wing-tip, neuration complex (Fig. 550), prefurca (*i.e.* basal section of R_s) very short; antennæ with a clubbed style; proboscis with fleshy expanded tip, palpi vestigial; at most one ocellus. About 130 species; widespread, but not common; often flies of large size. (Mỳdas (Fig. 550), widespr.; **Dolichogáster, Ectỳphus, Leptomỳdas** (Fig. 549), **Nomoneùra,** Nearc.; **Cephalócera,** Ethiop.; **Miltùnus, Triclònus,** Austr.). (*MYDÁSIDÆ*).
                                                        MYDÀIDÆ
Body usually with bristles, face bearded; fourth vein not curving forward, neuration not abnormal, prefurca long (Fig. 553); proboscis adapted for piercing, not fleshy, palpi usually prominent; three ocelli. A large family of nearly 4000 species, widespread, especially in warm localities; adults predatory on flying insects. Robber-flies. .... **ASÍLIDÆ**

a. Palpi one-jointed; antennæ with slender terminal arista; mesopleural bristles wanting; abdomen with eight segments . . . . b

   Palpi two-jointed; antennæ with or without a thickened terminal style, very rarely with a terminal arista c

b. Marginal cell open; very slender species with few hairs and bristles; claws long, pulvilli absent; ovipositor without whorl of spines. (**Leptogáster, Euscelídia, Psílonyx**) . . . . **LEPTOGASTRÌNÆ**

   Marginal cell closed and petiolate; less slender, or robust species, bristly rather than hairy; pulvilli present; ovipositor often with a crown of spines. (**Asìlus, Cerdístus, Dýsmachus, Èrax** (Fig. 553), **Mallóphora, Philodìcus, Ommàtius, Báctria** (= *Prómachus*), **Proctacánthus, Tolmèrus**) . . . . **ASILÌNÆ**

c. Marginal cell open, or rarely closed at extreme tip; mesopleural bristles wanting. (*DASYPOGONÌNÆ*)[1] . . . . d

   Marginal cell closed; mesopleural bristles present; male abdomen with seven (rarely six) segments; species often stout and very hairy. (*LAPHRIÌNÆ*)[1] . . . . f

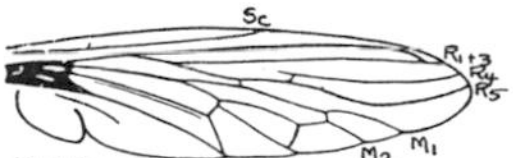

Figs. 553–555. Asilidæ

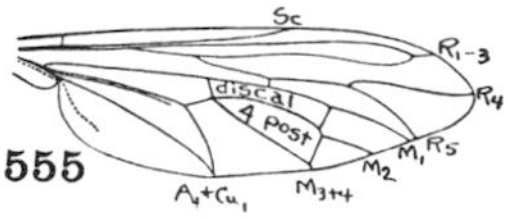

553. **Erax**, wing (Hine) Asilidæ.
554. **Stichopogon**, wing. Asilidæ.
555. **Atomosia**, wing. Asilidæ.

d. Abdomen of male with six segments. (**Laphýstia, Pérasis, Psilocùrus, Trichárdis, Trìclis**) . . . . **PYRTANIÌNÆ**

   Abdomen of male with seven, of female with eight segments . . . . . e

e. Front tibiæ without a claw-like apical projection. (**Anisopògon, Cyrtopògon, Dióctria, Habropògon, Heteropògon, Holopògon, Lasiopògon, Microstỳlum, Myiélaphus, Pycnopògon, Rhádinus, Stenopògon, Stichopògon** (Fig. 554)) . . . . . . **EREMOCNEMÌNÆ**

   Front tibiæ with a claw-like apical projection. (**Cenopògon, Cophùra, Dasypògon, Deromỳia, Isopògon, Nícocles, Saropògon, Selidopògon, Tarácticus**). (*DASYPOGONÌNÆ*, s. str.).

   ACANTHOCNEMÌNÆ

f. Small, usually dark colored; third antennal joint with a subapical thorn on upper side; side callouses of metanotum hairy or with blunt bristles; crossveins closing discal and fourth posterior cells

[1] The divisions of the Dasypogoninæ and Laphriinæ have less rank than the other two subfamilies of the Asilidæ, but are given because of the dominance of this family. The divisions of the Dasypogoninæ have no corresponding type genera.

usually in line with each other (Fig. 555); genitalia relatively small and ventrally placed. (Atomòsia (Fig. 555), Amathomỳia, Loewinélla) .... ATOMOSIÏNÆ

Moderate to large, rather heavily pubescent species; third antennal joint without subapical thorn; side pieces of metanotum never bristly; crossveins closing discal and fourth posterior cells not in the same line; genitalia free and usually large. (Làphria (= Làpria), Andrenosòma, Ctenòta, Dasýllis, Dásythrix, Lámpria, Lámyra, Nùsa, Pogonosòma) .... LAPHRIÏNÆ, s. str.

55. No functional frontal suture or lunule above antennæ, front uniformly chitinized, without an anterior median differentiated stripe; no alula 56

Frontal suture well developed as a horseshoe-shaped groove over the antennæ continuing down so as to separate the center of the face from the sides, frontal lunule present as a crescentic sclerite between the antennæ and the frontal suture (Fig. 594),[1]

Figs. 556, 557. Cyclorrhaphous Antennæ and Tarsus

556. *Antennæ*: A, **Dolichopus**, Dolichopodidæ; B, **Drapetis** (Williston) Empididæ; C, **Apivora** (Williston) Syrphidæ; D, **Salmacia** (Williston) Tachinidæ; E, **Glossina** (Hegh) Glossinidæ.

557. **Musca**, end of tarsus, showing hair-like empodium (Kellogg) Muscidæ.

middle part of front nearly always differentiated from the orbits; calypteres and alula usually pronounced; arista almost always dorsal; costa not extended to hind margin of wing; first two dorsal segments of abdomen more or less fused 64

56. Venation not of the types represented by Figs. 570 and 571, a closed cell (discal or discal and second basal) usually formed between the branches of the media, wings neither with radial branches concentrated near costa and medial veins extending obliquely across field of wing (as in Fig. 570), nor of lanceolate

[1] The frontal suture is forced open by the protrusion of the ptilinum, an eversible sac, for prying off the lid of the puparium at the time of emergence of the adult. Newly emerged flies of this group sometimes show the ptilinum; in older flies the ptilinum is withdrawn and the frontal suture closes to form the characteristic seam over the antennæ. The lid of the puparium opens by a circular cleft (see Fig. 763), hence the significance of the group-name Cyclorrhapha, meaning circular seam. In the coördinate group Orthorrhapha (including couplets 36 to 54) the pupa case opens by a dorsal straight longitudinal seam (see Fig. 707) and accordingly the frontal suture and ptilinum are not developed.

shape with long second vein and ambient costa (as in Fig. 571); antennæ evidently two- or three-jointed, the apical joint not spherical; male sometimes holoptic.........................57
Venation peculiar, of the type represented by Fig. 570 or Fig. 571; no discal cell; eyes of both sexes widely separated............59

57. Alular edge of wing without hairy bristles; posterior crossvein (m-m) usually present and then always located much beyond the anterior cross vein (r-m); anal cell acute (Fig. 563), rectangular (Fig. 561), rounded (Fig. 565) or obtuse (Fig. 560), when the anal cell is acute, the basal cells are relatively long and the subcosta is either vestigial or terminates in the costa; hind tarsi with first joint longer than second................................58
Alular edge of wing with feathery bristles; basal cells and discal cell very small, r-m and m-m cross-veins in same transverse line, anal cell short and acute, the anal vein reaching margin, medial branches disjoined basally, Sc ending in R_1; both sexes dichoptic; postocular cilia present; hind metatarsus shorter than next joint. (Sciadócera, (Fig. 584), Austr.; Archíphora, Neotrop.)
SCIADOCÉRIDÆ

58. Anterior crossvein (r-m) located beyond basal fourth of wing, discal cell usually separate from second basal, third vein often forked, often four posterior cells, *i.e.* M_2 separate from M_3, Sc vestigial or ending in costa, R_1 ending near middle of wing; calypteres minute; eyes usually with a small incision at the antennæ; seriate postocular cilia wanting; antennal style usually terminal; proboscis usually rigid; male genitalia not inflexed; dull colored species, almost never metallic. A large family of over 2000 species, widespread, but principally Holarctic and Neotropical...**EMPÍDIDÆ**

a. Anal and discal cells complete, or if either is incomplete the front coxæ are very long and the front legs are raptorial, or else the anal angle of the wing is rectangular........................b
Discal cell united with second basal (Fig. 561), anal cell and anal vein wanting or incomplete, three posterior cells, Sc vestigial or wanting, third vein always simple. (Corynèta (= *Tachydròmia*), Drápetis (Fig. 556b), Chersodròmia, Coloboneùra, Elaphropèza, Micrémpis, Platypálpus (Fig. 561), Stílpon, Tachypèza, Tachyémpis). (*TACHYDROMIÌNÆ*) .... **CORYNETÌNÆ**

b. Anal angle of wing not projecting, costa weakly but visibly continuing around hind margin of wing, anal crossvein (Cu_1) acute, perpendicular, or rounded, rarely obtusely closing anal cell; front coxæ longer than posterior pairs; proboscis short; eyes broadly separated on the front; mesopleuræ oblique..................c
Anal angle more or less distinct, if the wings taper uniformly toward base, the mesopleuræ are vertical or the hind margin of the wing is thin; front coxæ not elongate; male often holoptic...e

c. Front legs raptorial, located well forward, front coxæ subequal to femora in length; radial sector arising closer to anterior crossvein than to humeral crossvein. (Hemerodròmia, Chelífera (Fig. 564), Chelípoda, Colàbris, Drymodròmia, Monodròmia, Phyllodròmia).
    HEMERODROMIÏNÆ
    Legs slender, the front pair not distant from the others, the coxæ not long and the femora not thick; radial sector arising nearer base of wing .... d

d. Second antennal joint connected with third by a finger-like projection on inner side; no anal cell; restricted to southern hemisphere. (Ceratómerus, Icásma) .... CERATOMERÌNÆ
    Second antennal joint normal; anal cell present; mostly found about swiftly running brooks and waterfalls. (Atalánta (= Clinócera), Boreodròmia, Dolichocéphala, Heleodròmia, Oreothàlia (Fig. 562), Synamphótera, Trichopèza, Wiedemánnia). (CLINOCER-ÌNÆ) .... ATALANTÌNÆ

e. Anal crossvein forming a distinct angle with basal part of anal vein; proboscis rarely longer than head; thorax often highly arched...f
    Anal crossvein recurved and confluent with underside of anal cell, the anal vein usually an independent fold; proboscis often long, rarely porrect; antennæ usually three-jointed. (Émpis (Fig. 560), Glòma, Hesperémpis, Hílara, Hilarémpis (Fig. 558), Hormopèza, Iteáphila, Microphòrus, Oreogèton, Rhamphomỳia.)
    EMPIDÌNÆ

f. Anal cell as long as second basal, or longer, its outer angle acute; Sc distinct .... g
    Anal cell shorter than or about as long as second basal cell, its outer angle obtuse or right; Sc weak; proboscis short. (Ocydròmia, Anthàlia, Bicellària, Euthyneùra, Hoplocýrtoma, Leptopèza, Œdàlea, Trichìna) .... OCYDROMIÏNÆ

g. Discal cell emitting three veins, costa visibly continuing on hind margin; proboscis short and incurved; antennæ three-jointed; thorax not highly arched. (Brachýstoma (Fig. 559), Anomalémpis, Blepharoprócta, Homalocnèmis). (Including HOMALOCNEM-ÌNÆ) .... BRACHYSTOMATÌNÆ
    Discal cell emitting two veins; proboscis rigid, porrect; antennæ two-jointed; thorax greatly arched. (Noèza (=Hỳbos), Euhỳbos (Fig. 563), Meghỳperus, Lactistomỳia, Sýndyas, Synèches). (HYBOTÌNÆ) .... NOEZÌNÆ

Anterior crossvein located within basal fifth of wing (Fig. 566), discal cell always confluent with second basal, R_1 ending much beyond middle of wing, third vein never forked, three posterior cells, i.e. M_1 and M_2 fused, Sc when complete ending in R_1; calypteres rather large and fringed; a row of postocular cilia present; proboscis almost always soft; male genitalia more or less

inflexed under abdomen; color usually metallic green. A large family of over 2000 species, widespread, principally Holarctic and Neotropical (*DOLICHÓPIDÆ*) .... **DOLICHOPÓDIDÆ**
a. Fourth vein typically broken, the front fork widely diverging and angulately approaching the third vein (Fig. 566); head short and broad, occiput concave, vertex sunken, ocellar triangle prominent;

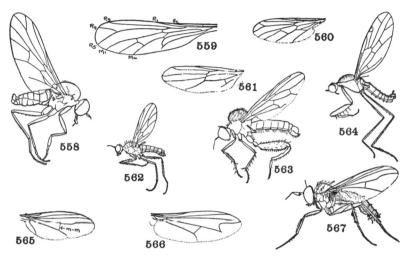

Figs. 558–567. Empididæ, Dolichopodidæ

558. **Hilarempis,** male. Empididæ.
559. **Brachystoma,** wing. Empididæ.
560. **Empis,** wing. Empididæ.
561. **Platypalpus,** wing. Empididæ.
562. **Oreothalia,** male. Empididæ.
563. **Euhybos,** male (Melander) Empididæ.
564. **Chelifera,** male (Melander) Empididæ.
565. **Dolichopus,** wing. Dolichopodidæ.
566. **Psilopodinus,** wing (Aldrich) Dolichopodidæ.
567. **Argyra,** male (Cole) Dolichopodidæ.

hypopygium free, its appendages visible; slender species with short and broad thorax, long narrow abdomen and long slender legs. (**Chrysosòma, Condylostỳlus, Leptorèthrum, Mesórhaga, Psilopodìnus** (Fig. 566), **Scìapus, Tenùopus**). (*AGONOSOMAT-ÌNÆ, LEPTOPODÌNÆ, PSILOPODÌNÆ, SCIAPODÌNÆ*).
                                                  CHRYSOSOMATÌNÆ
Fourth vein not angulately fractured though sometimes bowed; vertex not sunken; thorax longer than broad.................b
b. First antennal joint bare, or if exceptionally hairy then the occiput

is concave and fitting against the thorax, or the palpi are broad, or the hypopygium is not free...............................c

First antennal joint pubescent; occiput convex; face of male usually narrow and with only a weak indication of a transverse impression; palpi small; alar callus present; hind crossvein distant from margin; middle tibiæ with an apical set of five bristles; hypopygium large, rather free, with evident and often large lamellæ; robust and bristly species. (Dolíchopus (Fig. 556A, 565), Hercóstomus, Hypophýllus, Orthochìle, Paraclìus, Pelastoneùrus, Sybistròma, Tachýtrechus) .... DOLICHOPODÌNÆ

c. Proboscis stout, with an incurved hook; coxæ spined; front femora basally with two divergent spine-like bristles; maritime species. (Aphrosỳlus, Teneríffa) .... APHROSYLÌNÆ
Proboscis not furnished with a hook-like piercing organ; coxæ and front femora not so spined................................d

d. Face usually broad, with evident transverse impression...........e
Face usually narrow, with an incomplete transverse impression, which is sometimes entirely wanting, at least in male.........h

e. Arista dorsal; postvertical bristles evident; palpi usually very broad, applied against proboscis; occiput usually convex; hypopygium small, not free, with small to large appendages...............f
Arista apical or subapical; postverticals minute or wanting; occiput concave; thorax with a prescutellar bare, flattened area; hypopygium long, without long evident appendages; alar callus not distinct. (Medètera, Dolichóphorus, Oligochætus, Thrýpticus; Saccopherónta, Ethiop.) .... MEDETERÌNÆ

f. Hind crossvein nearly parallel with hind margin of wing, fourth vein bent forward and ending before wing-tip; upper occiput concave; no acrostichal bristles; hypopygium sunk into sixth segment. (Plagioneùrus, America).......PLAGIONEURÌNÆ
Hind crossvein nearly transverse, located close to hind margin of wing, the distal segment of fifth vein short...................g

g. Acrostichal bristles absent. (Thinóphilus, Eucóryphus, Peòdes, Schænóphilus, Ethiop.) .... THÌNOPHILÌNÆ
Acrostichals present. (Hydróphorus, Liáncalus, Orthoceràtium, Scéllus) .... HYDROPHORÌNÆ

h. Third antennal joint usually long and narrow, with apical arista, second joint transverse; occiput convex; middle tibiæ with apical ring of bristles; hypopygium long and free. (Rhàphium, Eutársus, Machærium, Pórphyrops, Syntórmon, Sýstenus, Xiphándrium).
RHAPHIÌNÆ
Third antennal joint triangular or spherical, short, rarely somewhat lengthened with dorsal arista..............................i

i. Hypopygium large and free, appendages more or less conspicuous; thorax short, scarcely longer than broad, with prescutellar area;

abdomen long; legs slender and without set of apical bristles on middle tibiæ. (**Neurigòna, Oncopỳgius**).....NEURIGONÌNÆ
Hypopygium usually small, rarely free, often hidden, the appendages never large though visible from beneath................j

j. Abdomen and legs elongate; antennæ located very high; ocellar triangle prominent; no pulvilli; hind margin of first abdominal segment raised. (**Stolidosòma,** Neotrop.).

STOLIDOSOMATÌNÆ

Abdomen short and robust; thorax longer than broad; middle tibiæ tipped with set of bristles.................................k

k. Occiput rather concave; arista dorsal or subapical; hypopygium cap-shaped or hemispherical, usually with four or more strong bristles and only rarely with distinct appendages; body bristly, usually apex of abdomen furnished with bristles. (**Diáphorus, Árgyra** (Fig. 567), **Asýndetus, Chrysòtus, Leucóstola, Melanóstolus, Trigonócera**) ....DIAPHORÌNÆ
Occiput convex; third antennal joint short-triangular, pubescent, with dorsal arista; face of male narrow; hypopygium small, rarely free and with appendages; usually small, weakly bristly species, the apex of abdomen without bristles......................l

l. Acrostichals wanting. (**Xanthochlòrus, Chrysotìmus, Lamprochròmus; Micromórphus,** Ethiop.).........XANTHOCHLORÌNÆ
Acrostichals present, in one or two more or less evident rows. (**Campsicnèmus Sympýcnus, Syntormoneùra**).

CAMPSICNEMÌNÆ

Suborder Brachycera, Section Cyclorrhapha

59. Radial veins stout, running into the costa near middle of wing, medial veins weak and extending obliquely across wing, no crossveins and therefore no basal cells (Fig. 570); antennæ placed low, apparently single-jointed because the minute basal joints are set in a cavity of the third joint, provided with a long, apical or subdorsal, three-jointed arista; palpi projecting, not jointed; hind legs long, their femora compressed; first and second abdominal segments separate; small, humpbacked, quick-running flies of characteristic form. Widespread, many species, mostly Holarctic; including most myrmecophilous genera of flies, some of which are specialized and degenerate forms. (See couplet 163).
HYPÓCERA ....PHÓRIDÆ

ɪ. Propleuræ lateral in position, visible from the sides, prothoracic spiracle not visible from above............................b
Propleuræ small, anterior in position, the humeri formed by the mesonotum, prothoracic spiracle visible from above; female usually wingless; ant-guests. (**Platýphora** (=*Ænigmàtias*), **Ænigmatístes,**

Assmuthèrium, Microplatýphora, Psyllomỳia). (*ÆNIGMATI-ÎNÆ*)................................. PLATÝPHORÌNÆ

b. Tibiæ usually with one or several long preapical bristles; lower frontal bristles when present curving obliquely upward; mesopleuræ usually undivided; both sexes winged. (**Phòra** (= *Trineùra*), **Aneurìna, Beckerìna, Chætoneuróphora** (Fig. 569), **Conícera, Diploneùra, Gymnoscèlia, Hypócera, Paraspiníphora** (Fig. 568), **Psoróphaga, Tríphleba**..................... PHORÌNÆ

Tibiæ without any long preapical bristles, bare or ciliate on the edge; twŏ or four supra-antennal proclinate bristles; female often wingless or with aborted wings. (**Metopìna, Apocéphalus,**

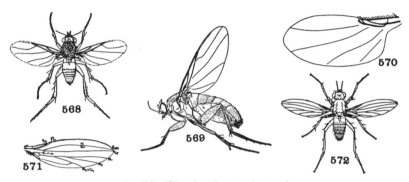

Figs. 568–572. Phoridæ, Lonchopteridæ

568. **Paraspiniphora** (Verrall) Phoridæ.
569. **Chætoneurophora** (Cole) Phoridæ.
570. **Megaselia**, wing. Phoridæ.
571. **Lonchoptera**, wing of female. Lonchopteridæ.
572. **Lonchoptera**, male (Verrall) Lonchopteridæ.

Chonocéphalus, Gymnóphora, Ecitomỳia, Megasèlia (= *Aphiochæta*) (Fig. 570), **Pseudactèon, Pulicíphora** (= *Stethópathus*), **Rhyncophoromỳia, Syneùra, Wandolléckia**). (*PULICÍPHÓRIDÆ, STETHOPÁTHIDÆ*) .... METOPINÌNÆ

Wings rather pointed at tip, lanceolate (Fig. 571), costa encompassing entire wing, basal cells very small, second vein (R_3) ending almost at wing-tip, anterior crossvein not obvious, no discal cell, the three branches of media arising from a common stalk from the apex of the second basal cell, Cu_1 of female curving forward and ending in M_4 at middle of wing-length, thus forming an apparent anal cell (Fig. 571), of male short and reaching hind margin (Fig. 572), veins largely setulose above; oral margin bristly; third antennal joint rounded, with a long subterminal bristle; thorax with bristles but no hairs. Principally Palæarctic, few species, males rare. (Lonchóptera or Musidòra (Figs. 571, 572))......LONCHOPTÉRIDÆ or MUSIDÓRIDÆ

60. Proboscis small, very rarely elongated; front never as broad as the width of the eye, no functioning lunule suture above antennæ, eyes of male usually meeting; face without subantennal grooves....61
Proboscis distinctly longer than head, slender, stiff and often folding (Fig. 578); head wider than thorax, front broad in both sexes, a functioning lunule present; face with a groove or grooves under the porrect antennæ, buccal cavity large, palpi short; no body bristles; abdomen clavate, deflexed at tip; first posterior cell pointed, anterior crossvein near middle of discal cell. Widespread, about 500 species; parasitic on wasps, bees and Orthoptera. (See couplet 87). .... CONÓPIDÆ

a. Vertex and tibiæ without bristles; anal cell rather long and pointed; ovipositor not excessively long...........................b
Vertex with bristles, tibiæ spurred; anal cell small; ovipositor very long; face carinate, proboscis long and geniculate; third antennal joint with subdorsal three-jointed arista. (Stylogáster, mainly Neotrop.) ....STYLOGASTRÌNÆ

b. Third antennal joint with dorsal two-jointed arista; proboscis usually hinged at middle, the distal part folding back; ocelli present....c
Third antennal joint with short apical style; ocelli usually vestigial; proboscis directed forward, not geniculate at middle; abdomen constricted toward base. (Cònops (Fig. 577), Brachyglóssum, Physocéphala (Fig. 579), Tropidomỳia)...........CONOPÌNÆ

c. Anal cell equal to second basal cell; ovipositor large and folding forward under abdomen. (Dalmánnia (Fig. 578), Paramyòpa).
DALMANNIÌNÆ
Anal cell much longer than second basal; ovipositor not extending forward under abdomen. (Myòpa, Melanosòma, Sìcus, Thecóphora (= Oncomỳia), Zòdion) (ZODIONÌNÆ)....MYOPÌNÆ

61. First posterior cell (R₅) open, though sometimes narrowed, no extra vein crossing the anterior crossvein (r-m). (If the anal cell is narrowly open at the margin see Bombyliidæ, Cyrtosiinæ, couplet 53, j)..62
First posterior cell (R₅) closed (Fig. 574), usually an extra vein between the third (R₅) and fourth (M₁) veins and crossing the anterior crossvein (r-m); costa continuing around margin or stopping at wing-tip; anal cell closed just before wing-margin, therefore short-petiolate, the vein closing discal cell parallel with margin; head and body usually without bristles; arista dorsal, very rarely terminal; male usually holoptic; ocelli always present.

Characteristically showy flower-flies with yellow markings; quick fliers and good hoverers; cosmopolitan, about 3000 species.

SÝRPHIDÆ

a. Antennæ elongate, porrect................................b
   Antennæ moderate in length, drooping, if elongate and porrect not placed on a produced front............................e
b. First posterior cell without stump of a vein from the third vein....c
   First posterior cell with a stump of a vein from the third vein which almost divides the cell into two............................d
c. Antennæ inserted on a strong frontal process; a single red abdominal band. (**Psàrus**)........................**PSARÌNÆ**
   Antennæ inserted on the flattened front; abdomen marked with several reddish bands. (**Antìopa** (= *Chrysotóxum*)). (*CHRYSO-TOXÌNÆ*) ....**ANTIOPÌNÆ**

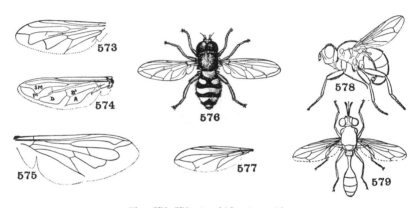

Figs. 573–579. Syrphidæ, Conopidæ

573. **Microdon,** wing (Williston) Syrphidæ.
574. **Tubifera,** wing. Syrphidæ.
575. **Copestylum,** wing. Syrphidæ.
576. **Syrphus,** male (Metcalf) Syrphidæ.
577. **Conops,** wing. Conopidæ.
578. **Dalmannia,** male (Cole) Conopidæ.
579. **Physocephala** (Lugger) Conopidæ.

d. Arista dorsal; face rounded and pilose; scutellum usually armed and emarginate; sometimes antennæ of male split into two or four parts; larvæ and pupæ developing in ant nests. (**Mìcrodon** (Fig. 573), **Mixogáster, Rhopalosýrphus**). (Including *MASARÝGIDÆ*, Neotrop., with antennæ of male split into lobes).

MICRODONTÌNÆ

Style terminal, antennæ on frontal processes; face not with abundant pile. (Cerìòides (= Cèria, = Sphyximórpha)) . . . CERIOIDÌNÆ

e. Anterior crossvein located before middle of discal cell, nearly always rectangular . . . . .f
Anterior crossvein near or beyond middle of discal cell, usually oblique . . . . .n

f. Wholly black or metallic tinted species, if abdomen is spotted with yellow, the facial profile is parallel with eye-margin and face and eyes are pubescent; front of mesonotum pubescent . . . . . . .g
Pale color marks present on head, thorax and abdomen i

g. Antennæ with terminal bristle. (Callícera) . . . . . . CALLICERÌNÆ
Antennæ with dorsal arista . . . . .h

h. Third antennal joint very large, orbicular, thick; abdomen concave below, genitalia entirely hidden from dorsal view, body thickly punctate. (Nausigáster) . . . . NAUSIGASTRÌNÆ
Third antennal joint smaller; abdomen not strongly concave below, the genitalia usually largely visible from above. (Chilòsia, Chrysogáster, Cnèmodon, Heríngia, Orthoneùra, Pipìza, Psilòta).
CHILOSIÌNÆ

i. Lower part of face strongly projecting . . . . .j
Lower part of face not strongly projecting .l

j. Face distinctly projecting conically downward; third antennal joint stout, with thickened three-jointed arista. (Pelecócera, Chamæsýrphus, Ischyróptera) . . . . PELECOCERÌNÆ
Face not projecting downward, but strongly produced forward; third antennal joint not stout and not with thickened arista . . . .k

k. Alula very small; abdomen clavate; hind femora thickened. (Sphegìna, Neoáscia) . . . . SPHEGINÌNÆ
Alula normal; abdomen short, not constricted at base. (Brachyòpa, Rhíngia) . . . . BRACHYOPÌNÆ

l. Humeral calli and the region between them destitute of pile; marginal cell open, vein closing first posterior cell usually parallel with margin; arista bare or pubescent . . . . .m
Humeral calli and the interhumeral region more or less pilose; marginal cell closed, vein closing first posterior cell distally recurrent; arista heavily plumose; hind coxæ with hair behind. (Apívora (= Volucélla) (Fig. 556 C), Copestỳlum (Fig. 575), Temnócera). (VOLUCELLÌNÆ) . . . . APIVORÌNÆ

m. Abdomen elongate, basally narrow. (Báccha, Dòros, Salpingogáster, Spathiogáster). . . . . BACCHÌNÆ
Abdomen oval, not narrow at base nor clavate. (Sýrphus (Fig. 576), Asarcìna, Dídea, Eriozòna, Lasiópticus (= Scæva), Leucozòna, Melanóstoma, Páragus, Platychìrus, Pyrophæna, Sphærophòria, Xanthográmma) . . . . SYRPHÌNÆ

n. Third vein bending deeply into first posterior cell (Fig. 574); femora

with conspicuous patch of black spinules near base. (Tubífera
(= Erístalis) (Fig. 574), Arctosýrphus, Helóphilus, Lampètia
(= Mèrodon) (L. equéstris, Narcissus bulb-fly), Lìops, Mallòta,
Megáspis, Mesémbrius, Myátropa). (ERISTALÌNÆ).

TUBIFERÌNÆ

Third vein not bending deeply into first posterior cell ....o

o. Arista plumose. (Cínxia (= Sericomỳia), Arctóphila, Condídea,
Conosýrphus, Pararctóphila). (ARCTOPHILÌNÆ, SERI-
COMYIÌNÆ) ....CINXIÌNÆ

Arista bare or pubescent ....p

p. Apical crossvein recurrent, usually with a stump of a vein at the
angle. (Zélima (= Eumèrus)). (EUMERÌNÆ)...ZELIMÌNÆ

Apical crossvein oblique, at most very slightly recurrent at apex ..q

q. Marginal cell closed and petiolate. (Milèsia) ......MILESIÌNÆ

Marginal cell open. (Xylòta, Brachypálpus, Callipróbola, Cynorrhìna,
Myiolépta, Penthesílea (= Criorrhìna), Sphecomỳia, Spilomỳia,
Syrítta, Temnóstoma, Tropídia) ....XYLOTÌNÆ

62. Proboscis firm, styliform, porrect or short; male genitalia terminal,
more or less asymmetrical; subcosta evanescent, not reaching
costa, anal angle of wing more or less rectangular, no alula, costa
interrupted at fourth vein; arista usually thread-like and terminal
(Fig. 563). (Subfamily Noezinæ, see couplet 58, g.)

EMPÍDIDÆ, part

Proboscis very small and soft; male genitalia forming a hypopygium inflexed under the abdomen; subcosta complete, ending
in costa 63

63. Antennæ with terminal arista; face small and broad; anal angle of
wing more or less full, basal cells small, second basal much
shorter than discal cell; hind tibiæ and tarsi dilated, especially
in male; head and thorax with bristles; female sometimes bright-
colored. About 100 species, principally Holarctic, some Nearctic,
Indoaustralian and Ethiopian. (Platypèza or Clýthia (Fig. 583),
Agathomỳia, Callomỳia, Calotársa (Fig. 582), Microsània, Opètia
(Fig. 581)). (MICROSANIÌNÆ)

PLATYPÉZIDÆ or CLYTHÌIDÆ

Antennæ with dorsal arista; face narrow; legs not dilated; head
and body without true bristles; head very large, usually spherical, consisting almost wholly of the eyes; anal angle of wings not
developed, second basal cell subequal to discal cell in length;
anal cell closed near margin; ovipositor large, with bulbous
base and long sword-like point, inflexed under abdomen. About
300 species, principally Holarctic and Australian, some Nearctic
and Ethiopian. (Pipùnculus or Dórylas (Fig. 580), Chálarus,
Nephróceros, Verrállia) ....PIPUNCÙLIDÆ or DORYLÀIDÆ

Schizophora

64. Coxæ close together, the legs attached ventrally; head movably
separated from thorax; adults not ectoparasites upon mammals,
birds or bees; rarely viviparous, in which case the new-born
young are very immature. (EUMYÌIDÆ, MUSCÒIDEA,
MYIODÀRIA) 65
Coxæ broadly separated from each other, the legs appearing attached toward the sides of the thorax and therefore sprawling
(Fig. 663); head often small and closely united with body, the
eyes more or less reduced, often wholly wanting, ocelli wanting

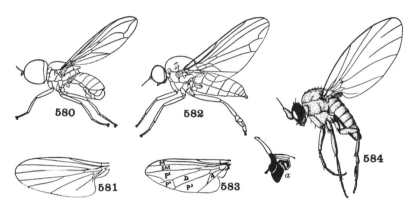

Figs. 580–584. Pipunculidæ, Platypezidæ, Sciadoceridæ

580. **Pipunculus,** male (Cole) Pipunculidæ.
581. **Opetia,** wing (Verrall) Platypezidæ.
582. **Calotarsa,** female; *a*, hind tibia and tarsus of male (Cole) Platypezidæ.
583. **Platypeza,** wing, Platypezidæ.
584. **Sciadocera** (Tonnoir) Sciadoceridæ.

or vestigial; adults usually much flattened, of a leathery or
horny structure, often wingless, living parasitically upon warm-
blooded vertebrates or upon the honey bee; viviparous, the new-
born larvæ well developed, ready for pupation, Braulidæ oviparous in bee-hives. (PUPÍPARA, EPROBOSCÍDEA, OMA-
LÓPTERA, NYMPHÍPARA) 146
65. Second antennal joint with a longitudinal seam along upper outer
edge which extends quite to the base; anterior orbits not differentiated above from the lateral vertex plates, bearing a row of
convergent lower frontal bristles which are more distant from
eye-margin than the upper frontal bristles are (Fig. 594); usually at least lower calypter large; posthumeral and intra-alar

bristles usually both present; thorax with a complete transverse suture before wings (Fig. 585); front of male usually narrow or the eyes meeting; subcosta always distinct and ending in costa, first vein (R_1) never short (Fig. 598); abdominal spiracles at least of segments two to five located in side margins of tergites, very rarely in the membrane. (CALYPTRÀTÆ, MUSCÁRIDÆ, MYODÀRIA SUPERIÒRA, SCHIZOMETÒPA, THECOSTÓMATA) 66

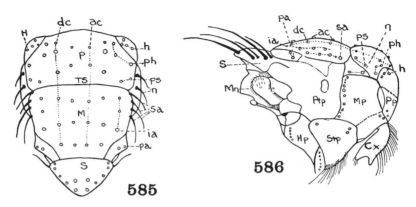

Figs. 585, 586. Calliphoridæ

585. **Calliphora,** thorax, dorsal view (Walton) Calliphoridæ.
586. **Calliphora,** thorax, lateral view (Walton) Calliphoridæ.

Sclerites: Cx, front coxa; H, humerus; Hp, hypopleura; M, posterior portion of mesonotum (metazona); Mp, mesopleura; Mn, metanotum; P, anterior portion of mesonotum (prozona); Pp, propleura; Ptp, pteropleura; S, scutellum; Stp, sternopleura.

Bristles: ac, acrostichals; dc, dorsocentrals; h, humerals; ia, intra-alars; n, notopleurals; pa, post-alars; ph, posthumerals; ps, presutural; sa, supra-alars.

c, calypteres; TS, transverse suture separating prozona from metazona.

Second antennal joint without such a seam (except *Loxocera,* couplet 131); anterior orbits usually separated above from lateral vertex plates, or the latter alone developed and bearing fronto-orbital bristles (if exceptionally the fronto-orbital bristles are located on the orbits the lower ones are closer to the eye-margin than the upper ones are); lower calypter vestigial or undeveloped; posthumeral bristles absent; thorax without a complete transverse suture in front of wings, posterior callosity usually absent; a visible membrane connecting the dorsal and ventral sclerites of the abdomen, in which the spiracles are nearly always located (if spiracles are in tergites, *e.g.* Chloropidæ and Ephydridæ, the subcosta is imperfect); front of both sexes of nearly equal width, or if wider in female the greater width is due to a widening of the middle stripe; fourth vein (M_1) nearly straight, never angulate or with an appendage; often very small species. (ACALYPTRATÆ, BORBORÒIDEA, HAPLOSTÓMATA, MUSCÀRIA HOLOMETÒPA, MYO-DÀRIA INFERIÒRA) 78

66. Mouthparts functional; usually with sternopleural bristles at least, often very bristly species, hypopleura with seriate bristles or hairy. 69

Mouth-opening small, the mouthparts vestigial or wanting; vibrissæ and bristles undeveloped, no sternopleural bristles; front broad in both sexes; antennæ set in the facial groove or grooves; lower calypter with margin only slightly pubescent, hypopleura with long hair. Bot flies. (ŒSTROIDEA) 67

67. Head apparently closed below, the small mouth-opening filled by the proboscis with which it is connected by a membrane, mouth-parts atrophied or even wanting, the proboscis never angled at base; arista always bare. 68

Head with a deep groove beneath, mouthparts present though very small, proboscis angled at base, withdrawn in the oral groove, palpi usually not visible; arista bare or plumose; first posterior cell usually open. (*CUTETERÉBRIDÆ*) ....CUTERÉBRIDÆ

a. Third antennal joint long, three times as long as second joint; antennal pit large and deep; arista hairy above; no facial carina. Neotropical. ....b

Third antennal joint rounded; antennal pit shallow c

b. Epistoma rather broad, projecting obliquely forward; arista long-plumose. (**Pseudogamètes, Alouattamỳia**, on monkeys).
PSEUDOGAMETÌNÆ

Epistoma very narrow; arista with hairs above only. (**Dermatòbia**, on cattle, horse, man) ....**DERMATOBIÌNÆ**

c. Arista plumose; no bristles; facial carina present. Large species; rodent parasites; N. and S. Am. (**Cutérebra** (Fig. 589), **Bogèria**).
CUTEREBRÌNÆ

Arista bare ....d

d. Second antennal joint trilobed; apical cell sometimes closed; front projecting. Elephant parasites. (**Cobbóldia** (Fig. 591) India; **Platycobbóldia, Rodhainomỳia**, Africa) ....**COBBOLDIÌNÆ**

Second antennal joint not trilobed; apical cell open; front more or less convex; bumble-bee-like parasites of Cervidæ; Europe and N. Am. (**Cephenomỳia, Pharyngomỳia**). **CEPHENOMYIÌNÆ**

68. Middle part of face narrow; hypopleura with fan of strong hairs; first posterior cell usually closed and long petiolate. (**Œstrus**,

sheep, goats (Fig. 590), **Cephalópsis,** camel, **Hippœstrus,** horse, **Pharyngóbolus,** elephant, **Rhinœstrus,** horse, hippopotamus).

ŒSTRIDÆ

Middle part of face forming a wide slightly convex shield-shaped plate; hypopleuræ with bundle of hairs; first posterior cell open; antennal pits deep. (**Hypodérma,** ruminants; **Dermatœstrus,** antelope; **Œdamágena,** reindeer; **Œstromỳia,** rodents).

HYPODERMÁTIDÆ

69. Hypopleuræ and pteropleuræ with one or more vertical rows of bristles or hairs (Fig. 586); fourth vein (M_1) curving or bending forward, narrowing or closing first posterior (apical) cell, often with a spur (M_2) at the bend (Fig. 598); when three sternopleural bristles present usually but one behind. (TACHINÒI-DEA) 70

Hypopleuræ without a vertical series of strong bristles below spiracle, if rarely the hypopleural bristles are present there is no row of bristles on pteropleura (in *Stomoxys,* which has a porrect rigid proboscis (Fig. 602), both hypopleural and pteropleural hairs are present); when three sternopleural bristles present usually two behind; ventral membrane usually distinct; postscutellum not developed convexly. (ANTHOMYIÀRIA) . . 75

70. Postscutellum little developed, not convexly prominent (Fig. 586), if more or less prominent the metathoracic spiracular covering is not in two parts but covers the entire lower portion, leaving a small opening in middle above; middle segments of abdomen rarely with rather strong hairs; second ventral segment of abdomen more or less overlapping edges of the dorsal segments. . . 71

Postscutellum strongly developed in the form of a transverse rounded ridge often projecting as far as apex of scutellum; dorsal segments of abdomen with strong bristles in addition to finer hairs, their edges overlapping all the ventral segments 73

71. Hindmost posthumeral bristle located lateral to the presutural bristle (Fig. 585) (sometimes absent in *Engyzops*); propleura and prosternum hairy (bare in *Pollenia* (Fig. 600) which has matted metallic hairs on mesonotum); generally two notopleural bristles, rarely three; arista generally long-plumose; body usually metallic blue or green; fifth ventral segment of male with a split hind margin, sometimes prominently developed; eyes of male touching or approximated, of female separated. Cosmopolitan. (*METOPÌIDÆ*) . . . .**CALLIPHÓRIDÆ**

a. Cheeks narrow, about one-fifth eye-height; arista plumose to end; curve of fourth vein broadly rounded, basal vein sometimes setose; metathoracic spiracle with its front and back ends equally rounded; postscutellum usually well developed. (**Mesembrinélla, Huascaromúsca,** Neotrop.) . . . . **MESEMBRINELLÌNÆ**

Cheeks subquadrate, about half the eye-height; curve of fourth vein
usually angulate; postscutellum not strongly developed.......b
b. Basal section of radius (stem vein) with distinct setulæ or hairs on
posterior upper side...c
Basal vein not setulose on posterior upper side..................d
c. Occipital orbits wide; lower calypter subtruncate at apex, concave
on outer margin, haired on part of upper surface; the small

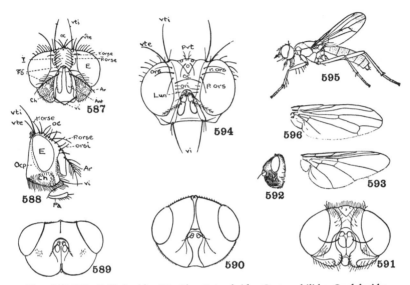

Figs. 587–596. Calliphoridæ, Œstridæ, Cuterebridæ, Gasterophilidæ, Cordyluridæ

587. **Calliphora**, head from front (Walton) Calliphoridæ: Ant, antenna; Ar, arista;
Ch, cheek; E, eye; FS, frontal suture; I, interfrontalia; Ocp, occiput; Pa,
palpus; oc, ocellar bristles; orsi, inner row of upper orbital bristles; p. orse,
proclinate bristle in outer row of upper orbitals; r. orse, reclinate bristles in
outer row of upper orbitals; vi, vibrissæ; vte, exterior vertical bristle; vti,
inner vertical bristle.
588. **Calliphora**, profile of head (Walton) Calliphoridæ. Lettering as for Fig. 587.
589. **Cuterebra**, head from front. Cuterebridæ.
590. **Œstrus**, head from front. Œstridæ.
591. **Cobboldia**, head from front (Rodhain and Bequaert) Cuterebridæ.
592. **Gasterophilus**, head from side (Cole) Gasterophilidæ.
593. **Gasterophilus**, wing (Cole) Gasterophilidæ.
594. **Cordylura**, head from front. Cordyluridæ: Lun, frontal lunule; ori, lower
set of fronto-orbital bristles; ors, upper set of fronto-orbitals; p.ors, proclinate
bristle of upper set; pvt, postverticals; r.ors, reclinate fronto-orbital bristles
of upper set; vi, vibrissæ; vte, outer vertical bristle; vti, inner vertical
bristle.
595. **Parallelomma**, female (Cole) Cordyluridæ.
596. **Scopeuma**, wing. Cordyluridæ.

rounded callosity below base of wing often with erect hairs. (**Phórmia** (*P. regina*, Black blowfly); **Apaulìna**, N. Amer., **Protocallíphora**, Palæarc., bird nest parasites; **Callítroga** (= *Cochliomỳia*, *Compsomỳia*) (*C. macellària*, Screw-worm), **Hemilucília**, **Paralucília**). (*CHRYSOMYIÌNÆ*) . . . . **PHORMIÌNÆ**
Occipital orbits very narrow; lower calypter rather narrowly rounded at apex, nearly straight on outer margin, bare above; subalar callosity bare or without distinct hairs; arista pectinate. (**Rhínia**, **Metállea**, **Rhyncomỳia**, **Stomatorhìna**) . . . . **RHINIÌNÆ**

d. Prosternum and propleura hairy; mesonotum without crinkly hairs; hairs of parafacial stripe not reaching lower margin of eyes . . . . e
Prosternum and center of propleura bare; mesonotum with crinkly hairs; parafacial hairs extending to lower margin of eyes. (**Pollènia** (*P. rùdis*, Cluster-fly (Fig. 600), **Melanodéxia**; **Anthracomỳia**, Austr.) . . . . **POLLENIÌNÆ**

e. Lower calypter bare above; parafacials entirely bare; parasquamal tuft present. Greenbottle flies. (**Lucília**, **Bufolucília**, **Phænícia**. Including *PHUMOSIÌNÆ:* **Phumòsia**, **Caiùsa**, **Euphomòsia**).

LUCILIÌNÆ

Lower calypter pilose above; parafacials usually partially setose; parasquamal tuft absent. Bluebottle flies. (**Callíphora** (Figs. 585–588), **Acronèsia**, **Cynomỳia**, **Onèsia**) . . . . **CALLIPHORÌNÆ**

Hindmost posthumeral bristle placed higher than or level with the presutural bristle; propleura and prosternum bare, thorax not with matted hairs, often four notopleural bristles; arista bare or hairy on basal half; eyes not contiguous, front of male narrow, or as wide as in female 72

72. Calypteres large and round, reaching scutellum; fifth ventral segment of male abdomen with a straight hind margin, or entirely absent; arista generally plumose only on basal half, sometimes bare; eyes bare. Flesh-flies . . . . **SARCOPHÁGIDÆ**

a. Head quadrangular in profile; arista usually plumose, rarely only pubescent; third and fourth sternites more or less evident, though not completely covering the margins of the tergites; theca of penis rarely with spine; front of male usually more or less narrow and without orbital bristles; more than two sternopleural bristles present (see Fig. 586, Stp.). Larvæ of most species feeding on carrion, some parasitic on grasshoppers. (**Sarcóphaga**, **Àgria**, **Helicòbia**, **Blæsóxipha**, **Ravínia**, **Sarcóphila**, **Sarcotáchina**, **Tephromỳia**). (*SAROTHROMYÌNÆ*, *STEPHANOSTOMÁTIDÆ*).

SARCOPHAGÌNÆ

Head not quadrangular in profile; third and fourth sternites less evident, covering margins of tergites; theca of penis usually with spine; arista bare or with very short pubescence; two sterno-pleural bristles present; front often with orbital bristles . . . . b

b. Middle tibiæ near the middle with a single extensor bristle; cheeks rather narrow, eyes large, front of both sexes of nearly equal breadth; arista sometimes with weak pubescence; third and fourth sternites completely covered. Larvæ feeding on supplies stored in nests of various bees and wasps. (Miltográmma, Apódacra, Craticùlina, Hilarélla, Metòpia, Opsídia, Pediasiomỳia, Pachyoph-thálma, Senotaínia). (*METOPIÌNÆ*). MILTOGRAMMATÌNÆ

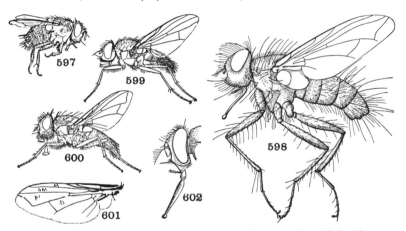

Figs. 597–602. Tachinidæ, Dexiidæ, Anthomyiidæ, Muscidæ, Calliphoridæ

597. **Belvosia.** Tachinidæ.
598. **Ptilodexia.** Dexiidæ.
599. **Limnophora** (Cole) Anthomyiidæ.
600. **Pollenia** (Cole) Calliphoridæ.
601. **Musca,** wing. Muscidæ.
602. **Stomoxys,** head. Muscidæ.

Middle tibiæ with at least two bristles near the middle; eyes small, cheeks broad, face broader than vertex, front of female broader than of male; arista bare c

c. Antennæ very short; genitalia large; sternites two to five large, open; eyes very small. (Paramacronýchia, Nemoræa, Eur.; Brachycòma, Wohlfártia) . . . . PARAMACRONYCHIÌNÆ
Antennæ normal; genitalia small; sternites two to five more or less covered . . . . d

d. Tergites three and four with discal macrochætæ, body bristly; eyes pubescent; theca fused with penis, forceps long. (Rhaphiochæta, Brachymèra, Eur.) . . . . RHAPHIOCHÆTÌNÆ
Tergites three and four without discal macrochætæ, body with

short bristles; eyes bare; theca free, penis without membrane.
(Amòbia, Hóplisa, Morínia) .... AMOBIÌNÆ

Calypteres narrow, with the inner edge generally bending away
from scutellum; fifth ventral segment of male split to the middle;
arista pubescent; eyes sometimes hairy. Larvæ parasitic on sow-
bugs, snails, beetles, etc. (Rhinóphora, Frauenfeldia, Macquártia,
Melanóphora, Phỳto). (Including *STACKELBERGOMYÌIDÆ*,
a dune-living European fly with deep cheeks, flat body, incrassate
legs and imperfect apical cell.) .... RHINOPHÓRIDÆ

73. Ventral membrane more or less evident between the reduced
sternites and the margins of the tergites, if not the female
abdomen is tipped by an under-folded claw (*Phania*); abdomen
destitute of stout bristles; facial plate more or less convexly produced nose-like below the vibrissal angles and fused with the
lowest part (epistome). Larvæ parasitic on bugs and beetles.
(Phàsia, Alóphora, Cystogáster, Clytiomỳia, Leucóstoma, Phània,
Phorántha, Rhodagỳne (= *Gymnosòma*), Trichópoda). (Including *GYMNOSOMÁTIDÆ* with four, not five, abdominal segments) .... PHASÌIDÆ
Ventral membrane not visible; abdomen bearing some stout bristles;
facial plate flattened, at most slightly produced.............74

74. Antennæ inserted usually at or below middle of eyes, the arista
usually hairy; no presutural intra-alar bristle; ventral segments
of abdomen concealed below the meeting edges of the tergites;
legs often relatively long. Larvæ parasitic in beetles. (Déxia,
Cylindromỳia (= *Ocýptera*), Loewia, Myiócera, Ptilodéxia (Fig.
598), Rhynchodéxia, Rutíllia, Thelaìra, Therèsia). (Including the
Australian *RUTILLÌIDÆ*, with nasute epistoma, reduced sternites and usually metallic color.)................... DEXÌIDÆ
Antennæ inserted above middle of eyes, the arista usually bare,
rarely short-pubescent (Fig. 556D); intra-alar bristles usually extending in front of suture, if not the ventral segments broadly
visible, or the fifth ventral of male is vestigial; at least two post-
humeral and three posterior intra-alar bristles. Tachina flies.
Larvæ mostly endoparasitic in caterpillars and other insects.
(Táchina or Larvævora, Áphria, Árchytas, Belvòsia (Fig. 597),
Echinomỳia, Ernéstia, Exorísta, Frontìna, Linnæmỳia, Masícera,
Nemoræa, Phorócera, Peletèria, Plàgia, Salmàcia (= *Gonia*) (Fig.
556 D), Siphòna, Stúrmia, Winthemia, Zeníllia). Including
EXORÍSTIDÆ, MASICÉRIDÆ, HISTRICÌIDÆ, etc.).
TACHÍNIDÆ or LARVÆVÓRIDÆ [1]

---

[1] This dominant group has been divided by several taxonomists into about sixty
so-called families, which do not have the rank of the dipterous subfamilies presented
in the previous portions of the key. Because the limits of these groups have not been
agreed on by the students of the muscoid flies and because there is no satisfactory

75. Fourth vein (M_1) often bending forward to narrow the apical cell at the margin (Fig. 601); if the apical cell is not narrowed then the eyes are not widely separated, or cruciate bristles are present on the front, and the lower calypter is longer than the upper, and the abdomen proper contains only five segments; if the eyes are widely separated (the females and some males) the oval, more or less bristly abdomen is distinctive; scutellar suture complete. (MUSCÒIDEA) 76

Apical cell not narrowed at margin (Fig. 596); no cruciate frontal bristles; eyes broadly separated in both sexes; lower calypter not longer than the upper; scutellar suture interrupted in the middle; abdomen more or less elongate, with six segments before the genitalia (the first two fused together, as usual). (*SCATO-MÝZIDÆ, SCATOPHÁGIDÆ, SCOPEUMÁTIDÆ*).
CORDYLÙRIDÆ

a. Propleural bristle absent; usually one sternopleural and five dorso-central bristles; first vein bare above........................b

Propleural bristle present; one to three sternopleurals c

b. Head broad; palpi spoon-shaped or leaf-like. (**Hydromỳza, Acanthocnèma, Microprosòpa, Pogonòta, Spathióphora**).
HYDROMYZÌNÆ

Head rounded; palpi narrow; heavily pollinose species. (**Scopeùma** (= *Scathóphaga*) (Fig. 596), **Coniostérnum, Ceratinóstoma, Scatomỳza**). (*SCATOPHAGÌNÆ*) ...... SCOPEUMATÌNÆ

c. Front femora and tibiæ at most with single row of bristles beneath.. d

Front femora with two rows of flexor bristles, front tibiæ with single or double rows; first vein bare above. (**Noréllia, Acantholèna, Norellisòma**) .... NORELLIÌNÆ

d. Palpi without long hairs; face short; legs strong. (**Clidogástra, Cochliàrium, Gymnomèra**) ....CLIDOGASTRÌNÆ

Palpi usually with apical bristle; face long; first vein usually setose above. (**Cordylùra** (Fig. 594), **Amaurosòma, Gonárcticus, Megophthálma, Parallelómma** (Fig. 595), **Scoliaphleps**).
CORDYLURÌNÆ

76. Either the hypopleural or pteropleural bristles or hairs present (Fig. 586); basal bristles of abdomen reduced; fourth vein bending or curving forward (straight in *Eginia*); arista feathered to tip...77

---

published key no attempt is here made to present subdivisions of the Tachinidæ. Even the distinctions between the conventional families Dexiidæ and Tachinidæ have broken down of recent years with the discovery of annectant genera. Perhaps the best solution is to consider but two subfamilies, Dexiinæ and Tachininæ, with a unique army of legions, cohorts and tribes of genera comprising the latter. (See page 7.) (An exhaustive recent work is the twelve-volume Manual of Myiodaires by C. H. T. Townsend, completed in 1942.)

Neither the hypopleural nor pteropleural hairs or bristles present; abdomen usually bristly; fourth vein curving backward (if curving forward the arista is not feathered to the tip); arista sometimes bare (Fig. 599)....................ANTHOMYÌIDÆ

a. Anal vein complete, faint apically but reaching margin...........b
   Anal vein not distinctly traceable to margin.....................c
b. Eyes of male close together on the narrowed front; calypteres large.
   (Anthomỳia, Chortóphila (*C. antíqua*, Onion maggot, *C. brássicæ*, Cabbage maggot, *C. cilicrùra* (=*florilèga*), Seedcorn maggot), Ègle, Hammomỳia, Hylemỳia (*H. coarctàta*, Wheat bulb fly), Hydrophòria, Opsolàsia, Pegomỳia (*P. hyoscyami*, Beet-fly, *P. rubívora*, Raspberry cane maggot), Phórbia, Pycnoglóssa). (*HY-LEMYIÌNÆ, PEGOMYIÌNÆ*)........... ANTHOMYIÌNÆ
   Eyes of both sexes widely separated by the broad front; calypteres small. (Fucéllia, Chiròsia, Mycóphaga, Myopìna).
                                                    FUCELLIÌNÆ
c. Lower sternopleural bristle wanting, or if present, closer to one of the upper sternopleurals than to the other....................d
   Lower sternopleural equidistant from the two upper; front in both sexes one-third the width of the head, each orbit with one long backward-directed bristle on upper half; thorax with but one pair of presutural dorsocentral bristles; lower stigmatal bristle directed downward; eyes of both sexes usually widely separated. (Cœnòsia, Chelísia, Atherígona, Limnospìla, Lispocéphala, Schœnomỳza) .... CŒNOSIÌNÆ
d. Pteropleura with a central group of hairs; palpi dilated apically, usually conspicuously dilated; front of both sexes equal to eyewidth, the interfrontalia without cruciate bristles; parafacials with some hairs on their entire length. (Líspa)...........LISPÌNÆ
   Pteropleura usually without such group of hairs, but if haired, the front of the male is narrower than that of the female; palpi not conspicuously dilated; parafacials bare below base of antennæ...e
e. Hind tibiæ of male with a strong dorsal bristle just beyond middle..f
   Hind tibiæ of male without such a strong dorsal bristle.........g
f. Anal vein very short, stopping abruptly, the seventh vein (axillary or A2) more or less distinctly curved forward around the apex of the first anal; female with wholly convex front, the broad orbits (and in males with wide front also) bearing two frontoorbital bristles on upper half directed outward over eyes, or the upper one directed slightly backward; middle tibiæ of male more or less densely pubescent and often swollen on inner side. (Fánnia, Cœlomỳia, Piezùra)....................FANNIÌNÆ
   Axillary vein not curving around end of anal vein; front of female more or less projecting forward, orbits not with two upper frontoorbitals curving outward over eyes in either sex; middle tibiæ

of male not pubescent or swollen. (Arícia (=*Phaònia*), Allœostỳlus, Diályta, Hèra, Hydrotæa, Ophỳra, Pogonomỳia). (*PHAO-NIÌNÆ*, including *HYDROTÆÌNÆ*) .... ARICIÌNÆ

g. Thorax with an uneven number of dark stripes, or unmarked; scutellum with only the larger basal and subapical bristles; face and oral margin usually produced; third and fourth veins parallel or slightly convergent, rarely divergent; usually sparsely short-setose. (Limnóphora (Fig. 599)) .... LIMNOPHORÌNÆ
Thorax with an even number of dark stripes, or rarely unmarked; scutellum usually with stout discal, prebasal and preapical bristles in addition to the basals and subapicals; face usually vertical, rarely produced; third and fourth veins usually divergent or parallel; usually strongly setose. (Mydæa (including Spilogáster), Azèlia, Hebecnèma, Helìna) .... MYDÆÌNÆ

77. Proboscis needle-like, porrect, at rest completely ensheathed by the long slender palpi; arista strongly plumose with feathered hairs (Fig. 556E); prosternum membranous; middle coxæ separated by the forward-projecting metasternum; abdominal spiracles located in the membrane between tergites and sternites. Tsetse flies. (Glossìna, Ethiop.) (Fig. 556 E) .... GLOSSÍNIDÆ
Proboscis, if elongate and porrect, not ensheathed by the palpi; hairs of arista not feathered; prosternal plate developed; abdominal spiracles located in second to fifth tergites .... MÚSCIDÆ

a. Proboscis of both sexes elongate, rigid, fitted for piercing and sucking blood, the labella not enlarged; arista with long hairs on upper side, bare or pubescent below; lower calypter rounded posteriorly, its inner basal margin well separated from the lateral basal angles of scutellum. (Stomóxys (*S. cálcitrans*, Stable fly (Fig. 602)), Bdellolárynx, Hæmatòbia, Lyperòsia (*L. írritans*, Horn fly); Haphóspatha, Eur., Afr.; Hæmatobósca, China).
STOMOXYDÌNÆ
Proboscis not heavily chitinized, the labella fleshy, fitted for lapping ....b

b. Apical cell widely open, the fourth vein gently curving back; hypopleural bristles present above hind coxæ; pteropleural bristles absent beneath root of wing. (Egínia, Palæarc.) .... EGINIÌNÆ
Apical cell narrowed; hypopleural bristles nearly always absent, pteropleural bristles or hairs often present; lower calypter with posterior curvature more or less transverse, the inner basal angle very close to and often touching or underlying the basal lateral angle of scutellum. (Músca (*M. doméstica*, Housefly (Figs. 557, 601), Cordylòbia (*C. anthropóphaga*, Tumbu-fly, Ethiop.), Dasýphora, Graphomỳia, Mesembrìna, Moréllia, Muscìna, Myiospìla, Pyréllia, Synthesiomỳia) .... MUSCÌNÆ

78. Mouth-opening small, the mouthparts vestigial; antennæ sunken in the facial grooves which form a rounded pocket, arista bare; vibrissæ and bristles absent, no sternopleural or pteropleural bristles; scutellar suture broadly interrupted at middle; ovipositor sturdy and inflexed under abdomen; costa ending at third vein (R_5) which terminates much before tip of wing, the apical cell widely open (Fig. 593). Horse botflies, cosmopolitan. (Gasteró-philus (Figs. 592, 593) Gyrostígma, Rhingogastróphilus).

GASTEROPHÍLIDÆ

Mouth-opening normal, the mouthparts functioning; third and fourth veins usually parallel or converging, very rarely markedly diverging; larvæ not internal parasites of horses, etc. 79

79. Costa entire, no indication of a break near the end of the subcosta nor near the humeral crossvein: Sc nearly always distinctly sepa-rated from R_1 and ending in the costa an appreciable distance before R_1 which usually terminates near or beyond middle of wing (see Fig. 608). 80

Costa fractured just before end of subcosta (best seen by trans-mitted light), or if Sc is imperfect the costa is visibly broken or constricted before end of first vein (R_1) (Fig. 603), or at least with an indication of such fracture; sometimes with an addi-tional break near the humeral crossvein (Fig. 658). 106

80. Subcosta complete, ending in the costa, usually free from R_1, rarely closely approximated to it, rarely wanting; anal cell present. 81

Subcosta incomplete, developed only at base and continuing as an evanescent fold, not attaining the costa; anal cell faint or absent; postvertical bristles divergent. 105

81. Vibrissæ present at the vibrissal angle of the head, in distinction to peristomial or buccal bristles or hairs. 82

Definite vibrissæ absent. 85

82. Palpi well developed. 83

Palpi very small, vestigial; anterior orbital bristles never developed; head spherical, cheeks narrow; arista bare or nearly so; posterior spiracle usually with at least one bristle; abdomen somewhat elongate and usually narrowed at base; black scavenger flies. Cosmopolitan . . . . SÉPSIDÆ

a. Postvertical bristles wanting; head broadened, with projecting eyes. (Eurychoromỳia) . . . . EURYCHOROMYIÌNÆ

Postverticals present and diverging; if absent, the head is not broad-ened . . . . b

b. First and second basal cells united. (Pandòra (Fig. 608), widespr.; Saltélliseps, Ethiop., Asiat.). PANDORÌNÆ

Basal cells separate. c

c. Thorax verrucose, subshining, pubescence fine, forming a sheen;

dorsal abdominal segments devoid of bristles and setæ. (**Toxó-poda, Paratoxópoda,** mainly Ethiop.)..........TOXOPODÌNÆ
Thorax not verrucose, at least mesopleuræ shining, hairs short, not forming a sheen; abdomen often with bristles.................d
d. Postocular and mesopleural bristles wanting. (**Themìra** (Fig. 607), **Enícita,** Holarc.; **Protothemìra,** Palæarc.)........THEMIRÌNÆ
At least mesopleural bristle present...........................e

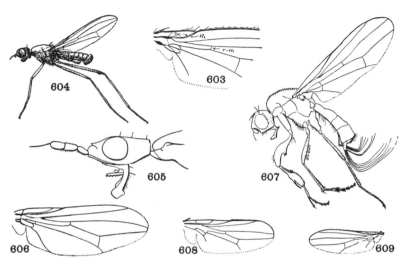

Figs. 603–609. Micropezidæ, Neriidæ, Tanypezidæ, Sepsidæ

603. **Trichoscelis,** basal portion of wing. Trichoscelidæ.
604. **Paracalobata,** male (Cole) Micropezidæ.
605. **Nerius,** profile of head. Neriidæ.
606. **Tanypeza,** wing. Tanypezidæ.
607. **Themira,** male. Sepsidæ.
608. **Pandora,** wing. Sepsidæ.
609. **Sepsis,** wing (Cole) Sepsidæ.

e. Front femora of male more or less excised before end and provided with varying sets of bristles, thorns or prongs; orbital bristle weak or wanting. (**Sépsis** (Fig. 609), cosmop.; **Lasiosépsis,** Eur., Ethiop.) ....SEPSÌNÆ
Front femora not excised toward end, with or without rows of bristles but without spinigerous tubercles.....................f
f. A strong orbital bristle present on each side; abdomen of both sexes without bristles; postocular bristle strong. (**Meròplius,** widespr.).
MEROPLIÌNÆ

Orbital bristle weak or wanting, or if present, the postocular bristle
is weak or wanting. (Nemópoda, Perochæta, Sepsidomórpha,
Holarc.) .... NEMOPODÌNÆ

83. Thorax convex; cheeks, pleuræ and legs not remarkably bristly;
postvertical bristles divergent.............................84
Mesonotum and scutellum more or less flattened; head, body and
legs coarsely bristly (Fig. 613). Seashore species. (See couplet
94) .... CŒLÓPIDÆ

84. Second antennal joint usually with an angulate projection from
the exterior edge (Fig. 635); interfrontal cross-bristles often present; tibiæ usually with preapical bristles; anal vein abbreviated,
not reaching margin. (See couplets 114 and 136)....CLUSÌIDÆ
Second antennal joint without angular projection; no interfrontal
cross-bristles; tibiæ without preapical bristles; anal vein continuing
as a fold almost to margin. (See couplet 116). (Acténoptera,
(=Gymnomỳza), Palæarc.)........NEOTTIOPHÍLIDÆ, part

85. First posterior cell (R$_5$) closed or much narrowed at apex due to
the convergence of both third and fourth veins (wide in Nothybidæ, couplet 88, which have remarkably long prosternum); abdomen elongate; legs long, or very long and slender..........86
First posterior cell widely open, if narrowed, the abdomen is short
and the legs are not unusually long and slender..............90

86. Eyes large, the cheeks and posterior orbits narrow; upper occiput
concave 87
Eyes moderately large, front not narrow, cheeks and posterior orbits
not distinctly narrow, face often greatly retreating, occiput usually large; ocellar and humeral bristles absent................89

87. Proboscis very long and geniculate; ovipositor elongate; arista terminal. (See couplet 60.) (Stylogáster, Am., Afr.).
                              CONÓPIDÆ, part
Proboscis and ovipositor not elongate; arista dorsal; hind metatarsi
with basal group of bristles...............................88

88. Ocellar and humeral bristles present, though sometimes small;
prothorax small; first vein (R$_1$) setulose; front of male narrow.
(Tanypèza (Fig. 606), Polphopèza, Scipopèza, Tritanypèza,
mainly Neotrop.) .... TANYPÉZIDÆ
Ocellar and humeral bristles absent; thorax elongate, the prosternum
prominent, the front legs attached behind middle of thorax; hind
femora without bristles on posterior edge; first vein bare; front
of both sexes wide. (Nothỳbus, Malay.).......NOTHÝBIDÆ

89. Arista dorsal, located toward base of the third antennal joint; front
legs shorter than posterior pairs from which they are widely
separated, the front coxæ short; propleuræ scarcely produced in
front; second antennal joint without projection; palpi usually
small. Mostly tropical. (MICROPÉZIDÆ)..........TÝLIDÆ

a. Front rather uniform in sculpturing; ocelli placed in back; antennæ approximate; male genitalia turgid..........................b
Front with well-marked areas; ocelli near middle of head; antennæ separated; male genitalia relatively inconspicuous. (Tæniáptera, Callobatìna, Cardiacéphala, Grallomỳza, Grallopèza, Hoplocheilòma, Ptílosphen, Rainièria (= *Tanýpoda*), Scipòpus). (*RAI-NIERIÌNÆ, TANYPODÌNÆ*) ....TÆNIÁPTERÌNÆ
b. Front opaque; hind tibiæ without extensor bristle; second basal separated from discal cell. (Trepidària (= *Calóbata*), Calobatélla, Cnodacóphora, Paracalóbata) (*CALOBÁTIDÆ*).
TREPIDARIÌNÆ
Front shining; hind tibiæ with extensor setæ; second basal and discal cells confluent. (Tỳlos (= *Micropèza*), Cliopèza, Cryógonus, Metopobráchia, Neriocéphalus). (*MICROPEZÌNÆ*).
TYLÌNÆ

Arista apical or subapical (Fig. 605); front legs longer than posterior pairs, the front coxæ lengthened, thus placing the front legs close to the middle pair; propleuræ strongly developed beneath in front of front coxæ; second antennal joint with a finger-like process on inside edge; palpi long. Mostly tropical. (Nèrius (Fig. 605), Macrótoma, Odontoloxòzus, Odontoscèlia, Telostỳlus).
NERÌIDÆ
90. Eyes prominently bulging, the vertex sunken; scutellum often large and grooved; femora and usually hind tibiæ greatly enlarged; anal cell rather large; prelabrum well developed......91
Eyes less prominent, vertex not sunken; first posterior cell widely open, if rarely narrowed the femora are not thick...........92
91. First vein ending far beyond subcosta, first posterior cell usually narrowed apically due to the angulation of the fourth vein at apex of discal cell; posterior spiracle with a group of bristles; palpi broad. Principally Neotropical. (Rhopalomèra, Apophorhýnchus, Krœberia, Rhýtidops, Willistoniélla (Fig. 610)).
RHOPALOMÉRIDÆ
First vein ending close to subcosta, first posterior cell widely open; posterior spiracle without group of bristles; palpi narrow. (See couplet 126). (Rhinótora (Fig. 611), Neotrop., Ethiop.).
RHINOTÓRIDÆ
92. Some or all tibiæ with preapical bristle on extensor side; ovipositor short, retractile 93
Tibiæ without extensor preapical bristle; in case preapical bristles are present either the ovipositor is long and chitinized, or the first vein is setulose, or the anal crossvein (Cu_1) is broken.....97
93. Scutellum never broadly covering the wings and abdomen.......94
Scutellum enormously enlarged and convexly inflated, covering the abdomen and the wings when at rest (Fig. 615); nearly bristleless

flies with shortened thorax, antennæ porrect, arista subapical, prelabrum large; abdominal sternites very small; alula large, discal and second basal cells confluent. Indoaustralian and African. (Celỳphus (Fig. 615), Acelỳphus, Parcelỳphus, Spaniocelỳphus).

CELÝPHIDÆ

94. Thorax convex; cheeks, pleuræ and legs not remarkably bristly; last tarsal joint not flattened..................................95

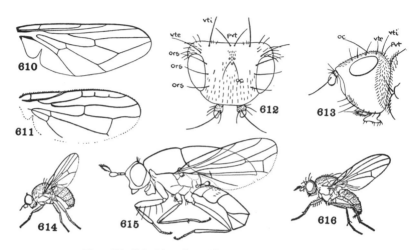

Figs. 610–616. Rhopalomeridæ, Rhinotoridæ, Cœlopidæ, Chamæmyiidæ, Celyphidæ, Lauxaniidæ

610. Willistoniella, wing. Rhopalomeridæ.
611. Rhinotora, wing. Rhinotoridæ.
612. Orygma, head from above. For lettering see Fig. 594. Cœlopidæ.
613. Orygma, head in profile. Cœlopidæ.
614. Leucopis (Cole) Chamæmyiidæ.
615. Celyphus. Celyphidæ.
616. Minettia (Cole) Lauxaniidæ.

Mesonotum and scutellum flattened; head, body and legs coarsely bristly; last tarsal joint flat and enlarged. Seashore species. (PHYCODRÓMIDÆ) .... CŒLÓPIDÆ

a. Postvertical bristles convergent or parallel; metathoracic spiracle without bristles; propleural bristle absent. (Cœlòpa, Fucomỳia).

CŒLOPÌNÆ

Postverticals divergent; metathoracic spiracle with group of bristles; propleural present. (See couplet 83.) (Orýgma (Figs. 612, 613)).

ORYGMATÌNÆ

95. Postvertical bristles convergent or crossing; second antennal joint
with dorsal bristle; one or two sternopleural bristles and one
mesopleural present; lower edge of front femora bearing bristles;
anal and second basal cells small, anal vein abruptly shortened
(Fig. 616); two or one fronto-orbital bristles, the lower often
directed inward. Many genera, mostly tropical. (Lauxània, Asiló-
stoma, Calliòpe, Camptoprosopélla, Griphoneùra, Halidayélla,
Homoneùra, Lauxaniélla, Minéttia (Fig. 616), Pachycerìna,
Pelomỳza, Sapromỳza, Sapromyzosòma, Steganópsis, Trigonometò-
pus). (Including *TRIGONOMETÓPIDÆ* with front horizontal). (*SAPROMÝZIDÆ*) .... LAUXANÌIDÆ
Postverticals parallel or divergent, rarely wanting; second antennal
joint rarely with dorsal bristle; mesopleural and usually sternopleural bristles wanting; front femora not bristly beneath; anal
vein reaching margin, at least as a fold.....................96

96. Prelabrum pronounced, not retractable with the infolding of the
proboscis; first vein ending beyond middle of wing; femoral
bristles undeveloped. A rather small family; principally Holarctic .... DRYOMÝZIDÆ

a. Cheeks evenly pubescent; third antennal joint spherical, antennæ
separated; oral margin not protruding, palpi without apical bristle;
anterior dorsocentral bristles present. (Helcomỳza (= Actòra),
Heterochìla, Macromelandèria, Œdoparèna) .. HELCOMYZÌNÆ
Cheeks with a bare groove; third antennal joint compressed, longer
than broad, antennæ not separated; oral margin protruding, palpi
with apical bristle; anterior dorsocentral bristle absent; middle
femora with posterior row of bristles. (Dryomỳza, Neuróctena
(Fig. 619)) .... DRYOMYZÌNÆ

Prelabrum vestigial, rarely chitinized, not touching oral margin
when the proboscis is extended; first vein ending at middle of
wing; femora setulose, their bristles developed, a characteristic
bristle usually present near middle of anterior face of middle
femora (Fig. 617). Many genera and species; widespread, largely
Holarctic. (*TETANOCÉRIDÆ*) .... SCIOMÝZIDÆ

a. Abdomen of female with seven segments, ovipositor not retractile;
arista subapical; front femora not bristly. (Tetanùra).
                              TETANURÌNÆ
No ovipositor; apical segments of female abdomen, beyond fifth,
retractile; arista basal; front femora with bristles.............b
b. Propleural bristle present; front usually without differentiated
median polished stripe; second antennal joint short. (Sciomỳza
(Fig. 618), Mélina, Oidemátops, Phæomỳia, Pherbéllia (= Ditæ-
nia), Pterómicra) .... SCIOMYZÌNÆ

Propleural bristle wanting; front usually with a distinct polished median stripe, rarely subshining; second antennal joint long. (Tetanócera, Antichæta, Díctya, Élgiva, Hedroneùra, Hoplodíctya, Euthýcera, Límnia, Pœcilógrapha, Renócera, Salticélla, Sépedon (Fig. 617), Statínia (= Coremácera)). (EUTHYCERÌNÆ).

TETANOCERÌNÆ

97. Head produced on each side into a lateral process bearing the eye at the tip and the antennæ widely distant from each other on the eye-stalk (Fig. 621), frontal lunule flattened; subcosta weak

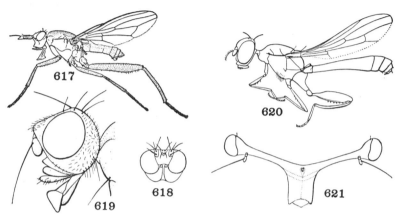

Figs. 617–621. Sciomyzidæ, Dryomyzidæ, Megamerinidæ, Diopsidæ

617. **Sepedon** (Cole) Sciomyzidæ.
618. **Sciomyza,** head from front (Hendel) Sciomyzidæ.
619. **Neuroctena,** head from side. Dryomyzidæ.
620. **Syringogaster.** Megamerinidæ.
621. **Diopsis,** head from front. Diopsidæ.

and parallel with first vein, third vein arising from second near middle of wing, discal cell confluent with second basal; front femora more or less thickened; scutellum bituberculate. A small family, mainly tropical. (Diópsis (Fig. 621), Diasemópsis, Megálabops, Sphyracéphala, Teleópsis) ....DIÓPSIDÆ

Head not produced so that the eyes are stalked and the antennæ are distantly separated; third vein arising from second toward base of wing; scutellum not bituberculate....................98

98. Anal crossvein (Cu_1) not angulate, the anal cell not acutely produced (Fig. 608), first vein bare; ovipositor retractile, not prominent. (If legs and thorax are unusually elongate, see Nothybidæ, couplet 88) 99

Anal crossvein usually angulate so that the anal cell is acutely produced (Fig. 624), or at least the anal cell apically angled, first vein usually setulose above; ovipositor chitinized and more or less projecting, usually flattened; post-vertical bristles diverging or parallel; palpi developed. (If Indomalayan, elongate flies with slender legs and prominent prothorax, see Phytalmiidæ, couplet 107) 101

99. Hind femora long, thickened and spinose beneath; basal cells lengthened, anal vein usually reaching margin; abdomen elongate, slender at base, clavate; postvertical bristles wanting. A small family; Europe, N. America, Oceania. (Megamerìna (= Líssa), Syringogáster (Fig. 620), Syrittomỳia, Texàra) .... MEGAMERÍNIDÆ
Hind femora rarely thickened, not biseriately spinose beneath; basal cells short, anal vein abbreviated; postverticals present, though sometimes small 100

100. Postvertical bristles diverging; palpi vestigial; front legs of male often more or less deformed and bristly; at least abdomen more or less shining, the base narrowed. (See couplet 82) .... SÉPSIDÆ
Postverticals converging, sometimes wanting; palpi developed; femora not spinose; usually densely gray-pruinose species, the oval abdomen usually pictured with paired brown spots. Europe, N. America, Asia. (Chamæmỳia (= Ochthíphila), Acrometòpia, Leucòpis, (Fig. 614), Leucopomỳia, Paraleucòpis, Pseudodínia). (OCHTHIPHÍLIDÆ) .... CHAMÆMYȈDÆ

101. First and third veins usually bare; first posterior cell sometimes apically narrowed or rarely closed; body often metallic; head large, hemispherical, front broad, eyes not bulging, proboscis stout. (Ulídia, Acrostícta, Chætópsis (Fig. 625), Chrysomỳza, Œdòpa, Euxésta (Fig. 624), Mosíllus (= Myodìna), Seóptera, Stenerétma, Tímia). (CHÆTÓPSIDÆ) .... ULIDȈDÆ
First vein usually setulose or hairy, when bare either the first posterior cell is not narrowed, or the eyes protrude, or the costal cell is very large 102

102. Ocelli present; ovipositor flattened......................... 103
Ocelli usually absent; basal joint of ovipositor large and conical; front projecting, face retreating, mouth-opening small, clypeus small, proboscis not heavy; second antennal joint elongate; no propleural bristle, prothoracic stigma with a row of hairs; third vein bare .... PYRGÓTIDÆ

a. Third antennal joint rounded; subcosta normal or weak before the end. (Pyrgòta (Fig. 622), Adapsília, Bromóphila, Campylócera, Hypotýphla, Teretrùra, Trichempòdia) .....PYRGOTÍNÆ

Third antennal joint pointed or angulate at tip; subcosta distant from costa, suddenly broken and ending at right angle. (Toxùra, Acropyrgòta, Epicerélla) .... TOXURÍNÆ

103. Third antennal joint round or short-ovate; first vein ending much
beyond subcosta; eyes rather protuberant; face vertical, excavated
in middle, without antennal grooves, prelabrum small; mesonotum
bristly in back only; propleural bristle weak or wanting, sternopleural bristle present; non-metallic flies. (Pterocálla (Fig.
623), Callopístria, Dasymetòpa, Myénnis, Pseudotephrìtis, Stylophthal-
mỳia) .... PTEROCÁLLIDÆ
Third antennal joint with sharpened apex; antennal grooves distinct; subcostal cell not large............................104

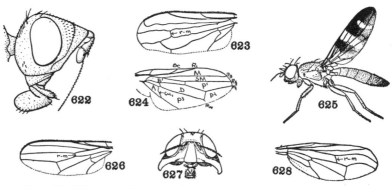

Figs. 622–628. Pyrgotidæ, Pterocallidæ, Ulidiidæ, Richardiidæ, Phytalmiidæ

622. **Pyrgota**, profile of head. Pyrgotidæ.
623. **Pterocalla**, wing (Williston) Pterocallidæ.
624. **Euxesta**, wing. Ulidiidæ.
625. **Chætopsis** (Cole) Ulidiidæ.
626. **Cœlometopia**, wing (Williston) Richardiidæ.
627. **Phytalmodes**, head from front (Bezzi) Phytalmiidæ.
628. **Phytalmodes**, wing (Bezzi) Phytalmiidæ.

104. Propleural and usually sternopleural bristles absent, three supra-
alar bristles; mouth-opening very large, clypeus large, proboscis
heavy, palpi broad. A large group, mainly tropical. (Including
CEPHALÍIDÆ) .... PLATYSTOMÁTIDÆ

a. Upper occiput usually convex; abdomen stalked, elongate; basal
cells of wing diminutive; sternopleurals usually present; ant-like
species. (Myrmecomỳia, Delphínia, Myrmecothèa, Tritóxa).
                                    MYRMECOMYIÎNÆ
Upper occiput never convex; abdomen not ant-like, if elongate no
sternopleurals present; basal cells not small....................b
b. Epistome convexly projecting above oral margin. (Tráphera,
Lùle, Pìara, Xíria) .... TRAPHERÌNÆ
Epistome not convexly projecting............................c

c. Abdomen slender, much longer than wide, usually compressed; third antennal joint much longer than wide, arista not long-plumose, the distal part bare; at most one weak fronto-orbital bristle. (Stenopterìna, Antineùra, Duomỳia, Elassogáster, Lamprophthálma, Xenáspis) .... STENOPTERINÎNÆ
Abdomen usually elliptical or short-oval, if slender either the arista is feathered to apex, or antennæ shorter, or two fronto-orbitals present ....d

d. Abdomen spindle-shaped, broadest at middle or beyond middle; lower calypter small. (Rivéllia, Cleitàmia, Diácrita, Ídana, Laglaisia) .... RIVELLIÎNÆ
Abdomen broadly oval, widest before middle, or very small and narrowly joined to thorax. (Platýstoma, Achìas, Brèa, Bromóphila, Euprosòpia, Lamprogáster, Loxoneùra, Naùpoda, Peltacanthìna, Scholástes) .... PLATYSTOMATÎNÆ

Propleural and sternopleural bristles present, four supra-alar bristles, anterior dorsocentral bristle present; mouthparts less developed, cheeks broad. (Otìtes (= Órtalis), Anacámpta, Hérina, Dorýcera, Melièria (= Ceróxys), Tétanops, Tephronòta). (Including CEROXÝDIDÆ, DORYCÉRIDÆ). (ORTALÍDIDÆ). OTÍTIDÆ

105. Discal cell complete (sometimes open in Sphyroperíscelis), anterior crossvein near middle of wing, costa extending only to third vein (R₅) (to fourth vein in Cỳamops and Períscelis), second vein (R₃) long, ending near tip of wing; vibrissæ absent. Europe, America, Ceylon. (Períscelis, Cỳamops, Marbènia, Neoscùtops, Podócera, Sphyroperíscelis (Fig. 629), Scùtops)
PERISCELÍDIDÆ
Discal cell entirely wanting, anterior crossvein located near base of wing, costa extending to fourth vein, second vein very short, ending close to first vein; vibrissæ present. (See couplet 132.) (Astìa (= Astèia) (Fig. 645), Liomỳza, Sigaloéssa (= Crepidohámma), Stenómicra, Uranùcha) .... ASTÎIDÆ

106. Typically heavy-bodied flies (Fig. 633), with broad, five-segmented abdomen and with rows of bristles on thorax, abdomen and legs (Anthophasia with tergites fused and apical bristles alone present on abdomen); second antennal joint as long as third or longer, arista bare; vibrissæ present; third vein close to second and ending much before wing-tip, costa stopping before tip of wing, first and third veins bristly above at least at base, subcosta distinct, obliquely ascending at tip, anal cell prolonged into a sharp point. Bright-colored flies, 7–18 mm. in length, with banded wings, resembling stout tachinids. (Tachinísca (Fig. 633), Peru, Bolivia; Anthophàsia (= Tachinœstrus), Tachiniscídia, Ethiop.).
TACHINÍSCIDÆ
Not large, heavy-bodied, or very bristly flies.................107

BULLETIN: MUSEUM OF COMPARATIVE ZOOLOGY

107. Legs long and slender, thorax large, prothorax often neck-like, abdomen long and clavate, the basal segment as long as remainder of abdomen; first posterior cell not narrowed; one or no fronto-orbital bristle, no postvertical, propleural, sternopleural or dorso-central bristles, two scutellars; arista long-plumose; cheeks often produced as lateral processes. Indomalayan, African. (**Phytálmia** (= *Elaphomyia*), **Angítula, Angitulòides, Atopógnathus, Clito-dòca, Giraffomỳia, Phytalmòdes** (Figs. 627, 628), **Terastiomỳia**).
PHYTALMĬIDÆ
Legs not unduly long and slender, prothorax not neck-like, body not suggestive of the Neriidæ......................................108

108. Costa broken only at end of subcosta (Fig. 639)..............109
Costa broken near humeral crossvein in addition to the subcostal break (Fig. 658), rarely (*Acartophthalmus*, couplet 136), the costa broken only at humeral crossvein...................133

109. Subcosta complete, ending in costa, usually independent of first radial vein (Fig. 630); second basal and anal cells complete (except Aulacogastridæ, couplet 113 (Fig. 631), with second basal and anal cells confluent)...........................110
Subcosta incomplete or vestigial, the apical portion represented as a fold, not ending independently in the costa (Fig. 646)....122

110. Vibrissæ present at the vibrissal angle (Fig. 635).............111
Vibrissæ absent, only peristomial hairs or setæ; no preapical tibial bristle 119

111. Cheek-plates continuing on the front, bearing inclinate lower fronto-orbital bristles (Fig. 594); tibiæ in addition to preapical and apical bristles usually with other bristles; metanotal suture continuous; anal crossvein straight or weakly curved, the tip of the anal cell angulate. (See couplet 75)..........**CORDYLÙRIDÆ**
Cheek-plates not continuing on the front, lower fronto-orbitals therefore not present; mesonotal cross-suture interrupted in the middle 112

112. Postvertical (postocellar) bristles divergent (Fig. 634), parallel or wanting 113
Postvertical (occipital) bristles convergent or cruciate (Fig. 637); foremost fronto-orbital bristle reclinate; costa often setose.....117

113. Second basal and discal cells confluent, anterior crossvein located before middle of cell, costa thin but not broken near humeral crossvein; no postvertical bristles; a graded series of oral bristles in addition to the vibrissæ; tibiæ without preapical bristles. (**Aulacogáster** (Figs. 631, 632), Holarc.) **AULÁCOGÁSTRIDÆ**
Second basal and discal cells separated......................114

114. Frontal orbits reaching the anterior edge of the front and bearing two to four fronto-orbital bristles (Fig. 636); second antennal joint nearly always with a triangular projection on the exterior

side; preapical bristles usually present on tibiæ. (See couplet 84).
(*CLUSIÓDIDÆ, HETERONEÙRIDÆ*) . . . . CLUSÌIDÆ

a. Postvertical bristles distant from each other, eyes hairy, arista short; costa broken only at humeral crossvein, Sc diverging from R_1. (See couplet 136.) (**Acartophthálmus** (Fig. 636), Holarc.).
ACARTOPHTHALMÌNÆ

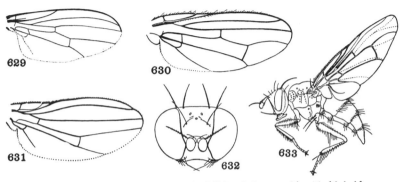

Figs. 629–633. Periscelididæ, Neottiophilidæ, Aulacogastridæ, Tachiniscidæ

629. **Sphyroperiscelis,** wing. Periscelididæ.
630. **Neottiophilum,** wing. Neottiophilidæ.
631. **Aulacogaster,** wing. Aulacogastridæ.
632. **Aulacogaster,** head from front. Aulacogastridæ.
633. **Tachinisca** (Kertesz) Tachiniscidæ.

Postverticals (postocellars) close together, eyes bare, arista twice as long as antennæ or more; costa broken at Sc. Mostly tropical. (**Clùsia** (Fig. 635), **Chætoclùsia, Clusiòdes** (=*Heteroneùra*), **Czernýola, Heteromeríngia, Sobarocéphala** (Fig. 634)).
CLUSIÌNÆ

Frontal orbits shortened, fronto-orbital bristles absent, or one or two pairs present; second antennal joint without triangular projection on exterior side 115
115. Eyes round, occiput convex; no ovipositor 116
Eyes large, semicircular, occiput concave, front of male about one-fifth width of head; female with long ovipositor. (See couplet 121). (**Lonchæa**) . . . . LONCHÆIDÆ
116. Costa spinose, first radial vein hairy above, anal vein reaching margin; four or five sternopleural bristles present; two fronto-orbital bristles; ocellar triangle large. (See couplet 84.) (**Neottióphilum** (Fig. 630), Eur., larvæ ectoparasites of nestling birds).
NEOTTIOPHÍLIDÆ

Costa not spinose, first vein not hairy, anal vein abbreviated; two
sternopleurals, one or no fronto-orbital. (**Pióphila**, cosmop. (*P.
càsei*, Cheese skipper); **Amphipògon, Mycetaùlus**, Holarc.; **Pro-
chylìza**, Nearc.) .... PIOPHÍLIDÆ

117. Orbital plates bearing the fronto-orbital bristles short (Fig. 637),
one or two reclinate fronto-orbitals, set in from the eyes, the foremost near middle of front; subcosta strong and clearly independent
of R_1, from which it diverges at apex, R_1 ending near two-fifths
the wing-length (Fig. 638); preapical tibial bristles present. A
rather large family, mainly Holarctic......... **HELOMÝZIDÆ**

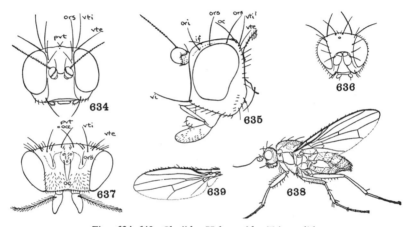

Figs. 634-649. Clusiidæ, Helomyzidæ, Trixoscelidæ

634. **Sobarocephala**, head from front. Clusiidæ.
635. **Clusia**, head in profile view. Clusiidæ.
636. **Acartophthalmus**, head from front. Clusiidæ.
637. **Suillia**, head from above. Helomyzidæ.
638. **Œcothea** (Cole) Helomyzidæ.
639. **Trixoscelis**, wing. Trixoscelidæ.

a. No propleural bristle; anal vein not reaching margin; the strip
bearing the upper fronto-orbital bristle reaching inward from
the eye-margin (Fig. 637). (**Suíllia** (=*Helomyza*, auct.) (Fig.
637), **Allophỳla, Didymochæta, Pórsenus**). (*HELOMYZÌNÆ*
auct.) .... **SUILLIÌNÆ**
Propleural bristle present; anal vein nearly or quite reaching margin; the fronto-orbital strip extending only along the eye-margin.
(**Helomỳza** (= *Blepharóptera*, = *Lèria*), **Amœbalèria, Anoró-
stoma, Eccoptomèra, Neolèria, Œcòthea** (Fig. 638), **Scoliocéntra,
Tephróchlamys**). (*LERIÌNÆ*).............. **HELOMYZÌNÆ**

Orbital plates longer, nearly attaining level of antennæ, the two or three fronto-orbital bristles close to eye-margin and the foremost in anterior portion of front; subcosta weak, parallel with R_1 with which it fuses at tip, R_1 shorter, ending at basal fourth to two-fifths of wing, anal vein not reaching margin (Fig. 639) 118

118. All tibiæ with preapical bristles; two fronto-orbital bristles; propleural bristle present, presutural dorsocentral bristles strong; costa spinulose. (**Trixóscelis** (= *Geomyza* Loew, = *Diástata* Malloch) (Fig. 639), Neóssus, Psiploplàgia, Spilóchroa, Zagònia). (*GEOMÝZIDÆ* auctt., part, *TRICHOSCÉLIDÆ*).

TRIXOSCÉLIDÆ

Tibiæ without preapical bristles; two or three fronto-orbitals; propleurals absent; palpi short; costa not spinulose; ground color yellow. Holarctic. (**Chyromỳia** (= *Chiromyia*, = *Peletóphila*), Aphaniosòma) .... **CHYROMYÌIDÆ**

119. Second segment of abdomen typically with lateral bristles; first radial vein bare, slightly deflected near apex to form a small stigmal area beyond the subcostal break; femora often thickened and furnished with spines; wings pictured with a few spots or clouds, anal crossvein recurved, anal cell not acutely pointed; eyes sometimes stalked. Many genera and species, mostly tropical. (**Richárdia, Cœlometòpia** (Fig. 626), **Cóniceps, Epiplàtea, Hemixántha, Melanolòma, Odontomèra, Setéllia, Stenomàcra**).

RICHARDÌIDÆ

Second segment of abdomen without lateral bristles; first vein not forming a characteristic stigma; femora not thickened........120

120. Anal crossvein recurved, anal vein continued beyond anal cell (Fig. 641); one fronto-orbital bristle, postvertical bristles parallel or slightly diverging; head not triangular in profile; ovipositor with definite non-retractile base..............................121

Anal crossvein straight, anal vein vestigial (Fig. 646); three to five usually weak fronto-orbitals, postocellar bristles diverging; upper part of face swollen, separating the antennæ, cheeks wide, front wide, the ocellar triangle large; third antennal joint spherical; no ovipositor. (See couplet 127.) (**Cánace** (Fig. 646), **Xanthocánace**) .... **CANACEÌDÆ**

121. Head hemispherical in profile, eyes large and vertically semicircular, cheeks narrow, front narrow, in male one-fourth to one-fifth width of head; post-vertical bristles close together; third antennal joint more or less cylindrical; metallic black species. (See couplet 115.) (**Lonchæa** (Fig. 641))................**LONCHÆIDÆ**

Head globular, eyes round, front more than one-third width of head; third antennal joint orbicular; more or less pale-colored species, wings patterned...................**PALLOPTÉRIDÆ**

a. Costa without bristles; prothoracic bristle absent; tibiæ without preapical bristle. (Pallóptera (Fig. 640))....PALLOPTERÌNÆ
Costa with bristles; prothoracic bristle present; tibiæ with two preapical bristles. (Eurygnathomỳia)....EURYGNATHOMYIÌNÆ

122. Anal cell complete or nearly so; arista pubescent..............123
Anal cell entirely wanting; no preapical bristles. (If hind metatarsi are short and thickened see Leptoceridæ, couplet 142)....132

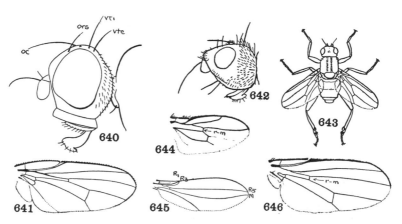

Figs. 640–646. Pallopteridæ, Lonchæidæ, Thyreophoridæ, Sphæroceridæ, Leptoceridæ, Astiidæ, Canaceidæ

640. **Palloptera,** head from side. Pallopteridæ.
641. **Lonchæa,** wing. Lonchæidæ.
642. **Thyreophora,** head in profile view. Thyreophoridæ.
643. **Sphærocera,** dorsal aspect (Howard) Sphæroceridæ.
644. **Leptocera,** wing (Spuler) Leptoceridæ.
645. **Astia,** wing. Astiidæ.
646. **Canace,** wing. Canaceidæ.

123. Hind metatarsi shortened and incrassate (Fig. 643); no sternopleural bristle, vibrissæ strong, dorsocentral bristles weak. Cosmopolitan, dung flies. (**Sphærócera** (Fig. 643), **Copromỳza** (= *Cýpsela, Bórborous*), **Lotòbia, Scatóphora** (= *Olìna*)). (*BORBÓRIDÆ, CYPSÉLIDÆ*) ....SPHÆROCÉRIDÆ
Hind metatarsi not short and thick........................124

124. Postvertical bristles converging, presutural dorsocentral bristle present, fronto-orbital bristles directed outward, interfrontal crossbristles usually present, one sternopleural bristle. (If preapical tibial bristles are present see Trixoscelidæ, couplet 117). Seashore species. (**Tethìna, Neopelomỳia, Pelomỳia, Phycomỳza, Rhicnoéssa**) ....TETHÍNIDÆ

Postvertical bristles diverging or absent, if (Anthomyzidæ, couplet 130) converging then presutural dorsocentral bristles are not developed and the two prominent fronto-orbital bristles are reclinate 125

125. Preapical tibial bristles present; postocellar bristles diverging; two reclinate and one inclinate fronto-orbital bristle present; vibrissæ present; one presutural and three postsutural dorso-central bristles; terminal segments of female abdomen slender and retractile. (Odínia, Neoalticomèrus, Tráginops) .... ODINÌIDÆ

Preapical tibial bristles absent, or insect otherwise disagreeing from preceding description 126

126. Eyes protuberant; scutellum usually tuberculate and medially grooved; front femora thickened; second basal and anal cells relatively large; at least base of anal vein firm; two reclinate fronto-orbital bristles, vibrissæ present, no postvertical bristles. Neotropical and Ethiopian. (See couplet 91). (Rhinótora (Fig. 611)).

RHINOTÓRIDÆ

Eyes not bulging; scutellum not tuberculate; front femora not enlarged; basal cells usually small 127

127. Subcosta uniformly firm though thin, separate from first radial vein almost to its tip, second basal and anal cells very small, anal crossvein straight, anal vein indicated by a weak fold (Fig. 646); no sternopleural bristle, postocellars diverging, three to five superior orbitals directed outward; ocellar triangle large, reaching edge of the front, antennæ well separated, the third joint orbicular. (See couplet 120.) (If second basal cell is open, two fronto-orbitals present, the anterior proclinate and the posterior reclinate, no postverticals, but sternopleurals present, see Aulacogastridæ, couplet 113). (Cánace (Fig. 646), Xanthocánace) ...... CANACÈIDÆ

Subcosta apically much weakened 128

128. Distinct vibrissæ present at the vibrissal angle of the face 129

Vibrissæ absent, though bristles may occur on the middle part of the cheeks; anal vein firm for some distance beyond anal cell, except when wings lack anal angle 131

129. Second basal cell present; sternopleural bristles present 130

Second basal cell open, fourth vein vestigial beyond discal cell; postvertical bristles diverging or parallel; pleuræ without bristles except the propleural; hind metatarsi not short. (Cypselosòma, Formosa) ...... SPHÆROCÉRIDÆ, CYPSELOSOMATÌNÆ

130. Postvertical (postocellar) bristles diverging; anterior fronto-orbital present and directed inward; seventh segment of female abdomen long and chitinized, not retractile; basal joint of arista shorter than broad. A large family, including many leaf-mining species; widespread. (Agromỳza (A. parvicórnis, Corn blotch leaf-miner; A. símplex, Asparagus miner), Cerodónta, Domomỳza, Liriomỳza

(*L. pusilla,* Serpentine leaf-miner), **Melanagromỳza, Napomỳza, Phytomỳza** (Fig. 647) (*P. chrysanthemi,* Chrysanthemum leaf-miner)). (*PHYTOMÝZIDÆ*) . . . . AGROMÝZIDÆ
Postvertical (occipital) bristles converging, rarely absent; base of female genitalia retractile; basal joint of arista longer than broad. (**Anthomỳza, Anagnòta, Ischnomỳia, Mumetòpia, Paranthomỳza, Stiphrosòma**) . . . . ANTHOMÝZIDÆ

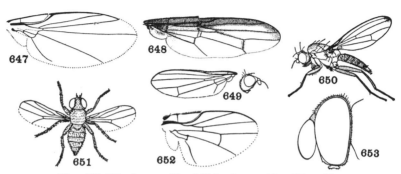

Figs. 647–653. Agromyzidæ, Psilidæ, Opomyzidæ, Chloropidæ, Cryptochætidæ

647. **Phytomyza,** wing. Agromyzidæ.
648. **Chyliza,** wing (drawn by Cole) Psilidæ.
649. **Psila,** wing and profile of head (Cole) Psilidæ.
650. **Geomyza** (Cole) Opomyzidæ.
651. **Oscinella,** dorsal aspect (Lugger) Chloropidæ.
652. **Cryptochætum,** wing. Cryptochætidæ.
653. **Cryptochætum,** head from side. Cryptochætidæ.

131. One presutural and two or three postsutural dorsocentral bristles present; postvertical bristles minute or absent; one sternopleural bristle; ocellar triangle small. (**Opomỳza, Anomalochæta, Geo- mỳza** (=*Balióptera,* not *Trixoscelis*) (Fig. 650). (*GEOMÝZ- IDÆ,* part) . . . . OPOMÝZIDÆ
No presutural (very rarely one) and at most two postsutural dorso- central bristles present; postvertical bristles diverging or absent; no sternopleural; ocellar triangle large. (*LOXOCÉRIDÆ*).
                                                                    PSÍLIDÆ

a. Anal cell closed by a straight crossvein; no or one notopleural bristle; third antennal joint elongate oval to very long . . . . .b
Anal cell closed by a curved crossvein; head spherical, third an- tennal joint rounded; two notopleurals, two scutellars. (**Stron- gylophthalmỳia, Chamæpsìla** (*C. ròsæ,* Carrot rust fly).
                                            STRONGYLOPHTHALMYIÌNÆ

b. Occiput concave; metapleural callus velvety; anal cell distinctly shorter than second basal. (Chylìza (Fig. 648)). . . CHYLIZÌNÆ
Occiput convex; metapleural callus bare; anal cell not shorter than second basal. (Psìla (Fig. 649), Loxócera) . . . . PSILÌNÆ

132. Ocellar triangle large (Fig. 651); arista bare, pubescent, or heavily feathered; postvertical bristles convergent or absent; second vein (R_3) long, ending beyond middle of wing; fifth vein with a curvature near middle of discal cell. A large, widespread family. (*OSCÍNIDÆ, TITANÌIDÆ*) . . . . CHLORÓPIDÆ

a. Costa reaching to tip of third vein, or a little beyond; inner bristle weak or absent. (Chlòrops (= Óscinis, Titània), Chloropísca, Eurìna, Ectecéphala, Meromỳza) . . . . CHLOROPÌNÆ
Costa reaching to tip of fourth vein; inner vertical bristles well developed . . . . b

b. Inner vertical bristle weaker than outer. (Oscinélla (= Botanòbia, Óscinis auctt., Oscinosòma) (Fig. 651), Elachíptera, Gaùrax, Hippelàtes, Madìza (= Siphonélla), Notonaùlax). (*BOTANOBI-ÌNÆ, OSCINOSOMATÌNÆ*) . . . . OSCINELLÌNÆ
Inner vertical bristle stronger than outer c

c. Second vein close to first vein and to costa, the submarginal cell wide. (Heríngium, Córsica) . . . . HERINGIÌNÆ
Second vein normal; front femora thickened; a stout cheek-bristle present; humeral bristle present. (Siphonellópsis, Lasiopleùra).
SIPHONELLOPSÌNÆ

Ocellar triangle small; arista loosely feathered; postvertical (pre-ocellar) bristles diverging; second vein very short, ending close to first vein. Few species. (See couplet 105.) (Astìa (Fig. 645), Sigaloéssa) . . . . ASTÌIDÆ

133. Subcosta free from first vein, ending steeply in the costal break much before the end of the first vein (Fig. 657), anal cell angular, often drawn out into an acute point, at least first vein setulose, wings usually banded or spotted; inclinate lower fronto-orbital bristles present; no vibrissæ, but oral hairs developed; no preapical tibial bristles; seventh segment of female abdomen long and chitinized. A large family, including many species of fruit flies, many tropical. (*TEPHRÍTIDÆ, TRYPANÈIDÆ*).
TRYPÉTIDÆ or EURIBÌIDÆ

a. Chætotaxy incomplete, the following bristles lacking, ocellar, inner occipital, postvertical, humeral, presutural, dorsocentral and sterno-pleural; second basal cell usually widened; antennæ elongate; sixth tergite of female short . . . . b
Chætotaxy complete, preceding bristles usually present; second basal cell not widened; antennæ usually short c

b. Femora more or less spinose beneath; transverse suture of mesonotum complete; abdomen long, cylindrical. (Adràma, Mera-
canthomỳia, Indoaustr.) .... ADRAMÌNÆ
Femora not spinose beneath; transverse suture of mesonotum interrupted in middle; abdomen ovate or clavate. (Dàcus (Fig.
656), Palæarc. (D. òleæ, Olive fly); Bactrócera, Indoautsr. (B.
cucúrbitæ, Melon fly); Chætodàcus, Pélmatops, Indomal.; Lep-
tóxyda, Ethiop.; Toxotrýpana, Neotrop. (T. curvicauda, Papaya
fly)) .... DACÌNÆ

c. Sixth abdominal tergite shorter than fifth; occipital bristles of hind
margin of eye slender and pointed; wings banded or marked
with brown or hyaline. (Trypèta, Acídia, Aciùra, Anástrepha
(A. lùdens, Orange maggot), Carpomỳia, Ceratìtis (C. capi-
tàta, Mediterranean fruit-fly or Medfly; C. ròsæ, Natal fruit-
fly), Epòchra (E. canadénsis, Currant fruit-fly), Euríbia (= Tephrìtis Latr. 1805, not 1804, = Uróphora), Neaspilòta, Platypà-
rea, Procecidóchares and Œdáspis, Rhagóletis (R. cingulàta,
Cherry maggot; R. pomonélla, Apple maggot), Straussia, Trypànea (= Uréllia, Loew), Zonosèma). (CERATITÌNÆ).
TRYPETÌNÆ or EURIBIÌNÆ
Sixth abdominal tergite of female at least as long as fifth; occipital
bristles on hind margin of eye usually stout and blunt; wings
or at least crossveins with numerous small spots. (Tephrìtis Latr.
1804, Actinóptera, (= Uréllia), Ensìna, Euarésta, Euròsta (Fig.
657) (E. solidáginis, Goldenrod gallmaker), Eutrèta, Ictérica,
Oréllia, Schistópterum, Teréllia, Trypànea, Xyphòsia). (TEREL-
LIÌNÆ, TRYPANEÌNÆ) .... TEPHRITÌNÆ

Subcosta ending closer to first vein, not steeply bent toward costa,
or vestigial; lower fronto-orbital usually wanting 134
134. Subcosta complete, ending in costa independently of R_1, second
basal and anal cells well formed; postvertical bristles diverging 135
Subcosta incomplete, vestigial, or ending in R_1, second basal and
anal cells usually weak or absent 137
135. Vibrissæ absent; anal cell more or less acute, often drawn out into
an acute lobe, second basal cell moderately large; female with
chitinized ovipositor. Refer to couplet 101, Otitid series.
Vibrissæ present; anal cell not produced 136
136. Antennæ retractile into deep grooves, face retreating, eyes round
and small (Fig. 642); scutellum very long, flattened, tipped with
two setigerous tubercles; two vibrissæ. A small family; Eur., Afr.,
Austr. (Thyreóphora (Fig. 642), Centrophlebomỳia, Dasyphle-
bomỳia, Piophilosòma) .... THYREOPHÓRIDÆ

Antennæ not retractile, the face flattened, vertical; subcostal break not evident. (**Acartophthálmus,** Holarc. (See couplet 114)).

CLUSÏIDÆ, part

137. Arista lacking, antennæ inserted high on head, the apparent third joint long and leaf-like; no postvertical, orbital, vibrissal or other bristles, but body including mesopleuræ setulose; eyes large, ver-

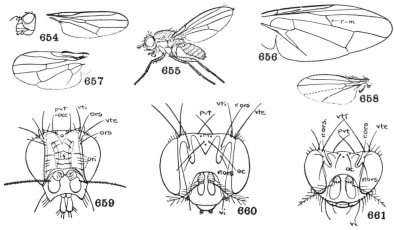

Figs. 654–661. Ephydridæ, Trypetidæ, Milichiidæ, Carnidæ, Drosophilidæ, Diastatidæ

654. **Parydra,** head in side view and wing (Cole) Ephydridæ.
655. **Drosophila** (Cole) Drosophilidæ.
656. **Dacus,** wing. Trypetidæ.
657. **Eurosta,** wing (Williston) Trypetidæ.
658. **Meoneura,** wing. Carnidæ.
659. **Desmometopa,** head from front. Milichiidæ.
660. **Cyrtonotum,** head from front. Diastatidæ.
661. **Diastata,** head from front. Diastatidæ.

tical, cheeks linear; proboscis short; scutellum triangular, with sharp margin; calypteres without cilia. A small Indoaustralian group, parasitic on scale insects, introduced into America. (**Cryptochætum** (= *Lestóphonus*) (Figs. 652, 653)).

CRYPTOCHÆTIDÆ

Arista present; fronto-orbital bristles present (*Lipochæta,* couplet 139, a, with no arista or bristles, has small antennæ); scutellum with rounded edge..138

138. Postvertical bristles diverging; vibrissæ absent, but often oral and facial hairs variously developed; sternopleural bristles usually present 139

Postverticals convergent or parallel, rarely wanting; vibrissæ present 140

139. Pubescent, without bristles, scutellum margined with fine bristles; cheeks broad and hairy; front hairy, produced as a subconical process over the antennæ. (**Sélachops, Eur.**, an aberrant genus).

AGROMÝZIDÆ, part

Usually bare, or nearly bare of pubescence; front not produced; second basal and anal cells not formed. A large family, mainly Holarctic. (*HYDRÉLLIDÆ, NOTIPHÍLIDÆ*). EPHÝDRIDÆ

a. Antennæ small, widely separated, inserted in cavities; no arista; eyes pubescent; bristleless, gray, seacoast flies. (**Lipochæta**).

LIPOCHÆTÌNÆ

Antennæ close together, arista developed .... b

b. Second antennal joint with a spinous bristle at its upper distal edge, or middle tibiæ with a strong extensor bristle; mouth-parts usually small c

Second antennal joint without a spinous bristle; middle tibiæ without a strong extensor bristle .... e

c. Posterior buccal area separated from the concave lower part of occiput by a sharp ridge; clypeus generally narrow but projecting apron-like; parafacials expanding below into the cheeks; no reclinate fronto-orbital bristles. (**Gymnòpa, Athyroglóssa, Cerometòpon, Ochtheròidea**) .... GYMNOPÌNÆ

No sharp post-buccal ridge, the cheeks rounding into the occiput; parafacials paralleling the orbits; lateral frontal bristles proclinate and reclinate .... d

d. Dorsocentral and acrostichal bristles rarely present. (**Psilòpa** (=*Ephygròbia*), **Atíssa, Allotrichòma, Discocerìna** (=*Clasiòpa*), **Discomỳza, Trimerìna**) .... PSILOPÌNÆ

Acrostichals usually and one or more dorsocentral bristles always present. (**Notíphila, Dichæta, Ilýthea, Paralímna**).

NOTÍPHILÌNÆ

e. Mouth-opening small; eyes usually pubescent. (**Hydréllia, Hydrìna** (=*Philýgria*), **Glenánthe, Axýsta**) .... HYDRELLIÌNÆ

Mouth-opening large; eyes without evident pubescence .... f

f. Face with median area bare and facial series of bristles parallel with orbits; anterior dorsocentrals absent or undeveloped. (**Napæa, Brachydeùtera, Hyadìna, Lytogáster, Párydra** (Fig. 654), **Pelìna**).

NAPÆÌNÆ

Face with median area setulose and facial series of bristles divergent from orbits above; anterior dorsocentrals usually well developed. (**Éphydra, Cœnia, Scatélla, Scatóphila, Teichomỳza**).

EPHYDRÌNÆ

140. Inflexed lower fronto-orbital bristles wanting, the lowest or the middle of the superior fronto-orbitals may be proclinate, reclinate, or directed outward.......................................141
    Inflexed lower fronto-orbitals present; interfrontal cruciate bristles usually present...145
141. Second basal and anal cells lacking; no proclinate fronto-orbital bristles 142
    At least anal cell formed, anal vein present almost to margin; interfrontal cruciate bristles absent; foremost or middle fronto-orbital bristle almost always proclinate.....................143
142. Hind metatarsi not short and stout; middle tibiæ not bristly; fronto-orbital bristles reclinate; only one row of acrostichals; ovipositor large, broadly oval, compressed so that the lateral margins form narrow ridges. (**Pseudopomỳza**, Eur., aberrant genus).
                                         MILICHÌIDÆ, part
    Hind metatarsi short and thickened; middle tibiæ bristly; interfrontal cruciate bristles present, fronto-orbitals directed outward; fourth vein continued beyond discal cell only as a fold (Fig. 644). (**Leptócera** (= *Limosìna*) (Fig. 644), Ceróptera, Nèrea).
                                              LEPTOCÉRIDÆ
143. Both fronto-orbital bristles reclinate; interfrontalia wanting; preapical bristles present on all tibiæ. (**Cnemospàthis**, Juan Fernandez Islands) .... **CNEMOSPÁTHIDÆ**
    One fronto-orbital bristle proclinate........................144
144. Subcosta complete, costa usually spinose; mesothorax raised anteriorly, mesopleuræ with bristles, sternopleural bristles present.
                                               DIASTÁTIDÆ

   a. Proclinate fronto-orbital bristle arising in front of reclinate ones, both remote from eyes (*Apsinota* has only uppermost fronto-orbital present); arista loosely long-plumose (Fig. 660). (**Cyrtonòtum** (= *Diplocentra*) (Fig. 660), Apsinòta, Parapsinòta, Thaumastóphila) .... **CYRTONOTÌNÆ**
    Proclinate fronto-orbital behind the foremost reclinate pair, close to eyes; arista short-plumose. (**Diástata** (= *Calopterélla*) (Fig. 661), Campichæta, Euthychæta, Tryptochæta)...**DIASTATÌNÆ**

    Subcosta evanescent beyond base, costa not spinose; mesopleuræ rarely bristly; proclinate fronto-orbital bristle not closer to the eyes than the reclinate ones are. A large family, mostly tropical.
                                            DROSOPHÍLIDÆ

   a. Sternopleural bristle absent, mesopleuræ bristly; hind tibiæ without preapical bristles; anal cell apically open; metallic colored. (**Camílla**, Palæarc.) .... **CAMILLÌNÆ**
    Sternopleural bristle present, no mesopleural bristles; hind tibiæ usually with preapical bristles.............................b

b. Discal and second basal cells separated by a pigmented crossvein . . . c
Discal and second basal cells united. (**Drosóphila** (Fig. 655) (*D. melanogáster* or *ampelóphila*, Pomace fly, the laboratory fly of experimental genetics), **Cacóxenus, Chymomỳza, Cladochæta, Gítona, Leucophénga; Diathoneùra,** Neotrop.; **Liodrosóphila,** Malay, **Mycodrosóphila, Scaptomỳza, Zygóthrica**) . . . . DROSOPHILÌNÆ
c. Middle tibiæ with dorsal row of bristles; eyes longest horizontally. (**Stégana,** largely Neotrop.; **Protostégana**) . . . . . STEGANÌNÆ
Middle tibiæ outwardly without bristles; eyes longest vertically. (**Amiòta** (= *Phórtica*), **Orthostégana, Sinophthálmus**). (*PHORTICÌNÆ*) . . . . AMIOTÌNÆ

145. Postvertical bristles convergent; proboscis usually long and geniculate; oral hairs smaller than vibrissæ. (*PHYLLOMỲZIDÆ*).
MILICHÌIDÆ

a. Costa prolonged as a pointed lappet at end of Sc, last section of fourth vein at most twice as long as preceding; calypteres with long cilia; cheeks very narrow, mesopleuræ often bristly. (**Milíchia, Milichiélla,** widespr.; **Ophthalmomỳia, Pholeomỳia,** Am.; **Pseudomilíchia,** Nearc.) . . . . MILÍCHIÌNÆ
Costa not prolonged as a lappet at the subcostal break, last section of fourth vein at least three times preceding; calypteres rarely with dense cilia; mesopleuræ rarely with bristles. (**Phyllomỳza, Mallochiélla** (= *Madìza*), Holarc.; **Desmometòpa** (Fig. 659), widespr.; **Aldrichomỳza, Eusiphòna, Paramỳia,** Nearc.). (*MADIZÌNÆ*) . . . . PHYLLOMYZÌNÆ

Postverticals parallel; proboscis short; some oral bristles as strong as the vibrissæ; ocellar triangle wide. (**Cárnus** (= *Cenchridòbia*), Palæarc.; **Meoneùra** (Fig. 658) Holarc., Ethiop.; **Hemeromỳia** (= *Paramadìza*) Nearc.; **Rhodesiélla,** Ethiop.) . . . . CÁRNIDÆ

Pupipara

146. Mesonotum short, resembling the abdominal segments, no scutellum, abdomen completely sessile; eyes minute, no ocelli, antennæ set in lateral grooves; vertex without bristles; last tarsal joint broad, bearing an inflexed comb of many microscopic teeth. Small convex wingless insect, widespread, commensal with the honeybee. (See couplet 177.) (**Braùla** (Fig. 662), Bee-louse).
BRAULIDÆ

Thorax distinct from abdomen, scutellum developed; head with bristles; two claws present, the tarsal comb not developed; winged or wingless species, parasitic on birds or mammals 147

147. Head small, capable of folding back into a groove on the flattened and expanded mesonotum; prosternum produced; eyes if present

represented at most by two facets; wingless, long-legged species, parasitic on bats. Bat-tick flies. (See couplet 178.) (Nyctéribia (Fig. 663), Bacília, Cyclopòdia, Penicillídia) ..NYCTERIBÌIDÆ Head not folding back upon the mesonotum which is not strongly flattened and expanded; abdominal segments more or less fused 148

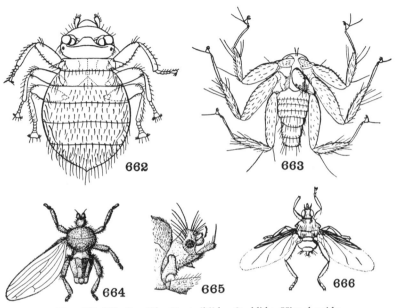

Figs. 662–666. Braulidæ, Nycteribiidæ, Streblidæ, Hippoboscidæ

662. **Braula,** dorsal aspect. Braulidæ.
663. **Nycteribia,** dorsal aspect. Nycteribiidæ.
664. **Trichobius,** dorsal aspect (Brues) Streblidæ.
665. **Trichobius,** profile of head (Brues) Streblidæ.
666. **Pseudolfersia,** dorsal aspect (Lugger) Hippoboscidæ.

148. Palpi broader than long, projecting leaf-like in front of head; wings when present usually with distinct parallel veins and outer cross-veins, at least the principal veins not crowded forward; claws simple; almost always ectoparasites of bats. Bat flies. (See couplet 179.) (Strébla, Aspidóptera, Ascodípteron, Megistópoda, Nycteróphila, Pterellípsis, Trichòbius (Figs. 664, 665)).

STRÉBLIDÆ

Palpi slender and elongate, forming a sheath for the proboscis; wings if present with the stronger veins crowded along the costa

(Fig. 666); tarsal claws strong and often armed with a series of small teeth; head and body often flattened: parasites of birds and mammals except bats. (See couplet 179)......HIPPOBÓSCIDÆ

a. Ocelli often present, or when absent the anal cell is formed.....b
   Ocelli absent; anal cell usually not formed.....................c
b. At most with functional wings having greatly reduced venation, usually with vestigial wings which have almost disappeared in the sheep-tick. (**Lipoptèna,** Holarc.; **Melóphagus** (*M. ovìnus,* Sheep-tick, cosmop.); **Echéstypus,** Ethiop.) (*MELOPHAGÌNÆ*).
                                                        LIPOPTENÌNÆ
   Wings functional or vestigial, anal cell usually present. (**Ornithomỳia,** cosmop.; **Ornithœca,** mostly Indoaustr.; **Ornithopértha,** Neotrop.; **Stenópteryx, Cratærrhìna,** Palæarc.)
                                                        ORNITHOMYIÌNÆ
c. Wings well developed.......................................d
   Wings vestigial, anal vein closing anal cell. (**Allobósca,** Ethiop.).
                                                        ALLOBOSCÌNÆ
d. Pronotum not visible from above. (**Olférsia,** cosmop.; **Icósta,** Malay.; **Lỳnchia,** widespr.) ....OLFERSIÌNÆ
   Pronotum visible from above usually as a light colored ring. (**Hippobósca,** mostly Palæarc.)..............HIPPOBOSCÌNÆ

Wingless Diptera, or with Vestigial Wings

149. Antennæ and mouthparts absent; body at most pupiform......150
     Antennæ and mouthparts present; body as in other adult flies..151
150. Completely submarine; legs vestigial. (**Pontomỳia,** female, Samoa (see couplet 159))
                                    CHIRONÓMIDÆ or TENDIPÉDIDÆ, part
     Boring in the skin of bats; completely sac-like, head, thorax and abdomen undifferentiated, without sutures. (**Ascodípteron,** female (Fig. 676), widespr. (see couplet 179)). (*ASCODIP-TÉRIDÆ*) .....STRÉBLIDÆ, Subfam. ASCODIPTERÌNÆ
151. Antennæ free, consisting of more than six joints which are all more or less similar; palpi usually plainly jointed; bristles not developed. (NEMATÓCERA) 152
     Antennæ consisting of three or less joints, rarely six; palpi not jointed; bristles often present. (BRACHÝCERA) 160
152. Female with long chitinized ovipositor; mesonotum typically with a V-shaped suture 153
     No chitinized ovipositor; mesonotum without transverse V-shaped suture 154
153. Flagellum of antennæ short, thin and long-haired. (**Chiònea** (Fig. 672), Snow-flea, apterous, Holarc.; **Zalùsa,** Falkl. Isl.; **Zaluscòdes,** Antarc.) ....LIMONÌIDÆ, part

Flagellum not much thinner than basal joints of antennæ; wings strap-shaped. (See couplet 7). (**Típula**, female, widespr.).

TIPÙLIDÆ, part

154. Eyes meeting over the antennæ............................155
Eyes widely separated on the front; mouthparts reduced 158

155. Abdomen enormously swollen, the apical four segments forming a slender projection; antennæ long, filiform or moniliform. Termite guests. (**Termitomástus** (Fig. 670), Neotrop.).

CECÍDOMYÌIDÆ or ITONÍDIDÆ, Subfam. TERMITOMAS-TÌNÆ

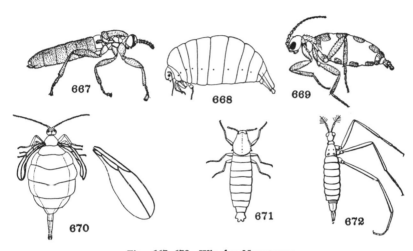

Figs. 667–672. **Wingless Nematocera**

667. **Thripomorpha** (Enderlein) Scatopsidæ.
668. **Dahlica** (Dahl) Mycetophilidæ.
669. **Pnyxia** (Schmitz) Sciaridæ.
670. **Termitomastus**, dorsal view and wing (Silvestri) Cecidomyiidæ.
671. **Clunio** (Carpenter, Bezzi) Chironomidæ.
672. **Chionea** (Johnson) Tipulidæ.

Abdomen formed otherwise 156

156. Claws dentate, pulvilli absent; antennal joints clavate and verticillate. (See couplet 17). (**Wasmanniélla**, Palæarc.).

CECÍDOMYÌIDÆ or ITONÍDIDÆ, part

Claws simple 157

157. Scutellum and halteres present; legs strong. (See couplet 22). (**Cobóldia**, myrmecophilous, Nearc.; **Thripomórpha** (Fig. 667), Palæarc.) ....SCATÓPSIDÆ, part

Scutellum absent; legs slender .. SCIÁRIDÆ or LYCORÌIDÆ, part

Two types of genera may be distinguished:

a. Small halteres and wing-stumps present. (**Austroscìara**, female only, in termite nests, Austr.; **Aptanógyna, Bértea, Calcaromỳia, Dasyscìara**, Palæarc.)

b. Halteres and wings wanting. (**Epídapus**, Holarc.; **Pnýxia** (Fig. 669), Potato-scab mite, Nearc.; **Schmítzia**)

158. Termite guests; antennæ 14-jointed; no ocelli; wings with several veins. (See couplet 14). (**Termitadélphus, Termitodípteron,** Neotrop.) ....**PSYCHÓDIDÆ**, part
Not termite guests 159

159. Mesothorax large, forming a hood over base of head; abdomen constricted at thorax; halteres present. (See couplet 35). (**Clùnio** (Fig. 671), maritime, Palæarc.; **Eretmóptera**, maritime, Nearc.; **Pontomỳia**, male, marine, legs for swimming, Samoa; **Bélgica,** Jacobsiélla, Patagonia). (*ERETMOPTÉRIDÆ*)
CHIRONÓMIDÆ or **TENDIPÉDIDÆ**, part
Mesothorax small, not projecting over head; abdomen broadly sessile with thorax; halteres and scutellum undeveloped. (**Dáhlica** (Fig. 668), Palæarc.)
Probably **MYCETOPHÍLIDÆ** or **FUNGIVÓRIDÆ**

160. Empodium pulvilliform, legs long; eyes and ocelli well developed; antennæ six-jointed, short, without arista; thorax convex; apterous. (See couplet 40). (**Boreòides**, Austral.). ...**CHIROMÝZIDÆ**, part
Empodium not pulvilliform 161

161. Physogastrous termite guests, the abdomen greatly swollen and anal segments inflexed under venter; arista feathered; mouth-parts free; legs not compressed. (**Termitoxènia** (Fig. 678), Ind., Afr.; **Termitomỳia**, Afr.; **Odontoxènia**, Java).
TERMITOXENìIDÆ
Not physogastrous, or if rarely so, the anus terminal 162

162. Head large, overlapping thorax; abdomen small, not evidently segmented; eyes present; antennæ in grooves, the last joint with apical arista. (**Thaumatóxena** (Fig. 673), Eur. Afr.)
THAUMATOXÉNIDÆ
Head not overlapping thorax 163

163. Antennæ consisting apparently of one globular joint, more or less sunk in cavities on the head, arista long and thin, bare or pubescent, three-jointed; legs, especially hind pair, robust and compressed: mostly myrmecophilous or termitophilous females. (See couplet 59). (**Pulicíphora, Chonocéphalus,** widespr.; **Platýphora** (= *Ænigmàtias = Oniscomyia*), Holarc.; **Acontistóptera** (Fig. 674), **Commóptera, Ecitomỳia, Adelopteromỳia,** Neotrop.; **Psyllomỳia, Ænigmatístes, Ænigmatopœus,** Ethiop.). (*STETHOPÁTHIDÆ*) ....**PHÓRIDÆ**, part
Antennæ two- or three-jointed; legs never compressed 164

164. Coxæ not separated by sternum; abdomen segmented; not parasitic on warm-blooded animals or on the honey-bee 165
Coxæ separated by sternum; segmentation of abdomen sometimes obscure; parasitic on birds, mammals, or on the honey-bee 177

165. No frontal lunule or suture immediately over antennæ; third antennal joint more or less tapering 166
A ∩-shaped frontal suture over the antennæ; third antennal joint more or less ovate, with dorsal arista; palpi at most one-jointed 167

166. Arista or style usually terminal, if dorsal (*Thinodromia*) the body is heavily gray pollinose. (See couplet 58). (**Ariasélla, Dusmetìna, Pieltània,** S. Europe; **Thinodròmia,** maritime, Pacific Coast of N. Am.) . . . . EMPÍDIDÆ, part
Arista dorsal, body metallic (*Emperoptera*), or brown (*Schœnophilus*). (See couplet 58). (**Emperóptera** (Fig. 675), Hawaii; **Schœnóphilus,** Antarctic) . . . . DOLICHOPÓDIDÆ, part

167. Hind metatarsi shorter than following joint. (See couplet 123). (**Aptilòtus,** Holarc.; **Apterìna,** Palæarc.; **Ántrops, Anatalánta** (Fig. 677), **Phthítia, Siphlópteryx,** Antarc.)
SPHÆROCÉRIDÆ, part
Hind metatarsi longer than following joint 168

168. Mouth-opening large. (See couplet 139). (**Amalópteryx, Chamæbósca,** Antarc.; **Scatóphila**) . . . . EPHÝDRIDÆ, part
Mouth-opening normal 169

169. Arista loosely plumose. (See couplet 143). (**Drosóphila,** in vestigial-winged or apterous condition) . . . . DROSOPHÍLIDÆ, part
Arista pubescent or bare 170

170. Legs woolly pubescent 171
Legs not woolly pubescent 172

171. Legs stout (cf. couplet 96). (**Pezomỳia,** Falkland Isl.)
DRYOMÝZIDÆ, part
Legs long and slender. (**Mormotomỳia,** Afr.)
MORMOTOMỲIIDÆ

172. Mesonotum with well developed bristles on anterior portion . . 173
Mesonotum without strong dorsocentral bristles 174

173. Thorax flattened; legs hairy; femora of *Icaridion* robust and with heavy spinous bristles beneath. (Cf. couplet 94). (**Apetènus, Icarídion,** Antarc.) . . . . CŒLÓPIDÆ, part
Thorax convex; legs with bristles. (See couplet 76). (**Cœnòsia** sp., Antarc.) . . . . ANTHOMYÌIDÆ, part

174. Legs lengthened and slender. (Cf. couplet 89). (**Calycópteryx,** Antarc.) . . . . TÝLIDÆ, part
Legs not elongate 175

175. Head without bristles, ocellar triangle large. (See couplet 132).
(Alómbus, Afr.; Myrmecomórpha, Eur.) CHLORÓPIDÆ, part
Head with vertical and frontal bristles, ocellar triangle not large . 176

176. Wings developing normally, but breaking off at base. (See couplet 145). (Cárnus (= Cenchridòbia), Eur.) ...CÁRNIDÆ, part
Wings reduced, not dehiscent. (Cf. couplet 131). (Penguístus, Chile) .... OPOMÝZIDÆ

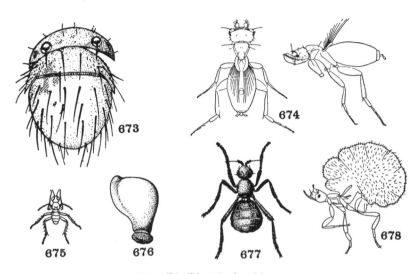

Figs. 673–678. Wingless Diptera

673. **Thaumatoxena** (Trägårdh) Thaumatoxenidæ.
674. **Acontistoptera** (Brues), dorsal and side views. Phoridæ.
675. **Empæroptera,** dorsal view (Grimshaw) Dolichopodidæ.
676. **Ascodipteron,** degenerate female (Adensamer) Streblidæ.
677. **Anatalanta** (Enderlein, Bezzi) Sphæroceridæ.
678. **Termitoxenia,** side view (Bugnion) Termitoxeniidæ.

177. Mesonotum short and resembling abdominal segments, no scutellum; parasitic on the honey-bee. (See couplet 146). (Braùla (Fig. 662), cosmop.) .... **BRAULIDÆ**
Thorax distinct from abdomen, scutellum developed; parasitic on birds or mammals 178

178. Head small, movable, thrown back into a groove of the thorax; thorax incompletely chitinized; completely apterous. Bat parasites. (See couplet 147). (Basília, Nycteríbia (Fig. 663), Penicillídia, widespr.; Cyclopòdia, Eucampsípoda, Ind., Ethiop.)
NYCTERIBÌIDÆ

Head not folding back on the thorax; mesonotum completely
chitinized 179
179. Head fitting into an emargination of the thorax; palpi forming a
sheath for proboscis; eyes more or less reduced, oval or round;
antennæ set in grooves. (See couplet 148). (**Lipoptèna** (wings
developing normally, but dehiscent at base), widespr.; **Melóphagus** (*M. ovìnus*, Sheep-tick), cosmop.; **Allobósca**, Madagascar)
HIPPOBÓSCIDÆ, part
Head with a fleshy movable neck; palpi broad, projecting; eyes
wanting or vestigial. (See couplet 148). Bat parasites. (**Ascodípteron,** male, wings normal but dehiscent at base. (See
couplet 150 for female), widespr.; **Aspidóptera, Megistópoda,
Metelásmus, Paradyschíria, Pterellípsis**). .....STRÉBLIDÆ, part

KEY TO THE LARVAE OF THE PRINCIPAL
FAMILIES OF DIPTERA [1]

1. Head complete (Figs. 679–704), or the posterior portion with deep
longitudinal incisions; mandibles moving horizontally, fitted for
chewing; more than three larval stages: body consisting of
thirteen segments in addition to head; with nine pairs of spiracles.
(NEMATÓCERA) 3
Head incomplete, without a strongly developed upper arcuate
plate (Figs. 705–737); mandibles moving vertically, mouthparts essentially sucking: body comprising fewer than thirteen
segments and only exceptionally with as many as nine pairs of
spiracles. (BRACHÝCERA) 2
2. Mandibles normally sickle-shaped, not protruding much beyond
apices of the well-developed maxillæ, often much shorter, maxillary palpi distinct (Fig. 686); antennæ well developed, situated
on the upper surface of a slightly arcuate chitinized dorsal plate;
no free pharyngeal skeleton within the head capsule, the exo-
skeleton of the head at least dorsally indicated. (ORTIIÓR-
RHAPHA) 25
Mandibles short and hook-like, usually capable of protrusion much
beyond the poorly developed maxillæ, palpi rarely visible; antennæ poorly developed or absent, when present situated on a
membranous surface; a free pharyngeal skeleton present; head
very poorly developed, completely unchitinized dorsally.
(CÝCLÓRRHAPHA) 38
3. Head incomplete, consisting of two parts, the anterior more or less
chitinized above, the posterior unchitinized and bearing the
eye spots; thorax and abdomen comprising thirteen segments;
usually with a "wishbone" or chitin plate on under side of

[1] Based on Malloch: Bull. Ill. State Lab. Nat. Hist., **12,** art. 3. (1917).

second thoracic segment, at least in mature larvæ; larvæ peripneustic, *i.e.* with series of lateral spiracles; mandibles apparently absent; antennæ long, two- or three-jointed. Usually
feeding on plant sap, many larvæ gall makers, some feed on
aphids, scale insects, mites, etc. Very small insects. (Fig. 679,
Retinodiplòsis) .... CECIDOMYÏIDÆ or ITONÍDIDÆ
Without such combination of characters 4

4. Abdominal segments with deep constrictions between them (Fig.
682), venter with series of sucking disks. Clinging to rocks in
swift-running streams 5
Abdomen without a series of large sucking disks for attachment to
rocks in swift-running water 6

5. Ventral sucking disks median, one on the anterior complex segment and usually one on each of the five following segments;
head, thorax and first two abdominal segments fused to form a
rather small first segment; mandibles three-toothed. (Fig. 682,
Bibiocéphala) .... BLEPHAROCÉRIDÆ
Ventral sucking disks lateral, placed on the prolongations of the
abdominal segments; thoracic segments distinct; mandibles deeply
incised, the outer arm fringed with a comb of long teeth;
antennæ long, two-branched .... DEUTEROPHLÉBÏIDÆ

6. Head incomplete behind, more or less retractile within thorax, either
with three deep wedge-shaped slits, two on dorsum and one on
ventral side (Fig. 685), or the ventral surface very poorly chitinized
and the dorsal posteriorly in the form of four slender heavily
chitinized rods, with a weakly chitinized divided plate on anterior
half of dorsum 7
Head capsule complete, *i.e.* at least bounded above behind and not
divided into plates or rods; mandibles opposed 8

7. End of abdomen with six radiating protuberances; body with
regularly placed bristles; head heavily chitinized, dorsally slightly
arcuate and with two longitudinal slits, ventrally rounded and
with a central slit; antennæ longer than maxillary palpi; labium
pointed, not divided into two parts, the anterior margin dentate;
mandibles very stout, with two apical teeth. Larvæ in damp
soil, feeding on roots, or as scavengers, sometimes in water. Larvæ
of *Tipula*, etc., known as Leatherjackets. (Fig. 995, **Típula**)
TIPÚLIDÆ
End of abdomen with at most five radiating processes as well as
single or double breathing tubes; if six apical processes are present the labium is subdivided centrally; body usually without
regularly placed bristles, frequently with dense surface pilosity;
head more or less retracted, sometimes weakly chitinized and
without distinct labium; antennæ sometimes short and slender
and not as long as maxillary lobe; mandibles never with only

two teeth. Mostly aquatic, or living in wet ground, sometimes carnivorous, some species are terrestrial and green from feeding on leaves. (Figs. 683, 685, Limònia; Fig. 684, Dicranòta)

LIMONÌIDÆ

8. The three thoracic segments fused to form a complex more or less dilated mass (Fig. 987); head freely movable, chitinized, at least in mature larvæ with faceted eyes; eighth abdominal segment typically with a stout protruding breathing tube, ninth segment with four anal gill-flaps and with a brush of hairs. Aquatic, free-swimming or suspended. (Fig. 680, Sayomỳia; Fig. 987, Cùlex) ....CULÍCIDÆ

a. Antennæ prehensile, with strong apical spines.... CORETHRÌNÆ
Antennæ not prehensile, without strong apical spines ....b

b. Eighth segment without respiratory tube, the spiracles sessile

ANOPHELÌNÆ

Eighth segment with respiratory tube at least as long as wide....c

c. Mouth-brush composed of ten stout rods ......MEGARHINÌNÆ
Mouth-brush each composed of thirty or more hairs ....d

d. Anal segment with a pair of ventral hairs or tufts ..SABETHÌNÆ
Anal segment with median ventral brush, usually large but at least four separate hairs or tufts ....CULICÌNÆ

The three thoracic segments separate 9

9. A many-toothed chitinized mentum or labial plate (Fig. 694) present on the underside of the head, which is divided into submentum and mentum in primitive forms; larvæ peripneustic only in the aquatic Simuliidæ where the spiracles are vestigial...........10

Mentum more or less reduced or completely wanting, at most three-dentate in the terrestrial and peripneustic Bibionidæ; lateral plates of head capsule usually connected ventrally behind by a chitinous bridge 16

10. Posterior portion of abdomen swollen (Fig. 985), the last segment ventrally armed with a sucking disk which bears concentric series of bristles by means of which the larvæ hold on to rocks in the swiftly running streams in which they live; mouth on each side with a large jointed maxilla which bears a fan-like arrangement of long hairs; thorax with a pair of closely fused pseudopods; minute spiracles opening on all abdominal segments, i.e. larvæ peripneustic. (Fig. 985, Simùlium or Melusìna)

SIMULÌIDÆ or MELUSÍNIDÆ

Body not club-shaped and fitted with terminal sucking disk, nor with large fan-like oral appendages (in Dixidæ the maxillæ bear a small fan); larvæ metapneustic, with only the last pair of spiracles, or amphipneustic, with only the first and last pairs ..11

11. First and second abdominal segments each dorsally with two
    wart-like elevations resembling pseudopods (Fig. 681), the apices
    of which are armed with many small hook-like setæ; behind the
    posterior spiracles two pairs of fringed processes and a terminal
    bristly tube: occurring in cold streams. (Figs. 681, 686, Díxa)

    DÍXIDÆ

    First and second abdominal segments without dorsal elevated
    processes 12

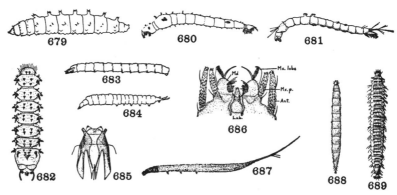

Figs. 679–689. Nematocerous Larvæ

679. **Retinodiplosis,** side view (Malloch) Cecidomyiidæ.
680. **Sayomyia,** side view (Malloch) Culicidæ.
681. **Dixa,** side view (Malloch) Dixidæ.
682. **Bibiocephala,** dorsal view (Malloch) Blepharoceridæ.
683. **Limonia,** side view (Malloch) Limoniidæ.
684. **Dicranota,** side view (Malloch) Limoniidæ.
685. **Limonia,** head capsule (Malloch) Limoniidæ.
686. **Dixa,** anterior extremity (Malloch) Dixidæ.
687. **Bittacomorpha,** side view (Hart) Ptychopteridæ.
688. **Psychoda,** dorsal view (Malloch) Psychodidæ.
689. **Psychoda,** dorsal view (Malloch) Psychodidæ.

12. Last abdominal segments retractile, terminating in a long slender
    respiratory tube, ventral pseudopods present and equipped with
    bristles: aquatic larvæ. (Fig. 687, **Bittacomórpha**).

    PTYCHOPTÉRIDÆ or LIRIOPÈIDÆ

    Abdomen not terminating in a long thin bare respiratory tube ...13
13. Thorax and abdomen with a secondary segmentation (Figs. 688,
    689) due to the presence of narrow transverse chitinized bands,
    three bands on most of the segments, or the apical segment in
    the form of a short chitinized tube; rarely the ventral segments
    bear a central series of sucker-like disks; body tapering at each

end. Occurring in sewage, dung, fungi and tree-holes. (Figs. 688, 689, **Psychòda**) .... PSYCHÓDIDÆ
Dorsum without narrow strap-like bands, apical segment not in the form of a short chitinized tube; ventral abdominal segments never with sucking disks 14

14. Mentum projecting, with chitinized cutting edge; labrum movable; four finger-like anal gills; head capsule with peculiar pointed processes; penultimate segment dorsolaterally humped; prothorax with leg-stumps. Living in woods, on damp rocks; rare.
THAUMALÈIDÆ
Mentum not projecting in the form of a cutter; labrum fixed 15

15. Either very slender, tapering toward each end, without thoracic or anal pseudopods or surface hairs (Fig. 691), or stouter, with well defined segments which are armed with strong bristles, some of which are lanceolate (Fig. 692); one pair of prothoracic pseudopods present, a single anal pseudopod present or not. Terrestrial, living in manure or under bark, etc., or in water. (Fig. 692, **Forcipomỳia**; Fig. 691, **Palpomỳia**).
CERATOPOGÓNIDÆ or HELÈIDÆ
Usually cylindrical (Figs. 690, 693, 695) rarely with thoracic segments swollen; without distinct body bristles but often with soft hairs, the last segment usually with a dorsal tuft of hairs; pseudopods usually present, one pair each on prothorax and anal segment. Mostly aquatic, living in sand-tubes (Bloodworms), some marine, rarely terrestrial. (Fig. 695, **Spaniótoma**; Fig. 690, **Chirónomus** or **Téndipes**; Figs. 693, 694, **Tánypus**)
CHIRONÓMIDÆ or TENDIPÉDIDÆ

16. Larvæ peripneustic, *i.e.* most abdominal segments with spiracles .. 17
Larvæ amphipneustic, *i.e.* only first and last pairs of spiracles present, or metapneustic, *i.e.* only the posterior pair of spiracles remaining; or thoracic and abdominal spiracles not evident 22

17. Antennæ elongate; body furnished with some conspicuous bristles or hairs 18
Antennæ usually short and inconspicuous, sometimes apparently absent; body without conspicuous bristles; principally inhabiting fungi 19

18. Anal spiracles at the apices of long stalk-like process (Fig. 704); no false segment immediately behind the head. Living in decaying vegetation, rotting fruits, excrement, or under old bark. (Fig. 704, **Scatópse**) .... SCATÓPSIDÆ
Anal spiracles sessile, metathoracic spiracles present; a fully developed false segment behind the head armed dorsally with spinose processes (Fig. 696). Larvæ principally scavengers living in soil, sometimes prevalent about dung, sometimes destructive to root crops. (Fig. 696, **Bíbio**) .... BIBIÓNIDÆ

19. Dorsal or clypeal sclerite of head (præfrons) not distinctly tapering behind; antennæ two-jointed ....BOLITOPHÍLIDÆ

Dorsal or clypeal sclerite of head conspicuously tapering posteriorly; antennæ almost indistinguishable 20

20. Lateral plates of head meeting on ventral line only for a short space immediately behind the mouth-opening, then widely

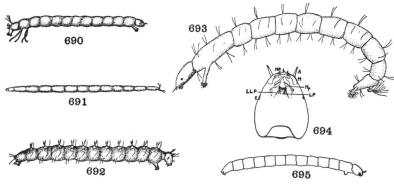

Figs. 690–695. Nematocerous Diptera, Larvæ

690. **Chironomus,** side view (Malloch) Chironomidæ.
691. **Palpomyia,** side view (Malloch) Ceratopogonidæ.
692. **Forcipomyia,** side view (Malloch) Ceratopogonidæ.
693. **Tanypus,** side view (Brues) Chironomidæ.
694. **Tanypus,** ventral view of head (Malloch) Chironomidæ.
695. **Spaniotoma,** side view (Malloch) Chironomidæ.

diverging and not connected at posterior margin; maxillæ and mandibles apparently grown together to form a pair of many-toothed rasping organs. (Fig. 698, **Exèchia**; Fig. 701, **Lèia**).

MYCETOPHÍLIDÆ or FUNGIVÓRIDÆ

Lateral plates of head connected for a short space behind the mouth-opening and again near posterior margin; maxillæ and mandibles distinctly separated from each other, the mandibles apically tridentate 21

21. Clypeal sclerite reaching back to the occipital margin of the head-capsule; body segmentation distinct; especially on venter where the outline is moniliform; armed with spines which have two or three points ....DITOMYÍIDÆ

Clypeal sclerite shorter, not attaining the occipital margin of the head-capsule; segmentation distinct but not moniliform; spines simple. Living in soil, essentially as scavengers. (Fig. 703, **Scìara** or **Lycòria**) ....SCIÁRIDÆ or LYCORÍIDÆ

22. Clypeal sclerite (præfrons) tapering behind to a point; head free,

body flattened, each abdominal segment with secondary incisures, last segment with four fleshy lobes surrounding the spiracles. Living in humus soil and under leaves. (Fig. 699, **Petaurísta**)

PETAURÍSTIDÆ

Clypeal sclerite not tapering behind to a point.................23

23. Antennæ undeveloped, appearing as pale round spots on sides of head; ventral surface of head with sclerites contiguous anteriorly, widely separated posteriorly. Living in slimy webs on fungi. (Fig. 702, **Ceróplatus**) ....**CEROPLÁTIDÆ**

Antennæ pedunculate, usually well developed; ventral surface of head with sclerites contiguous on entire length, not separated widely posteriorly; body slender, tapering, abdominal segments each with a single constriction near anterior margin 24

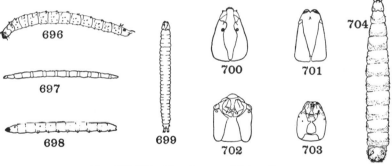

Figs. 696–704. Nematocerous Diptera, Larvæ

696. **Bibio,** side view (Malloch) Bibionidæ.
697. **Mycetobia,** side view (Malloch) Mycetobiidæ.
698. **Exechia,** side view (Malloch) Mycetophilidæ.
699. **Petaurista,** dorsal view (Malloch) Petauristidæ.
700. **Silvicola,** head (Malloch) Silvicolidæ.
701. **Leia,** head (Malloch) Mycetophilidæ.
702. **Ceroplatus,** head, ventral view (Malloch) Ceroplatidæ.
703. **Sciara,** head, ventral view (Malloch) Sciaridæ.
704. **Scatopse,** dorsal view (Malloch) Scatopsidæ.

24. Apical segment with five short but distinct processes around the spiracular disk; mandibles apically rounded and furnished with dense rows of long bristles; the thin ventral chitinous bridge posteriorly connecting the lateral plates not broken. Scavengers, occurring in decaying vegetable matter, manure, and sometimes in sewage. (Fig. 700, **Silvícola**) ....**SILVICÓLIDÆ**

Apical segment with minute processes around the spiracular disk; mandibles apically tridentate; the thin chitinous ventral bridge extending posteriorly between the lateral plates interrupted in the middle. Occurring in sap flow of trees. (Fig. 697, Mycetòbia)

MYCETOBÌIDÆ

Brachycera Orthorrhapha

25. Posterior spiracles approximated, situated within a terminal or subterminal cleft or chamber, usually concealed, or with a terminal breathing tube; body usually shagreened or wholly or in part longitudinally striated 26

Posterior spiracles rather widely separated, visible, situated on apical segment, which may be truncated, chitinized, or armed with apical processes, or upon penultimate or antepenultimate segment; body not shagreened or visibly striated 28

26. Head not retractile, bristly, body 11-segmented, flattened, surface finely shagreened, without pseudopods; spiracular fissure transverse, sometimes rather small; pupæ enclosed in larval skin 27

Head retractile; body 12-segmented, cylindrical, not shagreened, usually longitudinally striated, abdomen with a girdle of pseudopods on each segment; spiracular fissure vertical; pupæ free. Usually aquatic, or semiaquatic; predaceous ...... TABÁNIDÆ

27. Peripneustic, i.e. with lateral abdominal spiracles on most segments. Aquatic, or living in semiliquid matter, under bark, in manure, or on rotting vegetation. (Fig. 705, Stratiomỳia; Fig. 706, Hermètia) .... STRATIOMYÌIDÆ

Amphipneustic, i.e. only prothoracic and last abdominal spiracles present. Living under bark. (Fig. 707, Sólva) ...... SÓLVIDÆ

28. Posterior spiracles situated on apical segment 29

Posterior spiracles situated on penultimate or antepenultimate segment 34

29. Projecting portion of head and the flattened apical plate of last abdominal segment heavily chitinized, the former cone-shaped, entirely closed except at extreme apex, not retractile; apical abdominal segment obliquely truncate and with projecting processes 30

Projecting portion of head more or less retractile, not pointed cone-shaped, the movable parts not enclosed; last abdominal segment without a heavily chitinized flattened terminal plate .31

30. Head about twice as long as its greatest width; thoracic segments not chitinized above, each with two internal separated chitinized plates; body without long hairs; apical plate very large; spiracles vertically elongated, apical paired protuberances small, widely separated, each with a short hair on inner side. Living in soil or decaying wood. (Fig. 711, Cœnomỳia).

CŒNOMYÌIDÆ

Head at least three times as long as its greatest width; at least the first and second thoracic segments chitinized above, no internal chitinized plates present; body with a number of long hairs, four of which in a vertical series on each abdominal segment are very noticeable; apical plate rather small, spiracles rounded, apical paired protuberances large, fused basally, each with a number of rather long hairs. Living under bark or in soil. (Fig. 708, Xylóphagus or Erínna) ....**XYLOPHÁGIDÆ** or **ERÍNNIDÆ**

31. Posterior spiracles widely separated, located in an apical transverse cleft; head very small, retractile; mature larvæ stout, cy-

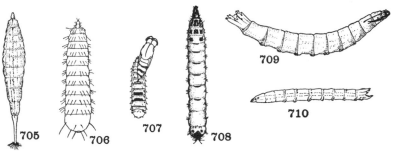

Figs. 705–710. Orthorrhaphous Diptera, Larvæ

705. **Stratiomyia**, dorsal view (Johannsen) Stratiomyiidæ.
706. **Hermetia**, dorsal view (Malloch) Stratiomyiidæ.
707. **Solva**, emergence showing withdrawal of pupa from puparium (Greene) Solvidæ.
708. **Xylophagus**, dorsal view (Greene) Xylophagidæ.
709. **Aphrosylus**, side view (Wheeler) Dolichopodidæ.
710. **Dolichopus**, side view (Malloch) Dolichopodidæ.

lindrical, bare, dorsally with three oval swellings and ventrally with a transverse creeping pad on each segment. Endoparasitic in beetles .... **NEMESTRÍNIDÆ**
Spiracles not located in an apical transverse cleft 32

32. Labial plate and rods behind it flat in one plane, or wanting, or fused with the capsule 33
Labial plates and rods meeting angularly, grown together in front V-like, in profile appearing bent and usually united behind with the tentorial rods; head mostly membranous, even above to the triangular dorsal plate; usually amphipneustic. Predatory, mostly living in moist earth, some aquatic, some under bark, some in decaying vegetable matter.
Fig. 713, **Drápetis** .... **EMPÍDIDÆ**
Fig. 709, **Aphrosy̆lus**; Fig. 710, **Dolíchopus**..**DOLICHOPÓDIDÆ**

33. Head capsule long, in large part internal, reaching back to the mesothorax, dorsal plate very long, pear-shaped, broader behind;

hind spiracles ending separately in two plates or tracheal gills. (Fig. 716, **Athèrix;** Figs. 712 and 717, **Chrysopìla**)

RHAGIÓNIDÆ

Head capsule short, the dorsal plate not covering the part inset in the thorax, the internal part flat or divided into rods; apical abdominal segment without projecting processes, the spiracles very small; endoparasites of spiders ....**ACROCÉRIDÆ**

34. Posterior spiracles situated on the antepenultimate segment, abdominal segments one to six subdivided, the body apparently consisting of twenty segments exclusive of the head; head free, slightly longer than broad and not set into the thorax 35

Posterior spiracles situated on penultimate segment; abdominal segments simple, the body apparently consisting of eleven or twelve segments exclusive of the head 36

35. Posterior dorsal internal extension of head (*i.e.* the two fused metacephalic rods lying in prothorax and mesothorax) spatulate at apex; ventral posterior projections in the form of two short chitinized rods. Living in soil and decaying wood, predatory, locomotion serpentine, assisted by the mouthparts. (Fig. 718, **Psilocéphala**) ....**THERÉVIDÆ**

Posterior dorsal internal extension of head not spatulate at apex; ventral posterior projections absent. Found in fungi, rotten wood and in houses, in carpets and furniture; predatory.

SCENOPÍNIDÆ or OMPHRÁLIDÆ

36. Penultimate abdominal segment longer than the ultimate, with a deep transverse depression near its apex giving it the appearance of two distinct segments; ultimate segment terminating in a sharp ridge with a median sharp point, on each side of which dorsally and ventrally are situated four very closely approximated hairs similar to those of Asilidæ. Living in decaying wood, predatory on beetle grubs. (Fig. 715, **Mỳdas**). .....**MYDÀIDÆ**

Penultimate abdominal segment shorter than ultimate, or if longer without a deep transverse depression; apical segment not as above, the hairs not closely approximated 37

37. Thoracic segments each with two long hairs, one on each side on ventro-lateral margin; apical segment with six or eight long hairs; head well developed, porrect and more or less cone-shaped when viewed from above, appearing flattened when viewed from the side; penultimate segment usually shorter than ultimate or not much longer; body held straight. Living in soil and decaying wood, predaceous. (Fig. 719, **Báctria**) ....**ASÍLIDÆ**

Thoracic segments without hairs, or with very weak hairs; apical segment without distinguishable hairs; head not much protruded, directed downward, not cone-shaped, with a dorsal protuberance when viewed from the side; penultimate segment distinctly longer than ultimate; body usually semicircularly curled at rest. Parasites, inquilines or predators, in nests of bees and wasps, egg-cases of grasshoppers, etc. (Fig. 714, Sparnopòlius) ....BOMBYLÌIDÆ

Cyclorrhapha

38. Maxillæ and palpi present, near the very small bent mandibles; body comprising only nine distinct segments, the head and pro-thoracic and the metathoracic and first abdominal segments

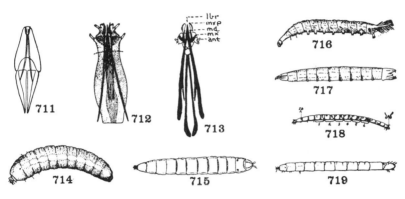

Figs. 711–719. Orthorrhaphous Diptera, Larvæ

711. **Cœnomyia**, cephalopharyngeal skeleton (Malloch) Cœnomyiidæ.
712. **Chrysopila**, cephalopharyngeal skeleton (Malloch) Rhagionidæ.
713. **Drapetis**, internal skeleton (Malloch): ant, antenna; lbr, labrum; md, mandible; mx, maxilla; mxp, maxillary palpus. Empididæ.
714. **Sparnopolius**, side view (Malloch) Bombyliidæ.
715. **Mydas**, dorsal view (Malloch) Mydaidæ
716. **Atherix**, side view (Greene) Rhagionidæ.
717. **Chrysopila**, side view (Malloch) Rhagionidæ.
718. **Psilocephala**, side view (Malloch) Therevidæ.
719. **Bactria**, side view (Malloch) Asilidæ.

appearing grown together; much flattened, seed-like, scarcely twice as long as broad; head bearing underneath on each side a triangular flap, retractile into the thorax; frontal sac opening directly into the upper surface of the head; incisures chitinized above, side margins with many incisions, venter membranous, apical segment with two filiform appendages. Living in mud and about decaying organic matter. (Fig. 723, Lonchóptera or Musidòra) ....LONCHOPTÉRIDÆ or MUSIDÒRIDÆ
Maxillæ not developed, only the mouth-hooks present; frontal sac opening in an atrium in the mouth cavity 39

39. Upper lip projecting forward between and below the two mouth-hooks, distally hooked or toothed, the mouth-hooks porrect, single-pointed or more often toothed; body with eleven incisures, lengthened, anteriorly tapering, posteriorly blunt or the eighth abdominal segment tube-like; metapneustic, *i.e.* terminal spiracles alone present. Living in many situations, in dung, carrion, ant nests, etc. ....PHÓRIDÆ

Mentum never extending between the two mouth-hooks as a point or hook except in Aphis-eating Syrphidæ, in which case the lateral rods of the mentum are produced forward over the mentum and fuse to form a projecting pointed upper lip; mostly amphipneustic, *i.e.* anterior pair as well as terminal spiracles present 40

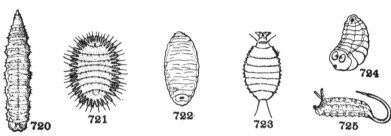

Figs. 720–725. Aschizous Diptera, Larvæ

720. Syrphus, dorsal view (Metcalf) Syrphidæ.
721. Callimyia, dorsal view (de Meijere) Platypezidæ.
722. Pipunculus, dorsal view (Perkins) Pipunculidæ.
723. Lonchoptera, dorsal view (de Meijere) Lonchopteridæ.
724. Conops (Brauer) Conopidæ.
725. Tubifera, side view (Metcalf) Syrphidæ.

40. Larva broad and depressed, in dorsal aspect appearing to have only nine or ten segments because the head and prothorax are inflexed to the under surface, the sides of the body with long projecting bristles and sometimes deeply incised and serrate; posterior spiracles not or but little prominent, rather widely separated, placed at the base of the last segment, prothoracic spiracles prominent. Developing in fungi. (Fig. 721, Callimyia)
PLATYPÉZIDÆ or CLYTHÏIDÆ

Of other conformation 41

41. Hind spiracles three- or four-parted, separate from each other on a common chitin plate some distance before the tip of the body; acephalous, mouthparts very indistinct, the mouth-hooks sessile; body comprising ten or eleven segments. Endoparasitic on Homoptera. (Fig. 722, Pipúnculus or Dórylas)
PIPUNCÙLIDÆ or DORYLÀIDÆ

If the posterior spiracles are located on a common chitin plate
they are contiguous to each other 42

42. Posterior spiracles close together at the end of a tracheal tube of
greater or less length, which is sometimes chitinized and sometimes greatly extensile; mouthparts various, absent in "rattail"
larvæ (Fig. 725), developed in the species living in wood, and
in the "Aphis-lions" (*Syrphus*, etc.) the mouthparts are specialized
into piercing organs; larvæ apparently acephalous, body with
about eleven obscure segments, skin usually rough, form diverse,
conical, more or less cylindrical, even hemispherical. Food habits
various, under bark, in tuber-roots, about sewage, in ant or bee
nests, or free-living and preying on aphids. (Fig. 720, Sýrphus;
Fig. 725, **Tubifera**) ....**SÝRPHIDÆ**
Acephalous, true maggots, usually conically tapering (Figs. 728–
737), sometimes stout warbles (Fig. 727). (The vast residue of
the Diptera are insufficiently known to tabulate as to families,
the following incomplete artificial key being largely based on
food habits). (MUSCÒIDEA) 43

43. Endoparasites of insects or higher animals 44
Not parasitic 50

44. Parasites of insects 45
Parasites of mammals, turtles, frogs, etc. 48

45. Body oval or pyriform, with distinct segments; antennæ wart-like,
tipped with a chitinous ocellus-like ring; posterior spiracular
plates large, round or reniform. Living within the abdomen
of wasps or bees. (Fig. 724, **Cònops**) ....**CONÓPIDÆ**
Body more or less elongate, segmentation less evident 46

46. Posterior end of body rather truncate or broadly rounded, without
long processes 47
Posterior end of body terminating in two slender tail-like processes,
two to five times length of body; young larva hairy on posterior
half of body. Living within Cottony cushion scale. (Fig. 736,
Cryptochætum) ....**CRYPTOCHÆTIDÆ**

47. Posterior spiracular plates with a button. Endoparasites of various
insects in their early stages..**TACHÍNIDÆ** or **LARVÆVÒRIDÆ**
Posterior spiracular plates without a button. (Figs. 731 and 732 D,
Sarcóphaga) ....**SARCOPHÁGIDÆ**

48. Body not strongly tapering, often obese, usually provided with
numerous strong chitinous spines 49
Body strongly tapering in front (Fig. 731), at most with girdles of
minute spines. (Figs. 731 and 732 D, **Sarcóphaga**)
SARCOPHÁGIDÆ

49. Warbles living under skin of various ungulates, rodents, dogs and
man, or in nasal sinuses or throat of various animals; body with
strong spines or not. (Fig. 727, **Cutérebra**) ..**CUTERÉBRIDÆ**

Bot parasites in the stomach and intestines, principally of horses. (Fig. 726, Gasteróphilus) ....GASTEROPHÍLIDÆ
50. Body with lateral and dorsal spinose processes. (Fig. 728, Homalomỳia) ....ANTHOMYÌIDÆ, part
    Body without such spinose processes 51
51. Body truncate or broadly rounded posteriorly 52
    Body with one or two posterior processes; rather small species ...57
52. Only one mandibular hook; posterior spiracular plates with sinuous slits (Fig. 732 A); no distinct fusiform pads on the side

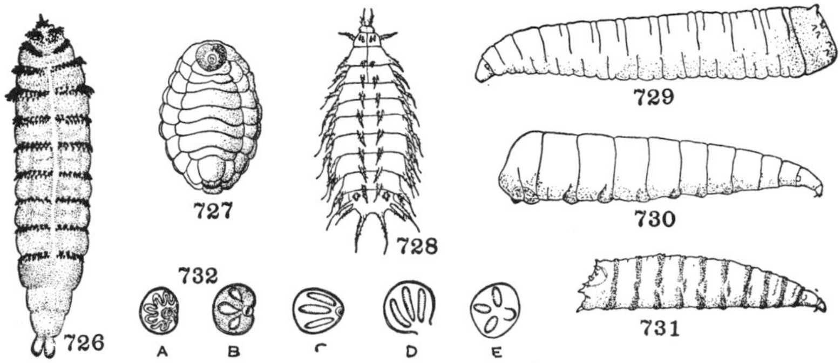

Figs. 726–732. Cyclorrhaphous Diptera, Larvæ

726. **Gasterophilus,** dorsal view (Hadwen and Cameron) Gasterophilidæ.
727. **Cuterebra,** ventral view (Brauer) Cuterebridæ.
728. **Homalomyia,** dorsal view (Banks) Anthomyiidæ.
729. **Pegomyia,** side view (Frost) Anthomyiidæ.
730. **Musca,** side view (Banks) Muscidæ.
731. **Sarcophaga,** side view (Greene) Sarcophagidæ.
732. Left posterior spiracle (Banks): A, **Musca,** Muscidæ; B, **Muscina,** Muscidæ; C, **Calliphora,** Calliphoridæ; D, **Sarcophaga,** Sarcophagidæ; E, **Tritoxa,** Otitidæ.

margins of the segments; posterior end of body with few if any conical processes, anterior end very slender. (Fig. 730, Músca)
                                                    MÚSCIDÆ, part
    With two mandibular hooks; slits of posterior spiracular plates not sinuous 53
53. Distinct tubercles above anal area; often processes around spiracular field; side margins of segments often with fusiform swollen areas 54
    No tubercles above anal area; no distinct processes around spiracular field 59
54. Slits in spiracular plates rather short and arranged radially 55
    Slits slender, subparallel to each other 56

55. Two tubercles above anal area; posterior spiracular field with distinct processes around it. (Fig. 729, **Pegomỳia**)

ANTHOMYÌIDÆ, part

Four or more tubercles above anal area; slits of spiracular plate usually pointed at inner end. (Fig. 732 B, **Muscìna**)

MÚSCIDÆ, part

56. Posterior spiracular plates each with a button, slits rather transverse. (Fig. 732 C, **Callíphora**) .... CALLIPHÓRIDÆ

a. Larva with sclerotized area on ventral part of third segment

MESEMBRINELLÌNÆ

Larva without such sclerotized area .... b

b. Third instar larva with spiracular button within closed peritreme which extends between the slit-like apertures .... RHINIÌNÆ

Third instar larva with circular peritreme, which does not extend between the three apertures c

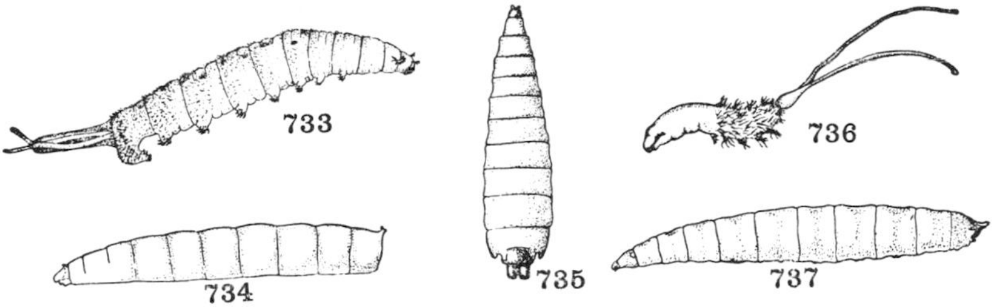

Figs. 733–737. Acalyptrate Diptera, Larvæ

733. **Parydra**, side view (Jones) Ephydridæ.
734. **Agromyza**, side view (Frost) Agromyzidæ.
735. **Drosophila**, dorsal view (Banks) Drosophilidæ.
736. **Cryptochætum**, side view (Smith and Compere) Cryptochætidæ.
737. **Scaptomyza**, side view (Frost) Drosophilidæ.

c. Peritreme incompletely formed .... PHORMIÌNÆ

Peritreme completely encircling the spiracles .... d

d. Peritreme strongly chitinized .... CALLIPHORÌNÆ

Peritreme weak .... POLLENIÌNÆ

Posterior spiracular plates without buttons, slits rather vertical, plates at bottom of a pit. (Figs. 731, 732 D, Sarcóphaga)

SARCOPHÁGIDÆ

57. Posterior end of body with respiratory and usually forked anal tube; venter with prolegs furnished with curved hooks. Aquatic larvæ. (Fig. 733, **Párydra**) .... EPHÝDRIDÆ

Posterior end of body with two short fleshy processes 58

58. Processes bearing spiracular plates. (Fig. 735, **Drosóphila**; Fig. 737, **Scaptomỹza**) .... DROSOPHÍLIDÆ
Processes not bearing spiracular plates .... PIOPHÍLIDÆ
59. Spiracular plates on black tubercles; lateral fusiform areas rather weak though distinct; rather slender larvæ. (Fig. 732 E, **Tritóxa**) OTÍTIDÆ
Spiracular plates barely if at all elevated; lateral fusiform areas indistinct; spiracular plates often contiguous or nearly so, slits long and subparallel, no button . . **TRYPÉTIDÆ** or **EURIBÍIDÆ**

KEY TO THE PUPAE OF THE PRINCIPAL FAMILIES OF DIPTERA [1]

1. Pupa free, not enclosed within the indurated last larval moult, or if so the head is distinct as in the larva, or the puparium is slightly flattened dorso-ventrally, its texture leathery, not chitinous, and the anterior respiratory organs not distinguishable; adult, or pupa, emerging through a rectangular, T-shaped split on dorsum of larval skin (see Fig. 707) 2
Pupa coarctate, *i.e.* enclosed within the indurated last larval moult, and usually barrel-shaped and brown in color; head always retracted, the chitinous portion occupying a position on the inner side of the ventral surface of the puparium; anterior respiratory organs distinct, either protruded from the antero-lateral angles of the head extremity or from dorsum of base of abdomen; adult emerging usually by forcing off the rounded anterior extremity of the puparium in cap-like form (see Fig. 763), or the dorsal half of the thoracic portion — the lines of cleavage being along the lateral margins to a point at base of abdomen; rarely emergence is through rectangular splitting of the dorsum of the puparium (Figs. 760–764) .... CYCLORRHAPHA [2]
2. Antennæ much elongated, distinctly visible beneath the pupal skin, normally curving well over upper margin of eyes and extending to or beyond base of wing, in some cases almost to apex of wing; head without strong thorns (except in some Cecidomyiidæ and a few Tipulidæ; thoracic respiratory organs much elongated or sessile; abdomen in species with short antennæ sometimes unarmed. (NEMATÓCERA) 3
Antennæ shorter, projecting downward and outward, not curving over the eyes nor reaching nearly to base of wing; head usually with strong thorns or horns; thoracic respiratory organs sessile, rarely stalk-like; abdomen usually armed with strong spines or

[1] Based largely on Malloch: Bull. Ill. State Lab. Nat. Hist., **12**, art. 3 (1917).
[2] The pupae of this large and important group are so imperfectly known that it is impossible to present a key to the families.

bristles, or if unarmed there are only four or five distinct pairs
of abdominal spiracles. (ORTHÓRRHAPHA) 26
3. Head with several strong thorns in a vertical series on the median
line; pupæ living in galls on various parts of plants; sometimes
pupa enclosed in the hardened larval skin and resembling a
flaxseed ....**CECIDOMYÌIDÆ** or **ITONÍDIDÆ**, part
Head without strong thorns, or if at base of each antenna there is
a protuberance it is not sharp; pupæ not enclosed in galls on

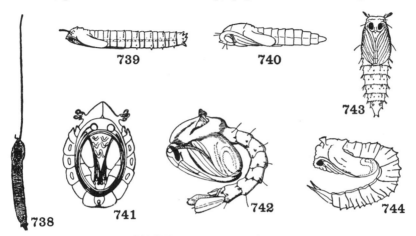

739 **740**

743

738 **741** **742** **744**

Figs. 738–744. Nematocerous Diptera, Pupæ

738. **Bittacomorpha**, dorsal view (Hart) Ptychopteridæ.
739. **Pachyrrhina**, side view (Malloch) Tipulidæ.
740. **Monardia**, side view (Malloch) Cecidomyiidæ.
741. **Deuterophlebia**, ventral view (Pulikovsky) Deuterophlebiidæ.
742. **Anopheles**, side view (Howard) Culicidæ.
743. **Psychoda**, ventral view (Malloch) Psychodidæ.
744. **Dixa**, side view (Malloch) Dixidæ.

living plants, usually free and not enclosed in larval skin, but if
so enclosed the larval moult does not resemble a muscid puparium 4
4. Thoracic respiratory organs sessile; abdomen without strong thorns
or leaf-like elevations; legs straight 5
Thoracic respiratory organs stalked, or if sessile the abdomen has
strong thorns or leaf-like elevations, or the legs are recurved
against base of abdomen and apex of thorax, or the coxæ do
not conceal the sternopleura and the scape of the antennæ is
almost globose; legs straight or recurved 9
5. Legs short, apices of hind tarsi projecting slightly beyond apices

of wings; antennæ short, curved across middle of eye. (Fig.
747, **Bíbio**) .... **BIBIÓNIDÆ**
Legs elongate, usually all tarsi projecting for a considerable distance
beyond apices of wings; antennæ elongate, extending to or beyond
bases of wings 6

6. Antennæ almost straight, noticeably flattened, extending to bases
of wings; thorax not much swollen in front, its anterior profile
not declivous. (Fig. 749, **Ceróplatus**) .... **CEROPLÁTIDÆ**
Antennæ distinctly curved, not flattened, extending beyond bases
of wings 7

7. Thorax conspicuously swollen, almost globose, its anterior profile
declivous; sternopleura concealed. (Fig. 750, **Lèia**).
              MYCETOPHÍLIDÆ or **FUNGIVÒRIDÆ**
Thorax not conspicuously swollen, the anterior profile not sloping
downward 8

8. Scape of antennæ much swollen, globose; abdominal spiracles
small or absent; sternopleura enlarged, not concealed by fore
coxæ and femora ...... **CHIRONÓMIDÆ** or **TENDIPÉDIDÆ**
Scape of antennæ not much swollen; abdominal spiracles distinct;
sternopleura not visible, concealed by the large coxæ and femora
of the fore legs.
(Fig. 740, **Monárdia**) .. **CECIDOMYÌIDÆ** or **ITONÍDIDÆ**, part
(Fig. 748, **Scìara** or **Lycoria**) .. **SCIÁRIDÆ** or **LYCORÌIDÆ**, part

9. Thoracic respiratory organs slender, long and tube-like; legs straight,
extending well beyond apices of wings; body without armature
except a pair of hairs on anterior margin of head; sternopleura
concealed .... **CECIDOMYÌIDÆ** or **ITONÍDIDÆ**, part
               SCIÁRIDÆ or **LYCORÌIDÆ**, part
Species without such combination of characters, abdomen usually
with hairs or spines, or the sternopleura is exposed 10

10. Pupa in a pocket-shaped or slipper-shaped cocoon consisting of coarse
threads, from the wide, open end of which project the thoracic
respiratory filaments: aquatic, living in swiftly running streams.
(Figs. 745, **Simùlium** or **Melusìna**).
               SIMULÌIDÆ or **MELUSÍNIDÆ**
Pupa free, or if enclosed or partly so the cocoon is not pocket-like
and respiratory organs do not consist of tube-like branches 11

11. Pupa when seen from above oval or rounded in outline, the abdomen at base not conspicuously narrower than thorax, so that the
lateral outline is continuous; dorsal surface with strong integument; venter with sucking disks for adhering to rocks in running
streams where the pupæ occur 12
Pupa with abdomen well differentiated from thorax, the dorsum
membranous, or if strong and almost chitinized surface spines
are developed 14

12. Antennæ excessively long, each forming a double coil on the venter; three pairs of lateral sucking disks; respiratory filaments short tubular. (Fig. 741, **Deuterophlèbia**)...**DEUTEROPHLEBÌIDÆ**
    Antennæ not twice coiled; ventral sucking disks median.......13
13. Thoracic respiratory organs lamelliform, consisting of four flat plates, the broad sides of which are contiguous. (Fig. 746, **Bibiocéphala**) .... **BLEPHAROCÉRIDÆ**
    Thoracic respiratory organs simple, tube-like. (Maurìna, N. and S. Am.) .... **PSYCHÓDIDÆ**, part

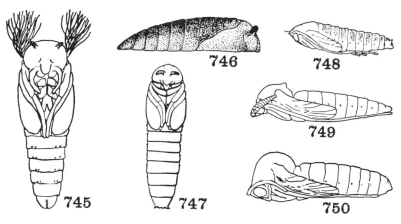

Figs. 745–750. Nematocerous Diptera, Pupae

745. **Simulium,** ventral view (Malloch) Simuliidæ.
746. **Bibiocephala,** side view (Malloch) Blepharoceridæ.
747. **Bibio,** ventral view (Malloch) Bibionidæ.
748. **Sciara,** side view (Malloch) Sciaridæ.
749. **Ceroplatus,** side view. Ceroplatidæ.
750. **Leia,** side view (Malloch) Mycetophilidæ.

14. Apical abdominal segment terminating in two or four paddle-like or fin-shaped organs which are fringed on all or part of outer surface by strap-like hairs; or if the apical segment terminates in two long subconic processes the tarsi are recurved against the ventral surface of the base of the abdomen and apex of thorax so that they do not extend beyond apices of wings...........15
    Apical segment of abdomen obtuse, armed with short or elongate spines or thorns, or if ending in a pair of long, slender processes they are more or less oval in transverse section and without strap-like hairs; tarsi generally entirely straight, rarely the apices of the hind pair incurved slightly, but never recurved as above stated...20

15. Thoracic respiratory organs terminating in numerous thread-like filaments .... CHIRONÓMIDÆ or TENDIPÉDIDÆ, part
Thoracic respiratory organs consisting of a single stem, in some cases with a few long, or many short, scale-like surface hairs, but never terminating in numerous thread-like filaments; occasionally the thoracic respiratory organs not elevated..........16
16. Thoracic respiratory organs not elevated; sternopleura exposed. CHIRONÓMIDÆ or TENDIPÉDIDÆ
Thoracic respiratory organs conspicuously elevated..............17
17. Thoracic respiratory organs situated close to anterior margin of thorax; no stellate hairs on thorax and abdomen.
CHIRONÓMIDÆ or TENDIPÉDIDÆ, part
Thoracic respiratory organs situated close to middle of thoracic dorsum 18
18. Apical abdominal segment ending in two or four broad, flat, paddle-like plates. (Fig. 742, **Anopheles**; Fig. 997, **Culex**).
CULÍCIDÆ, part
Apical abdominal segment ending in two long subconical processes 19
19. Apical processes armed with short hairs at apices and on middle of outer margin .... CULÍCIDÆ, part
Apical processes unarmed. (Fig. 744, **Díxa**)............DÍXIDÆ
20. Apices of legs not extending beyond apices of wings............21
Apices of posterior legs at least extending beyond apices of wings ..22
21. Apical segment of abdomen ending in two conical processes.
CERATOPOGÓNIDÆ or HELÈIDÆ
Apical segment of abdomen ending in two upper and two lower short thorns. (Fig. 743, **Psychòda**)...........PSYCHÓDIDÆ
22. Thoracic respiratory organs long, bifid; apical abdominal segment rounded, without processes; abdominal spiracles pedunculate.
SCATÓPSIDÆ
Thoracic respiratory organs simple; apical abdominal segment not rounded, generally armed with protuberances..............23
23. Thoracic respiratory organs elevated but little above disk of thorax; tarsi of fore legs overlapping those of middle pair, which overlap the hind ones, all rather closely fused together and to wings.
SILVICÓLIDÆ
Thoracic respiratory organs very conspicuously elevated; legs otherwise formed 24
24. Thoracic respiratory organs equal in length, rarely one twice as long as the other; all tarsi distinct.......................25
Thoracic respiratory organs of very different length, one short, the other very long; front tarsi overlapping middle pair. (Fig. 738, **Bittacomórpha**) ....PTYCHOPTÉRIDÆ or LIRIOPÈIDÆ
25. Abdominal segments each with one transverse row, sometimes with

two rows, of thorn-like protuberances; palpi recurved at apices. (Fig. 739, **Pachyrrhìna**) .... TIPÙLIDÆ
Abdominal segments rarely with distinct thorn-like protuberances, usually with weak hairs; palpi straight, not recurved at apices.
LIMONÏIDÆ

Orthorrhapha

26. Pupa enclosed within the last larval moult....................27
    Pupa free 28
27. Thoracic segments one and two each with a smooth plate on dorsum; apical segment with a transverse series of short teeth

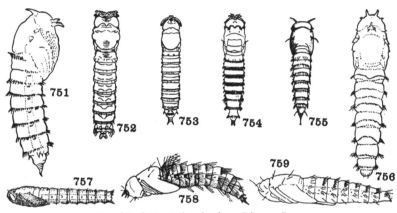

Figs. 751–759. Orthorrhaphous Diptera, Pupæ

751. **Mydas**, side view (Greene) Mydaidæ.
752. **Cœnomyia**, dorsal view (Greene) Cœnomyiidæ.
753. **Rhachicerus**, dorsal view (Greene) Solvidæ.
754. **Xylophagus**, dorsal view (Greene) Xylophagidæ.
755. **Psilocephala**, dorsal view (Malloch) Therevidæ.
756. **Dasyllis**, dorsal view (Greene) Asilidæ.
757. **Chrysopila**, side view (Malloch) Rhagionidæ.
758. **Sparnopolius**, side view (Malloch) Bombyliidæ.
759. **Rhamphomyia**, side view (Malloch) Empididæ.

near base on ventral surface; pupal skin largely or entirely withdrawn from puparium during emergence. (Fig. 707, **Sólva**).
SÓLVIDÆ
Thoracic segments without smooth dorsal plates; pupal skin not withdrawn from puparium during emergence.
STRATIOMYÏIDÆ
28. Prothorax with a large aperture mesad of and connected with the spiracle .... TABÁNIDÆ

Prothorax without such an aperture.........................29

29. Head without strong forwardly directed thorns, at most with one thorn on base of antenna which is directed to the side; abdominal armature weak, becoming gradually stronger toward apex; wings short, extending to or slightly beyond apex of basal abdominal segment; apices of hind tarsi at most extending slightly beyond apices of wings; abdomen with seven pairs of spiracles..30

Head usually with strong thorns, or if these are absent the abdominal armature is stronger on basal or second segment than it is on apical, or there are less than seven pairs of abdominal spiracles; apices of hind tarsi usually extending distinctly beyond apices of wings.......................................33

Figs. 760–764. Cyclorrhaphous Diptera, Pupæ

760. **Didea,** dorsal view (Metcalf) Syrphidæ.
761. **Criorhina,** dorsal view (Greene) Syrphidæ.
762. **Pipunculus,** dorsal view (Perkins) Pipunculidæ.
763. **Exorista,** side view (Greene) Tachinidæ.
764. **Sarcophaga,** side view (Greene) Sarcophagidæ.

30. Antennal sheaths much thickened at base, apical portion slender, styliform, the whole directed almost straight downward. (Fig. 757, Chrysopìla) .... RHAGIÓNIDÆ

Antennal sheaths thickened throughout their length, the apical portion generally more or less distinctly annulated, the whole directed either straight sideways or in a slightly downward direction....31

31. Antennal sheaths showing much more than ten annulations. (Fig. 753, Rhachícerus) ....SÓLVIDÆ, RHACHICERÍNÆ

Antennal sheaths showing not more than ten annulations.......32

32. Antennal sheaths very stout, not over twice as long as their basal breadth; face with a small sharp protuberance on each side a little mesad of the vertical line of apices of antennæ and slightly above middle of face, and at the base of each are two short hairs on the inner side; two very strong postspiracular abdominal bristles on each segment. (Fig. 752, Cœnomỳia).

CŒNOMYÌIDÆ

Antennal sheaths distinctly annulated, slender, about four times as long as their basal breadth; face without protuberances; postspiracular abdominal bristles slender, eight to ten on each segment. (Fig. 754, **Xylóphagus** or **Erínna**).

XYLOPHÁGIDÆ or ERÍNNIDÆ

33. Head without strong thorns; abdomen with three or four distinct pairs of spiracles and without spinose armature. ACROCÉRIDÆ

Head usually with strong thorns, at least with elevated ridge-like antennal sheath and several small carinated elevations; abdomen with seven pairs of spiracles and spinose armature.......34

34. Head with two thorns.......................................35

Head with more than two thorns or with several short tubercles. . 36

35. Abdomen with a single transverse series of spines on each dorsal segment; wing with a long thorn at base. (Fig. 755, **Psilocéphala**) .... THERÉVIDÆ

Abdomen with two transverse series of spines on each dorsal segment; wing without thorn at base.

SCENOPÍNIDÆ or OMPHRÁLIDÆ

36. Upper pair of cephalic thorns directed sideways and slightly upward; apices of wings extending to or very slightly beyond apex of first abdominal segment; apices of middle tarsi not extending to apices of wings. (Fig. 751, **Mỳdas**)....................MYDÀIDÆ

Upper pairs of cephalic thorns directed forward, at most slightly divergent apically, generally slightly curved downward, or head without strong upper thorn............................37

37. Head with strong thorns, or if they are absent the abdomen has the dorsal transverse armature consisting of very strong thorns and intervening long slender hairs; apices of antennæ obtuse....38

Head very rarely with strong thorns, two carinate elevations present on upper anterior margin; antennæ with attenuated apices; body without thorns, sometimes with bristles...............39

38. Lower median portion of face with a closely approximated pair of stout thorns which are occasionally fused almost to apices; abdomen with the transverse armature of dorsal segments consisting of short flattened thorns and long slender hairs, the thorns usually appearing as if attached to, rather than forming part of the abdomen and sometimes turned up at bases and apices. (Fig. 758, **Sparnopòlius**) .... BOMBYLÌIDÆ

Lower median portion of face without thorns; abdomen with the transverse armature consisting of alternating long and short thorns (except in *Leptogaster*). (Fig. 756, **Dasýllis**)........ASÍLIDÆ

39. Cephalic armature consisting of two carinated elevations on upper anterior margin, on each of which is a very long hair; antennal sheaths raised above level of face, tapering apically, directed downward and slightly outward; proboscis often much elongated. (Fig. 759, **Rhamphomỳia**) .... EMPÍDIDÆ

Similar to Empididæ, but proboscis never elongated.

DOLICHOPÓDIDÆ

LITERATURE ON DIPTERA, GENERAL

ADAMS, C. F. Diptera Contributions. Kansas Univ. Sci. Bull., **2**, pp. 21–47 (1903).
New Diptera. Ibid., **2**, pp. 433–455 (1904); **3**, pp. 149–208 (1905).

AUSTEN, E. E. British Blood-sucking Flies. British Mus. (Nat. Hist.), 74 pp. (1906).
African Blood-sucking Flies. Ibid., 221 pp. (1909).
Blood-sucking Flies (Palestine). Bull. Ent. Res., **12**, pp. 107–124 (1921).
Blood-sucking Diptera (Mesopotamia). Ibid., **13**, pp. 275–290 (1923).
Blood-sucking Diptera (Dardanelles). Ibid., **16**, pp. 1–23 (1925).

BANKS, C. S. Blood-sucking Insects. Philippine Jour. Sci., **14**, pp. 163–189 (1919).

BANKS, N. Dipterous Larvæ. U. S. Agr. Dept. Ent. Tech. Bull., **22**, 44 pp. (1912).

BECKER, T. Neue Dipteren. Mitt. zool. Mus. Berlin, **10**, pp. 1–93 (1921).

BEQUAERT, J. Medical and Economic Entomology (Amazon). Med. Rept. Rice Exped., Harvard, **2**, pp. 157–257 (1926).
Medical and Economic Entomology (Africa). Rept. Harvard Afr. Med. Exped., **2**, pp. 797–1001 (1931).

BEZZI, M. Mosche ematofaghe. Rend. R. Inst. Lombardo, **40**, pp. 433–460 (1907).
Diptères cavernicoles. Arch. Zool., **8**, 87 pp. (1911). Atti Soc. Italiana Sci. Nat., **53**, pp. 207–230 (1914).
Reduction of Wings. Nature, **7**, pp. 55–182 (1916).

CANZANELLI, A. Diptera of Fungi. Comment. Pontif. Accad. Sci., **5**, pp. 211–282 (1941).

CASTRO, A. R. Economic Diptera (Spain). Consejo Sup. Invest. Cienc., 101 pp. (1945).

COQUILLETT, D. W. New Diptera (North America). Proc. Ent. Soc. Washington, **6**, pp. 166–192 (1904).
Type Species of North American Genera of Diptera. Proc. U. S. Nat. Mus., **37**, pp. 499–647 (1910).

CURRAN, C. H. New Diptera. American Mus. Novitat., **339**, 13 pp. (1929); **492**, 13 pp. (1931); **526**, 13 pp., **534**, 15 pp. (1932); **673**, 11 pp. (1933).
Families and Genera of North American Diptera. 512 pp., New York (1934).
American Diptera. Bull. American Mus. Nat. Hist., **80**, pp. 51–84 (1942).

CURRAN, C. H., G. C. CRAMPTON et al. Diptera of Connecticut. Bull. Connecticut Geol. Nat. Hist. Surv., **64**, pp. 175–182 (1942).

DE MEILLON, B. Insects of Medical Importance (South Africa). Publ. So. Afr. Inst. Med. Res., **32**, pp. 195–248; **33**, pp. 249–308 (1934); **36**, pp. 323–366 (1935).
Biting Insects (Ethiopia). Jour. Ent. Soc. South Africa, **7**, pp. 38–67 (1944); **10**, pp. 110–124 (1947).

EDWARDS, F. W., H. OLDROYD and J. SMART. British Blood-sucking Flies. Brit. Mus. (Nat. Hist.), 156 pp. (1939).

ENDERLEIN, G. Exotic Flies. Stettiner Ent. Ztg., **1911**, pp. 135–209. Zweiflügler. Tierwelt Mitteleuropas, **6**, Teil 3, 259 pp. (1936).

FREY, R. Brachycera (Arctic Siberia). Mem. Acad. Sci. Russ. Phys.-Math., (8) 29, no. 10, 35 pp. (1915).

GARRETT, C. B. D. New Diptera. Privately printed, Cranbrook, B. C., 12 & 16 pp. (1925).

GRAHAM-SMITH, G. S. Flies in Relation to Disease. Cambridge Univ., 292 pp. (1913).

GRIMSHAW, P. H. Diptera. Fauna Hawaiiensis, III, 77 pp. (1901).

Guide to Literature, British Diptera. Proc. R. Phys. Soc. Edinburgh, 20, pp. 78–117 (1917).

Key to Families, British Diptera. Ibid., 22, pp. 187–215 (1934).

GRÜNBERG, K. Blutsaugenden Diptera. 188 pp., Fischer, Jena (1907).

Diptera (Germany). Süsswasserfauna Deutschlands, Heft 2A, 312 pp. (1910).

HENDEL, F. New Diptera (Wiener Museum). Wiener Ent. Ztg., 26, pp. 223–245 (1907).

Meigen's 1800 paper. Verh. zool.-bot. Ges. Wien., 58, pp. 43–69 (1908).

Zweiflügler. Tierwelt Deutschlands, pt. 2, 135 pp. (1928).

HENDEL, F., and M. BEIER. Diptera. In Kükenthal, Handb. Zool. Berlin, 4, Heft 2, Lief. 8–11, pp. 1729–1998 (1936).

HENNIG, W. Families of Diptera. Zool. Anz., 116, pp. 161–175 (1936).

HINDLE, E. Blood-sucking Flies. Cambridge Univ., 398 pp. (1914).

JAMES, M. T. Myiasis in Man. Misc. Publ. U. S. Dept. Agric., 631, 175 pp. (1947).

JOHANNSEN, O. A. Aquatic Diptera. Mem. Cornell Univ. Agr. Exp. Sta., 164, 71 pp. (1934); 177, 62 pp. (1935); 205, 84 pp. (1937); 210, 56 pp. (1937).

KEILIN, D. Diptères vivipares. Arch. Zool., 55, pp. 393–415 (1916).

Diptera Living on Mollusks. Parasitol., 11, pp. 430–455 (1919).

LAMEERE, A. Classification of Diptera. Mem. Soc. Ent. Belgique, 12, pp. 105–140 (1906).

Diptera. In Précis de Zoologie. Publ. Inst. Zool. Torley-Rousseau, 5, pp. 71–160 (1936).

LEVY, L. Aquatic Metamorphoses of Diptera. Ann. Biol. Lacustre, 9, pp. 201–248 (1920).

LINDNER, E. Families of Diptera. Fliegen Palaearkt. Reg., 1, pp. 81–144 (1930).

Diptera. Biol. Tiere Deutschlands, pt. 38, 40 pp. (1923).

LUNDBECK, W. Diptera Danica. Kopenhagen, 7 vols. (1907–1927).

LUTZ, A., and M. NUNEZ TOVAR. Blood-sucking Diptera of Venezuela. Estud. zool. parasitol. venezolanas Rio Janeiro, pp. 7–64 (1928).

MALLOCH, J. R. Classification, based on Larval and Pupal Characters. Illinois State Lab. Nat. Hist., 12, pp. 161–410 (1917).

Diptera. Mem. Carnegie Mus., 12, pt. 2, pp. 13–32 (1934).

MEIGEN, J. G. Nouvelle classification, Paris, 1800. Facsimile in Bull. Zool. Nomenclat., 1, pp. 121–160 (1945).

MEIJERE, J. C. H. DE. Diptera. In Bronn's Tierreich, 5, Abt. 3, Lief. 1–4, 64 pp. (1916).

Mining Diptera. Tijdschr. Ent., 88, pp. 49–62 (1947).

NEAVE, A. S. Blood-sucking Insects (East Africa). Bull. Ent. Res., 3, pp. 275–323 (1912).

PATTON, W. S. Diptera of Medical and Veterinary Importance. Philippine Jour. Sci., 27, pp. 177–200, 397–411 (1925). Ann. Trop. Med. Parasitol.,

26, pp. 347–405 (1932); **27**, 108 pp. (1933); **29**, pp. 19–32, 199–230, 303–315, 483–496 (1935); **30**, 107 pp. (1936); **31**, 64 pp. (1937).

PEARCE, E. K. Typical Flies (Britain). London, 3 photographic atlases (1928).

PENNAK, R. W. Aquatic Insects (Colorado). Univ. Colo. Stud., (D) **2**, pp. 353–383 (1947).

PETERSON, A. Head of Diptera. Illinois Biol. Monogr., **3**, no. 2, 114 pp. (1916).

SABROSKY, C. W. Family Nomenclature in Diptera. Verh. 7, Internat. Kongr. Ent., Berlin, **1**, pp. 599–612 (1939).

SEEVERS, C. H. Termitophilous Diptera (Neotropical). Field Mus. Zool. Ser., **24**, pp. 175–193 (1941).

SÉGUY, E. Parasitic Insects of Man and Domestic Animals. Paris, 422 pp. (1924).

　　Les mouches parasites des oiseaux. La Terre et la Vie, **2**, pp. 520–532 (1932).

　　Mouches phytophages. Encycl. Ent. (B) II, **6**, pp. 145–197 (1932); **7**, pp. 167–264 (1934).

　　Blood-sucking Flies (France). Trav. Nat. Loing, **6**, pp. 78–107 (1932).

　　Domestic Flies. Bull. Ass. Nat. Loing, **16**, pp. 85–144 (1933).

　　La vie des mouches et des moustiques. Paris, 254 pp. (1938).

　　Nematocera and Brachycera (Omo). Mem. Mus. Hist. Nat. Paris, **8**, pp. 319–380 (1938).

　　Mouches parasites. Encycl. Ent. (A), **21**, pp. 1–436 (1941).

　　Biologie des Diptères. Ibid., **26**, 609 pp. (1950).

SERGENT, E. Blood-sucking Diptera. Paris, 305 pp. (1907).

SMART, J. Insects of Medical Importance. British Mus. (Nat. Hist.), 272 pp. (1944).

STACKELBERG, A. A. Blood-sucking Diptera, Keys. Rev. Microbiol. Epidemiol., **5**, pp. 43–56 (1926).

STEBBINS, F. A. Insect Galls. Bull. Mus. Nat. Hist., Springfield, Mass., 1910, 138 pp.

STONE, A. Generic Names of Meigen, 1800. Ann. Ent. Soc. America, **34**, pp. 404–418 (1941).

SURCOUF, J., and R. GONZALEZ-RINCONES. Blood-sucking Diptera (Venezuela). Dipt. Nematoc. vulnerants. Paris, 320 pp. (1911). Arch. Parasitol., **15**, pp. 248–314 (1912).

SZILADY, Z. Dipterenstudien. Ann. Mus. Nat. Hungarici, **24**, pp. 586–611 (1926).

TUXEN, S. L. Danske Dipterer, Keys to Families. Ent. Medd., **24**, pp. 43–70 (1943).

　　Hot Springs of Iceland. Zool. Iceland, **1**, pt. 11, 206 pp. (1944).

TWINN, C. R. et al. Biting-flies (Manitoba). Canadian Jour. Res., **26**, pp. 334–357 (1948).

VERRALL, G. H. British Flies. Vol. **8**, 691 & 121 pp. (1901). Vol. **5**, 780 & 34 pp. (1909).

VILLENEUVE, J. Etudes diptérologiques. Wiener Ent. Ztg., **26**, pp. 247–263 (1907); **29**, pp. 79–85 (1910).

WALTON, W. R. Parasitic and Predacious Diptera. Proc. U. S. Nat. Mus., **48**, pp. 171–186 (1914).

WILLIAMS, F. X. Hydrophilous Diptera. Proc. Hawaiian Ent. Soc., **10**, pp. 85–119 (1938); **10**, pp. 281–315 (1939); **11**, pp. 313–338 (1943).

WILLISTON, S. W. Manual of Diptera, 3rd ed. (North America). New Haven, Conn. 405 pp. (1908).

WINGATE, W. J. English Diptera. Trans. Nat. Hist. Soc., (n.s.) 2, 416 pp. (1906).

CATALOGUES AND LISTS

ALDRICH, J. M. Catalogue of North American Diptera. Smithsonian Misc. Coll., 46, 680 pp. (1905).

New Diptera. Proc. U. S. Nat. Mus., 66, art. 18, 36 pp. (1925); 69, art. 22, 26 pp. (1926); 74, art. 1, 25 pp. (1928); 81, art. 9, 28 pp. (1932).

ALEXANDER, C. P. Bibliography of Aquatic Insects. Bull. Illinois State Nat. Hist. Surv., 15, pp. 439–535 (1925).

ANDREWS, W. W. British Dipterological Literature. Ent. Rec., 43, 7 pp. (1931).

ARIAS, J. Diptera of Catalunya. Inst. d'Estudis Catalana, Barcelona, 56 pp. (1917).

AUDCENT, H. L. F. Diptera (Bristol). Proc. Bristol Nat. Soc., 27, pp. 409–470 (1949); 28, pp. 45–132 (1951).

BAKER, C. F. Diptera. Invertebrata Pacifica, 1, pp. 17–40 (1904).

BAUDYS, E. Galls of Moravia (in Czech). Acta Univ. Agric. Silvicult. Bruensis, C 43, 64 pp. (1948).

BECKER, T. Diptera (Egypt). Mitt. zool. Mus. Berlin, 2, Heft 21, 185 pp. (1903).

Diptera (Algeria and Tunis). Zeitschr. syst. Hymenopt. Dipt., 6, pp. 1–16, 97–114, 145–158, 273–287, 353–367 (1906); 7, pp. 33–61, 97–128, 225–256, 369–407 (1907).

Diptera (Central Asia). Ann. Mus. Zool. Acad. Sci., St. Petersburg, 12, pp. 253–317 (1907).

Diptera (Canary Isl.). Mitt. zool. Mus. Berlin, 4, pp. 1–206 (1908).

Diptera (Tunis). Ann. Mus. Nat. Hungarici, 13, pp. 301–330 (1915).

Diptera (Arctic Ural). Mém. Acad. Imp. Sci., St. Petersburg, 28, no. 7, 67 pp. (1915).

Diptera (Sudan). Denkschr. Akad. Wiss. Wien, 98, pp. 57–82 (1923).

BECKER, T. et al. Diptera (South Arabia). Ibid., 71, no. 2 (1907); pp. 131–160 (1931).

Diptera (Corsica). Deutsche Ent. Zeitschr., 1910, pp. 655–665; 1911, pp. 62–100.

BECKER, T., and P. STEIN. Persian Diptera. Ann. Mus. Zool. Acad. Sci., St. Petersburg, 17, pp. 503–654 (1912).

Diptera (Morocco). Ibid., 18, pp. 62–95 (1913).

BECKER, T., M. BEZZI, K. KERTESZ, and P. STEIN. Katalog der Paläarktischen Diptera. Budapest, 4 vols. 1936 pp. (1903–1907).

BEZZI, M. Ditteri Eritrei. Bull. Soc. Ent. Italiana, 37, pp. 195–304 (1905); 39, pp. 3–199 (1908).

Diptera (South Africa). Denkschr. Med. Naturw. Ges. Jena, 13, pp. 179–201 (1908).

Diptera (Syria and Egypt). Brotéria, Zool., 8, pp. 37–65 (1909).

Diptera Ibericæ. Ibid., 10, pp. 114–156 (1912).

Philippine Diptera. Philippine Jour. Sci., 8, pp. 305–332 (1913); 12, pp. 107–159 (1917).

Ditteri (Africa). Boll. Lab. Zool. Portici, **8**, pp. 279–308 (1914).

Alpine Diptera (Italy). Mem. Soc. Italiana Sci. Nat. Milan, **9**, 164 pp. (1918).

Ditteri (West Africa). Ann. Mus. Civ. Genova, **5**, pp. 1–44 (1912); **9**, pp. 1–17 (1920).

Diptera (Tunis). Ann. Mus. Civ. Stor. Nat., **50**, pp. 97–139 (1920).

Diptera (Seychelles). Parasitol., **15**, pp. 75–102 (1923).

Diptera (Giglio Isl., Italy). Ann. Mus. Civ. Stor. Nat., **50**, pp. 291–354 (1926).

BEZZI, M., and C. G. LAMB. Diptera (exclud. Nematocera) from Rodriguez Island. Trans. Ent. Soc. London, **1925**, pp. 537–573 (1926).

BRÈTHES, J. Catalogo Dipteros (del Plata). An. Mus. Nac. Buenos Aires, **16**, pp. 277–305 (1907).

BRIMLEY, C. S. Diptera of North Carolina. Ent. News, **33**, pp. 20–26, 230, 232, 294–298 (1922).

BROOKS, A. R. New Canadian Diptera. Canadian Ent., **77**, pp. 78–96 (1945).

BRYAN, E. H. Hawaiian Diptera. Proc. Hawaiian Ent. Soc., **8**, pp. 399–468 (1934).

COLE, F. R. Diptera (California). Rept. Laguna Marine Sta., **1**, pp. 150–162 (1912).

Diptera (Pribilof Isl.). Proc. California Acad. Sci., **12**, pp. 160–177 (1921).

COLE, F. R., and A. L. LOVETT. Oregon Diptera. Ibid., **9**, pp. 221–255 (1919); **11**, pp. 197–344 (1921). Ent. News, **34**, pp. 205–209 (1923).

COLLART, A. Mining Diptera (Belgium). Bull. Mus. Roy. Hist. Nat. Belgique, **18**, 10 pp. (1942).

COLLIN, J. E. Diptera (Greenland). Ann. Mag. Nat. Hist., (10) **7**, pp. 67–91 (1931).

CURRAN, C. H. Diptera from Congo. American Mus. Novitat., **246**, 18 pp. (1927). Bull. American Mus. Nat. Hist., **57**, pp. 33–89, 327–399 (1928); **58**, pp. 167–187 (1928).

Nearctic Diptera. Canadian Ent., **59**, pp. 79–92 (1927).

Diptera (Africa). American Mus. Novitat., **340**, 15 pp. (1929).

Diptera (Fiji and New Caledonia). Ibid., **375**, 15 pp. (1929).

Diptera from Harrison Park, N. Y. Bull. American Mus. Nat. Hist., **61**, pp. 21–115 (1930).

Diptera (Galapagos Isl.). Nyt Mag. Naturvidensk., **71**, pp. 347–366 (1932).

Diptera (British Guiana). Bull. American Mus. Nat. Hist., **66**, pp. 287–532 (1934).

Diptera (Africa). American Mus. Novitat., **836**, 17 pp. (1936).

CURRAN, C. H., C. P. ALEXANDER and E. T. CRESSON. Expedition to Polynesian and Melanesian Islands, Diptera. Proc. California Acad. Sci., **4** (22), pp. 1–66 (1936).

CZERNY, L., and G. STROBL. Spanische Dipteren. Verh. K. K. zool.-bot. Ges. Wien, **59**, pp. 121–301 (1909).

CZIZEK, K. Dipterenfauna Mährens. Zeitschr. Mähr. Landesmus. Brünn, **6**, pp. 182–234 (1906).

EDWARDS, F. W. Diptera (Sumatra). Jour. Fed. Malay States Mus., **8**, pp. 7–59 (1919).

EDWARDS, F. W. and E. E. AUSTEN. Diptera (Dutch New Guinea). Trans. Zool. Soc. London, **20**, pp. 391–422 (1915).

ENCOBET, J. A. Catalogue of Diptera (Spain). Mem. Soc. España Hist. Nat., **7**, pp. 61–246 (1912).

ENDERLEIN, G. Diptera (Antarctic). Kongl. Svenska Vet. Handl., **48**, no. 3, pp. 93–111 (1912).
  Diptera (Alai-Pamis Exped.) Deutsches Ent. Ztg., **1933**, pp. 129–146 (1934).
  Diptera of Juan Fernandez and Easter Islands. Nat. Hist. Fern. Easter Isl., **3**, pp. 643–680 (1940).

ESAKI, T. et al. Diptera. In Iconographia Insect. Japonicorum, Tokyo, 242 pp. (1932).

FORDHAM, W. J. List of Diptera (Durham). Trans. Nat. Hist. Soc. Northumberland, **7**, pp. 197–265 (1945).

FREY, R. Diptera (Finland). Acta Soc. Faun. Fl. Fennica, **34**, no. 6, pp. 1–59 (1911).
  Diptera (Ceylon). Finska Vet. Soc. Forh., **59** A, no. 20, 36 pp. (1917).
  Diptera (Saren). Naturw. Untersuch. Sarekgebirges, **4**, pt. 6, pp. 665–696 (1916).
  Dipteren aus Archangelsk. Acta Soc. Faun. Fl. Fennica, **46**, no. 2, 32 pp. (1918).
  Diptera (South America). Finska Vet. Soc. Forh., **60** A, no. 14, 35 pp. (1919).
  Diptera (Canary Isl.) Soc. Sci. Fennicæ, Comment. Biol., **6**, 237 pp. (1936).
  Diptera (Azores). Ibid., **8**, no. 10, 114 pp. (1945).
  Diptera (Madeira). Ibid., **8**, no. 16, 47 pp. (1950).
  Diptera (Lapland). Notulæ Ent., **30**, pp. 5–18 (1950).

GOETGHEBUER, M. Diptera of Temporary Lakes of Dunes. Bull. Ann. Soc. Ent. Belgique, **68**, pp. 18–92 (1928).

GRAENICHER, S. Diptera (Wisconsin). Bull Wisconsin Nat. Hist. Soc., **10**, pp. 171–185 (1913).

HARDY, G. H. Australian Diptera. Proc. Linn. Soc. New South Wales, **58**, pp. 408–420 (1933); **64**, pp. 34–50, 345–352 (1939); **65**, pp. 484–493 (1940); **66**, pp. 223–232 (1941); **70**, pp. 135–146 (1945); **71**, pp. 65–71 (1946).

HENDEL, F. American Diptera. Deutsche Ent. Zeitschr., **1913**, pp. 617–636; **1914**, pp. 151–176.
  Notes on Diptera. Verh. zool.-bot. Ges. Wien, **81**, pp. 28–43 (1931).
  Subantarctic Diptera. Ann. Naturh. Mus. Wien, **48**, pp. 179–193 (1937).

HENDRICKSON, G. O. Insects of Iowa Prairies. Iowa State Coll. Jour. Sci., **4**, pp. 125–148, 198–202 (1930).

HENNIG, W. Diptera (Formosa). Ent. Beihefte, **8**, pp. 1–239 (1941).

HENRIKSEN, K. L., and W. LUNDBECK. Diptera (Greenland). Meddel. Groenland, **21**, pp. 557–664 (1917).

HUNTER, W. D. Catalogue of Diptera (South America) to Mydaidæ. Trans. American Ent. Soc., **26**, pp. 258–298 (1900); **27**, pp. 121–155 (1901).

HUTTON, F. W. Catalogue of New Zealand Diptera. Colonial Mus. New Zealand, Wellington, pp. 1–70 (1881).

JOHNSON, C. W. Diptera (Bermuda). Psyche, **15**, pp. 69–80 (1908).
    Diptera (New Jersey). Ann. Rept. New Jersey State Mus., **1909**, pp.
    703–814 (1910).
    Diptera (Florida). Bull. American Mus. Nat. Hist., **32**, pp. 37–90
    (1913). Ann. Ent. Soc. America, **6**, pp. 443–452 (1913).
    Diptera (Jamaica). Bull. American Mus. Nat. Hist., **41**, pp. 421–449
    (1919) (with C. T. Brues).
    Diptera (Mt. Desert). Insect Fauna Mt. Desert Isl., pp. 161–227 (1927).
    Diptera (Labrador). Psyche, **36**, pp. 129–146 (1929).
    Diptera (New England). Occ. Pap. Boston Soc. Nat. Hist., **7**, 326 pp.
    (1925).
    Diptera (Nantucket). Publ. Maria Mitchell Assn., Nantucket, **3**, pp.
    120–159 (1930).
KARL, O. Diptera. Tierwelt Nord- u. Ostsee, **19**, no. 11, pp. 33–84 (1930).
KERTESZ, K. Catalogus Dipterorum. Budapest, 7 vols. 2438 pp. (1902–1910).
KNOWLTON, G. F. et al. Diptera (Utah). Utah Agr. Exp. Sta., mimeogr. ser.
    200, pt. 5, 22 pp. (1939).
KOLOSOV, Y. M. Catalog of Diptera (Ural). Oblast. Sverdlovsk Bact. Inst.,
    1928, 16 pp. (In Russian).
KRÖBER, O. Diptera (Argentina). Konowia, **8**, pp. 170–193 (1928).
    Diptera (Schleswig-Holstein). Verh. Ver. naturw. Heimatforsch., **22**,
    pp. 19–78 (1931); **23**, pp. 63–113 (1932); **24**, pp. 45–156 (1935).
LAMB, C. G. Diptera. Subarctic Isls. New Zealand, Wellington, pp. 129–145
    (1909).
LUNDSTRÖM, C., and R. FREY. Diptera (North European Russia). Acta Soc.
    Faun. Fl. Fennica, **37**, no. 10, 20 pp. (1913).
MALLOCH, J. R. Diptera (Costa Rica). Trans. American Ent. Soc., **40**, pp.
    1–36 (1914).
    Diptera (Canada). Rep. Canadian Arctic Exped., 3 C, pp. 34–89 (1919).
    Diptera (Pribilof Isl.). North American Fauna, **46**, pp. 170–227 (1923).
    Australian Diptera. Proc. Linn. Soc. New South Wales, **48–66**, 39 pts.
    700 pp. (1923–1941).
    Oriental Diptera. Philippine Jour. Sci., **31**, pp. 491–512 (1926).
    Diptera. British Mus., Insects of Samoa, **6**, fasc. 9, pp. 329–366 (1935).
    Diptera (New Guinea). Proc. Linn. Soc. New South Wales, **64**, pp.
    97–154, 169–180, 409–465 (1939).
MATSUMURA, F. Coleoptera, Diptera (Sachalin). Jour. Coll. Agric. Sapporo,
    4, 145 pp. (1911).
MEIJERE, J. C. H. DE. Southasiatic Diptera. Tijdschr. Ent., **50–67**, 1180 pp.
    (1907–1924); Bijdr. Dierk., **18**, pp. 83–118 (1904).
    Diptera (Indo-Australian). Ann. Mus. Nat. Hungarici, **4**, pp. 165–196
    (1906).
    Diptera (Arctic). Fauna Arctica, **5**, pp. 13–72 (1910).
    Diptera (Simalu). Tijdschr. Ent., **58**, Suppl., pp. 1–63 (1915).
    Diptera (North New Guinea). Ibid., pp. 98–139 (1915).
    Diptera (New Guinea). Res. Exped. Sci. Neerl. Nieuw Guinea, **9**,
    pp. 305–386 (1903).
    Diptera (Holland). Tijdschr. Ent., **71**, pp. 11–83 (1928); **78**, pp. 188–
    230 (1935); **82**, pp. 118–136 (1939); **87**, pp. 1–25 (1946).

NUNEZ TOVAR, M. Diptera (Venezuela). Trab. Contrib. 4th Congr. Venez. Med., Maracay, 41 pp. (1924).

OUELLET, J. Catalogue of Diptera (Quebec). Nat. Canadien, 68, pp. 121–141 (1941).

PARAMONOV, S. J. Diptera (Australia). Ann. Mag. Nat. Hist., (12) 3, pp. 515–534 (1950).

PARENT, O. Diptera (Egypt). Bull. Soc. Roy. Ent. Egypte, 1925, pp. 153–185.

POPPIUS, B., C. LUNDSTRÖM and R. FREY. Dipteren (Sarekgebiet). Naturw. Untersuch. Sarekgebirg., 4, pp. 665–696 (1917).

RIEDEL, M. P. Subalpine Diptera (Silesia). Zeitschr. Wiss. Insekt.-biol., 25, pp. 71–81 (1930).

ROHDENDORF, B. B. Diptera (USSR). Inst. Zool. Acad. Sci., Moscow, 19, 500 pp. (1937).

SACK, P. Diptera (Poland). Bayer Akad. Wiss. Abh. math.-naturw. Abt., Suppl.-Band, pp. 259–277 (1925–32).

SÉGUY, E. Diptères d'Espagne. Mem. Soc. Ent. Zaragoza, 3 A, 30 pp. (1929).

Diptères du Maroc. Mem. Soc. Sci. Nat. Maroc, 24, 206 pp. (1930).

Diptères (Mozambique). Mem. Mus. Zool. Univ. Coimbra, 67, pp. 5–80 (1933).

Diptères de Chine. Encycl. Ent. (B) 7, pp. 1–28 (1934).

Diptères d'Afrique. Ibid., 7, pp. 63–80 (1934).

Diptères d'Espagne. Mem. Acad. Cienc. Zaragoza, 3, 54 pp. (1934).

Diptères (Azores). Ann. Soc. ent. France, 105, pp. 11–26 (1936).

Diptères (France). Faune de France, Paris, fasc. 8, 216 pp. (1937).

Diptera. Miss. Biol. Paese Borana, Rome, 3, no. 2, pp. 123–148 (1939).

Diptera (French Antarctic Isl.). Mem. Mus. Hist. Nat. Paris, 14, pp. 203–267 (1940).

Diptères (Morocco). Ann. Soc. ent. France, 110, pp. 1–23 (1941); Rev. franç. Ent., 16, pp. 152–161 (1949).

Diptera (Ivory Coast). Ann. Soc. ent. France, 109, pp. 109–130 (1941).

Diptera (Biology and Taxonomy). Encycl. Ent. (B) 10, pp. 105–150 (1946).

SENIOR-WHITE, R. A. Diptera (India). Mem. Dept. Agr. India, Ent. Ser., 7, pp. 83–169 (1922).

Diptera (Ceylon). Spolia Zeylandica, 11, pp. 381–395 (1921); 12, pp. 195–206, 375–406 (1924); 13, pp. 9–12 (1925).

SHIRAKI, T. New Diptera (Japan). Trans. Nat. Hist. Soc. Formosa, 22, pp. 259–280, 331–336, 487–493 (1932).

SOUKUP, J. List of Diptera (Peru). Bol. Mus. Hist. Nat. Prado, 9, pp. 119–142 (1945).

SPEISER, P. Diptera (Kilimandjaro). Schw. Exped. Kilimandjaro, 10, 210 pp. (1907–1910).

Diptera (German East Africa). Berliner Ent. Zeitschr., 52, pp. 127–149 (1907). Beitr. Tierkunde, Widmungsschr., Königsberg, 1924, pp. 90–156 (1924).

Dipteren (Ethiopia). Wiener Ent. Ztg., 40, pp. 81–99 (1923).

STACKELBERG, A. A. Les mouches de l'URSS. Tabl. Anal. Leningrad, 7, 742 pp. (1933).

STRICKLAND, E. H. Diptera of Alberta. Canadian Jour. Res. Zool. Sci., 16, pp. 177–219 (1938); 24, pp. 157–173 (1946).

STROBL, P. G. Diptera of Balkan Peninsula. Glasnik Zem. Mus. Bosni Herce-govini, 14, pp. 461–517 (1902). (In Serbian).
Spanische Dipteren, pt. 2. Mem. R. Soc. España Hist. nat., 3, pp. 271–422 (1906).
Dipteren von Steiermark, pt. 2. Mitt. Naturw. Ver. Steiermark, Graz, 46, pp. 45–293 (1910).
STUARDO ORTIZ, C. Catalogo Dipteros (Chile). Santiago, Chile, Minist. Agric., 250 pp. (1946).
THALHAMMER, J. Diptera Hungariæ. Budapest, pp. 5–76 (1918).
TILLYARD, R. J. et al. Insects of Macquarie Isl. Sci. Rept. Australian Antarct. Exped., Ser. C, 5, pt. 8, pp. 1–35 (1920).
TIMON-DAVID, J. Diptères du Mont Blanc. Ann. Fac. Sci. Marseille, 10, pp. 3–51 (1937).
TUCCIMEI, G. Catalogue of Diptera (Rome). Boll. Soc. Zool. Ital., 1907, pp. 125–158.
TUCKER, E. S. Diptera (Kansas, Colorado). Kansas Univ. Sci. Bull., 4, pp. 83–108 (1907).
TWINN, C. R. et al. Biting Flies (Manitoba). Canadian Jour. Res. Zool. Sci., 26, pp. 334–347 (1948).
VILLENEUVE, J. Diptera (Syria). Voyage Zool. Gadeau Kerville, 1, pp. 317–331 (1926).
VIMMER, A. Katalog der Dipteren Böhmens. Cas. Ceske Spol. Ent. Prague, 7, pp. 90–94 (1910); 9, pp. 49–80 (1912).
Diptera (Puno). Bol. Mus. Hist. Nat. "Javier Prado," Lima, 4, no. 14, pp. 360–372 (1940).
WASHBURN, F. L. Diptera of Minnesota. Bull. Minnesota Agr. Exp. Sta., 93, 168 pp. (1905).
WENGENMAYR, X. Dipteren (Bayern). Ber. Naturw. Ver. Augsburg, 49, pp. 18–80 (1931).
WHITE, J. H. List of Diptera (Lincolnshire). Trans. Lincolnshire Nat. Union, 11, pp. 163–175 (1947).
WINN, A. F., and G. BEAULIEU. List of Diptera (Quebec). 24th Rept. Quebec Soc. Prot. Plants, Suppl., 100 pp. (1932).

SUBORDER NEMATOCERA

ALEXANDER, C. P. Radial Field of Nematocerous Diptera. Proc. Linn. Soc. New South Wales, 52, pp. 42–72 (1927).
BISCHOFF, W. Die Köpfe der Oligoneuralarven. Arch. Naturg., 88 A, Heft 6, pp. 1–51 (1923).
BRUNETTI, E. Nematocera. Fauna British India, Diptera, 1, 581 pp. (1912).
Catalogue of Nematocera (Orient). Rec. Indian Mus., 17, 276 pp. (1920).
COE, R. L. et al. Nematocera. Handbook of British Insects, 9 (2), 216 pp., Roy. Ent. Soc. London (1950).
COQUILLETT, D. W. New Nematocera. Jour. New York Ent. Soc., 13, pp. 56–69 (1905).
CRAMPTON, G. C. Phylogeny of Nematocera. Psyche, 31, pp. 238–242 (1924). Proc. Ent. Soc. Washington, 27, pp. 68–91 (1925). Ann. Ent. Soc. America, 18, pp. 49–74 (1925). Ent. News, 37, pp. 33–38, 65–70 (1926).

EDWARDS, F. W. Nematocera (South America) Mission Arc. Meridien Amérique du Sud, **10**, pp. 143–162 (1919).

Nematocera (North Borneo). Jour. Fed. Malay States Mus., **16**, pp. 486–504 (1931).

Nematocera (Spitzbergen). Ann. Mag. Nat. Hist., (9) **10**, pp. 193–215 (1922); **14**, pp. 162–174 (1924).

Philippine Nematocera. Notulæ Ent., **6**, pp. 33–44 (1926).

Phylogeny of Nematocera. Verh. 3 Internat. Ent. Kongr. Zürich, **2**, pp. 111–130 (1926).

Nematocera (Borneo). Jour. Sarawak Mus., **3**, pp. 243–278 (1926).

Nematocera (Ceylon). Spolia Zeylandica, **14**, pp. 117–128 (1927).

Nematocera (East Indies). Treubia, **6**, pp. 154–172 (1925); **9**, pp. 352–370 (1927).

Nematocera (Samoa). Insects of Samoa, **6**, fasc. 2, pp. 23–102, British Mus. (1928).

Nematocera (Yunnan and Tibet). Ann. Mag. Nat. Hist., (10) **1**, pp. 681–703 (1928).

Nematocera (Corsica). Encycl. Ent. (B) II, **4**, pp. 157–189 (1928).

Nematocera (Fed. Malay St.) Jour. Fed. Malay States Mus., **14**, 139 pp. (1928).

Nematocera (Philippines). Notulæ Ent., **9**, pp. 1–14, 70–81 (1929).

Nematocera, part (Patagonia). Diptera of Patagonia and South Chile, pt. II, fasc. 3, pp. 77–119, British Mus. (1930).

Nematocera (Dutch East Indies). Treubia, **14**, pp. 137–152 (1932).

Nematocera (Mt. Kinabalu). Jour. Fed. Malay States Mus., **17**, pp. 223–296 (1933).

Nematocera (Gulf of Guinea). Ann. Mag. Nat. Hist., (10) **14**, pp. 321–336 (1934).

GOETGHEBUER, M. Nematocera (Belgium). Bull. Ann. Soc. Ent. Belgique, **74**, pp. 35–48 (1934).

GRACE, G. Nematocera. Naturalist, **1926**, pp. 133–136, 173–176, 211–216.

HARANT, H., and J. RICHARD. Larves de Nematocères. Bull. Soc. Etud. Sci. Nat. Beziers, **41**, pp. 76–89 (1938).

HENNIG, W. Thalassophile Nematocera. Tierwelt Nord- u. Ostsee, **27**, pp. 85–102 (1935).

JOHANNSEN, O. A. Aquatic Nematocera. Bull. New York State Mus., **68**, pp. 327–448 (1903); **86**, pp. 76–327 (1905).

Nematocera (exclusive of Chironomidæ). Mem. Cornell Agric. Exp. Sta., **164**, 71 pp. (1934).

KEILIN, D. Larvæ of some Nematocera. Ann. Mag. Nat. Hist., (9) **3**, pp. 33–42 (1919).

KIEFFER, J. J. Nematocera (Europe). Ann. Soc. Sci. Bruxelles, **30**, pp. 311–358 (1906).

LUNDSTRÖM, C. Nematocera (Finland). Acta Soc. Faun. Fl. Fennica, **37**, no. 10, 20 pp. (1913).

Nematocera (Arctic Siberia). Mem. Acad. Imp. Sci. Petrograd, Phys. Math., (8) **29**, no. 8, 33 pp. (1915).

MALLOCH, J. R. Nematocera. Bull. Illinois Lab. Nat. Hist., **10**, pp. 213–243 (1914).

DeMeillon, B. Nematocera (Ethiopia). Jour. Ent. Soc. South Africa, **5,** pp. 87–98 (1942); **6,** pp. 90–113 (1943).

Reidel, M. R. Nematocera (New Guinea). Ann. Mus. Nat. Hungarici, **18,** pp. 129–144 (1921).

Séguy, E. Nematocères piqueurs. Faune de France, **12,** 109 pp. (1925). Nematocères. Ibid., **36,** 368 pp. (1940).

Stackelberg, A. A. Nematocera (Petrograd). Petrogr. Agron. Inst. Sci. Res., C, no. **10,** 16 pp. (1922).

Storå, R. Nematocera (Finland). Notul. Ent., **19,** pp. 16–30 (1939).

Surcouf, J., and P. Gonzales-Rincones. Diptères piqueurs (Venezuela). Arch. Parasitol., **15,** pp. 248–314 (1912).

Wahlgren, E. Nematocera (Sweden). Uppsala, 273 pp. (1921).

Wesche, W. Phylogeny of Nematocera. Biol. Bull., **23,** pp. 250–270 (1912).

TIPULOIDEA

Abreu, E. S. Tipulidos (Canary Isl.). Mem. R. Acad. Barcelona, (3) **19,** 19 pp. (1926). Limonidos (Canary Isl.). Ibid., **18,** 132 pp. (1923).

Alexander, C. P. Holarctic Tipulidæ in U. S. National Museum. Proc. U. S. Nat. Mus., **72,** no. 2698, 17 pp. (1927).

Crane-flies (Canadian Arctic). Rept. Canadian Arct. Exped., **3,** pp. 3–30 (1919). Canadian Ent., **51,** pp. 191–199 (1919).

Nearctic Crane-flies. Bull. Brooklyn Ent. Soc., **25,** pp. 71–77, 276–282 (1930); **26,** pp. 177–184 (1931); **33,** pp. 71–78 (1938); **34,** pp. 92–100 (1939); **35,** pp. 84–89 (1940); **36,** pp. 12–17 (1941); **42,** pp. 131–135 (1947); **44,** pp. 15–20, 98–104, 152–157 (1949); **45,** pp. 41–48, 156–160 (1950).

New Nearctic Crane-flies. Canadian Ent., **48,** pp. 42–53 (1916); **49,** pp. 22–31, 61–64, 199–211 (1917); **50,** pp. 60–71, 158–165, 242–246, 381–386, 411–416 (1918); **51,** pp. 162–172, 191–199 (1919); **52,** pp. 109–112, 224–229 (1920); **53,** pp. 132–137 (1921); **59,** pp. 184–193 (1927); **61,** pp. 15–22 (1929); **72,** pp. 151–155 (1940); **73,** pp. 85–90, 206–213 (1941); **74,** pp. 206–212 (1942); **75,** pp. 13–20, 139–145 (1943); **76,** pp. 57–62, 166–172, 217–222 (1944); **77,** pp. 1–6, 140–144, 186–191, 204–208 (1945); **78,** pp. 155–159 (1946); **79,** pp. 68–73 (1947); **80,** pp. 166–171 (1948).

New Crane-flies (Eastern U. S. and Canada). Ent. News, **36,** pp. 200–204, 229–230 (1925); **37,** pp. 44–50, 291–297 (1926); **38,** pp. 181–184 (1927); **40,** pp. 44–49 (1929); **51,** pp. 83–85, 99–103 (1940); **52,** pp. 192–196 (1941); **55,** pp. 125–129, 241–247 (1944); **57,** pp. 245–252 (1947); **61,** pp. 163–171 (1950).

New Crane-flies (U. S. and Canada). Jour. Ent. Zool., **36,** pp. 89–94 (1944); Proc. Acad. Nat. Sci. Philadelphia, **1914,** pp. 579–606; **1915,** pp. 458–515; **1916,** pp. 486–549.

Crane-flies (Western U. S. and Canada). Ent. News, **54,** pp. 45–51, 253–258 (1943); **56,** pp. 126–132, 155–161 (1945); **57,** pp. 65–71, 173–179 (1946); **58,** pp. 61–67, 205–209 (1947); **59,** pp. 121–128, 207–214 (1948); **60,** pp. 39–45 (1949); **61,** pp. 29–35 (1950).

Tipulidæ (Western North America). Proc. U. S. Nat. Mus., **64,** no. 2500, 16 pp. (1924).

Western Tipulidæ. Pan-Pacific Ent., **20**, pp. 91–97 (1944); **21**, pp. 91–97 (1945); **23**, pp. 91–96 (1947); **26**, pp. 81–85 (1950). Great Basin Nat., **4**, pp. 89–100 (1943); **5**, pp. 93–103 (1944).

Crane-flies (U. S.). Ins. Inscit. Menstr., **3**, pp. 127–142 (1915).

Tipulidæ and Rhyphidæ (Pribilof Isl.). North American Fauna, **46**, pp. 159–169 (1923).

Crane-flies (Quebec). Canadian Ent., **61**, pp. 231–251 (1929); **63**, pp. 135–147 (1931).

Crane-flies (Ontario). Canadian Ent., **58**, pp. 236–240 (1926); **60**, pp. 54–60 (1928).

Crane-flies (Alberta). Canadian Ent., **59**, pp. 214–225 (1927).

Crane-flies (New England). Occ. Pap. Boston Soc. Nat. Hist., **5**, pp. 169–174 (1925); pp. 223–231 (1927); pp. 267–278 (1930); **8**, pp. 273–293 (1936).

Crane-flies (New York). Mem. Agric. Exp. Sta., Cornell, **25**, pp. 767–993 (1919). Bull. Brooklyn Ent. Soc., **17**, pp. 58–62 (1922); **19**, pp. 57–64 (1924); **24**, pp. 22–29, 295–302 (1929).

Crane-flies (Connecticut). Bull. Conn. Geol. Nat. Hist. Surv., **64**, pt. 4, pp. 183–486 (1942).

Tipuloidea (Great Smoky Mts.). American Midl. Nat., **24**, pp. 602–644 (1940); **26**, pp. 281–319 (1941).

Tipuloidea (Colorado). Ibid., **29**, pp. 147–179 (1943).

Tipuloidea (Yellowstone Park). Ibid., **30**, pp. 718–764 (1943); **33**, pp. 391–439 (1945).

Tipuloidea (Texas, Arizona). Ibid., **35**, pp. 484–531 (1946).

Tipuloidea (Utah). Ibid., **39**, pp. 1–82 (1948).

Tipuloidea (Washington). Ibid., **42**, pp. 257–333 (1949).

Crane-flies (California). Bull. So. California Acad. Sci., **44**, pp. 33–45 (1945); **45**, pp. 1–16 (1946); **46**, pp. 35–50 (1947). Proc. California Acad. Sci., **10**, pp. 35–52 (1920).

Ptychopteridæ. Gen. Insectorum, **188**, 12 pp. (1927). Bull. Brooklyn Ent. Soc., **32**, pp. 140–143 (1937); **38**, pp. 37–42 (1943); **42**, pp. 19–24 (1947).

Tipula (Western North America). Bull. Brooklyn Ent. Soc., **40**, pp. 33–37 (1945); **41**, pp. 45–51, 65–71 (1946).

Brachypremna. Jour. New York Ent. Soc., **20**, pp. 225–236 (1912).

Tanypremna and Megistocera. Ibid., **22**, pp. 205–218 (1914).

Cylindrotomidæ. Gen. Insectorum, **187**, 16 pp. (1927).

Limnophila (Eastern North America). Bull. Brooklyn Ent. Soc., **22**, pp. 56–64, 110–115 (1927).

Eriopterinæ (United States, Canada). Jour. New York Ent. Soc., **37**, pp. 49–58 (1929).

Crane-flies, Biology. Jour. Ent. Zool., **6**, pp. 12–34, 105–118 (1914); **7**, pp. 1–8, 142–158 (1915); **11**, pp. 67–74 (1919).

Crane-flies (Jamaica). Ent. Bull. Dept. Sci. Agr. Jamaica, **4**, suppl., pp. 4–14 (1928).

Crane-flies (Puerto Rico). Jour. Dept. Agr. Puerto Rico, **16**, pp. 347–387 (1932).

Tipulidæ (West Indies). Jour. Agr. Univ. Porto Rico, **20**, pp. 877–882 (1937); **21**, pp. 179–190, 523–534 (1937); **23**, pp. 91–130 (1939).

Tipulidæ (Panama). Ann. Ent. Soc. America, **27,** pp. 55–73 (1934). Encycl. Ent. (B) II, **10,** pp. 91–104 (1946).

Crane-flies (Mexico). Ann. Ent. Soc. America, **18,** pp. 341–362 (1925); **19,** pp. 158–176 (1926); **20,** pp. 301–318 (1927); **21,** pp. 101–119 (1928); **31,** pp. 393–412 (1938); **32,** pp. 70–90 (1939); **33,** pp. 140–161 (1940); **39,** pp. 119–139, 522–541 (1946). Ann. Esc. Nac. Cienc. Biol. Mexico, **4,** pp. 213–253 (1946).

Crane-flies (South America). Ann. Ent. Soc. America, **19,** pp. 378–394 (1926); **21,** pp. 623–641 (1928); **22,** pp. 768–788 (1929); **23,** pp. 721–740 (1930); **24,** pp. 622–642 (1931); **28,** pp. 313–331 (1935); **29,** pp. 749–769 (1936); **30,** pp. 598–617 (1937); **34,** pp. 231–254 (1941); **36,** pp. 103–127 (1943); **37,** pp. 298–322 (1944); **38,** pp. 256–280 (1945); **42,** pp. 101–119 (1944); **45,** pp. 119–135 (1952). Trans. Ent. Soc. London, **1922,** pp. 34–64.

Neotropical Tipulidæ. Jour. New York Ent. Soc., **27,** pp. 132–154 (1919); **28,** pp. 1–13 (1920); **35,** pp. 265–278 (1927); **36,** pp. 47–59, 355–367 (1928); **37,** pp. 89–99, 395–407 (1929); **38,** pp. 109–120 (1930); **39,** pp. 109–122 (1931); **46,** pp. 327–337 (1938); **48,** pp. 105–116 (1940); **49,** pp. 139–148, 345–356 (1941); **50,** pp. 135–146, 251–262 (1942); **51,** pp. 199–212 (1943); **52,** pp. 45–57, 369–383 (1944); **53,** pp. 49–61, 279–291 (1945); **54,** pp. 293–307 (1946); **55,** pp. 173–184 (1947); **56,** pp. 137–148 (1948); **57,** pp. 253–265 (1949); **59,** pp. 99–110 (1951).

Tipulidæ (Tropical America). Knowia, **16,** pp. 55–66 (1937). Rev. Ent. Rio Janeiro, **9,** pp. 426–441 (1938); **10,** pp. 622–677 (1939); **11,** pp. 894–908 (1940); **12,** pp. 322–337 (1941); **14,** pp. 485–502 (1943); **16,** pp. 373–393 (1945); **17,** pp. 375–400 (1946); **18,** pp. 65–100, 317–360 (1947); **19,** pp. 149–190, 509–556 (1948); **20,** pp. 589–616 (1949); **21,** pp. 161–211 (1950).

Neotropical Crane-flies in Hungarian National Museum. Ent. News, **24,** pp. 404–412, 439–449 (1913); **25,** pp. 202–215, 351–363 (1914).

Brazilian Tipulidæ. Rev. Ent. Rio Janeiro, **6,** pp. 10–23 (1936); **7,** pp. 233–246 (1937); **8,** pp. 318–332 (1938); **9,** pp. 247–260 (1938); **10,** pp. 428–444 (1939); **11,** pp. 382–397 (1940); **13,** pp. 166–182, 421–437 (1942); **14,** pp. 291–306 (1943); **15,** pp. 19–34, 292–312 (1944); **16,** pp. 210–243 (1945).

Crane-flies (South Brazil). Encycl. Ent. (B) II, **9,** pp. 23–36 (1938).

Neotropical Tipulidæ. Ann. Mag. Nat. Hist., (10) **20,** pp. 481–504 (1937); (11) **1,** pp. 336–362 (1937); (11) **2,** pp. 416–438 (1938); (11) **3,** pp. 186–209 (1939); (11) **5,** pp. 275–297 (1940); (11) **6,** pp. 194–222 (1940); (11) **8,** pp. 105–132, 240–265, 313–344 (1941); (11) **9,** pp. 219–245, 338–370, 424–448, 759–790 (1942); (11) **10,** pp. 217–245, 522–552, 738–765 (1943); (11) **11,** pp. 154–182, 284–311, 586–616 (1944); (11) **12,** pp. 8–28, 234–264, 390–419, 579–609, 734–765 (1946); (11) **13,** pp. 740–767 (1947); (11) **14,** pp. 256–280, 388–414, 552–577 (1948); (12) **1,** pp. 391–417 (1948).

Crane-flies (Andes). Jour. New York Ent. Soc., **21,** pp. 193–212 (1913).

Crane-flies (Br. Guiana, Colombia, Peru). Trans. American Ent. Soc., **40,** pp. 223–255 (1914); **42,** pp. 1–32 (1916).

Tipulidæ (Venezuela). Bol. Ent. Venezolana, **2**, pp. 17–26, 125–144 (1943); **3**, pp. 35–50, 143–160, 171–192 (1944); **4**, pp. 59–78 (1945); **6**, pp. 37–105 (1947). Zoologica, **35**, pp. 33–56 (1950).

Crane-flies (Chile). Bol. Sanid. Veg. Chile, **3**, pp. 117–135 (1943). Agric. Technica, **5**, pp. 5–23 (1945).

Tipulidæ (Chile). Rev. Chilena Hist. Nat., **38**, pp. 173–179 (1934); **39**, pp. 49–105 (1935); **42**, pp. 276–282 (1938); **43**, pp. 176–184 (1939).

Tipulidæ (Patagonia). Arkiv Zool., **13**, pp. 1–32 (1920). British Mus., Diptera of Patagonia and South Chile, **1**, 240 pp. (1929).

Tipulidæ (São Paulo). Pap. Avulsos, Dept. Zool., São Paulo, **2**, pp. 39–77 (1942); **6**, pp. 241–282 (1945); **7**, pp. 1–43 (1945). Rev. Ent. Rio Janeiro, **20**, pp. 461–487 (1948). Livro homenagem, d'Almeida, Soc. brasil. Ent., São Paulo, **1**, pp. 1–9 (1946).

Crane-flies (Argentina). Ent. News, **31**, pp. 215–221 (1920); **32**, pp. 72–76, 175–179, 292–295 (1921); **33**, pp. 207–210 (1922); **34**, pp. 181–186, 309–313 (1923); **35**, pp. 61–65 (1924).

Neotropical Tipula. Rev. Ent. Rio Janeiro, **16**, pp. 330–356, 415–440 (1945); **17**, pp. 172–201 (1946).

Tipula (Chile). Rev. Chilena Hist. Nat., **32**, pp. 276–286 (1929).

Neotropical Teucholabis. Encyl. Ent. (B) II, **4**, pp. 17–28 (1927). Rev. Ent. Rio Janeiro, **17**, pp. 375–400 (1946).

Neotropical Eriopterini. Ibid., **18**, pp. 65–100 (1947).

Neotropical Hexatomini. Ibid., **19**, pp. 149–190 (1948).

Neotropical Limonia. Ibid., **21**, pp. 161–221 (1950).

Tanyderidæ. Gen. Insectorum, 189, 13 pp. (1927).

Neotropical Tanyderidæ. Proc. U. S. Nat. Mus., **44**, pp. 331–335 (1913).

Neotropical Limnobiinæ. Ibid., **44**, pp. 481–549 (1913).

Neotropical Antochini. Psyche, **20**, pp. 40–54 (1913); **21**, pp. 33–45 (1914).

Neotropical Rhipidiæ. Bull. Brooklyn Ent. Soc., **8**, pp. 6–17 (1912).

Neotropical Sigmatomera. Encycl. Ent. (B) II, **5**, pp. 155–162 (1930).

Crane-flies (Russian Arctic). Rept. Norwegian Exped. Novaya Zemlya, 1921, no. 5, 16 pp. (1922).

Crane-flies (Tropical Africa). Rev. Zool. Africaine, **11**, pp. 1–16, 369–383 (1923); **14**, pp. 165–184 (1926); **19**, pp. 337–367 (1930).

Tipulidæ (Congo). Bull. American Mus. Nat. Hist., **43**, art. 11, pp. 9–20 (1920).

African Crane-flies in Paris Museum. Bull. Mus. Hist. Nat. Paris, **1920**, 14 pp. (1920).

Tipulidæ (Central Africa). Arkiv Zool., **16**, no. 18, 15 pp. (1924).

Crane-flies (Liberia and Belgian Congo). Harvard African Med. Exped., **2**, pp. 1004–1021 (1930).

Ethiopian Tipulidæ. Encycl. Ent. (B) II, **7**, pp. 49–62 (1934).

Crane-flies (South Africa). Ann. South African Mus., **17**, pp. 139–184 (1917); **18**, pp. 181–230 (1921).

African Tipulidæ. Occ. Pap. Nat. Mus. So. Rhodesia, **6**, pp. 1–11 (1937).

Exotic Tipulidæ (Africa). Proc. Roy. Ent. Soc. London (B), **14**, pp. 95–102 (1945); **15**, pp. 132–139 (1946); **17**, pp. 18–24 (1948); **18**, pp. 153–159 (1949); **19**, pp. 85–89 (1950).

Dolichopeza (South Africa). South African Jour. Nat. Hist., **5**, pp. 39–48 (1925).

Ethiopian Tipulidæ. Ann. Mag. Nat. Hist., (9) **5**, pp. 52–62, 337–351, 465–472 (1920); (9) **7**, pp. 305–322 (1921); (9) **8**, pp. 161–175, 309–320 (1921).

African Crane-flies. Ibid., (9) **6**, pp. 1–44, 336–364 (1920); (9) **7**, pp. 98–118 (1921).

Crane-flies (Madagascar). Mem. Inst. Sci. Madagascar, A, **5**, pp. 33–63 (1951).

Oriental Tipulidæ. Rec. Indian Mus., **29**, pp. 167–214 (1927); **44**, pp. 29–72 (1942).

Ptychopteridæ (Burma and British India). Arkiv Zool., **38** A, no. 2, 10 pp. (1946).

Tipulidæ (Eastern China). Notes ent. chinoise, Mus. Heude., **4**, pp. 1–28, 65–88 (1937); **8**, pp. 1–28 (1940).

Tipulidæ (China). Sci. Jour. Lingnan Univ., **11**, pp. 505–508 (1932); **17**, pp. 337–356 (1938); **19**, pp. 105–119, 121–132 (1940); **20**, pp. 177–184 (1942); **21**, pp. 15–30 (1945).

Tipulidæ (North-west China). Arkiv Zool., **27** A, no. 17, 24 pp. (1934).

Tipulidæ (East China). Ibid., **30** B, no. 6, 5 pp. (1938).

Crane-flies (East Asia). Encycl. Ent. (B) II, **2**, fasc. 2, pp. 87–93 (1925).

Exotic Tipulidæ (China). Proc. Roy. Ent. Soc. London (B), **12**, pp. 173–180 (1943).

Asiatic Crane-flies. Bull. Mus. Hist. Nat. Paris, **1923**, pp. 67–103 (1923).

Crane-flies (Korea). Trans. Roy. Ent. Soc. London, **95**, pp. 227–246 (1945).

Tipulidæ (Kamchatka). Arkiv Zool., **19** A, no. 9, 10 pp. (1927).

Crane-flies (Siberia). Proc. U. S. Nat. Mus., **68**, no. 2605, 21 pp. (1925).

Crane-flies (East Asia). Jour. New York Ent. Soc., **26**, pp. 66–75 (1918).

Tipulidæ (Eastern Asia). Philippine Jour. Sci., **31**, pp. 363–383 (1926); **35**, pp. 455–488 (1928); **36**, pp. 455–485 (1928); **40**, pp. 317–348, 519–547 (1929); **42**, pp. 59–83, 507–535 (1930); **43**, pp. 507–536 (1930); **44**, pp. 339–368 (1931); **49**, pp. 105–136, 373–406 (1932); **50**, pp. 129–162 (1933); **51**, pp. 369–408, 507–544 (1933); **52**, pp. 131–166, 305–348, 395–442 (1933); **53**, pp. 267–300 (1934); **54**, pp. 309–343, 443–471 (1934); **55**, pp. 19–60, 133–164 (1934); **56**, pp. 339–372, 525–562 (1935); **57**, pp. 81–148, 195–225 (1935); **58**, pp. 213–252, 385–426 (1935); **59**, pp. 225–257 (1935); **60**, pp. 165–204, 323–360 (1936); **61**, pp. 113–149, 169–203 (1936); **62**, pp. 143–180 (1937); **63**, pp. 365–404 (1937); **66**, pp. 93–134, 221–259, 309–342, 439–478 (1938); **67**, pp. 129–166 (1938); **71**, pp. 39–76, 169–204 (1940); **73**, pp. 375–420 (1940); **76**, pp. 27–66 (1941). Rec. South Australian Mus., **8**, pp. 525–606 (1947).

Tipulidæ (New Guinea). Proc. Linn. Soc. New South Wales, **40**, pp. 51–70 (1935); **41**, pp. 169–183, 322–340 (1936); **46**, pp. 138–144 (1941).

Pediciinæ (British India, Burma). Arkiv Zool., **42** A, no. 2, pp. 1–21 (1949).

Crane-flies (Java). Proc. U. S. Nat. Mus., **49**, pp. 157–193 (1915).

Tipulidæ of Sunda Expedition (Sumatra, Java, Bali). Archiv Hydrobiol., suppl. **9,** pp. 135–191 (1931).

Tipuloidea (Sumatra). Supplementa Ent., **15,** pp. 90–102 (1927).

Tipulidæ (Pacific Islands). Ann. Mag. Nat. Hist., (9) **13,** pp. 33–49 (1924).

Exotic Tipulidæ (Dutch East Indies). Proc. Roy. Ent. Soc. London (B), **13,** pp. 74–80 (1944).

Crane-flies (Fiji Isl.). Ann. Ent. Soc. America, **7,** pp. 239–246 (1914).

Tipulidæ (Papua). Proc. Linn. Soc. New South Wales, **41,** pp. 122–127 (1936).

Tipulidæ (New Caledonia and Samoa). Encycl. Ent. (B) II, **5,** pp. 83–92 (1929).

Tipulidæ (New Caledonia). Proc. Hawaiian Ent. Soc., **12,** pp. 235–244 (1945). Trans. Roy. Ent. Soc. London, **99,** pp. 361–393 (1948). Ann. Ent. Soc. America, **41,** pp. 137–148 (1948).

Tipulidæ (Marquesas). Bull. Bishop Mus., **98,** pp. 87–92 (1932).

Tipulidæ (Society Isl.). Ibid., **113,** pp. 53–56 (1933).

Tipulidæ (Guam). Ibid., **172,** pp. 195–198 (1942).

Tipulidæ (Southeast Pacific). Occ. Pap. Bishop Mus., **18,** pp. 337–347 (1947).

Crane-flies (Hawaiian Isl.). Ann. Ent. Soc. America, **12,** pp. 25–30 (1919). Proc. Hawaiian Ent. Soc., **5,** pp. 249–251 (1923). (Australasia) Ibid., pp. 252–260 (1923).

Checklist of Tipulidæ (Oceania). Occ. Pap. Bishop Mus., **9,** no. 21, 12 pp. (1932).

Crane-flies (Formosa and Luzon). Philippine Jour. Sci., **22,** pp. 467–481 (1923).

Tipulidæ (Philippines). Ibid., **21,** pp. 373–384 (1922); **27,** pp. 71–81 (1925); **28,** pp. 369–377 (1925); **33,** pp. 291–307 (1927); **40,** pp. 239–273 (1929); **41,** pp. 287–314 (1930); **43,** pp. 277–303 (1930); **45,** pp. 263–296, 415–448 (1931); **46,** pp. 9–38, 269–304, 447–477 (1931); **47,** pp. 163–195 (1931); **48,** pp. 21–49, 597–638 (1932); **49,** pp. 231–276 (1932); **53,** pp. 429–468 (1934).

Crane-flies (Japan). Canadian Ent., **45,** pp. 197–210, 285 295, 313–322 (1913); **46,** pp. 157–164, 205–211, 236–242 (1914). Ann. Ent. Soc. America, **11,** pp. 443–449 (1918); **12,** pp. 327–342 (1919); **16,** pp. 57–76 (1923); **17,** pp. 59–74, 431–448 (1924); **40,** pp. 350–371 (1947); **43,** pp. 418–436 (1950). Ins. Inscit. Menstr., **12,** pp. 49–55, 150–159 (1924). Philippine Jour. Sci., **24,** pp. 531–610 (1924). Trans. American Ent. Soc., **46,** pp. 1–26 (1920). Ent. Mag., **3,** pp. 122–127 (1919).

Tipulidæ (Pacific Isl.). Annot. Zool. Japonenses, **19,** pp. 198–221 (1940).

Tanyderidæ (Japan). Ibid., **13,** pp. 273–281 (1932).

Trichoceridæ (Japan). Konowia, **9,** pp. 103–108 (1930).

Tipulidæ (Australia). Ann. Mag. Nat. Hist., (9) **8,** pp. 546–563 (1921); (9) **13,** pp. 177–194, 359–380, 499–523 (1924); (9) **18,** pp. 169–193 (1926); (9) **19,** pp. 16–38, 177–196 (1927); (9) **20,** pp. 33–54, 353–372 (1927); (10) **1,** pp. 82–108, 217–241, 577–601 (1928); (10) **2,** pp. 337–362 (1928); (10) **3,** pp. 49–71, 327–346, 468–489 (1929); (10) **5,** pp. 136–156, 370–388 (1930); (10) **6,** pp. 114–136 (1930); (10) **7,** pp. 17–36, 153–172 (1931); (10) **8,** pp. 145–166 (1931); (10) **12,** pp. 335–357 (1933); (10)

13, pp. 240–264 (1934); (10) **16**, pp. 329–354 (1937); (11) **13**, pp. 740–767 (1947); (12) **1**, pp. 391–417 (1948); (12) **3**, pp. 301–324, 672–695, 935–959 (1950).

Crane-flies (South Australia). Rec. South Australian Mus., **2**, pp. 223–270 (1922).

Australian Tipulidæ, Proc. Linn. Soc. New South Wales, **47**, pp. 581–590 (1922); **69**, pp. 1–15 (1944).

Crane-flies (New South Wales). Ibid., **53**, pp. 51–70 (1928).

Tipulidæ (Australia). Ibid., **57**, pp. 1–23 (1932).

Trichoceridæ (Australia). Ibid., **51**, pp. 299–304 (1926).

Tanyderidæ (Australia). Ibid., **53**, pp. 367–374 (1928); **55**, pp. 219–230 (1930).

Molophilus (Australia). Ibid., **54**, pp. 137–144 (1929); **59**, pp. 179–189 (1934).

Australian Crane-flies. Proc. Roy. Soc. Queensland, **32**, no. 7, pp. 92–109 (1920).

Crane-flies (Queensland). Mem. Queensland Mus., **7**, pt. 1, 12 pp. (1920).

Crane-flies (Malaya and North Australia). Rev. Suisse Zool., **43**, no. 4, pp. 73–97 (1936).

Tasiocera (Australia). Encycl. Ent. (B) II, **4**, pp. 117–123 (1928).

Tanyderidæ (Australasia). Pan-Pacific Ent., **22**, pp. 51–55 (1946).

Tipuloidea (New Zealand). Philippine Jour. Sci., **38**, pp. 157–199 (1929).

Crane-flies (New Zealand). Ann. Ent. Soc. America, **15**, pp. 223–238 (1922). Trans. New Zealand Inst., **55**, pp. 641–660 (1924). Rec. Canterbury Mus., **2**, pp. 163–170 (1924); **3**, pp. 459–467 (1932); **4**, pp. 219–230 (1939); **4**, pp. 281–288 (1940).

Australasian Tipulidæ (New Zealand). Ann. Mag. Nat. Hist., (9) **9**, pp. 145–160, 297–315, 505–524 (1922); (9) **10**, pp. 83–99, 557–573 (1922); (9) **11**, pp. 97–111, 193–208 (1923); (9) **12**, pp. 97–112, 194–212, 265–281, 376–393 (1923); (9) **13**, pp. 561–579 (1924); (9) **14**, pp. 289–306 (1924); (9) **15**, pp. 634–651 (1925); (9) **16**, pp. 65–81 (1925); (9) **17**, pp. 65–83, 521–548 (1926).

ALEXANDER, C. P., and W. L. McATEE. Tipuloidea (District of Columbia). Proc. U. S. Nat. Mus. **58**, pp. 385–435 (1920).

AUDCENT, H. British Tipulidæ. Trans. Ent. Soc. South England, **8**, pp. 1–34 (1932).

British Liriopeidæ. Trans. Soc. British Ent., **1**, pp. 103–118 (1934).

BANGERTER, H. Neue Eriopterili. Mitt. Schweiz. Ent. Ges., **20**, pp. 353–380 (1947).

BARNES, H. F. Crane-flies of Carnavonshire. North West Nat., **1**, pp. 17–34 (1926).

BROWN, E. E., and A. B. DUNCAN. List of Tipulidæ (Solway). Scottish Nat., **61**, pp. 156–168 (1949).

BRUCH, C. List of Argentine Tipulas. Physis, **5**, pp. 320–324 (1922); **17**, pp. 3–35 (1939).

BRUNETTI, E. Oriental Tipulidæ. Rec. Indian Mus., **15**, pp. 255–340 (1918).

CZIZEK, K. Tipulidæ (Moravia). Zeitschr. Mähr. Landesmus., 11, pp. 193–285 (1911).

Mährischen Liriopidæ. Ibid., 17, pp. 1–16 (1919).

Limnobiidæ und Cylindrotomidæ. Cas. Morav. Mus. Zem., Libau, 28–29, pp. 289–495 (1933).

DICKINSON, W. E. Crane-flies (Wisconsin). Bull. Public Mus. Milwaukee, 8, pp. 139–260 (1932).

DIETZ, W. G. Tipula, Key. (America). Ann. Ent. Soc. America, 6, pp. 461–484 (1913).

Tipula. Trans. American Ent. Soc., 40, pp. 345–363 (1914).

Ormosia. Ibid., 42, pp. 135–146 (1916).

Pachyrhina. Ibid., 44, pp. 105–140 (1918).

List of Crane-flies from Pennsylvania. Ibid., 47, pp. 233–268 (1921).

Tipula. Ann. Ent. Soc. America, 14, pp. 1–14 (1921).

DOANE, R. W. New Western Tipulas. Ann. Ent. Soc. America, 5, pp. 41–61 (1912).

EDWARDS, F. W. Tipulidæ (Sladen Exped. Indian Ocean). Trans. Linn. Soc. London, (2) 15, pp. 195–213 (1912).

Styringomyia. Trans. Ent. Soc. London, 1914, pp. 206–227. Ann. Mag. Nat. Hist., (9) 13, pp. 265–274 (1924).

Malayan Tipulidæ. Ann. Mag. Nat. Hist., (8) 17, pp. 349–361 (1916).

Formosan Tipulidæ. Ibid., (8) 18, pp. 245–269 (1916); (9) 8, pp. 99–115 (1921).

Old World Erioceras. Ibid., (9) 8, pp. 67–99 (1921).

British Limnobiidæ. Trans. Ent. Soc. London, 1921, pp. 196–230.

Crane-flies (New Zealand). Trans. New Zealand Inst., 54, pp. 265–352 (1923).

Tipulidæ (Philippines). Notulæ Ent., 6, pp. 33–44 (1926).

Malayan Tipulidæ. Bull. Raffles Mus., 7, pp. 52–74 (1932).

British Crane-flies with Short Palpi. Trans. Soc. British Ent., 5, 168 pp. (1938).

EDWARDS, F. W., and D. KEILIN. Trichoceridæ Gen. Insectorum, 190, pp. 30–37 (1928).

ENDERLEIN, G. Tipulidæ. Zool. Jahrb. Syst., 32, pp. 1–88 (1912).

GOETGHEBUER, M., and A. TONNOIR. Catalogue of Tipulidæ (Belgium). Bull. Soc. Ent. Belgique, 2, pp. 104–112, 131–147 (1920); 3, pp. 47–58, 105–125 (1921).

HUTTON, F. W. Tipulidæ of New Zealand. Trans. New Zealand Inst., 32, pp. 22–51 (1899).

KUNTZE, A. Eriopterinæ (Palæarctic). Ann. Naturh. Hofmus. Wien, 28, pp. 361–388 (1914).

Limoniinæ (Palæarctic). Zool. Jahrb. Syst., 43, pp. 371–432 (1920).

LACKSCHEWITZ, P. Palæarctic Tipulidæ, s. lat. Ann. Naturh. Staatsmus. Wien, 50, pp. 68–122 (1939).

LENZ, F. Metamorphose Cylindrotomiden. Arch. Naturg., 85, A, Heft 6, pp. 113–146 (1920).

LUNDSTROM, C. Tipulidæ (Finland). Acta Soc. Faun. Fl. Fennica, 29, no. 2, 27 pp. (1907).

Cylindrotomidæ, Limnobiidæ (Finland). Ibid., 29, no. 8,. 32 pp. (1907).

MASAKI, J. Tipulinæ (Japan). Mushi, 6, pp. 74–95 (1933).

Meijere, J. C. H. de. Limnobiidæ (Palæarctic). Tijdschr. Ent., 62, pp. 52–97 (1919); 63, pp. 46–86 (1920); 64, pp. 54–118 (1921).

Needham, J. G. Crane-flies, Habits. Rept. New York State Ent., 23, pp. 199–248 (1908).

Nielsen, P. Ptychoptera (Denmark). Afhandl. Meddel., Fl. Fauna Kjöben-havn, 1, pp. 16–19 (1921).
    Stankelben (Tipulidæ). Danmarks Fauna, 28, 165 pp. (1925).

Pierre, C. Catalogue of Tipulidæ (France). Ann. Soc. Linn. Lyon, 65, pp. 63–76 (1919); 67, pp. 73–77 (1921).
    Tipulidæ of France. Faune de France, 8, Diptères. 159 pp. (1924).
    Tipulinæ. Gen. Insectorum, 186, 68 pp. (1926).

Rimsky-Korsakow, A. Chionea. Zeitschr. Wiss. Insekt.-biol., 20, pp. 69–76, 99–105 (1925).

Rogers, J. S. Crane-flies (Tennessee). Occ. Pap. Mus. Zool. Univ. Michigan, 215, 50 pp. (1930).
    Polymera, Biology. Ibid., 268, 13 pp. (1933).
    Crane-flies (Florida). Ecol. Monogr., 3, 74 pp. (1933).
    Crane-flies (Michigan). Misc. Publ. Mus. Zool. Univ. Michigan, 53, 128 pp. (1942).

Saito, S. Tipulidæ (Iwateken). Ent. World, Tokyo, 8, pp. 375–386 (1940).

Seligo, A. Liriope. Ber. Westpreuss. bot. zool. Ver. Danzig, 50, pp. 231–247 (1928); 51, pp. 83–84 (1929).

Sellke, K. Tipulidæ, Biology. Zeitschr. Wiss. Zool., 148, pp. 465–555 (1936).

Szilady, Z. Tipulidæ (Hungary). Mat. Term. Ert., Budapest, 56, pp. 622–633 (1937). (In Magyar)

Tjeder, B. Swedish Prionocera. Opusc. Ent., 13, pp. 75–99 (1948).

Tokunaga, M. Trichoceridæ (Japan). Tenthredo, 2, pp. 137–148 (1938).
    Marine Tipulidæ. Kontyu, 14, pp. 133–148 (1940).

PSYCHODIDÆ

Abonnenc, E., and H. Floch. Key to Phlebotomus. Bol. Ent. Venezolana, 6, pp. 1–24 (1947).

Abreu, E. S. Psychodidæ (Canary Isl.). Mem. R. Acad. Barcelona, 22, pp. 91–128 (1930).

Addis, C. J. Phlebotomus, Keys (U. S.). Trans. American Micros. Soc., 64, pp. 328–332 (1945).

Adler, S. Sandflies (Cyprus). Bull. Ent. Res., 36, pp. 497–511 (1946).

Adler, S. et al. Phlebotomus (Belgian Congo). Rev. Zool. Bot. Africaines, 18, pp. 72–89 (1929).
    Sandflies (Persia, Palestine). Bull. Ent. Res., 21, pp. 529–539 (1930).
    Sandflies (Mediterranean). Proc. Roy. Soc. London (B), 108, pp. 464–480 (1931).

Akalin, M. S. Phlebotomus in Anatolia. Türk. Zeitschr. Hyg. Ankara, 2, no. 2, pp. 114–127 (1941). (In Turkish)

Alexander, C. P. Bruchomyinæ. Proc. U. S. Nat. Mus., 75, no. 2778, 9 pp. (1929). Rev. Ent. Rio Janeiro, 11, pp. 793–799 (1940).
    Tanyderidæ (Australasian). Pan-Pacific Ent., 22, pp. 51–55 (1946).
    Ptychopteridæ. Bull. Brooklyn Ent. Soc., 32, pp. 140–143 (1937); 38, pp. 37–42 (1943); 42, pp. 19–24 (1947).

BRUNETTI, E. Psychodidæ (India). Rec. Indian Mus., 2, pp. 369–384 (1908).
CAUSEY, C. R., and R. G. DAMASCENO. Flebotomus (Amazon). Rev. Serv. Saude Publ. Rio Janeiro, 1, pp. 179–191 (1947); pp. 625–710 (1948). Mem. Inst. Oswaldo Cruz, 42, pp. 17–29 (1945); pp. 645–660 (1946).
COSTA LIMA, A. DA. Phlebotomos americanos. Ibid., 26, pp. 15–69 (1932). Rev. Ent. Rio Janeiro, 4, pp. 427–429 (1934).
  Flebotomos (Amazon). Acta Medica, Rio Janeiro, 7, pp. 7–19 (1941).
COUTINHO, J. O., and M. PEREIRA BARRETTO. Flebotomos (São Paulo). Rev. Biol. Hyg., 10, pp. 89–103 (1940); 11, pp. 74–83 (1941).
DAMESCENO, R. G. et al. Phlebotomus (Amazon). Rev. Serv. Saude Publ., 2, pp. 817–842 (1949).
DAMPF, A. Flebotomidos (Mexico). Rev. Soc. Mexicana Hist. Nat., 5, pp. 237–254 (1945); 8, pp. 205–213 (1948). An. Escuela Nac. Cienc. Biol., 4, pp. 423–449 (1947). Medicina, Mexico, 27, pp. 179–183 (1947).
  Flebotomidos americanos. Rev. Ent. Rio Janeiro, 18, pp. 296–316 (1947).
DYAR, H. G. Phlebotomus. American Jour. Hyg., 10, pp. 112–124 (1929).
EATON, A. E. Psychodidæ (Indian Ocean). Trans. Linn. Soc. London, (2) 15, pp. 423–432 (1912).
ENDERLEIN, G. Klassification der Psychodiden. Deutsche Ent. Zeitschr., 1936, pp. 81–112 (1937).
FAIRCHILD, G. B., and M. HERTIG. Phlebotomus (Panama). Ann. Ent. Soc. America, 40, pp. 610–623 (1948); 41, pp. 247–257, 455–467 (1948); 43, pp. 523–533 (1950); 44, pp. 395–429 (1951). Proc. Ent. Soc. Washington, 52, pp. 91–95 (1950).
FAIRCHILD, G. B., and H. TRAPIDO. Phlebotomus (West Indies). Ann. Ent. Soc. America, 13, pp. 405–417 (1950).
FEUERBORN, H. J. Psychodidæ, Larvæ. Verh. 1 Int. Ver. Limnol. Kiel, 1, pp. 181–213 (1923).
  Halobionte Psychodiden. Mitt. Geograph. Ges. Lübeck, (2) 31, pp. 127–152 (1926).
FLOCH, H., and E. ABONNENC. Phlébotomes du Venezuela. Publ. Inst. Pasteur Guyane, 178, pp. 1–24 (1948). Bol. Ent. Venezolana, 8, pp. 77–101 (1950).
  Phlébotomes (French Guiana). Publ. Inst. Pasteur Guyane, 161, pp. 1–17 (1947).
FLOCH, H., and R. CHASIGNET. Phlébotomes (French Guiana). Ibid., 152, 3 pp.; 155, 3 pp.; 157, 3 pp. (1947).
FRANÇA, C. Phlebotomus. Broteria, 17, pp. 102–160 (1919). Bull. Soc. Portugaise, 8, pp. 215–236 (1920). Arch. Inst. Pasteur Africaine, 1, pp. 103–106, 279–284 (1921). Bull. Soc. Pasteur Sci. Nat., 8, pp. 1–24 (1921); 9, pp. 9–18 (1922).
FREEMAN, P. Nemopalpus (South America). Ent. Mon. Mag., 110, pp. 85–88 (1949).
GALLIARD, H., and V. NITZULESCU. Phlebotomus du Gabon. Ann. Parasit. Hum. Comp., 9, pp. 233–246 (1931).
HASEMAN, L. Psychodidæ (North America). Trans. American Ent. Soc., 33, pp. 299–333 (1907).
KEILIN, D., and P. TATE. Larvæ of some Psychodidæ. Parasitol., 29, pp. 247–258 (1937).
KINCAID, T. Psychodidæ (Pacific States). Ent. News, 10, pp. 30–37 (1899).

KIRK, R., and D. J. LEWIS. Phlebotomus (Sudan). Trans. Roy. Soc. Trop. Med. Hyg., **40**, pp. 869–888 (1947).

Ethiopian Phlebotomus. Ann. Trop. Med. Parasitol., **42**, pp. 322–333 (1948). Trans. Roy. Ent. Soc. London, **102**, pp. 383–510 (1951).

LANGERON, M., and V. NITZULESCU. Phlébotomes de France. Ann. Parasit. Hum. Comp., **10**, pp. 286–294 (1932).

LARROUSE, F. Phlebotomus. Travail Lab. Parasitol. Paris, 106 pp. (1921).

LEWIS, D. J., and R. KIRK. Phlebotcmus (Ethiopian). Proc. Roy. Ent. Soc. London (A), **24**, pp. 51–55 (1949).

LUTZ, A., and A. NEIVA. Phlebotomus (Brazil). Mem. Inst. Oswaldo Cruz, **4**, pp. 84–95 (1912).

MANGABEIRA, O. Flebotomus. Ibid., **36**, 55 pp. (1941); **37**, 58 pp. (1942).

MEIRA, M. T. V., and G. F. TIAGO. Phlebotomus (Lisbon). An. Inst. Med. Trop., **1**, pp. 269–288 (1944).

NEWSTEAD, R. Phlebotomus (Maltese Isl.). Bull. Ent. Res., **2**, pp. 47–78 (1911). London Jour. Roy. Army Corps, **18**, pp. 613–625 (1912); **19**, pp. 28–41, 162–174 (1912).

Phlebotomus. Bull. Ent. Res., **5**, pp. 179–192 (1915).

NITZULESCU, V. Phlebotomus (Jugoslavia). Ann. Parasit. Hum. Comp., **7**, pp. 494–505 (1929).

Phlébotomes européens. Ibid., **9**, pp. 122–133, 271–275 (1931).

PATTON, W. S., and E. HINDLE. Phlebotomus (North China). Proc. Roy. Soc. London (B), Biol. Sci., **100**, pp. 405–412 (1926); **102**, pp. 533–551 (1928).

PEREIRA BARRETTO, M. Early Stages of Phlebotomus. An. Fac. Med. Univ. São Paulo, **17**, pp. 357–427 (1941).

Flebotomus (Brazil). Rev. Brasil. Biol. Rio Janeiro, **6**, pp. 427–434, 527–536 (1946).

Flebotomus (America). An. Fac. Med. Univ. São Paulo, **22**, pp. 1–27 (1946).

Flebotomus, Key. Ibid., **22**, pp. 279–293 (1946). Pap. Avulsos, Dept. Zool., São Paulo, **8**, pp. 239–247 (1947).

Catalogo dos flebotomos americanos. Arq. Zool. São Paulo, **5**, pp. 177–242 (1947).

PEREIRA BARRETTO, M. et al. Flebotomos de São Paulo. Pap. Avulsos, Dept. Zool., São Paulo, **1**, pp. 143–158, 177–191, 223–236 (1941). Rev. Brasil. Biol. Rio Janeiro, **3**, pp. 183–189 (1943).

Bruchomyinæ. Livro homenagem, d'Almeida, Soc. brasil. Ent., São Paulo, **1**, pp. 55–75 (1946).

Flebotomos americanos. Ibid., **1**, pp. 77–101 (1946).

PERFIL'EV, P. P. Phlebotomus. Mag. Parasit. Leningrad, **2**, pp. 73–83 (1931). (In Russian)

Sandflies of Turkmenistan. Murghab Ent. Exped. 1930, Acad. Sci. Soviet Rep., 1932, pp. 119–141.

Phlebotomus. Trud. Tadzhik Sect. Acad. Sci. USSR, **5**, pp. 29–51 (1935). (In Russian)

Phlebotominæ (USSR). Faune de l'URSS, Diptères, **3**, no. 2, 144 pp., Inst. Zool. Acad. Sci. URSS, Moscow (1937).

Sandflies (USSR). Trav. Acad. Milit. Med. Leningrad, **19**, pp. 75–95 (1939); **25**, pp. 272–283 (1941). (In Russian)

Popov, P. Phlebotomus. Russ. Jour. Trop. Med., **1926,** no. 4, pp. 31–48. (In Russian)

Quate, L. W., and W. W. Wirth. Maruina. Wasmann Jour. Biol., **9,** pp. 151–166 (1951).

Rapp, W. F. Check-lists of Psychodidæ. (North America). Jour. New York Ent. Soc., **52,** pp. 201–209 (1944); (South and Central America) **53,** pp. 21–30; (Europe) pp. 117–126; (Asia, Australia) pp. 211–217; (Africa) pp. 247–257 (1945); (Pacific Islands) **54,** pp. 291–292 (1946).

Raynal, J. Phlébotomes d'Indochine. Arch. Inst. Pasteur Indochine, **6,** pp. 349–374 (1936).

Phlébotomes (North China). Ibid., **7,** pp. 37–99 (1937).

Raynal, J., and H. Gaschen. Phlébotomes d'Indochine. Bull. Soc. Path. Exot., **27,** pp. 559–567, 670–679, 858–862 (1934).

Raynal, J., and P. LeGac. Phlebotomus (Madagascar). Bull. Soc. Path. Exot., **30,** pp. 76–90 (1937).

Ristorcelli, A. Phlébotomes du Maroc. Arch. Inst. Pasteur Maroc, **2,** pp. 521–533 (1941); **3,** pp. 105–109 (1945).

Root, F. M. Phlebotomus. American Jour. Hyg., **20,** pp. 233–246 (1934).

Rosario, F. del. Psychoda (America). Philippine Jour. Sci., **59,** pp. 85–148 (1936).

Psychodinæ (Philippines). Ibid., **59,** pp. 553–571 (1936).

Roubaud, E., and J. Colas-Belcour. Phlebotomus (Tunis). Arch. Inst. Pasteur Tunis, **26,** pp. 59–80 (1927).

Satchell, G. H. Larvæ of British Psychoda. Parasitol., **38,** pp. 51–69 (1947).

Larvæ of British Pericoma. Trans. Roy. Ent. Soc. London, **100,** pp. 411–447 (1949).

Psychodidæ (New Zealand). Ibid., **101,** pp. 147–178 (1950).

Schwetz, J. Phlebotomus (Congo). Bull. Inst. Roy. Colon. Belge, **8,** pp. 521–547 (1937); **14,** pp. 1–93 (1944).

Sinton, J. A. Phlebotomus (India). Indian Jour. Med. Res., **10–21,** 33 papers, about 350 pp. (1923–1933).

Asiatic Phlebotomus. Ibid., **16,** pp. 297–324 (1928).

Theodor, O. Phlebotominæ (Old World). Bull. Ent. Res., **39,** pp. 85–115 (1948).

Tonnoir, A. L. Psychodidæ (Belgium). Ann. Soc. Ent. Belgique, **59,** pp. 1–17, 138–140 (1919); **60,** pp. 149–157, 180–187 (1920); **62,** pp. 49–88, 125–136, 153–181 (1922).

Psychodidæ (Africa). Rev. Zool. Africaine, **8,** fasc. 2, pp. 127–147 (1920). Bull Soc. Ent. Egypte, **1921,** pp. 80–111 (1922).

Psychodidæ (Patagonia). Diptera of Patagonia and South Chile, **2,** fasc. 1, 32 pp., British Mus. (1929).

Psychodidæ (India). Rec. Indian Mus., **35,** pp. 53–75 (1933).

Phlebotomus (Australia). Bull. Ent. Res., **26,** pp. 137–147 (1935).

Psychodidæ. Ruwenzori Exped. 1934–35, **1,** pp. 35–80, British Mus. (1939).

British Psychodidæ. Trans. Soc. British Ent., **7,** pp. 21–64 (1940).

Yao, Y. T., and C. C. Wu. Phlebotomus (China). Chinese Med. Jour. Peiping, **60,** pp. 73–80 (1941).

Zariquiey Alvares, R. Phlebotomus (Spain). Graellsia, Madrid, **2,** pp. 15–20 (1944).

CULICIDÆ

ABBOTT, P. W. Culicidæ (Sudan). Proc. Roy. Ent. Soc. London (B), **17,** pp. 37–48 (1948).

ACHUNDOW, I. Induced Modifications in Anopheles. Arch. Schiffs- u. Tropenhyg., **32,** pp. 547–561 (1928).

AFRIDI, M. K. et al. Anopheles. Jour. Malaria Inst. India, **3,** pp. 1–51 (1940).

AITKEN, T. H. G. Anopheles (California). Proc. 6 Pacific Sci. Congr. 1939, **4,** pp. 463–484 (1941).

    Culicidæ (Lower California). Proc. California Acad. Sci., (4) **24,** pp. 161–170 (1942).

    Anophelines (North America). Univ. California Publ. Ent., **7,** pp. 273–364 (1945).

ANDUZE, P. J. Culicidæ (Venezuela). Bol. Acad. Cienc., **10,** pp. 331–373 (1947).

ANTUNES, P. C. A., and A. SILVA RAMOS. Culex. Bol. Biol. São Paulo, **4,** pp. 374–385 (1939).

APFELBECK, V. Culicidæ (Jugoslavia). Acta Soc. Ent. Jugoslav., **5–6,** pp. 49–61 (1932).

ARNETT, R. H., JR. Culicidæ. Syst. Nat. Zool., **1,** pp. 1–15 (1946).

    Culicines (Panama). Jour. New York Ent. Soc., **55,** pp. 185–200 (1947); **56,** pp. 175–193 (1948); **57,** pp. 233–251 (1949); **58,** pp. 99–115 (1950).

ASHWORTH, J. H. Anophelines (Scotland). Proc. Roy. Soc. Edinburgh, **47,** pp. 81–93 (1927).

AYROSA GALVAO, A., and R. G. DAMASCENO. Anophelines. An. Fac. Med. Univ. São Paulo, **20,** pp. 73–87 (1944).

AYROSA GALVAO, A., and J. LANE. Nyssorhynchus. Ibid., **12,** pp. 269–288 (1937). Rev. Biol. Hyg. São Paulo, **8,** pp. 37–45 (1937).

AZIZ, M. Anophelines (Cyprus). Health Dept. Pap. Cyprus, **4,** 32 pp. (1934).

BAEZA CUÉLLAR, M. Culicidos hematófagos. Madrid, 158 pp. (1933).

BAISAS, F. E. Anopheles (Philippines). Philippine Jour. Sci., **44,** pp. 425–448 (1931).

    Philippine Mosquitoes. Ibid., **56,** pp. 485–497 (1935); **57,** pp. 63–80, 167–178 (1935); **59,** pp. 65–84 (1936); **61,** pp. 205–220 (1936); **78,** pp. 43–73 (1950). Mon. Bull. Bur. Health Philippines, **15,** pp. 291–339 (1936); **16,** pp. 205–242 (1936); **18,** pp. 175–232 (1938); **22,** pp. 31–47 (1946); **23,** pp. 197–207 (1947).

BARBER, M. A. Anopheles (New Mexico). American Jour. Trop. Med., **19,** pp. 345–356 (1939).

BARNES, M. E. Anopheles (Siam). Jour. Nat. Hist. Soc. Siam, **6,** pp. 65–79 (1923).

BARNES, R. C., H. L. FELTON, and C. A. WILSON. List of Mosquitoes (New York). Mosquito News, **10,** pp. 69–84 (1950).

BARRAUD, P. J. Culicinæ (India). Indian Jour. Med. Res., **10,** pp. 772–788, 934–942 (1923); **11,** pp. 214–228, 475–505 (1923); **11,** pp. 845–865, 971–990, 1259–1282 (1924); **12,** pp. 15–22, 39–46, 139–142, 427–434 (1924); **14,** pp. 331–350 (1926); **14,** pp. 523–563 (1927); **15,** pp. 653–670 (1928); **16,** pp. 357–375 (1928).

Anophelines (India). Rec. Malaria Surv. India, **3**, pp. 507–525 (1933).
Megarhini and Culicini. Fauna of British India, Diptera, **5**, 463 pp. (1934).

BARRAUD, P. J., and S. R. CHRISTOPHERS. Mosquitoes (Siam). Rec. Malaria Surv. India, **2**, pp. 269–285 (1931).

BATES, M. Anopheles spp. Ann. Ent. Soc. America, **33**, pp. 343–356 (1940).
Anopheles (Albania). Proc. Ent. Soc. Washington, **43**, pp. 37–58 (1941).
Natural History of Mosquitoes. Macmillan Co., New York. 379 pp. (1949).

BEAN, J. L. Mosquitoes (Maine). Canadian Ent., **78**, pp. 25–28 (1946).

BEDFORD, G. A. H. Mosquitoes (South Africa). Rep. Vet. Res. South Africa, **14**, pp. 883–990 (1928).

BEKLEMISHEV, V. et al. Anopheles, Biology (USSR). Mag. Parasit. Moscow, **6**, pp. 147–168 (1936). Bull. Soc. Nat. Moscow, **50**, sect. Biol., no. 1–2, pp. 56–73 (1945). (In Russian)

BELKIN, J. N. Tripteroides (Solomon Isl.). Proc. U. S. Nat. Mus., **100**, pp. 201–274 (1950).
Chætotaxy of Mosquito Larvæ. American Midl. Nat., **44**, pp. 678–698 (1950).

BELKIN, J. N. et al. Anophelines (Solomon and New Hebrides). Jour. Parasitol., **31**, pp. 241–265 (1945).

BELLAMY, R. E. Mosquito Larvæ (Georgia). Ibid., **28**, pp. 299–310 (1942).

BENARROCH, E. I. Anophelines (Venezuela). Biol. Soc. Venezolana Cienc. Nat., **4**, pp. 178–190 (1934).

BEQUAERT, J. Culicidæ (Liberia, Belgian Congo). Contrib. Inst. Trop. Biol. Med., **5**, pp. 825–846 (1930).

BERBERIAN, D. A. Anopheles (Syria, Lebanon). Jour. Palest. Arab. Med. Assn., **1**, pp. 120–146 (1946).

BERG, K. Corethra, Biology. K. Danske Vidensk. Selsk. Skr., **13**, 101 pp. (1937).

BEYER, G. E. Mosquitoes (Louisiana). Quart. Bull. Louisiana Bd. Health, **14**, pp. 54–84 (1923).

BISHOPP, F. C. et al. Mosquitoes. Proc. Ann. Meet. New Jersey Mosq. Exterm. Assoc., **35**, pp. 46–65 (1948).

BLACKLOCK, D. B., and A. M. EVANS. Anophelines (Sierra Leone). Ann. Trop. Med. Parasitol., **20**, pp. 59–83 (1926).

BLANCHARD, R. Les moustiques. Paris, 673 pp. (1905).

BODDY, D. W. Culicids of Washington. Pan-Pacific Ent., **24**, pp. 85–94 (1948).

BOHART, R. M. Philippine Mosquitoes. U. S. Bur. Med. Surg. Dept. Navy, **580**, 88 pp. (1945).
Culicines (China). Ibid., **961**, 23 pp. (1946).
Neoculex (North America). Ann. Ent. Soc. America, **41**, pp. 330–345 (1948).

BOHART, R. M., and R. L. INGRAM. Mosquitoes (Okinawa). U. S. Bur. Med. Surg. Dept. Navy, **1055**, 110 pp. (1946).

BONNE-WEPSTER, J. Tæniorhynchus. Meded. Dienst. Volksgezond, **19**, pp. 116–212, 387–399 (1930).
Mosquitoes (New Guinea). Treubia, **19**, pp. 305–322 (1948).

BONNE-WEPSTER, J., and C. BONNE. List of Mosquitoes (Dutch Guiana). Ins. Inscit. Menstr., 11, pp. 123–127 (1923).
    Mosquitoes (Surinam). Amsterdam, 558 pp. (1925).
    Mosquitoes (South America). Ins. Inscit. Menstr., 9, pp. 1–25 (1921).
BONNE-WEPSTER, J., and S. L. BRUG. Stegomyia (Dutch East Indies). Geneesk. Tijdschr. Nederlandsch-Indië Bijbl., 2, pp. 39–119 (1932).
    Culicid Larvæ. (Dutch East Indies). Geneesk. Tijdschr., 79, pp. 1218–1279 (1939).
BOREL, E. Moustiques (Cochin-China). Arch. Inst. Pasteur Indochine, 4, 423 pp. (1928); 8, pp. 41–75 (1928); 9, pp. 23–82 (1929).
    Les moustiques de la Cochinchine. 423 pp., Masson et cie., Paris (1930).
BOYD, M. F. Anopheline Bionomics. American Jour. Hyg., 9, pp. 346–370 (1929); 12, pp. 449–466 (1930).
BRAGA, J. M. Culicideos de Portugal. Inst. Zool. Univ. Porto, 83 pp. (1931).
BRESSLAU, E. Mosquito Eggs. Biol. Centralbl., 40, pp. 337–355 (1920).
BRÈTHES, J. Mosquitoes (Argentina). Bol. Inst. Ent. Pat. Veg., 1, pp. 1–48 (1912). An. Mus. Nac. Buenos Aires, 28, pp. 193–218 (1916). Physis, 8, pp. 305–315 (1926).
BROLEMANN, H. W. Culex des Pyrénées. Ann. Soc. Ent. France, 87, pp. 425–440 (1919); 88, pp. 65–103 (1919).
BROOKE, G. E. Malayan Culicidæ. Singapore Nat., 1, pp. 41–58 (1922).
BROWN, W. L., JR. Mosquito Survey (Pennsylvania). Jour. New York Ent. Soc., 56, pp. 219–232 (1948).
BRUG, S. L. Oriental Mosquitoes. Geneesk. Tijdschr. Nederlandsch-Indië, 63, pp. 635–640 (1923); 65, pp. 661–671 (1925). Vereen. Bevord. Geneesk., 1924, 53 pp. Bull. Ent. Res., 14, pp. 433–442 (1924); 25, pp. 501–519 (1934).
    Culicidæ (Sunda Expedition). Arch. Hydrobiol. Suppl., 9, 42 pp. (1931).
BRUG, S. L., and J. BONNE-WEPSTER. Mosquitoes (Malaya). Chronica Naturæ, Batavia, 103, pp. 179–197 (1947).
BRUG, S. L., and F. W. EDWARDS. Culicidæ (Sumatra). Tijdschr. Ent., 74, pp. 241–261 (1931).
BRUNETTI, E. Oriental Culicidæ. Rec. Indian Mus., 4, pp. 403–517 (1912); 10, pp. 15–73 (1914).
BÜTTIKER, W. Mosquitoes, Biology (Switzerland). Mitt. Schweiz. Ent. Ges., 21, 148 pp. (1948).
BUXTON, P. A., and G. H. E. HOPKINS. Mosquitoes (Polynesia, Melanesia). London Sch. Hyg. Trop. Med., 260 pp. (1927).
CAMBOURNAC, F. J. C. Culicidæ (Aguas de Moura). Ann. Inst. Med. Trop. Lisbon, 1, pp. 247–268 (1944).
CAMPOS, F. Catalogue of Culicidæ (Ecuador). Rev. Coll. Nac. Rocafuerte, 5, pp. 20–30 (1921).
    Mosquitoes (Guayaquil). Ibid., 7, pp. 3–49 (1925).
CARPENTER, S. J. Mosquitoes (Arkansas). Ark. State Bd. Health, 87 pp. (1941).
CARPENTER, S. J. et al. Mosquitoes (South U. S.). Monogr. Am. Midland Nat., 3, 292 pp. (1946).
CARTER, H. F. Anophelines (Ceylon). Ceylon Jour. Sci., Med. Sci., 1, pp. 57–97 (1925).
    Mosquitoes (Ceylon). Ibid., Zool., 24, pp. 85–115 (1950).

CARTER, H. F. et al. Malaria and Anophelines (Ceylon). Colombo, Govt. Printer, 84 pp. (1927).
  Culicines (Ceylon). Ceylon Jour. Sci. (B), 23, pp. 135–151 (1948).
CARVALHO PEREIRA, M. DE. Culicidæ (East Africa). An. Inst. Med. Trop. Lisbon, 3, pp. 341–372 (1946).
CASTILLO, R. L. Anopheles (Ecuador). Quito, 14 pp. (1944). Rev. Asos. Esc. Cienc. Quim. Guayaquil, 3, 16 pp. (1944).
CAUSEY, O. R. et al. Brazilian Anophelines. American Jour. Hyg., 39, pp. 1–7 (1944). Rev. Serv. Saude Publica, 1, pp. 293–384 (1947).
CERQUEIRA, N. L. Mosquitos da Bolivia. Mem. Inst. Oswaldo Cruz, 39, pp. 1–36 (1943).
CHANDLER, S. C. Malarial Mosquitoes (Illinois). Bull. Illinois Nat. Hist. Surv., 13, pp. 307–328 (1920).
CHANG, T. L. Anophelines (Yunnan). Chinese Med. Jour., 58 (2), pp. 8–233 (1940).
CHOW, C. Y. Chinese Anophelinæ. Jour. Nat. Malaria Soc., 8, pp. 121–131 (1949).
CHRISTOPHERS, S. R. Color-markings in Anophelinæ. Ann. Trop. Med. Parasitol., 7, pp. 45–100 (1913).
  Anophelini. Mem. Ind. Med. Res. Calcutta, 3, 105 pp. (1924).
  Mosquitoes (Madeira, Canary Isl.). Ind. Jour. Med. Res., 17, pp. 518–530 (1929).
  Anopheline Fauna (India). Rec. Malaria Surv. India, 2, pp. 305–332 (1931). Fauna of British India, Diptera, 4, 371 pp. London (1933).
CHRISTOPHERS, S. R. et al. Anophelines (India). Health Bull. Calcutta, 10, 22 pp. (1927).
  Malaria Survey. Ibid.. 14, 147 pp. (1928); 2nd edit. 174 pp. (1931); 3rd edit. 206 pp. (1936); 4th edit. 208 pp. (1939).
  Eggs of Indian Anopheles. Rec. Malaria Surv. India, 2, pp. 161–192 (1931).
  Anopheles. Ibid., 2, pp. 481–493 (1931).
  Anophelines (Sierra Leone). Indian Jour. Med. Res., 18, pp. 1133–1166 (1931).
CILENTO, R. W. Australian Mosquitoes and Malaria. Commonwealth Australia, Dept. Health Serv. Publ., 3, 141 pp. (1924).
CLAVERO, G. Aëdinos de España. Rev. Sanid. Hig. Publ., 20, pp. 1–28 (1946).
COHER, E. I. Culicidæ. Ent. Americana, 28, pp. 75–112 (1949).
COLLESS, D. H. Anophelines (Borneo). Proc. Linn. Soc. New South Wales, 73, pp. 71–119 (1948).
COOLING, L. E. Mosquitoes (Australia). Commonwealth Australia, Dept. Health Serv. Publ., 1, 24 pp. (1924); 2, 61 pp. (1924); 8, 40 pp. (1924).
COQUILLETT, D. W. Classification of Mosquitoes. U. S. Dept. Agr. Bull. Ent., Tech. Ser., 11, 31 pp. (1906).
CORRADETTI, A. Anophelines (Italian East Africa). Riv. Biol. Colon., 3, pp. 419–429 (1940).
  Anophelines. Riv. Parassit. Rome, 7, pp. 43–48 (1943).
CORREA, R. R., and A. S. RAMOS. Anofelinos (São Paulo). Arq. Hig. Saude Publ., 7, pp. 37–48 (1942); 9, pp. 125–152 (1944).

Costa Lima, A. da. Anopheles (Brazil). Suppl. Mem. Inst. Oswaldo Cruz, 3, pp. 91–113 (1928); 12, pp. 275–293 (1929). Sciencia Med., 6, pp. 249–251, 334–341, 406–411 (1928).
    Sabethes. Mem. Inst. Oswaldo Cruz, 25, pp. 51–64 (1931).
    Megarhinus. Ibid., 25, pp. 307–315 (1931).
    Tæniorhynchus. Ibid., 30, pp. 453–469 (1935).
    Sabetineos. An. Acad. Brasil. Cienc., 15, pp. 295–308 (1943).
Cova-Garcia, P. Anofelinos (Venezuela). Pub. Div. Malariol. Soc., 2, 34 pp. (1939). Conf. Sanit. Panamericaine, Caracas, 12, no. 1, 208 pp. (1946).
Covell, G. Anophelines (India, Ceylon). Mem. Indian Med. Res., 5, 84 pp.; 7, 117 pp. (1927). Rec. Malaria Surv. India, 2, pp. 225–268 (1931). Health Bull. Delhi, 17, 43 pp. (1936).
Crawford, R. Some Anopheline Pupæ (Malaya). Singapore, Govt. Ptg. Off., 110 pp. (1938).
D'Abrera, V. St. E. Anopheline Eggs (Ceylon). Jour. Malaria Inst. India, 5, pp. 337–359 (1944).
Darsie, R. F. Anopheline Pupæ (U. S.). Rev. Ent. Rio Janeiro, 20, pp. 509–530 (1949).
Davis, D. E. Mosquito Larvæ, Habits (Brazil). Rev. Ent. Rio Janeiro, 15, pp. 221–235 (1944).
Davis, N. C. Mosquitoes (South America). Ann. Ent. Soc. America, 26, pp. 277–295, 619–639 (1933).
Day, M. F. Mosquitoes (U. S.) Trans. Acad. Sci. St. Louis, 31, pp. 29–45 (1943).
Deane, L. M., O. R. Causey, and M. P. Deane. Brazilian Anophelines. Monogr. American Jour. Hyg., Ser. 18, pp. 1–18, 21–31, 35–50 (1946). Rev. Serv. Saude Publ., 1, pp. 827–965 (1948).
Del Ponte, E. Bibliography, Malarial Mosquitoes. Rev. Soc. Ent. Argentina, 3, pp. 81–94 (1928).
De Meillon, B. Anophelini (Africa). Publ. South African Inst. Med. Res., 28, pp. 275–375 (1931); 49, 272 pp. (1947).
Del Vecchio, G. Anopheles (Littoria). Rend. Inst. San. Publ. Rome, 4, pp. 614–650 (1941).
Dickinson, W. E. Mosquitoes (Wisconsin). Bull. Public Mus. Milwaukee, 8, pp. 269–305 (1944).
Diemer, J. Biotypen van Anopheles. Proefschr. Rijksuniv., 256 pp. (1935).
Doucet, J. Anopheles (Madagascar). Publ. Inst. Tech. Sci. Tananarive-Tsimbazaza, 198 pp. (1951).
    Culicidæ (Lake Alaotra). Mem. Inst. Sci. Madagascar, A, 3, pp. 121–146 (1949).
Duren, A. N. Culicidæ (Belgian Congo). Ann. Soc. Belge Med. Trop., 9, pp. 97–115 (1929).
    Anopheles (Belgian Congo). Ibid., 18, pp. 557–580 (1938).
Duret, J. P. List of Mosquitoes (Argentina). Rev. Soc. Ent. Argentina, 14, pp. 297–318 (1950).
Dyar, H. G. Mosquitoes. Proc. Biol. Soc. Washington, 19, pp. 133–142, 159–172 (1906).
    Mosquitoes (California). Ins. Inscit. Menstr., 4, pp. 80–90 (1916); 5, pp. 11–21 (1927).

Mosquitoes (Canada). Ins. Inscit. Menstr., **7**, pp. 11–39 (1919). Trans. Roy. Canadian Inst., **13**, pp. 71–120 (1921).

Mosquitoes (British Columbia, Yukon). Ins. Inscit. Menstr., **8**, pp. 1–27 (1920).

Culex, Subgenus Chœroporpa. Ibid., **8**, pp. 54–81 (1920).

Aëdes. Ibid., **9**, pp. 69–80 (1921).

Hæmagogus. Ibid., **9**, pp. 101–114 (1921).

Mosquitoes (U. S.). Proc. U. S. Nat. Mus., **62**, art. 1, 119 pp. (1922).

Mosquitoes (Panama). Ins. Inscit. Menstr., **11**, pp. 167–186 (1923); **13**, pp. 101–195 (1925).

Mosquitoes. Ibid., **11**, pp. 36–50, 64–72, 81–96, 118–121, 186–190 (1923).

Sabethids. Ibid., **12**, pp. 97–107 (1924).

Culicidæ (America). Jour. Washington Acad. Sci., **14**, pp. 472–486 (1924).

Mosquitoes (Philippines). Ins. Inscit. Menstr., **13**, pp. 66–89 (1925).

Mosquitoes of the Americas. Publ. Carnegie Inst., **387**, 616 pp. (1928).

Dyar, H. G., and F. Knab. Culicid Larvæ. Jour. New York Ent. Soc., **14**, pp. 169–230 (1906).

Megarhinus. Smithsonian Misc. Coll., **48**, pp. 241–258 (1906).

Mosquitoes (Tropical America). Proc. U. S. Nat. Mus., **35**, no. 1632, pp. 53–70 (1908).

Culex (U. S.). Ins. Inscit. Menstr., **5**, pp. 170–183 (1917).

Dyar, H. G., and R. C. Shannon. Uranotænia. Ibid., **12**, pp. 187–192 (1924).

Chaoborinæ. Ibid., **12**, pp. 201–216 (1924).

Echstein, F. Stechmücken. Zentralbl. Bakt. Jena, **82**, pp. 57–68 (1918); **83**, pp. 281–294 (1919); **84**, pp. 223 240 (1920).

Edwards, F. W. Culex (Africa). Bull. Ent. Res., **2**, pp. 241–286 (1911).

Culicidæ (Africa). Ibid., **3**, pp. 1–53, 241–250, 373–385 (1912).

Mosquitoes (Sweden). Ent. Tidskr., **42**, pp. 46–52 (1921).

Mosquitoes (Palæarctic). Bull. Ent. Res., **12**, pp. 263–351 (1921).

Oriental Culicines. Indian Jour. Med. Res., **10**, pp. 249–293, 430–474 (1922); **14**, pp. 1–9 (1923); **15**, pp. 257–270 (1925); **17**, pp. 101–131 (1926); **18**, pp. 267–284 (1928); **21**, pp. 287–306, 541–545 (1930).

Culicidæ (Australia). Ibid., **14**, pp. 351–401 (1923).

Zanzare (Palæarctic). Riv. Malariol. Rome, **5**, 152 pp. (1926).

Moustiques (Belgian Congo). Rev. Zool. Africaine, **15**, fasc. 3, pp. 1–49 (1927).

Chaoborinæ. Ann. Mag. Nat. Hist., (10) **6**, pp. 528–540 (1930).

Culicidæ. Gen. Insectorum, **194**, 258 pp. (1932).

Culicine Adults and Pupæ (Ethiopian). Mosquitoes of Ethiopian Region, **3**, 499 pp. British Mus. (1941).

Edwards, F. W., and D. H. C. Given. Early Stages of Mosquitoes (Singapore). Bull. Ent. Res., **18**, pp. 337–357 (1928).

Edwards, F. W., and S. P. James. British Mosquitoes. British Mus. Econ. Ser., **4A**, 27 pp. (1925); revised edit., 30 pp. (1934).

Ekbloom, T., and R. Ströman. Anophelines, Biology. C. R. 2 Congr. Internat. Paludisme, Algiers, **1**, pp. 256–276 (1931).

Evans, A. M. Mosquitoes (South America). Ann. Trop. Med. Parasitol., **16**, 213 pp. (1922); **18**, 12 pp. (1924).

Mosquitoes (Sierra Leone). Ibid., **19**, pp. 119–124 (1925); **20**, pp. 97–108 (1926).

Mosquitoes (Africa). Ibid., **26**, pp. 85–108 (1932).

African Anophelines. Ibid., **25**, pp. 129–143 (1931). Mem. Liverpool Sch. Trop. Med., **3**, 78 pp. (1927).

Mosquitoes of Ethiopian Region, **2**, 404 pp. British Mus. (1938).

FALLERONI, D. Fauna anofelica italiana. Riv. Malariol. Rome, **5**, pp. 553–593 (1926).

FARNER, D. S. et al. Aëdes. U. S. Naval Med. Bull., **44**, pp. 37–53 (1945).

Mosquitoes (Pacific area). U. S. Bur. Med. Surg., **983**, 64 pp. (1946).

FAVR, V. V. Malaria in Russia. Kharkov, 344 pp. (1903).

FELT, E. P. Mosquitoes (New York). Bull. New York State Mus., **79**, pp. 241–400 (1904); **97**, pp. 442–497 (1905).

FENG, LAN-CHOU. Anopheles Larvæ and Pupæ (China). Nat. Med. Jour. China, **17**, pp. 493–512 (1931).

Mosquitoes (China). Verh. 7 Internat. Kongr. Ent., **3**, pp. 1579–1588 (1939).

FERGUSON, E. W. Mosquitoes (New South Wales). Rept. Dir. Gen. Publ. Health New South Wales, **1925**, pp. 187–191.

FERMI, C. Anofelinologia. Riv. Malariol. Rome, **5**, pp. 113–131, 286–302 (1926).

FLOCH, H., and E. ABONNENC. Anopheles (French Guiana). Publ. Inst. Pasteur Guyane, **144**, 9 pp. (1947).

Culex (French Guiana). Ibid., **146**, 8 pp. (1947).

Culicines (French Guiana). Ibid., **148**, 12 pp. (1947).

Nyssorhynchus (Guianas). Bull. Soc. Path. Exot. Paris, **40**, 457–462 (1948).

FREEBORN, S. B., and B. BROOKMAN. Mosquitoes (California). Univ. California Publ. Ent., **3**, pp. 333–460 (1926).

Mosquitoes (Western U. S.). U. S. Publ. Health Serv., mimeogr. ser., 23 pp. (1943).

GABALDON, A. et al. Estudios sobre Anopheles. Publ. Div. Malariol., **5**, 50 pp. (1940); **7**, 57 pp. (1941).

GALLIARD, H. Culicines du Gabun. Ann. Parasit. Hum. Comp., **9**, 24 pp. (1931); **10**, 40 pp. (1932).

GAPUZ, R. B., and D. SANTIAGO. Key to Anopheles. Philippine Jour. Sci., **78**, pp. 127–133 (1950).

GARNHAM, P. C. C. et al. Mosquitoes (Kenya). Bull. Ent. Res., **36**, pp. 473–496 (1946).

GASCHEN, H. Anophèles de Suisse. Mém. Soc. Vaud. Sci. Nat., **6**, pp. 279–306 (1940).

GATER, B. A. R. Malayan Mosquitoes. Malay. Med. Jour., **8**, pp. 39–45, 96–101, 180–189, 277–283 (1933).

Anophelines (Malaya). Singapore, Govt. Ptg. Off., 242 pp. (1935).

GERRY, B. I. Cuban Mosquitoes. Ann. Ent. Soc. America, **25**, pp. 31–75 (1932).

GIAQUINTO-MIRA, M. Distribution of Mosquitoes (Ethiopia). Riv. Malariol. Rome, **29**, pp. 281–313 (1950).

GIL COLLADO, J. Culícidos (Isl. Fernando Po). Eos, **11**, pp. 311–329 (1936).

GILES, G. M. Handbook of Mosquitoes. London, 530 pp. (1902).

GILLETT, J. D. Tæniorhynchus, Subgenus Coquillettidia. Bull. Ent. Res., **36**, pp. 425–438 (1946).

GJULLIN, C. M. Aëdes (Pacific Coast). Proc. Ent. Soc. Washington. **39**, pp. 252–266 (1937).

    Aëdes (North America). Ibid., **48**, pp. 215–236 (1946).

GOELDI, E. A. Mosquitos no Para. Mem. Mus. Goeldi, **4**, 154 pp. (1905). Review: F. Knab, Jour. New York Ent. Soc., **14**, pp. 57–76 (1906).

GOETGHEBUER, M. Catalogue of Culicidæ (Belgium). Bull. Ann. Soc. Ent. Belgique, **65**, pp. 209–219 (1925).

GOMPERTS, H. C. Anophelini (Dutch East Indies). Thesis, Univ. Amsterdam, 58 pp. (1924).

HADDOW, A. J. Mosquitoes in Plant Axils (Uganda). Bull. Ent. Res., **39**, pp. 185–212 (1948).

HAGA, J. Aanteekening muskieten. Geneesk. Tijdschr. Nederlandsch-Indië, **64**, pp. 815–834 (1924).

HANCOCK, G. L. R. Uganda Mosquitoes and Larvæ. Bull. Soc. Ent. Egypte, **1930**, pp. 38–56 (1930).

HARMSTON, F. C., and G. F. KNOWLTON. Mosquito Records (Idaho). Pan-Pacific Ent., **22**, pp. 148–156 (1946).

HARRIS, W. V. Culicinæ (Tanganyika). Bull. Ent. Res., **33**, pp. 181–193 (1942).

HAYES, W. P. Bibliography of Immature Mosquitoes. Ent. News, **55**, pp. 144–145, 183–189 (1944).

HEADLEE, T. J. Mosquitoes (New Jersey). Bull. New Jersey Exp. Sta., **276**, 135 pp. (1915); **328**, 229 pp. (1921).

    Mosquitoes of New Jersey. 326 pp., Rutgers Univ. Press, New Brunswick (1945).

HEARLE, E. Mosquitoes of Fraser Valley, British Columbia. Rept. Nat. Res. Council, Ottawa, **17**, 94 pp. (1926).

    Mosquitoes (British Columbia). Proc. Ent. Soc. British Columbia, **24**, pp. 11–19 (1927).

    Culicidæ in Great Plains, Canada. Trans. Roy. Soc. Canada, V **23**, pp. 85–101 (1929).

HILL, G. F. North Australian Mosquitoes. Commonwealth Australia Dept. Health Serv. Publ., **21**, 32 pp. (1922). Proc. Roy. Soc. Victoria, **37**, pp. 61–77 (1925).

HILL, N. D. Mosquitoes (Kansas). Trans. Kans. Acad. Sci., **42**, pp. 255–265 (1939).

HILL, R. B.. and C. M. HILL. Mosquitoes of Jamaica. Bull. Inst. Jamaica, Sci. Ser., **4**, pp. 1–60 (1949).

HO, C. Culicids of Peiping. Bull. Fan Mem. Inst. Biol. **2**, pp. 107–175 (1931).

HOCKING, B., et al. Mosquitoes (Manitoba). Canadian Jour. Res., Zool., **28**, pp. 58–80 (1950).

HODGKIN, E. P. Anopheles. Trans. Roy. Ent. Soc. London, **101**, pp. 281–334 (1950).

HOFFMAN, C. C. Distribution of Anopheles in Veracruz. Dept. Salubr. Publica, Mexico, 76 pp. (1929).

HOPKINS, G. H. E. Larvæ of Ethiopian Mosquitoes. Bull. Ent. Res., **22**, pp. 89–104 (1931). Mosquitoes of Ethiopian Region, **1**, 250 pp. British Mus. (1936). Bull. Ent. Res., **33**, pp. 175–178 (1942).

Howard, C. W. Mosquitoes (Minnesota). Rept. Minnesota State Ent., **16,** pp. 73–92 (1916).

Howard, L. O., H. G. Dyar and F. Knab. Mosquitoes (North and Central America). Carnegie Inst. Washington, 4 vols., 1064 pp. (1912–1917).

Howland, L. J. English Mosquito Larvæ. Jour. Ecol., **18,** pp. 81–125 (1930).

Hsiao, T., and R. M. Bohart. Mosquitoes (Japan). U. S. Bur. Med. Surg., **1095,** 44 pp. (1946).

Ingram, A., and J. W. S. MacFie. Pupæ of African Mosquitoes. Bull. Ent. Res., **8,** pp. 73–91, 135–154 (1917).

Ingram, A., and B. De Meillon. South African Mosquito Survey. Publ. South Africa Inst. Med. Res., **22,** 81 pp. (1927); **24,** 87 pp. (1929).

Iwata, M. Malarial Mosquitoes. Bull. Takarazuka Insectarium, **7,** pp. 1–10 (1941). (In Japanese)

Jackson, R. B. Anopheline Larvæ (Hong Kong). Chinese Med. Jour., **53,** pp. 259–270 (1938).
    Anophelines. Ibid., **53,** pp. 563–576 (1938).

Johannsen, O. A. Culicidæ. Bull. New York State Mus., **68,** pp. 388–429 (1903).

Jolly, G. G. Mosquito Survey of Rangoon. 55 pp. (1933).

Kerr, J. A. West African Mosquitoes, Habits. Bull. Ent. Res., **24,** pp. 493–510 (1933).

King, W. V., and G. H. Bradley. Culex erraticus. Ann. Ent. Soc. America, **30,** pp. 345–357 (1937).
    Anopheles (Nearctic). Publ. American Assoc. Adv. Sci., **15,** pp. 63–78 (1941).

King, W. V., G. H. Bradley and T. E. McNeel. Mosquitoes of Southeastern United States. Misc. Publ. U. S. Dept. Agric., **336,** 96 pp. (1942).

King, W. V., and H. Hoogstraal. Mosquitoes (East Indies). Proc. Ent. Soc. Washington, **48,** 58 pp. (1946).
    Culex (New Guinea). Proc. Biol. Soc. Washington, **50,** pp. 143–154 (1946).

Kirkpatrick, T. W. Mosquitoes (Egypt). Bull. Soc. Roy. Ent. Egypte, **1924,** pp. 362–388 (1925). Govt. Press, Cairo, 224 pp. (1925).

Kissileva, E. Culicidæ (Siberia). Med. Parasit. Dis. Moscow, **5,** pp. 220–240 (1936). (In Russian)

Knight, K. L. Aëdes (Orient). Jour. Washington Acad. Sci., **36,** pp. 270–280 (1946). Ann. Ent. Soc. America, **40,** pp. 624–649 (1947).
    Aëdes (Pacific). Jour. Washington Acad. Sci., **37,** pp. 315–325 (1947).
    Aëdes. Proc. Ent. Soc. Washington, **50,** pp. 1–8 (1948).

Knight, K. L., and R. M. Bohart. Mosquitoes of Australasia. Nat. Res. Council, Div. Med. Sci., Washington, 71 pp. (1944).

Knight, K. L., and R. W. Chamberlain. Mosquito Pupæ. Proc. Helminth. Soc. Washington, **15,** pp. 1–18 (1948).

Knight, K. L., and H. S. Hurlbert. Mosquitoes of Ponape Island. Jour. Washington Acad. Sci., **39,** pp. 20–34 (1949).

Knight, K. L., and J. L. Laffoon, Aëdes (Orient). Trans. American Ent. Soc., **72,** pp. 102–225 (1946).

Knight, K. L., and P. F. Mattingly. Orthopodomyia Mosquitoes. Proc. Ent. Soc. Washington, **52,** pp. 1–20 (1950).

KNIGHT, K. L., and L. E. ROZEBOOM. Aëdes. Proc. Biol. Soc. Washington, 59, pp. 83–98 (1946).

KOIDZUMI, M. Mosquitoes (Formosa). Rept. Sci. Inst. Taihoku, Formosa, 8, 158 pp. (1920). (In Japanese)

Anophelines (Formosa). Zool. Mag. Tokyo, 37, pp. 314–377 (1925). (In Japanese)

KOMP, W. H. Mosquitoes (U. S.). U. S. Publ. Health Repts., 38, pp. 1061–1080 (1923).

Anopheles. Ann. Ent. Soc. America, 30, pp. 492–529 (1937).

Nyssorhynchus. Ibid., 34, pp. 791–807 (1941).

Anopheles (Mexico, Central America, West Indies). Publ. American Assoc. Adv. Sci., 15, pp. 88–97 (1941).

Anophelines (Caribbean). Bull. Nat. Inst. Health, 179, 195 pp. (1942).

Microculex (Colombia). Proc. Ent. Soc. Washington, 52, pp. 147–157 (1950).

KOMP, W. H., and L. E. ROZEBOOM. Melanoconion. Proc. Ent. Soc. Washington, 53, pp. 121–137 (1951).

KUMM, H. W. Distribution of Malarial Mosquitoes. American Jour. Hyg. Monogr. Ser., 18, 178 pp. (1929).

KUMM, H. W. et al. Mosquitoes (Costa Rica). American Jour. Trop. Med., 20, pp. 385–422 (1940).

Mosquitoes (El Salvador). Ibid., 22, pp. 399–415 (1942).

Hæmagogus (Colombia). American Jour. Hyg., 43, pp. 13–28 (1946).

KUNTZE, A. Culicidæ (Europe). Deutsche Ent. Zeitschr., 1920, pp. 363–383.

LAFACE, L. Anofelini italiani. Riv. Malariol. Rome, 5, pp. 44–48 (1926).

Anofelini (Italian Colonies). Riv. Parassitol., 1, suppl. 1, 120 pp. (1937).

LAFFOON, J. Aëdes (Philippines). Jour. Washington Acad. Sci., 36, pp. 228–245 (1946).

LANE, J. Mosquitoes (São Paulo). Bol. Inst. Hyg. São Paulo, 60, 15 pp. (1936).

Culicideos (Matto Grosso). Rev. Mus. Paulista, 20, pp. 173–206 (1936).

Catalogue of Mosquitoes (Neotropical). Bol. Biol., São Paulo, Monogr., 1, 218 pp. (1939).

Non-Hæmatophagous Culicidæ. Bol. Biol., São Paulo (N. S.) 4, pp. 99–113, 386–393 (1939).

Megarhinini (Brazil). Rev. Ent. Rio Janeiro, 15, pp. 172–190 (1944).

LANE, J., and N. L. CERQUEIRA. Sabetíneos. Arq. Zool., São Paulo, 3, pp. 473–849 (1942).

LANE, J., and A. NEGHME. Anopheles pictipennis. Biologica, Santiago, 4, pp. 83–93 (1946).

LANE, J., and L. WHITMAN. New Culex (Brazil). Rev. Ent. Rio Janeiro, 14, pp. 389–408 (1943).

LANG, W. D. Handbook of British Mosquitoes. 125 pp., British Mus. (1920).

LEE, D. J. Armigeres. Proc. Linn. Soc. New South Wales, 69, pp. 215–225 (1944).

Tripteroides. Ibid., 70, pp. 219–275 (1946).

LEE, D. J., and A. R. WOODHILL. Anophelines (Australasia). Monogr. Dept. Zool. Univ. Sydney, 2, 209 pp. (1944).

LEESON, H. S. Anophelines (Southern Rhodesia). Mem. London Sch. Hyg. Trop. Med., 4, 55 pp. (1931).

Anophelines (West Africa). Bull Ent. Res., 30, pp. 129–161 (1939).

LEHMANN, K. B. Steckmücken Unterfrankens. Deutsche Ent. Zeitschr., **1925**, pp. 420–438 (1926).

LEICESTER, G. F. Culicidæ (Malaya). Stud. Inst. Med. Federated Malay States, **3**, pt. 3, pp. 18–269 (1908).

LEVI CASTILLO, R. Anofelinos (Ecuador). Guayaquil, 172 pp. (1945).

Atlas of South American Anophelinæ. Filantropic Soc., Guayaquil, 207 pp. (1949).

LEWIS, D. J. Mosquitoes of Wicken Fen. Nat. Hist. Wicken Fen, **6**, pp. 548–559 (1932).

Culicines (Eritrea). Bull. Ent. Res., **34**, pp. 279–285 (1943).

Culicidæ (Sudan). Trans. Roy. Ent. Soc. London, **95**, pp. 1–24 (1945).

LI, FENG-SWEN. Anophelines of the World. Yearb. Bur. Ent. Hangchow, **1932**, pp. 71–98 (1933).

LI, F.-S., and SHIH-CHENG WU. Mosquitoes of Hangchow. Ibid., **1933**, pp. 97–123 (1933).

Culicine Larvæ in Hangchow. Ibid., **1934**, pp. 95–120 (1935).

Chinese Culicini. Ent. Phytopath. Hangchow. **3**, pp. 44–90 (1935). (In Chinese)

LIVIDAS, G. A., and J. C. SPHANGOS. Anophelines (Greece). Athens Sch. Hyg., **1**, pp. 69–107 (1941).

LOWRY, P. R. Mosquitoes of New Hampshire. Bull. New Hampshire Agric. Exp. Sta., **243**, 23 pp. (1929).

LUDLOW, C. S. Disease-bearing mosquitoes. Bull. War Dept. Office Surg. Gen., **4**, 97 pp. (1914).

LUTZ, A., and A. NEIVA. Megarininas. Mem. Inst. Oswaldo Cruz, **5**, pp. 129–141 (1913).

MACARTHUR, W. P. Mosquitoes of Shanghai. Jour. Roy. Army Med. Corps, London, **52**, pp. 241–247 (1929).

MACFIE, J. W., and A. INGRAM. Domestic Mosquitoes of Accra. Bull. Ent. Res., **7**, pp. 161–178 (1916).

West African Mosquitoes. Ibid., **13**, pp. 409–442 (1923).

MACGREGOR, M. E. Handbook of Mosquito Surveys. London, 293 pp. (1927).

MACKERRAS, I. M. Mosquitoes of Sydney District. Australian Naturalist, **6**, pp. 33–42 (1926).

Australian Mosquitoes. Proc. Linn. Soc. New South Wales, **52**, pp. 33–41, 284–298 (1927).

MAIL, G. A. Mosquitoes of Montana. Bull Montana Agr. Exp. Sta., **288**, 72 pp. (1934).

MANGKOEWINOTO, R. M. M. Anophelinen van West-Java. Meded. Burgerl. Geneesk. Nederlandsch-Indië, **2**, pp. 41–82 (1919).

MARCHOUX, E. Paludisme. Nouv. Traité Méd. Therap., **5**, 366 pp. (1926).

MARCUZZI, G. Culicidæ (Albania). Riv. Parassitol. Rome, **7**, pp. 155–167 (1943).

MARDARE, I. Aëdes (Rumania). Anal. Acad. Romane, (3) **18**, pp. 397–460 (1943).

MARKS, E. N. Queensland Mosquitoes. Pap. Dept. Biol. Univ. Queensland, **2**, 118 pp. (1948).

MARSHALL, J. F. British Mosquitoes. 341 pp., British Mus. (1938).

MARTINI, E. Anopheles (Hamburg). Abh. Naturw. Ver. Hamburg, **21**, Heft 2, 32 pp. (1920).

Stechmücken (Europe). Arch. Schiffs-Tropenhyg., **24**, 267 pp. (1920).

German Mosquitoes. Wiener Ent. Ztg., **39**, pp. 97–104 (1922).

Mosquitoes (Central Europe). Ent. Mitt., **11**, pp. 106–126 (1922).

Stechmücken. Zool. Jahrb. Syst., **46**, pp. 517–590 (1923).

Stechmückenfragen. Arch. Hydrobiol., **14**, pp. 726–740 (1924).

Stechmücken von Saratow. Arb. Biol. Wolga-Sta., **8**, pp. 189–227 (1926).

Culicids of Volga Region. Abh. Geb. Auslandsk. Hamburg Univ., **29**, pp. 21–61 (1928).

Culicidæ (Palæarctic). Fliegen Palæarkt. Reg., **11–12**, 398 pp. (1929–1931).

Culiciden (South America). Rev. Ent. Rio Janeiro, **1**, pp. 199–219 (1931).

Mosquitoes (Mexico). Bol. Tec. Dept. Salubr. Publica, Mexico (A), no. 1, 65 pp. (1935).

MATHESON, R. Genera of Culicidæ. Canadian Ent., **56**, pp. 157–161 (1924).

Mosquitoes (North America). 313 pp., Comstock Publ. Co., Ithaca, New York (1944).

Culicidæ (Connecticut). Bull. Connecticut Geol. Nat. Hist. Surv., **68**, pp. 1–48 (1946).

MATHESON, R., and R. C. SHANNON. Anophelines (Northeastern America). Ins. Inscit. Menstr., **11**, pp. 57–72 (1923).

MATTINGLY, P. F. Anophelini (West Africa). Ann. Trop. Med. Parasitol., **38**, pp. 189–200 (1944).

Ethiopian Mosquitoes, Early Stages. Ibid., **41**, pp. 239–252 (1947).

Forest Mosquitoes (West Africa). Bull. Ent. Res., **40**, pp. 149–168, 387–402 (1949).

McLINTOCK, J. Mosquitoes (Winnipeg). Canadian Ent., **76**, pp. 89–104 (1944).

MEILLON, B. DE. Anophelines (South Africa). Publ. South African Inst. Med. Res., **28**, pp. 275–375 (1931); Ibid., **49**, pp. 1–272 (1947).

MEILLON, B. DE et al. Anophelines (Portuguese East Africa). Docum. Trim., Moçambique, **23**, pp. 69–83 (1940).

Culicini (Mozambique). Ibid., **27**, pp. 69–77 (1941).

Culicini, Larvæ and Pupæ (Ethiopian). Bull. Ent. Res., **36**, pp. 85–101 (1945).

MENDOZA, J. B. Anopheles (Philippines). Mon. Bull. Bur. Health Philippines, **23**, pp. 171–184 (1947).

MITCHELL, E. G. Mosquito Life. 281 pp., G. P. Putnam and Sons, N. Y. (1907).

MOCHIZUKI, D. Culicidæ (Fukuoka District). Mag. Fukuoka Med. Coll., **7**, 65 pp. (1913). (In Japanese)

MONTSCHADSKY, A. Culiciden Larven. Bull. Acad. Sci. URSS, **1927**, pp. 479–498.

MORISHITA, K. Oriental Anophelines. Jour. Med. Assoc. Formosa, **31**, pp. 176–204 (1932). (In Japanese)

Anophelines (Formosa). Trans. Nat. Hist. Soc. Formosa, **26**, pp. 347–355 (1936). Jour. Med. Assoc. Formosa, **35**, pp. 888–897 (1936). Zool. Mag. Tokyo, **48**, pp. 573–579 (1936).

MULLIN-DIAZ, E. Anopheles (Uruguay). Comun. Zool. Mus. Hist. Nat. Montevideo, **1**, no. 3, 8 pp. (1943).

NATVIG, G. R. Danish and Fennoscandian Culicinæ. Norsk Ent. Tidsskr. Suppl., 1, 567 pp. (1948).

NETTO, A. S. Mosquitoes (Rio Grande do Sul). Thesis, Fac. Med. Porto Alegre, 103 pp. (1940).

NUNEZ TOVAR, M. Mosquitos y Flebotomos de Venezuela. Trab. Contrib. 4 Congr. Venez. Med., Maracay, 46 pp. (1924).

OLIVEIRA COUTINHO, J. DE. Anopheles, Subgenus Kerteszia, and Malaria. Thesis, Univ. São Paulo Fac. Med., 87 pp. (1946).
    Anopheles (Brazil). Ibid., 117 pp. (1947).

ORLOWA, A. A.. and S. D. SCHACHOW. Culicidæ and Phlebotominæ (Turkmen). Arch. Schiffs- u. Tropenhyg., 34, pp. 593–608 (1930).

ORSONO-MESA, E. Anopheles. Caldasia, Bogotá, 4, pp. 431–451 (1947).

OWEN, W. B. Mosquitoes (Minnesota). Tech. Bull. Minnesota Exp. Sta., 126, 75 pp. (1937).

PAINE, R. W. Mosquitoes of Fiji. Fiji, Dept. Agric., 29 pp. (1935); 2nd edit., Bull. Fiji Dept. Agric., no. 22, 35 pp. (1943).

PAINE, R. W., and F. W. EDWARDS. Mosquitoes from Solomon Islands. Bull. Ent. Res., 20, pp. 303–316 (1929).

PANDAZIS, G. Culicides de Grèce. Acta Inst. Mus. Zool. Univ. Athens, 1, pp. 1–27 (1935). 6 Congr. Intern. Ent., 1935, pp. 911–935 (1940).

PAVLOVSKY, E. N. Investigating Mosquitoes. Rev. Microbiol. Epidemiol., Saratov, 4, pp. 77–118 (1925). Leningrad Zool. Mus. Acad. Sci. URSS, 76 pp. (1927). Zool. Acad. Sci. URSS, no. 14, 176 pp. (1935). (In Russian)

PELAEZ, D. Anofelinos de Mexico. Ciencia, Mexico, 6, pp. 69–77 (1945).

PENN, G. H. Anopheline Pupæ (Nearctic). Jour. Nat. Malaria Soc., 8, pp. 50–69 (1949).
    Mosquito Pupæ (New Guinea). Pacific Sci., 3, pp. 3–85 (1949).

PEREIRA, M. DE C. Culicidæ (Mozambique). Ann. Inst. Med. Trop., 3, pp. 341–372 (1946).

PERRY, W. J. Mosquitoes (New Hebrides). Pan-Pacific Ent., 22, pp. 9–18 (1946).

PERYASSU, A. Culicideos (Brazil). Trab. Inst. Manguinhos, 1908, 409 pp.
    Anophelineos (Brazil). Arch. Mus. Nac. Rio Janeiro, 23, pp. 9–104 (1921).
    Catalogo culicideos Brasil. Folha Medica Rio Janeiro, 5, 12 pp. (1923).

PETRISHCHEVA, P. A. Culicidæ, Biology. Trudy Leningrad Akad. Nauk. Izuch. proizvodet. Sil Ser. Turkmensk., 6, 85–104 (1934).

PETROCCHI, J. Argentine Mosquitoes. Rev. Inst. Bact. Buenos Aires, 3, pp. 83–93 (1923).

PEUS, F. Ecology of Local Culicidæ. Zeitschr. Desinfect. Berlin, 21, pp. 76–81, 92–98 (1929).
    Anopheles (Mediterranean). Hyg. Zool. Monogr. Biol., 8, 150 pp. (1942).

PHILIP, C. B. Ethiopian Uranotænia. Bull. Ent. Res., 22, pp. 183–193 (1931).

PINTO, C. Mosquitoes (South America). Rev. Med.-Cir. Brasil, 40, pp. 285–309 (1932).

PLETNJOW, E. A. Biologie der Mücken (Tomsk). Arch. Naturgesch., 92, A, Heft 12, 27 pp. (1928).

PRADO, A. Culicideos de São Paulo. Mem. Inst. Butantan, 6, pp. 191–212 (1931).

PRITCHARD, A. E., and H. D. PRATT. List of Mosquitoes (Puerto Rico). Repts. U. S. Publ. Health Serv., 59, pp. 221–233 (1944).

PURI, I. M. Indian Anophelines. Indian Jour. Med. Res., 16, pp. 519–528 (1928). Rec. Malaria Surv. India, 5, pp. 265–273 (1935); 6, pp. 177–211 (1936). Govt. India, Health Bull., 16, 65 pp. (1930); 4th edit., 109 pp. (1941).
    Anophelines (Indian). Mem. Indian Med. Res., 21, 227 pp. (1931).
    Collecting Mosquitoes. Govt. India, Health Bull., no. 13 (Malaria Bull., no. 5), 57 pp. (1940).
    Distribution of Anopheline Mosquitoes. Indian Jour. Malariol., 2, pp. 67–107 (1948).

REES, D. M. Mosquitoes (Utah). Bull. Univ. Utah, 33, no. 7, 99 pp. (1943).

REEVES, W. C. Mosquitoes (California). Proc. 12 Ann. Conf. Mosq. Control, 14 pp. (1942).

REID, J. A. Anopheles. Trans. Roy. Ent. Soc. London, 101, pp. 281–318 (1950).

REMPEL, J. G. Mosquito Larvæ (Canada). Canadian Jour. Res., D 28, pp. 207–248 (1950).

RICHARDS, A. G. Mosquitoes (Long Island). Bull. New York State Mus., 316, pp. 85–180 (1938).

RILEY, W. A. List of Canton Mosquitoes. Lingnan Sci. Jour., 11, pp. 25–35 (1932).

RILEY, W. A., and LIANG-YU WU. Anophelines of China. Ibid., 11, pp. 175–191 (1932).

RIPSTEIN, C. Mosquitoes (Mexico). An. Inst. Biol. Mexico, 6, pp. 63–70, 213–233 (1935).

ROOT, F. M. Anopheline Larvæ. American Jour. Hyg., 2, pp. 379–392 (1922). Nyssorhynchus (Brazil). Ibid., 6, pp. 684–717 (1926).
    Mosquitoes (Haiti). Ibid., 7, pp. 463–469 (1927); (Brazil), 7, pp. 470–480 (1927).
    Culex (Brazil). Ibid., 7, pp. 574–598 (1927).

ROSS, E. S., and H. R. ROBERTS. Mosquito Atlas, I. Anopheles (Nearctic). II. Anopheles (Old World). 44 + 44 pp. American Ent. Soc., Philadelphia (1943).

ROSS, H. H. Mosquitoes (Illinois). Bull. Illinois Nat. Hist. Surv., 24, pp. 1–96 (1947).

ROTH, L. M. Culex of Southeastern U. S. Jour. Kansas Ent. Soc., 16, pp. 117–133 (1943).
    Anopheles of Southeastern U. S. American Midl. Nat., 31, pp. 96–110 (1944).
    Mosquito Behavior. Ibid., 40, pp. 265–352 (1948).

ROUBAUD, E. Anophelisme en extrême-orient. 434 pp., Paris (1936).

ROWE, J. A. Mosquitoes (Iowa). Iowa State Coll. Jour. Sci., 16, pp. 211–225 (1942).

ROZEBOOM, L. E. Nyssorhynchus, Eggs (Panama). American Jour. Hyg., 27, pp. 95–107 (1938).
    Anopheles (Caribbean). Publ. Amer. Assoc. Adv. Sci., 15, pp. 98–107 (1941).

Mosquitoes (Oklahoma). Tech. Bull. Oklahoma Exp. Sta., **16,** 56 pp. (1942).

ROZEBOOM, L. E., and A. GABALDON. Anopheles. American Jour. Hyg., **33,** pp. 88–100 (1941).

ROZEBOOM, L. E., and H. W. KOMP. Culex, Subgenus Melanoconion. Ann. Ent. Soc. America, **43,** pp. 75–114 (1950).

Culex, Subgenus Microculex. Proc. Ent. Soc. Washington, **52,** pp. 147–160 (1950).

RUSSELL, P. F., and F. E. BAISAS. Larvæ of Anopheles (Philippines). Philippine Jour. Sci., **55,** pp. 307–336 (1934).

Anopheles. Ibid., **59,** pp. 15–64 (1936).

RUSSELL, P. F., L. E. ROZEBOOM, and A. STONE. Anophelines of the World. 152 pp., American Ent. Soc., Philadelphia, (1943).

RUSSELL, P. F., L. S. WEST, and R. D. MANWELL. Classification of Anophelines. In Practical Malariology, pp. 587–657, Saunders, Philadelphia (1946).

RYBINSKY, S. B. Moustiques (Ukraine). Bull. Soc. Zool. France, **58,** pp. 18–29 (1933).

SAHARAGI, M., and Y. MIHARA. Catalogue of Culicidæ (Japan). Insect World, Gifu, **31,** pp. 362–368 (1927).

SALEM, H. H. Mosquitoes (Sinai). Publ. Egyptian Univ. Fac. Med., **16,** 31 pp. (1938).

SANDOSHAM, A. A. Malaria in Malaya. Sayonan Tokubetu-si, 288 pp. (1944).

Anophelines (Malaya and Thailand). 95 pp., Singapore (1945).

SCHLAIFER, A., and D. E. HARDING. The Mosquitoes of Tennessee. Jour. Tennessee Acad. Sci., **21,** pp. 241–256 (1946).

SCHNEIDER, A. Culicidæ (Bonn). Verh. Naturh. Ver. Bonn, **70,** pp. 1–54 (1913).

SCHWETZ, J. Mosquitoes (Belgian Congo). Rev. Zool. Africaine, **15,** pp. 271–319 (1927). Bull. Soc. Path. Exotique, **20,** pp. 170–192 (1927). Ann. Soc. Belge Med. Trop., **10,** pp. 25–65 (1930). Mem. Inst. Roy. Colon. Belge, **14,** no. 1, 93 pp. (1944).

SÉGUY, E. Les moustiques de France. Bull. Mus. Hist. Nat. Paris, **26,** pp. 51–58, 141–147, 223–230, 322–329, 407–414, 512–519 (1920).

Histoire naturelle des moustiques de France. 225 pp., Paris (1923).

Mosquitoes (North East Africa). Encycl. Ent. (A), **1,** 257 pp. (1924).

French Mosquitoes. Trav. Nat. Loing, **2,** pp. 5–20 (1928); **5,** pp. 19–93 (1931).

SENEVET, G. Nymphes de Culicides. Arch. Inst. Pasteur Algérie, **8,** pp. 297–382 (1930); **9,** pp. 17–112 (1931); **10,** pp. 204–254 (1932).

Nymphes Anophelines. C. R. 2 Congr. Internat. Paludisme, **1,** pp. 69–154 (1931). Arch. Inst. Pasteur Algérie, **12,** pp. 29–76 (1934).

Anophèles de la France et de ses colonies. Encycl. Ent. (A), **19,** 400 pp. (1934).

Moustiques (Martinique). Arch. Inst. Pasteur Algérie, **14,** pp. 123–134 (1936).

Culicides (Algeria). Ibid., **14,** pp. 432–448 (1936).

Moustiques (French Guiana). Ibid., **15,** pp. 352–382 (1937).

Moustiques (Guadeloupe). Ibid., **16,** pp. 176–190 (1938).

Culex (North Africa). Ibid., **23,** pp. 48–65 (1945); **25,** pp. 107–136 (1947).

Anopheles. Ibid., **26**, pp. 149–161 (1948).

SENEVET, G., and E. ABONNENC. Anophelines (French Guiana). Ibid., **16**, pp. 486–512 (1938); **17**, pp. 62–134, 217–281, 466–480, 585–597 (1939).
Sabethines. Ibid., **20**, pp. 336–348 (1942).

SENEVET, G., and M. PRUNNELLE. Anopheles (Algeria). Ibid., **6**, pp. 468–485 (1928).

SENIOR-WHITE, R. A. Culicidæ of Ceylon. Indian Jour. Med. Res., **8**, pp. 304–325 (1920). Spolia Zeylandica. **13**, pp. 213–222 (1925).
Catalogue of Indian Culicidæ. 124 pp., Govt. Ptg. Off., Calcutta (1923).
Mosquito Ecology. Bull. Ent. Res., **16**, pp. 187–248 (1926).
Larvæ of non-Anophelines. Spolia Zeylandica, **14**, pp. 61–76 (1927).

SHANNON, R. C. Brazilian Culicidæ. Proc. Ent. Soc. Washington, **33**, pp. 1–27, 125–164 (1931).
Anophelines (Amazon). Proc. Ent. Soc. Washington, **35**, pp. 117–143 (1933).
Mansonia (Amazon). Ibid., **36**, pp. 99–110 (1934).

SHANNON, R. C., and N. C. DAVIS. Anophelini of Bahia, Brazil. Ann. Ent. Soc. America, **23**, pp. 467–505 (1930).

SHANNON, R. C., and E. DEL PONTE. Culicidos en la Argentina. Rev. Inst. Bact. Buenos Aires, **4**, pp. 549–590 (1926); **5**, pp. 29–147 (1927).

SIMMONS, J. S., and T. H. G. AITKEN. Anophelines. U. S. Army Med. Bull. Carlisle, Pa., no. **59**, 213 pp. (1942).

SMITH, J. B. Mosquitoes of New Jersey. Rept. New Jersey Exp. Sta., 482 pp. (1904).

SOMEREN, E. C. C. Ethiopian Culicidæ. Trans. Roy. Ent. Soc. London, **96**, pp. 109–124 (1946); **97**, pp. 177–186 (1946).

SPEER, A. J. Parasites of Mosquitoes. Bull. U. S. Hyg. Lab., **146**, 36 pp. (1927).

STACKELBERG, A. A. Culicinæ de URSS. Moscow Inst. Zool. Acad. Sci., **3**, no. 4, 258 pp. (1937).
Culicidæ of Russia. Faune de l'URSS., Leningrad Acad. Sci., **1**, 169 pp. (1927). (In Russian)
Anopheles of URSS. Rev. Microbiol. Epidemiol., **4**, pp. 20–42 (1925). (In Russian)

STANTON, A. T. Anopheles, Larvæ (Malaya). Bull. Ent. Res., **6**, pp. 159–172 (1916).

STONE, A., and R. M. BOHART. Mosquitoes (Australasia). Proc. Ent. Soc. Washington, **46**, pp. 207–225 (1944).

STONE, A., and G. H. PENN. Culex (Solomon Isls.). Ibid., **50**, pp. 109–120 (1948).

STOREY, G. Egyptian Mosquitoes and Larvæ. Bull. Soc. Ent. Egypte, **1918**, pp. 84–105 (1919).

STRICKLAND, C., and K. L. CHOWDBURY. Anophelines of India, Ceylon, and Malaya. Thacker, Spink, and Co., Calcutta, 67 pp. (1927); Suppl., 36 pp. (1931).

SWELLENGREBEL, N. H. List of Indian Anopheles. Tijdschr. Ent., **63**, pp. 96–108 (1920).
List of Anopheles (Malay Archipelago). Bull. Ent. Res., **11**, pp. 77–92 (1920).
Anophelinen (Dutch East Indies). Meded. Kolon. Inst. Amsterdam, **15**, 155 pp. (1921).

SWELLENGREBEL, N. H., and E. RODENWALDT. Die Anophelen von Nieder-
ländsch-Ostindien. 242 pp. Fischer, Jena (1932).
SYMES, C. B. Anopheles, Larvæ (East Africa). Rec. Med. Res. Lab. Kenya, 2,
78 pp. (1931).
TATE, H. D., and D. B. GATES. Mosquitoes (Nebraska). Res. Bull. Nebr. Exp.
Sta., 133, 27 pp. (1944).
TAYLOR, F. H. Culicidæ (Papua). Trans. Roy. Ent. Soc. London, 1914,
pp. 185–205.
    Culicidæ in Maclean Museum. Proc. Linn. Soc. New South Wales, 38,
pp. 747–760 (1914).
    Australian Culicidæ. Ibid., 39, pp. 454–469 (1914); 40, pp. 178–184
(1915); 43, pp. 826–843 (1919).
    Australian Anopheles. Trans. Congr. Far East Trop. Med., 3, pp. 143–
163 (1930).
    List of Australian Culicidæ. Commonwealth Australia, Dept. Health
Serv. Publ., 1, 24 pp. (1934).
    Intermediary Hosts of Malaria. Ibid., 5, 100 pp. (1944).
THEOBALD, F. V. Culicidæ. 5 vols., 2459 pp. British Mus. (1901–1910).
    Culicidæ. Gen. Insectorum, 26, 50 pp. (1905).
    Catalogue of Culicidæ (Hungarian National Museum). Ann. Mus. Nat.
Hungarici, 3, pp. 61–119 (1905).
    Culicidæ (Sladen Exped. Indian Ocean). Trans. Linn. Soc. London,
(2) 15, pp. 81–94 (1912).
THIBAULT, J. K. Mosquitoes of Arkansas. Proc. Ent. Soc. Washington, 12,
pp. 13–26 (1910).
THOMSON, R. C. M. Anopheles. Bull. Ent. Res., 38, pp. 527–558 (1948).
THURMAN, E. B., and P. T. JOHNSON. Culiseta Larvæ. Pan-Pacific Ent., 26,
pp. 179–187 (1951).
TORRES CANAMARES, F. Anopheles (Spain). Rev. Sanid. Hig. Publ., 18, pp.
629–636 (1944). Eos, 20, pp. 233–245 (1945).
    Culicidos (Cuenca). Rev. Sanid. Hig. Publ., 19, reprint, 15 pp. (1945).
TOUMANOFF, C. Anopheles au Tonkin. Bull. Soc. Path. Exot., 25, pp. 770–
788 (1932).
TOWNSEND, C. H. T. Mosquitoes of the Rio Tapajos. Rev. Ent. Rio Janeiro,
4, pp. 486–499 (1934).
TULLOCH, G. S. Mosquitoes of New England. Psyche, 37, pp. 234–244 (1930).
    Mosquitoes of Puerto Rico. Jour. Agric. Univ. Puerto Rico, 21, pp. 137–
167 (1937).
    Mosquitoes of Massachusetts. Psyche, 46, pp. 113–136 (1939).
UNTI, O., and A. S. RAMOS. Fauna Anofelica (Paraiba). Arq. Hig. Saude
Publ. São Paulo, 8, no. 19, pp. 21–34 (1943).
URBINO, C. M. Eggs of Anopheles. Mon. Bull. Bur. Health Philippines, 16,
pp. 261–275 (1936).
VAN DINE, D. L. Mosquitoes in Hawaii. Bull. Hawaiian Agr. Exp. Sta., 6,
30 pp. (1904).
VARGAS, L. Mosquitoes (America). Rev. Inst. Salubr. Enferm. Trop., 1, pp.
189–198 (1940).
    Anopheles (Mexico). Gaceta Medica Mexico, 71, pp. 107–123 (1941).
    Anopheles. Rev. Inst. Salubr. Enferm. Trop., 4, pp. 57–77 (1943). Riv.
di Paran., 11, pp. 73–84 (1950).

Anopheles (Mexico). Rev. Inst. Salubr. Enferm. Trop., **4,** pp. 359–370 (1943).

Aëdes, Bionomics. Rev. Soc. Mexicana Hist. Nat., **9,** pp. 91–119 (1948).

Aëdes (America). Rev. Inst. Salubr. Enferm. Trop., **10,** pp. 327–344 (1949); **11,** pp. 61–69 (1950).

Vogel, R. Stechmücken Württembergs. Jahresh. Vaterl. Naturk. Württemberg, **85,** pp. 258–277 (1929); **89,** pp. 175–186 (1933).

Waterston, J. Mosquitoes in Macedonia. Jour. Roy. Army Med. Corps, London, **38,** pp. 334–349 (1922).

Wesenberg-Lund, C. Culicidæ, Biology. Naturens Verden, **3,** 74 pp. (1919). Pupæ of Mosquitoes. Festschr. Zschokke, Basle, no. **23,** 17 pp. (1921).

Weyer, F. Die Malaria-Ueberträger. 141 pp. Thieme, Leipzig (1939). Anopheles. Deutsche Tropenmed. Zeitschr., **46,** pp. 441–456, 461–480 (1942).

Wharton, R. H. Harpagomyia. Proc. Linn. Soc. New South Wales, **72,** pp. 58–69 (1947).

Wigglesworth, V. B. Early Stages of Mosquitoes (West Africa). Bull. Ent. Res., **20,** pp. 59–69 (1929).

Wirth, W. W. Melanoconion. Proc. Ent. Soc. Washington, **47,** pp. 199–210 (1945).

Wolfs, J. Moustiques (Belgian Congo). Ann. Soc. Belge Med. Trop., **26,** pp. 95–104 (1946).

Woodhill, A. R., and G. Pasfield. Mosquito Larvæ. Proc. Linn. Soc. New South Wales, **66,** pp. 201–214 (1941).

Wu, Shi-Cheng. Mosquitoes (Hangchow). Yearb. Bur. Ent. Hangchow, **1935,** pp. 46–53 (1936).

Yamada, S. Japanese Aëdes. Annot. Zool. Japonenses, **10,** pp. 45–81 (1921). Anophelines of Japan. Sci. Rept. Govt. Inst. Infect. Diseases, **3,** pp. 215–241 (1924); **4,** pp. 447–493 (1925).

Yao, Y. T., and L. C. Ling. Anophelini (Southwest China). Japanese Jour. Exp. Med., **15,** pp. 121–136 (1937).

Zaitzev, P. Mosquitoes of Caucasus. Trav. Zool. Tiflis, **1,** pp. 1–31 (1934). (In Russian)

Zetek, J. Anopheles (Panama). Proc. Med. Assoc. Canal Zone, **13,** pp. 29–56 (1920).

DIXIDÆ, NYMPHOMYIIDÆ

Cooper, J. L., and W. F. Rapp. Checklist of Dixidæ of the World. Canadian Ent., **76,** pp. 247–252 (1944).

Edwards, F. W. British Chaoborinæ and Dixinæ. Ent. Mon. Mag., **56,** pp. 264–270 (1920).

Goetghebuer, M. Les Dixidæ de Belgique. Bull. Soc. Ent. Belgique, **2,** pp. 18–29 (1920); **3,** pp. 183–188 (1921).

Johannsen, O. A. Dixidæ (North America). Psyche, **30,** pp. 52–58 (1923).

Lane, J. Dixinæ e Chaoborinæ. Rev. Ent. Rio Janeiro, **13,** pp. 81–148 (1942); **14,** pp. 162–166 (1943).

Martini, E. Dixinæ (Palæarctic). Fliegen Palæarkt. Reg., **33,** pp. 20–43 (1929).

NOWELL, W. R. Dixidæ (North America). Microentomology, 16, pp. 187–270 (1951).

PEUS, F. Dixidæ (Europe). Norsk Ent. Tidsskr., 4, pp. 117–127 (1936).

SMITH, F. K. Larvæ of Dixa. Jour. New York Ent. Soc., 36, pp. 263–286 (1928).

TOKUNAGA, M. Nymphomyia. Annot. Zool. Japonenses, 13, pp. 559–569 (1932). Mushi, Fukuoka, 8, pp. 41–52 (1935). Philippine Jour. Sci., 56, pp. 127–214 (1935).

TONNOIR, A. L. Dixidæ (New Zealand). Rec. Canterbury Mus., 2, pp. 221–233, 311–316 (1925).

CHIRONOMIDÆ

ABREU, E. S. Tendipedidos (Canary Isl.). Mem. R. Acad. Barcelona, 14, no. 2, pp. 159–326 (1918).

ALBRECHT, O. Chironomidenlarven (Austria). Verh. 2 Internat. Verein. Limnol., Innsbruck, 1923, pp. 183–209 (1924).

ANDERSON, F. S. Ceratopogonid and Chironomid Metamorphosis. Medd. Grønland, 116, 95 pp. (1937).

BAUSE, E. Metamorphosis Tendipediden. Arch. Hydrobiol. Suppl., 2, 128 pp. (1914).

BERG, C. O. Chironomidæ from Potamogeton. Ecol. Monogr., 20, pp. 83–101 (1950).

BRANCH, H. E. Chironomid Egg Masses. Trans. Kansas Acad. Sci., 34, pp. 151–157 (1931).

BRUNDIN, L. Chironomidæ (Sweden). Arkiv Zool., 39, A, 95 pp. (1947).
    Tanytarsus Metamorphosis. Ibid., 41 A, 22 pp. (1948).

CARTER, H. F. Leptoconops. Bull. Ent. Res.. 12, pp. 1–28 (1921).

DECKSBACH, M. Russian Chironomid Larvæ. Zool. Anz., 79, pp. 19–104 (1928).
    Chironomid Biology. Arch. Hydrobiol., 25, pp. 365–382 (1933).

DIBB, J. R. Tanypinæ. Ent. Mon. Mag., 65, pp. 213–217 (1929).

EDWARDS, F. W. Marine Chironomidæ. Proc. Zool. Soc. London, 1926, pp. 779–806.
    Chironomidæ (Britain). Trans. Roy. Ent. Soc. London, 77, pp. 279–428 (1929).
    Chironomidæ (Patagonia). Diptera of Patagonia and South Chile, 2, fasc. 5, pp. 233–324, British Mus. (1931).

GIBSON, N. H. E. Chironomidæ. Trans. Roy. Ent. Soc. London, 95, pp. 263–294 (1945).

GOETGHEBUER, M. Chironomidæ (Belgium). Ann. Biol. Lacustre, 6, pp. 148–172 (1913); 11, pp. 38–62, 173–186 (1922); 12, pp. 103–120 (1923). Mem. Acad. R. Bruxelles, 2, 48 pp. (1914). Mem. Mus. R. Hist. Nat. Belgique, 8, fasc. 4, pp. 1–208 (1921).
    Chironomidæ, Tanypodinæ. Faune de France, 15, 83 pp. (1927). Chironomariæ, Ibid., 18, 174 pp. (1928). Chironomidæ, Ibid., 23, 204 pp. (1932).
    Catalogue of Chironomids of Belgium. Bull. Ann. Soc. Ent. Belgique, 73, pp. 363–372 (1933); 74, pp. 209–213, 391–405 (1934); 75, pp. 63–72 (1935); 78, pp. 131–136 (1938); 81, pp. 187–197 (1945).

Tendipedidæ. Fliegen Palæarkt. Region, **13**, 5 pts., 360 pp. (1933–1949).

Chironomidæ in Vienna Museum. Ann. Naturh. Mus. Wien, **46**, pp. 91–115 (1933).

Chironomidæ (Greenland). Skr. Svalb. og Ishavet, **53**, pp. 19–31 (1933).

Chironomidæ (Bavaria). Bull. Ann. Soc. Ent. Belgique, **74**, pp. 334–350 (1934).

Chironomidæ. Arch. Hydrobiol., **30**, pp. 669–692 (1936).

Chironomidæ (Belgian Congo). Rev. Zool. Bot. Africaines, **28**, pp. 453–492 (1936).

Chironomidæ (Lapland). Bull. Ann. Soc. Ent. Belgique, **80**, pp. 55–72 (1940).

Chironomides du Tyrol. Bull. Mus. R. Hist. Nat. Belgique, **17**, fasc. 37, 8 pp. (1941).

Chironomides (Bas-Escaut). Bull. Ann. Soc. Ent. Belgique, **86**, pp. 141–163 (1950).

Chironomidæ and Ceratopogonidæ. Bull. Ann. Soc. Ent. Belgique, **71**, pp. 211–218; **72**, pp. 125–130, 287–294 (1931); **73**, pp. 209–221 (1933); **79**, pp. 219–229, 378–389 (1939); **81**, pp. 187–197 (1945). Bull. Mus. R. Hist. Nat. Belgique, **17**, fasc. 67, 12 pp. (1941). Biol. Jahrb., **11**, pp. 35–44 (1944).

Chironomidæ and Ceratopogonidæ (Congo). Rev. Zool. Bot. Africaines, **24**, pp. 129–151 (1933); **25**, pp. 191–205 (1934); **27**, pp. 145–181, 351–366 (1935).

GOETGHEBUER, M., and F. LENZ. Podonominæ. Fliegen Palæarkt. Region, **13f**, 19 pp. (1939).

GOUIN, F. Chironomid Metamorphosis (Alsace-Lorraine). Rev. française Ent., **3**, pp. 151–173 (1936).

GRIPEKOVEN, H. Mining Tendipedidæ. Arch. Hydrobiol. Suppl., **2**, pp. 129–230 (1914).

HAUBER, U. A. Pentaneura (Iowa). American Midl. Nat., **34**, pp. 496–503 (1945).

Tanytarsus (Iowa). Proc. Iowa Acad. Sci., **51**, pp. 451–461 (1945).

Tendipedinæ (Iowa). American Midl. Nat., **38**, pp. 456–465 (1947).

HESSE, A. J. Marine Clunionines (South Africa). Trans, Roy. Ent. Soc. London, **82**, pp. 27–40 (1934).

JOHANNSEN, O. A. Chironomidæ. Bull. New York State Mus., **86**, pp. 76–316 (1905); **124**, pp. 264–285 (1908). Aquatic Diptera, pt. 3, Mem. Cornell Univ. Agr. Exp. Sta., **205**, 84 pp. (1937); pt. 4, Ibid., **210**, 52 pp. (1937).

Pentaneura. Jour. New York Ent. Soc., **54**, pp. 267–289 (1946).

Chironomidæ and Ceratopogonidæ (Dutch East Indies). Arch. Hydrobiol., **9**, pp. 403–447, 493–507, 715–732 (1932); **11**, pp. 503–552 (1932).

KIEFFER, J. J. Chironomidæ. Gen. Insectorum, **42**, 78 pp. (1906).

Chironomidæ (Indian Ocean). Trans. Linn. Soc. London, (2) **14**, pp. 315–366 (1910–11).

Chironomidæ (India, Egypt). Mem. Indian Mus., **2**, pp. 181–242 (1910).

Chironomidæ (India). Rec. Indian Mus., **6**, pp. 113–177, 319–350 (1911); **9**, pp. 119–197 (1913).

Chironomidæ. Bull. Soc. Hist. Nat. Metz, **27**, pp. 1–60 (1911).

Chironomidæ (Ceylon). Spolia Zeylandica, **8**, pp. 1–24 (1912).
Tendipedidæ (Formosa). Supplementa Ent., **1**, pp. 27–43 (1912). Ann. Mus. Hungarici, **14**, pp. 81–121 (1916).
Chironomidæ (Germany). Bull. Soc. Hist. Nat. Afrique Nord, **5**, pp. 7–36 (1913).
Chironomidæ and Cecidomyidæ (East Africa). Voyage Alluaud, Dipt, 43 pp. (1913).
Chironomidæ (South Africa). Ann. South African Mus., **10**, pp. 259–270 (1914).
Tendipedidæ (Faroe Isl.). Zool. Jahrb., **39**, pp. 103–120 (1915).
Chironomidæ (Central Europe). Arch. Hydrobiol. Suppl., **2**, pp. 472–482, 785–808 (1915–1921). Broteria, **13**, pp. 65–87 (1915); Bull. Soc. Hist. Nat. Moselle, **30**, pp. 11–110 (1924).
Chironomidæ (Australia). Ann. Mus. Hungarici, **15**, pp. 175–208 (1917).
Chironomidæ of America. Ibid., **15**, pp. 292–364 (1917).
Chironomidæ of Africa and Asia. Ibid., **16**, pp. 31–139 (1918).
Chironomidæ of Europe. Ibid., **17**, pp. 1–160 (1919).
Chironomidæ (Palæarctic). Ent. Mitt., **7**, pp. 35–52, 94–110, 163–170, 177–188 (1918).
Chironomidæ of the North Polar Region. Ibid., **8**, pp. 38–48, 110–124 (1919).
Chironomidæ (Courland). Ann. Soc. Sci. Bruxelles, **40**, pp. 275–298 (1921).
Chironomidæ (Formosa). Ann. Soc. Linn. Lyon, **68**, pp. 149–163 (1921); **69**, pp. 27–41 (1922).
Chironomidæ (Africa). Ann. Soc. Ent. France, **90**, pp. 1–56 (1921); **91**, pp. 1–72 (1922); **92**, pp. 149–204 (1923).
Chironomidæ (Philippines, Formosa). Philippine Jour. Sci., **18**, pp. 557–593 (1921).
Chironomariæ. C. R. Ann. Soc. Sci. Bruxelles, **40**, pp. 269–277 (1921).
Chironomidæ (Palæarctic). Bull. Soc. Hist. Nat. Moselle, **29**, pp. 51–109 (1921); Ann. Soc. Sci. Bruxelles, **41**, pp. 355–367 (1922); **42**, pp. 71–128, 138–180 (1923).
Chironomidæ (Russian Arctic). Rept. Norwegian Exped. Novaya Zemlya, **1921**, no. 2, 24 pp. (1922); **1921**, no. 9, 11 pp. (1923).
Chironomidæ (Argentina). Ann. Soc. Sci. Bruxelles, **44**, pp. 73–92 (1925).
Chironomidæ (Egypt). Bull. Soc. Roy. Ent. Egypte, **8**, pp. 244–313 (1925).
Chironomiden der Hochmoore. Beitr. Kunde Estlands, Reval, **10**, pp. 145–163 (1925).
Tanytarsus (Europe). Ann. Soc. Sci. Bruxelles, **44**, pp. 218–230 (1925).
Chironomides des Zehlaubruches. Schr. Phys. Oekon. Ges. Königsberg, **66**, pp. 287–312 (1929).
KIEFFER, J. J., and A. THIENEMANN. Chironomid Metamorphosis. Zeitschr. Wiss. Insekt.-Biol., **4**, 60 pp. (1908).
KRÜGER, F. Atanytarsus. Arch. Hydrobiol., **33**, pp. 208–256 (1938).
KRUSEMAN, G. Tendipes. Tijdschr. Ent., **76**, pp. 119–216 (1933). Tendipedidæ (Malaya). Bijdr. Dierk., **27**, pp. 408–412 (1939).

LENZ, F. Phænocladius. Arch. Hydrobiol., **14**, pp. 453–469 (1923).
 Chironomidæ (Balaton Lake). Arch. Balatonicum, **1**, pp. 129–144 (1926).
 Salzwasser-Chironomus. Mitt. Geogr. Ges. Lübeck, (2) **31**, pp. 153–169 (1926).
 Chironomidæ (Norway). Nyt Mag. Naturf. Oslo, **66**, 82 pp. (1927).
 Medd. Zool. Mus., no. **12**, pp. 111–192 (1928).
 Chironomariæ, Larvæ and Pupæ (Dutch East Indies). Arch. Hydrobiol. Suppl., **15**, pp. 1–29 (1937).
 Parachironomus. Arch. Hydrobiol., **32**, pp. 700–714 (1938).
 Chironomariæ, Early Stages. Ibid., **38**, pp. 1–69 (1941).
 Cryptochironomus, Metamorphosis. Zool. Anz., **133**, pp. 29–41 (1941).
LIPINA, N. Chironomid Larvæ (Oka-Bassin). Arb. Biol. Oka-Sta., **4**, pp. 72–122 (1926); **5**, pp. 37–48 (1927). (In Russian)
 Chironomid Larvæ from River Plants. Trav. Soc. Nat. Charkow, **52**, pp. 287–319 (1929). (In Ukrainian)
LUNDSTRÖM, C. Chironomidæ (Finland). Acta Soc. Faun. Fl. Fennica, **33**, no. 10, 47 pp. (1910).
MALLOCH, J. R. Chironomidæ (Illinois). Bull. Illinois State Lab. Nat. Hist., **10**, pp. 275–543 (1915); **11**, pp. 305–363 (1915).
MARCUZZI, G. Tendipedidæ (Italy). Atti Acad. Padova, **57**, pp. 149–174 (1942). Hydrobiol., **1**, pp. 183–209 (1949).
MARGALEF LOPEZ, R. Quirnomidos. Graellsia, Madrid, **2**, pp. 3–13, 65–76, 165–181 (1944); **3**, pp. 13–22 (1945).
MUELLER, A. Tanypinæ. Verh. zool.-bot. Ges. Wien, **73**, pp. 98–111 (1923).
PAGAST, F. Chironomiden in Kurland. Folia Zool. Hydrobiol., **3**, pp. 199–248 (1931).
RÜBSAAMEN, E. H. Chironomidæ. Exped. Antarctique Belge, Zool. Ins., pp. 75–85 (1906).
SOOT-RYEN, T. List of Tendipedidæ (Norway). Arsh. Tromsø Mus., **64**, pp. 9–24 (1943).
SPÄRCK, R. Bibliography of Chironomid Metamorphosis. Ent. Medd., **14**, pp. 32–109 (1922).
 Chironomidæ (Greenland). Ibid., **23**, pp. 432–442 (1943).
STONE, A., and W. W. WIRTH. Clunio. Proc. Ent. Soc. Washington, **49**, pp. 201–224 (1947).
STUART, T. A. Chironomid Larvæ. Trans. Roy. Soc. Edinburgh, **60**, pp. 475–502 (1942).
THIENEMANN, A. Chironomid Metamorphosis. Verh. Nat. Ver. Bonn, **65**, pp. 201–212 (1908).
 Marine Chironomidæ. Arch. Hydrobiol. Suppl., **2**, pp. 443–471 (1915).
 Tanypinæ, Metamorphosis. Ibid., **2**, pp. 565–654 (1916).
 Freshwater Chironomids (Westfal). Jahresber. Prov-Ver. Wiss., **46**, pp. 19–63 (1918).
 Chironomid Metamorphosis. Arch. Hydrobiol. Suppl., **2**, pp. 809–850 (1921). Arch. Hydrobiol., **19**, pp. 585–623 (1928). Stettiner Ent. Ztg., **95**, pp. 3–23 (1934); **96**, pp. 201–224 (1935); **97**, pp. 43–65 (1936).
 Lundstroemia. Zool. Anz., **58**, pp. 331–344 (1924).
 Tanytarsus, Metamorphosis. Arch. Hydrobiol., **20**, pp. 93–123 (1929).
 Orthocladiariæ, Metamorphosis. Deutsche Ent. Zeitschr., **1933**, pp. 1–38.

Phænocladius Metamorphosis. Encycl. Ent. (B) II, **7**, pp. 29–46 (1934).
Alpine Chironomidæ. Arch. Hydrobiol., **30**, pp. 167–262 (1936).
Chironomid Metamorphosis. Festchr. E. Strand, **1**, pp. 531–553 (1936).
Chironomid Larvæ and Pupæ (India). Zoogeogr., **3**, pp. 145–158 (1936).
Chironomidæ (Lapland). Stettiner Ent. Ztg., **98**, pp. 165–185 (1937).
Arch. Hydrobiol. Suppl., **17**, 253 pp. (1941).
Podonominæ. Internat. Rev. Hydrobiol., **35**, pp. 65–99 (1937). Zool. Anz., **128**, pp. 161–176 (1939).
Orthocladiinæ, Metamorphosis. Deutsche Ent. Zeitschr., **1939**, pp. 1–19.
Arch. Hydrobiol., **39**, pp. 551–664 (1944).
Trichocladius. Ibid., **39**, pp. 294–315 (1942).
Pseudosmittia. Acta Biotheor. Leiden, **7** A, pp. 117–134 (1943).
THIENEMANN, A., and J. J. KIEFFER. Chironomids. Verh. Naturhist. Ver. Westfalens, **72**, pp. 1–58 (1915).
Schwedische Chironomiden. Arch. Hydrobiol. Suppl., **2**, pp. 483–554 (1916).
THIENEMANN, A., and K. MAYER. Diamesa, Larvæ and Pupæ. Zool. Anz., **103**, pp. 1–12 (1933).
THIENEMANN, A. et al. Terrestrial Chironomidæ. Zool. Anz., **127**, pp. 246–258 (1939); **132**, pp. 24–40, 238–244 (1940); **133**, pp. 137–146, 244–253 (1941).
TOKUNAGA, M. Marine Tanytarsus. Philippine Jour. Sci., **50**, pp. 327–344 (1933).
Chironomidæ (Japan). Ibid., **59**, pp. 525–552 (1936); **60**, pp. 71–85, 303–321 (1936); **62**, pp. 21–65 (1937); **65**, pp. 313–383 (1938); **69**, pp. 297–345 (1939); **72**, pp. 255–311 (1940). Tenthredo, **1**, pp. 9–32 (1936).
Chironomidæ and Ceratopogonidæ (Micronesia). Philippine Jour. Sci., **71**, pp. 205–230 (1940).
TOWNES, H. K. Tendipedini (Nearctic). American Midl. Nat., **34**, pp. 1–206 (1945).
VIMMER, A. Pelopini (Europe). Acta Soc. Sci. Nat. Morav., **4**, pp. 41–84 (1927). (In Czech)
WALLEY, G. S. Tanypus. Canadian Ent., **57**, pp. 271–278 (1926). Ann. Ent. Soc. America, **21**, pp. 581–592 (1928).
WIRTH, W. W. Clunione Midges. Univ. California Publ. Ent., **8**, pp. 151–182 (1949).
Thalassomyia and Telmatogeton. Proc. Hawaiian Ent. Soc., **13**, pp. 117–191 (1947).
WUNDSCH, H. Tendipedid Larvæ. S. B. Ges. Naturf. Freunde, **1942**, pp. 33–58 (1943).
ZAVREL, J. Chironomid Metamorphosis. Acta Soc. Sci. Nat. Morav., **3**, fasc. 8, pp. 251–282 (1926). (In Czech)
Chironomids in Radesina. Sbornik Klubu Prir., **8**, pp. 93–102 (1926).
Chironomiden aus Wigry-See. Arch. Hydrobiol., **17**, pp. 195–220 (1926).
Chironomid Larvæ and Pupæ. Acta Soc. Sci. Morav., **4**, pp. 85–95 (1927); **11**, no. 10, pp. 1–29 (1939); **13**, no. 7, pp. 10–28 (1941). Zpravy Kom. Prir. Vyzk. Moravy, **18**, 52 pp. (1929). (In Czech)

Corynoneuriariæ, Early Stages. Arch. Hydrobiol., 19, pp. 651–665 (1928).

Tanypodinæ Larvæ and Pupæ (Sumatra). Arch. Hydrobiol. Suppl., 11, pp. 604–624 (1933).

Chironomid Larvæ from Caves. Arch. Hydrobiol., 40, pp. 250–264 (1943).

Ablabesmyia. Bull. Inst. Acad. Prague, 44, pp. 225–237 (1944).

Brillia. Vestn. Ceske Zool. Spolec., 9, pp. 182–196 (1944). (In Czech)

ZAVREL, J., and A. THIENEMANN. Metamorphose der Tanypinen. Arch. Hydrobiol. Suppl., 2, pp. 566–654 (1916); 655–784 (1921).

CERATOPOGONIDÆ

CARTER, H. F., A. INGRAM, and J. W. S. MACFIE. Ceratopogoninæ (Gold Coast). Ann. Trop. Med., 14, pp. 187–274, 309–331 (1920); 15, pp. 177–212 (1921).

COLAÇO, A. T. F. Culicoides (Transvaal). An. Inst. Med. Trop. Lisbon, 3, pp. 217–266 (1946).

COSTA LIMA, A. DA. Culicoides (Neotropical). Mem. Inst. Oswaldo Cruz, 32, pp. 411–422 (1937).

DE MEILLON, B. Ceratopogonidæ. Pub. South African Inst. Med. Res., 38, pp. 136–207 (1936).

Ceratopogonidæ (South Africa). Jour. Ent. Soc. South Africa, 1, pp. 9–25; 2, pp. 7–17 (1939). Trans. Roy. Ent. Soc. London, 90, pp. 455–466 (1940).

DOVE, W. E., D. G. HALL, and J. B. HULL. Salt Marsh Sand Fly Problem. Ann. Ent. Soc. America, 25, pp. 505–527 (1932).

EDWARDS, F. W. Ceratopogonidæ (Britain). Trans. Ent. Soc. London, 74, pp. 389–426 (1926).

FLOCH, H., and E. ABONNENC. Ceratopogonidæ (French Guiana). Publ. Inst. Pasteur Guyane, 1942, no. 37, 10 pp.; no. 42, 4 pp.; no. 55, 6 pp. (1942).

FOX, I. Culicoides (Caribbean). Ann. Ent. Soc. America, 39, pp. 248–258 (1946).

GOETGHEBUER, M. Ceratopogoninæ (Belgium). Mem. Mus. R. Hist. Nat. Belgique, 8, fasc. 3, 116 pp. (1920).

Catalogue of Ceratopogonidæ (Belgium). Bull. Ann. Ent. Soc. Belgique, 73, pp. 363–372 (1933).

Ceratopogonidæ (Belgian Congo). Expl. Parc Nat. Albert, 55, 21 pp. (1948).

GOETGHEBUER, M., and F. LENZ. Heleidæ. Fliegen Palæarkt. Region, 13a, pp. 1–133 (1934).

HILL, M. A. Culicoides, Life Cycle. Ann. Trop. Med. Parasitol., 41, pp. 55–115 (1947).

HOFFMAN, W. A. Culicoides. American Jour. Hyg., 5, pp. 274–301 (1925).

INGRAM, A., and J. W. S. MACFIE. Ceratopogoninæ (West Africa). Ann. Trop. Med. Parasitol., 15, pp. 313–347 (1921); 16, pp. 243–282 (1922); 18, pp. 377–392, 533–593 (1924).

Ceratopogoninæ (Nyasaland). Bull. Ent. Res., 15, pp. 283–288 (1925).

Ceratopogonidæ (Patagonia). Diptera of Patagonia and South Chile, 2, fasc. 1, pp. 155–232, British Mus. (1931).

Ceratopogonidæ (New Zealand). Ann. Trop. Med. Parasitol., 25, pp. 195–209 (1931).

JOHANNSEN, O. A. Ceratopogoninæ (Malaya). Arch. Hydrobiol. Suppl., 9, pp. 403–448 (1931).
Ceratopogoninæ of Americas. Ann. Ent. Soc. America, 36, pp. 761–791 (1944).

KIEFFER, J. J. Ceratopogonidæ (Europe). Ann. Soc. Sci. Bruxelles, 41, pp. 230–238 (1922).
Ceratopogonidæ (Java). Ibid., 43, pp. 134–143 (1923).
Ceratopogon (Sahara). Arch. Inst. Pasteur Algérie, 1, pp. 654–683 (1923).
Ceratopogonidæ (Europe). Ibid., 2, pp. 391–408 (1924); 3, pp. 405–430 (1925); 4, pp. 96–107 (1926).
Ceratopogonidæ (France). Faune de France, 11, 139 pp. (1925).

KONO, H., and H. TAKAHASI. Culicoides (Japan). Ins. Matsumurana, 14, pp. 69–77 (1940).

LANE, J. Clinohelia (Neotropical). Rev. Ent. Rio Janeiro, 15, pp. 249–261 (1944).
Ceratopogonidæ (Neotropical). Ibid., 16, pp. 357–372 (1945); 17, pp. 202–215 (1946); 18, pp. 197–214, 438–447 (1947).
Forcipomyia and Culicoides. Arq. Fac. Hig. Saude Publ., 1, pp. 159–170 (1947).

LEE, D. J. Australasian Ceratopogonidæ. Proc. Linn. Soc. New South Wales, 72, pp. 313–356 (1947); 73, pp. 57–70 (1948).

LENZ, F. Ceratopogoninæ (Dutch East Indies). Arch. Hydrobiol., 12, pp. 196–223 (1933).

LUTZ, A. Ceratopogoninæ (Brazil). Ibid., 4, pp. 1–33 (1912); 5, pp. 45–73 (1913); 6, pp. 81–99 (1914).

MACFIE, J. W. S. Ceratopogonidæ. Ann. Mag. Nat. Hist., (10) 9, pp. 485–499 (1932).
Biting Midges (New Zealand). Ann. Trop. Med. Parasitol., 26, pp. 23–53 (1932).
Ceratopogonidæ from Wings of Dragon Flies. Tijdschr. Ent., 75, pp. 265–283 (1932).
Ceratopogonidæ (Malaya). Ann. Trop. Med. Parasitol., 28, pp. 177–195, 279–293 (1934).
Ceratopogonidæ (Sumatra). Tijdschr. Ent., 77, pp. 202–231 (1934).
Ceratopogonidæ (Society Isl.). Bull. Bishop Mus., 113, pp. 75–80 (1935).
Ceratopogonidæ (Marquesas Isl.). Ibid., 114, pp. 93–103 (1935).
Ceratopogonidæ (Trinidad). Ann. Mag. Nat. Hist., (10) 20, pp. 1–18 (1937).
Ceratopogonidæ. Ruwenzori Exped., 1, pp. 81–107, British Mus., (1939).
Ceratopogonidæ (New Guinea). Proc. Linn. Soc. New South Wales, 64, pp. 356–368 (1939).
Ceratopogonidæ (Brazil). Rev. Ent. Rio Janeiro, 10, pp. 137–219, 481–482 (1939).
Ceratopogonidæ. Trans. Roy. Ent. Soc. London, 89, pp. 1–12 (1939).
Ceratopogonidæ. Ann. Trop. Med. Parasitol., 34, pp. 13–30 (1940).

Ceratopogonidæ (British Guiana, Trinidad). Proc. Roy. Ent. Soc. London (B), **9**, pp. 179–195 (1940).
Ceratopogonidæ (Egypt). Ibid., **12**, pp. 145–159 (1943).
Culicoides (Mexico). Ann. Trop. Med. Parasitol., **42**, pp. 67–87 (1948).
MAYER, K. Ceratopogonidæ, Metamorphosis. Arch. Hydrobiol. Suppl., **13**, pp. 166–202 (1934). Arch. Naturges., **3**, pp. 205–288 (1934).
OKADA, T. Biting Midges. Jour. Coll. Agric. Imp. Univ. Tokyo, **15**, pp. 13–31 (1941).
PAINTER, R. H. Ceratopogonidæ (Honduras). Ann. Rept. Med. Dept. United Fruit Co., **15**, pp. 245–262 (1926).
PEREIRA BARRETTO, M. Culicoides. An. Fac. Med. Univ. São Paulo, **20**, pp. 89–105 (1944).
RIETH, J. T. VON. Metamorphosis of Ceratopogoninæ. Arch. Hydrobiol. Suppl., **2**, pp. 377–443 (1915).
ROOT, F. M., and W. A. HOFFMAN. Culicoides (North America). American Jour. Hyg., **25**, pp. 150–176 (1937).
SAUNDERS, L. G. Forcipomyia, Life History. Parasitol., **16**, pp. 164–213 (1924).
SIMOES BARBOSA, F. A. Culicoides (Neotropical). An. Soc. Biol. Pernambuco, **7**, pp. 3–30 (1947).
SMITH, L. M., and H. LOWE. Ceratopogon (California). Hilgardia, **18**, pp. 157–183 (1948).
SOOT-RYEN, T. List of Heleidæ (Norway). Arsh. Mus. Tromsø, **64**, pp. 1–9 (1943).
THIENEMANN, A. Dasyhelea, Larvæ and Pupæ. Mitt. Geogr. Ges. Lübeck, (2) **31**, pp. 102–126 (1926).
THOMSEN, L. Ceratopogonidæ (New York). Jour. New York Ent. Soc., **43**, pp. 283–296 (1935).
Ceratopogonidæ. Mem. Cornell Univ. Agric. Exp. Sta., **210**, pp. 57–80 (1937).
TOKUNAGA, M. Palpomyia and Bezzia. Tenthredo, **2**, pp. 273–313 (1939).
Ceratopogonidæ (Japan). Ibid., **3**, pp. 58–186 (1940).
Ceratopogonidæ (Caroline Isl.). Annot. Zool. Japonenses, **20**, pp. 109–119 (1941).
VARGAS, L. Culicoides, Catalogue. Rev. Soc. Mexicana Hist. Nat., **10**, pp. 191–218 (1950).
VIMMER, A. Ceratopogoninæ. Sbornik Ent. Odd. Nar. Mus., **10**, pp. 130–144 (1932). (In Czech)
WATERSTON, J. Sand-flies, Bionomics. Ann. Trop. Med. Parasitol., **16**, pp. 69–92 (1922).
WIRTH, W. W. Probezzia (North America). Proc. Ent. Soc. Washington, **53**, pp. 25–34 (1951).
Culicoides (Alaska). Ann. Ent. Soc. America, **44**, pp. 75–86 (1951).
ZILAHI-SABESS, G. Heleidæ (Hungary). Acta Univ. Szeges Biol., **4**, pp. 39–45 (1936). Arb. Ungarisches Biol. Forsch. Ins., **8**, pp. 196–206 (1936). Folia Ent. Hungarica, **5**, pp. 10–133 (1940). (In Magyar)

THAUMALEIDÆ

BEZZI, M. Taumaleidi italiano. Boll. Lab. Zool. Gen. Agr., **7**, pp. 227–266 (1913).

COLLART, A. Thaumaleidæ de Belgique. Bull. Mus. Roy. Hist. Nat. Belgique, 21, fasc. 5, 8 pp. (1945).

DYAR, H. G., and R. C. SHANNON. Thaumaleidæ (North America). Jour. Washington Acad. Sci., 14, pp. 432–434 (1924).

EDWARDS, F. W. Thaumaleidæ. Zool. Anz., 82, pp. 121–142 (1929).

LINDNER, E. Thaumaleidæ. Fliegen Palæarkt. Region, 3, 16 pp. (1930).

SIMULIIDÆ

ABREU, E. S. Melusinidæ (Canary Isl.). Mem. R. Acad. Cienc. Barcelona, 17, 48 pp. (1922).

D'ANDRETTA, C., and M. A. V. Simulium (Neotropical). Mem. Inst. Oswaldo Cruz, 43, pp. 85–152 (1945); 44, pp. 401–412 (1946); 45, pp. 667–677 (1947). Pap. Avulsos, Dept. Zool., São Paulo, 8, no. 2, pp. 23–37 (1947); 8, no. 13, pp. 145–180 (1947). Arq. Zool. São Paulo, 5, pp. 637–647 (1948). Rev. brasil. Biol., 9, pp. 55–66 (1949).

BARANOFF, N. Serbian Simuliidæ. Neue Beitr. Syst. Ins., 3, pp. 161–164, 183–194 (1926).

BEQUAERT, J. Simuliidæ (Guatemala). Dept. Trop. Med. Harvard, 6, pp. 175–224 (1934).
    Simuliidæ (Belgian Congo). American Jour. Trop. Med. Suppl., 18, pp. 116–136 (1938).

BRADT, S. Puerto Rican Black Flies. Puerto Rico Jour. Pub. Health Trop. Med., 8, pp. 69–78 (1932).

BRICENO-IRAGORRY, L. Simuliidæ (Venezuela). Bol. Lab. Clin. L. Razetti, Caracas, 2, pp. 110–116 (1941).

DALMAT, H. T. New Simuliidæ (Guatemala). Ann. Ent. Soc. America, 42, pp. 538–553 (1949); 43, pp. 137–151 (1950); 44, pp. 31–58 (1951).

DE MEILLON, B. Ethiopian Simuliidæ. Bull. Ent. Res., 21, pp. 185–200 (1930).
    Simuliidæ and Ceratopogonidæ (Mozambique). Estaç. Anti-Malar., 27 pp. (1943).

DOROGOSTAISKII, V. et al. Black flies in Eastern Siberia. Mag. Parasitol., 5, pp. 107–204 (1935). (In Russian)

DRUMMOND, F. H. N. West Australian Simuliidæ. Jour. Roy. Soc. West Australia, 18, pp. 1–12 (1933).

DYAR, H. G., and R. C. SHANNON. Simuliidæ (North America). Proc. U. S. Nat. Mus., 69, art. 10, 54 pp. (1927).

EDWARDS, F. W. British Simuliidæ. Ent. Mon. Mag., 51, pp. 305–309 (1915). Bull. Ent. Res., 6, pp. 23–42 (1915); 11, pp. 211–246 (1920).
    Simuliidæ (Patagonia). Diptera of Patagonia and South Chile, 2, fasc. 1, pp. 121–154, British Mus. (1931).
    Simuliidæ (Java, Sumatra). Arch. Hydrobiol. Suppl., 13, pp. 92–138 (1934).

EMERY, W. T. Simulium. Kansas Univ. Sci. Bull., 8, pp. 323–362 (1914).

ENDERLEIN, G. Simuliidæ. Zool. Anz., 53, pp. 43–46 (1921).
    Simuliidæ (Palæarctic). S. B. Ges. Naturf. Freunde, 1920, pp. 212–224 (1921).
    Distribution of Simuliidæ. Zool. Anz., 62, pp. 201–211 (1925).
    Cnetha. Wiener Ent. Ztg., 46, pp. 73–78 (1929).

Classification of Simuliidæ. Arch. Klassif. Phylogen. Ent., 1, pp. 77–97 (1930). Deutsche Ent. Zeitschr., 1933, pp. 273–292 (1934). Kriebelmücken (Leinegebietes). Arch. Wiss. Prakt. Tierheilk., 63, pp. 475–528 (1931).

FAIRCHILD, G. B. Simuliidæ (Panama). Ann. Ent. Soc. America, 33, pp. 701–719 (1940).

FROST, S. W. Simuliidæ (Pennsylvania). Ent. News, 60, pp. 129–133 (1949).

GIBBINS, E. G. Ethiopian Simuliidæ. Trans. Roy. Ent. Soc. London, 81, pp. 37–51 (1933); 82, pp. 51–97 (1934). East African Med. Jour., 18, pp. 210–218 (1941).
Simuliidæ (Congo). Ann. Trop. Med. Parasitol., 30, pp. 133–150 (1936).
Simuliidæ (Uganda). Trans. Roy. Ent. Soc. London, 85, pp. 217–242 (1936). Bull. Ent. Res., 28, pp. 289–309 (1937).
Simuliidæ. Ruwenzori Exped. 1934–35, 1, pp. 11–27, British Mus. (1939).

GRENIER, P. Simuliidæ of France. Physiol. Comp. Oecol., 1, pp. 165–330 (1949).

GRENIER, P., and J. DOUCET. Simulies de Madagascar. Mem. Inst. Sci. Madagascar, (A), 3, pp. 301–323 (1949).

HEARLE, E. Black Flies (British Columbia). Proc. Ent. Soc. British Columbia, 1932, pp. 5–19.

HOFFMANN, C. C. Simulidos (Chiapas). An. Inst. Biol. Univ. Mexico, 1, pp. 293–306 (1930).

IRIARTE, D. R. Simuliidæ (Venezuela). Bol. Lab. Clin. L. Razetti, Caracas, 14, pp. 333–347; 15, pp. 401–482 (1946).

JOBBINS-POMEROY, A. W. Simulium, Bibliography. Bull. U. S. Dept. Agr., 329, 48 pp. (1916).

JOHANNSEN, O. A. Simulidæ (U. S.). Bull. New York State Mus., 68, pp. 336–388 (1903).

KNAB, F. Simuliidæ (North Chile). An. Zool. Aplic., 1, pp. 17–22 (1914).
Simuliidæ (Peru). Proc. Biol. Soc. Washington, 27, pp. 81–86, 123–124 (1914).

LANE, J., and C. E. PORTO. Simulideos (Neotropical). Bol. Biol. São Paulo, 4, pp. 168–176 (1939).

LANE, J., and M. A. VULCANO. Simulideos, Buccal Armature. Rev. Ent. Rio Janeiro, 14, pp. 430–440 (1943).

LEÓN, J. R. DE. Simúlidos (Guatemala). 12 pp., Guatemala (1945); 23 pp. (1948).

LEWIS, D. J. Simuliidæ (Sudan). Trans. Roy. Ent. Soc. London, 99, pp. 475–496 (1948).

LUNDSTRÖM, C. Melusinidæ (Finland). Acta Soc. Faun. Fl. Fennica, 34, no. 12, 24 pp. (1911).

LUTZ, A. Simulium (Brazil). Mem. Inst. Oswaldo Cruz, 1, pp. 124–146 (1909); 2, pp. 213–266 (1910).

MACKERRAS, M. J. and I. M. Simuliidæ (Queensland). Australian Jour. Sci. Res., 1, pp. 231–270 (1948).
Simuliidæ (Australasia). Proc. Linn. Soc. New South Wales, 73, pp. 372–405 (1948).

MALLOCH, J. R. American Black Flies. U. S. Dept. Agr. Bur. Ent. Tech. Bull., 26, 71 pp. (1914).

Meeser, C. C. V. Simuliidæ (North Rhodesia). Proc. Rhodesian Sci. Assoc., 39, pp. 28–42 (1942).

Metcalf, C. L. Black flies (Adirondacks). Bull. New York State Mus. 289, pp. 1–78 (1932).

Nicholson, H. P., and C. E. Mickel. Blackflies (Minnesota). Tech. Bull. Minnesota Exp. Sta., 192, 64 pp. (1950).

O'Kane, W. C. Simuliidæ, Bionomics. Tech. Bull. New Hampshire Exp. Sta., 32, 24 pp. (1926).

Petersen, A. Natural History of Danish Simuliidæ. Skr. Kgl. Danske Vidensk. Selsk. Naturv. Math. Afd., (8) 5, pp. 237–339 (1924).

Pinto, C. Simulidæ (Central and South America). 7 Reun. Soc. Argentina Patagonia Reg. Norte, pp. 661–763 (1932).

Porto, C. E. Simulideos (Neotropical). Bol. Biol. brasil, 4, pp. 369–373 (1939).

Puri, I. M. Life History of Simuliidæ. Parasitol., 17, pp. 295–369 (1925).

Roubaud, E., and P. Grenier. Simulium (West Africa). Bull. Soc. Path. Exot., 36, pp. 281–311 (1943).

Rubtzov, I. A. Simuliidæ, Biology. Mag. Parasitol. Leningrad, 6, pp. 169–200 (1936). (In Russian)
    Simuliidæ (USSR). Moscow Inst. Zool. Acad. Sci., 23, 533 pp. (1940). (In Russian.)

Séguy, E. Simulium (Central Europe). Eos, 1, pp. 231–238 (1925).

Shiraki, T. Simuliidæ (Japanese Empire). Mem. Fac. Sci. Agr. Taihoku, 16, 90 pp. (1935).

Smart, J. Simuliidæ (British Guiana, Lesser Antilles). Trans. Roy. Ent. Soc. London, 90, pp. 1–11 (1940).
    British Simuliidæ. Sci. Publ. Freshwater Biol. Assoc., 9, 57 pp. (1944).
    Simuliidæ, Classification. Trans. Roy. Ent. Soc. London, 95, pp. 463–528 (1945).

Smith, L. M., and H. Lowe. Black Gnats (California). Hilgardia, 18, pp. 157–183 (1948).

Stains, G. S., and G. F. Knowlton. Simuliidæ (Western U. S.). Ann. Ent. Soc. America, 36, pp. 259–280 (1943).

Tonnoir, A. L. Australasian Simuliidæ. Bull. Ent. Res., 15, pp. 213–255 (1925).

Tucker, E. S. Blackflies in Louisiana. Trans. Kansas Acad. Sci., 29, pp. 65–75 (1920).

Twinn, C. R. Blackflies (Eastern Canada). Canadian Jour. Res., 14, pp. 97–150 (1936).
    Blackflies (Utah, Idaho). Canadian Ent., 70, pp. 48–55 (1938).

Ussing, H. Simulier's Naturhistorie. Vidensk. Medd. Dansk. Nat. For., 80, pp. 517–541 (1925).

Vargas, L. Simúlidos Mexicanos. Rev. Inst. Salubr. Enferm. Trop., 2, pp. 115–122 (1941); 3, pp. 229–250 (1942).
    Simúlidos (Neotropical). Rev. Soc. Mexicana Hist. Nat., 4, pp. 135–146 (1943); 6, pp. 71–82 (1945). 251 pp., Inst. Salubr. Enferm. Trop., Mexico (1945).

Vargas, L., and A. Diaz Najera. Simúlidos de Mexico. Rev. Inst. Salubr. Enferm. Trop., 7, pp. 99–192 (1946); 9, pp. 65–79, 321–369 (1948); 10, pp. 283–319 (1949).

WHARTON, R. H. Simulidæ (New Guinea). Proc. Linn. Soc. New South Wales, **72**, pp. 357–366 (1948).

WU, YI FANG. Simulium, Biology. Pap. Michigan Acad. Sci., **13**, pp. 543–599 (1931).

ZAHAR, A. R. Black-flies, Ecology (Scotland). Jour. Animal Ecol., **20**, pp. 33–62 (1951).

BLEPHAROCERIDÆ AND DEUTEROPHLEBIIDÆ

BARNARD, K. H. Blepharoceridæ (South Africa). Jour. Ent. Soc. South Africa, **10**, pp. 3–15 (1947).

BEZZI, M. Blefaroceridæ (Italy). Bull. Soc. Ent. Italiana, **44**, pp. 1–144 (1913).
Blefaroceridæ (New Zealand). Ibid., **45**, pp. 115–129 (1914).

BISCHOFF, W. Liponeura (Belgium). Zool. Anz., **58**, pp. 253–261 (1924); **59**, pp. 250–281 (1924).
Blepharoceridæ, Early Stages. Ibid., **60**, pp. 231–251 (1924).
Blepharoceridæ (Palæarctic). Ergebn. Zool., Jena, **7**, pp. 209–278 (1926).
Zool. Jahrb. Syst., **54**, pp. 449–466 (1928). Zool. Anz., **92**, pp. 9–17 (1930).

BRODSKII, K. Blepharoceridæ. Zool. Anz., **90**, pp. 129–146 (1930). Trav. Inst. Zool. Acad. Sci. URSS, **4**, pp. 71–105 (1937). (In Russian)
Deuterophlebia. Zeitschr. Morph. Oekol. Tiere, **18**, pp. 289–321 (1930).

CAMPBELL, J. W. Blepharoceridæ (New Zealand). Trans. New Zealand Inst., **53**, pp. 258–288 (1921); **54**, pp. 260–264 (1923).

EDWARDS, F. W. Deuterophlebiidæ. Ann. Mag. Nat. Hist., (9) **9**, pp. 379–387 (1922).
Blepharoceridæ (Patagonia). Diptera of Patagonia and South Chile, **2**, fasc. 2, pp. 33–75, British Mus. (1929).

HOFENEDER, H. Larven der Blepharoceriden. Verh. zool.-bot. Ges. Wien, **77**, pp. 82–98 (1927).

KELLOGG, V. L. Blepharoceridæ (North America). Proc. California Acad. Sci., **3**, sec. Zool. 3, pp. 187–226 (1903).
Blepharoceridæ. Gen. Insectorum, **56**, 15 pp. (1907).

KITAKAMI, S. Blepharoceridæ (Japan). Mem. Coll. Sci. Kyoto, B **6**, pp. 53–108 (1931); **12**, pp. 115–136 (1937); **14**, pp. 341–351 (1938).
Deuterophlebiidæ (Japan). Annot. Zool. Japonenses, **17**, pp. 487–513 (1938).
Blepharoceridæ (Formosa). Mem. Coll. Sci. Kyoto, B **16**, pp. 59–74 (1941).

KOMAREK, J. Blepharoceridæ (Jugoslavia). Acta Ent. Jugosl., **5–6**, pp. 8–22 (1932).

KOMAREK, J., and A. VIMMER. Blepharocerid Larvæ (Europe). Ann. Biol. Lacustre, **11**, pp. 63–77 (1922).
Blepharoceridæ (Balkans). Mitt. Naturw. Inst. Sofia, **7**, pp. 1–35 (1934).

LINDNER, E. Blepharoceridæ and Deuterophlebiidæ. Fliegen Palaearkt. Reg., **2**, 36 pp. (1930).

LUTZ, A. Blepharoceridæ (Brazil). Mem. Inst. Oswaldo Cruz, **12**, pp. 16–43 (1920).

MANNHEIMS, B. J. Blepharoceridæ, Biology and Morphology. 115 pp. Noske, Leipzig (1935).

Blepharoceridæ, Synonymy. Mitt. Deutsche Ent. Ges., **7**, pp. 90–96 (1937); **9**, pp. 57–63 (1939).
Pennak, R. W. Deuterophlebiidæ. American Mus. Novit., **1276**, 10 pp. (1945).
Tillyard, R. J. Blepharoceridæ (Australia). Australian Zool., **2**, pp. 159–172 (1922). New Zealand Jour. Sci. Tech., **5**, pp. 101–107 (1922).
Tonnoir, A. L. Blepharoceridæ. Australian Zool., **3**, pp. 47–59, 135–142 (1923).
    Blepharoceridæ (Tasmania). Ann. Biol. Lacustre, **13**, pp. 5–69 (1924).
    Blepharocerid Larvæ and Pupæ (India). Rec. Indian Mus., **32**, pp. 161–214 (1930); **34**, pp. 269–275 (1932).
Vimmer, A., and J. Komarek. Larvæ of Blepharoceridæ. Casopis Praze, **18**, pp. 37–55 (1921).
Walley, G. S. Blepharoceridæ. Canadian Ent., **59**, pp. 112–115 (1927).
Yie, S. Deuterophlebia (Japan). Trans. Nat. Hist. Soc. Formosa, **23**, pp. 271–296 (1933).

SILVICOLOIDEA

Correa, R. R. Olbiogaster (Neotropical). Livro homenagem, d'Almeida, Soc. brasil. Ent., São Paulo, **12**, pp. 141–148 (1946).
    Anisopodidæ (South America). Pap. Avulsos, Dept. Zool., São Paulo, **8**, no. 8, pp. 97–107 (1947).
Edwards, F. W. Anisopodidæ. Ann. Mag. Nat. Hist., (9) **12**, pp. 475–493 (1923).
    Anisopus (Europe). Ent. Mon. Mag., **62**, p. 113 (1926).
    Anisopodidæ (Sumatra). Tijdschr. Ent., **74**, pp. 262–280 (1931).
Edwards, F. W., and D. Keilin. Protorhyphidæ, Anisopodidæ, Pachyneuridæ and Trichoceridæ. Gen. Insectorum, **190**, 41 pp. (1928).
Kertesz, K. Rhyphidæ. Ter'mészetr. Füzet., **25**, pp. 4–6 (1902).
Lindner, E. Phryneidæ, Petauristidæ. Fliegen Palæarkt. Reg. **1a, 1b**, pp. 1–22 (1930).
Müller, M. Rhyphus und Mycetobia, Larvæ. Arch. Naturg., **88**, A, Heft 2, 44 pp. (1922).
Okada, I. Phryneidæ and Pachyneuridæ (Japan). Jour. Fac. Agric. Hokkaido Imp. Univ., **42**, pp. 221–238 (1938).

MYCETOPHILIDÆ, s. lat.

Abreu, E. S. Fungivoridæ (Canary Isl.). Mem. R. Acad. Cienc. Barcelona, **16**, 154 pp. (1920).
Coher, E. I. Mycomyia (Neotropical). Rev. Ent. Rio Janeiro, **21**, pp. 561–580 (1950).
Czizek, K. Epidapus. Wiener Ent. Ztg., **34**, pp. 365–377 (1915); **36**, pp. 283–291 (1921).
Edwards, F. W. Mycetobia, Systematic Position. Ann. Mag. Nat. Hist. (8) **17**, pp. 108–115 (1916).
    Ditomyinæ. Ibid. (9) **7**, pp. 431–436 (1921).
    British Fungus-gnats. Trans. Roy. Ent. Soc. London, **1924**, pp. 505–669 (1925). Ent. Mon. Mag., **77**, pp. 21–32, 67–82 (1941).

Mycetophilidæ and Bibionidæ (South Africa). Ann. South African Mus., **19**, pp. 601–616 (1925).

Ceroplatinæ (Australia). Proc. Linn. Soc. New South Wales, **54**, pp. 162–175 (1929).

Mycetophilidæ (Neotropical). Rev. Ent. Rio Janeiro, **2**, pp. 138–149 (1932); **3**, pp. 303–322 (1933); **4**, pp. 354–372 (1934); **11**, pp. 440–465 (1940).

Neoempheria (Neotropical). Novit. Zool., **42**, pp. 107–130 (1940).

Mycetophilidæ (Matto Grosso). Rev. Ent. Rio Janeiro, **12**, pp. 303–314 (1941).

EDWARDS, F. W., and D. KEILIN. Pachyneuridæ. Gen. Insectorum, **190**, pp. 27–29 (1928).

ENDERLEIN, G. Lycoridæ. Arch. Naturg., **77**, Band 1, Suppl. 3, pp. 116–201 (1911).

Mycetophilidæ (Indian Ocean). Trans. Linn. Soc. London, (2) **14**, pp. 59–81 (1910).

Sciaridæ (Indain Ocean). Percy Sladen Exped., **4**, no. 13, pp. 181–194 (1912).

Sciaridæ and Scatopsidæ. Zool. Anz., **40**, pp. 261–282 (1912).

FISHER, E. G. Fungus gnats. Jour. New York Ent. Soc., **45**, pp. 387–400 (1937). Trans. American Ent. Soc., **64**, pp. 195–200 (1938).

Costa Rican Mycetophilidæ. Ibid., **65**, pp. 227–236 (1939).

Ditomyiinæ, Diadocidiinæ and Ceroplatinæ. Ibid., **67**, pp. 275–301 (1941).

FREY, R. Sciaridæ. Notulæ Ent., **22**, pp. 5–44 (1942); **27**, pp. 33–112 (1948).

JOHANNSON, O. A. Fungus-gnats (North America). Bull. Maine Agr. Exp. Sta., **172, 180, 196, 200**, 308 pp. (1909–1912).

Mycetophilidæ. Gen. Insectorum, **93**, 141 pp. (1909).

LACKSCHEWITZ, P. Fungivoriden (East Baltic). Arb. Naturf. Ver., **21**, pp. 1–47 (1937).

LANDROCK, K. Bolitophila. Berliner Ent. Zeitschr., **57**, pp. 33–51 (1912).

Pilzmücken Mährens. Zeitschr. Mähr. Landesmus., **12**, pp. 273–322 (1912); **14**, pp. 14–93 (1914); **15**, pp. 59–66 (1916); **17**, pp. 17–75 (1919); Wiener Ent. Ztg., **40**, pp. 163–171 (1923).

Macroccra. Ibid., **36**, pp. 67–102 (1917).

Mycetophilidæ (Europe). Ibid., **37**, pp. 55–72, 107–120 (1918).

Cordyla (Palæarctic). Konowia, **5**, pp. 64–69, 200–204 (1926).

Mycetophilidæ (Palæarctic). Fliegen Palæarkt. Reg., **8**, 196 pp. (1926–1927).

Fungivora. Cas. Morav. Mus. Zem., Brno, **27**, pp. 441–466 (1932).

Mycetophilidæ. Tierwelt Deutschlands, **38**, 166 pp. (1940).

LANE, J. Mycetophilidæ (Brazil). Rev. Ent. Rio Janeiro, **17**, pp. 339–360 (1947); **18**, pp. 448–458 (1947); **19**, pp. 231–278 (1948). Rev. brasil. Biol., **8**, pp. 247–254 (1948).

Ceroplatinæ (Neotropical). Rev. Ent. Rio Janeiro, **19**, pp. 437–458 (1948). Dusenia, Curitiba, **1**, pp. 23–69, 139–144 (1950).

Leia (Brazil). Rev. brasil. Biol., **10**, pp. 121–131 (1950).

LENGERSDORF, F. Sciaridæ of Wien Museum. Konowia, **5**, pp. 122–129, 247–255 (1926). Wiener Ent. Ztg., **43**, pp. 31–38 (1926).

Sciaridæ from Formosa. Supplementa Ent., **16**, pp. 104–108 (1927).

Lycoriidæ. Fliegen Palæarkt. Reg., **7**, 71 pp. (1928–1930).
Lycoriden (Mexico). Arb. Morph. Taxon. Ent., **11**, pp. 123–130 (1944).
LENGERSDORF, F., and R. LERUTH. Mycetophilidæ cavernicoles. Bull. Mus. Roy. Hist. Nat. Belgique, **16**, pp. 1–24 (1940).
LUNDSTRÖM, C. Mycetophilidæ (Finland). Acta Soc. Faun. Fl. Fennica, **29**, 50 pp. (1906); **32**, 67 pp. (1909); **39**, 24 pp. (1914).
Mycetophilidæ (Europe). Ann. Mus. Nat. Hungarici, **9**, pp. 390–419 (1911); **10**, pp. 514–522 (1912); **11**, pp. 305–322 (1913).
MADWAR, S. Mycetophilidæ, Immature Stages. Philos. Trans. (B), **227**, pp. 1–110 (1937).
MANSBRIDGE, G. H. Biology of Ceroplatinæ and Macrocerinæ. Trans. Roy. Ent. Soc. London, **81**, pp. 75–92 (1933).
NIELSEN, P. Danish Fungus-gnats. Ent. Medd., **23**, pp. 120–131 (1943).
OKADA, I. Bolitophilinæ (Japan). Insecta Matsumurana, **9**, pp. 12–18 (1934).
Fungivoridæ (Honshu). Tenthredo, **3**, pp. 24–44 (1940).
Pilzmücken (Japan). Jour. Fac. Agr. Hokkaido Imp. Univ., **42**, pp. 267–335 (1939).
PETTEY, F. W. Sciara. Ann. Ent. Soc. America, **11**, pp. 319–343 (1918).
SCHULZE, R. Mycetophilidenlarven. Zool. Jahrb. Syst., **46**, pp. 433–462 (1924).
SHAW, F. R. Phylogeny of Mycetophilidæ. Ann. Ent. Soc. America, **41**, pp. 189–199 (1948).
SHAW, F., and J. LANE. Neotropical Leia. Rev. brasil. Biol., **10**, pp. 253–256 (1950).
SOOT-RYEN, T. List of Lycoridæ (Norway). Norsk Ent. Tidsskr., **6**, pp. 74–80 (1942).
STACKELBERG, A. A. Macroceratidæ (Europe). Rev. Ent. USSR, **28**, pp. 17–29 (1945). (In Russian)
Fungivoridæ (Leningrad). Ent. Obozr, Moscow, **30**, pp. 94–102 (1948). (In Russian)
STEENBERG, C. M. Phronia. Vidensk. Medd., **78**, 69 pp. (1924).
Phronia Larvæ. Ent. Medd. Copenhagen, **23**, pp. 337–351 (1943).
TOLLETT, R. Ditomyiinæ, Bolitophilinæ (Belgium). Bull. Mus. Roy. Hist. Nat. Belgique, **19**, fasc. 59, 20 pp. (1943).
TONNOIR, A. L. Mycetophilidæ (Australia). Proc. Linn. Soc. New South Wales, **54**, pp. 584–614 (1929).
TONNOIR, A. L., and F. W. EDWARDS. Mycetophilidæ (New Zealand). Trans. Proc. New Zealand Inst., **57**, pp. 747–878 (1927).
VAN DUZEE, M. C. Mycetophilidæ (California, Alaska). Proc. California Acad. Sci., **17**, pp. 31–65 (1928).
VIMMER, A. Lycoriides, with Wingless Females. Bull. Ecole Sup. Agron. Brno, D **3**, 16 pp. (1926).

CECIDOMYIIDÆ

BAGNALL, R. S., and J. W. H. HARRISON. British Cecidomyidæ. Trans. Ent. Soc. London, **1917**, pp. 346–426 (1918).
BARNES, H. F. British Gall-midges of Economic Importance. Jour. South-eastern Agric. Coll., Wye, **24**, pp. 65–146 (1927).
British Gall-midges. Ent. Mon. Mag., **63**, pp. 164–172, 211–221 (1927).
Lestodiplosis (Britain). Ibid., **64**, pp. 68–75, 142–148 (1928).

Biology of Gall-midges. Sci. Progr., **29**, pp. 73–86 (1934).
Check-list of Cecidomyidæ (Oceania). Occ. Pap. British Mus., **13**, pp. 61–66 (1937).
Check-list of Cecidomyidæ (New Zealand). Trans. Roy. Soc. New Zealand, **67**, pp. 115–121 (1937).
Some Gall-midges. Ann. Appl. Biol., **26**, pp. 319–347 (1939).
Gall-midges of Coffee. Rev. Zool. Bot. Africaines, **32**, pp. 324–336 (1939).
Gall-midges of Fruit. Crosby Lockwood, London, 184 pp. (1948).
Gall-midges of Ornamental Plants. Ibid., 165 pp. (1948).
Gall-midges of Trees. Ibid., 270 pp. (1951).

BAUDYS, E. Galls of Moravia. Acta Univ. Agric. Silvicult. Brno, C **43**, pp. 1–64 (1948).

BAYER, E. Zoocecidæ. Cas. Morav. Mus. Zem. Brno, **17–19**, pp. 15–168, 469–529 (1921). (In Czech)

BEUTENMUELLER, W. Gall-producing Insects (New York). American Mus. Jour., **4**, pp. 24–34 (1904).
Cecidomyiidæ. Bull. American Mus. Nat. Hist., **23**, pp. 385–400 (1907).

CALLAN, E. M. Gall-midges (West Indies). Rev. Ent. Rio Janeiro, **11**, pp. 730–758 (1940).

COUDERC, J. Cécidomyie de la violette. Bull. Soc. Hist. Nat. Toulouse, **65**, pp. 193–279 (1933).

DOCTERS VAN LEEUWEN, J. and W. M. Zoocecidia (East Indies). Bot. Gardens, Buitenzorg, 601 pp. (1926).

DOMBROVSKAYA, E. Cecidomyiids (Kamennaja Steppe). Trav. Inst. Zool. Acad. Sci. URSS., **3**, pp. 409–428 (1936). (In Russain)
Cecidomyids (Western USSR). Ibid., **4**, pp. 117–147 (1937).

EDWARDS, F. W. British Lestremiinæ. Proc. Roy. Ent. Soc. London (B), **7**, 66 pp. (1938).

FELT, E. P. Cecidomyiidæ. Bull. New York State Mus., **104, 110, 124, 165, 175, 180, 186, 198, 200, 202, 257,** 1643 pp. (1906–1925).
American Gall-midges. Jour. Econ. Ent., **4**, pp. 451–484, 546–559 (1911).
Itonididæ, Generic Synopsis. Jour. New York Ent. Soc., **19**, pp. 31–62 (1911); **20**, pp. 236–248 (1912).
Gall-midges (New England). Psyche, **20**, pp. 133–147 (1913); **21**, pp. 109–114 (1914).
New Gall-midges. Proc. U. S. Nat. Mus., **48**, pp. 195–211 (1915).
New Gall-midges (Asia). Jour. New York. Ent. Soc., **23**, pp. 173–184 (1915).
Western Gall-midges. Ibid., **24**, pp. 175–196 (1916).
Gall-midges (Philippine). Philippine Jour. Sci. Biol., **13**, pp. 281–324 (1918).
Gall-midges (Java). Treubia, **1**, pp. 139–151 (1921).
Gall-midges (Orient). Lingnan Sci. Jour., **7**, pp. 423–474 (1929).
Plant-galls and Gall-makers. 364 pp., Comstock Publ. Co., Ithaca (1940).
Micromyini (North America). Ent. Americana, **27**, pp. 1–86 (1947).

FORSIUS, J. Cecidomyider i Finland. Notulæ Ent., **2**, pp. 52–57 (1922).

HOUARD, C. Zoocécididies (North Africa). Ann. Soc. Ent. France, **81**, 236 pp. (1912).

Galls in Museum d'Histoire Naturelle, Paris. Marcellia Avellino, **14–24,** 721 pp. (1915–1928). (Mostly botanical).
Oak galls (North America). 549 pp., Libr. Sci. Hermann, Paris (1940).
Galls (U. S. and Mexico). Ann. Ent. Soc. France, **112,** pp. 1–64 (1947).
KAPUSCINSKI, S. Cecidies (Poland). Kosmos, **61,** pp. 137–185 (1936). Trav. Inst. Rech. For. Pologne, (A) **20,** pp. 3–86 (1937). (In Polish)
KIEFFER, J. J. Cecidomyiidæ (Europe, Algeria). Ann. Soc. Ent. France, **69,** pp. 181–472 (1900).
Cecidomyies gallicoles. Ann. Soc. Sci. Bruxelles, **28,** pp. 329–350 (1904). Bull. Soc. Hist. Nat. Metz, **23,** pp. 67–80 (1904).
Cecidomyies xylophiles. Ann. Soc. Sci. Bruxelles, **28,** pp. 367–410 (1904).
Cecidomyidæ (Seychelles). Trans. Linn. Soc. London, (2) **14,** pp. 315–330 (1911).
Cecidomyies. Marcellia Avellino, **11,** pp. 219–235 (1912).
Cecidomyies (East Africa). Bull. Soc. Hist. Nat. Afrique Nord, **5,** pp. 87–114 (1913).
Cecidomyiidæ. Gen. Insectorum, **152,** 346 pp. (1913).
MANI, M. S. Indian Itonididæ. Rec. Indian Mus., **36–38,** 126 pp. (1934–1938). Indian Jour. Ent., **4–7,** 65 pp. (1942–1945).
Gall-midges (India). Bull. Ent. Res., **38,** pp. 439–448 (1947).
MIMEUR, J. M. Zoocecidies du Maroc. Encycl. Ent. (A), **24,** pp. 3–259 (1949).
PAINTER, R. H. Dipterous Gall-makers (Texas). Jour. Kansas Ent. Soc., **8,** pp. 81–97 (1935).
PRITCHARD, A. E. Micromyini. Ent. Americana, **27,** pp. 1–87 (1947).
Catotrichini and Catochini. Ann. Ent. Soc. America, **40,** pp. 662–671 (1948).
Lestremiinæ. Univ. California Publ. Ent., **8,** pp. 239–275 (1951).
RÜBSAAMEN, E. H. Deutsche Gallmücken. Zeitschr. Wiss. Insektenbiol., **7,** 36 pp. (1911); **8,** 29 pp. (1912).
Exotic Gallmücken. S. B. Ges. Naturf. Freunde, **1915,** pp. 431–482.
Oligotropharien und Lasiopterarien. Ibid., **1915,** pp. 485–567.
Asphondylarien (Germany). Ibid., **1916,** pp. 1–12.
Cecidomyid-studien. Ibid., **1917,** pp. 36–99. Deutsche Ent. Zeitschr., **1921,** pp. 33–52.
Gallbildungen. Handb. Ent., **2,** pp. 219–248 (1926).
RÜBSAAMEN, E. H., and H. HEDICKE. Cecidomyiden und ihre Cecidien. Zoologica, **29,** Heft 77, pp. 1–264, 329–350 (1926–1939).
SENIOR-WHITE, R. Catalogue of Indian Cecidomyidæ. Catalogue of Indian Insects, **15,** 23 pp. Calcutta (1928).
TAVARES, J. S. Cecidias Brazileiras. Broteria, **15–21,** 8 pts., 445 pp. (1917–1922).
Cynipides e Cecidomyias (Argentina). Ibid., **20,** pp. 97–158 (1922).
Anadiplosariæ. Marcellia Avellino, **17,** pp. 57–73 (1921).
THOMPSON, W. T., and E. P. FELT. Catalogue of American Galls. 116 pp., Nassau, N. Y. (1915).
WAHLGREN, E. Cecidiologiska. Ent. Tidskr., **65,** pp. 50–121 (1944).

BIBIONIDÆ, HESPERINIDÆ, SCATOPSIDÆ

BRUNETTI, E. Oriental Bibionidæ. Rec. Indian Mus., 27, pp. 443–450 (1925).

DUDA, O. Scatopsidæ. Konowia, 7, pp. 259–297 (1929).
Bibionidæ. Fliegen Palæarkt. Reg., 4, 75 pp. (1930).
Scatopsidæ. Ibid., 5, 62 pp. (1929).

EDWARDS, F. W. Bibionidæ and Scatopsidæ (Britain). Ann. Appl. Biol., 12, pp. 263–275 (1925).
Mycetophilidæ and Bibionidæ (South Africa). Ann. South African Mus., 19, pp. 601–616 (1925).
Bibionidæ, Scatopsidæ, Anisopodidæ (Sumatra). Tijdschr. Ent., 74, pp. 262–280 (1931).
Bibionidæ (Brazil). Ann. Mag. Nat. Hist., (11) 2, pp. 321–330 (1938).

ENDERLEIN, G. Sciaridæ and Scatopsidæ. Zool. Anz., 40, pp. 261–282 (1912).

GOETGHEBUER, M. Scatopsidæ (Belgium). Biol. Jaarb., 12, pp. 22–30 (1945).

HARDY, D. E. New Bibionidæ (Nearctic America). Proc. Utah Acad. Sci., 14, pp. 199–213 (1937).
Plecia (New World). Jour. Kansas Ent. Soc., 13, pp. 15–27 (1940). Canadian Ent., 74, pp. 105–116 (1942).
Philia. Jour. Kansas Ent. Soc., 15, pp. 127–134 (1942); 24, pp. 74–94 (1951).
Bibionidæ (Nearctic). Univ. Kansas Sci. Bull., 30, pp. 367–548 (1945).
Bibionidæ. Ruwenzori Exped. 1934–35, 1, pp. 109–127 British Mus. (1948).
Bibio (Africa). Jour. Kansas Ent. Soc., 23, pp. 137–153 (1950).
Bibionidæ (Pacific). Proc. Hawaiian Ent. Soc., 14, pp. 75–85 (1950); 257–275 (1951).

LUNDSTRÖM, C. Bibionidæ (Finland). Acta Soc. Faun. Fl. Fennica, 33, no. 1, 16 pp. (1910).
Bibionidæ (Palæarctic). Ann. Mus. Nat. Hungarici, 11, pp. 388–397 (1913).

MCATEE, W. L. Scatopsidæ (District of Columbia). Proc. Ent. Soc. Washington, 23, pp. 120–124 (1921).
Bibionidæ (Nearctic). Proc. U. S. Nat. Mus., 60, art. 11, 27 pp. (1921).

MELANDER, A. L. Scatopsidæ (Nearctic). Bull. Washington Agr. Exp. Sta., 130, 21 pp. (1916).

MORRIS, H. M. Bibionidæ, Larvæ and Pupæ. Bull. Ent. Res., 12, pp. 221–232 (1921); 13, pp. 189–195 (1922).

OKADA, I. Bibionidæ (Japan). Jour. Fac. Agric. Hokkaido Imp. Univ., 42, pp. 189–220 (1938).

OUCHI, V. Diptera Sinica, Bibionidæ. Jour, Shanghai Sci. Inst., (3) 4, pp. 289–297 (1940).

SUBORDER BRACHYCERA, DIVISION ORTHORRHAPHA

AUDCENT, H. List of Orthorrhapha of Bristol. Proc. Bristol Nat. Soc., 27, pp. 409–470 (1949).

BECKER, T. Brachycera (East Africa). Voyage Allaud et Jeannel, Paris, pp. 147–190 (1915).

Fauna Faeröensis, Brachycera. Zool. Jahrb. Syst., **39**, pp. 121–134 (1915). Brachycera (South America). Mission Arc. Meridien Amérique Sud, **10**, pp. 163–215 (1919).

BEZZI, M. Brachycera and Athericera (Fiji Isl.). 220 pp. British Mus. (1928).

BRUNETTI, E. Brachycera (British India). Fauna of British India, Diptera, **1**, 401 pp. (1920).

COLE, F. R., J. R. MALLOCH, and W. L. McATEE. Tromoptera (District of Columbia). Proc. Ent. Soc. Washington, **26**, pp. 181–195 (1924).

FREY, R. Neue Brachycera (Finland). Notulæ Ent., **10**, pp. 82–94 (1930); **12**, pp. 81–85 (1932).
Brachycera (Sunda Isl. and North Australia). Rev. Suisse Zool., **41**, pp. 299–339 (1934).
Brachycera (Madeira). Ark. Zool., **31** A, no. 20, 18 pp. (1939).

GRAENICHER, S. Bombyliidæ, Syrphidæ, Conopidæ (Wisconsin). Bull. Wisconsin Nat. Hist. Soc., **8**, pp. 32–44 (1910); **9**, pp. 66–72 (1911).

HARDY, G. H. Some Genera of Australian Brachycera. Proc. Linn. Soc. New South Wales, **46**, pp. 285–300 (1921).
Phylogeny of Brachycera. Ibid., **52**, pp. 380–386 (1927)-

HUTTON, F. W. Brachycera (New Zealand). Trans. New Zealand Inst., **33**, pp. 1–95 (1900).

KARL, O. Brachycera (Pomerania). Stettiner Ent. Ztg., **96**, pp. 106–130, 242–261 (1935); **97**, pp. 108–136, 318–330 (1936); **98**, pp. 125–159 (1937).

KEISER, F. Orthorrhapha (Switzerland). Ergebn. Wiss. Untersuch. Schweiz. Nat. Park., **2**, 198 pp. (1947).

LAMB, C. G. Orthorrhapha. Sladen Exped. Seychelles. Trans. Linn. Soc. London, (2) **18**, pp. 361–416 (1922).

MALLOCH, J. R. Rhagionidæ, Therevidæ, Lonchopteridæ (Patagonia). Diptera of Patagonia and South Chile, pp. 199–257, 283 British Mus. (1932).

OLDROYD, H. Rhagionidæ, Tabanidæ, Asilidæ, Bombyliidæ. Ruwenzori Exped. 1934–35, **2**, pp. 13–47 British Mus. (1939).
Tabanidæ, Asilidæ, Bombyliidæ (Abyssinia). Ann. Mag. Nat. Hist., (11) **5**, pp. 192–203 (1940).

RICARDO, G. Stratiomyiidæ, Tabanidæ, Asilidæ (Samoa). Insects of Samoa, **6**, fasc. 3, pp. 109–122 British Mus. (1929).

RINGDAHL, O. Brachycera (Sweden). Ent. Tidskr., **62**, pp. 1–23 (1941).

SÉGUY, E. Brachycera of France. Faune de France, **13**, 308 pp. (1926).

SHANNON, R. C., and S. W. BROMLEY. Radial Venation in Brachycera. Ins. Inscit. Menstr., **12**, pp. 137–140 (1924).

SPEISER, P. Brachycera. Zool. Jahrb. Syst., **43**, pp. 194–220 (1920).

WAHLGREN, E. Brachycera (Sweden). Ent. Tidskr., **28**, 191 pp. (1907–1910).

WHITE, A. Brachycera (Tasmania). Pap. Roy. Soc. Tasmania, **1914**, pp. 35–74; **1915**, pp. 1–59; **1916**, pp. 148–288.

STRATIOMYIOIDEA

AUBERTIN, D. Stratiomyiidæ (Patagonia). Diptera of Patagonia and South Chile, **5**, fasc. 2, pp. 93–105 British Mus. (1930).

BEZZI, M. Allognosta. Deutsche Ent. Zeitschr., **1908**, pp. 471–475.
Chiromyza (South America). Ann. Ent. Soc. America., **15**, pp. 117–124 (1922).

Brunetti, E. Stratiomyiidæ (Orient). Rec. Indian Mus., 1, pp. 85–132 (1907); 25, pp. 45–180 (1923).
   Stratiomyiidæ (Belgian Congo). Rev. Zool. Africaine, 14, pp. 122–136 (1926).
Carrera, M. and J. Lane. Stratiomyiidæ and Tabanidæ. Arq. Mus. Paranaense, 4, pp. 127–136 (1945).
Collart, A. Stratiomyiidæ (Belgium). Bull. Ann. Soc. Ent. Belgique 73, pp. 121–141 (1933).
Curran, C. H. Stratiomyiidæ (Canada). Trans. Roy. Soc. Canada, sect. V, (3), 21, pp. 191–228 (1927).
Enderlein, G. Stratiomyiidæ, Subfamilies. Zool. Anz., 43, pp. 289–315, 577–615 (1914); 44, pp. 1–25 (1915).
   Xylophagidæ. Zool. Anz., 43, pp. 533–552 (1913).
   Stratiomyiidæ. Mitt. Zool. Mus. Berlin, 10, pp. 153–214 (1921).
Grünberg, K. Stratiomyiidæ (Cameroons, Spanish Guinea). Ibid., 8, pp. 43–70 (1915).
Hardy, G. H. Stratiomyiidæ (Australia). Pap. Proc. Roy. Soc. Tasmania, 1920, pp. 33–64 (1921). Proc. Roy. Soc. Queensland, 43, pp. 50–55 (1932), 44, pp. 41–49 (1932).
   Chiromyzinæ (Australia). Proc. Linn. Soc. New South Wales, 45, pp. 532–542 (1921); 49, pp. 360–370 (1924).
Hill, G. F. Stratiomyiidæ (Australia). Ibid., 44, pp. 450–462 (1919).
James, M. T. Hermetia (U. S.). Bull. Brooklyn Ent. Soc., 30, pp. 165–170 (1935).
   Adoxomyia (Nearctic). Pan-Pacific Ent., 11, pp. 62–64 (1935). Proc. Ent. Soc. Washington, 45, pp. 163–171 (1943).
   Odontomyia (Nearctic). Ann. Ent. Soc. America, 29, pp. 517–550 (1936).
   Geosarginæ (Nearctic). Canadian Ent., 67, pp. 267–275 (1936). Lloydia, 4, pp. 300–309 (1941).
   Stratiomyiidæ (Colorado, Utah). Jour. Kansas Ent. Soc., 9, pp. 33–48 (1935).
   Stratiomyiinæ, Classification. Trans. American Ent. Soc., 62, pp. 31–36 (1936).
   Beridinæ (Nearctic). Ann. Ent. Soc. America, 32, pp. 543–548 (1939).
   Stratiomyiidæ (Neotropical). Jour. Kansas Ent. Soc., 12, pp. 32–40 (1939). Proc. U. S. Nat. Mus., 86, art. 3065, pp. 595–607 (1939). Rev. Ent. Rio Janeiro, 11, pp. 119–149 (1940).
   Euparyphus. Pan-Pacific Ent., 15, pp. 49–56 (1939).
   Stratiomyiidæ (Palæarctic Asia). Ibid., 17, pp. 12–32 (1941).
   Myxosarginæ. Ibid., 18, pp. 49–60 (1942).
   Rhaphiocerinæ (Neotropical). Ann. Ent. Soc. America, 36, pp. 365–382 (1943).
   Stratiomyiidæ (Solomon Isl.). Proc. U. S. Nat. Mus., 98, no. 3228, pp. 187–213 (1948).
   Stratiomyiidæ (New Caledonia, Hebrides). Jour. Washington Acad. Sci., 40, pp. 248–260 (1950).
Johannsen, O. A. Stratiomyia Larvæ and Pupæ. Jour. New York Ent. Soc., 30, pp. 141–153 (1928).

KERTESZ, K. Notacanthen. Ann. Mus. Nat. Hungarici, **6**, pp. 321–374 (1908);
7, pp. 369–397 (1909); **12**, pp. 449–557 (1914); **14**, pp. 123–218 (1916);
18, pp. 153–176 (1921); **20**, pp. 85–129 (1923).
Pachygastrinen. Allat. Közlem, **15**, pp. 107–119, 201 (1916).
LENZ, F. Metamorphose der Stratiomyiden. Arch. Naturg., **89** A, Heft 2, pp. 39–62 (1923).
LINDNER, E. Stratiomyiidæ (Brazil). Senckenbergiana, **10**, pp. 235–244 (1928).
Stratiomyiidæ (Paraguay). Arch. Naturg., **92** A, Heft 12, pp. 94–103 (1928).
Stratiomyiidæ and Rhagionidæ (Amazon). Ann. Naturh. Mus. Wien, **43**, pp. 257–268 (1929).
Stratiomyiidæ (South America). Rev. Ent. Rio Janeiro, **1**, pp. 304–312 (1931); **3**, pp. 199–205 (1933); **5**, pp. 396–413 (1935). Senckenbergiana, **15**, pp. 325–334 (1933).
Stratiomyiidæ (Ethiopian). Deutsche Ent. Zeitschr., **1934**, pp. 291–316 (1935).
Stratiomyiidæ (Madagascar). Konowia, **15**, pp. 33–60 (1936).
Stratiomyiidæ (Indo-Australian). Ann. Mag. Nat. Hist., (10) **20**, pp. 370–394 (1937).
Stratiomyiidæ (Congo). Bull. Mus. Roy. Hist. Nat. Belgique, **14**, no. 54, 35 pp. (1936).
Stratiomyiidæ. Fliegen Palæarkt. Reg., **18**, 218 pp. (1938).
Stratiomyiidæ. Ruwenzori Exped. 1934–35, **2**, pp. 1–11 British Mus. (1939).
Stratiomyiidæ (China). Deutsche Ent. Zeitschr., **1939**, pp. 20–36 (1939).
Stratiomyiidæ (Manchukuo). Arb. Morph. Taxon. Ent., **8**, pp. 94–98 (1941).
Stratiomyiidæ (Chile). Ann. Naturh. Mus. Wien, **53**, pp. 89–100 (1944).
Stratiomyiidæ (Neotropical). Ann. Mag. Nat. Hist., (12) **1**, pp. 782–821, 851–891 (1949).
Stratiomyiidæ (South America). Rev. Ent. Rio Janeiro, **22**, pp. 245–264 (1951).
LUNDBECK, W. Stratiomyiidæ. Diptera Danica, **1**, pp. 13–82 (1907).
MALLOCH, J. R. Pachygasterinæ. Ann. Ent. Soc. America, **8**, pp. 305–320 (1915).
MELANDER, A. L. Nemotelus. Psyche, **10**, pp. 171–183 (1903).
Several Nearctic Genera. Canadian Ent., **36**, pp. 14–24, 53–54 (1904).
MILLER, D. Beridinæ (New Zealand). Trans. New Zealand Inst., **49**, pp. 172–194 (1917).
OUCHI, V. Diptera Sinica, Stratiomyiidæ. Jour. Shanghai Sci. Inst., (3) **4**, pp. 265–285 (1940).
PLESKE, T. Stratiomyiinæ and Pachygastrinæ (Palæarctic). Ann. Mus. Zool. Acad. Sci. Russie, **23**, pp. 325–338 (1922).
Stratiomyiinæ (Palæarctic). Notulæ Ent., **4**, pp. 14–25, 65–73 (1924).
Pachygastrinæ (Palæarctic). Encycl. Ent. B II, **1**, pp. 95–103 (1924).
Clitellarinæ (Palæarctic). Ibid., **1**, pp. 105–119, 162–188 (1924).
Eulalia (Palæarctic). Ibid., **2**, pp. 23–40 (1925).
Stratiomyiidæ (Palæarctic). Eos, **2**, pp. 385–420 (1926).
Stratiomyiidæ (Siberia). Ann. Mus. Zool. Acad. Sci. Leningrad, **31**, pp. 181–206 (1930).

Séguy, E. Stratiomyiidæ (France). Faune de France, 13, pp. 16–90 (1926). Erinnidæ and Coenomyiidæ. Encycl. Ent. B II, 2, pp. 181–184 (1926). Konowia, 7, pp. 85–87 (1928).

Steyskal, G. C. Xylomyia and Solva. Pap. Michigan Acad. Sci., 31, pp. 181–190 (1947).

Szilady, Z. Notacantha. Tierwelt Deutschlands, 26, pp. 1–39 (1932). Stratiomyiidæ (Palæarctic). Ann. Hist. Nat. Mus. Hungarici, 34, pp. 88–101 (1941).

Verrall, G. H. Stratiomyiidæ. British Flies, 5, pp. 51–229 (1909).

White, A. Stratiomyiidæ (Australia). Proc. Linn. Soc. New South Wales, 41, pp. 71–100 (1916).

RHAGIONOIDEA

Aldrich, J. M. Symphoromyia (North America). Proc. U. S. Nat. Mus., 49, pp. 113–142 (1915).

Becker, T. Leptidæ (Palæarctic). Ent. Nachricht., 26, pp. 97–116 (1900). Neue Rhagionidæ. Zeitschr. Wiss. Insektenbiol., 2, pp. 41–48, 54–64, 69–72 (1922).

Bezzi, M. Rhagionidæ and Empididæ (Formosa). Ann. Mus. Nat. Hungarici, 10, pp. 442–495 (1912). Supplementa Ent., 3, pp. 65–78 (1914). Rhagionidæ (South Africa). Ann. South African Mus., 23, pp. 297–324 (1926).

Brunetti, E. Leptidæ (Orient). Rec. Indian Mus., 2, pt. 5, pp. 417–436 (1910).

Carrera, M. Rachicerus. Pap. Avulsos, Dept. Zool., São Paulo, 5, pp. 119–134 (1945).

Enderlein, G. Xylophagidæ. Zool. Anz., 43, pp. 533–552 (1913).

Ferguson, E. W. Blood-sucking Leptidæ (Australia). Jour. Roy. Soc. New South Wales, 49, pp. 233–243 (1915).

Greene, C. T. Leptidæ, Larvæ and Pupæ. Proc. U. S. Nat. Mus., 70, art. 2, pp. 1–20 (1926).

Hardy, D. E. Chrysopilus. American Midl. Nat., 41, pp. 143–167 (1949).

Hardy, D. E., and J. U. McGuire. Ptiolina (Nearctic). Jour. Kansas Ent. Soc., 20, pp. 1–15 (1947).

Leonard, M. D. Rhagionidæ (Nearctic). Mem. American Ent. Soc., 7, 181 pp. (1930).

Lindner, E. Rhagionidæ. Fliegen Palæarkt. Reg., 20, 49 pp. (1925). Ptiolina (Europe). Arb. Morph. Taxon. Ent., 9, pp. 230–241 (1942).

Lundbeck, W. Leptidæ. Diptera Danica, 1, pp. 133–157 (1907).

Malloch, J. R., C. T. Greene, and W. L. McAtee. Rhagionidæ (District of Columbia). Proc. Ent. Soc. Washington, 33, pp. 213–220 (1931).

Pechuman, L. L. Vermilio (New World). Bull. Brooklyn Ent. Soc., 33, pp. 84–89 (1938).

Pleske, T. Erinnidæ, Coenomyiidæ. Faune de France, 13, pp. 81–90 (1926).

Séguy, E. Rhagionidæ. Faune de France, 13, pp. 90–118 (1926).

Szilady, Z. Rhagionidæ. Tierwelt Deutschlands, 26, pp. 40–54 (1932). Ann. Mus. Nat. Hungarici, 28, pp. 229–270 (1934). Konowia, 14, pp. 92–93 (1935).

Verrall, G. H. Leptidæ. British Flies, 5, pp. 232–319 (1909).

Wheeler, W. M. Vermilio and Lampromyia. In Demons of the Dust, New York, 378 pp. (1931).

TABANOIDEA

AUSTEN, E. E. Phlebotomic Diptera (Tabanidæ) (Africa). Ann. Mag. Nat. Hist., (8) **1**, pp. 209–228, 401–428 (1908); **2**, pp. 94–116, 274–301, 352–356 (1909); **6**, pp. 337–356 (1910); **9**, pp. 353–369 (1912).

New Tabanidæ. Ibid., (8) **9**, pp. 1–33 (1912); **10**, pp. 240–243 (1912).

Tabanidæ (Africa). Bull. Ent. Res., **2**, pp. 279–290 (1912); **3**, pp. 113–136, 329–338, 399–416 (1912); **4**, pp. 283–300 (1914).

Chrysops (Africa). Ann. Mag. Nat. Hist., (7) **20**, pp. 507–520 (1907).

Tabanidæ (Palestine). Bull. Ent. Res., **10**, pp. 277–321 (1920); **13**, pp. 151–160 (1922); **14**, pp. 421–432 (1924).

Tabanidæ (Siam). Ibid., **12**, pp. 431–455 (1922).

Pantophthalmidæ. Proc. Zool. Soc. London, **1923**, pp. 551–598 (1923).

Pangoniinæ (Ethiopia). Ibid., (C) **107**, pp. 32–34; (B) **107**, pp. 263–293 (1937).

BEQUAERT, J. Pangoniinæ (Belgian Congo). Rev. Zool. Africaine, **2**, pp. 218–231 (1913).

Critique on Tabanidæ. Psyche, **31**, pp. 24–40 (1924).

Tabanidæ (Belgian Congo). Rept. Harvard Afric. Exped. Trop. Med., **2**, pp. 858–971 (1930).

Tabanidæ (Yucatan). Jour. New York Ent. Soc., **39**, pp. 533–553 (1931).

Tabanidæ of Congo Expedition. American Mus. Novit., **539**, 19 pp. (1932).

Tabanidæ (Antilles). Rev. Ent. Rio Janeiro, **11**, pp. 253–369 (1940).

Tabanidæ (Trinidad). Bull. Ent. Res., **30**, pp. 447–453 (1940). Psyche, **51**, pp. 12–21 (1944).

BEQUAERT, J., and W. T. DAVIS. Tabanidæ (Staten Island). Bull. Brooklyn Ent. Soc., **18**, pp. 113–122 (1923).

BEQUAERT, J., and S. RENJIFO-SALCEDO. Tabanidæ (Colombia). Psyche, **53**, pp. 52–86 (1946).

BORGMEIER, T. Neotropical Tabanidæ, Nomenclature. Rev. Ent. Rio Janeiro, **3**, pp. 286–303 (1933).

BOUVIER, G. Tabanidæ (Switzerland). Mitt. Schweiz. Ent. Ges., **19**, pp. 409–466 (1945).

BRENNAN, J. M. Pangoniinæ (Nearctic). Univ. Kansas Sci. Bull., **22**, pp. 249-401 (1935).

BRÈTHES, J. Los Tabánidos del Plata. Estudios Univ. Buenos Aires, **21**, 79 pp. (1921).

CAMERON, A. E. Bionomics of Tabanidæ of Canadian Prairie. Bull. Ent. Res., **17**, 42 pp. (1926).

CARTER, H. F. Some African Tabanidæ. Ann. Trop. Med., **9**, pp. 173–196 (1915).

CHAGNON, G., and O. FOURNIER. Les Tabanides du Québec. Nat. Canadien, **70**, pp. 49–84 (1943).

DRENSKY, P. Tabanidæ (Bulgaria). Mitt. Naturw. Inst. Sofia, **2**, pp. 55–128 (1929). (In Bulgarian)

EDWARDS, F. W. Hæmatopota (Africa). Bull. Ent. Res., **7**, pp. 145–159 (1916).

EFFLATOUN, H. C. Egyptian Tabanidæ. Mem. Soc. Roy. Ent. Egypte, **4**, fasc. 1, 114 pp. (1930).

ENDERLEIN, G. Pantophthalmidæ. Zool. Anz., 41, pp. 97–118 (1912); S. B. Ges. Naturf. Freunde, 1930, pp. 361–376 (1931).
New Tabanid Genera. Deutsche Ent. Zeitschr., 1923, pp. 544–555.
Ein neues Tabanidensystem. Mitt. Zool. Mus. Berlin, 10, pp. 333–351 (1922); 11, pp. 253–409 (1925).

FAIN, A. Tabanides congolais. Rev. Zool. Bot. Africaines, 40, pp. 139–150 (1947).

FAIRCHILD, G. B. Acanthocera. Rev. Ent. Rio Janeiro, 10, pp. 14–27 (1939).
Chlorotabanus and Cryptotylus. Ibid., 11, pp. 713–722 (1940).
Dichelacera. Ann. Ent. Soc. America, 33, pp. 683–700 (1940).
Chrysops (Panama). Proc. Ent. Soc. Washington, 44, pp. 1–8 (1942).
Leucotabanus and Fidene (Panama). Ann. Ent. Soc. America, 34, pp. 629–646 (1941).
Bellardia (Panama). Psyche, 49, pp. 8–17 (1942).
Neotabanus (Panama). Ann. Ent. Soc. America, 35, pp. 153–182 (1942).
Scione. Ibid., 35, pp. 183–199 (1942).
Stenotabanus. Ibid., 35, pp. 289–309 (1942).
Tabanus (Panama). Ibid., 35, pp. 441–474 (1942).
Supra-specific Categories, Tabanidæ. Canadian Ent., 73, pp. 2–14 (1941).
Tabanidæ, Synonymy. Psyche, 57, pp. 117–127 (1950).
Tabanidæ (Connecticut). Connecticut State Nat. Hist. Surv., 75, pp. 1–31 (1950).
Tabanidæ (Neotropical). Ann. Ent. Soc. America, 44, pp. 441–462 (1951).

FATTIG, P. W. Tabanidæ (Georgia). Bull. Emory Univ. Mus., 4, 26 pp. (1946).

FERGUSON, E. W. Australian Tabanidæ. Proc. Roy. Soc. Victoria, 33, pp. 1–29 (1921). Rec. South Australian Mus., 1, pp. 365–379 (1921). Proc. Linn. Soc. New South Wales, 47, pp. 245–263 (1922). Bull. Ent. Res. 16, pp. 293–306 (1926).
Pangoniinæ (Australia). Bull. Ent. Res., 14, pp. 251–263 (1924).

FERGUSON, E. W., and M. HENRY. Tabanidæ (New South Wales). Proc. Linn. Soc. New South Wales, 44, pp. 828–849 (1920).

FERGUSON, E. W., and G. F. HILL. Tabanidæ (Australia). Proc. Linn. Soc. New South Wales, 45, pp. 460–467 (1920); 48, pp. 381–435 (1923).

FRAGA, A. Tabanidæ (Chile). Com. Mus. Concepción, 1, pp. 19–27, 30–37, 56–58 (1936); pp. 90–96 (1936).
Osca. Rev. Chilena Hist. Nat., 42, pp. 66–74 (1939).
Parosca. Ibid., 45, pp. 108–116 (1943).

GHIDINI, G. Tabanidi d'Italia. Arch. Zool. Ital., 22, pp. 371–493 (1936). Mem. Soc. Ent. Ital., 69, pp. 129–175 (1937).

GOFFE, E. R. British Tabanidæ. Trans. Ent. Soc. South England, 1930, pp. 43–114 (1931).

GOETGHEBUER, M. Catalogue of Tabanidæ (Belgium). Bull. Ann. Soc. Ent. Belgique, 66, pp. 109–114 (1926).

HARDY, G. H. Tabanus (Tasmania). Stylops, 3, pp. 43–48 (1934).
Tabanus (Australia). Proc. Roy. Soc. Queensland, 59, pp. 169–178 (1948).

HINE, J. S. Tabanidæ of Ohio. Ohio Acad. Sci. Spec. Pap., 5, 63 pp. (1903).
Tabanidæ (U. S. and Canada). Ohio Nat., 5, pp. 217–248 (1904).
Horseflies (Louisiana). Circ. Louisiana Crop Pest Comm., 6, 43 pp.
(1906). Bull. Louisiana Exp. Sta., 93, 59 pp. (1907).
Neotropical Tabanidæ. Ohio Jour. Sci., 20, pp. 185–192, 311–319 (1920).
Occ. Pap. Mus. Zool. Univ. Michigan, 162, 35 pp. (1925).
ISAAC, P. V. Indian Tabanidæ. Mem. Dept. Agric. India, Ent. Ser., 8, pp.
93–108 (1925).
KARIYA, S. Tabanidæ. Cat. Japanese Insects, Tokyo, 6, 23 pp. (1936).
KNAB, F. Stibasoma. Proc. U. S. Nat. Mus., 46, pp. 407–412 (1913).
KNOWLTON, G. F., and T. O. THATCHER. Utah Horseflies. Proc. Utah Acad.
Sci., 11, pp. 291–294 (1934).
KONO, H., and H. TAKAHASI. Tabanidæ (Japan). Ins. Matsumurana, 13, pp.
147–162 (1939); 14, pp. 6–24 (1939).
Tabanidæ, Larvæ and Pupæ. Kontyu, 14, pp. 1–22 (1940). (In Japanese)
KRÖBER, O. Palæarctic Chrysops. Zool. Jahrb. Syst., 43, pp. 41–160 (1920).
Palæarctic Tabanidæ. Arch. Naturg., 88 A, Heft 8, pp. 114–164 (1922);
89 A, Heft 12, pp. 55–118 (1923); 90, A, Heft 9, pp. 1–195 (1924).
Tabanidæ (Philippines). Ibid., 90 A, Heft 1, 27 pp. (1924).
Egyptian Tabanidæ. Bull. Soc. Roy. Ent. Egypte, 1925, pp. 77–137.
Chrysopini (Neotropical). Konowia, 4, pp. 210–375 (1925).
Tabanidæ. Fliegen Palæarkt. Reg., 19, 146 pp. (1925).
Chrysops (Nearctic). Stettiner Ent. Ztg., 87, pp. 209–353 (1926).
Chrysops (Africa). Zool. Jahrb. Syst., 53, pp. 175–268 (1927).
Diachlorinæ. Beih. Arch. Schiffs-Tropenhyg., 32, pp. 73–123 (1928).
Tabanidæ (Amazon). Ann. Naturh. Mus. Wien, 43, pp. 244–255 (1929).
Chrysopini (Indo-Australian). Zool. Jahrb. Syst., 56, pp. 463–528
(1929).
Neotropical Tabanidæ. Zool. Anz., 83, pp. 47–63, 115–137 (1929); 86,
pp. 248–265 (1930); 90, pp. 69–86 (1930).
Phæotabanus. Ibid., 86, pp. 273–300 (1930).
Macrocormus and Chlorotabanus. Ibid., 87, pp. 1–18 (1930).
Silviini. Ibid., 88, pp. 225–238 (1930).
Pitocerini. Ibid., 88, pp. 305–312 (1930).
Pangoniini. Ibid., 89, pp. 211–228 (1930).
Sackenomyia. Ibid., 90, pp. 1–12 (1930).
Straba and Poecilosoma. Ibid., 94, pp. 67–89 (1931).
Esenbeckia. Ibid., 94, pp. 245–257 (1931).
Fidena. Ibid., 95, pp. 17–37 (1931).
Gymnochela. Ibid., 96, pp. 49–61 (1931).
Patagonian Tabanidæ. Diptera of Patagonia and South Chile, 5, fasc. 2,
pp. 106–161 British Mus. (1930).
Stenotabaninæ and Lepidoselaginæ (South America). Encycl. Ent. B II,
5, pp. 101–144 (1930).
Scione (South America). Stettiner Ent. Ztg., 91, pp. 141–174 (1930).
Tabanidæ (New Zealand). Ibid., 92, pp. 58–89 (1931).
Tabanidæ (Neotropical). Ibid., 92, pp. 275–305 (1931). Rev. Ent. Rio
Janeiro, 2, pp. 185–202 (1932); 4, pp. 222–276, 291–333 (1934).

Therevidæ and Tabanidæ. Deutsche Ent. Zeitschr., 1928, pp. 417–434 (1929).

Pelecorhynchinæ and Melpiinæ (South America). Mitt. Zool. Mus. Hamburg, 44, pp. 149–196 (1931).

Tabanidæ (South America). Ann. Mus. Nat. Hungarici, 27, pp. 329–350 (1931).

Dichelacerinæ (South America). Rev. Ent. Rio Janeiro, 1, pp. 282–296 (1931).

Bellardiinæ and Tabaninæ (South America). Ibid., 1, pp. 400–417 (1931).

Esenbeckia. Ibid., 2, pp. 52–93 (1932).

Bellardiinæ (Neotropical). Ibid., 2, pp. 289–302 (1932).

Stibasoma. Stettiner Ent. Ztg., 93, pp. 241–259 (1932).

Tabanidæ. Tierwelt Deutschlands, 26, pp. 55–99 (1932).

Catalogue of Tabanidæ (Palæarctic). Acta Inst. Mus. Zool. Univ. Atheniensis, 2, pp. 57–245 (1939).

Dicladocera. Ver. Deutsch. Kolon. u. Uebersee-Mus., 3, pp. 58–92 (1940).

LANDROCK, K. Tabanidæ (Austria). Verh. Naturf. Ver. Brünn, 63, pp. 133–151 (1932).

LUNDBECK, W. Tabanidæ. Diptera Danica, 1, pp. 85–132 (1907).

LUTZ, A. Tabanidæ (Brazil). Zool. Jahrb. Suppl., 10, pp. 619–692 (1909). Mem. Inst. Oswaldo Cruz, 3, pp. 65–84 (1911); 5, pp. 142–191 (1913); 6, pp. 69–80 (1914) with Neiva, A.; 7, pp. 51–119 (1915).

LUTZ, A. and G. M. OLIVEIRA CASTRO. Esenbeckia. Mem. Inst. Oswaldo Cruz, 30, pp. 543–562 (1935).

Melpia. Ibid., 32, pp. 169–183 (1936).

MACCREARY, D. Tabanidæ (Delaware). Bull. Univ. Delaware Exp. Sta., 226, 41 pp. (1940).

MACKERRAS, I. M., and M. E. FULLER. Pelecorhynchus. Proc. Linn. Soc. New South Wales, 67, pp. 9–76 (1942).

MARCHAND, W. Chrysops, Early Stages. Jour. New York Ent. Soc., 25, pp. 149–163 (1917).

Tabanidæ, Early Stages. Monogr. Rockefeller Inst. Med. Res., 13, 203 pp. (1920).

MCATEE, W. L., and W. R. WALTON. Tabanidæ (District of Columbia). Proc. Ent. Soc. Washington, 20, pp. 188–206 (1919).

MIDDLEKAUFF, W. W. Horseflies or Deerflies (California). Bull. Cal. Insect Surv., 1, pp. 1–24 (1950).

NEAVE, S. A. Tabanidæ of Nyasaland, Life Histories. Bull. Ent. Res., 5, pp. 287–320 (1915).

NEIVA, A. Tabanidæ (Rio Janeiro). Mem. Inst. Oswaldo Cruz, 6, pp. 69–80 (1914).

NIESCHULZ, O. Tabanidæ, Distribution in Dutch East Indies. Zeitschr. Angew. Ent., 22, pp. 131–142 (1935).

Larvæ of Tabanus. Zeitschr. Parasitenk., 7, pp. 639–656 (1935).

OLDROYD, H. Tabanidæ (New Guinea). Proc. Linn. Soc. New South Wales, 72, pp. 125–142 (1947); 73, pp. 304–361 (1948).

OLSOUFIEFF, H. G. Tabanidæ (Leningrad). Mag. Parasit. Leningrad, 4, pp. 111–201 (1934).

Tabanidæ (Urals). Ibid., Moscow, **5**, pp. 205–215 (1935).
Tabanidæ (Western Siberia). Ibid., **6**, pp. 201–245 (1936).
Tabanidæ (USSR). Faune de l'URSS, **7**, no. 2, 433 pp. Inst. Zool. Acad. Sci. (1937).
Tabanidæ (Caucasus). Trav. Sect. Zool. Acad. Sci. URSS, **3**, pp. 45–90 (1941). (In Russian)

OUCHI, V. Diptera Sinica, Tabanidæ. Jour. Shanghai Sci. Inst., (3) **4**, pp. 175–189 (1939).

PATTON, W. S. Gadflies of Mesopotamia. Indian Jour. Med. Res., **7**, pp. 735–750 (1920).

PECHUMAN, L. L. List of Tabanidæ (Venezuela). Bol. Ent. Venezolana, **1**, pp. 51–58 (1942).

PEREIRA BARRETTO, M. Tabanidæ (Brazil). An. Fac. Med. Univ. São Paulo, **23**, pp. 77–85, 89–111 (1947); **24**, pp. 63–91 (1949). Rev. Ent. Rio Janeiro, **19**, pp. 401–417, 481–488 (1948). Rev. brasil. Biol., **9**, pp. 39–48 (1949).

PHILIP, C. B. Tabanidæ (Minnesota). Tech. Bull. Univ. Minn. Exp. Sta., **80**, 132 pp. (1931).
Tabanus. Canadian Ent., **68**, pp. 148–160 (1936); **69**, pp. 35–40, 49–58, 207–208 (1937). Ohio Jour. Sci., **36**, pp. 149–156 (1936). Ann. Ent. Soc. America, **43**, pp. 240–248 (1950).
Chrysops. Proc. Ent. Soc. Washington, **37**, pp. 153–161 (1936).
Apatolestes. Bull. Brooklyn Ent. Soc., **36**, pp. 185–199 (1941).
Tabanidæ, Tribes. Canadian Ent., **73**, pp. 2–14 (1941).
Nearctic Tabanidæ. Ibid., **73**, pp. 105–110, 141–153 (1941). Proc. New England Zool. Club, **21**, pp. 55–68 (1942). Psyche, **49**, pp. 25–40 (1942). Ann. Ent. Soc. America, **43**, pp. 115–122 (1950).
Nearctic Pangoniinæ. Proc. Ent. Soc. Washington, **43**, pp. 113–130 (1941). Ann. Ent. Soc. America, **42**, pp. 451–460 (1949).
Catalogue of Nearctic Tabanidæ. American Midl. Nat., **37**, pp. 257–324 (1947); **43**, pp. 430–437 (1950).
Tabanidæ (Egypt). Bull. Soc. Fouad Ent., **32**, pp. 77–83 (1948).

RAPP, W. F. and W. E. SNOW. Catalogue of Pantophthalmidæ. Rev. Ent. Rio Janeiro, **16**, pp. 252–254 (1945).

RICARDO, G. Pangoninæ. Ann. Mag. Nat. Hist., (7) **5**, pp. 167–182 (1900); **8**, pp. 286–315 (1901); **9**, pp. 366–381, 424–438 (1902).
Tabanidæ. Ibid., **14**, pp. 349–372 (1904).
Tabanidæ (Orient). Rec. Indian Mus., **4**, pp. 111–255, 321–399 (1911).
List of South African Tabanidæ. Ann. South African Mus., **10**, pp. 447–461 (1914).
Australian Tabanidæ. Ann. Mag. Nat. Hist., (8) **15**, pp. 270–291; **16**, pp. 16–39, 259–286 (1915).

ROWE, J. A., and G. F. KNOWLTON. Tabanus (Utah). Canadian Ent., **67**, pp. 238–244 (1935).

SCHUURMANS STEKOVEN, J. H. Tabanids from Buru. Treubia, **5**, pp. 299–330 (1924).
Tabanids of Dutch East Indies. Treubia, **6**, Suppl., 551 pp. (1926). Tijdschr. Ent., **70**, pp. 1–36 (1927). Zool. Jahrb. Syst., **54**, pp. 425–448

(1928). Zool. Anz., **92**, 109–111 (1930). Tijdschr. Ent., **75**, Suppl., pp. 78–83 (1932).

Tabanidæ (East Indies). Arch. Naturg., **1**, pp. 56–94 (1932).

Schwardt, H. H. Arkansas Horseflies. Bull. Arkansas Agr. Exp. Sta., **256**, 27 pp. (1930); **332**, 66 pp. (1936).

Early Stages of Tabanidæ. Jour. Kansas Ent. Soc., **14**, pp. 1–15 (1931).

Segal, B. Chrysops (New York). Jour. New York Ent. Soc., **44**, pp. 51–78, 125–154 (1936).

Séguy, E. Tabanidæ (France). Faune de France, **13**, pp. 119–157 (1926).

Tabanidæ (Madagascar). Mem. Inst. Sci. Madagascar, A, **3**, pp. 277–300 (1949).

Senior-White, R. A. Catalogue of Tabanidæ (India). Catalogue of Indian Insects, **12**, 70 pp. Calcutta (1927).

Shannon, R. C., and J. Hadjinicolaou. List of Tabanidæ (Greece). Acta Inst. Mus. Zool. Univ. Atheniensis, **1**, pp. 160–172 (1936).

Shiraki, T. Tabanidæ (Formosa, Japan). Taihoku Agr. Exp. Sta. Formosa, 1918, 442 pp.

Stammer, H. J. Die Larven der Tabaniden. Zeitschr. Morph. Oekol. Tiere, **1**, pp. 121–170 (1924).

Stone, A. Bionomics of Tabanidæ. Ann. Ent. Soc. America, **23**, pp. 261–304 (1930).

Tabaninæ (Nearctic). Misc. Publ. U. S. Dept. Agric., **305**, 171 pp. (1938).

Tabanidæ from Venezuela. Bol. Ent. Venezolana, **3**, pp. 125–138 (1944).

Surcouf, J. M. R. Tabanus d'Afrique. Paris, 1909, 258 pp.

Tabanidæ (South America). Mission Arc Meridien Amérique Sud, **10**, pp. 217–233 (1919).

Tabanidæ. Gen. Insectorum, **175**, 205 pp. (1921). Critique: Bequaert, Psyche, **31**, pp. 24–40 (1924).

Tabanidæ (Southwest Europe). Encycl. Ent. (A), **5**, 261 pp. (1924).

Tabanus (Syria). Voy. Gadeau Kerville en Syrie, **1**, pp. 339–350 Paris (1926).

Szilady, Z. Tabanus. Ent. Mitt., **4**, pp. 93–107 (1915).

Tabanidæ (Palæarctic). Ann. Mus. Nat. Hungarici, **12**, pp. 661–673 (1914).

Chrysops (Palæarctic). Arch. Naturg., **83**, pp. 85–135 (1917).

Horseflies. Biol. Hungarica, **1**, fasc. 1, pp. 1–39 (1923); **1**, fasc. 7, pp. 1–30 (1926).

Taylor, F. H. Australian Tabanidæ. Proc. Linn. Soc. New South Wales, **40**, pp. 806–815; **44**, pp. 41–71 (1919). Rec. Australian Mus., **12**, no. 5, pp. 53–70 (1918).

Tendeiro, J. Tabanidæ (Portuguese Guinea). Bol. Cultural Guiné Portuguesa, **6**, pp. 435–447 (1947).

Toumanoff, C. Tabanidæ (Indochina). Rev. Med. Franç. Extreme-Orient, Hanoi, **19**, pp. 1075–1087 (1941).

Vanderyst, R. P. R. Tabanides du Congo Belge. Bull. Agric. Congo Belge, **19**, pp. 607–630 (1928).

Verrall, G. H. Tabanidæ. British Flies, **5**, pp. 320–439 (1909).

Vianna Martins, A. Tabanidæ (Minas Geraes). Trab. Inst. Biol. Dias, **1940**, 233 pp.

WEBB, J. L., and R. W. WELLS. Horseflies in Relation to Western Agriculture. Bull. U. S. Dept. Agric., **1218**, 36 pp. (1924).

WEHR, E. E. Tabanidæ (Nebraska). Univ. Studies Nebraska, **22**, pp. 107–118 (1922).

WHITE, A. Tabanidæ and Therevidæ (Tasmania). Proc. Roy. Soc. Tasmania, **1915**, pp. 1–59 (1916).

THEREVOIDEA (THEREVIDÆ, SCENOPINIDÆ)

BECKER, T. Therevidæ. Verh. zool.-bot. Ges. Wien, **62**, pp. 289–319 (1912). Thereva. Konowia, **1**, pp. 16–34 (1922).

COLE, F. R. Therevidæ (North America). Proc. U. S. Nat. Mus., **62**, art. 4, 140 pp. (1923). Canadian Ent., **57**, pp. 84–88 (1925).

COLLIN, J. E. British Therevidæ. Proc. Roy. Phys. Soc. Edinburgh, **23**, pp. 95–102 (1948).

CRESSON, E. T. Scenopinidæ. Trans. American Ent. Soc., **33**, pp. 109–114 (1907).

ENGLISH, K. M. I. Biology of Therevidæ (Australia). Proc. Linn. Soc. New South Wales, **75**, pp. 345–359 (1950).

HARDY, D. E. Omphralidæ (North America). Jour. Kansas Ent. Soc., **17**, pp. 31–51 (1944).

KRÖBER, O. Omphralidæ. Ann. Mus. Nat. Hungarici, **2**, pp. 174–210 (1913). Therevidæ. Gen. Insectorum, **148**, 69 pp. (1913). Tierwelt Deutschlands, **26**, pp. 100–122 (1932).
Scenopinidæ. Gen. Insectorum, **161**, 15 pp. (1914).
Scenopinidæ and Therevidæ. Bull. Soc. Roy. Ent. Egypte, **1923**, pp. 70–107; **1929**, pp. 73–80.
Therevidæ and Omphralidæ. Mitt. Mus. Naturh., Hamburg, **31**, pt. 2, pp. 29–74 (1913).
Omphralidæ, Conopidæ and Therevidæ. Konowia, **7**, pp. 1–23, 113–134 (1928).
Therevidæ. Fliegen Palæarkt. Reg., **26**, 60 pp. (1925).
Omphralidæ. Ibid., **27**, 8 pp. (1925).
Therevidæ (New Zealand). Stettiner Ent. Ztg., **93**, pp. 122–142 (1932).
Therevidæ (South Africa). Ann. Transvaal Mus., **14**, pp. 103–134 (1931). Konowia, **12**, pp. 289–299 (1933).
Omphralidæ (Belgian Congo). Rev. Zool. Bot. Africaines, **28**, pp. 258–286 (1936).
Omphralidæ. Stettiner Ent. Ztg., **98**, pp. 211–231 (1937).
Catalogue of Palæarctic Therevidæ. Acta Inst. Mus. Zool. Univ. Atheniensis, **1**, pp. 269–321 (1937).

LUNDBECK, W. Therevidæ and Scenopinidæ. Diptera Danica, **2**, pp. 132–160 (1908).

MANN, J. S. Therevidæ (Australia). Australian Zool., **5**, pp. 151–194 (1928); **6**, pp. 17–49 (1929); **7**, pp. 325–344 (1933).

OSTEN SACKEN, C. R. Therevidæ. Verh. zool.-bot. Ges. Wien, **62**, pp. 289–319 (1912).

SÉGUY, E. Therevidæ and Omphralidæ. Faune de France, **13**, pp. 255–279 (1926).

VANSCHUYTBROECK, P. Therevidæ. Expl. Parc Nat. Albert, **70**, pp. 7–20 (1951).

VERRALL, G. H. Therevidæ and Scenopinidæ. British Flies, **5**, pp. 537–602 (1909).

ASILIDÆ

BACK, E. A. Robberflies (North America). Trans. American Ent. Soc., **35**, pp. 137–400 (1909).

BANKS, N. Dasyllis. Bull. Brooklyn Ent. Soc., **12**, pp. 52–55 (1917).

BECKER, T. Revision of Loew's Asilica. 91 pp., Vienna (1923).

Dioctria. Konowia, **2**, pp. 1–18, 171–179 (1923).

Asilidæ (Formosa). Ent. Mitt., **14**, pp. 62–85, 123–139, 240–250 (1925).

BEZZI, M. Stichopogon. Ann. Mus. Nat. Hungarici, **8**, pp. 129–159 (1910).

Lasiopogon. Bull. Lab. Zool. Portici, **11**, pp. 250–281 (1917).

Cyrtopogon (Italy). Mem. Soc. Ent. Italiana, **5**, pp. 42–70 (1927).

BROMLEY, S. W. Asilidæ (Cuba). Ann. Ent. Soc. America, **22**, pp. 272–294 (1929).

Proagonistes. Ann. Mag. Nat. Hist., (10) **6**, pp. 209–224 (1930).

List of Robberflies (Ohio). Sci. Bull. Ohio State Univ., **1**, no. 2, pp. 1–18 (1931).

Stenopogon. Ann. Ent. Soc. America, **24**, pp. 427–435 (1931). Jour. New York Ent. Soc., **45**, pp. 291–309 (1937).

Asilidæ (Patagonia). Diptera of Patagonia and South Chile, **5**, fasc. 3, pp. 261–282, British Mus. (1932).

Robber-Flies (Texas). Ann. Ent. Soc. America, **27**, pp. 74–113 (1934).

New Asilidæ (Belgian Congo). Rev. Zool. Bot. Africaines, **26**, pp. 404–415 (1935).

New Asilidæ (India). Rec. Indian Mus., **37**, pp. 219–230 (1935). Indian Jour. Agr. Sci., **8**, pp. 863–888 (1938).

Diogmites (U. S.). Jour. New York Ent. Soc., **44**, pp. 225–237 (1936).

Asilidæ (South Africa). Ann. Transvaal Mus., **18**, pt. 2, pp. 125–146 (1936).

Robber-flies (Utah). Proc. Utah Acad. Sci., **14**, pp. 99–109 (1937).

Robber-flies (Madagascar). Trans. American Ent. Soc., **68**, pp. 11–21 (1942).

Robber-flies (China). Lingnan Sci. Jour., **21**, pp. 87–105 (1945).

Asilidæ (Connecticut). Bull. Connecticut Geol. Nat. Hist. Surv., **69**, 48 pp. (1948).

Asilidæ (Florida). Ann. Ent. Soc. America, **43**, pp. 227–239 (1950).

Asilidæ. American Mus. Novit., **1532**, 36 pp. (1951).

BROWN, C. J. D. Asilidæ (Utah). Trans. American Ent. Soc., **54**, pp. 295–320 (1929).

CARRERA, M. Leptogastrinæ. Pap. Avulsos, Dept. Zool., São Paulo, **4**, pp. 85–94 (1944).

Asilidæ (Neotropical). Arq. Zool. São Paulo, **7**, 148 pp. (1949).

Asilidæ (Brazil). Rev. brasil. Biol., **10**, pp. 99–111 (1950).

Prolepsis (Argentina). Dusenia, Curitiba, **1**, pp. 83–90 (1950).

CARRERA, M., and M. A. V. D'ANDRETTA. Asilideos do Mexico. Pap. Avulsos, Dept. Zool., São Paulo, **9**, pp. 159–192 (1950).

COLE, F. R., and J. WILCOX. Lasiopogon and Alexiopogon. Ent. Americana, 18, 90 pp. (1938).

CURRAN, C. H. Cyrtopogon. Canadian Ent., 55, pp. 92–95, 116–125, 132–142, 169–174, 185–190 (1923).

Asilidæ (Belgian Congo). American Mus. Novit., 272, 18 pp. (1927). Ommatius. Ibid., 327, 6 pp. (1928). Asilidæ. Ibid., 425, 21 pp. (1930); 487, 25 pp. (1931).

Mallophora. Jour. New York Ent. Soc., 49, pp. 269–284 (1941).

DAKIN, W. T., and M. G. C. FORDHAM. Asilidæ (West Australia). Ann. Mag. Nat. Hist., (9) 10, pp. 517–530 (1922).

EFFLATOUN, H. Asilidæ (Egypt). Mem. Soc. Roy. Ent. Egypte, 4, pp. 1–443 (1934–1937).

ENDERLEIN, G. Tropical Asilidæ. Zool. Anz., 44, pp. 241–263 (1914).

Dasypogoninæ and Archilaphrinæ. Wiener Ent. Ztg., 33, pp. 151–174 (1914).

ENGEL, O. Gonioscelis (Africa). Mitt. Zool. Mus., Berlin, 12, pp. 159–176 (1925).

Asilidæ (South Africa). Ann. Transvaal Mus., 12, pp. 132–180 (1927); 13, pp. 154–171 (1929); 14, pp. 253–283 (1932).

Larvæ of Leptidæ and Asilidæ. Trans. Roy. Soc. South Africa, 18, pp. 147–162 (1928).

Asilidæ (Chaco Exped.). Konowia, 8, pp. 457–474 (1930).

Asilidæ. Tierwelt Deutschlands, 26, pp. 127–204 (1932).

Asilidæ (China). Ark. Zool., 25 A, no. 22, 17 pp. (1934).

Asilidæ. Fliegen Palæarkt. Reg., 24, 491 pp. (1925–1930).

FATTIG, P. W. Asilidæ (Georgia). Bull. Emory Univ. Mus., 3, 33 pp. (1945).

FREY, R. Oriental Leptogaster. Notulæ Ent., 17, pp. 38–52 (1937).

GEMIGNANI, E. V. Mallophora (Argentina). Rev. Soc. Ent. Argentina, 3, pp. 133–144 (1930).

HARDY, G. H. Australian Asilidæ. Proc. Linn. Soc. New South Wales, 45, pp. 185–202 (1920); 51, pp. 305–312, 643–657 (1926); 52, pp. 387–398 (1937); 53, pp. 469–473 (1928); 54, pp. 353–360 (1929); 55, pp. 249–260 (1930).

Cerdistus (Australia). Ibid., 51, pp. 643–657 (1926); 54, pp. 80–88 (1929).

Stenopogon (Australia). Proc. Roy. Soc. Queensland 39, pp. 119–123 (1928).

Ommatius (Australia). Ibid., 40, pp. 61–65 (1928).

Brachyrrhopalini. Ibid., 41, pp. 59–72 (1930).

Asilidæ (Australia). Ann. Mag. Nat. Hist. (10) 13, pp. 498–525; 14, pp. 1–35 (1935); 16, pp. 161–187, 405–426 (1935).

HERMANN, F. Asilidæ. Zeitschr. syst. Hymenopt. Dipt., 6, pp. 129–144 (1906); 7, pp. 1–16, 65–78 (1907).

Asilidæ (South America). Abh. Deutsches Akad. Naturf., 96, 275 pp. (1912).

Mydaidæ and Asilidæ (Formosa). Ent. Mitt., 3, 41 pp. (1914).

Asilidæ (Formosa). Arch. Naturg., 82 A, Heft 5, pp. 1–35 (1917).

Laxenecera. Deutsche Ent. Zeitschr., 1919, pp. 337–358.

Systematik der Asiliden. Zool. Jahrb. Syst., 43, pp. 161–194 (1920).

Leptogastrinæ, Holcocephala. Verh. zool.-bot. Ges. Wien, **74**, pp. 140–191 (1926).

HINE, J. S. Asilus. Ann. Ent. Soc. America, **2**, pp. 136–170 (1909).

Promachus and Protacanthus. Ibid., **4**, pp. 153–172 (1911).

Erax. Ibid., **12**, pp. 103–157 (1919).

HOBBY, B. M. British Asilidæ and Prey. Proc. Trans. Ent. Soc. South England, **1930**, pp. 1–42 (1931).

Rhodesian Asilidæ and Prey. Jour. Anim. Ecol., **4**, pp. 90–112 (1935).

Bactria (Ethiopian). Ent. Mon. Mag., **72**, pp. 182–199, 232–249, 274–278 (1936).

HSIA, KAI-LING. Leptogastrinæ (China). Sinensia, **19**, pp. 23–56 (1949).

JAMES, M. T. Robber-flies (Colorado). Jour. Kansas Ent. Soc., **14**, pp. 27–53 (1941); **15**, pp. 124–236 (1942).

JONES, P. R. Asilidæ (Nebraska). Trans. American Ent. Soc., **33**, pp. 273–286 (1907).

LUNDBECK, W. Asilidæ. Diptera Danica, **2**, pp. 1–87 (1908).

McATEE, W. L. Laphria and Nusa. Ohio Nat., **19**, pp. 143–170 (1918); pp. 244–248 (1919).

McATEE, W. L., and N. BANKS. Asilidæ (District of Columbia). Proc. Ent. Soc. Washington, **22**, pp. 13–33 (1920).

MELANDER, A. L. Cyrtopogon. Psyche, **30**, pp. 102–119 (1923).

Lasiopogon. Ibid., pp. 136–144 (1923).

Asilidæ, Various Genera. Ibid., pp. 207–219 (1923).

MELIN, D. Swedish Asilidæ, Biology. Zool. Bidrag, **8**, pp. 1–317 (1923).

OLDENBERG, L. Lasiopogon. Deutsche Ent. Zeitschr., **1924**, pp. 441–448.

OLDROYD, H. Hoplistomerus. Trans. Roy. Ent. Soc. London, **90**, pp. 307–318 (1940).

PANDELLÉ, E. Asilus (Europe). Rev. Ent., France, **24**, pp. 44–98 (1905).

PRITCHARD, A. E. New Asilidæ (Southwestern U. S.). American Mus. Novit., **813**, 13 pp. (1935).

Holcocephala and Taracticus. Jour. New York Ent. Soc., **46**, pp. 11–21, 179–190 (1938).

Haplopogon and Cophura. Ann. Ent. Soc. America, **34**, pp. 350–354 (1941); **36**, pp. 281–309 (1943).

Aphamartina. Proc. Ent. Soc. Washington, **43**, pp. 131–140 (1941).

RICARDO, G. Australasian Asilidæ. Ann. Mag. Nat. Hist., (8) **9**, pp. 473–488, 585–594 (1912); (8) **10**, pp. 142–160, 350–360 (1912); (8) **11**, pp. 147–166, 409–451 (1913).

Asilinæ. Ibid., (9) **3**, pp. 44–79 (1919); (9) **5**, pp. 169–185, 209–240, 377–392, 433–444 (1920).

Asilidæ (South Africa, Orient). Ibid., (9) **8**, pp. 175–192 (1921); (9) **15**, pp. 234–282 (1925).

SÉGUY, E. Asilidæ of France. Faune de France, **17**, 190 pp. (1927).

STACKELBERG, A. A. Asilidæ (USSR). Faune Petropolit., **13**, 21 pp. (1922). (In Russian)

THORPE, W. H. Larvæ and Pupæ of Hyperechia. Trans. Roy. Ent. Soc. London, **75**, pp. 177–185 (1927).

VERRALL, G. H. Asilidæ. British Flies, **5**, pp. 614–754 (1909).

WILCOX, J. Stichopogon. Pan-Pacific Ent., **12**, pp. 201–212 (1936); **13**, pp. 37–45 (1937).

Ommatius, Key. Bull. Brooklyn Ent. Soc., **31**, pp. 172–176 (1936).
Heteropogon, Key. Ibid., **36**, pp. 50–56 (1941).
Nicocles, Key. Ibid., **40**, pp. 161–165 (1945).
WILCOX, J., and C. H. MARTIN. Coleomyia. Ibid., **30**, pp. 204–213 (1935).
Cyrtopogon (North American). Ent. Americana, **16**, 94 pp. (1936).
Nanocyrtopogon. Ann. Ent. Soc. America, **29**, pp. 449–459 (1936).
Dioctria (North America). Ent. Americana, **21**, 38 pp. (1941).

MYDAIDÆ, APIOCERIDÆ

ARIAS, J. Mydaidæ (Spain). Inst. Nac. Cienc. Zool., **15**, 40 pp. (1914).
BEQUAERT, J. Mydaidæ (Africa). Rev. Zool. Bot. Africaines, **31**, pp. 129–152 (1936). Bull. Mus. Roy. Hist. Nat. Belgique, **16**, no. 30, 26 pp. (1940).
BEZZI, M. Mydaidæ (South Africa). Ann. South African Mus., **19**, pp. 191–234 (1924).
CAZIER, M. A. Apioceratidæ. American Midl. Nat., **25**, pp. 589–631 (1941).
HARDY, D. E. Nomoneura and Nemomydas. Wasmann Jour. Biol., **8**, pp. 9–37 (1950).
HARDY, G. H. Australian Mydaidæ. Proc. Linn. Soc. New South Wales, **50**, pp. 139–144 (1925).
HARMANN, F. Apioceriden. Deutsche Ent. Zeitschr., **1909**, Beiheft, pp. 104–122.
JOHNSON, C. W. Mydaidæ. Proc. Boston Soc. Nat. Hist., **38**, pp. 131–145 (1926).
MACKERRAS, I. M. Australian Mydaidæ. Proc. Linn. Soc. New South Wales, **53**, pp. 539–543 (1928).
NORRIS, K. R. Apioceridæ (West Australia). Jour. Roy. Soc. West Australia, **22**, pp. 49–70 (1936).
PAINTER, R. H. Apiocera. Ann. Ent. Soc. America, **25**, pp. 350–357 (1932).
Apioceratidæ. Univ. Kansas Sci. Bull., **24**, pp. 187–203 (1936).
RAPP, W. F., and W. E. SNOW. Catalogue of Apioceridæ. Pan-Pacific Ent., **21**, pp. 157–160 (1945).
SACK, P. Mydaidæ. Fliegen Palæarkt. Reg., **23**, 28 pp. (1934).
SÉGUY, E. Mydaidæ. Encycl. Ent. (B) II, **4**, pp. 129–156 (1928).

BOMBYLIIDÆ

D'ANDRETTA, M. A. V., and M. CARRERA. Toxophorinæ (Brazil). Dusenia, Curitiba, **1**, pp. 351–374 (1950).
AUSTEN, E. E. Thyridanthrax. Bull. Ent. Res., **20**, pp. 151–164 (1929).
New Bombyliidæ (Palæarctic). Ann. Mag. Nat. Hist., (10) **18**, pp. 181–204 (1936).
Bombyliidæ of Palestine. 188 pp., British Mus. (1937).
BECKER, T. Usia. Berliner Ent. Zeitschr., **50**, pp. 193–228 (1905).
Apoclea. Ibid., **53**, pp. 276–294 (1908).
Genera of Bombyliidæ. Ann. Mus. Zool. St. Petersburg, **17**, pp. 421–502 (1912).
Villa, Anastœchus, Systœchus. Ann. Mus. Nat. Hungarici, **14**, pp. 17–67 (1916).

Bezzi, M. Systropus. Redia, **2**, pp. 262–279 (1904).

Bombyliidæ (Central Africa). Trans. Roy. Ent. Soc. London, **1911**, pp. 605–656 (1912).

Bombyliidæ (South Africa). Ann. South African Mus., **18**, pp. 1–180, 469–478 (1921). Broteria, **20**, pp. 64–86 (1922).

Bombyliidæ (Africa). Ann. Mus. Civ. Genova, **49**, pp. 98–114 (1920).

Bombyliidæ and Syrphidæ (Africa). Voy. Alluaud et Jeannel, pp. 315–351, Paris (1923).

Bombyliidæ of the Ethiopian Region. 390 pp. British Mus. (1924).

Bombyliidæ (Egypt). Bull. Soc. Roy. Ent. Egypte, **17**, 1924, pp. 159–242 (1925); **18**, 1925, pp. 244–273 (1926).

Brunetti, E. Catalogue of Oriental Bombyliidæ. Rec. Indian Mus., **2**, pp. 437–492 (1909).

Canizo, J. del. Bombyliidæ. Bol. Pat. Veg. Ent. Agric. Madrid, **12**, pp. 77–99 (1944).

Cole, F. R. Pœcilanthrax. Jour. New York Ent. Soc., **25**, pp. 67–80 (1917).

Bombyliidæ (Lower California). Proc. California Acad. Sci., **12**, pp. 289–314, 457–481 (1923).

Curran, C. H. Exoprosopa. American Mus. Novit., **415**, 16 pp. (1930).

Edwards, F. W. Bombyliidæ, Nemestrinidæ, Cyrtidæ (Patagonia). Diptera of Patagonia and South Chile, **5**, fasc. 2, pp. 162–197, British Mus. (1930).

Comptosia and Allies. Encycl. Ent., (B II, Dipt.) **7**, pp. 81–112 (1934).

Efflatoun, H. C. Bombyliidæ Homœophthalmæ. Bull. Soc. Fouad Ent., **29**, pp. 1–482 (1945).

Enderlein, G. Systropodinæ. Wiener Ent. Ztg., **43**, pp. 69–92 (1926).

Engel, E. O. Bombyliidæ. Fliegen Palæarkt. Reg., **25**, 619 pp. (1932–1937).

Bombyliidæ and Asilidæ (China). Mitt. Münchner Ent. Ges., **30**, pp. 72–84 (1940).

Hardy, G. H. Bombyliidæ and Cyrtidæ (Australia). Pap. Proc. Roy. Soc. Tasmania, **1920**, pp. 33–64; **1921**, pp. 41–83 (1922).

Notes on Australian Bombyliidæ. Ibid., **1923**, pp. 72–86 (1924).

Hesse, A. J. Bombyliidæ (Kalahari Exped.). Ann. Transvaal Mus., **17**, pp. 161–184 (1936).

Bombyliidæ (South Africa). Ann. South African Mus., **34**, pp. 1–1053 (1938).

Johnson, C. W. Bombylius (Eastern U. S.). Psyche, **14**, pp. 95–100 (1907).

Lundbeck, W. Bombyliidæ. Diptera Danica, **2**, pp. 88–132 (1908).

Maughan, L. Bombyliidæ (Utah). Jour. Kansas Ent. Soc., **8**, pp. 27–80 (1935).

Melander, A. L. Oligodranes. Ann. Ent. Soc. America, **39**, pp. 451–495 (1946).

Aphœbantus. Ibid., **43**, pp. 1–46 (1950).

Some Smaller Bombyliidæ. Pan-Pacific Ent., **26**, pp. 139–156 (1950).

Painter, R. H. Lepidophora. Trans. American Ent. Soc., **51**, pp. 119–127 (1925).

Parabombylius. Ent. News, **37**, pp. 73–78 (1926).

Villa. Ohio Jour. Sci., **26**, pp. 205–212 (1926).

Bombyliidæ (Honduras). Ann. Ent. Soc. America, **23**, pp. 793–807 (1930).

Heterostylum. Jour. Kansas Ent. Soc., **3**, pp. 1–7 (1930).

Bombyliidæ (China). Lingnan Sci. Jour., **11**, pp. 341–374 (1932).

Geron (U. S.). Trans. American Ent. Soc., **58**, pp. 139–168 (1932).
Bombyliidæ (Panama). American Mus. Novit., **642**, 10 pp. (1933).
New Bombyliidæ. Jour. Kansas Ent. Soc., **6**, pp. 5–18 (1933).
Bombyliidæ. Trans. Kansas Acad. Sci., **42**, pp. 267–301 (1939).
PARAMONOV, S. J. Heterotropus. Konowia, **4**, pp. 110–114 (1925).
Lomatia. Neue Beitr. Syst. Insektenk., **3**, pp. 41–46, 78–84, 95–100, 112–116, 176–182 (1926).
Dischistus. Ibid., **3**, pp. 155–161 (1926).
Hemipenthes, Thyridanthrax. Encycl. Ent. (B) II, **3**, pp. 150–190 (1926).
Anastœchus. Neue Beitr. Syst. Insektenk., **3**, pp. 127–137. Arch. Naturg., **91**, A, Heft 1, pp. 46–55 (1926).
Platypygus. Konowia, **5**, pp. 85–92 (1926).
Bombylius. Mem. Acad. Sci. Ukraine, Kiev, (Phys. Sci. Math.), **3**, pp. 77–184 (1926).
Exoprosopa. Ibid., **6**, Livr. 2, pp. 181–303 (1928).
Bombyliidæ. Ibid., **11**, Livr. 2, pp. 65–232 (1929).
Cytherea, Anastœchus. Ibid., **15**, Livr. 3, pp. 355–481 (1930).
Amictus, Lyophlæba. Ibid. (Nat. Sci.), **9**, pp. 1–218 (1931).
Bombyliidæ (Northwest China). Ark. Zool., **26** A, no. 4, 7 pp. (1934).
Anthrax. Trav. Mus. Zool. Kiev, **16**, pp. 3–31 (1936); **18**, pp. 69–159 (1937). (In Russian)
Bombyliid Genera (Recent and Fossil). Rep. Inst. Zool. Biol. Kiev, **23**, pp. 51–88 (1939). (In Ukrainian)
Bombyliinæ (USSR). Inst. Zool. Acad. Sci. URSS, **25**, 414 pp. (1940).
Bombyliidæ (America). Eos, **13** (1937), pp. 13–43 (1940).
Bombyliidæ. Ibid., **23**, pp. 79–102, 207–220 (1947).
Triplœchus and Sericosoma. Rev. Ent. Rio Janeiro, **18**, pp. 183–192, 361–369 (1947).
Lyophlæbia. Ibid., **19**, pp. 115–148 (1948).
Lepidophora. Ibid., **20**, pp. 631–643 (1949).
Usia. Eos, **26**, pp. 341–378 (1951).
ROBERTS, F. H. S. Bombyliidæ (Australia). Proc. Linn. Soc. New South Wales, **53**, pp. 90–144, 413–455 (1928); **54**, pp. 553–583 (1929).
RUIZ, H. F. Comptosia (Chile). Rev. Univ. Santiago, **24**, pp. 111–126 (1939).
SACK, P. Spongostylum (Palæarctic). Abh. Senckenbergisches Naturf. Ges., **30**, pp. 503–548 (1909).
SÉGUY, E. Bombyliidæ. Faune de France, **13**, pp. 178–254 (1926).
Cyrtosia (Mediterranean). Rev. franç. Ent., **16**, pp. 83–85 (1949).
SENIOR-WHITE, R. Bombyliidæ, Catalogue. Catalogue of Indian Insects, **3**, 31 pp., Calcutta (1923).
VENTURI, F. Usia (Italy). Redia, **33**, pp. 127–142 (1948).
VERRALL, G. H. Bombyliidæ. British Flies, **5**, pp. 474–536 (1909).

NEMESTRINIDÆ, ACROCERIDÆ

ANDREWS, H. W. Cyrtidæ. Proc. Trans. South London Ent. Soc., **1939**, pp. 78–79 (1939).
ARIAS, J. Nemestrinidæ (Spain). Trav. Mus. Nac. Cienc. Nat. Zool., **13**, 33 pp. (1913).

Bequaert, J. Hirmoneura (North America). Jour. New York Ent. Soc., **27**, pp. 301–306 (1919).
    Nemestrinidæ (Rhodesia, New Guinea). Psyche, **32**, pp. 4–22 (1925).
    Nemestrinidæ (North America). Ibid., **37**, pp. 286–297 (1930).
    Lasia (North America). American Mus. Novit., **455**, 11 pp. (1931).
    Nemestrinidæ in Röder Collection. Zool. Anz., **100**, pp. 13–33 (1932).
    Nemestrinidæ. Jour. New York Ent. Soc., **42**, pp. 163–184 (1934).
    Oriental Nemestrinidæ. Psyche, **42**, pp. 123–141 (1935).
    Nemestrinidæ (Palæarctic). Bull. Ann. Soc. Ent. Belgique, **78**, pp. 292–310 (1938).
    Catalogue of Recent and Fossil Nemestrinidæ (America). Psyche, **54**, pp. 194–207 (1947).
Bezzi, M. Genera of Cyrtidæ. Bol. Soc. Ent. Italiana, **55**, pp. 99–105 (1923).
    Nemestrinidæ (South Africa). Ann. South African Mus., **19**, pp. 164–190 (1924).
Brunetti, E. Cyrtidæ. Ann. Mag. Nat. Hist., (9) **18**, pp. 561–606 (1926).
Cockerell, T. D. A. Nemestrinidæ. Trans. American Ent. Soc., **34**, pp. 247–253 (1908).
Cole, F. R. Cyrtidæ (North America). Ibid., **45**, pp. 1–79 (1919).
    Thyllis and Megalybus. Canadian Ent., **51**, pp. 54–62 (1919).
Hardy, G. H. Australian Nemestrinidæ. Proc. Linn. Soc. New South Wales, **49**, pp. 448–460 (1924); **70**, pp. 135–146 (1946).
Johnson, C. W. Acrocera. Psyche, **22**, pp. 198–203 (1915).
Lichtwardt, B. Nemestrina (Palæarctic). Zeitschr. syst. Hymenopt. Dipt., **7**, pp. 433–451 (1907).
    Nemestrinidæ. Deutsche Ent. Zeitschr., **1909**, pp. 113–123, 507–514, 643–651; **1910**, pp. 589–624.
Lindner, E. Cyrtidæ. Fliegen Palæarkt. Reg., **21**, 36 pp. (1936).
Lundbeck, W. Acroceridæ. Diptera Danica, **1**, pp. 157–163 (1907).
Mackerras, I. M. Australasian Nemestrinidæ. Proc. Linn. Soc. New South Wales, **50**, pp. 489–561 (1925).
Paramonov, S. J. Nemestrinus (Palæarctic). Eos, **21**, pp. 279–295 (1945).
Pleske, T. Acroceridæ (Palæarctic). Konowia, **9**, pp. 156–173 (1930).
Plomley, N. J. B. Oncodes. Rec. Queensland Victoria Mus., **2**, pp. 17–30 (1947).
Sabrosky, C. W. Ogcodes and Acrocera. American Midl. Nat., **31**, pp. 385–413 (1944).
    Acroceratidæ. Ibid., **39**, pp. 382–430 (1948).
Sack, P. Nemestrinidæ. Fliegen Palæarkt. Reg., **22**, 42 pp. (1933).
    Cyrtidæ. Ibid., **21**, 36 pp. (1936).
Séguy, E. Oncodidæ and Nemestrinidæ. Faune de France, **13**, pp. 157–175 (1926).
Stuardo, C. Hirmoneura (Chile). Rev. Chilena Hist. Nat., **36**, pp. 61–81 (1932).
    Trichophthalma (Chile). Ibid., **38**, pp. 214–248 (1934).
    Nemestrinidæ (Argentina). Physis, **17**, pp. 77–94 (1940).
Verrall, G. H. Nemestrinidæ and Acroceridæ. British Flies, **5**, pp. 440–469 (1909).
Wandolleck, B. Inflatæ. 30 pp., Leipzig, B. G. Teubner (1914).

EMPIDIDÆ

BEZZI, M. Indo-australian Empididæ. Ann. Mus. Nat. Hungarici, 2, pp. 320–361 (1904).

    Neotropical Empididæ. Ibid., 3, pp. 424–460 (1905). Nova Acta Akad. Naturf. Halle, 91, pp. 293–407 (1910).

    Rhagionidæ and Empididæ (Formosa). Ann. Mus. Nat. Hungarici, 10, pp. 442–495 (1912). Supplementa Ent., 3, pp. 65–78 (1914).

    Empis (Palæarctic). Deutsche Ent. Zeitschr., 1909, Beiheft, pp. 85–103.

    Empididæ of Caves. Bull. Mus. Roy. Hist. Nat. Belgique, 18, 11 pp. (1942).

BRUNETTI, E. Indian Empididæ. Rec. Indian Mus., 9, pp. 11–45 (1913).

COLLIN, J. E. Empididæ (Britain). Ent. Mon. Mag., 62, pp. 146–152, 185–190, 213–219, 231–237 (1926); 63, pp. 20–29, 61–67, 93–98 (1927).

    New Zealand Empididæ in the British Museum. 110 pp., British Mus. (1928).

    Empididæ (Patagonia). Diptera of Patagonia and South Chile, 4, 334 pp. (1933).

    Pipunculidæ and Empididæ (Ussuri). Proc. Roy. Ent. Soc. London, (B) 10, pp. 218–248 (1941).

CURRAN, C. H. Empididæ (Panama). American Mus. Novit., 467, 25 pp. (1931).

ENGEL, E. Atalanta. Deutsche Ent. Zeitschr., 1918, pp. 1–80, 197–268 (1918).

    Empididæ (Chaco Exped.). Konowia, 7, pp. 245–251 (1928).

    Empididæ. Fliegen Palæarkt. Reg., 28, 384 pp. (1945).

FREY, R. Empididæ (Finland). Acta Soc. Faun. Fl. Fennica, 37, pp. 3–89 (1913).

    Rhamphomyia. Notulæ Ent., 2, pp. 1–10, 34–45, 65–77 (1922); 29, pp. 91–119 (1950).

    Hybotinen (Formosa and Philippines). Ibid., 18, pp. 52–62 (1938).

    Platypalpus (Palæarctic). Ibid., 23, pp. 1–19 (1943).

HARDY, G. H. Australian Empididæ. Australian Zool., 6, pp. 237–250 (1930).

JONES, C. G. Empididæ. Ruwenzori Exped. 1934–35, 2, pp. 257–323, British Mus. (1940).

KUNTZE, A. Empis. Zeitschr. syst. Hymenopt. Dipt., 6, pp. 209–216, 297–304 (1906); 7, pp. 25–32, 155–160 (1907).

LUNDBECK, W. Empididæ. Diptera Danica, 3, pp. 1–324 (1910).

MELANDER, A. L. Empididæ. Trans. American Ent. Soc., 28, pp. 195–367 (1902).

    Drapetis. Ann. Ent. Soc. America, 11, pp. 183–221 (1918).

    Empididæ. Gen. Insectorum, 185, pp. 1–434 (1927).

    Microphorus. Pan-Pacific Ent., 16, pp. 5–11, 59–69 (1940).

    Some New Empididæ. Psyche, 52, pp. 79–87 (1945).

    Iteaphila and Apalocnemis. Bull. Brooklyn Ent. Soc., 41, pp. 29–40 (1946).

    Coptophlebia. Pan-Pacific Ent., 22, pp. 105–117 (1946).

    Hemerodromiinæ. Jour. New York Ent. Soc., 55, pp. 237–273 (1947).

MILLER, D. Empididæ (New Zealand). Trans. New Zealand Inst., 45, pp. 198–206 (1911); 54, pp. 437–467 (1923).

Oldenberg, L. Rhamphomyia. Arch. Naturg., 80 A, Heft 9, pp. 69–91 (1915); 82, Heft 1, pp. 153–164 (1916); 83, Heft 6, pp. 14–27 (1917). Deutsche Ent. Zeitschr., 1922, pp. 339–347.

    Empididæ (Alps). Zool. Jahrb. Syst., 43, pp. 221–234 (1920).

    Rhamphomyia (Palæarctic). Konowia, 6, pp. 1–29 (1927).

Wahlgren, E. Empididæ (Sweden). Ent. Tidskr., 31, pp. 41–95 (1910).

DOLICHOPODIDÆ

Aldrich, J. M. Keys to Various Genera. Trans. American Ent. Soc., 30, pp. 269–286 (1904).

    Hydrophorus (Nearctic). Psyche, 18, pp. 45–70 (1911).

    Dolichopus and Hydrophorus (Alaska). Proc. U. S. Nat. Mus., 61, art. 25, 18 pp. (1922).

Becker, T. Dolichopodidæ (Palæarctic). Nova Acta Leop.-Carol. Akad. Naturf. Halle, 102, pp. 115–361 (1917); 103, pp. 205–315 (1918); 104, pp. 37–212 (1918).

    American Dolichopodidæ. Abh. zool.-bot. Ges. Wien, 13, pp. 1–394 (1922).

    Indo-australian Dolichopodidæ. Capita Zool., 1, pp. 1–247 (1922).

    Ethiopian Dolichopodidæ. Ent. Mitt., 12, pp. 1–50 (1923).

Cregan, M. B. Dolichopodid Mouthparts. Illinois Biol. Monogr., 18, pp. 1–68 (1941).

Curran, C. H. Dolichopodidæ (South Africa). Ann. Transvaal Mus., 10, pp. 212–232 (1924); Ann. South African Mus., 23, pp. 377–416 (1926).

    Dolichopodidæ (Africa). Rev. Zool. Africaine, 14, 39 pp. (1926): Ann. Mag. Nat. Hist., (9) 19, pp. 1–16 (1927).

    Dolichopodidæ (Belgian Congo). Rev. Zool. Africaine, 13, pp. 103–122 (1925).

    Rhaphium (Nearctic). Trans. Roy. Canadian Inst., 15, pp. 249–260 (1926); 16, pp. 99–179 (1927).

    Chrysosoma (Ethiopian). Rev. Zool. Africaine, 15, pp. 241–266 (1927).

Enderlein, G. Exotic Psilopodini. Zool. Jahrb. Suppl., 15, Band 1, pp. 367–408 (1912).

Frey, R. Dolichopodidæ (Finland). Acta Soc. Faun. Fl. Fennica, 40, 80 pp. (1915).

Greene, C. T. Tachytrechus. Proc. U. S. Nat. Mus., 60, art. 17, 21 pp. (1922).

    Scellus. Ibid., 65, art. 16, 18 pp. (1924).

Hardy, G. M. Dolichopodidæ (Australia). Australian Zool., 6, pp. 124–134 (1930).

Harmston, F. C., and G. F. Knowlton. Sympycnus (Utah). Ann. Ent. Soc. America, 33, pp. 395–403 (1940).

    Campsicnemus (North America). Bull. Brooklyn Ent. Soc., 37, pp. 10–17 (1942).

James, M. T. Dolichopus (Colorado). Trans. American Ent. Soc., 65, pp. 209–226 (1939).

Knezy, G. Dolichopus (Hungary). Folia Ent. Hungarica, 2, pp. 1–20 (1929). (In Magyar)

Lamb, C. G. Dolichopodidæ (Samoa). Insects of Samoa, 6, fasc. 3, pp. 125–139, British Mus. (1929).

LUNDBECK, W. Dolichopodidæ (Denmark). Diptera Danica, 4, 416 pp. (1912).
MERCIER, L., and O. PARENT. Dolichopodidæ (Normandy). Bull. Soc. Linn. Normandie, (7) 8, pp. 67–88 (1925).
PARENT, O. Dolichopodidæ (Belgium). Ann. Soc. Sci. Bruxelles, 41, pp. 238–248, 340–346 (1922).

Dolichopodidæ, Palæarctic Genera: Chrysotus, ibid., 42, pp. 281–312 (1923); Thrypticus, ibid., 44, pp. 46–69 (1925); Aphrosylus, ibid., 44, pp. 93–127 (1925); Diaphorus, ibid., 44, pp. 221–294 (1925); Medetera, ibid., 47, pp. 1–26 (1927); Tachytrechus, ibid., 47, pp. 83–89 (1927); Dolichopus, ibid., 48, pp. 30–36 (1929).

Tachytrechus (France). Encycl. Ent. (B) II, 1, pp. 19–64 (1924).

New Dolichopodidæ (Europe). Ibid., 3, pp. 23–40 (1926); 4, pp. 45–96 (1927); 7, pp. 113–140 (1934).

Dolichopodidæ from Far East (Palæarctic). Ibid., 4, pp. 111–149 (1927).

Catalogue of Dolichopodidæ (France). Ann. Soc. Linn. Lyon, 72, pp. 94–101 (1926).

Dolichopodidæ (Egypt). Bull. Soc. Roy. Ent. Egypte, 1927, pp. 60–67; 1929, pp. 42–58, 151–190; 1934, pp. 112–138.

Hercostomus (Palæarctic). Ann. Soc. Ent. France, 96, pp. 209–213 (1927).

Dolichopodidæ (Pyrenees). Butll. Inst. Catalana Hist. Nat. Barcelona, 9, pp. 56–72 (1929).

Condylostypus (America). Ann. Soc. Sci. Bruxelles (B) 49, pp. 74–87 (1929).

Dolichopodidæ from Röder's Collection. Ibid., 49, pp. 169–246 (1929).

Dolichopodidæ (Brazil). Ann. Naturh. Mus. Wien, 44, pp. 5–26 (1930).

New Dolichopodidæ in Paris Museum. Mem. Soc. Sci. Bruxelles, 50, pp. 86–115 (1930).

Dolichopodidæ (South America). Abh. Mus. Dresden, 18, pp. 1–22 (1931).

Dolichopodidæ (Sunda Isl.). Encycl. Ent. (B) II, 6, pp. 103–123 (1932).

Sympycnus (South America). Encycl. Ent. (B) II, 6, pp. 41–70 (1932).

Dolichopodidæ (Australia). Ann. Soc. Sci. Bruxelles (B), 52, pp. 105–176 (1932); 53, pp. 170–187 (1933); 53, pp. 325–441 (1933).

Dolichopodidæ (Neotropical). Bull. Ann. Soc. Ent. Belgique, 73, pp. 163–186 (1933).

Dolichopodidæ (Chaco Exped.). Konowia, 11, pp. 241–259 (1933).

Dolichopodidæ (Congo). Rev. Zool. Bot. Africaines, 24, pp. 1–49 (1933); 27, pp. 112–129 (1935).

Dolichopodidæ exotiques. Mem. Soc. Nat. Sci. Cherbourg, 41 (1929–1933), pp. 257–312 (1934).

Dolichopodidæ (Belgian Congo). Bull. Mus. Roy. Hist. Nat. Belgique, 12, fasc. 15, 19 pp. (1936); 13, fasc. 18, 19 pp. (1937).

Dolichopodidæ (Ethiopian). Rev. Zool. Bot. Africaines, 28, pp. 317–327 (1936); 32, pp. 256–282 (1939).

Dolichopodidæ. Bull. Ann. Soc. Ent. Belgique, 77, pp. 125–148 (1937).

Dolichopodidæ. Faune de France, 35, 720 pp. (1938).

Dolichopodidæ (Hawaii). Konowia, 16, pp. 67–84 (1937); pp. 209–219 (1938). Proc. Hawaiian Ent. Soc., 10, pp. 225–249 (1939).

Dolichopodidæ (Neotropical). Arb. Morph. Taxon. Ent., 6, pp. 140–151 (1939).

Dolichopodidæ (New Guinea). Proc. Linn. Soc. New South Wales, 64, pp. 155–168 (1939).

RINGDAHL, O. Swedish Dolichopodidæ. Ent. Tidskr., 49, pp. 179–201 (1928).

STACKELBERG, A. Dolichopus (Siberia). Ann. Mus. Zool. Acad. Sci. Leningrad, 31, pp. 135–163 (1930) (In Russian). Zool. Anz., 84, pp. 169–180 (1929). Dolichopodidæ. Fliegen Palæarkt. Reg., 29, 224 pp. (1930–1941).

VAN DUZEE, M. C. Various Nearctic Genera: Neurigona, Ann. Ent. Soc. America, 6, pp. 22–60 (1913); Pelastoneurus, ibid., 16, pp. 30–48 (1925); Thinophilus, ibid., 19, pp. 35–49 (1926); Polymedon, ibid., 20, pp. 123–126 (1927). Thripticus, Psyche, 22, pp. 84–88 (1915); Asyndetus, ibid., 23, pp. 88–94 (1916); Medeterus, ibid., 35, pp. 36–42 (1928), Proc. California Acad. Sci., (4) 9, pp. 257–270 (1919). Sciapus, Ent. News, 26, pp. 17–26 (1915); Porphyrops, ibid., 34, pp. 239–243 (1923). Xiphandrium, Trans. American Ent. Soc., 48, pp. 79–87 (1922); Syntormon, ibid., 50, pp. 257–287 (1925). Paraphrosylus, Pan-Pacific Ent., 1, pp. 73–78 (1924); Hydrophorus, ibid., 3, pp. 4–11 (1927); Sympycnus, ibid., 7, pp. 35–47, 51–63 (1930). Diaphorus, Bull. Buffalo Soc. Nat. Sci., 11, no. 2, pp. 161–194 (1915); Chrysotus, ibid., 13, no. 3, pp. 1–52 (1924). Argyra, Proc. U. S. Nat. Mus., 66, art. 23, pp. 1–43 (1925).

Dolichopodidæ (Alaska). Ohio Jour. Sci., 23, pp. 241–264 (1923). Proc. U. S. Nat. Mus., 63, art. 21, 16 pp. (1923).

Dolichopodidæ. Ent. News, 25, pp. 433–443 (1914); 28, pp. 123–128 (1917); 29, pp. 45–51 (1918); 41, pp. 53–55 (1930). Psyche, 28, pp. 120–129 (1921); 30, pp. 63–73 (1923); 32, pp. 178–189 (1925); 33, pp. 45–52 (1926). Occ. Pap. Boston Soc. Nat. Hist., 5, pp. 101–106 (1924).

New Dolichopodidæ (West Indies). American Mus. Novit., 262, 10 pp. (1927); 521, 14 pp. (1932). Ent. News, 43, pp. 183–187 (1932).

Dolichopodidæ (Neotropical). Proc. U. S. Nat. Mus., 74, no. 2755, 64 pp. (1929). American Mus. Novit., 483, 26 pp. (1931); 484, 14 pp. (1931); 569, 22 pp. (1932). Ann. Mag. Nat. Hist., (10) 7, pp. 243–255 (1931).

Dolichopodidæ (Patagonia). Diptera of Patagonia and South Chile, 5, fasc. 1, 92 pp. British Mus. (1930).

Dolichopodidæ (Canal Zone). Bull. American Mus. Nat. Hist., 61, pp. 161–206 (1931).

Dolichopodidæ and Phoridæ (Galapagos). Proc. California Acad. Sci., 21, pp. 65–74 (1933).

New Dolichopodidæ (North America). American Mus. Novit., 599, 27 pp. (1933); 655, 20 pp. (1933).

Dolichopodidæ (Hawaii). Proc. Hawaiian Ent. Soc., 8, pp. 307–356 (1933).

VAN DUZEE, M. C., F. R. COLE and J. M. ALDRICH. Dolichopus (North America). Bull. U. S. Nat. Mus., 116, 304 pp. (1921).

VAN DUZEE, M. C., and C. H. CURRAN. Nearctic Dolichopus, Males. American Mus. Novit., 683, 26 pp. (1934); Females, Ibid., 684, 17 pp. (1934).

WAHLGREN, E. Swedish Dolichopodidæ. Ent. Tidskr., 33, 54 pp. (1912).

Division CYCLORRHAPHA, Series ASCHIZA

AUDCENT, H. List of Cyclorrhapha (Bristol). Proc. Bristol Nat. Soc., **28,** pp. 45–132 (1950).
HENNIG, W. Kopulationsapparat der Cyclorrhapha. Zeitschr. Morph. Oekol. Tiere, Berlin, **31,** pp. 328–370 (1936).
KEILIN, D. Larves de Diptères Cyclorhaphes. 184 pp. (1915).
WAHLGREN, E. Aschiza. Ent. Tidskr., **30,** 86 pp. (1909).
ZIMIN, L. Cyclorrhaphous Larvæ. 115 pp. (1948). (In Russian)

LONCHOPTERIDÆ

ACZEL, M. Musidoridæ. Ann. Mus. Nat. Hungarici, **33,** pp. 109–121 (1940).
COLLIN, J. E. Lonchoptera (British). Ent. Mon. Mag., **74,** pp. 60–65 (1938).
CURRAN, C. H. Lonchopteridæ (North America). American Mus. Novit., **696,** 7 pp. (1934).
CZERNY, L. Musidoridæ. Fliegen Palæarkt. Reg., **30,** 16 pp. (1934).
DUDA, O. Lonchoptera. Konowia, **6,** pp. 89–99 (1927).
LUNDBECK, W. Lonchopteridæ (Denmark). Dipt. Danica, **5,** pp. 1–18 (1916).
MEIJERE, J. C. H. DE. Lonchopteridæ (Palæarctic). Tijdschr. Ent., **49,** pp. 44–98 (1906).

PHOROIDEA

ABREU, E. S. Phoridæ (Canary Isl.). Mem. Acad. Cienc., Barcelona, **17,** no. 1, 90 pp. (1921).
BECKER, T. Phoridæ (Europe). Abh. K. K. zool.-bot. Ges. Wien, **1,** 100 pp. (1901).
BOHART, G. E. Phoridæ (Guam). Proc. U. S. Nat. Mus., **96,** no. 3205, pp. 397–416 (1947).
BORGMEIER, T. Phoridæ. Arch. Mus. Nac. Rio Janeiro, **24,** pp. 323–346 (1923); **25,** pp. 85–281 (1925).
Phoridæ (Brazil). Vozes de Petropolis, **17,** 15 pp. (1923). Bol. Mus. Nac. Rio Janeiro, **1,** pp. 167–202 (1924); **2,** pp. 39–52 (1926).
Phorideos myrmecophilos. Arch. Inst. Biol. São Paulo, **1,** pp. 159–192 (1928); **4,** pp. 209–228 (1931). Rev. Ent. Rio Janeiro, **6,** pp. 23–37 (1936).
Xanionotum. Ibid., **2,** pp. 369–380 (1932).
Ueber attophile Phoriden. Zool. Anz., **82,** pp. 493–517 (1929).
Melaloncha. Rev. Ent. Rio Janeiro, **4,** pp. 167–189 (1934); **9,** pp. 39–53 (1938).
Coniceromyia. Ibid., **21,** pp. 281–299 (1950).
BORGMEIER, T., and H. SCHMITZ. Phoridæ (Brazil). Zeitschr. Deutsche Ver. São Paulo, **3,** pp. 127–181 (1922).
BRUES, C. T. Phoridæ (Indo-Australian). Ann. Mus. Nat. Hungarici, **3,** pp. 541–555 (1905).
Phoridæ (North America). Trans. American Ent. Soc., **29,** pp. 331–404 (1903).
Phoridæ. Gen. Insectorum, **44,** 21 pp. (1906).
Systematic Affinities of Phoridæ. Biol. Bull., **12,** pp. 349–359 (1907).
Phoridæ (Formosa). Ann. Mus. Nat. Hungarici, **9,** pp. 530–559 (1911).
Psyche, **31,** pp. 206–223 (1924).

Catalogue of Phoridæ. Bull. Wisconsin Nat. Hist. Soc., **12**, pp. 85–152 (1915).

Aphiochæta. Ins. Inscit. Menstr., **6**, pp. 183–194 (1916).

Phoridæ (Grenada). Bull. Mus. Comp. Zool., **62**, pp. 499–506 (1919).

Phoridæ (Philippines). Proc. American Acad. Arts Sci., **70**, pp. 365–466 (1936).

Phoridæ (Neotropical). Psyche, **51**, pp. 151–161 (1944).

Phoridæ (Connecticut). Geol. Nat. Hist. Surv. Connecticut, **75**, pp. 33–85 (1950).

COLLIN, J. E. Phoridæ (Seychelles). Trans. Linn. Soc. London, (2) **15**, pp. 105–118 (1912).

ENDERLEIN, G. Phoridæ (Southern Brazil). Stettiner Ent. Ztg., **73**, pp. 16–45 (1912). (Critique: Borgmeier, Rev. Ent. Rio Janeiro, **5**, pp. 427–470 (1935)).

KEMNER, N. A. Flügeln der Termitoxenien. 6 Congr. Int. Ent., Madrid, 1935, pp. 275–294 (1940).

LERUTH, R. Phoridæ (Belgium). Bull. Mus. Roy. Hist. Nat. Belgique, **12**, no. 36, 23 pp. (1936).

LUNDBECK, W. Phoridæ (Denmark). Dipt. Danica, **6**, pp. 69–447 (1922).

Aphiochæta (Denmark). Vidensk. Medd. Dansk Naturh. Foren., **71**, pp. 1–34 (1920).

New Phoridæ (Denmark). Ibid., **72**, pp. 129–143 (1921).

MALLOCH, J. R. British Phoridæ. Ann. Scott. Nat. Hist., **1910**, pp. 15–21, 87–92.

Phoridæ (U. S.). Proc. U. S. Nat. Mus., **43**, pp. 411–529 (1913).

MEIJERE, J. C. H. DE. Puliciphora. Zool. Jahrb. Suppl., **15**, 1, pp. 141–154 (1912).

PATTON, W. S. Aphiochæta (India). Jour. Indian Med. Res., **9**, pp. 683–691 (1922).

SCHMITZ, H. Myrmecophilous Phoridæ. Zool. Jahrb. Syst., **37**, pp. 509–566 (1914).

Myrmecophilous and Termitophilous Phoridæ. Jaarb. Natuurh. Genootsch. Limburg, **1913**, pp. 123–133 (1914). Deutsche Ent. Zeitschr., **1915**, pp. 465–507.

Thaumatoxena. Zool. Anz., **45**, pp. 548–564 (1915).

Termitophilous Diptera. Zool. Jahrb. Syst., **39**, pp. 211–266 (1916).

Keys to European Phoridæ. Jaarb. Natuurh. Genootsch. Limburg, **1917**, pp. 79–150; **1918**, pp. 146–164; **1919**, pp. 91–154.

Ecitophilous Phoridæ. Publ. Mus. Nac. Rio Janeiro, **4**, 29 pp. (1924).

Phoridæ. Natuurh. Maandbl., **13**, pp. 138–143, 148–150 (1924); **15**, 6 pp. (1926); **16**, 76 pp. (1927); **17**, 26 pp. (1928); **29**, 20 pp. (1940); **30**, 7 pp. (1941); **37**, pp. 37–44 (1948).

New Phoridæ. Encycl. Ent. (B) II, **2**, pp. 73–85 (1925).

Phoridæ (Formosa). Ent. Mitt., **15**, pp. 46–57 (1926).

Phoridæ (Freiburg). Mem. Soc. Fribourg, **1**, pp. 117–136 (1926).

Trineura (Palæarctic). Konowia, **6**, pp. 144–160 (1927).

Sciadoceridæ and Phoridæ (Patagonia). Diptera of Patagonia and South Chile, **6**, fasc. 1, 42 pp., British Mus. (1929); fasc. 2, 6 pp. (1931).

Phoridae. Revision der Phoriden, Dümmler's, Berlin u. Bonn., 211 pp. (1929).

Nepenthes Phoriden. Arch. Hydrobiol. Suppl., **9**, pp. 449–471 (1932).
Neue Europäische Phoriden. Tijdschr. Ent., **78**, pp. 79–94 (1935).
Neue Phoriden (Palæarctic). Broteria, **31**, pp. 5–16 (1935).
Paraspinophora. Ibid., **31**, pp. 155–173 (1935).
Phoridæ (Portugal). Ibid., **34**, pp. 163–179 (1938); **35**, pp. 8–17, 180–
193 (1939); **36**, pp. 49–74 (1940).
Misotermes. Treubia, **16**, pp. 369–391 (1938).
Phoridæ (Ireland). Proc. Roy. Irish Acad., **44**, sect. B, pp. 173–204
(1938).
Phoridæ. Fliegen Palæarkt. Reg., **33**, pp. 1–240 (1938–49).
Termitoxeniidæ. Broteria, **34**, pp. 22–40, 55–70, 132–162 (1938); **35**,
pp. 53–63, 133–148 (1939). 6 Congr. Int. Ent., Madrid, 1935, pp. 9–15
(1940).
Phoridæ (New Zealand). Natuurh. Maandbl., **28**, 31 pp. (1939).
Phoridæ (Madeira, Azores). Broteria, **37**, pp. 151–160 (1941).
Phoridæ (Austria). Ann. Naturh. Mus. Wien, **56**, pp. 375–399 (1948).
Phoridæ, Smaller Genera. Rev. Ent. Rio Janeiro, **20**, pp. 237–252 (1949).
SILVA FIGUEROA, C. Phoridæ (Chile). Bol. Mus. Nac. Chile, **9**, pp. 5–21 (1916).
SILVESTRI, F. Phoridæ termitofili dei Brasile. Acta Pontificia Accad. Sci., **10**,
pp. 281–295 (1946).
TRÄGÅRDH, I. Thaumatoxena. Ark. Zool., **4**, 12 pp. (1908).
Cryptopteromyia. Zool. Jahrb. Syst., **28**, pp. 329–348 (1909).
WASMANN, E. Termitoxenia. Zeitschr. Wiss. Zool., **70**, pp. 289–298 (1901).
Termitoxeniiden (Orient). Ann. Soc. Ent. Belgique, **57**, pp. 16–22
(1913).
WOOD, J. H. Notes on British Phora. Ent. Mon. Mag., **42**, pp. 186–196, 262–
266 (1906); **48**, pp. 94–99, 166–180 (1912).

SYRPHIDÆ

ANDREU, J. Spanish Syrphidæ. Bol. Soc. Ent. España, **9**, pp. 98–126 (1926).
ANDRIES, M. Microdon. Zeitschr. Wiss. Zool., **103**, pp. 299–361 (1912).
BANKS, N., C. T. GREENE, W. L. McATEE and R. C. SHANNON. Syrphidæ (District of Columbia). Proc. Biol. Soc. Washington, **29**, pp. 173–204 (1916).
BEAN, J. L. Tubifera (Eristalis) Hypopygium. Canadian Ent., **81**, pp. 140–
152 (1949).
BECKER, T. Helophilus. Berliner Ent. Zeitschr., **55**, pp. 213–232 (1910).
Neue Syrphidæ. Mitt. Zool. Mus. Berlin, **10**, pp. 1–93 (1921).
BEZZI, M. Syrphidæ (West Africa). Ann. Mus. Civ. Genova, **45**, pp. 400–443
(1912).
Syrphidæ of the Ethiopian Region. 146 pp., British Mus. (1915).
Platynochætus. Mem. Soc. Ent. Italiana, **3**, pp. 215–227 (1925).
Ethiopian Syrphidæ. Broteria, ser. Zool., **18**, pp. 131–142 (1920); **19**,
pp. 5–22 (1921).
BHATIA, M. L. Aphidophagous Syrphid Larvæ. Parasitol., **31**, pp. 79–129
(1939).
CAMPBELL, R. E., and W. M. DAVIDSON. Aphidophagous Syrphidæ. Bull.
Southern California Acad. Sci., **23**, pp. 3–9, 59–71 (1924).
CARRERA, M., H. DE SOUZA LOPES and J. LANE. Microdontinæ (Neotropical).
Rev. brasil. Biol. Rio Janeiro, **7**, pp. 471–486 (1947).

CHENG, C. T. Syrphidæ (China). Biol. Bull. Fukien Univ., 1, pp. 41–70 (1940). (In Chinese)

COLE, F. R. Sphegina. Ent. News, 35, pp. 39–44 (1924).

CURRAN, C. H. Syrphus. Canadian Ent., 53, pp. 152–159 (1921).

Nearctic Pipiza. Proc. California Acad. Sci., (4) 11, pp. 345–393 (1921).

Brachyopa. Ann. Ent. Soc. America, 15, pp. 239–255 (1922).

New Chilosia (Canada). Canadian Ent., 54, p. 19–20, 67–72 (1922).

Pipizella. Trans. American Ent. Soc., 49, pp. 339–345 (1923).

Chrysotoxum. Canadian Ent., 56, pp. 34–40 (1924).

Cynorhina. Ibid., 56, pp. 193–196 (1924).

Neoascia. Proc. Ent. Soc. Washington, 27, pp. 51–62 (1925).

Syrphidæ (North America). Kansas Univ. Sci. Bull., 15, pp. 1–216 (1924).

Volucella. Ann. Ent. Soc. America, 19, pp. 50–66 (1926). American Mus. Novit., 413, 23 pp. (1930); 1027, 7 pp. (1939); 1028, 17 pp. (1939).

Syrphidæ (South Africa). Bull. American Mus. Nat. Hist., 57, pp. 44–83 (1927).

Syrphidæ (Malaya, Borneo). Jour. Fed. Malay States Mus., 14, pp. 141–324 (1928); 16, pp. 290–376 (1931).

Baccha. American Mus. Novit., 403, 16 pp. (1930); 1041, 12 pp. (1939).

Eristalinæ. Ibid., 411, 27 pp. (1930).

Mesogramma. Ibid., 405, 14 pp. (1930).

Syrphidæ (West Indies, Central America). Ibid., 416, 11 pp. (1930).

Syrphidæ (Neotropical). Ibid., 882, 17 pp. (1936); 1086, 14 pp. (1940).

Syrphidæ (African). Ibid., 1025, 11 pp. (1939); 1026, 10 pp. (1939).

Syrphidæ (North America). Bull. American Mus. Nat. Hist., 78, pp. 243–304 (1941).

Syrphidæ (Guadalcanal). American Mus. Novit., 1364, 17 pp. (1947).

Spilomyia (North America). Ibid., 1492, pp. 1–11 (1951).

CURRAN, C. H., and C. L. FLUKE. Helophilus (Nearctic). Trans. Wisconsin Acad. Sci., 22, pp. 207–281 (1926).

DAVIDSON, W. M. Melanostoma. Trans. American Ent. Soc., 48, pp. 35–47 (1922).

DRENSKY, P. Syrphidæ (Bulgaria). Mitt. Bulgarischen Ent. Ges., 8, pp. 109–131 (1934). (In Bulgarian)

EFFLATOUN, H. C. Syrphidæ (Egypt). Mem. Soc. Roy. Ent. Egypte, 2, fasc. 1, 123 pp. (1922). Bull. Soc. Roy. Ent. Egypte, 18, pp. 274–283 (1926); 19, pp. 295–304 (1936).

FERGUSON, E. W. Syrphidæ (Australia). Proc. Linn. Soc. New South Wales, 51, pp. 137–183, 517–544 (1926).

FLUKE, C. L. Syrphidæ (Wisconsin). Trans. Wisconsin Acad. Sci., 20, pp. 215–253 (1921).

Xanthogramma. Ibid., 26, pp. 289–310 (1931).

Syrphus (America). Ibid., 28, pp. 63–128 (1933).

High Altitude Syrphids. Ann. Ent. Soc. America, 23, pp. 133–144 (1930).

Epistrophe. Ent. Americana, 15, pp. 1–56 (1935).

New Syrphids (South America). American Mus. Novit., 941, 14 pp. (1937).

New Syrphids (North and Central America). Ann. Ent. Soc. America, **32**, pp. 365–375 (1939).

Syrphini Related to Syrphus (Neotropical). American Mus. Novit., **1201**, 24 pp. (1942).

Melanostomini (Neotropical). Ibid., **1272**, 29 pp. (1945).

Syrphidæ (Alaska). Proc. U. S. Nat. Mus., **100**, no. 3256, pp. 39–54 (1949).

Syrphus, Male Genitalia. Trans. Wisconsin Acad. Sci., **40**, pp. 115–148 (1950).

Volucella. American Mus. Novit., **1503**, 33 pp. (1951).

Fluke, C. L., and F. M. Hull. Cheilosia, Subgenus Chilomyia. Trans. Wisconsin Acad. Sci., **36**, pp. 327–347 (1946).

Cartosyrphus (North America). Ibid., **37**, pp. 221–263 (1947).

Frey, R. Syrphinæ. Notulæ Ent., **25**, pp. 152–172 (1945).

Hase, A. Eristalis Larvæ. Zool. Anz., **68**, pp. 33–51 (1926).

Heiss, E. M. Syrphidæ, Larvæ and Pupæ. Bull. Univ. Illinois, **36**, 142 pp. (1938).

Hervé-Bazin, J. Syrphidæ (Belgian Congo). Rev. Zool. Africaine, **3**, pp. 68–102, 279–298 (1913).

Syrphidæ (Japan). Ann. Soc. Ent. France, **83**, pp. 398–416 (1914).

Lathryophthalmus. Ann. Sci. Nat. (Zool.), Paris, (10) **6**, pp. 125–152 (1923).

Syrphides (French Indo-China). Encycl. Ent. (B) II, **3**, pp. 61–110 (1926).

Hine, J. S. Alaskan Helophilus. Ohio Jour. Sci., **23**, pp. 192–200 (1923).

Hull, F. M. Eristalis (North America). Ibid., **25**, pp. 11–42, 285–310 (1925).

Didea. Ann. Ent. Soc. America, **18**, pp. 277–280 (1925).

Syrphidæ (Samoa). Insects of Samoa, **6**, fasc. 4, pp. 191–198, British Mus. (1929).

New Syrphidæ. Trans. American Ent. Soc., **56**, pp. 139–150 (1930).

Sphegina. Ibid., **61**, pp. 373–382 (1935).

Check-list of Syrphids (Australia). Jour. Fed. Malay States Mus., **13**, pp. 190–212 (1936).

Check-list of Syrphids (Oceania). Occ. Pap. Bishop Mus., **13**, pp. 79–87 (1937).

Exotic Syrphid Flies. Psyche, **44**, pp. 12–32 (1937). Jour. Washington Acad. Sci., **27**, pp. 165–176 (1937).

Syrphid Flies (Madagascar). Proc. Acad. Nat. Sci. Philadelphia, **92**, pp. 309–334 (1941).

New Syrphidæ. Psyche, **48**, pp. 149–165 (1941); **49**, pp. 19–24, 84–107 (1942).

Meromacrus. American Mus. Novit., **1200**, 10 pp. (1942). Bull. Mus. Hist. Nat. Javier Prado, **9**, pp. 104–118 (1945).

Volucella and Microdon. Ann. Mag. Nat. Hist., (11) **10**, pp. 18–40, 702–720 (1943).

Mesogramma. Ent. Americana, **23**, pp. 1–41 (1943). American Mus. Novit., **1480**, 22 pp. (1951).

Baccha. Ent. Americana, **23**, pp. 42–98 (1943); **27**, pp. 89–291 (1949). Bull. Brooklyn Ent. Soc., **39**, pp. 56–64 (1944). Rev. Ent. Rio Janeiro, **18**, pp. 395–410 (1947).

Syrphidæ in British Museum. Ann. Mag. Nat. Hist., (11) 11, pp. 21–61 (1944); (12) 3, pp. 603–624 (1950).

Microdon in British Museum. Ibid., (11) 11, pp. 241–261 (1944).

Syrphidæ in Museum of Comparative Zoology. Psyche, 51, pp. 22–45 (1944).

Syrphidæ (South America). Rev. Ent. Rio Janeiro, 15, pp. 34–54 (1944).

Quichuana. American Mus. Novit., 1317, 17 pp. (1946).

Lepidostola. Ibid., 1326, 15 pp. (1946).

Syrphidæ (Neotropical). Ent. News, 59, pp. 1–12 (1948); 60, pp. 225–234 (1949).

Some Syrphidæ. Psyche, 54, pp. 230–240 (1947).

Some Volucella. Ibid., 56, pp. 26–40 (1949).

New Eristalinæ. Ibid., 56, pp. 120–138 (1949).

Genera of Syrphidæ, Recent and Fossil. Trans. Zool. Soc. London, 26, pp. 257–408 (1949).

Some Syrphidæ (South America). Rev. Ent. Rio Janeiro, 21, pp. 225–236 (1950).

Mesogramma (Neotropical). American Mus. Novit., 1480, 22 pp. (1951).

HULL, F. M., and C. L. FLUKE. Cheilosia and Hiatomyia. Bull. American Mus. Nat. Hist., 94, pp. 303–401 (1950).

JOHNSON, C. W. Syrphidæ (New England). Psyche, 23, pp. 75–80, 159–163 (1916).

Chrysotoxum (New England). Occ. Pap. Boston Soc. Nat. Hist., 5, pp. 97–100 (1924).

JONES, P. R. Syrphidæ (Nebraska). Jour. New York Ent. Soc. 15, pp. 87–100 (1907).

Syrphidæ (Colorado). Ann. Ent. Soc. America, 10, pp. 219–231 (1917). Bull. Colorado Agr. Exp. Sta., 269, 72 pp. (1922).

KANERVO, E. Syrphidæ (Siberia). Ann. Ent. Fennici, 4, pp. 145–170 (1938).

KERTESZ, K. Ceria (South America). Termes. Füzet., 25, pp. 85–90 (1902).

Syrphidæ (Hungary). Rovartani Lapok., 22, pp. 1–12 (1915). (In Magyar)

KRÜGER, F. Biology of Syrphid Larvæ. Zeitschr. Morph. Oekol. Tiere, 6, pp. 83–149 (1926).

LANE, J., and M. CARRERA. Cerioides. Rev. Ent. Rio Janeiro, 14, pp. 167–173 (1943).

LATTA, R., and F. R. COLE. Eumerus. Mon. Bull. Dept. Agric. California, 22, pp. 142–152 (1933).

LUNDBECK, W. Syrphidæ (Denmark). Dipt. Danica, 5, pp. 18–591 (1916).

MALLOCH, J. R. Sphegina. Ent. News, 33, pp. 266–270 (1922). Proc. Biol. Soc. Washington, 35, pp. 141–144 (1922).

MATSUMURA, S., and J. ADACHI. Economic Syrphidæ (Japan). Ent. Mag. Kyoto, 2, pp. 1–36 (1916); 2, pp. 133–152 (1917); 3, pp. 14–46 (1917); 3, pp. 128–144 (1919).

METCALF, C. L. Syrphidæ, Life-histories. Ohio Nat., 11, pp. 337–344 (1911); 12, pp. 397–404, 477–488, 533–541 (1912); 13, pp. 81–91 (1913).

Syrphidæ (Ohio). Ohio Univ. Bull., 17, no. 31, pp. 1–123 (1913).

Syrphidæ (Maine). Bull. Maine Exp. Sta., **253**, pp. 193–264 (1916); **263**, pp. 153–176 (1917).

Syrphidæ (North Carolina). Jour. Elisha Mitchell Soc., **32**, pp. 95–112 (1916).

Syrphidæ, Male Genitalia. Ann. Ent. Soc. America, **14**, pp. 169–214 (1921).

MILLER, D. Syrphidæ (New Zealand). Trans. New Zealand Inst., **53**, pp. 289–333 (1921).

OSBURN, R. C. Syrphidæ (British Columbia). Canadian Ent., **40**, pp. 1–14 (1908).

PARAMONOV, S. Merodon. Encycl. Ent. (B) II, **2**, pp. 143–160 (1925).

Lampetia (Merodon). Trav. Mus. Zool. Kiev, **17**, pp. 3–13 (1936). (In Russian)

PEREIRA BARRETTO, M., and J. LANE. Microndotinæ. Rev. Ent. Rio Janeiro, **18**, pp. 139–148 (1947).

SACK, P. Salpinogaster and Meromacrus. Zool. Jahrb. Syst., **43**, pp. 235–272 (1920).

Syrphidæ (Paraguay). Arch. Naturg., Abt. A, **87**, Heft 3, pp. 127–149 (1921).

Syrphidæ (Formosa). Ibid., **87**, Heft 11, pp. 258–276 (1922). Stettiner Ent. Ztg., **88**, pp. 305–320 (1927). Konowia, **7**, pp. 182–190 (1928).

Syrphidæ (Philippines, Malaya). Philippine Jour. Sci., **29**, pp. 563–596 (1926).

Syrphidæ (Palæarctic). Tierwelt Deutschlands, **20**, pp. 1–142 (1930). Fliegen Palæarkt. Reg., **31**, 451 pp. (1928–1932).

Neue Syrphiden aus Mandschukuo. Ann. Morph. Taxon. Ent., **8**, pp. 186–192 (1941).

SHANNON, R. C. Syrphidæ. Proc. Ent. Soc. Washington, **19**, pp. 101–113 (1916). Proc. Biol. Soc. Washington, **29**, pp. 195–203 (1916). Bull. Brooklyn Ent. Soc., **16**, pp. 65–72, 120–128 (1921); **17**, pp. 30–42 (1922); **18**, pp. 17–21 (1923).

Chilosia (North America). Ins. Inscit. Menstr., **10**, pp. 117–145 (1922). Ceriodinæ. Ins. Inscit. Menstr., **13**, pp. 48–65 (1925). Jour. Washington Acad. Sci., **17**, pp. 38–55 (1927).

Sphecomyia. Pan-Pacific Ent., **2**, pp. 43–44 (1925).

Xylotinæ. Proc. U. S. Nat. Mus., **69**, art. 9, 52 pp. (1926).

Chrysotoxinæ. Ibid., **69**, art. 11, 20 pp. (1926).

Syrphidæ (South America). Ibid., **70**, art. 9, 34 pp. (1927).

Temnostoma. Proc. Ent. Soc. Washington, **41**, pp. 215–224 (1939).

SHANNON, R. C., and D. AUBERTIN. Syrphidæ (Patagonia). Diptera of Patagonia and South Chile, **6**, fasc. 3, pp. 120–170, British Mus. (1933).

SHIRAKI, T. Syrphidæ (Japan). Mem. Taihoku Imp. Univ., Ent., **1**, 446 pp. (1930).

SPEISER, P. Ueber einige Syrphiden. Wiesbaden Jahrb. Ver. Naturk., **66**, pp. 117–146 (1914).

Beiträge zur Syrphiden. Weiner Ent. Ztg., **41**, pp. 42–55 (1924).

STACKELBERG, A. Syrphidæ (Petrograd). Rev. Russe Ent., **15**, pp. 197–217 (1915).

Zelima (= Xylota). Deutsche Ent. Zeitschr., **1925**, pp. 279–288.

Cynorrhina (Palæarctic). Konowia, **7**, pp. 252–258 (1928).

Suster, P. M. Syrphides de Roumanie. Bull. Sect. Sci. Acad. roumaine, **25**, pp. 557–570 (1923); **28**, pp. 668–675 (1926).

Szilady, Z. Syrphidæ (Palæarctic). Ann. Mus. Nat. Hungarici, **33**, pp. 54–70 (1940).

Telford, H. S. Syrphidæ (Minnesota). Tech. Bull. Univ. Minnesota Exp. Sta., **140**, 76 pp. (1939).

Thornley, A. Syrphidæ (Cornish). Trans. Soc. British Ent., Southampton, **2**, pp. 87–114 (1935).

Verrall, G. H. Syrphidæ. British Flies, **8**, pp. 127–676 (1901).

Callicera. Trans. Ent. Soc. London, **1913**, pp. 323–333.

Wahlgren, E. Syrphidæ (Sweden). Ent. Tidskr., **30**, pp. 1–86 (1929).

Wehr, E. E. Syrphidæ (Nebraska). Univ. Stud. Nebraska, **22**, pp. 119–162 (1924).

Wheeler, W. M. Microdon. Jour. New York Ent. Soc., **16**, pp. 202–213 (1908).

CONOPIDÆ

Aldrich, J. M. Stylogaster. Proc. U. S. Nat. Mus., **78**, no. 2852, 27 pp. (1930).

Banks, N. Zodion and Myopa. Ann. Ent. Soc. America, **9**, pp. 191–200 (1916).

Becker, T. Neue Conopidæ. Konowia, **1**, pp. 195–208, 282–295 (1922).

Bohart, R. M. Dalmannia. Pan-Pacific Ent., **14**, pp. 132–136 (1938).

Physocephala of Western U. S. Ibid., **17**, pp. 141–144 (1941).

Brunetti, E. New African Conopidæ. Ann. Mag. Nat. Hist., (9) **15**, pp. 97–112 (1925); **16**, pp. 101–112 (1925).

Camras, S. Zodion. Pan Pacific Ent., **20**, pp. 121–128 (1944).

Occemyia (North America). Ann Ent. Soc. America, **38**, pp. 216–222 (1945).

Chen, S. H. Conopidæ (China). Notes Ent. Chinoise, **6**, pp. 161–231 (1939).

Kröber, O. Physocephala, Melanosoma, Dalmannia. Arch. Naturg., Abt. A, **80**, Heft 10, pp. 43–94 (1914).

Physocephala (Africa, North America). Ibid., **80**, Heft 11, pp. 81–110 (1914).

Conopidæ, Smaller Genera. Ibid., **81**, Heft 1, pp. 35–89 (1915).

Physocephala (Indo-Australian, South America). Ibid., **81**, Heft 4, pp. 84–145 (1915).

Conops (North and South America). Ibid., **81**, Heft 5, pp. 121–160 (1915).

Myopa, Conops, Occemyia. Ibid., **81**, Heft 7, pp. 23–107 (1916).

Conops (Palæarctic). Ibid., **81**, Heft 11, pp. 35–60 (1916).

Conopidæ, Subfamilies. Ibid., **83**, Heft 7, pp. 141–143 (1919).

Catalogue of Conopidæ. Ibid., **83**, Heft 8, pp. 1–91; Heft 9, pp. 1–52 (1919).

Stylogaster. Ent. Mitt., **3**, pp. 338–353 (1914).

Conopidæ (Egypt). Bull. Soc. Roy. Ent. Egypte, **1923**, pp. 57–70 (1924).

Conopidæ. Fliegen Palæarkt. Reg., **35**, 48 pp. (1924–1925).

Conopidæ (Philippines). Philippine Jour. Sci., **34**, pp. 331–347 (1927).

Conopidæ. Konowia, **6**, pp. 122–143 (1927).

Conopidæ (Central Europe). Tierwelt Deutschlands, **20**, pp. 119–142 (1930).

Conopidæ (South Africa). Ann. Transvaal Mus., 14, pp. 49–102 (1931). Konowia, 12, pp. 272–288 (1933).

Conopidæ (Northwest China). Ark. Zool., 26, A, no. 8, pp. 15–18 (1934).

Conopidæ, Catalogue and Key. Acta Inst. Mus. Zool. Univ. Atheniensis, 1, pp. 121–159 (1936).

Conopidæ. Ann. Mag. Nat. Hist., (11) 4, pp. 362–395, 454–468, 525–544, 594–607 (1939); (11) 5, pp. 64–82, 203–245 (1940).

MEIJERE, J. C. H. DE. Conopidæ. Tijdschr. Ent., 46, pp. 144–225 (1903); 55, pp. 184–207 (1912).

OUCHI, V. Conopidæ (China). Jour. Shanghai Sci. Inst., (3) 4, pp. 191–214 (1939).

PARSONS, C.T. Conopidæ (West Indies, Bermuda). Psyche, 47, pp. 27–37 (1940).

Classification of Conopidæ (North America). Ann. Ent. Soc. America, 41, pp. 223–246 (1948).

SÉGUY, E. Conopidæ (Western Europe). Encycl. Ent. (A), 9, pp. 9–52 (1928).

Generic Synopsis of Conopidæ (Holarctic). Livre Jubil. Bouvier, pp. 299–302 (1936).

SOUZA LOPES, H. DE. Stylogaster. Arch. Inst. Biol. Veg. Rio Janeiro, 3, pp. 257–293 (1937).

SZILADY, Z. Conopidæ (Hungary). Math. Termeszet. Ert., 41, pp. 215–229 (1925). (In Hungarian)

TONNOIR, A. Conopidæ de Belgique. Bull. Soc. Ent. Belgique, 3, pp. 67–78 (1921).

VAN DUZEE, M. C. Conopidæ (North America). Proc. California Acad. Sci., (4) 16, pp. 573–604 (1927).

Conopidæ (Rocky Mountains). Ann. Ent. Soc. America, 27, pp. 315–323 (1934).

VAN SCHUYTBROECK, P. Conopidæ. Expl. Parc Nat. Albert, Brussels, 70, pp. 21–25 (1951).

PIPUNCULIDÆ

ACZEL, M. Dorylaidæ. Zool. Anz., 125, pp. 15–23, 49–69 (1939); 132, pp. 149–170 (1940). Deutsche Ent. Zeitschr., 1943, pp. 1–27.

Tömösvaryella. Ann. Hist. Nat. Hungarici, 37, pp. 75–130 (1944).

Dorylaidæ. Acta Zool. Lilloana, Tucumán, 6, pp. 5–168 (1948).

BECKER, T. New Pipunculidæ. Wiener Ent. Ztg., 38, pp. 123–132, 149–167 (1921).

CRESSON, E. T. Pipunculidæ (North America). Trans. American Ent. Soc., 36, pp. 267–320 (1910).

CURRAN, C. H. Pipunculus. Canadian Ent., 59, pp. 290–303 (1927).

HARDY, D. E. Dorylaidæ. Jour. Kansas Ent. Soc., 13, pp. 101–114 (1940); 21, pp. 88–91 (1948).

Dorylaidæ (Nearctic). Univ. Kansas Sci. Bull., 39, pp. 1–231 (1943).

Dorylaidæ. Jour. Kansas Ent. Soc., 20, pp. 146–153 (1947).

Dorylaidæ (Neotropical). Psyche, 55, pp. 1–15 (1948). Jour. Kansas Ent. Soc., 21, pp. 124–133 (1948). Rev. Ent. Rio Janeiro, 21, pp. 433–448 (1950).

New Rhagionidæ and Dorylaidæ. Wasmann Coll., **7**, pp. 129–137 (1948).

Dorylaidæ (Africa). Mem. Inst. Roy. Sci. Nat. Belgique, (2), fasc. **36**, 80 pp. (1949).

Dorylaidæ. Expl. Parc Nat. Albert, Brussels, **62**, 53 pp. (1950).

KERTESZ, K. Dorylaidæ (Formosa). Ann. Mus. Nat. Hungarici, **10**, pp. 285–299 (1912).

Dorylaidæ. Ibid., **13**, pp. 386–392 (1915).

LUNDBECK, W. Pipunculidæ (Denmark). Dipt. Danica, **6**, pp. 1–69 (1922).

PERKINS, R. C. L. Pipunculidæ (Australia, Hawaii). Bull. Hawaiian Sugar Planters Assn., Ent., **1**, pp. 123–157 (1905).

SACK, P. Dorylaidæ. Fliegen Palæarkt. Reg., **32**, 57 pp. (1935).

VERRALL, G. H. Pipunculidæ. British Flies, **8**, pp. 60–126 (1901).

WAHLGREN, E. Pipunculidæ (Sweden). Ent. Tidskr., **31**, pp. 209–217 (1910).

PLATYPEZIDÆ and SCIADOCERIDÆ

CZERNY, L. Clythiidæ. Fliegen Palæarkt. Reg., **34**, 29 pp. (1930).

JOHNSON, C. W. Platypezidæ. Occ. Pap. Boston Soc. Nat. Hist., **5**, pp. 51–58 (1923).

KESSEL, E. L. Platypezina. Wasmann Coll., **7**, pp. 47–64 (1948).

Callomyia (California). Ibid., **7**, pp. 139–148 (1948).

Protoclythia. Ibid., **7**, pp. 257–275 (1949).

KESSEL, E. L., and J. V. KARABINOS. American Smoke Flies, Microsania. Ibid., **7**, pp. 23–30 (1947).

LUNDBECK, W. Platypezidæ (Denmark). Dipt. Danica, **7**, pp. 1–39 (1927).

SCHMITZ, H. Sciadoceridæ. Diptera of Patagonia and South Chile, **6**, no. 1, pp. 1–11, British Mus. (1929).

TONNOIR, A. L. Sciadocerinæ. Rec. Canterbury Mus., **3**, pp. 31–38 (1926).

VERRALL, G. H. Platypezidæ. British Flies, **8**, pp. 11–59 (1901).

CALYPTRATÆ, General

AWATI, P. II. Chætotaxy in Muscidæ. Indian Jour. Med. Res., **3**, pp. 135–148, 510–529; **4**, pp. 123–139 (1916).

BEDFORD, G. A. H. Check-list of Muscidæ and Œstridæ Causing Myiasis (South Africa). Rept. Vet. Res. South Africa, **11, 12**, pp. 483–491 (1926).

BEZZI, M. Non-pupiparous Diptera Parasitic on Birds. Parasitol., **14**, pp. 29–46 (1922).

Miodarii superiori (East Africa). Boll. Lab. Zool. Agr. Portici, **6**, pp. 45–104 (1912).

BRAUER, F., and J. E. BERGENSTAMM. Zweiflügler. 7 pts., (1880–1894), 760 pp. Facsimile reprint, Junk (1923).

EMDEN, F. I. VAN. Muscidæ (Ethiopia). Bull. Ent. Res., **32**, pp. 251–275 (1941).

Anthomyiinæ. Ruwenzori Exped., **2**, no. 6, pp. 325–710, British Mus. (1951).

GREENE, C. T. Puparia of Muscoid Flies. Proc. U. S. Nat. Mus., **60**, no. 2405, pp. 1–39 (1921). Proc. Ent. Soc. Washington, **27**, pp. 157–163 (1925).

HALL, D. G. New Muscoids in U. S. Nat. Museum. Proc. U. S. Nat. Mus., **84**, no. 3011, pp. 201–216 (1937).

JAMES, M. T. Myiasis in Man. U. S. Dept. Agr. Misc. Publ., **631,** 175 pp. (1948).

MALLOCH, J. R. Exotic Muscaridæ. Anthomyiidæ. Ann. Mag. Nat. Hist., (9) **7,** pp. 161–173, 420–431 (1921); **8,** pp. 225–239, 414–425 (1921); **9,** pp. 271–280 (1922); **10,** pp. 132–143, 379–391, 573–587 (1922); **11,** pp. 664–675 (1923); **12,** pp. 177–194 (1923). Muscidæ. Ibid., (9) **12,** pp. 505–528 (1923). Anthomyiidæ. Ibid., (9) **13,** pp. 409–424 (1924); **14,** pp. 257–274, 513–522 (1924). Muscarinæ. Ibid., (9) **15,** pp. 131–142 (1925). Muscidæ and Calliphoridæ. Ibid., (9) **16,** pp. 81–100, 361–377 (1925); **17,** pp. 489–510 (1926); **18,** pp. 496–522 (1926); **20,** pp. 385–424 (1927); (10) **1,** pp. 465–494 (1928). Key to Stomoxydinæ. Ibid., (10) **2,** pp. 307–319 (1928). Sarcophagidæ. Ibid., (10) **2,** pp. 321–327 (1928); **4,** pp. 249–257 (1929). Pyrgotidæ, Calliphoridæ. Ibid., (10) **3,** pp. 249–280 (1929). Caliphoridæ. Ibid., (10) **3,** pp. 545–564 (1929). Anthomyiidæ, Calliphoridæ. Ibid., (10) **4,** pp. 97–120 (1929); **5,** pp. 465–484 (1930). Anthomyiidæ. Ibid., (10) **4,** pp. 322–341 (1929); **16,** pp. 217–240 (1935). Calliphoridæ. Ibid., (10) **7,** pp. 185–200 (1931). Cylindromyiinæ, Tachiniscidæ. Ibid., (10) **7,** pp. 314–340 (1931). Cordyluridæ. Ibid., (10) **8,** pp. 425–446 (1931); **15,** pp. 242–266 (1935). Stomoxydinæ. Ibid., (10) **9,** pp. 377–405, 421–447, 501–518 (1931). Tachinidæ. Ibid., (10) **10,** pp. 297–330 (1932); **16,** pp. 321–343, 562–597 (1935).

Calyptratæ (New England). Psyche, **31,** pp. 193–204 (1924).

Calyptratæ of Federated Malay States. Jour. Fed. Malay States Mus., **13,** pp. 203–205 (1926); **14,** pp. 453–458 (1929); **16,** pp. 116–153 (1930); **17,** pp. 646–685 (1935).

Calyptratæ (New Zealand). Rec. Canterbury Mus., **3,** pp. 289–331 (1930), 377–422 (1931), 431–455 (1932). Trans. Roy. Soc. New Zealand, **68,** pp. 161–258 (1938).

Calyptratæ (East Indies). Mem. Mus. Roy. Hist. Nat. Belgique, **4,** fasc. 10, pp. 3–24 (1934).

NIELSEN, J. C. Entoparasitiske Muscidelarver. Vidensk. Meddel. Dansk Naturh. Foren., **64,** pp. 215–248 (1913).

PATTON, W. S. Mesopotamian Houseflies. Indian Jour. Med. Res., **7,** pp. 751–777 (1920).

Myiasis-producing Diptera. Bull. Ent. Res., **12,** pp. 239–261 (1921).

REINHARD, H. J. New Muscoids. Bull. Brooklyn Ent. Soc., **32,** pp. 62–74 (1937); **34,** pp. 61–74 (1939). Jour. Kansas Ent. Soc., **17,** pp. 57–72 (1944); **20,** pp. 15–24, 95–126 (1947).

ROUBAUD, E. Myiasis of Man and Animals (Africa). 250 pp., Paris (1914).

RUSSELL, H. Indian Parasitic Flies. Jour. Bombay Nat. Hist. Soc., **28,** pp. 370–380, 703–718, 957–969 (1922).

SÉGUY, E. Mouches parasites (Europe). Encycl. Ent. (A) **9,** 240 pp. (1928). Muscidæ. Gen. Insectorum, **205,** 595 pp. (1937).

SENIOR-WHITE, R. A. Indian Muscoids. Rec. Indian Mus., **32,** pt. 2, pp. 65–75 (1930).

SHANNON, R. C., and E. DEL PONTE. Argentine Calyptratæ. Rev. Inst. Bact. Buenos Aires, **4,** no. 5, pp. 549–590 (1926); **5,** no. 1, pp. 141–147 (1927).

STEIN, P. Cyclorrhapha schizophora (Central Asia). Ann. Mus. Zool. Acad. Sci. St. Petersburg, **12,** pp. 318–372 (1907).

Tao, S. M. Early Larvæ of Common Flies. American Jour. Hyg., **7**, pp. 735–761 (1927).

Thompson, W. R. Morphogenesis in Muscoids. Trans. Ent. Soc. London, **77**, pp. 195–244 (1929).

Townsend, C. H. T. Muscoid Taxonomy. Smithsonian Misc. Coll., **51**, no. 1803, 138 pp. (1908).

New Muscoidea (South America). Proc. U. S. Nat. Mus., **43**, pp. 301–367 (1912).

Relationships of Muscoid Flies. Canadian Ent., **45**, pp. 37–60 (1913).

New Muscoid Flies. Ins. Inscit. Menstr., **1**, pp. 144–148 (1913); **2**, pp. 10–16, 29–32, 42–48, 81–96, 123–128, 133–144, 153–160, 169–176, 183–187 (1914); **3**, pp. 91–104 (1915).

Muscoidea (U. S.). Jour. New York Ent. Soc., **23**, pp. 216–234 (1915).

New Muscoid Flies (Neotropical). Proc. U. S. Nat. Mus., **49**, pp. 405–440 (1915). Wiener Ent. Ztg., **44**, pp. 143–154 (1928). Rev. Chilena Hist. Nat., **32**, pp. 365–382 (1929).

New Genera of Muscoid Flies. Proc. U. S. Nat. Mus., **49**, pp. 617–633 (1916).

Muscoidea (Brazil). Bull. American Mus. Nat. Hist., **35**, pp. 15–22 (1916); **37**, pp. 221–233 (1917).

Oriental and African Muscoidea. Philippine Jour. Sci., **29**, pp. 529–544 (1926).

Muscoidea (Sumatra). Supplementa Ent., **14**, pp. 14–42 (1926); **16**, pp. 56–76 (1927).

New Muscoidea (Holarctic). Ins. Inscit. Menstr., **14**, pp. 24–41 (1926).

Œstromuscoid Flies. Rev. Ent. Rio Janeiro, **1**, pp. 65–104, 157–183, 313–354, 437–479 (1931). Ann. Mag. Nat. Hist., (10) **8**, pp. 369–391 (1931); (10) **9**, pp. 33–57 (1932). Jour. New York Ent. Soc., **40**, pp. 439–479 (1932).

Muscoideos (South America). Rev. Mus. São Paulo, **15**, pt. 1, pp. 205–386 (1927).

Muscoidea (Philippines). Philippine Jour. Sci., **33**, pp. 279–290 (1927); **34**, pp. 365–397 (1927).

Œstromuscoid Flies (Neotropical). Rev. Ent. Rio Janeiro, **4**, pp. 201–212, 390–406 (1934); **5**, pp. 216–233 (1935).

Manual of Myiology. 12 vols., 3780 pp., São Paulo, C. Townsend e Filhos (1934–1942).

Villeneuve, J. Myodaires supérieurs (China). Bull. Mus. Roy. Hist. Nat. Belgique, **13**, no. 34, 16 pp. (1937).

Myodaires supérieurs (Africa). Ibid., **13**, no 27, 4 pp. (1937); **13**, no. 35, 4 pp. (1937); **14**, no. 38, 16 pp. (1938).

Myodaires (South Africa). Ann. South African Mus., **15**, pp. 469–515 (1916). Rev. Zool. Africaine, **14**, pp. 64–69 (1926).

Myodaires supérieurs (Africa). Rev. Zool. Africaine, **3**, pp. 24–46, 146–156 (1913); **3**, pp. 429–441 (1914).

Myodaires supérieurs (Madagascar). Ibid., **4**, pp. 191–209 (1914).

Myodaires supérieurs (Formosa). Ibid., **15**, pp. 387–397 (1927).

Myodaires supérieurs (South Africa). Ibid., **8**, pp. 151–162 (1920).

Myodaires supérieurs nouveaux. Ann. Bull. Soc. Ent. Belgique, **68,** pp. 47–52 (1928); **69,** pp. 61–68, 99–105 (1929).
WAHLGREN, E. Schizophora (Sweden). 416 pp., Stockholm (1927).

CALLIPHORIDÆ, SARCOPHAGIDÆ

ALDRICH, J. M. Sarcophaga and Allies (North America). Thomas Say Foundation, **1,** 302 pp. (1916). Proc. U. S. Nat. Mus., **78,** no. 2855, 39 pp. (1930).
ALLEN, H. W. Miltogrammini (North America). Ibid., **68,** art. 9, 106 pp. (1926).
AUBERTIN, D. Hemipyrellia. Proc. Zool. Soc. London, **1931,** pp. 497–509.
Lucilia. Jour. Linn. Soc. London, **38,** pp. 389–436 (1933).
BARANOFF, N. Sarcophaga. Neue Beitr. Syst. Insektenk., **4,** pp. 142–153 (1929).
BEZZI, M. Calliphoridæ (South Pacific Isl.). Bull. Ent. Res., **17,** pp. 221–247 (1927).
BLANCHARD, E. E. Sarcofagidos argentinos. Physis, **17,** pp. 791–858 (1939); **19,** pp. 133–172 (1942).
BÖTTCHER, G. Male Sarcophagas. Deutsche Ent. Zeitschr., **1912,** pp. 343–350, 525–544.
BUXTON, P. A. Sarcophagidæ (Samoa). Insects of Samoa, **6,** fasc. 3, pp. 141–150, British Mus. (1929).
CURRAN, C. H. Tricyclea. Ann. Mag. Nat. Hist., (9) **19,** pp. 527–533 (1927).
Hoplacephala. Ibid., (10) **2,** pp. 417–427 (1928).
Calliphoridæ (Africa). American Mus. Novit., **506,** 22 pp. (1931).
Sarcophagidæ (Belgian Congo). Ibid., **727,** 31 pp. (1934).
ENDERLEIN, G. Sarcophagid Studies. Konowia, **7,** pp. 147–153 (1928).
Sarcophaginæ, Classification. Arch. Klass. Phylog. Ent. Wien, **1,** pp. 1–56 (1928).
ENGEL, E. O. Rutiliidæ. Zool. Jahrb. Syst., **50,** pp. 339–376 (1925).
GREENE, C. T. Puparia and Larvæ of Sarcophagidæ. Proc. U. S. Nat. Mus., **66,** no. 2566, 26 pp. (1925).
HALL, D. G. Sarcophaginæ (Patagonia). Diptera of Patagonia and South Chile, **7,** fasc. 3, pp. 347–375, British Mus. (1937).
Blowflies of North America. Thomas Say Foundation, **4,** 477 pp. (1948).
HALL, D. G., and G. E. BOHART. Sarcophagidæ of Guam. Proc. Ent. Soc. Washington, **50,** pp. 127–136 (1948).
HALLOCK, H. C. Sarcophaginæ (New York). Jour. New York Ent. Soc., **48,** pp. 127–153, 201–231 (1940); **50,** pp. 215–240 (1942).
HARDY, G. H. Calliphora. Proc. Linn. Soc. New South Wales, **62,** pp. 17–26 (1937).
Sarcophaginæ (Australia, New Zealand). Ibid., **68,** pp. 17–32 (1943).
Calliphoridæ (Australia). Proc. Roy. Soc. Queensland, **51,** pp. 133–146 (1940); **57,** pp. 53–56 (1947).
HO, C. Sarcophaga (China). Bull. Fan Mem. Inst. Biol., **3,** pp. 345–360 (1932).
Sarcophaga (Hainan Isl.). Ibid., **6,** pp. 207–215 (1936).
Sarcophaga (Java). Ann. Trop. Med. Parasitol., **32,** pp. 279–285 (1938).
JOHNSTON, T. H., and G. H. HARDY. Sarcophaga (Australia). Proc. Linn. Soc. New South Wales, **48,** pp. 94–129 (1923). Proc. Roy. Soc. Queensland, **35,** pp. 21–42 (1923).

JOHNSTON, T. H., and O. W. TIEGS. Australian Sarcophagidæ. Ibid., **33**, pp. 46–90 (1922); **34**, pp. 77–104, 181–190 (1922). Rec. Australian Mus., **13**, pp. 175–188 (1922).

LAAKE, E. W., E. C. CUSHING and H. E. PARISH. Screwworm Flies. U. S. Dept. Agr. Tech. Bull., **500**, 24 pp. (1936).

MALLOCH, J. R. Exotic Rhiniinæ. Ann. Mag. Nat. Hist., (9) **18**, pp. 496–522 (1926).

 Calliphoridæ (Australia). Proc. Linn. Soc. New South Wales, **52**, pp. 299–335 (1927).

 Calliphoridæ (Africa). Ann. Mag. Nat. Hist., (10) **3**, pp. 272–278; **4**, pp. 97–120 (1929).

MATTOS, W. B. Sarcophagidæ (São Paulo). 115 pp., São Paulo (1919).

MILLER, D. Blow-flies (New Zealand). Monogr. Cawthron Inst., **2**, 68 pp. (1939).

PATTON, W. S., and E. C. CUSHING. Calliphoridæ, Genitalia. Ann. Trop. Med. Parasitol., **28**, pp. 107–130, 205–223, 305–314 (1934).

PARKER, R. R. Ravinia and Böttcheria (New England). Proc. Boston Soc. Nat. Hist., **35**, pp. 1–77 (1914).

PRADO, A., and F. DA FONSECA. Sarcophagidæ (São Paulo). Rev. Med. Cirurg. Brasil, **40**, pp. 35–39 (1932). Mem. Inst. Butantan, **7**, pp. 161–171 (1932).

RICHARDS, O. W. British Lucilias. Trans. Ent. Soc. London, **74**, pp. 255–260 (1926).

ROHDENDORF, B. Miltogramminen-Studien. Zool. Anz., **62**, pp. 80–85 (1925); **71**, pp. 157–169 (1927). Encycl. Ent. (B) II, **2**, pp. 61–72 (1925). Ent. Mitt., **15**, pp. 394–397 (1926).

 Calliphoridæ, Genitalia. Rev. Zool. Russe, **6**, pp. 83–128 (1926). (In Russian)

 Sarcophagidæ, Subfamilies. Konowia, **7**, pp. 319–321 (1928).

 Sarcophagids Parasitic on Acridids. Uzbekistan Exp. Sta. Prot. Plants, **14**, 66 pp. (1929). (In Russian) Bull. Plant Prot. Ent., **3**, pp. 171–190 (1932). (In Russian)

 Sarcophaginæ. Fliegen Palæarkt. Reg., **39**, 128 pp. (1930–1935).

 Sarcophaginæ (Sichote-Alin). Trans. Sikhote-Alin St. Res. Moscow, **2**, pp. 87–110 (1938). (In Russian)

 Stackelbergomyiidæ. C. R. Acad. Sci. URSS, **63**, pp. 455–458 (1948).

ROUBAUD, E. Auchmeromyies (Calliphorines) (Africa). Bull. Sci. France et Belgique, **47**, pp. 105–202 (1913).

SALEM, H. H. Sarcophaga (Egypt). Bull. Soc. Roy. Ent. Egypte, **20**, pp. 229–247 (1936).

 Wohlfartia. Publ. Egypt. Univ. Fac. Med., **13**, 90 pp. (1938).

 Agriella. Ibid., **14**, 16 pp. (1938).

 New Sarcophagas (Australasia). Bull. Inst. Egypt., **27**, pp. 183–213 (1946).

SÉGUY, E. Calliphoridæ (Western Europe). Encycl. Ent. (A), **9**, pp. 89–192 (1928).

 Chrysomyiini. Encycl. Ent. (B) II, **4**, pp. 101–116 (1928).

 Diptères parasites des sauterelles. Ibid., **6**, pp. 11–40 (1932).

 Calliphorines. Ibid., **8**, pp. 121–150 (1935).

 Sarcophagines et Rhinophorines. Encycl. Ent. (A), **21**, 436 pp. (1941).

 Calliphoridæ (Orient). Encycl. Ent. (B) II, **10**, pp. 81–90 (1946).

Lucilia (Europe). Entomologiste, Paris, **4**, pp. 172–178 (1948).
Les Calliphorides Thelychætiformes. Rev. brasiliera Biol., **9**, pp. 115–142 (1949).

SENIOR-WHITE, R. Sarcophaginæ (Orient). Rec. Indian Mus., **26**, pp. 193–283 (1924).
Oriental Rhiniinæ. Ibid., **27**, pp. 81–96 (1925).
Calliphoridæ (Orient). Ibid., **28**, pp. 127–140 (1926).

SENIOR-WHITE, R., D. AUBERTIN and J. SMART. Calliphoridæ (Orient). 288 pp. London (1940).

SHANNON, R. C. Calliphoridæ. Ins. Inscit. Menstr., **11**, pp. 101–118 (1923); **12**, pp. 67–81 (1924). Proc. Ent. Soc. Washington, **28**, pp. 115–139 (1926).

SHANNON, R. C., and I. D. DOBROSCKY. Protocalliphora. Jour. Washington Acad. Sci., **14**, pp. 247–253 (1924).

SMART, J. Calliphoridæ (Patagonia). Diptera of Patagonia and South Chile, **7**, fasc. 3, pp. 376–384, British Mus. (1937).

SMIT, B. Sheep Blow-flies (South Africa). Rep. Vet. Res. South Africa, **17**, pp. 299–421 (1931).

SMIT, B., and S. DU PLESSIS. Blow-flies (South Africa). Bull. Dept. Agric. South Africa, **13**, 19 pp. (1927).

SOUZA LOPES, H. DE. Sarcophagidæ (Neotropical). Arch. Inst. Biol. Veg., **3**, pp. 71–90 (1936).
Sarcophagidæ, Paratypes. Mus. Univ. São Paulo, **21**, pp. 839–853 (1936).
New Sarcophagidæ (Neotropical). Mem. Inst. Oswaldo Cruz, **33**, pp. 333–348 (1938).
Sarcophagidæ do Deutsches Entomologisches Museums. Ibid., **33**, pp. 555–565 (1938).
Helicobia. Rev. Ent. Rio Janeiro, **10**, pp. 497–517 (1939).
Udamopyga. Ibid., **11**, pp. 924–954 (1940).
Sarcophagidæ (Hawaii). Proc. Hawaiian Ent. Soc., **11**, pp. 53–56 (1941).
Sarcophagidæ (Neotropical). Arq. Zool. São Paulo, **2**, pp. 357–387 (1941).
Sarcophagid Larvæ. Mem. Inst. Oswaldo Cruz, **38**, pp. 127–163 (1943).
Notochæta. Ibid., **42**, pp. 503–550 (1945).
Sarcophagidæ (Mexico). Ibid., **44**, pp. 119–146 (1946); **45**, pp. 555–570 (1948).
New Neotropical Sarcophagidæ. Rev. brasiliera Biol., **6**, pp. 117–131 (1946).
Notochæta e Dexosarcophaga. Ibid., **10**, pp. 353–364 (1950).

THOMAS, H. T. Blowfly Genera (Szechuan, China). Proc. Zool. Soc. London, **121**, pp. 147–200 (1951).

TIENSUU, L. Sarcophagidæ (Finland). Acta Ent. Fennici, **5**, pp. 255–266 (1939).

TOWNSEND, C. H. T. Genera of Sarcophagini. Proc. Biol. Soc. Washington, **30**, pp. 189–198 (1917).
Indian Rhiniinæ. Rec. Indian Mus., **13**, pt. 4, pp. 185–202 (1917).

VENTURI, F. Miltogrammi e Metopiini (Italy). Redia, (2) **32**, pp. 119–139 (1947).

WARDLE, R. A. Calliphorinæ, Frequency in Great Britain. American Jour. Hyg., 26, pp. 441–464 (1927).

ZUMPT, F., and H. J. HEINZ. Calliphora and Sarcophaga, Male Terminalia. Ent. Mon. Mag., 86, pp. 207–216 (1950).

TACHINIDÆ, PHASIIDÆ, DEXIIDÆ

ALDRICH, J. M. Metallic Green Tachinids. Ins. Inscit. Menstr., 14, pp. 51–58 (1926).

Tachinids with Retracted Hind Crossvein. Trans. American Ent. Soc., 52, pp. 7–28 (1926).

Cylindromyia. Proc. U. S. Nat. Mus., 68, no. 2624, 27 pp. (1926).

Microphthalma. Ibid., 69, no. 2638, 8 pp. (1926).

Belvosia. Ibid., 73, no. 2729, 45 pp. (1928).

Spathimeigenia. Ibid., 80, no. 2911, 10 pp. (1931).

Tachinidæ (Patagonia). Diptera of Patagonia and South Chile, 7, fasc. 1, 170 pp., British Mus. (1934).

ALDRICH, J. M., and R. T. WEBBER. Phorocera. Proc. U. S. Nat. Mus., 63, art. 17, 90 pp. (1924).

ALLEN, H. W. Achætoneura. Trans. American Ent. Soc., 52, pp. 187–198 (1926).

List of Tachinidæ (Mississippi). Ann. Ent. Soc. America, 22, pp. 676–690 (1929).

ARNAUD, P. H. Paradejeania. Canadian Ent., 83, pp. 317–329 (1951).

BAER, W. Tachinidæ, Classification. Zeitschr. Angewandte Ent., 6, pp. 185–246 (1921); 7, pp. 97–163, 349–423 (1921).

BARANOFF, N. Serbian Dexiinæ. Encycl. Ent. (B) II, 3, pp. 56–60 (1926).

Serbian Tachinidæ. Ibid., 4, pp. 31–44 (1927). Let. Poljoprivr. Sta. Topcideru, 1, pp. 153–184 (1926). (In Serbian).

Echinomyia, Ocyptera (Jugoslavia). Inst. Hyg. Schule Volks. Zagreb, 2, 22 pp. (1929).

Carcelia. Ibid., 3, 45 pp. (1931). Trans. Roy. Soc. London, 82, pp. 387–408 (1934).

Tachinidæ (East Indies). Vet. Archiv, Zagreb, 4, pp. 472–485 (1934).

Tachinidæ (Palæarctic and Oriental). Ibid., 5, pp. 550–560 (1935).

Tachinidæ (Solomon and New Britain Isl.). Ann. Mag. Nat. Hist., (10) 17, pp. 97–113 (1936).

BEESON, C. F. C., and S. N. CHATTERJEE. Biology of Tachinidæ. Indian Forest Rec., 1, pp. 169–184 (1935).

BELANOVSKII, J. D. Tachinidæ (Kiev). Trav. Mus. Zool. Kiev, 10, pp. 17–42 (1931).

BEZZI, M. Fissicorn Tachinidæ. Proc. Linn. Soc. New South Wales, 48, pp. 647–659 (1923).

Euthera. Ibid., 50, pp. 275–283 (1925).

Tachinidæ (4th vein obliterated at apex). Ann. Mag. Nat. Hist., (9) 17, pp. 236–241 (1926).

BLANCHARD, E. E. Tachinidæ (La Plata). Rev. Mus. La Plata, Zool., 2, pp. 341–379 (1941); 3, pp. 123–161 (1943).

BROOKS, A. R. Ernestia (Canada). Canadian Ent., 75, pp. 66–78 (1943). Gonia (North America). 75, pp. 219–236 (1943). Linnæmyia (North

America). **76,** pp. 193–206 (1944). Girschneria. **77,** pp. 184–185 (1945). Rhodogyne (Gymnosoma). **77,** pp. 218–230 (1945). Leschenaultia (North America). **78,** pp. 169–182 (1947). Phasia complex (North America). Sci. Agr. Ottawa, **25,** pp. 647–679 (1945).

COQUILLETT, D. W. Tachinidæ. U. S. Dept. Agr. Tech. Ser. Bull., **7,** 156 pp. (1897).

CORTES, P. Sturmia (Chile). Bol. Mus. Nac. Hist. Nat. Chile, **22,** pp. 159–167 (1944).

COUPIN, L. Tachinides de Normandie. Bull. Soc. Sci. Nat. Rouen, (9) **74–75,** pp. 96–106 (1941).

CURRAN, C. H. Peleteria. Trans. Roy. Soc. Canada, **19,** sect. 5, pp. 225–257 (1925).

Cryptomeigenia and Tachinomyia. Ibid., **20,** pp. 155–171 (1926).
Lydella. Canadian Ent., **59,** pp. 11–24 (1927).
Tachinidæ (Africa). Bull. Ent. Res., **17,** pp. 319–340 (1927); **18,** pp. 103–128 (1927); **18,** pp. 237–245 (1928).
Archytas (America). Canadian Ent., **60,** pp. 201–208, 218–226, 249–256, 275–282 (1928).
Cylindromyia (Africa). Ann. Mag. Nat. Hist., (10) **14,** pp. 121–142 (1934).
Calodexia. American Mus. Novit., **685,** 21 pp. (1934).
Tachinidæ (Africa). Ibid., **751,** 25 pp. (1934); **985,** 8 pp. (1938); **1022,** 5 pp. (1939); **1111,** 11 pp. (1941).
New Tachinidæ. Proc. Linn. Soc. New South Wales, **63,** pp. 185–206 (1938).
Macromyia. American Mus. Novit., **1020,** 3 pp. (1939).
Phorocera. Ibid., **1063,** 13 pp. (1939).
Tachinidæ. Bull. American Mus. Nat. Hist., **89,** art. 2, 122 pp. (1947).

CUTHBERTSON, A. List of Tachinidæ (Rhodesia). Occ. Pap. Nat. Mus. Southern Rhodesia, **10,** pp. 5–19 (1941).
Tachinids and Hosts. Trans. Rhodesia Sci. Assn., **38,** pp. 88–118 (1941).

DAY, C. D. British Tachinidæ. Northwest Nat., **21,** suppl., pp. 1–32 (1946); **22,** suppl., pp. 65–150 (1947). Arbroath, T. Buncle and Co. (reprint) 150 pp. (1948).

DUPUIS, C. Phasiinæ cimicophages. Ann. Parasitol., **2?**, pp. 201–232, 397–441 (1947); **24,** pp. 503–646 (1950).

EMDEN, F. VAN. Phasiinæ (Ethiopia). Proc. Zool. Soc. London, **114,** pp. 389–436 (1945).
Dexiinæ (Ethiopia). Ibid., **116,** pp. 627–674 (1947).

ENDERLEIN, G. Rutiliinen. Veröff. Deutsch. Kol. Mus., **1,** pp. 397–436 (1936).

ENGEL, E. O. Hystriciidæ (Neotropical). Zool. Jahrb. Syst., **43,** pp. 273–328 (1920).
Rutiliidæ, *sensu lat.* Ibid., **50,** pp. 339–376 (1925).

FATTIG, P. W. Larvævoridæ (Georgia). Emory Univ. Mus. Bull., **1949,** pp. 1–38.

GARDNER, J. C. M. Tachinidæ, Puparia (India). Indian Forest Rec., Ent., **6,** pp. 227–251 (1940).

GREENE, C. T. Tachinids (with 4th vein evanescent). Proc. Ent. Soc. Washington, **36,** pp. 27–40 (1934).

Ho, C., and W. S. Patton. Portschinskia. Bull. Fan Mem. Inst. Biol., 7, pp. 145–158 (1937).

Jacentkovsky, D. Tachinidæ (Central Europe). Bull. Inst. Nat. Agron. Brünn, (D) 20, 7 pp. (1933); 22, 38 pp. (1934). Mitt. Naturw. Inst. Sofia, 9, pp. 109–134 (1936). Acta Soc. Ent. Cechosloveniae, 33, pp. 76–90 (1936). Acta Soc. Sci. Nat. Moravicae, 13, no. 4, pp. 1–64 (1941). Sborn. Ent. Odd. Zemsk. Mus., 19, pp. 76–80 (1941); 20, pp. 172–187 (1942); 21–22, pp. 380–395 (1944).

James, M. T. Leskiini (with Setulose R₁). Proc. U. S. Nat. Mus., 97, pp. 91–115 (1947).

Kramer, H. Tachiniden (Oberlausitz). Abh. Naturf. Ges. Görlitz, 27, pp. 117–166 (1911).

Lundbeck, W. Danish Tachinoidea. Diptera Danica, 7, pp. 40–560 (1927).

Malloch, J. R. Notes on Australian Tachinidæ. Proc. Linn. Soc. New South Wales, 52, pp. 336–353 (1927).
Catalogue of Australian Tachinidæ. Ibid., 53, pp. 651–662 (1928).
Keys to Australian Genera, Tachinidæ. Ibid., 54, pp. 283–343 (1929).
Key to Genera of Ormiini. Ann. Mag. Nat. Hist., (10) 3, pp. 278–280 (1929).

Mesnil, L. Tachinaires. Monogr. Sta. Lab. Rech. Agron. Paris, 1939, 67 pp.
Larvævoridæ. Verb. 7 Intern. Kongr. Ent., 1, pp. 319–328 (1939).
Larvævorinæ. Fliegen Palæarkt. Reg., 64, 104 pp. (1944–1949).
Phorocerini (Old World). Encycl. Ent. (B) II, 10, pp. 37–80 (1946).
Drino. Bull. Inst. Sci. Nat. Belgique, 25, no. 42, 38 pp. (1949).
Protachinidæ (Africa). Bull. Ann. Soc. Ent. Belgique, 86, pp. 104–117 (1950).

Morrison, F. O. Gonia (America). Canadian Jour. Res., 18, (D), pp. 336–362 (1940).

Müller, A. German Tachinidæ. Nova Acta Leop., Halle, 108, pp. 1–30 (1926). Konowia, 5, pp. 72–78, 233–246 (1926).

Petzold, W. Hypopygidium of Tachinidæ. 50 pp., Jena (1927).

Reinhard, H. J. New Tachinidæ (North America). Bull. Brooklyn Ent. Soc., 29, pp. 150–154, 186–196 (1934).
Ceratomyiella and Paradidyma (North America). Proc. U. S. Nat. Mus., 83, no. 2973, 43 pp. (1934).
Cuphocera. Ibid., 83, no. 2974, pp. 45–70 (1934).
New Genera and Species of Muscoids. Bull. Brooklyn Ent. Soc., 34, pp. 61–74 (1939).
Eumacronychia. Jour. New York Ent. Soc., 47, pp. 57–68 (1939).
Muscopteryx. Ann. Ent. Soc. America, 37, pp. 352–358 (1944).
New Species of Tachinidæ. Canadian Ent., 77, pp. 28–36 (1945). Jour. Kansas Ent. Soc., 18, pp. 66–77 (1945).
Minthozelia (U. S.). Ibid., 19, pp. 52–59 (1946).
Pseudochæta and Phenopsis (North America). Canadian Ent., 78, pp. 111–121 (1946).
Siphophyto and Coronimyia. Proc. Ent. Soc. Washington, 48, pp. 79–92 (1946).
Chaetophlepsis. Jour. Kansas Ent. Soc., 25, pp. 13–21 (1952).

Riedel, M. P. Tachinidæ (Frankfurt). Deutsche Ent. Zeitschr., 1934, pp. 252–272 (1935).

RINGDAHL, O. Tachinidæ (Norway). Aarsh. Tromsø Mus., 65, no. 4, p. 1–11 (1944).
    Tachinidæ (Sweden). Ent. Tidskr., 66, pp. 177–219 (1945).
ROHDENDORF, B. B. Egyptian Larvævoridæ. Bull. Soc. Roy. Ent. Egypte, 18, pp. 1–16 (1934).
ROWE, J. A. Fabriciella, Males. Ann. Ent. Soc. America, 24, pp. 643–678 (1931).
SABROSKY, C. W. Eudejeania. Proc. U. S. Nat. Mus., 97, no. 3215, pp. 141–156 (1947).
    Trichopodini. Jour. Washington Acad. Sci., 40, pp. 361–371 (1950).
SCHAFFNER, J. V., and C. I. GRISWOLD. Parasites of Macrolepidoptera. Misc. Publ. U. S. Dept. Agr., 188, 160 pp. (1934).
SELLERS, W. F. Zenillia. Proc. U. S. Nat. Mus., 93, no. 3157, 108 pp. (1943).
SENIOR-WHITE, R. Oriental Tachinidæ. Spolia Zeylandica, 13, pp. 103–119 (1924).
SOUZA LOPES, H. DE. Oxysarcodexia. Bol. Escuela Nac. Vet. Brasil, 1, pp. 62–134 (1946).
STEIN, P. Tachiniden Mitteleuropas. Arch. Naturg., Abt. A, 90, Heft 6, 271 pp. (1924). Critique: Villeneuve, Konowia, 10, pp. 47–74 (1931).
SUSTER, P. M. Tachinaires en Roumanie. Ann. Sci. Univ. Jassy, 14, pp. 525–535 (1927); 16, pp. 57–248 (1930); 16, pp. 585–600 (1931); 18, pp. 479–511 (1933). Bull. Sect. Sci. Acad. Roumaine, 15, pp. 219–234 (1932).
THORNLEY, A. Tachinidæ and Muscidæ (Cornish). Trans. Soc. British Ent., 2, pp. 87–114 (1935).
TOTHILL, J. D. Ernestia. Canadian Ent., 53, 20 pp. (1921).
    Gonia. Ibid., 56, 12 pp. (1924).
    Fabriciella. Ibid., 56, pp. 257–269 (1924).
VIMMER, A. Exorista. Acta Soc. Ent. Cechosloveniæ, 29, pp. 126–137 (1932). (In Czech)
    Tachinidæ (Czechoslovakia). Sborn. Ent. Odd. Nar. Mus., 11, pp. 99–127 (1933).
WAINWRIGHT, C. J. British Tachinidæ. Trans. Ent. Soc. London, 76, pp. 139–254 (1928); 80, pp. 405–424 (1932); 90, pp. 411–448 (1940).
WEBBER, R. T. Achætoneura. Proc. U. S. Nat. Mus., 78, no. 2853, 37 pp. (1930).
    Tachinomyia. Ibid., 90, no. 3108, pp. 287–304 (1941).
WEST, L. S. New Tachinidæ (New York). Jour. New York Ent. Soc., 33, pp. 121–135 (1925).
    Rhynchodexia. Pap. Michigan Acad. Sci., 34, pp. 109–118 (1948).

MUSCIDÆ AND GLOSSINIDÆ

ALDRICH, J. M. Mesembrinella (Neotropical). Proc. U. S. Nat. Mus., 62, art. 11, 24 pp. (1922).
AUSTEN, E. E. Monograph of the Tsetse-flies. 319 pp., British Mus. (1903).
    Handbook of the Tsetse-flies. 110 pp., British Mus. (1911).
AUSTEN, E. E., and E. HEGH. Tsetse-flies. Publ. British Imp. Bur. Ent., 188 pp. (1922).
BEZZI, M. Lyperosia. Arch. Parasitol., 15, pp. 1–38 (1911).

BRUNETTI, E. Oriental Bloodsucking Muscidæ. Rec. Indian Mus., **4**, no. 4, pp. 59–93 (1910).

CURRAN, C. H. African Muscidæ. American Mus. Novit., **776**, 27 pp. (1935); **788**, 17 pp. (1935); **931**, 14 pp. (1937); **974**, 17 pp. (1938).

EMDEN, F. VAN. Muscinæ and Stomoxydinæ. Ruwenzori Exped., **2**, no. 3, pp. 49–89, British Mus. (1939).

    Muscidæ (Abyssinia). Ann. Mag. Nat. Hist., (11) **8**, pp. 210–234 (1941); **14**, pp. 460–484 (1948).

    Dichætomyia (Ethiopian). Ibid., (11) **9**, pp. 673–701, 721–736 (1942).

    Muscidæ. Exped. to Southwest Arabia, **1**, pp. 161–175, British Mus. (1948).

    Muscidæ. Ruwenzori Exped., **2**, no. 6, pp. 325–710, British Mus. (1951).

ENDERLEIN, G. Stomoxinæ. Zeitschr. Angewandte Ent., **14**, pp. 356–368 (1929).

GAMINARA, A. Muscidæ y Calliphoridæ (Uruguay). Arch. Soc. Biol. Montevideo, Suppl. **5**, pp. 1237–1280 (1931).

HALL, D. G. New Muscoid Flies. Proc. U. S. Nat. Mus., **84**, no. 3011, pp. 201–216 (1937).

HEGH, E. Les Tsé-tsés. 742 pp., Bruxelles (1929).

HO, C. Blood-sucking Muscidæ (Peiping). Bull. Fan Mem. Inst. Biol., **6**, pp. 185–206 (1936).

HOUGH, G. DEN. Muscidæ (Somaliland). Proc. Acad. Nat. Sci. Philadelphia, **1898**, pp. 165–187.

    Muscidæ (South America). Kansas Univ. Quart., A, **9**, pp. 203–232 (1900).

JACK, R. W. Tsetse Fly in Rhodesia. Bull. Ent. Res., **10**, pp. 71–90 (1919).

KARL, O. Muscidæ (Germany). Tierwelt Deutschlands, **13**, 232 pp. (1928). Zool. Anz., **86**, pp. 161–174 (1930). Stettiner Ent. Ztg., **97**, pp. 137–140 (1936); **104**, pp. 64–77 (1943).

    Exotic Muscidæ. Arb. Morph. Taxon. Ent., **2**, pp. 29–49 (1935).

KATO, S. Muscinæ of Hokkaido. Kontyu, **11**, pp. 59–69 (1937). (In Japanese)

KRAMER, H. Muscidæ (Oberlausitz). Abh. Naturf. Ges. Görlitz, **28**, pp. 257–352 (1917).

MALLOCH, J. R. Key to Australian Muscidæ. Proc. Linn. Soc. New South Wales, **50**, pp. 45–46 (1925).

    Muscidæ (Sumatra). Ent. Mitt., **17**, pp. 290–303, 310–336 (1928).

    Anthomyiinae, Muscinæ (Buruana). Treubia, **7**, pp. 390–408 (1929).

    Muscidæ (Samoa). Insects of Samoa, **6**, fasc. 3, pp. 151–175, British Mus. (1929).

    Muscidæ (Patagonia). Diptera of Patagonia and South Chile, **7**, fasc. 2, pp. 171–346, British Mus. (1934).

NEWSTEAD, R., A. M. EVANS and W. H. POTTS. Tsetse-flies. Mem. Liverpool Sch. Trop. Med., N. S. **1**, 268 pp. (1924).

PATTON, W. S. Oriental Muscas. Philippine Jour. Sci., **23**, pp. 309–355 (1923). Glossina. Ann. Trop. Med. Parasitol., **28**, pp. 315–322, 579–588 (1934).

PATTON, W. S., and E. G. GIBBINS. The Metallic Muscini. Ibid., **28**, pp. 571–578 (1934).

PATTON, W. S., and R. SENIOR-WHITE. Oriental Muscas. Rec. Indian Mus., **26**, pp. 553–577 (1924).

Ringdahl, O. Muscinæ, Key. (Sweden). Ent. Tidskr., **50**, pp. 8–13, 273 (1929).

Muscidæ (Kamchatka). Ark. Zool., **21 A**, no. 20, 16 pp. (1930).

Prosalpia. Ent. Tidskr., **63**, pp. 134–146 (1942).

Muscidæ (Norway). Arsh. Tromsø Mus., **65**, no. 4, pp. 12–27 (1944).

Séguy, E. French Muscids. Trav. Nat. Loing, **3**, pp. 19–45 (1929).

Pollenia. Rev. franç. Ent., **1**, pp. 44–51 (1934).

Les Stomoxydines. Encycl. Ent. (B) II, **8**, pp. 15–59 (1935).

Snyder, F. M. Ethiopian Muscinæ. American Mus. Novit., **1533**, 42 pp. (1951).

Summers, S. L. M. Blood-sucking Muscidæ. Jour. London Sch. Trop. Med., **1**, pp. 189–205 (1912).

Surcouf, J. M. R. Muscidæ testaceæ. Nouv. Arch. Mus. Hist. Nat. Paris, (5) **6**, pp. 27–124 (1920).

Tiensuu, L. Muscidæ (Finland). Acta Soc. Faun. Fl. Fennica, **59**, no. 4, 56 pp. (1935). Acta Ent. Fennici, **5**, pp. 241–255 (1939).

Townsend, C. H. T. Connectant Forms between Muscoid and Anthomyoid Flies. Ann. Ent. Soc. America, **7**, pp. 160–167 (1914).

Zavattari, E. Affinity between Hippoboscidæ and Glossinidæ. Atti Soc. Italiana Sci. Nat., **67**, pp. 37–70 (1928).

Zumpt, F. Die Tsetsefliegen. 149 pp., Jena (1936).

Glossina, Sex Apparatus. Zeitschr. Parasitenk., **8**, pp. 546–560 (1936).

Stomoxydinæ. Zeitschr. Angewandte Ent., **25**, pp. 337–353 (1938). Verh. 7 Intern. Kongr. Ent., **3**, pp. 1723–1733 (1939).

Stomoxys (Africa, Orient). Zeitschr. Angewandte Ent., **27**, pp. 126–141 (1940).

ANTHOMYIIDÆ

Aldrich, J. M. Lispa (Nearctic). Jour. New York Ent. Soc., **21**, pp. 126–146 (1913).

Fucellia (North America). Proc. California Acad. Sci., **8**, pp. 157–179 (1918).

Philornis. Ann. Ent. Soc. America, **16**, pp. 304–309 (1923).

Becker, T. Lispa (Palæarctic). Zeitschr. f. Ent., **29**, pp. 1–70 (1904).

Cœnosiinæ (Corsica). Deutsche Ent. Zeitschr., **1911**, pp. 62–100.

Brooks, A. R. Root Maggot Flies (Canada). Canadian Ent., **83**, pp. 109–120 (1951).

Collin, J. E. British Limnophora. Ent. Mon. Mag., **7**, 32 pp. (1921).

Hammomyia and Hylephila. Trans. Ent. Soc. London, **1921**, pp. 305–326.

Emden, F. van. Cœnosiinæ. Ruwenzori Exped., **2**, no. 4, pp. 91–255, British Mus. (1940).

Anthomyiinæ (Ethiopian). Bull. Ent. Res., **32**, pp. 251–275 (1941).

Phaonia. Ann. Mag. Nat. Hist., (11) **10**, pp. 73–101 (1943).

Anthomyiinæ. Ruwenzori Exped., **2**, no. 6, pp. 325–710, British Mus. (1951).

Huckett, H. C. The Ovipositor of Anthomyiidæ. Ann. Ent. Soc. America, **14**, pp. 290–328 (1921).

Anthomyiinæ (New York). Mem. Cornell Agric. Exp. Sta., **77**, pp. 1–91 (1924).

Anthomyiidæ on Willow Catkins. Bull. Brooklyn Ent. Soc., **23**, pp. 70–83 (1928).

Hylemyia (Canada). Canadian Ent., **61**, pp. 93–96, 110–119, 136–144, 161–168, 180–190 (1929).

Limnophora. Jour. New York Ent. Soc., **40**, pp. 25–76, 105–158, 279–338 (1932).

Cœnosia. Trans. American Ent. Soc., **60**, pp. 57–118, 133–198 (1934).

Cœnosia and Limnophora. Jour. New York Ent. Soc., **44**, pp. 187–222 (1936).

Pegomyia. Trans. American Ent. Soc., **65**, pp. 1–36 (1939). Mem. American Ent. Soc., **10**, 131 pp. (1941).

Leucophora. Jour. New York Ent. Soc., **48**, pp. 335–364 (1940).

Hydrophoria. Ann. Ent. Soc. America, **37**, pp. 261–297 (1944).

Eremomyioides. Jour. New York Ent. Soc., **52**, pp. 361–368 (1944).

Hylemyia, Subgenera. Bull. Brooklyn Ent. Soc., **41**, pp. 110–125 (1946).

Botanophila. Jour. New York Ent Soc., **55**, pp. 1–33 (1947).

Pycnoglossa. Ibid., **57**, pp. 51–65 (1949).

Phorbia. Bull. Brooklyn Ent. Soc., **42**, pp. 109–125 (1948).

Paraprosalpia. Ibid., **45**, pp. 121–143 (1950).

Eremomyia (North America). Jour. New York Ent. Soc., **59**, pp. 75–91 (1951).

Hylemyia (North America). Proc. Ent. Soc. Washington, **53**, pp. 251–260 (1951).

JOHANNSEN, O. A. Anthomyiidæ (Eastern U. S.). Trans. American Ent. Soc., **42**, pp. 385–398 (1916).

KARL, O. Anthomyiidæ (Central Europe). Tierwelt Deutschlands, **13**, pp. 15–232 (1928).

Corrections and Additions. Zool. Anz., **86**, pp. 161–174 (1930). Stettiner Ent. Ztg., **97**, pp. 137–140 (1936); **104**, pp. 64–77 (1943).

KEILIN, D. Anthomyides with Carnivorous Larvæ. Parasitol., **9**, pp. 325–450 (1917).

MALLOCH, J. R. Anthomyidæ, Subfamilies. Canadian Ent., **49**, pp. 406–408 (1917).

Anthomyiidæ (North America). Trans. American Ent. Soc., **46**, pp. 133–196 (1920).

Anthomyidæ and Scatophagidæ (Katmai Exped.). Ohio Jour. Sci., **20**, pp. 267–288 (1920).

Cœnosiinæ. Ent. News, **32**, pp. 106–107, 201–205 (1921). Ann. Mag. Nat. Hist., (9) **10**, pp. 573–587 (1922).

Lispinæ, Genera. Ibid., (9) **10**, pp. 379–391 (1922).

Anthomyiidæ (Africa). Ibid., (9) **10**, pp. 573–587 (1922).

Phaoniinæ (North America). Trans. American Ent. Soc., **48**, pp. 227–282 (1923).

Keys to Various Australian Anthomyiidæ. Proc. Linn. Soc. New South Wales, **50**, pp. 36–45 (1925).

Indian Atherigona. Mem. Dept. Agric. India, Ent. Ser., **8**, pp. 110–126 (1925).

Philippine Dichætomyia. Philippine Jour. Sci., **26**, pp. 321–332 (1925).

Anthomyiidæ (Sumatra). Ent. Mitt., **17,** pp. 290–336 (1928).

Lispocephala (Hawaii). Proc. Hawaiian Ent. Soc., **7,** pp. 67–89 (1928).

RINGDAHL, O. Anthomyidæ (Sweden). Ent. Tidskr., **35,** pp. 142–154 (1914).

Nordische Anthomyiden. Ibid., **39,** pp. 148–194 (1918).

Phaonia. Ibid., **44,** pp. 117–140 (1923).

Mydæa and Helina. Ibid., **45,** pp. 39–66 (1924).

Hydrotæa. Ibid., **46,** pp. 7–20 (1925).

New Northern Muscidæ. Ibid., **47,** pp. 101–118 (1926).

Anthomyidæ (Northern Norway). Aarsh. Tromsø Mus., **49,** no. 3, 60 pp. (1928).

Hylemyia (Sweden). Ent. Tidskr., **54,** pp. 1–35 (1933).

Fannia (Sweden). Ibid., **55,** pp. 105–121 (1934).

Pegomyia (Sweden). Ibid., **59,** pp. 190–213 (1938).

Limnophora. Ibid., **62,** pp. 206–221 (1941).

Cœnosiinæ. Ibid., **66,** pp. 7–22 (1945).

Hydrophoria and Acroptena. Ibid., **67,** pp. 158–168 (1946).

Hylemyia. Aarsh. Tromsø Mus., **65,** no. 2, 16 pp. (1943).

SABROSKY, C. W. Ophyra (Pacific). Proc. Hawaiian Ent. Soc., **13,** pp. 423–432 (1949).

SCHNABL, J., and H. DZIEDZICKI. Die Anthomyiden. Nova Acta Leop., Halle, **95,** pp. 53–358 (1911).

SÉGUY, E. Anthomyides (Europe). Faune de France, **6,** 400 pp. (1923).

Etudes sur Anthomyides. Encycl. Ent. (B) II, **6,** pp. 71–82 (1932); **8,** pp. 97–116 (1935); **9,** pp. 109–120 (1938).

SHIZUO, K. Hylemyia. Bot. Zool. Tokyo, **7,** pp. 1367–1576 (1939). (In Japanese)

SNYDER, F. M. Myospila. American Mus. Novit., **1087,** 10 pp. (1940).

Mydæini (Neotropical). Ibid., **1141,** 22 pp. (1941).

Mydæa (Nearctic). Ibid., **1401,** 38 pp. (1949).

Phaoniinæ (Nearctic). Ibid., **1402,** 25 pp. (1949).

Neomuscina (Nearctic). Ibid., **1404,** 39 pp. (1949).

Lispinæ. Ibid., **1403,** 9 pp. (1949).

Helina. Bull. American Mus. Nat. Hist., **94,** pp. 109–160 (1949).

New Neotropical Muscidæ. American Mus. Novit., **1494,** 11 pp. (1951).

STEIN, P. Anthomyiidæ (East Africa). Berliner Ent. Ztg., **51,** pp. 33–80 (1906). Voy. Alluaud, Diptera, 1914, pp. 101–144.

Anthomyiden (Java). Tijdschr. Ent., **52,** pp. 205–271 (1909).

Anthomyidæ (Seychelles). Trans. Linn. Soc. London., (2) **14,** pp. 149–163 (1910).

Fucellia. Wiener Ent. Ztg., **29,** pp. 11–27 (1910).

Anthomyiden (Indo-Australian). Ann. Mus. Nat. Hungarici, **8,** pp. 545–570 (1910).

Anthomyiidæ (South America). Arch. Naturg., **77,** Heft 1, pp. 61–189 (1911).

Anthomyiden (Africa). Ann. Mus. Nat. Hungarici, **11,** pp. 457–583 (1913).

Anthomyiden (Germany). Arch. Naturg., **79** A, Heft 8, pp. 4–55 (1913).

Anthomyidæ (Formosa). Supplementa Ent., **4,** pp. 13–56 (1915).

Anthomyidæ (Europe). Arch. Naturg., **81** A, Heft 10, pp. 1–224 (1916).

Anthomyiden. Ann. Mus. Nat. Hungarici, 16, pp. 147–244 (1918).
  Genera of Anthomyidæ of World. Arch. Naturg., 83 A, Heft 1, pp. 85–178 (1919).
  Anthomyiidæ (North America). Ibid., 84 A, Heft 9, pp. 1–106 (1920). See Berliner Ent. Zeitschr., 42, pp. 161–288 (1897).
Stork, M. N. Anthomyidæ, Puparia. Tijdschr. Ent., 79, pp. 94–167 (1936).
Thomson, R. C. M. Anthomyiidæ, Biology. Parasitol., 29, pp. 273–358 (1937).
Vos-de Wilde, B. Larves de Cyclorrhaphes, specialement d'Anthomyides. 125 pp., Amsterdam (1935).

CORDYLURIDÆ

Becker, T. Scatomyzidæ. Berliner Ent. Zeitschr., 39, pp. 77–196 (1894).
Bezzi, M. Tapeigaster (Australia). Australian Zool., 3, pp. 72–78 (1923).
Coquillett, D. W. Scatophagidæ. Jour. New York Ent. Soc., 8, pp. 160–165 (1898).
Curran, C. H. Several Nearctic Genera. Canadian Ent., 59, pp. 253–261 (1927).
Emden, F. van. Scatophaginæ and Anthomyiinæ (Ethiopian). Bull. Ent. Res., 32, pp. 251–275 (1941).
Hendel, F. Cordyluridæ and Dryomyzidæ (Kamchatka). Ark. Zool., 31 A, no. 18, pp. 1–12 (1930).
James, M. T. Scopeuma. Ann. Ent. Soc. America, 43, pp. 343–353 (1950).
Johnson, C. W. Several Keys. Psyche, 34, pp. 100–104 (1927).
Malloch, J. R. Generic Key. Rept. Canadian Arctic Exped. 1913–1918, 3, C, pp. 75–81 (1919).
  Several Nearctic Genera. Ohio Jour. Sci., 20, pp. 286–288 (1920). Bull. Brooklyn Ent. Soc., 17, pp. 77–78 (1922). Ent. News 34, pp. 139–140, 175–180 (1923). North American Fauna, 46, pp. 201–207 (1923).
Ringdahl, O. Scopeumatidæ. Ent. Tidskr., 57, pp. 158–179 (1936).
Sack, R. Cordyluridæ. Fliegen Palæarkt. Reg., 62a, 103 pp. (1937).
Séguy, E. Acalypteræ et Scatophagidæ. Faune de France, 28, 832 pp. (1934).

ŒSTRIDÆ, CUTEREBRIDÆ, GASTEROPHILIDÆ

Austen, E. E. Cutiterebra. Ann. Mag. Nat. Hist., (6) 15, pp. 377–396 (1895); 16, pp. 147–155 (1895).
  New Cuterebra. Proc. Zool. Soc. London, 1933, pp. 699–713.
Bau, A. Oestridæ. Gen. Insectorum, 43, 31 pp. (1906).
  Cuterebra. Konowia, 10, pp. 197–240 (1931).
Bedford, G. A. H. Gastrophilus (South Africa). Rep. Dir. Vet. Res. Dept. Agric. Union South Africa, 1919, pp. 627–643.
Bergman, A. Œstridæ. Skand. Vet. Bakt. Path., 1916, pp. 309–340; 1917, pp. 1–34. Ent. Tidskr., 38, pp. 1–32, 113–146 (1917). Zeitschr. Infektionskr., 1919, pp. 67–91, 97–116, 179–201.
Bevan, W. J., and E. E. Edwards. Ox Warble Flies. Bull. Ent. Res., 41, pp. 639–662 (1951).
Cameron, A. E. Cuterebra (Canada). Parasitol., 18, pp. 430–435 (1926).
Carrera, M. Cuterebrideos do Brasil. Arq. Zool., São Paulo, 3, 11 pp. (1941).
Cross, H. E. Bot-flies (Punjab). Agric. Res. Inst. Pusa, 160, 16 pp. (1926).

DEL PONTE, E. Œstridæ (Argentina). Physis, Buenos Aires, **17**, pp. 525–534 (1939).

DINULESCU, G. Biologie des Gastrophiles. Ann. Sci. Nat., Paris, (10) **15**, 183 pp. (1932).

DOVE, W. E. Bots of Horses. U. S. Dept. Agric. Bull., **597**, 51 pp. (1918).

DRENSKY, P. Œstridæ (Bulgaria). Bull. Inst. Hist. Nat. Sofia, **6**, pp. 125–149 (1933). (In Bulgarian)

FLETCHER, T. B., and S. K. SEN. Indian Œstridæ. Jour. Centr. Bur. Anim. Husb. India, **4**, pt. 3, pp. 90–104; pt. 4, pp. 127–138 (1931).

HADWEN, S. Warble Flies. Canadian Dept. Agric. Health Anim. Bull., **16**, 200 pp. (1912).

KNIPLING, E. F. Hypoderma Larvæ. Jour. Parasitol., **21**, pp. 70–82 (1935).

KNIPLING, E. F., and A. L. BRODY. Cuterebrine Larvæ. Ibid., **26**, pp. 33–43 (1940).

LAAKE, E. W. Ox Warble Larvæ. Jour. Agric. Res., **21**, pp. 439–457 (1921).

LECLERCQ, M. Œstridæ (Belgium). Bull. Mus. Roy. Hist. Nat. Belgique, **24**, no. 41, 11 pp. (1948).

LUTZ, A. Œstridæ (Brazil). Mem. Inst. Oswaldo Cruz, **9**, pp. 94–113 (1917); **10**, pp. 118–137 (1918).

MACDOUGALL, R. S. Ox Bot Flies. Trans. Highl. Soc. Scotland, (5) **31**, pp. 94–121 (1919).

    Warble Flies of Cattle. Ibid., **1930**, 40 pp.

MOTE, D. C. Ox Warbles. Bull. Ohio Agric. Exp. Sta., **428**, 45 pp. (1928).

ONO, S. Warble Flies (Manchuria). Kitasato Arch. Exp. Med., **15**, pp. 199–246 (1938).

PARAMONOFF, S. J. Gastrophilidæ. Zeitschr. Parasitenk., **14**, pp. 27–37 (1949).

PLESKE, T. Œstridæ (Palæarctic). Ann. Mus. Zool. Leningrad, **26**, pp. 215–230 (1925).

RODHAIN, J., and J. BEQUAERT. Œstridæ (Congo). Bull. Soc. Path. Exot., **8**, pp. 765–778 (1915).

    Œstridæ (Africa). Bull. Sci. France et Belgique, **50**, pp. 53–165 (1916).
    Parasites of Elephant and Rhinoceros. Ibid., **52**, pp. 379–465 (1919).

    Œstridæ of Antelopes and Zebras. Rev. Zool. Africaine, **8**, pp. 169–228 (1920).

ROHDENDORF, B. Œstridæ (Belgian Congo). Ann. Parasit. Hum. Comp., **5**, pp. 193–213 (1927).

SÉGUY, E. Genera of Œstridæ. Encycl. Ent. (B) II, pt. 3, pp. 1–10 (1926).
    Œstridæ (Europe). Ibid. (A), pt. 9, pp. 53–88 (1928).

SHANNON, R. C. Bot-flies of Domestic Animals. Cornell Vet., **1922**, pp. 240–262.

TOWNSEND, C. H. T. Cuterebridæ. Ins. Inscit. Menstr., **5**, pp. 23–28 (1917).

WELLS, R. W., and E. F. KNIPLING. Gasterophilus in Horses. Iowa State Coll. Jour. Sci., **12**, pp. 181–204 (1938).

ACALYPTRATÆ, GENERAL

BEZZI, M., and J. S. TAVARES. Muscideos cecidogénicos (Brazil). Broteria, Zool., **14**, pp. 155–170 (1916).

DUDA, O. Acalyptrates (Africa, Orient). Ann. Mag. Nat. Hist., (10) **18**, pp. 337–351 (1936).

FREY, R. Mouthparts, Diptera schizophora. Acta Soc. Faun. Fl. Fennica, **48**, 245 pp. (1921).

HENDEL, F. Acalyptrates. Wiener Ent. Ztg., **29**, pp. 101–127, 307–313 (1910); **30**, pp. 19–46 (1911); **31**, pp. 1–20 (1912). Supplementa Ent., **2**, pp. 33–43, 77–112 (1913); **3**, pp. 90–117 (1914). Deutsche Ent. Zeitschr., **1914**, pp. 151–176; **1917**, pp. 33–47; **1933**, pp. 39–56. Ent. Mitt., **5**, pp. 294–299 (1916). Konowia, **1**, pp. 145–160, 253–265 (1922); **2**, pp. 203–215 (1924).

    Kritische Bemerkungen. Verh. zool.-bot. Ges. Wien, **81**, pp. 28–43 (1931).

    Egyptian Acalyptrates. Bull. Soc. Roy. Ent. Egypte, **1931**, pp. 1–12, 59–73.

    Acalyptrates (Kamchatka). Ark. Zool., **23** A, no. 7, pp. 1–12 (1932).

    Acalyptrates (Chaco Exped.). Konowia, **11**, pp. 98–110, 115–145 (1932).

    Acalyptrates (South America). Rev. Ent. Rio Janeiro, **3**, pp. 58–83, 213–224 (1933).

    Acalyptratæ, Except Chloropidæ. Ann. Naturh. Mus. Wien, **47**, pp. 61–106 (1936).

HERING, E. M. Neue Acalyptraten aus Manchukuo. Arb. Morph. Taxon. Ent., **7**, pp. 288–295 (1940).

LAMB, C. G. Acalyptrates, Sladen Exped. (Seychelles). Trans. Linn. Soc. London, (2) **15**, pp. 303–348 (1912); **16**, pp. 307–372 (1914).

MALLOCH, J. R. Borboridæ, Phoridæ and Agromyzidæ (Costa Rica). Trans. American Ent. Soc., **41**, pp. 8–36 (1914).

    Acalyptrates. Proc. U. S. Nat. Mus., **68**, no. 2622, 35 pp. (1926).

    Acalyptrates (Samoa). Clusiidæ, Sapromyzidæ, Insects of Samoa, Brittish Mus., **6**, fasc. **4**, pp. 199–213 (1929); Ortalidæ. Ibid., fasc. **5**, pp. 215–231 (1930); Lonchæidæ, Chloropidæ, Piophilidæ. Ibid., fasc. **6**, pp. 239–251 (1930); Trypetidæ. Ibid., fasc. **7**, pp. 253–266 (1931); Drosophilidæ, Ephydridæ, Sphæroceridæ. Ibid., fasc. **8**, pp. 267–329 (1934).

    Acalyptrata (Patagonia). Diptera of Patagonia and South Chile, British Mus., **6**, fasc. **4**, pp. 177–391 (1933); fasc. **5**, pp. 393–489 (1934); fasc. **6**, pp. 491–507 (1948).

SÉGUY, E. Acalyptères et Scatophagidæ. Faune de France, **28**, 832 pp. (1934).

SOOS, A. Acalypteren (Hungary). Arb. Ungarisches Biol. Forsch., **15**, pp. 309–323 (1943).

STURTEVANT, A. H. Acalyptratæ. American Mus. Novit., **76**, 12 pp. (1923).

THORNLEY, A. List of Cornish Acalyptrates. Trans. Soc. British Ent., **3**, pp. 155–171 (1936).

TONNOIR, A. L., and J. R. MALLOCH. New Zealand Acalyptratæ. Ephydridæ. Rec. Canterbury Mus., **3**, pp. 1–18 (1926); Sapromyzidæ. Ibid., pp. 19–26 (1926); Helomyzidæ. Ibid., pp. 83–100 (1927); Sciomyzidæ. Ibid., pp. 151–179 (1928).

WAHLGREN, E. Acalyptrates (Sweden). Ent. Tidskr., **1919**, pp. 225–322 (1919).

TYLIDÆ (MICROPEZIDÆ), NERIIDÆ, TANYPEZIDÆ

ACZEL, M. L. Tylininæ (Argentina); Catalogue of Tylidæ. Acta Zool. Lilloana, **8**, pp. 219–280, 309–389 (1950).

BERG, C. O. Micropezidæ, Biology (Solomon Isl.). Occ. Pap. Mus. Zool. Univ. Michigan, **503**, 14 pp. (1947).

COLLIN, J. E. British Micropezidæ. Ent. Rec., **57**, pp. 115–119 (1945).

CRESSON, E. T. Micropezidæ (North America). Trans. American Ent. Soc., **52**, pp. 260–274 (1926).

Neotropical Micropezidæ. Ibid., **56**, pp. 307–362 (1930).

Neriidæ and Micropezidæ (North America). Ibid., **64**, pp. 293–366 (1939).

CZERNY, L. Tylidæ and Neriidæ. Stettiner Ent. Ztg., **93**, pp. 267–302 (1932).

ENDERLEIN, G. Tanypezidæ. Zool. Anz., **42**, pp. 224–229 (1913). Deutsche Ent. Zeitschr., **1936**, pp. 39–47.

Micropezidæ. Arch. Naturg., **88** A, Heft 5, pp. 140–229 (1922). Deutsche Ent. Zeitschr., **1923**, pp. 540–543.

FISCHER, C. R. Tylidæ. Rev. Ent. Rio Janeiro, 2, pp. 15–24 (1932).

FREY, R. Micropezidæ. Notul. Ent., **7**, pp. 65–76 (1927).

African Tanypodinæ. Ann. Mag. Nat. Hist., (10) **3**, pp. 313–318 (1929).

HENNIG, W. Tylidæ. Stettiner Ent. Ztg., **95**, pp. 65–108, 294–330 (1934); **96**, pp. 27–67 (1935); **98**, pp. 46–50 (1937). Konowia, **14**, pp. 68–93, 192–216, 289–310 (1935); **15**, pp. 129–144, 201–239 (1936).

Tanypezidæ. Fliegen Palæarkt. Reg., **44**, 6 pp. (1937).

Tylidæ (Japan). Insecta Matsumurana, **13**, pp. 1–14 (1938).

KNAB, F., and R. C. SHANNON. Tanypezidæ (U. S.). Ins. Inscit. Menstr., **4**, pp. 33–36 (1916).

STEYSKAL, G. C. Micropezidæ (Solomon Isl.). Occ. Pap. Mus. Zool. Univ. Michigan, **502**, 11 pp. (1947).

Tylidæ (Australasian). Proc. U. S. Nat. Mus., **102**, no. 3294, pp. 161–180 (1952).

VAN DUZEE, M. C. Micropeza (Nearctic). Pan-Pacific Ent., 3, pp. 1–11 (1926).

VERBECKE, J. Tæniopterinæ. Expl. Parc Nat. Albert, **72**, 106 pp. (1951).

OTITID SERIES: PHYTALMIIDÆ, PLATYSTOMATIDÆ,
PTEROCALLIDÆ, PYRGOTIDÆ, RICHARDIIDÆ,
TACHINISCIDÆ, ULIDIIDÆ

BEZZI, M. Phytalmiides (Africa). Rev. Zool. Africaine, 12, pp. 225–239 (1924).

BEZZI, M., and J. R. MALLOCH. Pyrgotidæ (Australia). Proc. Linn. Soc. New South Wales, **54**, pp. 1–31 (1929).

CARRERA, M. Plagiocephalus. Pap. Avulsos, Dept. Zool. São Paulo, 9, pp. 259–268 (1950).

CHEN, S. H. Pyrgotidæ (China, Japan). Sinensia, **17**, pp. 47–74 (1946).

CRESSON, E. T. Ortalidæ. Trans. American Ent. Soc., **50**, pp. 225–241 (1924).

ENDERLEIN, G. Ortalinæ and Loxoneurinæ (Orient, Africa). Zool. Jahrb. Syst., **33**, pp. 347–378 (1912).

Pterocallinæ. Zool. Anz., **52**, pp. 211–219 (1921).

Platystominæ. Mitt. Zool. Mus. Berlin, **11**, pp. 97–153 (1924).

Phytalmiidæ. Arb. Morph. Taxon. Ent., 3, pp. 225–243 (1936).

Pyrgotidæ. S. B. Ges. Naturf. Freunde Berlin, **1941**, pp. 98–134 (1942).

FREY, R. Platystomidæ (Africa). Ann. Mag. Nat. Hist., (10) **9**, pp. 242–264 (1932).

FROST, S. W. Ortalidæ, Check-list (Pennsylvania). Ent. News, **40**, pp. 84–87 (1929).

HENDEL, F. Pyrgotinæ. Gen. Insectorum, 79, 33 pp. (1908).
　　Pterocallinæ. Ibid., 96, 50 pp. (1909). Deutsche Ent. Zeitschr., 1909, Beiheft, pp. 1–84.
　　Chrysomyza. Zool. Anz., 34, pp. 612–622 (1909).
　　Euxesta. Ann. Mus. Nat. Hungarici, 7, pp. 151–172 (1909).
　　Ulidiinæ. Wiener Ent. Ztg., 28, pp. 247–270 (1909). Gen. Insectorum, 106, pp. 1–76 (1910).
　　Richardiinæ. Ibid., 113, pp. 1–56 (1911). Deutsche Ent. Zeitschr., 1911, pp. 181–212, 239–270, 367–396.
　　Pyrgotinæ. Arch. Naturg., 79 A, Heft 11, pp. 77–117 (1913).
　　Platystoma. Zool. Jahrb. Syst., 35, Heft 1, pp. 55–126 (1913).
　　Platystominæ. Gen. Insectorum, 157, 179 pp. (1914). Abh. zool.-bot. Ges. Wien, 8, 410 pp. (1914).
　　Pyrgotidæ. Fliegen Palæarkt. Reg., 36, 15 pp. (1933). Encycl. Ent. (B) II, 7, pp. 111–156 (1934).
HENNIG, W. Otitidæ. Fliegen Palæarkt. Reg., 46, 47, 78 pp. (1939).
　　Richardiidæ. Rev. Ent. Rio Janeiro, 8, pp. 111–122 (1938).
　　Ulidiidæ. Fliegen Palæarkt. Reg., 45, 34 pp. (1940).
　　Psilidæ and Platystomidæ. Arb. Morph. Taxon. Ent., 7, pp. 304–318 (1940).
　　Platystomidæ. Fliegen Palæarkt. Reg., 48, 56 pp. (1945).
MALLOCH, J. R. Pyrgotidæ (Africa). Ann. Mag. Nat. Hist., (10) 3, pp. 249–261 (1929).
　　Tachiniscidæ. Ibid., 7, pp. 334–338 (1931).
　　Ortalidæ (New Guinea). Proc. Linn. Soc. New South Wales, 64, pp. 97–154, 169–180 (1939).
　　Otitidæ and Phytalmidæ (Solomon Isl.). Ann. Mag. Nat. Hist., (11) 6, pp. 66–98 (1940).
McALPINE, J. E. Herina (= Tephronota). Canadian Ent., 83, pp. 308–314 (1951).
SOUZA LOPES, H. DE. Ctenostylidæ. Arch. Inst. Biol. Veg., 2, pp. 247–253 (1935).
STEYSKAL, G. Diacrita. Bull. Brooklyn Ent. Soc., 41, pp. 149–154 (1946).

TRYPETIDÆ

ACZEL, M. L. Catalogue of Trypetidæ (Neotropical). Acta Zool. Lilloana, 7, pp. 177–328 (1949).
　　Xanthaciura. Ibid., 8, pp. 111–146 (1950).
ALDRICH, J. M. Procecidochares. Proc. U. S. Nat. Mus., 76, art. 2, 13 pp. (1929).
BAKER, A. C. et al. Mexican Fruit-fly. Misc. Publ. U. S. Dept. Agric., 531, 155 pp. (1944).
BATES, M. American Trypetidæ. Psyche, 40, pp. 48–56 (1933).
　　Trypetidæ (West Indies). Bull. Brooklyn Ent. Soc., 28, pp. 160–172 (1933).
　　Acrotænia. Rev. Ent. Rio Janeiro, 4, pp. 7–17 (1934).
　　Tephrellia. Pan-Pacific Ent., 11, pp. 103–114 (1935).
BENJAMIN, F. H. Trypetid Flies. U. S. Dept. Agric. Tech. Bull., 401, 95 pp. (1934).

BEZZI, M. Ceratitis, Anastrepha, Dacus. Boll. Lab. Zool. Portici, 3, pp. 273–313 (1909).
    Œdaspis (Italy). Marcellia, 12, pp. 144–156 (1913).
    Trypaneids (India). Mem. Indian Mus., 3, no. 3, pp. 53–175 (1913).
    Dacus (Ethiopian). Bull. Ent. Res., 6, pp. 85–101 (1915); 8, pp. 63–154 (1917).
    Dacus (Oriental). Ibid., 7, pp. 99–121 (1916).
    Ethiopian Fruit-flies. Ibid., 8, pp. 215–251 (1918); 9, pp. 13–46 (1919); 10, pp. 211–271 (1920); 15, pp. 73–155 (1924).
    Dacus (Philippines). Philippine Jour. Sci., 15, pp. 411–443 (1919).
    Urophora (America). Trans. Ent. Soc. America, 49, pp. 1–6 (1923).
    Trypaneidæ (Africa). Bull. Mus. Hist. Nat. Paris, 1923, pp. 523–530, 577–581.
    Tripaneidi (South Africa). Ann. South African Mus., 19, pp. 449–577 (1924). Boll. Lab. Zool. Portici, 18, pp. 276–300 (1926).
    Gastrozona and Tæniostola. Ibid., 18, pp. 258–267 (1926).
CHEN, S. H. Trypetinæ (China). Sinensia, 18, pp. 69–123 (1947).
COLLARD, A. Dacinæ (Congo). Bull. Mus. Roy. Hist. Nat. Belgique, 16, no. 13, pp. 1–26 (1940).
COLLIN, J. E. British Genera of Trypetidæ. Ent. Rec., 59, pp. 1–14 (1947).
COSTA LIMA, A. DA. Hexachæta. Ann. Acad. Brasiliera Sci., 7, pp. 233–250 (1935).
CRESSON, E. T. Rhagoletis. Trans. American Ent. Soc., 55, pp. 401–414 (1929).
CURRAN, C. H. Key to Genera of Trypaneidæ (North America). American Mus. Novit., 556, 19 pp. (1932).
DRENSKY, P. Trypetidæ (Bulgaria). Ann. Univ. Sofia, 39, pp. 69–126 (1943). (In Bulgarian)
EFFLATOUN, H. C. Trypaneidæ (Egypt). Mem. Soc. Roy. Ent. Egypte, 2, fasc. 2, 132 pp. (1924).
    Trypaneid Larvæ (Egypt). Bull. Soc. Roy. Ent. Egypte, 1927, pp. 17–50.
ENDERLEIN, G. Trypetidæ. Zool. Jahrb. Syst., 31, pp. 407–460 (1911); 43, pp. 336–360 (1920).
FROGGATT, W. W. Fruit-flies. Dept. Agric. New South Wales, 1909, 115 pp. Farmers' Bull., 24, 56 pp. (1910).
FROST, S. W. Leaf-mining Diptera. Mem. Cornell Univ. Agric. Exp. Sta., 78, 228 pp. (1924).
GREENE, C. T. Anastrepha. Proc. Ent. Soc. Washington, 36, pp. 127–179 (1934).
HARDY, D. E. Fruit-flies (Hawaii). Ibid., 51, pp. 181–205 (1949).
    Fruit-flies (Australia). Pacific Sci., 5, pp. 115–189 (1951).
HAYWARD, K. J. Moscas de frutas, Bibliography. Bol. Est. Exp. Agric. Tucumán, 31, 42 pp. (1940).
HENDEL, F. Dacus (Formosa). Supplementa Ent., 1, pp. 13–24 (1912).
    Anastrepha. Wiener Ent. Ztg., 33, pp. 66–70 (1914).
    Genera of Tephritinæ. Ibid., 33, pp. 73–98 (1914).
    Bohrfliegen Südamerikas. Abh. Ber. K. Zool. Anthrop. Mus. Dresden, 14, pp. 1–84 (1914).
    Tephritinæ (Formosa). Ann. Mus. Nat. Hungarici, 13, pp. 424–467 (1915).

Trypetidæ. Fliegen Palæarkt. Reg., **49**, 221 pp. (1927).

Bohrfliegen. Ent. Mitt., **17**, pp. 341–370 (1928).

HERING, E. M. Bohrfliegen. Mitt. Zool. Mus. Berlin, **22**, pp. 244–264 (1937).

Neue Bohrfliegen. Deutsche Ent. Zeitschr., **1938**, pp. 397–417.

Trypetidæ (Burma, British India). Ark. Zool., **30** A, no. 25, 56 pp. (1939).

New Trypetidæ. Verh. 7 Intern. Kongr. Ent., **1**, pp. 165–190 (1939).

Fruchtfliegen-Kunde. Siruna Seva, **1**, pp. 1–16 (1940); **2**, pp. 1–16 (1941); **3**, pp. 1–32 (1941); **4**, pp. 1–31 (1942); **5**, pp. 1–31 (1944).

Trypetidæ (German East Africa). Ann. Naturh. Mus. Wien, **51**, pp. 193–205 (1941).

Trypetidæ (Sunda Isl.). Arb. Morph. Taxon. Ent., **8**, pp. 24–45 (1941).

Fruchtfliegen. Mitt. Zool. Mus. Berlin, **25**, pp. 274–291 (1942). **Siruna** Seva, **6**, 16 pp. (1947).

IHERING, R. v. Muscas das fructas. Publ. Secr. Agr. Comm. São Paulo, 21 pp. (1905).

KIEFFER, J. J., and P. JORGENSEN. Gallenthiere (Argentina). Centralbl. Parasit. Infektionsk., **27**, pp. 362–444 (1910).

LOEW, H. Europäischen Bohrfliegen. 128 pp., Wien (1862). Reprint: Junk, Berlin (1923).

MALLOCH, J. R. Trypetidæ (Samoa). Insects of Samoa, **6**, fasc. 7, pp. 253–266, British Mus. (1931).

Trypetidæ (Solomon Isl.). Ann. Mag. Nat. Hist., (11) **4**, pp. 228–278 (1939).

Trypetidæ (New Guinea). Proc. Linn. Soc. New South Wales, **64**, pp. 409–465 (1939).

MIYAKE, T. Fruit-flies (Japan). Bull. Imp. Exp. Sta., **2**, pp. 85–165 (1919).

MUNRO, H. K. Fruit-flies of Wild Olives. Ent. Mem. Union South Africa Dept. Agric., **2**, pp. 5–17 (1924).

Biology Trypaneidæ (South Africa). Ibid., **3**, pp. 39–67 (1925); **5**, pp. 17–40 (1926); **6**, pp. 9–17 (1929).

Trypctids in South African Museum. Ann. South African Mus., **29**, pp. 1–39 (1929).

Trypctidæ from South Africa. Bull. Ent. Res., **20**, pp. 391–401 (1929); **22**, pp. 115–126 (1931).

African Trypetidæ. American Mus. Novit., **597**, 10 pp. (1933). Ent. Mem. Union South Africa Dept. Agric., 8, pp. 25–45 (1933); **9**, pp. 18–59 (1935).

Trypetidæ (Formosa). Arb. Physiol. Angewandte Ent., **2**, pp. 195–203, 253–271 (1935).

Indian Trypetidæ. Rec. Indian Mus., **37**, pp. 15–27 (1935).

Spathulina (Africa). Trans. Roy. Ent. Soc. London, **87**, pp. 417–430 (1939).

Trypetidæ (Africa). Jour. East African Nat. Hist. Soc., **14**, pp. 1–10 (1939). Jour. Ent. Soc. South Africa, **1**, pp. 26–46 (1939); **2**, pp. 139–164 (1939). Ann. Mag. Nat. Hist., (11) **13**, pp. 482–493 (1947). Mem. Ent. Soc. South Africa, **1**, 284 pp. (1947).

Dacinæ. Jour. Ent. Soc. South Africa, **11**, pp. 13–33 (1948).

Mesoclanis. Ibid., **13**, pp. 37–52 (1950).

PERKINS, F. A. Trypaneidæ (Australia and Orient). Proc. Roy. Soc. Queensland, 48, pp. 51–60 (1937); 49, pp. 120–144 (1938). Pap. Dept. Biol. Univ. Queensland, 1, no. 10, 35 pp. (1939).

PHILLIPS, V. T. Trypetidæ (North American). Jour. New York Ent. Soc., 31, pp. 119–154 (1923).
    Trypetid Larvæ. Mem. American Ent. Soc., 12, 161 pp. (1946).

PICKETT, A. D. Rhagoletis. Canadian Jour. Res., Zool. Sci., 15, pp. 53–75 (1937).

QUISENBERRY, B. F. Euaresta (U. S.). Jour. New York Ent. Soc., 58, pp. 9–38 (1950).
    Tephritis (Nearctic). Jour. Kansas Ent. Soc., 24, pp. 56–72 (1951).

SAUNT, J. W. Isle of Wight Trypetidæ. Proc. Isle Wight Nat. Hist. Soc., 4, pp. 33–40 (1947).

SEIN, F., JR. Anastrepha (Puerto Rico). Jour. Dept. Agric. Puerto Rico, 17, pp. 183–196 (1933).

SENIOR-WHITE, R. Catalogue of Indian Trypetidæ. Catalogue of Indian Insects, 4, 33 pp., Calcutta (1924).

SHIRAKI, T. Trypetidæ (Japan). Mem. Fac. Sci. Agric. Taihoku Univ., 8, Ent., 2, 509 pp. (1933).

SILVESTRI, F. Ceratitis. Boll. Lab. Zool. Portici, 7, pp. 3–26 (1912).
    Natural Enemies of Trypaneidæ. Bull. Ent. Agric. Hawaii, 3, 176 pp. (1914).

STONE, A. New Genus, near Anastrepha. Jour. Washington Acad. Sci., 29, pp. 340–350 (1939).
    Pseudodacus. Rev. Ent. Rio Janeiro, 10, pp. 282–289 (1939).
    Anastrepha. U. S. Dept. Agric. Misc. Publ., 439, 112 pp. (1942).

TRYON, H. Queensland Trypetidæ. Proc. Roy. Soc. Queensland, 38, pp. 176–224 (1927).

VARLEY, G. C. Life Histories of Trypetids. Proc. Roy. Ent. Soc. London (A), 12, pp. 109–122 (1937).

WILLE, J. Anastrepha (Peru). Inf. Estac. Exp. Agric. Lima, 27, 12 pp. (1934).
    Bol. Direcc. Agric. Ganaderia, Peru, 5, pp. 46–56 (1935).

ZIA, Y. Trypetidæ (China). Sinensia, 8, pp. 103–226 (1937).

ZIA, Y., and H. CHEN. Trypetidæ of North China. Ibid., 9, pp. 1–180 (1938).

DIOPSIDÆ, MEGAMERINIDÆ, RHINOTORIDÆ RHOPALOMERIDÆ, SEPSIDÆ

BEZZI, M. Toxopoda. Bull. Soc. Italiana Ent., 52, pp. 50–63 (1920).

BRUNETTI, E. Oriental Sepsinæ. Rec. Indian Mus., 3, pt. 4, pp. 343–372 (1909).
    Diopsidæ from Belgian Congo. Rev. Zool. Africaine, 14, pp. 73–84 (1926).

DUDA, O. Sepsidæ. Ann. Naturh. Mus. Wien, 39, pp. 1–153 (1925); 40, pp. 1–110 (1926).

EGGERS, F. Diopsidæ (East Africa). Zool. Jahrb. Syst., 49, pp. 469–500 (1925).

FISCHER, C. R. Rhopalomeridæ. Rev. Ent. Rio Janeiro, 2, pp. 441–450 (1932).

FREY, R. Sepsis (Finland). Deutsche Ent. Zeitschr., 1908, pp. 577–588.
    Sepsidæ (Palæarctic). Notul. Ent., 5, pp. 69–76 (1925).
    Diopsidæ (Philippines). Ibid., 8, pp. 69–77 (1928).

GOETGHEBUER, M., and F. BASTIN. Sepsidæ (Belgium). Bull. Ann. Soc. Ent. Belgique, **65**, pp. 123–137 (1925).

HAFEZ, M. Sepsidæ, Biology. Proc. Roy. Ent. Soc. London, A, **23**, pp. 9–104 (1948).

HENDEL, F. Megamerinidæ. Supplementa Ent., **2**, pp. 90–93 (1913).

Diopsiden (Africa). Wiener Ent. Ztg., **40**, pp. 33–42 (1923).

HENNIG, W. Diopsidæ, Copulatory Apparatus. Arb. Morph. Taxon. Ent., **8**, pp. 54–65 (1941).

Sepsidæ, Megamerinidæ, Diopsidæ. Fliegen Palæarkt. Reg., **39** a, b, c, 103 pp. (1941–1949).

LINDNER, E. Rhopalomeridæ. Deutsche Ent. Zeitschr., **1930**, pp. 122–137.

MELANDER, A. L., and A. SPULER. Sepsidæ and Piophilidæ. Bull. Washington Agric. Exp. Sta., **143**, 103 pp. (1917).

SÉGUY, E. Diopsidæ (Madagascar). Mem. Inst. Sci. Madagascar, 3 A, pp. 65–76 (1949).

SHILLITO, J. F. Diopsidæ. Novitat. Zool., **42**, pp. 147–164 (1940).

SOUZA LOPES, H. DE. Rhinotorinæ. Arch. Inst. Biol. Veg., **2**, pp. 19–26 (1935).

STEYSKAL, G. C. Sepsidæ, Generic Key (North America). Pan-Pacific Ent., **19**, pp. 93–95 (1943).

Themira, Key (Nearctic). Ent. News, **57**, pp. 93–95 (1946).

Australasian Sepsidæ. Pan-Pacific Ent., **25**, pp. 161–171 (1949).

CELYPHIDÆ, LAUXANIIDÆ

BECKER, T. Sapromyzidæ. Berliner Ent. Zeitschr., **40**, pp. 171–264 (1895).

CURRAN, C. H. Lauxaniidæ (Africa). American Mus. Novit., **979**, 18 pp. (1938).

CZERNY, L. Lauxaniidæ. Fliegen Palæarkt. Reg., **50**, 76 pp. (1932).

FREY, R. Philippine Lauxaniidæ. Acta Soc. Faun. Fl. Fennica, **56**, no. 8, pp. 1–44 (1927).

Celyphidæ. Notul. Ent., **21**, pp. 3–16 (1941).

HENDEL, F. Lauxaninæ. Gen. Insectorum, **68**, pp. 1–66 (1908).

Gattungen der Lauxaniiden. Encycl. Ent. (B) II, **2**, pp. 103–142 (1925).

HENNIG, W. Lonchæidæ and Lauxaniidæ. Acta Zool. Lilloana, **6**, pp. 333–429 (1948).

JACOBSON, G. Catalogue of Celyphidæ. Ann. Mus. Zool. Acad. Sci. St. Petersburg, **1896**, pp. 246–252.

KERTESZ, K. Sapromyza (Indo-Australia). Termesz. Füzetek, **23**, pp. 254–276 (1900).

Lauxaniidæ (Hungary). Math. Termesz. Ert., Budapest, **38**, pp. 352–359 (1921).

MALLOCH, J. R. Griphoneura. Proc. Biol. Soc. Washington, **38**, pp. 75–77 (1925).

Sapromyzidæ (Australia). Proc. Linn. Soc. New South Wales, **52**, pp. 399–421 (1927).

Sapromyzidæ. Proc. U. S. Nat. Mus., **73**, art. 23, 18 pp. (1928).

Oriental Sapromyzidæ. Ibid., **74**, art. 6, 97 pp. (1929).

Sapromyzidæ (Solomon Isl., New Caledonia). Novitat. Zool., **42**, pp. 131–146 (1940).

MALLOCH, J. R., and W. L. McATEE. Lonchæidæ, Pallopteridæ and Sapromyzidæ of Eastern U. S. Proc. U. S. Nat. Mus., **65**, art. 12, 26 pp. (1924).

MELANDER, A. L. Sapromyzidæ (Nearctic). Psyche, **20**, pp. 57–82 (1913).

SHEWELL, G. F. Lauxaniidæ (Quebec). Canadian Ent., **70**, pp. 102–118, 134–142 (1938).

Camptoprosopella. Ibid., **71**, pp. 130–141, 145–153 (1939).

Homoneura. Ibid., **71**, pp. 264–266 (1939).

TONNOIR, A. L., and J. R. MALLOCH. Sapromyzidæ (New Zealand). Rec. Canterbury Mus., **3**, pt. 1, pp. 19–26 (1926).

DRYOMYZIDÆ, MORMOTOMYIIDÆ, SCIOMYZIDÆ

AUSTEN, E. E. Mormotomyiidæ. Proc. Zool. Soc. London, **1936**, pp. 425–431.

CRESSON, E. T. Sciomyzidæ. Trans. American Ent. Soc., **46**, pp. 27–89 (1920).

FREY, R. Tetanocera (North Palæarctic). Notul. Ent., **4**, pp. 47–53 (1924).

HENDEL, F. Sciomyzidæ (Palæarctic). Abh. zool.-bot. Ges. Wien, **2**, pt. 2, 92 pp. (1902).

Sepedon (Ethiopian, Indo-malayan). Ann. Mus. Nat. Hungarici, **9**, pp. 266–277 (1911).

Cordyluridæ and Dryomyzidæ (Kamchatka). Ark. Zool., **21** A, no. 18, 12 pp. (1930).

KERTESZ, K. Tetanoceridæ (Hungary). Allatt. Kozlem., **14**, pp. 81–126 (1915). Math. Termesz. Ert., Budapest, **39**, pp. 124–130 (1922).

MALLOCH, J. R., and W. L. McATEE. Sciomyzidæ (District of Columbia). Ent. News, **34**, pp. 231–234 (1923).

MELANDER, A. L. Tetanoceridæ (Nearctic). Ann. Ent. Soc. America, **13**, pp. 305–322 (1920).

SACK, P. Sciomyzidæ. Fliegen Palæarkt. Reg., **37**, 87 pp. (1939).

STEYSKAL, G. C. Protodictya. Proc. Ent. Soc. Washington, **52**, pp. 33–39 (1950).

Sepedon (America). Wasmann Jour. Biol., **8**, pp. 271–297 (1951).

TONNOIR, A. L., and J. R. MALLOCH. Sciomyzidæ (New Zealand). Rec. Canterbury Mus., **3**, pt. 3, pp. 151–179 (1928).

VAN EMDEN, F. I. Mormotomyia. Proc. Roy. Ent. Soc. London, (B) **19**, pp. 121–128 (1950).

VERBECKE, J. Sciomyzidæ (Belgium). Bull. Mus. Roy. Hist. Nat. Belgique, **24**, no. 3, 31 pp. (1948).

LONCHÆIDÆ, NEOTTIOPHILIDÆ, PALLOPTERIDÆ, PIOPHILIDÆ, PSILIDÆ, THYREOPHORIDÆ

BEZZI, M. Lonchæidæ. Bull. Ent. Res., **9**, pp. 241–254 (1919); **11**, pp. 199–210 (1920).

Lonchæidæ (Australia). Australian Zool., **3**, pp. 183–185 (1923).

BLANCHARD, E. E. Lonchæidæ (Argentina). Rev. Invest. Agric., **2**, pp. 157–178 (1950).

COLLIN, J. E. British Psilidæ. Ent. Mon. Mag., **80**, pp. 214–224 (1944).

CZERNY, L. Neottiophilidæ. Fliegen Palæarkt. Reg., **38** b, pp. 11–15 (1931).

Lonchæidæ. Ibid., **43**, 40 pp. (1934).

DUDA, O. Piophila. Konowia, **3**, pp. 97–113, 153–203 (1924).

FREY, R. Psiliden (Palæarctic). Notul. Ent., **5**, pp. 47–50 (1925).
HENNIG, W. Psilidæ, Copulatory Apparatus. Arb. Morph. Taxon. Ent., **7**, pp. 304–318 (1940).
　　Pallopteridæ, Copulatory Apparatus. Ibid., **8**, pp. 54–65 (1941).
　　Psilidæ. Fliegen Palæarkt. Reg., **41**, 38 pp. (1941).
　　Piophilidæ. Ibid., **40**, 52 pp. (1943).
　　Lonchæidæ and Lauxaniidæ, Copulatory Apparatus. Acta Zool. Lilloana, **6**, pp. 333–429 (1948).
KERTESZ, K. Lonchæidæ (Indo-Australian). Termesz. Füzetek, **24**, pp. 82–87 (1901).
MALLOCH, J. R. New Lonchæidæ and Sapromyzidæ. Proc. Ent. Soc. Washington, **25**, pp. 45–53 (1923).
MALLOCH, J. R., and W. L. McATEE. Lonchæidæ, Pallopteridæ and Sapromyzidæ (Eastern U. S.). Proc. U. S. Nat. Mus., **65**, art. 12, 26 pp. (1924).
MELANDER, A. L. Psilidæ (Nearctic). Psyche, **27**, pp. 91–101 (1920).
　　Piophilidæ. Ibid., **31**, pp. 78–86 (1924).
MELANDER, A. L., and A. SPULER. Piophilidæ (North America). Bull. Washington Agric. Exp. Sta., **143**, pp. 53–76 (1917).

CŒLOPIDÆ, HELOMYZIDÆ, TRIXOSCELIDÆ

ALDRICH, J. M. Genera of Helomyzidæ. Ins. Inscit. Menstr., **14**, pp. 96–102 (1926).
ALDRICH, J. M., and P. S. DARLINGTON. Helomyzidæ. Trans. American Ent. Soc., **34**, pp. 67–100 (1908).
COLLIN, J. E. Helomyzidæ (Britain). Ent. Mon. Mag., **79**, pp. 234–251 (1943).
CURRAN, C. H. Anorostoma. American Mus. Novit., **676**, 9 pp. (1933).
CZERNY, L. Geomyza (*Trixoscelis*). Wiener Ent. Ztg., **22**, pp. 123–127 (1903).
　　Helomyzidæ. Ibid., **23**, pp. 199–244, 263–286 (1904). Konowia, **5**, pp. 53–56 (1926); **6**, pp. 35–49 (1927); **7**, pp. 52–55 (1928); **8**, pp. 87–92, 438–449 (1929); **10**, pp. 19–21 (1931); **11**, pp. 209–217 (1932); **12**, pp. 236–238 (1933); **14**, pp. 271–287 (1935); **16**, pp. 137–142 (1937). Abh. zool.-bot. Ges. Wien, **15**, 166 pp. (1924).
　　Helomyzidæ, Trichoscelidæ, Chiromyidæ. Fliegen Palæarkt. Reg., **53**, 56 pp. (1927).
HENNIG, W. Cœlopidæ. Ibid., **52**, 38 pp. (1937).
MALLOCH, J. R. Cœlopa (Nearctic). No. American Fauna, **46**, p. 214 (1923).
　　Spilochroa. Proc. U. S. Nat. Mus., **78**, art. 15, p. 29 (1931).
MERCIER, L., and L. TOLMER. Cœlopa (Europe, North America). Bull. Soc. Zool. France, **55**, pp. 238–242 (1930).
SABROSKY, C. W. Lutomyia. Occ. Pap. Mus. Zool. Univ. Michigan, **517**, 6 pp. (1949).
STEYSKAL, G. Suillia. Bull. Brooklyn Ent. Soc., **39**, pp. 173–176 (1945).
SZONDY, G. Helomyzidæ (Hungary). Folia Ent. Hungarica, **2**, pp. 74–88 (1929). (In Magyar)
TONNOIR, A. L., and J. R. MALLOCH. Helomyzidæ (New Zealand). Rec. Canterbury Mus., **3**, pp. 83–100 (1927).

SPHÆROCERIDÆ (BORBORIDÆ), LEPTOCERIDÆ

DAHL, F. Limosina. S. B. Ges. Naturf, Freunde, **6,** pp. 360–377 (1909).

DUDA, O. Limosina (Europe). Abh. zool.-bot. Ges. Wien, **10,** 240 pp. (1918).

Leptocera, Subgenera. Zool. Jahrb. Syst., **43,** pp. 433–446 (1920).

Sphærocera (Palæarctic). Tijdschr. Ent., **63,** pp. 1–39 (1920).

Borboridæ, Genera (South America). Ibid., **64,** pp. 119–146 (1921).

Borborus (Palæarctic). Arch. Naturg., 89 A, Heft 4, pp. 35–112 (1923).

Limosina (Europe). Verh. zool.-bot. Ges. Wien, **73,** pp. 163–180 (1923).

Leptocera (extra-European). Arch. Natur., 90 A, Heft 11, pp. 5–215 (1924).

Some European Limosinas. Konowia, **7,** pp. 162–174 (1928).

Sphæroceridæ. Fliegen Palæarkt. Reg., **57,** 182 pp. (1938).

GODDARD, W. H. Sphæroceridæ, Pupæ (British). Trans. Soc. British Ent., **5,** pp. 235–258 (1938).

GUIBE, J. Apterina. Bull. Biol. Paris, Suppl., **26,** 112 pp. (1939).

HAFEZ, M. Borboridæ, Biology. Proc. Roy. Ent. Soc., London, A, **24,** pp. 1–5 (1949).

MALLOCH, J. R. Borboridæ (Costa Rica). Trans. American Ent. Soc., **40,** pp. 1–24 (1914).

Sphærocera. Proc. Ent. Soc. Washington, **27,** pp. 117–123 (1925).

Sphæroceridæ (Samoa). Insects of Samoa, **6,** fasc. 8, pp. 267–329, British Mus. (1934).

RICHARDS, O. W. Sphæroceridæ (British). Proc. Zool. Soc. London, **1930,** pp. 261–345.

Sphæroceridæ (Patagonia). Diptera of Patagonia and South Chile, **6,** fasc. 2, pp. 62–84, British Mus. (1931).

Sphæroceridæ (Africa). Mem. Mus. Hist. Nat. Paris, **8,** pp. 381–406 (1938).

SABROSKY, C. W. Leptocera lutosa. Proc. Ent. Soc. Washington, **51,** pp. 1–24 (1949).

SPULER, A. Borboridæ, Genera (North America). Proc. Acad. Nat. Sci. Philadelphia, **75,** pp. 369–378 (1923).

Sphærocera and Aptilotus (Nearctic). Pan-Pacific Ent., **1,** pp. 66–71 (1924).

Leptocera (Nearctic). Ann. Ent. Soc. America, **17,** pp. 106–116 (1924). Psyche, **31,** pp. 121–135 (1924). Jour. New York Ent. Soc., **33,** pp. 70–84, 147–162 (1925). Canadian Ent., **57,** pp. 99–104, 116–124 (1925).

Borborus and Scatophora (Nearctic). Bull. Brooklyn Ent. Soc., **20,** pp. 1–16 (1925).

VAN SCHUYTBROECK, P. Sphæroceridæ (Belgium). Bull. Mus. Hist. Nat. Belgique, **18,** no. 19, 12 pp. (1942); **19,** no. 32, 12 pp. (1943).

Sphærocerinæ. Expl. Parc Nat. Albert, **52,** 43 pp. (1948).

CANACEIDÆ, EPHYDRIDÆ, TETHINIDÆ

BECKER, T. Ephydridæ (Palæarctic). Berliner Ent. Zeitschr., **41,** pp. 91–276 (1896). Fliegen Palæarkt. Reg., **56,** 115 pp. (1926).

BERG, C. O. Hydrellia, Bred from Potamogeton. Ann. Ent. Soc. America, **43,** pp. 374–398 (1950).

CRESSON, E. T. Paralimna. Trans. American Ent. Soc., 42, pp. 101–124 (1916).
Notiphila and Dichæta. Ibid., 43, pp. 27–66 (1917).
Ephydridæ (Costa Rica). Ibid., 44, pp. 39–68 (1918).
Gymnopinæ. Ibid., 47, pp. 325–343 (1922).
Exotic Ephydridæ. Ibid., 51, pp. 227–258 (1925).
New Ephydridæ and Micropezidæ. Ibid., 52, pp. 249–260 (1926).
Ephydridæ. Ibid., 55, pp. 165–195 (1929); 58, pp. 1–34 (1932).
Ephydridæ (Patagonia). Diptera of Patagonia and South Chile, 6, fasc. 2, pp. 85–116, British Mus. (1931).
New Genera and Species of Ephydridæ. Trans. American Ent. Soc., 60, pp. 199–222 (1934); 61, pp. 345–372 (1935); 62, pp. 257–270 (1937).
Notul. Acad. Nat. Sci. Philadelphia, 38, 10 pp. (1940).
Ochthera. Rev. Ent. Rio Janeiro, 8, pp. 24–40 (1938).
Discomyza. Notul. Acad. Nat. Sci. Philadelphia, 21, 12 pp. (1939).
Nostima (Neotropical). Ibid., 78, 8 pp. (1941).
Psilopodinæ. Trans. American Ent. Soc., 68, pp. 101–128 (1942).
Ilytheini. Ibid., 69, pp. 1–16 (1943).
Hydrellini, Hydrini, Ilytheini. Ibid., 70, pp. 159–180 (1944).
Psilopodinæ (Indo-Australian). Ibid., 71, pp. 47–75 (1945).
Psilopodinæ (Neotropical). Ibid., 71, pp. 129–163 (1946).
Notiphilini (North America). Ibid., 72, pp. 227–240 (1946).
Psilopinæ (Ethiopian). Ibid., 72, pp. 241–264 (1946).
Notiphilinæ (Neotropical). Ibid., 73, pp. 35–61 (1947). (Ethiopian). Ibid., 73, pp. 105–124 (1947). (Indo-Australian). Ibid., 74, pp. 1–28 (1948).
Napæinæ (North America). Ibid., 74, pp. 225–260 (1949).
CZERNY, L. Tethinidæ. Fliegen Palæarkt. Reg., 55, 8 pp. (1928).
HENDEL, F. Ephydridæ (Chaco Exped.). Konowia, 9, pp. 127–155 (1930).
Tethinidæ. Tijdschr. Ent., 77, pp. 37–54 (1934).
HENNIG, W. Tethinidæ. Ent. Rdsch. Stuttgart, 54, pp. 136–140 (1936).
Tethinidæ, Copulation Apparatus. Arb. Morph. Taxon. Ent., 6, pp. 81–94 (1939).
Ephydridæ, Metamorphosis. Ibid., 10, pp. 105–138 (1945).
JONES, B. J. Ephydridæ. Univ. California Publ. Ent., 1, pp. 153–198 (1906).
MALLOCH, J. R. Ephydridæ (Samoa). Insects of Samoa, 6, fasc. 8, pp. 267–329, British Mus. (1934).
MELANDER, A. L. Tethinidæ (North America). Jour. New York Ent. Soc., 59, pp. 187–212 (1951).
TONNOIR, A. L., and J. R. MALLOCH. Ephydridæ (New Zealand). Rec. Canterbury Mus., 3, pp. 1–18 (1926).
WIRTH, W. W. Scatella (Hawaii). Proc. Hawaiian Ent. Soc., 13, pp. 277–304 (1947).

CHLOROPIDÆ

BECKER, T. Chloropidæ (Palæarctic). Arch. Zool., 1, pt. 10, pp. 33–174, 197–200 (1910).
Chloropidæ (Ethiopian). Ann. Mus. Nat. Hungarici, 8, pp. 377–443 (1911).
Chloropidæ (Indo-Australian). Ibid., 9, pp. 35–170 (1911).

Chloropidæ (Nearctic). Ibid., **10**, pp. 21–120 (1912). (Neotropical). Ibid., **10**, pp. 121–256 (1912).
Chloropidæ (Abyssinia). Ann. Mus. Nat. Hungarici, **11**, pp. 147–167 (1913).
Chloropidæ, New Species. Ibid., **14**, pp. 423–453 (1916).
BECKER, T., and J. C. H. DEMEIJERE. Chloropidæ (Java). Tijdschr. Ent., **56**, pp. 283–307 (1913).
COLLIN, J. E. British Oscinellinæ. Trans. Roy. Ent. Soc. London, **97**, pp. 117–148 (1946).
CORTI, E. Crassiseta (Italy). Bull. Soc. Ent. Italiana, **40**, pp. 121–162 (1909).
DUDA, O. Chloropidæ (Neotropical). Folia Zool. Hydrobiol., **2**, pp. 46–128 (1930); **3**, pp. 159–172 (1931); **5**, pp. 41–48 (1933).
Oriental Chloropidæ. Stettiner Ent. Ztg., **91**, pp. 278–304 (1930).
Chloropidæ. Fliegen Palæarkt. Reg., **61**, 248 pp. (1932–1933).
Chloropidæ (Neotropical). Konowia, **12**, pp. 192–209 (1933); **13**, pp. 58–69, 101–110 (1934).
Chloropidæ (Orient, Australia). Arb. Morph. Taxon. Ent., **1**, pp. 39–60 (1934).
Chloropidæ (Sumatra). Tijdschr. Ent., **77**, pp. 55–161 (1934).
ENDERLEIN, G. Oscinosominæ. S. B. Ges. Naturf. Freunde, **1911**, pt. 4, pp. 185–244.
Oscinosominæ, Genera. Zool. Anz., **38**, pp. 10–13 (1911).
Chloropidæ. Ibid., **42**, pp. 351–374 (1913).
Heringiinæ. Ibid., **105**, pp. 191–194 (1934).
HALL, D. G. Pseudogorax. Jour. Washington Acad. Sci., **27**, pp. 255–261 (1937).
KUMM, H. W. Hippelates and Oscinella. Bull. Ent. Res., **27**, pp. 307–329 (1936).
LAMB, C. G. Exotic Chloropidæ. Ann. Mag. Nat. Hist., (8) **19**, pp. 33–58 (1917).
New Chloropidæ. Ibid., (10) **20**, pp. 421–432 (1937).
MALLOCH, J. R. Botanobiinæ. Proc. U. S. Nat. Mus., **46**, pp. 239–266 (1913).
Chloropidæ, Genera. Canadian Ent., **46**, pp. 113–120 (1914).
Botanobiinæ (Australia). Proc. Linn. Soc. New South Wales, **52**, pp. 434–445 (1927).
Exotic Chloropidæ. Ann. Mag. Nat. Hist., (10) **7**, pp. 473–492; **8**, pp. 49–70 (1931).
Chloropidæ (Australia). Proc. Linn. Soc. New South Wales, **63**, pp. 334–356 (1938); **65**, pp. 261–288 (1940); **66**, pp. 41–64 (1941).
ROCKWOOD, L. P. et al. Meromyza. U. S. Dept. Agric. Tech. Bull., **928**, 18 pp. (1947).
SABROSKY, C. W. Chlorops, Taxonomy. Ent. News, **46**, pp. 77–84 (1935).
Madiza, Vittate Species. Jour. Kansas Ent. Soc., **8**, pp. 105–116 (1935).
Chloropidæ (Kansas). Trans. American Ent. Soc., **61**, pp. 207–268 (1935).
Oscinella and Madiza. Ann. Ent. Soc. America, **29**, pp. 707–728 (1936).
Chloropisca (Nearctic). Canadian Ent., **68**, pp. 170–177 (1936).
Chloropidæ, Taxonomic Notes. Jour. New York Ent. Soc., **46**, pp. 417–434 (1938).

Chloropidæ (Oriental). Ann. Mag. Nat. Hist., (11) 6, pp. 418–427 (1940).

Oscinella. Canadian Ent., 72, pp. 214–230 (1940).

Chloropidæ of World, Genotypes. Ann. Ent. Soc. America, 34, pp. 735–765 (1941).

Ectecephala. Proc. Ent. Soc. Washington, 43, pp. 75–80 (1941).

Hippelates. Canadian Ent., 73, pp. 23–27 (1941).

Thaumatomyia. Ibid., 75, pp. 109–117 (1943).

Epimadiza (Africa). Ann. Mag. Nat. Hist., (11) 13, pp. 821–851 (1946).

Elachiptera (Nearctic). Jour. Washington Acad. Sci., 38, pp. 365–382 (1948).

Dicraeus (North America). Proc. Ent. Soc. Washington, 52, pp. 53–62 (1950).

Gaurax (Nearctic). Amer. Midl. Nat., 45, pp. 407–431 (1951).

Lasiopleura. Canadian Ent., 83, pp. 336–343 (1951).

Chloropidæ. Ruwenzori Exped., 1939, 2, no. 7, pp. 711–828, British Mus. (1951).

Séguy, E. Hippelates (Neotropical). Mem. Mus. Hist. Nat., Paris, 13, pp. 331–357 (1940).

ANTHOMYZIDÆ, CHAMÆMYIIDÆ, CHYROMYIIDÆ, OPOMYZIDÆ, CLUSIIDÆ

Becker, T. Peletophila. Zeitschr. syst. Hymenopt. Dipt., 4, pp. 129–133 (1904).

Bezzi, M. Chiromyia. Atti Soc. Italiana Sci. Nat., 43, pp. 177–181 (1904).

Coe, R. L. Chamæmyia (British). Ent. Mon. Mag., 78, pp. 173–190 (1942).

Collin, J. E. Aphaniosoma. Ann. Mag. Nat. Hist., (12) 2, pp. 127–147 (1949).

Czerny, L. Anthomyza (Palæarctic). Wiener Ent. Ztg., 21, pp. 249–254 (1902).

Heteroneuridæ. Ibid., 22, pp. 61–107 (1903).

Ochthiphilidæ. Ibid., 23, pp. 167–170 (1904).

Chiromyiidæ. Fliegen Palæarkt. Reg., 53, pp. 51–54 (1927). Konowia, 8, pp. 438–449 (1930).

Clusiidæ. Ibid., 54 A, pp. 1–12 (1928).

Anthomyzidæ. Ibid., 54, 8 pp. (1928).

Opomyzidæ. Ibid., 55, 15 pp. (1928).

Chamæmyiidæ. Ibid., 51, 24 pp. (1936).

Hennig, W. Clusiiden. Encycl. Ent. (B) II, 9, pp. 121–138 (1938).

Malloch, J. R. Chyromyia. Proc. Ent. Soc. Washington, 16, pp. 179–181 (1914).

Clusiodidæ. Ibid., 20, pp. 2–8 (1918).

Leucopis. Bull. Illinois Nat. Hist. Surv., 13, pp. 345–357 (1921). Ann. Mag. Nat. Hist., (9) 19, pp. 575–577 (1927).

Notes on Clusiodidæ. Occ. Pap. Boston Soc. Nat. Hist., 5, pp. 47–50 (1922).

Chamæmyiinæ (North America). Ann. Mag. Nat. Hist., (11) 6, pp. 265–274 (1940).

Melander, A. L. Agromyzidæ, Milichiidæ, Ochthiphilidæ. Jour. New York Ent. Soc., 21, pp. 219–273, 283–300 (1913).

MELANDER, A. L., and N. ARGO. Clusiidæ. Proc. U. S. Nat. Mus., **64**, art. 11, 54 pp. (1924).

AGROMYZIDÆ, CARNIDÆ, CRYPTOCHÆTIDÆ, MILICHIIDÆ, ODINIIDÆ

BARNES, H. F. Asparagus Miner. Ann. Appl. Biol., **24**, pp. 574–588 (1937).

BECKER, T. Milichinæ. Ann. Mus. Nat. Hungarici, **5**, pp. 507–550 (1907).

BEL'SKII, B. I. Minierfliegen. Rep. Zool. Mus. Kiev, **23**, pp. 89–103 (1939). (In Ukrainian)

BEZZI, M. Cryptochætum. Atti Soc. Italiana Sci. Nat., **58**, pp. 237–252 (1919).

BUHR, H. Agromyzid Mines (Southern Europe). Stettiner Ent. Ztg., **102**, pp. 73–119 (1941).

DUDA, O. Madizinæ (Palæarctic). Natuurh. Maandbl., **24**, pp. 14–16, 24–26, 37–40 (1935).

FREY, R. Finlands Agromyzider. Notul. Ent., **17**, pp. 82–96 (1937); **26**, pp. 13–55 (1946).

FROST, S. W. New Agromyzidæ (Central America). Ann. Ent. Soc. America, **29**, pp. 298–318 (1936).

HENDEL, F. Agromyzidæ (Palæarctic). Arch. Naturg., **84** A, Heft 7, pp. 109–174 (1918).

Milichiiden. Ent. Mitt., **8**, pp. 196–200 (1919).

Blattminierende Fliegen. Deutsche Ent. Ztg., **1923**, pp. 386–400.

Dipterenminen. Blattminen Europas, Vienna, **1**, 64 pp. (1926); **2**, 135 pp. (1928).

Agromyzidæ, Key to Genera. Zool. Anz., **69**, pp. 248–271 (1927).

Agromyzidæ. Fliegen Palæarkt. Reg., **59**, 570 pp. (1931–1936).

HENNIG, W. Milichiidæ, Carnidæ. Ibid., **60** A, 91 pp. (1937).

HERING, M. Key to Mines on Cratægus. Deutsche Ent. Zeitschr., **1921**, pp. 123–147.

Œkologie der blattminierenden Insektenlarven. Zool. Bausteine, Berlin, **1**, Heft 2, 254 pp. (1926).

Agromyzidæ. Tierwelt Deutschlands, Diptera, **6**, 172 pp. (1927).

Minenfauna der Canarischen Inseln. Zool. Jahrb. Syst., **53**, pp. 405–486 (1927).

Blattminierende Insekten. Ibid., **55**, pp. 535–588 (1928). Zeitschr. Angewandte Ent., **17**, pp. 431–471 (1930). Ent. Jahrb., **1935**, pp. 17–33.

Minenstudien. Zeitschr. Pflanzenkrankh., **44**, pp. 49–70 (1934).

Blattminen (Europe). 112 pp., Junk (1935).

New Agromyzidæ (Palæarctic). Eos, **19**, pp. 51–62 (1943). Notul. Ent., **29**, pp. 18–32 (1949).

KNAB, F. Cryptochætum. Ins. Inscit. Menstr., **2**, pp. 33–36 (1914).

LUNDQUIST, A. Agromyzidæ (Sweden). Opusc. Ent., **12**, pp. 61–76 (1947).

MALLOCH, J. R. Agromyzidæ. Proc. U. S. Nat. Mus., **46**, pp. 127–154 (1913).

Agromyza and Cerodonta. Ann. Ent. Soc. America, **6**, pp. 269–340 (1913).

Agromyzidæ, Notes. Ent. News, **25**, pp. 308–314 (1914).

Agromyza virens. Proc. U. S. Nat. Mus., **49**, pp. 103–108 (1915).

Agromyza. Canadian Ent., **50**, 11 pp. (1918).

Cryptochætum. Proc. Linn. Soc. New South Wales, **52**, pp. 421–423 (1927).

MEIJERE, J. C. H. DE. Agromyzidæ (Holland). Tijdschr. Ent., **67**, pp. 119–155 (1924).

Agromyzinæ, Larvæ. Ibid., **68**, pp. 195–293 (1925); **69**, pp. 227–317 (1926); **71**, pp. 145–178 (1928); **77**, pp. 244–290 (1934); **80**, pp. 167–243 (1937); **81**, pp. 61–116 (1938); **83**, pp. 160–188 (1940); **84**, pp. 13–20 (1941); **86**, pp. 61–76 (1943); **87**, pp. 65–74 (1946); **92**, pp. 15–33 (1950).

MELANDER, A. L. Agromyzinæ, Milichiinæ. Jour. New York Ent. Soc., **21**, pp. 219–273 (1913).

MENON, M. G. R. Cryptochætum. Indian Jour. Ent., **11**, pp. 1–8 (1949).

RYDEN, N. S. Agromyzidæ and Mines (Sweden). Ent. Tidskr., **47**, pp. 119–131 (1926).

THORPE, W. H. Cryptochætum, Key and Larvæ. Parasitol., **33**, pp. 131–148 (1941).

VENTURI, F. Ceredonta. Redia, **31**, pp. 191–226 (1946).

VIMMER, A. Leaf-miners in Böhmen. Acta Soc. Ent. Cechosloveniæ, **27**, pp. 54–66 (1930). (In Czech)

List of Plant Miners (Czechoslovakia). Arch. Prir. Vyzk. Cech., **18**, 159 pp. (1931). (In Czech)

WATT, M. N. Agromyza and Phytomyza (New Zealand). Trans. New Zealand Inst., **54**, pp. 465–489 (1923).

ASTIIDÆ, AULACOGASTRIDÆ, CNEMOSPATHIDÆ, DIASTATIDÆ, DROSOPIIILIDÆ, PERISCELIDÆ

BREUER, M. E., and C. PAVAN. Drosophila, Genitalia. Rev. brasiliera Ent., **10**, pp. 469–488 (1950).

BRYAN, E. H. Drosophilidæ (Hawaii). Proc. Hawaiian Ent. Soc., **10**, pp. 25–42 (1938).

BURLA, H. Drosophila, willistoni Group. Evolution, **3**, pp. 300–314 (1950).

Drosophila (Switzerland). Rev. Suisse Zool., **58**, pp. 23–175 (1951).

DEBARROS, R. Drosophila Speciation. Rev. brasiliera Biol., **10**, pp. 265–278 (1950).

DEMEREC, M. edit. Biology of Drosophila. 632 pp., Wiley, New York (1950).

DOBZHANSKY, T., and C. PAVAN. Drosophila (Brazil). Bol. Fac. Cien. Letr. São Paulo, **36**, pp. 7–72 (1943).

DUDA, O. Scaptomyza. Jahresh. Ver. Insektenk., **13**, pp. 57–69 (1921).

Oriental and Australian Drosophilidæ. Ann. Mus. Nat. Hungarici, **20**, pp. 24–59 (1923); **23**, pp. 241–250 (1926).

Drosophila (Europe). Ent. Meddel., **14**, pp. 246–313 (1924).

Drosophilidæ (Palæarctic, Oriental). Arch. Naturg., **90** A, Heft 3, pp. 172–234 (1924); (Southeast Asia). Ibid., pp. 235–259 (1924); (Neotropical). Ibid., **91** A, Heft 11, pp. 1–229 (1925).

Drosophilidæ (Costa Rica). Ann. Mus. Nat. Hungarici, **22**, pp. 149–229 (1925).

Drosophilidæ (Sumatra). Supplementa Ent., **14**, pp. 42–120 (1926).

Astiidæ (Old World). Deutsche Ent. Zeitschr., **1927**, pp. 113–147.

Hypselothyrea (Southeast Asia). Ann. Mus. Nat. Hungarici, **25**, pp. 79–90 (1928).

Periscelidæ, Astiidæ, Cyrtonotidæ. Fliegen Palæarkt. Reg., **58** A–F, 63 pp. (1934).

Drosophilidæ. Ibid., **58** G, 118 pp. (1935).

Drosophilidæ (Africa). Ann. Mus. Nat. Hungarici, **32**, pp. 1–57 (1939); **33**, pp. 19–53 (1940).

ENDERLEIN, G. Cnemospathidæ. Nat. Hist. Juan Fernandez, **3**, Zool., pp. 643–680 (1940).

FROTA-PESSOA, O. Hirtodrosophila. Rev. brasiliera Biol., **5**, pp. 469–483 (1945).

Clastopteromyia. Summa brasiliensis Biol., **1**, pp. 181–241 (1947).

HENDEL, F. Cyrtonotum. Deutsche Ent. Zeitschr., **1913**, pp. 618–630.

Scaptomyza. Zool. Anz., **76**, pp. 289–302 (1928).

HSU, T. C. Drosophilidæ, Male Genitalia. Univ. Texas Publ., **4920**, pp. 80–142 (1949).

KAHL, H. Leucophenga. Ann. Carnegie Mus., **11**, pp. 364–393 (1917).

KIKKAWA, H., and F. T. PENG. Drosophila (Japan). Japan. Jour. Zool., **7**, pp. 507–552 (1938).

MALLOCH, J. R. Exotic Drosophilidæ. Ann. Mag. Nat. Hist. (10) **6**, pp. 321–334 (1930).

Neotropical Drosophilidæ. Proc. U. S. Nat. Mus., **66**, art. 3, 11 pp. (1924).

Drosophilidæ (Samoa). Insects of Samoa, **6**, fasc. 8, pp. 267–329, British Mus. (1934).

MALLOCH, J. R., and W. L. McATEE. Drosophilidæ (District of Columbia). Proc. Biol. Soc. Washington, **37**, pp. 25–41 (1924).

MALOGOLOWKIN, C. Rhinoleucophenga. Rev. brasiliera Biol., **6**, pp. 415–426 (1946).

PATTERSON, J. T. Drosophila, virilis group. American Nat., **75**, pp. 523–539 (1941).

Drosophilidæ of Southwestern U. S. Univ. Texas Publ., **4313**, pp. 7–216 (1943).

PATTERSON, J. T., and G. B. MAINLAND. Drosophilidæ (Mexico). Ibid., **4445**, pp. 7–101 (1944).

PATTERSON, J. T., and W. S. STONE. Drosophila, virilis group. Ibid., **4920**, pp. 7–17 (1949).

PATTERSON, J. T., and R. P. WAGNER. Distribution of Drosophila. Ibid., **4313**, pp. 217–281 (1943).

PATTERSON, J. T., and M. R. WHEELER. Hirtodrosophila and Drosophila. Ibid., **4213**, pp. 67–109 (1942).

Catalogue of Drosophila. Ibid., **4920**, pp. 207–233 (1949).

PAVAN, C. A. B. Drosophila (Brazil). Bol. Fac. Univ. São Paulo, **86**, pp. 20–63 (1947).

SABROSKY, C. W. Asteiidæ. Ann. Ent. Soc. America, **36**, pp. 501–514 (1943).

SALLES, H. Genitalia of Drosophila. Summa brasiliensis Biol., **1**, pp. 311–383 (1947).

SPENCER, W. P. New Species of Drosophila, quinaria group. Univ. Texas Publ., **4213**, pp. 53–66 (1942).

SPIESS, E. B. Drosophila in New England. Jour. New York Ent. Soc., **57**, pp. 117–131 (1949).

STREISINGER, G. Drosophila, cardini group. Jour. New York Ent. Soc., **54**, pp. 105–113 (1946).

Sturtevant, A. H. Nearctic Drosophilas. Ann. Ent. Soc. America, **9**, pp. 325–342 (1916). Bull. American Mus. Nat. Hist., **38**, pp. 441–446 (1918). Carnegie Inst. Publ., **301**, 150 pp. (1921). Proc. Nat. Acad. Sci., **25**, pp. 137–141 (1939). Univ. Texas Publ., **4213**, pp. 1–51 (1942).

    Zygothrica. Proc. U. S. Nat. Mus., **58**, pp. 155–158 (1920).

    Oriental Drosophilidæ. Philippine Jour. Sci., **32**, pp. 361–374 (1927).

Sturtevant, A. H., and T. Dobzhansky. Drosophila, affinis group. American Nat., **70**, pp. 574–584 (1936).

Tan, C. C., T. C. Hsu and T. C. Sheng. Drosophila (China). Univ. Texas Publ., **4920**, pp. 196–206 (1949).

Wheeler, M. R. Drosophilidæ, Taxonomy. Ibid., **4920**, pp. 143–195 (1949); **5204**, pp. 162–218 (1952).

PUPIPARA

Aldrich, J. M. Hippoboscidæ, Table of Genera. Ins. Inscit. Menstr., **11**, pp. 75–79 (1923).

Austen, E. E. Hippoboscidæ. Ann. Mag. Nat. Hist., (7) **12**, pp. 255–266 (1903).

    Cratærina. Parasitol., **18**, pp. 350–360 (1926).

Bau, A. Pupipara (Chaco Exped.). Konowia, **9**, pp. 209–213 (1930).

Bequaert, J. Larger Species of Lynchia. Psyche, **40**, pp. 68–82 (1933).

    Hippoboscinæ. Psyche, **37**, pp. 303–326 (1930).

    Hippoboscidæ (Yucatan). Ibid., **38**, pp. 186–193 (1931). Carnegie Inst. Publ., **431**, pp. 547–576 (1933).

    Hippoboscidæ (Galapagos). Proc. California Acad. Sci., **21**, pp. 131–138 (1933).

    Hippoboscidæ, Notes. Psyche, **40**, pp. 68–82, 101–105 (1933); **46**, pp. 70–90 (1939).

    Lipoptena. Bull. Brooklyn Ent. Soc., **32**, pp. 91–101 (1937).

    Echestypus. Psyche, **47**, pp. 83–104 (1940).

    Hippoboscidæ (Antilles). Mem. Soc. Cubana Hist. Nat., **19**, pp. 305–327 (1941).

    Hippoboscidæ (Oceania). Occ. Pap. Bishop Mus., **16**, pp. 247–292 (1941).

    Pupipara (Venezuela). Bol. Ent. Venezolana, **1**, pp. 79–88 (1942).

    Brachypteromyia. Psyche, **49**, pp. 108–117 (1942).

    Melophaginæ. Ent. Americana, **22**, 220 pp. (1942).

    Lynchia. Psyche, **52**, pp. 88–104 (1945).

Bequaert, J., and M. Leclercq. Hippoboscidæ (Belgium). Bull. Ann. Soc. Ent. Belgique, **83**, pp. 77–84 (1947).

Braga, J. M. Pupíparos (Portugal). An. Fac. Cienc. Porto, **26**, pp. 230–237 (1941).

Collins, B. J. Nycteribia and Spinturnix. Bull. Nat. Inst. Health, **155**, pp. 743–765 (1931).

Corradetti, A. Nycteribiidæ (Italy). Riv. Malariol., **13**, pp. 338–352 (1934).

Corradetti, A., and G. Lupascu. Nycteribiidæ, Hypopygium. Riv. Parassit., **5**, pp. 85–99 (1941).

Costa Lima, A. da. Streblidæ (South America). Arch. Esp. Agric. Med. Vet., **5**, pp. 25–32 (1921).

CURRAN, C. H. Nycteribiidæ and Streblidæ. American Mus. Novit., **765**, 15 pp. (1935).

DRYENSKY, P. Pupipara (Bulgaria). Mitt. Bulgarischen Ent. Ges., **3**, pp. 89–104 (1926). (In Bulgarian)

DUDICH, E. Fledermausfliegen (Hungarian). Math. Termesz. Ert., Budapest, **41**, pp. 144–151 (1925).

EICHLER, W. Hippoboscids on Birds (Germany). Mitt. Ver. Sächs. Orn., **5**, pp. 126–130 (1937).

FALCOZ, L. Pupipara. Arch. Zool. Paris, **61**, pp. 521–552 (1923).

    Pupipara (New Caledonia). Nova Caledonia, A. Zool., **3**, pp. 81–96 (1923).

    Pupipara. Bull. Mus. Hist. Nat. Paris, **1924**, pp. 223–230, 309–315, 386–389 (1924).

    Pupipara (France). Faune de France, **14**, pp. 21–52 (1926).

    Pupipara (Samoa). Insects of Samoa, **6**, fasc. 1, 9 pp. (1927).

    Hippoboscidæ. Encycl. Ent. (B) II, **5**, pp. 27–54 (1930).

FERRIS, G. F. Ectoparasites on Bats. Ent. News, **27**, pp. 433–438 (1916).

    New World Nycteribiidæ. Ibid., **35**, pp. 191–199 (1924).

    Pupipara (Philippines). Philippine Jour. Sci., **27**, pp. 413–420 (1925); **28**, pp. 329–339 (1925); **34**, pp. 207–232 (1927); **43**, pp. 537–553 (1930).

    Hippoboscidæ (Borneo). Sarawak Mus. Jour., **3**, pp. 279–286 (1926).

    Hippoboscidæ (Samoa). Insects of Samoa, **6**, fasc. 1, pp. 10–21, British Mus. (1927).

FERRIS, G. F., and F. R. COLE. Hippoboscidæ. Parasitol., **14**, pp. 178–205 (1922).

GUIMARÃES, L. R. Trichobius (South America). Rev. Mus. Paulista, **23**, pp. 651–666 (1938).

    Basilia (South America). Arq. Zool. São Paulo, **5**, 87 pp. (1946).

HARDENBERG, J. D. F. Pupipara, Development. Zool. Jahrb. Anat., **50**, pp. 497–570 (1929).

HASE, A. Pupipara, Notes. Zeitschr. Parasitenk., **11**, pp. 637–651 (1940).

IMMS, A. D. Braula and Affinities. Parasitol., **34**, pp. 88–100 (1942).

JOBLING, B. Raymondia. Ibid., **22**, pp. 283–301 (1930).

    Nycteribosca. Ibid., **26**, pp. 64–97 (1934).

    Streblidæ, Subfamilies. Ibid., **28**, pp. 355–380 (1936).

    Trichobius. Ibid., **30**, pp. 358–387 (1938).

    Streblidæ (Africa). Ibid., **31**, pp. 147–165 (1939).

    Streblidæ (America). Ibid., **31**, pp. 486–497 (1939).

    Streblidæ, Key to American Genera. Ibid., **39**, pp. 315–329 (1949).

    Aspidoptera. Proc. Roy. Ent. Soc. London (B), **18**, pp. 135–144 (1949).

    Streblidæ (Pacific Isl.). Trans. Roy. Ent. Soc. London, **102**, pp. 211–246 (1951).

JOHNSON, C. W. Distribution of Hippoboscidæ. Psyche, **29**, pp. 79–85 (1922).

JOHNSON, P. Danish Louse-flies. Ent. Medd., **25**, pp. 278–298 (1948).

KARAMAN, T. S. Nycteribien Jugoslaviens. Bull. Soc Sci. Skoplje, **17**, pp. 9–20 (1937). (In Serbian)

KESSEL, Q. C. Notes on Streblinæ. Parasitol., **16**, pp. 405–414 (1924).

    Streblidæ of World. Jour. New York Ent. Soc., **33**, pp. 11–33 (1925).

LUTZ, A., A. NEIVA and A. DA COSTA LIMA. Pupipara (Brazil). Mem. Inst. Oswaldo Cruz, **7**, pp. 173–199 (1915).

MacArthur, K. Hippoboscidæ (Wisconsin). Bull. Publ. Mus. Milwaukee, **8**, pp. 373–440 (1948).

Massonat, E. Pupipara. Ann. Univ. Lyon, N. S. 1, **28**, pp. 1–356 (1909).

Muir, F. Ascodipteron. Bull. Mus. Comp. Zool. Harvard, **54**, pp. 349–366 (1912).

Musgrave, A. Nycteribiidæ (Australia). Rec. Australian Mus., **14**, pp. 289–300 (1925); **15**, pp. 263–276 (1927).

Ryberg, O. Bat Parasites. 330 pp., Univ. Lund, Stockholm (1947),

Schuurmans Stekhoven, J. H. Basilia (Venezuela). Zeitschr. Parasitenk., **3**, pp. 205–219 (1931).

 Pupipara and Tabanidæ (China). Lingnan Sci. Jour., **7**, pp. 497–510 (1929).

 Bat-flies (East Indies). Capita Zool., **8**, no. 4, pp. 1–37 (1939).

 Nycteribien (East Indies). Zeitschr. Parasitenk., **12**, pp. 507–537 (1942).

Scott, H. Nycteribiidæ (Orient). Ann. Mag. Nat. Hist., (8) **14**, pp. 209–235 (1914).

 Nycteribiidæ, Notes. Parasitol., **9**, pp. 593–610 (1917).

 Nycteribiidæ (India). Rec. Indian Mus., **27**, pp. 351–384 (1925).

 Australian Nycteribiidæ. Stylops, **1**, pp. 16–30 (1932).

Speiser, P. Streblidæ. Arch. Naturg., **66**, pp. 31–70 (1901).

 Nycteribiidæ. Ibid., **67**, pp. 11–77 (1901).

 Hippoboscidæ. Ann. Mus. Genova, **40**, pp. 553–560 (1901).

 Pupipara. Termesz. Füzetek, **25**, pp. 327–338 (1902). Zeitschr. syst. Hymenopt. Dipt., **2**, pp. 145–180 (1902).

 Hippoboscidæ. Ibid., **6**, pp. 347–360 (1905).

 Checklist of North American Pupipara. Ent. News, **18**, pp. 103–105 (1907).

 Distribution and Phylogeny, Pupipara. Zeitschr. Wiss. Insektenbiol., **4**, pp. 241–246, 301–305, 420–427, 437–447 (1908).

Stefanelli, A. Nycteribiidæ. Riv. Parassit., **6**, pp. 25–42, 61–86 (1942).

Swenk, M. H. Hippoboscidæ (North America). Jour. New York Ent. Soc., **24**, pp. 126–136 (1916).

Thompson, G. B. Nycteribiidæ and Streblidæ from Bats. (Pacific Isl.). Ent. Mon. Mag., **73**, pp. 200–208 (1937).

 Hippoboscidæ (Pacific Isl.). Ibid., **74**, pp. 14–17, 43–52 (1938).

 Hippoboscidæ (Ceylon). Ann. Mag. Nat. Hist., (11) **1**, pp. 315–319 (1938).

Zavattari, E. Affinity between Hippoboscidæ and Glossinidæ. Atti Soc. Italiana Sci. Nat., **67**, pp. 37–70 (1928).

METAMORPHOSES OF DIPTERA. Papers on several families

Anderson, F. S. Ceratopogonidæ and Chironomidæ (Greenland). Medd. Grønland, **116**, no. 1, 95 pp. (1937).

Andrews, H. W. Earlier Stages of Diptera. Proc. South London Ent. Nat. Hist. Soc., **1930**, pp. 17–29 (1930).

Banks, N. Dipterous Larvæ. U. S. Bur. Ent. Tech. Ser., **22**, 44 pp. (1912).

Harant, H., and J. Richard. Larves de Nematocères. Bull. Soc. Etud. Sci. Nat. Beziers, **41**, pp. 76–89 (1937).

HAYES, W. P. Bibliography of Keys. Ent. News, 49, pp. 246–251 (1938); 50, pp. 5–10, 76–82 (1939).

HENNIG, W. Larvenformen der Dipteren. Berlin, Akad. Verlag, 1, 184 pp. (1948); 2, 458 pp. (1950).

HERING, M. Die Blatt-minen (Middle and North Europe). 6 pts., 631 pp. W. Junk. (1935–1937).

   Blattminierenden Larven, Œcology, Zool. Bausteine 1, 253 pp. (1926). Biology of Leaf-miners. 420 pp., W. Junk, The Hague (1951).

JOHANNSEN, O. A. Aquatic Diptera. Mem. Cornell Exp. Sta., 164, 71 pp. (1934); 177, 62 pp. (1935).

MALLOCH, J. R. Larval and Pupal Characters. Bull. Illinois Lab. Nat. Hist., 13, pp. 161–410 (1917).

MEIJERE, J. C. H. DE. Dipteren Larven und Puppen. Zool. Jahrb. Syst., 40, pp. 177–322 (1916).

SÉGUY, E. Dipterous Larvæ Parasitic on Birds. Encycl. Ent. (B) II, 5, pp. 63–82 (1929).

   Diptères mineurs (Madagascar). Mém. Inst. Sci. Madagascar, 5 A, pp. 309–321 (1951).

SMITH, R. W., and T. U. FINLAYSON. Larvæ Parasitic on Grasshoppers. Canadian Jour. Res. D, Zool. Sci., 28, pp. 81–117 (1950).

VIMMER, A. Pupæ of Eucephalous Diptera. Acta Soc. Ent. Cechosloveniæ, 13, pp. 25–34 (1916).

VANEY, C. Larves et Métamorphoses des Diptera. Ann. Univ. Lyon, n.s. 1, fasc. 9, 178 pp. (1902).

ZIMIN, L. S. Key to Larvæ of Synanthropic Flies (Tadzhikistan). Keys to Fauna USSR., Moscow Zool., Inst., 28, 114 pp. (1948).

ORDER SIPHONÁPTERA

(SUCTÒRIA, APHANÍPTERA, ROPHOTEÌRA)

Small, wingless, strongly compressed, jumping insects, with dark colored, heavily chitinized bristly body and legs; parasitic in the adult condition on mammals, or rarely on birds. Head small, closely articulated with the thorax. Antennæ short and thick, with two large basal joints and an oval or elongate indistinctly jointed apical portion, lying in depressions behind the small, simple eyes which are sometimes wanting. Mouthparts fitted for piercing and sucking, the mandibles setiform, maxillæ blade-like; both pairs of palpi well developed. Thorax small, composed of three similar, freely movable segments. Abdomen large, composed of nine segments; cerci one-jointed. Legs large, stout; coxæ large, tarsi five-jointed with stout claws. Metamorphosis complete; larvæ elongate, cylindrical, legless, with well developed head and biting mouthparts; free living. Pupæ enclosed in cocoons. Fleas.

1. Most of the dorsal abdominal segments each bearing more than one transverse row of bristles; fronto-epicranial groove frequently present 2

Most of the dorsal abdominal segments with only a single transverse row of bristles, or without bristles..........................5

2. Gena (cheek) simple, not divided by a vertical groove or suture...3

Gena divided by a vertical suture; head with a "helmet" composed of the greatly reduced front and the anterior part of the greatly enlarged genæ; postantennal region of head with a dorsal swelling .... **STEPHANOCÍRCIDÆ**

3. Head simple at sides, seldom elongated, without a flattened, articulated lobe, on each side anteriorly; not parasitic on bats.......4

Head usually elongated, with two or three ventral flaps that project downward from the anterior corner of the head at the sides of the mouth opening; species parasitic on bats. (Ischnopsýllus, Myodopsýlla). (*CERÁTOPSÝLLIDÆ*) ..... **ISCHNOPSÝLLIDÆ**

4. Head without a comb-like series of spines on each cheek; front not reduced in size; abdomen usually with few apical spines and rarely with combs. (*CERATOPHÝLLIDÆ, VERMIPSÝLLIDÆ, MALACOPSÝLLIDÆ, MEGAPSÝLLIDÆ*, part).
DOLICHOPSÝLLIDÆ

a. Frontal notch or frontal tubercle, or both, present although sometimes weakly developed ....b

Frontal notch and frontal tubercle completely absent. (Uropsýlla, Malacopsýlla, Acanthopsýlla, Conorhinopsýlla). **UROPSYLLÍNÆ**

b. Antepygidial bristles absent or very poorly developed; abdomen of female frequently distended. (Vermipsýlla, Arctopsýlla).
VERMÍPSYLLÍNÆ

Antepygidial bristles present, conspicuous; abdomen not distended..c

c. Pronotum with a comb of spines. (Dolichopsýlla, Ceratophýllus, Ctenophýllus, Amphipsýlla) ...........DOLICHOPSYLLÍNÆ

Pronotum without a comb of spines. (Rhopalopsýllus, Parapsýllus).
RHOPALOPSYLLÍNÆ

Head with a comb-like series of spines on each cheek; front often reduced in size; combs often present on abdomen; apical spines of abdomen frequently numerous. (Including *CTENOPSÝLLIDÆ, CTENOPHTHÁLMIDÆ, TYPHLOCERÁTIDÆ, MALACOPSÝLLIDÆ, MEGAPSÝLLIDÆ, MACROPSÝLLIDÆ*).
HYSTRICHOPSÝLLIDÆ

a. Front never greatly reduced, forming at least one-half of the anterior margin of the head; cheeks usually not greatly enlarged, usually longest horizontally; eyes sometimes present.................b

Front greatly reduced, dorsal or antedorsal in position, forming less than one-half of the anterior margin of the head, furnished with one or two pairs of dermal pits and with never more than a vestigial frontal tubercle; cheeks greatly enlarged, longest in a vertical or nearly vertical direction; eyes absent or vestigial. (Leptopsýlla, Peromyscopsýlla) . . . . LEPTOPSYLLÌNÆ

b. Labial palpi with eight joints or less; cephalic comb of bristles seldom extending along both the ventral margin of the cheek and the anterior margin of the antennal groove c

Labial palpi with more than ten joints; cephalic comb extending along the ventral margin of the cheek and the anterior margin of the antennal groove. (Macropsýlla, Austr.).

MACROPSYLLÌNÆ

c. Front with a tubercle or notch, sometimes very poorly developed; comb on cheek with no more than six spines; small species. (Ctenophthálmus, Micropsýlla) . . . . . . CTENOPHTHALMÌNÆ

Front without trace of a tubercle or notch; comb on cheek with six or more spines; medium or large species. (Hystricopsýlla, Stenopònia) . . . . HYSTRICHOPSYLLÌNÆ

5. Thorax above longer than the first abdominal segment; abdomen of gravid female never greatly swollen; segments of abdomen each with a row of distinct bristles. (Figs. 766, 767, 768, 770).

PULÍCIDÆ

a. Mesoëpisternum separated from the epimeron by an internal vertical ridge . . . . b

Mesoëpisternum not separated from the epimeron. (Pùlex, Juxtapùlex) . . . . PULICÌNÆ

b. Fronto-epicranial suture indistinct or absent; postantennal region of head not, or only slightly, incrassate above. Ctenocephálides (= Ctenocéphalus) (C. fèlis, Cat-flea; C. cànis, Dog-flea), Xenopsýlla (= Lœmopsýlla) (X. cheòpis, Plague flea), Hoplopsýllus).

SPILOPSYLLÌNÆ

Fronto-epicranial suture (above the antennal groove) well developed; front considerably reduced, the fronto-genal angle almost as high as the level of the eye; post-antennal region of head incrassate above. (Chimæropsýlla, Ethiop.) . . . . . CHIMÆROPSYLLÌNÆ

Thorax greatly reduced in size, its length above shorter than that of the first abdominal segment; abdomen of gravid female greatly distended; bristles on abdomen weak or absent 6

6. Maxillæ with a long narrow, curved lamina which projects downward and backward; maxillary palpi as long as the front coxæ; head evenly rounded above; side pieces of metathorax extending over only the first abdominal segment; abdomen of fully matured female vermiform. (Hectopsýlla, Ind.) . . . . . HECTOPSÝLLIDÆ

Maxillæ without, or with a very short and broad projecting lamina, their palpi extending beyond the front coxæ; head strongly angulated anteriorly above; side pieces of metathorax extending over nearly two or three abdominal tergites; abdomen of fully matured female enormously swollen, globose (Fig. 765). (**Túnga** (= *Sarcopsýlla, Dermatóphilus*) (*T. pénetrans*, Chigoe or Jigger flea) tropicopol.; **Echidnóphaga** (*E. gallinàcea*, Sticktight or Hen flea) tropicopol.). (*SARCOPSÝLLIDÆ, ECHIDNOPHÁGIDÆ, DERMATOPHÍLIDÆ, RHYNCHOPRIÓNIDÆ*. **TÚNGIDÆ**

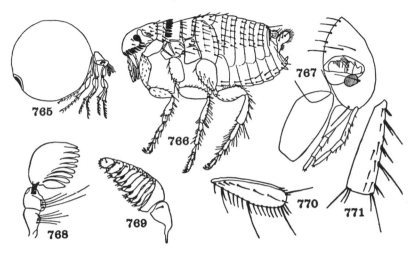

Figs. 765–771. Siphonaptera

765. **Tunga**, mature female (Butler) Tungidæ.
766. **Ctenocephalides** (Patton and Cragg) Pulicidæ.
767. **Xenopsylla**, side view of head (Fox) Pulicidæ.
768. **Ctenocephalides**, antenna (Patton and Cragg) Pulicidæ.
769. **Ceratophyllus**, antenna (Fox) Dolichopsyllidæ.
770. **Ctenocephalides**, hind tibia (Fox) Pulicidæ.
771. **Ceratophyllus**, hind tibia (Fox) Dolichopsyllidæ.

LITERATURE ON SIPHONAPTERA

BAKER, C. F. Revision of American Siphonaptera. Proc. U. S. Nat. Mus., **27**, pp. 265–469 (1904).
   Classification of American Siphonaptera. Proc. U. S. Nat. Mus., **29**, pp. 121–170 (1905).
BEIER, M. Siphonaptera. Kükenthal, Handbuch der Zoologie, **4**, Hälfte 2, Lief. 11, pp. 1999–2039, 54 figs. (1937).
COSTA LIMA, A. DA. Suctorios (pulgas). Insetos do Brasil, **4**, pp. 17–71, 42 figs. (1943).
COSTA LIMA, A. DA and C. R. HATHAWAY. Pulgas. Bibliografia, catalogo e animais por elas sugados. Monogr. Inst. Oswaldo Cruz, No. **4**, 517 pp. (1946).
DALLA TORRE. C. G. Aphaniptera orbis terrarum. Ber. naturw. med. Ver., Innsbruck, **39**, pp. 1–29 (1924).

DAMPF, A. Die Aphanipteren Westdeutschlands. Ber. bot. zool. Ver. Rhein-
lande, 1911, pp. 73–113 (1912).
Kritisches Verzeichnis der Aphaniptera Deutschlands. Ent. Mitt., 15,
pp. 377–386 (1926).
Notas sobre pulgas. I–VII. Rev. Soc. mexicana Hist., nat., 6, pp. 47–70,
17 figs. (1945).
EWING, H. E. Manual of External Parasites. 225 pp. Thomas, Springfield, Ill.,
and Baltimore, Md. (1929).
EWING, H. E. and I. Fox. Fleas of North America. Classification, Identifica-
tion, and Geographic Distribution. Misc. Publ., U. S. Dept. Agric., 500,
142 pp., 13 figs. (1943).
Fox, I. Fleas of Eastern United States. 191 pp. Ames, Iowa (1940).
HUBBARD, C. A. Fleas of Western North America. ix + 533 pp., 235 figs.
Iowa State Coll. Press, Ames (1947).
IOFF, J. Zur Systematik der Flöhe aus der Unterfamilie Ceratophyllinæ.
Zeitschr. f. Parasitenk., 9, pp. 73–124 (1937).
JANCKE, O. Flöhe oder Aphaniptera. Tierwelt Deutschlands, 35, pp. 1–42, 47
figs. (1938).
JELLISON, W. L. and N. E. GOOD. Index to Literature of Siphonaptera of North
America. National Health Bull., No. 178, iv + 193 pp. (1942).
JORDAN, H. E. K. On Thaumapsyllinæ, a New Subfamily of Bat-fleas. Proc.
Ent. Soc. Washington, 49, pp. 182–184, 2 figs. (1947).
JORDAN, K. and W. ROTHSCHILD. Revision of Sarcopsyllidæ. Thompson Yates
and Johnston Lab. Repts., 7, (1906).
Revision of the non-combed eyed Siphonaptera. Parasitology, 1, pp.
1–100 (1908).
KOHLS, G. M. Siphonaptera. A Study of the Species Infesting Wild Hares
and Rabbits in North America. National Inst. Health Bull., No. 175,
34 pp., 3 pls., 8 maps (1940).
LIU, C. Y. The Fleas of China. Philippine Journ. Sci., 70, pp. 1–122, 132
figs. (1939).
MACCHIAVELLO, A. Siphonaptera de la costa sur-occidental de America. Bol.
Ofic. Sanit. Panamericana, Washington, D. C., 27, pp. 412–460 (1948).
OUDEMANS, A. C. Anteekningen over Suctoria. Ent. Bericht. (numerous parts)
(1909–1917).
Neue Ansichten über die Morphologie des Flohkopfes, sowie über die
Ontogenie, Phylogenie und Systematik der Flöhe. Novit. Zool., 16, pp.
133–158 (1910).
Kritisch Overzicht du Nederlandische Suctoria. Tijdschr. v. Ent., 58,
pp. 60–97 (1915).
ROTHSCHILD, N. C. Synopsis of British Siphonaptera. Ent. Monthly Mag., 51,
pp. 49–112 (1915).
SÉGUY, E. Insectes ectoparasites (Mallophaga, Anoploures, Siphonaptera).
Faune de France, 43, pp. 461–543 (1944).
SHARIF, M. Revision of Indian Siphonaptera (Pulicidæ) Rec. Indian Mus.,
32, pp. 29–62 (1930).
TRAUB, R. Siphonaptera from Central America and Mexico. Fieldiana, Zool.
Mem., 1, 127 pp., 54 pls. (1950).
WAGNER, J. Ordnung: Flöhe, Aphaniptera (Siphonaptera, Suctoria). Tierwelt
Mitteleuropas, 6, Lief. 2, Teil 3, 24 pp. (1936).

Aphaniptera aus Süd-Peru (Stephanocircidæ). Zeitschr. Parasitenk., **9**, pp. 698–716 (1937).
Aphaniptera. In Bronn's Klassen u. Ordnungen Tierreichs, **5**, Abt. iii, Buch 13, Teil f, pp. 1–114, 100 figs. (1939).

ORDER COLEÓPTERA

(*ELEUTHERȦTA*; *ELYTRÓPTERA*)

Moderate-sized, small or minute, more rarely very large, hard-bodied insects. Head free, usually prominent, sometimes produced forward to form a snout or beak; mandibles well developed; maxillæ well developed, usually bilobed with the palpi three- to five-jointed; labial palpi shorter, two- or three-jointed; antennæ ten- or eleven-jointed, sometimes less, very rarely more, filiform or variously modified, often with the apical joints enlarged; ocelli nearly always absent. Prothorax free; two pairs of wings, the front pair (elytra) thickly chitinized, sheathing the meso- and metathorax and also nearly always the abdomen, almost always meeting in a straight line down the middle of the back; hind wings occasionally absent, front ones rarely reduced or absent. Legs homonomous, the tarsi usually with five or four joints; no cerci. Metamorphosis complete, the larvæ mandibulate. A very large and widely distributed group, including Beetles and Weevils.[1]

1. First ventral segment divided by the hind coxal cavities, so that its sides are separated from the usually very small median part (Fig. 772); the first three sternites (ventral abdominal segments) immovably united; antennæ usually filiform or nearly so; hind wings usually with a triangular or oval cell at the apex of an elongate discal cell. (Figs. 774, 777). (Suborder ADÉPHAGA) . 2
First visible sternite extending for its entire breadth behind the coxal cavities; hind wing wthout closed cell at apex of discal cell (except Cupidæ), the latter also often absent. (Figs. 775, 776, 778). (Suborder POLÝPHAGA) 9
2. Metasternum with a well-defined ante-coxal piece, marked off anteriorly by a distinct suture which extends across the whole width of the metasternum excepting the episterna; mostly terrestrial forms, a few aquatic 3
Metasternum with a much smaller ante-coxal piece, or none; aquatic or rarely subaquatic forms 5
3. Posterior coxæ expanded into large plates which almost entirely conceal the abdomen; antennæ 10-jointed; aquatic forms. (**Halíplus**, cosmop.; **Peltódytes** (*Cnemídotus*), Holarc.) . . . . . . **HALÍPLIDÆ**
Posterior coxæ not thus expanded; antennæ usually 11-jointed, but

[1] A few highly degenerate forms of more or less larviform appearance that will not otherwise run out in the key may be identified by reference to couplet **198**.

segments reduced in number, fused, or distorted in certain rare Carabidæ (paussids); terrestrial or at most subaquatic forms. (If the tarsi are two-jointed and the antennæ bead-like, see Jacobsoniidæ, couplet 119) 4

4. Antennæ inserted on the front, above the base of the mandibles; eyes prominent; head usually wider than the thorax, vertical, with

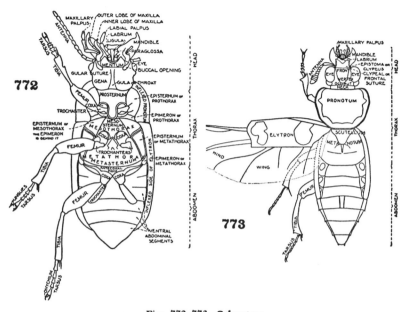

Figs. 772–773. Coleoptera

772. **Harpalus**, underside (Hayward) Carabidæ.
773. **Necrophorus**, wings spread on left side and removed on the right (Hayward) Silphidæ.

large mandibles. Tiger-beetles. (**Cicindèla**, cosmop.; **Megacéphala** (*Tétracha*), widespr.; **Oxychìla**, Neotrop.; **Mantíchora**, Afr.; **Tricóndyla**, Indoaustr.; **Pogonóstoma**, Madagascar; **Òmus,** Nearc.) . . . . **CICINDÉLIDÆ**

Antennæ inserted on the sides of the head between the base of the mandibles and the eyes; head usually narrower than the thorax and usually held horizontal. Ground beetles, etc. A very large, diverse, abundant and widespread family. (Figs. 772, 777, 783, 818). (**Calosòma, Scarìtes, Clivìna, Pteróstichus, Chlænius, Lèbia, Bráchinus**, cosmop. or widespr.; **Cárabus, Nèbria, Trèchus, Amàra, Hárpalus,** chiefly Nearc.; **Anophthálmus,** Eur.; **Pseudanophthál-**

mus, E. N. Am.; **Pseudomórpha,** Am.; **Sphallomórpha, Silphomór-pha,** Austr.; **Cryptocephalomórpha,** Indomal.; **Hydroporomórpha,** Afr.; **Ómophron,** widespr.; and very many other genera.) (Including *MORMOLÝCIDÆ* (**Mormólyce,** Malay.), *PAUSSIDÆ* (**Paússus, Cerápterus,** Ethiop.; **Arthrópterus,** Austr.; and **Homópterus,** Neotrop., represent this group of small myrmecophilous beetles with the antennæ often remarkably thickened by the fusion of the apical segments into a club, or forming a broad, more or less unsegmented lamina.), *PSEUDOMÓRPHIDÆ, OMOPHRÓN-IDÆ,* and many others) . . . .**CARÁBIDÆ** [1]

a. Both spurs of the front tibia apical, when present; metepimera visible behind the metepisterna; middle coxal cavities disjunct (reached by the mesepimera). (A few presumably primitive forms, including the paussids) . . . . .Division ISOCHÆTA (The following family names have recently been used for genera that are placed in this group: Trachypachỳidæ, Gehringìidæ, Ozænidæ, Metrìidæ).

One spur of front tibia more or less distant from the apex, often at the inner end of the comb-organ . . . . .b

b. No metepimera visible behind the metepisterna; middle coxal cavities disjunct (CARABÌNÆ of G. Horn, in part).
    Division SIMPLÍCIA
(The following family names have recently been used for genera that are placed in this group; Nebrìidæ, Migadópidæ, Eláphridæ, Omophrónidæ, Lorocéridæ, Siagónidæ, Cimbionótidæ).

Metepimera visible as lobes behind the metepisterna (Division LIMBÀTA) c

c. Body usually pedunculate; middle coxal cavities disjunct; antennæ in repose received in channels under the eyes (Scaritini of G. Horn) . . . . LIMBÀTA SCROBÍFERA ('The following family names have recently been used for genera that are placed in this group: Hilétidæ, Scarítidæ).

Body usually not pedunculate; middle coxal cavities conjunct (not reached by mesepimera) . . . . .d

d. Left and right parameres of male copulatory organ more or less alike, long, slender, with apical setæ; mandibles usually with a seta in the scrobe (Apotomini, Broscini, Psydrini, Bembidiini, and Pogonini of G. Horn) . . . . .LIMBÀTA STYLÍFERA

---

[1] It is not feasible at present to divide the enormous family Carabidæ into satisfactory subfamilies. An arrangement by G. Horn into three subfamilies (Carabinæ, Harpalinæ, Pseudomorphinæ; Trans. Amer. Ent. Soc., 9:103 (1881); Leconte and Horn (1883)) has been in use for many years, and a recent classification into "divisions" and "groups", has been proposed by Jeannel. However, neither of these arrangements is entirely satisfactory. Dr. P. J. Darlington, Jr., of the Museum of Comparative Zoology, has furnished us with the following summary of Jeannel's arrangement, which is presented here in the form of a key.

(The following family names have recently been used for genera that are placed in this group: Apotómidæ, Bróscidæ, Psýdridæ, Tréchidæ, Patróbidæ).

Left and right parameres more or less differentiated, usually without setæ ....e

e. Left paramere (and often also the right one) more or less spatulate; mandibles without a seta in the scrobe (most of Harpalinæ of G. Horn)........................LIMBÀTA CONCHÍFERA
(The following family names have recently been used for genera that are placed in this group: Perigónidæ, Cnemacánthidæ, Melanódidæ, Peleciidæ, Ctenodactýlidæ, Harpálidæ, Pterostíchidæ, Callístidæ, Glýptidæ, Panagæidæ, Licínidæ, Odacánthidæ, Masorèidæ, Lebìidæ, Orthogonìidæ, Ágridæ, Calophænidæ, Pentagonícidæ, Pericálidæ, Anthìidæ, Zùphidæ, Drýptidæ).

Left paramere very short and broad, partly clasping the base of the middle lobe (right paramere still more reduced); mandibles with a seta in the scrobe (Brachynini and Pseudomorphini of G. Horn) .... LIMBÀTA BALTEÍFERA
(The following family names have recently been used for genera that are placed in this group: Brachínidæ, Pseudomórphidæ).

5. Metasternum with a small ante-coxal piece which does not extend the whole width of the metasternum; rare and localized, subaquatic or aquatic forms................................6
Metasternum with no ante-coxal piece; many common and widespread, almost always aquatic forms........................7

6. Legs ambulatorial; subaquatic forms. (Amphizòa, W. N. Am., Centr. Asia) .... AMPHIZÒIDÆ
Legs natatorial; aquatic forms. (Hygròbia (Pelòbius), Palæarc., Austr.) .... HYGROBÌIDÆ

7. Antennæ like a string of beads, with globular joints; bark beetles (if tarsi are two-jointed, see the dubious genus *Jacobsonium*, couplet 119). (Rhysòdes, cosmop.; Rhysodiástes, widespr.).
                                    RHYSÓDIDÆ
Antennæ of a different conformation; aquatic forms.............8

8. Only the posterior legs modified for swimming; antennæ slender; eyes normal, not divided. Diving beetles. Water tigers. (Figs. 779, 781). (Canthỳdrus, Laccophilus, Bidéssus, Rhántus, cosmop.; Cybíster, Cœlámbus, widespr.; Hydróporus, Deronéctes, Ágabus, Acílius, Dytíscus, Holarc.) .... DYTÍSCIDÆ

a. Episternum of metathorax not reaching the middle coxal cavity...b
Episternum of metathorax reaching the middle coxal cavity.......d
b. Greatest anterior extension of the hind coxa near the middle (longitudinally) of the body; metasternum more or less pointed in the middle behind, and not marked by a transverse suture. (*NO-*

TÉRIDÆ) .... **NOTERÎNÆ**
Greatest anterior extension of the hind coxa nearer to the epipleura
than to the medial line of the body..........................c

c. Prosternal process not reaching the metasternum....**VATELLÎNÆ**
Prosternal process reaching the metasternum....**LACCOPHILÎNÆ**

d. Prosternum deflected between the front coxæ so that the prosternal
process is placed on a quite different plane of direction from that
of the prosternum; the latter not incrassate along middle; front
tarsi often 4-jointed....................................e
Prosternal process on the same plane of direction as the prosternum;
front tarsi 5-jointed.....................................f

e. Prosternal process much deflected from the plane of direction of
the prosternum. Front tarsi usually with only four joints.
HYDROPORÎNÆ

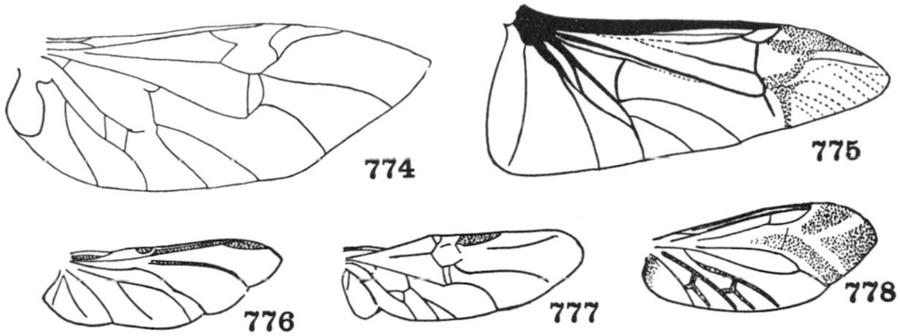

Figs. 774–778. Coleoptera

774. Hind wing of Adephaga (Kempers).
775. Hydrophilus, hind wing. Hydrophilidæ.
776. Necrophorus, hind wing (Kempers) Silphidæ.
777. Tachypus, hind wing (Kempers) Carabidæ.
778. Lygistopterus, hind wing (Kempers) Lycidæ.

Prosternal process but little deflected from the plane of direction
of the prosternum; front tarsi 5-jointed; scutellum not visible.
METHLÎNÆ

f. Inferior spur of hind tibia not or but little broader than the other..g
Inferior spur of the hind tibia dilated, much broader than the
other .... **CYBISTRÎNÆ**

g. Hind margins of joints of posterior tarsi not set with flattened and
appressed cilia ....h
Hind margins of joints of posterior tarsi provided externally with
flattened, appressed cilia.....................**HYDATICÎNÆ**

h. Spiracles of last two dorsal segments not, or but little, broader
than the preceding ones; outline of eye notched by the free margin
of front of head..........................**COLYMBETÎNÆ**

Spiracles of the last two dorsal segments enlarged, each on the penultimate segment being about one-fourth of the total breadth of the segment; circular outline of the eye uninterrupted.

DYTISCÌNÆ

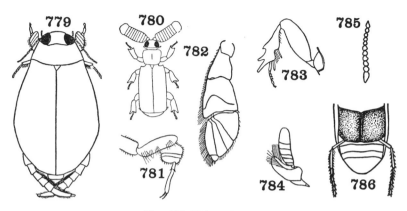

Figs. 779–786. **Coleoptera**

779. **Cybister** (Maxwell-Lefroy) Dytiscidæ.
780. **Arthropterus** (Westwood) Carabidæ.
781. **Dytiscus**, front tibia and tarsus of male (Kolbe) Dytiscidæ.
782. **Gyrinus**, hind leg (Berlese) Gyrinidæ.
783. **Scarites**, front leg (Kolbe) Carabidæ.
784. **Dineutes**, antenna. Gyrinidæ.
785. **Rhysodes**, antenna. Rhysodidæ.
786. **Haliplus**, coxal plate (Maxwell-Lefroy) Haliplidæ.

Middle and posterior legs modified for swimming; antennæ short, thickened; eyes divided into a separate upper and lower section. Whirligig beetles. (**Dineùtes, Gyrìnus**, widespr.; **Aulonogỳrus**, Old World; **Gyrètes**, Neotrop.; **Orectochìlus**, Palæarc., Indomal.; **Orectogỳrus**, Ethiop.; **Macrogỳrus**, Neotrop., Indoaustr.). (*GYR-INÒIDEA*) .... **GYRÍNIDÆ**

9. Antennæ clubbed or not, if clubbed, not with the club-joints lamellate; tarsi frequently with less than five joints; antennæ very rarely somewhat lamellate in certain aquatic Hydrophilidæ. (Figs. 793 to 813) 10

Antennæ with the last three to seven joints enlarged on one side to form a comb-like or lamellate club which can often be opened and closed (Figs. 814, 815, 816). Legs often fitted for digging; tarsi almost always 5-jointed, the front tarsi very exceptionally reduced or absent; larvæ with thick, curved body and well developed legs. Never aquatic. (LAMELLICÓRNIA) 176

10. Head not prolonged into a beak, gular sutures double, at least before and behind; prosternal sutures distinct; proepimera not meeting behind the prosternum............................11

Head generally prolonged in front of the eyes and snout-like (Figs. 787, 873, 878); gular sutures confluent along the median line or obsolete; proepimera united behind the prosternum, prosternal sutures wanting; antennæ usually elbowed (Fig. 879); palpi usually rigid; all tarsi apparently with four or three joints (Fig. 788); larvæ legless or with short legs. (RHYNCÓ PHORA) 165

11. Fourth and fifth tarsal joints if present, not immovably united, the articulation between them like that between the other joints (Fig. 789). (If rarely united, as in some Erotylidæ, the antennæ are clavate) 12

Fourth tarsal joint minute, fused with the fifth; tarsi usually densely pubescent below, with the first three joints dilated and with a sole, the third joint usually bilobed (Figs. 790, 791); antennæ filiform, rarely serrate or thickened apically; larvæ vegetarian. (PHYTÓPHAGA, CERAMBYCÒIDEA)................147

12. Hind tarsi with at least as many joints as the others............13

Hind tarsi four-jointed; front and middle tarsi five-jointed (rarely with the penultimate joint very short so that the hind tarsi are apparently three-jointed and the others apparently four-jointed; in very exceptional cases with the front tarsi five-jointed and both other pairs four-jointed). (HETERÓMERA). (See also Hemipeplidæ, couplet 49)..120

13. Maxillary palpi long and slender, almost always as long as or longer than the short antennæ; antennæ six- to ten-jointed, the outer joints forming a distinct, pubescent, sometimes asymmetrical club; elytra with an alula; small to large, almost always aquatic species (Figs. 775, 792). Water scavenger beetles. (**Hydræna, Cércyon, Enòchrus, Hýdrous** (=*Hydróphilus auctt.*) **Beròsus,** cosmop.; **Ochthèbius, Sphærídium, Laccòbius,** widespr.; **Hydróphilus, Helóphorus,** Holarc.; **Tropistérnus,** Am.). (PALPICÓRNIA, HYDROPHILÓIDEA) .... **HYDROPHÍLIDÆ**

a. Eyes normal, not divided.................................b
Eyes divided, each into two parts...............**AMPHIOPÌNÆ**

b. Second joint of posterior tarsi elongate, longer than third; first joint very short; pronotum at base as wide as elytra................c
Second joint of posterior tarsi short, about equal to the third.....d

c. Posterior tarsi oar-shaped; metasternum prolonged into a sharp elongate spine .... **HYDROPHILÌNÆ**
Posterior tarsi not oar-shaped; metasternum not prolonged into a spine .... **HYDROBIÌNÆ**

d. Pronotum at base narrower than the base of the elytra, with distinct longitudinal furrows .... **HELOPHORÌNÆ**
Pronotum at base not narrower than the base of the elytra, without distinct longitudinal furrows............................e
e. Clypeus emarginate; scutellum long, triangular; anterior coxal cavities open behind .... **SPERCHEÌNÆ**
Clypeus truncate; scutellum small and short; anterior coxal cavities closed behind. (*HYDRÆNIDÆ*).............**HYDRÆNÌNÆ**

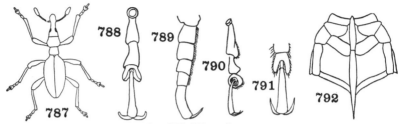

Figs. 787–792. Coleoptera

787. **Cylas** (Pierce) Cyladidæ.
788. **Camptocerus**, tarsus (Hopkins) Scolytidæ.
789. **Megalodacne**, tarsus. Erotylidæ.
790. **Leptinotarsa**, tarsus (Sharp) Chrysomelidæ.
791. **Saperda**, apical part of tarsus. Lamiidæ.
792. **Hydrophilus**, mesosternum (Berlese) Hydrophilidæ.

   Maxillary palpi much shorter than the antennæ, if rarely comparable to the antennæ in length the alula is absent and the last tarsal joint abnormally long (some Dryopidæ), or only the last joint is greatly lengthened (Telegeusidæ)....................14
14. Elytra short, exposing much of the abdomen; tergites entirely corneous in texture; wings usually present and folded beneath the elytra in repose; free portion of media atrophied or absent, not joining the cubitus to form a long closed axial cell. (If external parasites of the beaver, compare Platypsyllidæ, couplet 71). (STAPHYLINIFÓRMIA)........................15
   Elytra covering most of the abdomen, not much shortened and covering all or all but one, two or three abdominal segments; rarely much shortened in which case the wings either do not fold beneath the elytra or are wanting; tergites membranous or semi-membranous, except sometimes those of the two or three apical segments (five in the beaver parasite, *Platypsyllus*, couplet 71)..17
15. Abdomen flexible, not enlarged apically, parallel or tapering, with six to eight freely movable sternites; antennæ usually eleven-jointed; tarsi usually five-jointed; usually small, occasionally large, slender species. (If wings do not fold beneath elytra and maxillary palpi are flabellate, compare Atractoceridæ (couplet 91) or

if palpi are nearly as long as the antennæ, compare Telegeusidæ (couplet 92); or if body is very greatly flattened, compare Hemipeplidæ (couplet 49)) 87

Abdomen not flexible, swollen, oval, the segments anchylosed; usually only five sternites, rarely with seven or eight; antennæ often with less than eleven joints; tarsi three-jointed; small or minute, robust species; abdomen very much wider than the prothorax...16

16. Abdomen with five dorsal segments; antennæ five to eleven-jointed (usually 11), the last joint never truncate (Figs. 805, 821); maxillary palpi usually four-jointed. (Psélaphus, cosmop.; Eupléctus, Batrisòdes, widespr.; Achíllia (=Bryáxis), Tychus, Holarc.; Eupìnes, Indoaustr.) ....PSELÁPHIDÆ

Abdomen with three dorsal segments, antennæ with two to six joints (Fig. 813); maxillary palpi one-jointed. Small, myrmecophilus beetles. (Fústiger, Am.; Adrànes, Nearc.; Clàviger, Palæarc.; Artícerus, Austr.) ....CLAVIGÉRIDÆ

17. Tarsi five-jointed on at least one pair of legs, and almost always on all pairs 18
All tarsi with less than five joints..........................94

18. Abdomen with five sternites, or less........................19
Abdomen with at least six sternites.........................70

19. Five abdominal sternites....................................20
Only three visible sternites, the first very long; small beetles living in ants' nests; antennæ with only three joints, all but the two basal ones fused into a large club-shaped mass. (Gnóstus, S. Am., Florida) ....GNÓSTIDÆ

20. Front coxæ globular or transverse, usually projecting but little from the coxal cavities; trochanters never interstitial.............21
Front coxæ more or less conical and prominent 54

21. Front coxæ transverse, more or less cylindrical.................22
Front coxæ globular...35

22. Hind coxæ grooved to receive the femora.....................23
Hind coxæ flat, not grooved.................................30

23. Strongly convex beetles with more or less retractile legs; tibiæ dilated and usually grooved near the outer end to receive the tarsi; tibial spurs distinct 24
Slightly convex, oval species with non-retractile slender legs; tibial spurs more or less reduced.................................27

24. Antennæ inserted at the sides of the head....................25
Antennæ inserted on the front; head retracted; third joint of tarsi lobed; thorax margined; oval species. (Chelonàrium, Am.)
CHELONARÌIDÆ

25. Head prominent; mentum large, elongate and sub-elliptical; tarsi not lobed. (Nosodéndron, widespr.).......NOSODÉNDRIDÆ
Head retracted; mentum small and quadrate 26

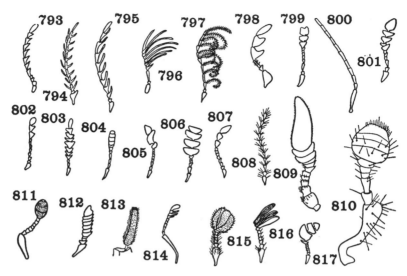

Figs. 793–817. Antennæ of Various Coleoptera

793. **Ludius** (Leconte and Horn) Elateridæ.
794. **Prionocyphon** (Leconte and Horn) Helodidæ.
795. **Corymbites** (Leconte and Horn) Elateridæ.
796. **Acneus** (Leconte and Horn) Helodidæ.
797. **Dendroides** (Leconte and Horn) Pyrochroidæ.
798. **Dorcatoma** (Leconte and Horn) Anobiidæ.
799. **Corynetes** (Leconte and Horn) Corynetidæ.
800. **Brontes.** Cucujidæ.
801. **Liodes** (Leconte and Horn) Histeridæ.
802. **Temnochilus** (Leconte and Horn) Ostomatidæ.
803. **Catoptrichus** (Leconte and Horn) Silphidæ.
804. **Colon** (Leconte and Horn) Silphidæ.
805. **Achillia** (Leconte and Horn) Pselaphidæ.
806. **Anogdus** (Leconte and Horn) Silphidæ.
807. **Aulicus** (Leconte and Horn) Cleridæ.
808. **Dasycerus** (Leconte and Horn) Lathridiidæ.
809. **Anthrenus** (Felt) Dermestidæ.
810. **Dendroctonus** (Felt) Ipidæ.
811. **Epierus** (Leconte and Horn) Histeridæ.
812. **Heterocerus** (Leconte and Horn) Heteroceridæ.
813. **Adranes** (Leconte and Horn) Clavigeridæ.
814. **Lucanus** (Leconte and Horn) Lucanidæ.
815. **Bolboceras** (Leconte and Horn) Geotrupidæ.
816. **Phyllophaga** (Leconte and Horn) Melolonthidæ.
817. **Phymaphora** (Leconte and Horn) Mycetæidæ.

26. Clypeus not distinct from the front; posterior coxæ almost touching one another. (Pedilóphorus, Syncalýpta, widespr.; Cýtilus, Býrrhus, Holarc. Lìöon, Nearc.) ....BÝRRHIDÆ
Clypeus separated from the front by a fine suture; posterior coxæ more or less widely separated. (Límnichus, widespr.)
LIMNÍCHIDÆ
27. Front coxæ with distinctly separated side-piece (trochantin)......28
Front coxæ without trochantin..............................29

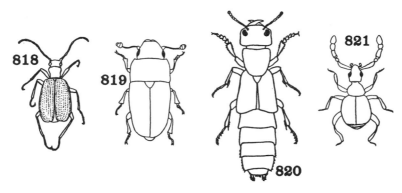

Figs. 818–821. Coleoptera

818. Brachinus. Carabidæ.
819. Glischrochilus (Felt) Nitidulidæ.
820. Staphylinus. Staphylinidæ.
821. Goniastes. (Westwood) Pselaphidæ.

28. First three tergites connate; last joint of tarsi long, with very large claws; small, aquatic or subaquatic beetles. (Drỳops Hèlichus, widespr.; Lùtrochus, Am.; Sóstea, Indomal.). (PÁRNIDÆ).
DRYÓPIDÆ
All tergites free; last tarsal joint not elongated, the claws not enlarged; terrestrial species.[1] (Dascíllus, Eubrìanax, Holarc.; Artemátopus, Neotrop.; Platydascýllus, E. Ind.; Veronàtus, Austr. (DASCÝLLIDÆ)) .... DASCÍLLIDÆ
29. Posterior coxæ at most moderately dilated internally. (Cỳphon, cosmop.; Helòdes (Elòdes), Scírtes, widespr.; (Figs. 794, 796, 825) (Including EUBRÌIDÆ, PTILODACTÝLIDÆ) (CYPHÓN-IDÆ) .... HELÓDIDÆ
Posterior coxæ very large. (Eucinètus, widespr.; Euscaphùrus, Nearc.) .... EUCINÉTIDÆ

[1] If front is narrowed and antennæ are much thickened on apical six joints.
BRACHYSPÉCTRIDÆ

30. Antennæ geniculate, very strongly clavate or capitate; elytra shortened, leaving two tergites uncovered; all tibiæ usually dilated, the
front ones usually toothed; head very much narrower than the
prothorax (if head is nearly as wide as prothorax and the clypeus
is rounded on the sides, see Synteliidæ, couplet 60; or if clypeus
bears a projection at each side, see Niponiidæ, couplet 44). (See
couplet 44) .... HISTÉRIDÆ, part
  Antennæ straight, not geniculate........................... 31
31. Tarsi more or less dilated, the first joint not shortened; fourth joint
very small; elytra not usually extending to the tip of the abdomen 32
  Tarsi slender; metatarsus very short; elytra entire, never truncate,
covering the abdomen. (**Tenebriòides, Ancỳrona,** widespr.; **Péltis,
Temnochìla,** Holarc., Neotrop.; **Nemosòma,** Eur., Am.; **Thýmalus,**
Holarc.). (Figs. 802, 823). (*TROGOSÍTIDÆ, TEMNOCHÍL-
IDÆ*) .... OSTOMÁTIDÆ
32. Maxillæ with well developed inner and outer lobe............33
  Maxillæ with only a single lobe (Fig. 819). (**Carpóphilus, Epuræa,**
cosmop.; **Meligèthes, Cryptárcha,** widespr.; **Nitídula,** Palæarc.,
Am.; **Omosìta,** Holarc.) .... NITIDÙLIDÆ
33. Antennæ clavate; elytra usually not covering the tip of the abdo-
men 34
  Antennæ filiform; elytra entirely covering the abdomen; moderately
large, elongate beetles. (**Parándra,** widespr.; **Archándra,** Palæarc.,
Neotrop.; **Neándra,** Nearc.) .... PARÁNDRIDÆ
34. Antennæ 11-jointed; with a three-jointed club; labrum free.
(**Brachýpterus,** widespr.) .... BRACHYPTÉRIDÆ
  Antennæ 10-jointed, with a two-jointed club; labrum fused with
the clypeus. (**Rhizóphagus, Anomóphagus,** Holarc.). (*RHY-
ZOPHÁGIDÆ*) .... RHIZOPHÁGIDÆ
35. First two or three sternites fused or immovably united..........36
  All sternites free, or at least separated by equally distinct sutures,
except in very rare cases............................... 37
36. First two sternites connate, the suture between them very weak;
antennæ serrate, very rarely pectinate in the male; tarsi with
membranous lobes beneath; last tarsal joint not lengthened, claws
moderate or small; active, hard-bodied beetles, of more or less
metallic color; not aquatic. (Fig. 824). (**Acmæódera, Antháxia,
Chrysobóthris, Ágrilus,** cosmop.; **Psilóptera, Stigmódera, Buprés-
tis,** widespr.; **Bráchys,** Am.; **Chrysóchroa,** Indomal.).
  　　　　　　　　　　　　　　　　　　　　　　　　　　BUPRÉSTIDÆ
  a. Middle coxal cavity formed entirely by the mesosternum (except
in certain South African species of *Julodis* and *Amblysterna*) ....b
  Middle coxal cavity formed laterally by the mesosternum and at
its posterior part by the metasternum........................e

b. Antennal pores scattered over two faces of the serrate joints........c
   Antennal pores concentrated in a depression or fovea on the serrate
   joints ....d
c. Posterior coxæ slightly dilated on their inner side, their posterior
   margin transverse and slightly sinuate; scutellum invisible; antennal pores hidden by silky pubescence..............JULODÌNÆ
   Posterior coxæ distinctly dilated on their inner side, their posterior
   margin oblique; antennal pores bare......THRINCOPŸGÌNÆ
d. Lateral pieces of the metathorax narrow.......POLYCESTÌNÆ
   Lateral pieces of the metathorax very broad; tergites membranous.
                                                         SCHIZOPÌNÆ
e. Lateral branches of mesosternum elongate (except in *Belionota*)....f
   Lateral branches of the mesosternum very short and set back on
   the sides, or invisible.......................................j
f. Antennal pores scattered over the two faces of the serrate joints...g
   Antennal pores concentrated in a depression or fovea on the serrate
   joints ....h
g. Scutellum absent, or hidden .... CHRYSOCHROÌNÆ
   Scutellum visible .... CHALCOPHORÌNÆ
h. Front not narrowed at the insertion of the antennæ; eyes not very
   close together, sometimes distant on the vertex...............i
   Front narrowed at the insertion of the antennæ; eyes strongly
   oblique and closely approaching one another on the upper surface .... CHRYSOBOTHRÌNÆ
i. Scutellum broad and acuminate behind; mentum large, triangular;
   poriferous foveæ terminal .... SPHENOPTERÌNÆ
   Scutellum at most moderate, never enlarged in front or acuminate
   behind; mentum strongly transverse; poriferous foveæ terminal
   or inferior .... BUPRESTÌNÆ
j. Front narrowed at the insertion of the antennæ; antennal cavities
   very large and situated at a considerable distance from the eyes;
   posterior coxæ not dilated on their inner side, with their posterior
   margins horizontal and slightly sinuate; poriferous foveæ terminal ....k
   Front not narrowed at the insertion of the antennæ; antennal cavities
   moderate and situated near the eyes; posterior coxæ dilated on
   their inner side, their posterior margin oblique; poriferous foveæ
   variable .... STIGMODERÌNÆ
k. Base of pronotum more or less sinuate............. AGRILÌNÆ
   Base of pronotum straight .... MASTOGENÌNÆ

   First three sternites connate; antennæ slender, slightly thickened
   externally; last joint of tarsi greatly elongated, with very large
   claws; small aquatic beetles. (Fig. 822). (Élmis (*Hélmis*), cosmop.; **Stenélmis**, widespr.; **Macrónychus**, Holarc.; **Rìolus, Lathél-
   mis**, Palæarc.) (*HÉLMIDÆ*).................... ÉLMIDÆ

37. Prosternum prolonged behind into a median process which is received in the mesosternum................................38
    Prosternum without such backwardly directed process (if rarely with such a process, it is not received in the mesosternum)....41
38. Prothorax loosely joined to the mesothorax, freely movable, its hind angles usually prolonged backward into teeth; prosternal spine loosely received in a notch in the mesosternum; front coxal cavities contained entirely in the prosternum.................39
    Prothorax firmly attached, not movable; front coxal cavities closed behind by the mesosternum. (**Drapètes, Thróscus** (= *Tríxagus*), cosmop.; **Paradrapètes, Aulonothróscus,** widespr.; **Páctopus,** Nearc.). (*TRIXÁGIDÆ*) .... **THRÓSCIDÆ**

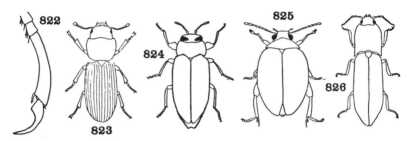

Figs. 822–826. Coleoptera

822. **Macronychus,** apical portion of tarsus. Elmidæ.
823. **Tenebrioides** (Back and Cotton) Ostomatidæ.
824. **Chrysobothris** (Chittenden) Buprestidæ.
825. **Scirtes** (Grandi) Helodidæ.
826. **Melanotus** (Hyslop) Elateridæ.

39. Hind coxæ laminate; trochanter short.........................40
    Hind coxæ not laminate; middle and hind trochanters very long; labrum short, transverse, connate with the clypeus; antennæ serrate (♀) or pectinate (♂). (**Ceróphytum,** Holarc, Neotrop.)
    CEROPHÝTIDÆ
40. Labrum visible, free; antennæ arising near the eyes under the frontal margin; last two sternites connected by a membranous suture; prosternum lobed in front; beetles capable of moving the prothorax by its basal joint with a sudden clicking motion. (If the middle coxæ are not distinctly separated, see couplet 74). Click-beetles, Wireworm beetles. (**Làcon, Drastèrius, Élater, Cardióphorus,** cosmop.; **Adelócera, Melanòtus, Álaus, Monocrepídius,** widespr.; **Pyróphorus,** Am., Austr.; **Dichrónychus,** Ethiop., Ind.). (Figs, 793, 795, 826). (Including *DICHRONÝCHIDÆ, PEROTHÓPIDÆ*) .... **ELATÉRIDÆ**

Labrum concealed; no membranous fold between the last two sternites; prosternum not lobed in front; antennæ inserted on the front between the eyes, received in transverse grooves on the front; not able to leap by the prothoracic joint. (Dro-

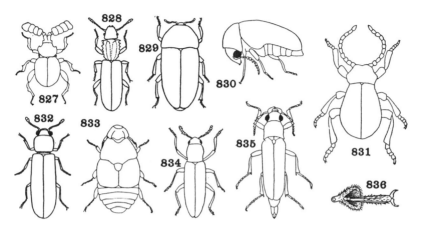

Figs. 827-836. Coleoptera

827. **Ectrephes** (Westwood) Ectrephidæ.
828. **Silvanus** (Chittenden) Silvanidæ.
829. **Dermestes** (Howard and Marlatt) Dermestidæ.
830. **Lasioderma** (Smith) Anobiidæ.
831. **Mezium** (Smith) Ptinidæ.
832. **Lyctus** (Hopkins) Lyctidæ.
833. **Platypsyllus** (Westwood) Platypsyllidæ.
834. **Languria.** Languriidæ.
835. **Cebrio** (Hyslop) Cebrionidæ.
836. **Moncedus,** tarsus (Sharp) Moncedidæ.

mæolus, Fórnax, cosmop.; Mélasis, Palæarc., Am.; Eucnèmis, Holarc.). (*EUCNÉMIDÆ*) ....MELÁSIDÆ
41. Hind coxæ in contact 42
 Hind coxæ not in contact, although very closely approximate in certain very much flattened species 43
42. Antennæ filiform; elytra with longitudinal rows of large pit-shaped punctures with ribs between; moderate-sized, elongate beetles. (Cùpes, widespr.; Ómma, Austr.) (*CUPÉDIDÆ*) ....CÙPIDÆ
 Antennæ clavate; elytra simple; very small or minute, convex, oval or rounded beetles. (Phálacrus, Ólibrus, Stílbus, widespr.)
 PHALÁCRIDÆ
43. Elytra shortened, leaving two segments of the abdomen exposed; antennæ elbowed, very strongly clavate or capitate (Fig. 811);

tibiæ compressed, the front pair usually toothed; hard-bodied, smooth and shining; small, convex or much flattened, rarely elongate, beetles 44

Elytra entire, covering the pygidium 45

44. Prothorax much wider than the head, its front margin concave; clypeus without projections; tarsi short (Fig. 801)   **HISTÉRIDÆ**

a. Prosternum simple, without lobe. (SAPRINOMÓRPHÆ) ......b
Prosternum with a median lobe anteriorly. (HISTEROMÓRPHÆ)
                                                              g

b. Club of antennæ short, rounded, usually but little longer than wide; scape not strongly angulate; antennal cavities, when present, open beneath c
Club of antennæ at least three times as long as broad; scape strongly angulate and usually greatly expanded; antennal cavities closed beneath by the sides of the prosternum ....**CHLAMYDOPSÌNÆ**

c. Body round, oval, or oblong-oval ....d
Body cylindrical, sometimes stoutly so ....e

d. Elytra with dorsal striæ, or at least with a sutural stria; pronotum without a lateral longitudinal groove. (**Saprìnus**, cosmop.)
                                                    SAPRINÌNÆ
Elytra without distinct dorsal striæ; a lateral groove sometimes present on pronotum ....**ABRÆÌNÆ**

e. Antennæ inserted under the margin of the front, anterior to the eyes ....f
Antennæ inserted on the front, the fossæ cutting into the margin of the front between the eyes. (Tribe Teretriini) ..**ABRÆÌNÆ**, part

f. Head horizontal, antennæ with eight joints in addition to the club. (**Trypanæus**) ....**TRYPANÆÌNÆ**
Head vertical; antennæ with seven joints in addition to the club
                                                    TRYPETICÌNÆ

g. Antennal scape normal, neither expanded nor strongly angulate ...h
Antennal scape expanded and strongly angulate. (**Hetærius, Yarmíster**, Am.) ....**HETÆRIÌNÆ**

h. Labrum with setigerous punctures i
Labrum without setigerous punctures. (**Híster, Hololépta, Platysòma, Margarinòtus**, widespr.) ....**HISTERÌNÆ**

i. Front tibiæ with a few teeth along the edge; antennal cavities completely open, usually lying just in front of the front coxa. (**Cárcinops**, Neotrop.; **Bacànius**, widespr.) ..**DENDROPHILÌNÆ**
Front tibiæ with many small teeth along the edge; antennal cavities at least partly closed beneath, lying in the anterior angles of the prothorax. (**Epièrus**, widespr.) ....**TRIBALÌNÆ**

Prothorax as wide as the head, its front margin straight; clypeus with a projection at each side; tarsi very long and slender; man-

dibles deflexed, moving at right angles to the long axis of the head.
(Nipònius, Indomal.) ....NIPONÌIDÆ

45. Antennæ consisting of only two apparent segments, the distal one greatly elongate, enlarged and flattened; minute, more or less globose beetles, living in ants' nests. (Fig. 827). (Éctrephes, Austr.) ....ECTRÉPHIDÆ
Antennæ normal, ten or eleven-jointed, filiform or clavate......46

46. Elytra each with a pair of large wax-like spots; antennæ short, with a four-jointed club; rather large beetles, with the prothorax widened behind. (Helòta, As., Indo-malay.) ....HELÓTIDÆ
Elytra not thus ornamented; prothorax not noticeably widened behind 47

47. Middle coxal cavities open externally, i.e. not closed by the meeting of the meso- and metasterna; body elongate, usually greatly flattened 48
Middle coxal cavities closed externally by the sterna 51

48. Maxillæ covered by corneous plates; front coxal cavities open behind. (Passándra, Ethiop., Neotrop.; Catógenus, widespr.; Scalídia, Am.). (Including SCALIDÌIDÆ) ..PASSÁNDRIDÆ
Maxillæ exposed 49

49. Tarsi with the third joint simple, not lobed 50
Tarsi with the third joint lobed; front coxal cavities closed behind (Fig. 839); elytra sometimes shortened. (Hemipéplus, widespr.; Diagrypnòdes, Austr.; Holopéplus, Neotrop.)...HEMIPÉPLIDÆ

50. Front coxal cavities open behind. (Figs. 800, 840). (Cùcujus, Læmophlœus, Bróntes, widespr.). (Including LÆMOPHLŒ-IDÆ, CATOGÉNIDÆ) ....CUCÙJIDÆ
Front coxal cavities closed behind. (Figs. 828, 839). (Silvànus, cosmop.; Nausíbius, widespr.) ....SILVÁNIDÆ

51. Prosternum not prolonged behind; small, oval, coarsely punctate species with the fourth tarsal joint short, the third lobed. (Diphýllus, Diplocœlus, widespr.) (BIPHÝLLIDÆ)
DIPHÝLLIDÆ
Prosternum prolonged behind, meeting the mesosternum 52

52. Front coxal cavities open behind (Fig. 840); small or minute species. (Lobèrus, Micrámbe, Cryptóphagus, Antheróphagus, widespr.; Cænóscelis, Atomària, Holarc.) ...CRYPTOPHÁGIDÆ
Front coxal cavities closed behind (Fig. 839) 53

53. Antennæ with an abrupt club; moderate-sized beetles usually black with orange markings. (Fig. 789). (Megalodácne, Dácne, widespr.; Epíscapha, Palæarc.). ....Some EROTÝLIDÆ
Antennæ gradually clavate, short; very small beetles. (Catopochròtus, Turkestan) ....CATOPOCHRÓTIDÆ

54. Hind coxæ dilated into plates which are grooved for the reception of the femora 55

Hind coxæ not thus dilated, not grooved for the reception of the
femora 59

55. Front coxal cavities closed behind (Fig. 839) 56
Front coxal cavities open behind (Fig. 840) 57

56. Second and third joints of tarsi lobed beneath; plate of hind coxæ
feeble; small pubescent beetles. (Bytùrus, Holarc., Neotrop.;
Satorýstia, Palæarc.) . . . . .BYTÙRIDÆ
Tarsi simple, not lobed; ocelli often present; small, coarsely
punctured beetles. (Derodóntus, Laricòbius, Peltástica, Holarc.)
DERODÓNTIDÆ

57. Antennæ with the last three joints much enlarged, forming a
strong club; small or rather small, often scaly beetles. (Derméstes,
Attágenus, Trogodérma, cosmop.; Anthrènus, widespr.; Crypto-
rhópalum, Neotrop., Austr.). (Figs. 809, 829) . . DERMÉSTIDÆ

a. Head without frontal ocellus; mouthparts not covered.
DERMESTÌNÆ
Head with frontal ocellus . . . . .b

b. Mouthparts not covered; anterior coxæ strongly projecting.
ATTAGENÌNÆ
Mouthparts covered by the prosternum or by the coxæ and tro-
chanters of the front legs c

c. Prosternum horizontal; hind coxæ not reaching the side margins
of the body, which is hairy or squamose . . . . .d
Prosternum vertical; hind coxæ reaching the side margins of the
body; upper surface bare and glabrous . . . . .ORPHILÌNÆ

d. Form oblong; posterior coxæ contiguous; upper surface with re-
cumbent hairs . . . . MEGATOMÌNÆ
Form short, round or short-oval; posterior coxæ not contiguous . .e

e. Upper surface squamose; head with deep antennal grooves beneath.
ANTHRENÌNÆ
Upper surface with stiff upright bristles; head without antennal
grooves beneath . . . . TRINODÌNÆ

Antennæ not capitate 58

58. Tarsi with a long, hairy pad (onychium) between the claws; tibial
spurs present, small; moderate-sized or large, elongate beetles
with prominent porrect head; antennæ usually flabellate in the
male, often with more than eleven joints. (Sándalus, widespr.;
Zénoa, Nearc.; Callirhìpis, Indo-Austr., Neotrop.; Rhipícera,
Austr., Neotrop.). (SANDÁLIDÆ, RHIPICERÁTIDÆ, RHIPI-
DOCÉRIDÆ . . . . .RHIPICÉRIDÆ
Onychium not developed, or very small; no tibial spurs; small,
usually oval or cylindrical beetles with the head strongly deflexed. (Figs. 798, 830). (Stegòbium (=Sitódrepa), Anòbium,

Catoràma, cosmop.; Ernòbius, widespr.; Hadrobrégmus, Lasio-
dérma, widespr.; Dorcátoma, Holarc.) (*ASPIDOPHÓRIDÆ*)
ANOBÌIDÆ

59. First joint of tarsi very short and indistinctly separated from the
    second 60
    First joint of tarsi distinct, when rarely very short, the first ventral
    segment is not elongate and the head not deflexed 62

60. All the tibiæ dilated and toothed externally; antennæ more or
    less geniculate, with a three-jointed club; head almost as wide
    as the prothorax; clypeus rounded on the sides; elytra not covering
    the tip of the abdomen; large beetles. (Syntèlia, Mex., Japan,
    India) . . . . SYNTELÌIDÆ
    Tibiæ not dilated or toothed 61

61. First sternite elongated, always much longer than the second;
    antennæ with a quite distinct, two-jointed club; small elongate
    beetles with prominent head not covered by the prothorax.
    Powder-post beetles. (Fig. 832). (Lýctus, cosmop.). LÝCTIDÆ
    First sternite not elongated; antennal club three- or four-jointed;
    head usually deflexed and protected by the prothorax; declivity
    of elytra often toothed or spined; elongate, more or less cylindri-
    cal beetles. (Bóstrichus, Psòa, Lichenóphanes, widespr.). (In-
    cluding *PSÒIDÆ*). (*APÁTIDÆ, BOSTRÝCHIDÆ*).
    BOSTRÍCHIDÆ

62. Hind coxæ flat or oval, not prominent 63
    Hind coxæ prominent internally, more or less conical 67

63. Fourth joint of tarsi extremely short, not visible from above; small
    beetles of rather bright colors. (Fig. 799). (Corynètes, Necròbia,
    cosmop.; Pelònium, widespr.; Phyllobænus, Orthopleùra, Am.;
    Epiphlœus, Neotrop.) . . . . CORYNÉTIDÆ
    Fourth joint of tarsi not abnormally short 64

64. Fifth segment of abdomen conically produced, as long as the three
    preceding ones, elytra not completely covering the abdomen.
    (Scaphídium, Scaphosòma, cosmop.; Bæócera, widespr.).
    SCÁPHIDÌIDÆ
    Fifth abdominal segment not elongated, not conically produced . .65

65. Antennæ 11-jointed, with a solid club, consisting of three almost
    entirely fused joints; very small beetles, with tufts of golden hairs
    at the sides of the prothorax or beneath the body, living in ants'
    nests. (Thoríctus, Palæarc., Ethiop.) . . . .   THORÍCTIDÆ
    Joints of antennal club not thus fused, or antennæ with fewer
    joints 66

66. Trochanters attached to the internal margin of the femora. (Fig.
    807). (Tíllus, Opìlo, Thanásimus, widespr.; Clèrus, Cyma-
    tódera, Hydnócera, Am.; Trichòdes, Holarc.) . . . . . . CLÉRIDÆ
    Trochanters interstitial, *i.e.* attached to the base of the femora.

(Fig. 831). (Ptìnus, Gíbbium, cosmop.; Mèzium, widespr.; Sphæricus, Holarc.) .... **PTÍNIDÆ**

67. Antennæ capitate, *i.e.* the last three joints forming a very abrupt club; elytra truncate; rather broad, slightly metallic beetles. (Sphærites, Holarc.) .... **SPHÆRÍTIDÆ**

  Antennæ simple, not clubbed 68

68. Prothorax very large, oval, longer than the elytra; hind coxæ very large, almost dividing the first sternite; antennæ very short; hind legs greatly thickened. Large beetles of burrowing habits. (Hypocéphalus, Neotrop.) ....**HYPOCEPHÁLIDÆ**

  Of a different conformation 69

69. Front coxæ with a distinct side-piece (trochantin). (See couplet 84) ....Some **DASÝTIDÆ**

  Front coxæ without trochantin; long narrow beetles. (Lyméxylon, Melittómma, widespr.; Hylecœtus, Holarc., Austr.) (See couplet 86) (*LYMEXYLÓNIDÆ*) ....**LYMEXÝLIDÆ**

70. Front coxæ flat, rounded or globular, small and not prominent ..71

  Front coxæ conical, prominent, usually large 75

71. Front coxæ flat; elytra not longer than the prothorax, exposing five abdominal segments; eyes absent; small flattened wingless beetles living as external parasites of beavers. (Fig. 833). (Platypsýllus, Holarc.). (*ACREIÓPTERA*). **PLATYPSÝLLIDÆ**

  Front coxæ rounded or globular; not such beetles 72

72. Last joint of tarsi not excessively lengthened; tarsal claws not enlarged 73

  Last joint of tarsi greatly lengthened; tarsal claws very large; first three sternites connate; small, aquatic beetles. (Psephènus, Am.; Psephènops, Tychepsephènus, Neotrop.; Metaeopsephènus, Holarc.) ....**PSEPHÉNIDÆ**

73. Prosternum prolonged behind into a process which is received in a notch in the mesosternum; prothorax loosely attached to the mesothorax 74

  Prosternum without such a backwardly directed process; eyes very small or wanting; rare, minute beetles living in the nests of rodents. (Leptìnus, Holarc.; Leptiníllus, Nearc.)....**LEPTÌNIDÆ**

74. Labrum fused with the clypeus; antennæ distant at base; tibial spurs well developed. (Fig. 835). (Cèbrio, Palæarc.; Scaptolènus, Am.; Cebriorhìpis, Indo-malay). (Including *CAVICOX-ÛMIDÆ*). .... **CEBRIÓNIDÆ**

  Labrum free; tibial spurs very weak. (Plastócerus, Am.; Phyllócerus, Palæarc.; Euthysànius, Aplástus, Nearc.). (*PHYLLOCÉRIDÆ*)
PLASTOCÉRIDÆ

75. Abdomen with six sternites 76

  Abdomen with seven or eight sternites. (MALACODÉRMATA, CANTHARÒIDEA) 89

76. Fifth segment of abdomen conical, as long as the three preceding segments together, the sixth minute. (See couplet 64).
SCAPHIDÌIDÆ
Fifth segment not conical nor excessively lengthened 77
77. Hind coxæ grooved for the reception of the femora; tarsi with a prominent hairy pad between the claws. (See couplet 58).
RHIPICÉRIDÆ
Hind coxæ simple, not grooved 78
78. Hind coxæ flat, not prominent, covered by the femora in repose; first joint of posterior tarsi usually very short and indistinct 79
Hind coxæ prominent, at least internally 80
79. Tarsi with the fourth joint of normal size; pronotum continuous with the propleura. (See couplet 66) . . . . CLÉRIDÆ
Tarsi with the fourth joint very small, indistinct; pronotum separated from the pleura by a marginal line. (See couplet 63).
CORYNÉTIDÆ
80. Hind coxæ widely separated 81
Hind coxæ approximated or contiguous 82
81. Eyes absent. (See couplet 82) . . . . a few SÍLPHIDÆ
Eyes present, coarsely granulated; small, more or less ovate, pubescent, brown beetles. (Scydmænus, cosmop.; Eucónnus, Steníchnus, widespr.; Leptomástax, Cephànium, Neùraphes, Palæarc.) . . . . SCYDMÆNIDÆ
82. Tibial spurs large; antennæ gradually thickened or clavate; hind tarsi slender, not widened. Carrion-beetles. (Figs. 773, 776, 803, 804, 806). (Sílpha, Càtops, Ptomóphagus, widespr., Bathýscia, Palæarc.; Nicróphorus, Nearc.; Liòdes, Holarc.). (Including CATÓPSIDÆ, or CATÓPIDÆ, LIÓDIDÆ, COLÓNIDÆ, ANISOTÓMIDÆ, pt.) . . . . SÍLPHIDÆ
Tibial spurs small or indistinct 83
83. Front coxæ with a distinct side piece (trochantin); rather small, usually soft-bodied species 84
Front coxæ without trochantin 85
84. Body with extensible vesicles. (Malthòdes, Malàchius, Holarc.; Cóllops) . . . . MALACHÌIDÆ
Body without extensible vesicles. (Mélyris, widespr.; Dásytes, Holarc., Neotrop.; Haplocnèmus, Palæarc.; Rhádalus, Nearc.; Astỳlus, Neotrop.). (Including RHADÁLIDÆ) (MELÝRIDÆ)
DASÝTIDÆ
85. Epimera of metasternum distinct; maxillary palpi simple; body more or less ovate. (Brathìnus, Nearc.) . . . . . . BRATHÍNIDÆ
Epimera of metasternum not visible; body elongate 86
86. Elytra shortened, exposing several of the abdominal segments; very small species; maxillary palpi simple in both sexes. (Micromálthus, Holarc.) . . . . MICROMÁLTHIDÆ

Elytra entire; maxillary palpi of the male flabellate. (**Hylecœtus,** Holarc., Austr.). (See couplet 69) . . . . Some **LYMEXȲLIDÆ**

87. Antennæ ten- or eleven-jointed, not abruptly capitate and not received in cavities; tarsi usually with more than three joints. (Fig. 820). (**Philónthus, Stènus, Aleóchara, Homalòta, Oxýtelus, Lathròbium, Tachýporus, Quèdius,** widespr.; **Staphylìnus,** Holarc., Neotrop.) . . . . **STAPHYLÍNIDÆ**

a. Antennæ inserted upon the front, near the inner margin of eyes . . b
Antennæ inserted on the anterior margin of the head c
Antennæ inserted under the sides of the front . . . . d

b. Posterior coxæ large, contiguous; antennæ not terminated by a distinct club . . . . **ALEOCHARÌNÆ**
Posterior coxæ small, widely separated; antennæ terminated by a distinct club . . . . **STENÌNÆ**

c. Antennæ approximate; prosternum developed in front of the anterior coxæ . . . . **XANTHOLINÌNÆ**
Antennæ distant; prosternum not developed in front of the anterior coxæ . . . . **STAPHYLINÌNÆ**

d. Prothoracic spiracles conspicuous on removing the front coxæ . . . . e
Prothoracic spiracles difficult to perceive on account of the prominence of the sides of the prothorax . . . . g

e. Posterior coxæ transverse . . . . f
Posterior coxæ triangular, prominent; antennæ capillary and verticillate-pilose . . . . **HABROCERÌNÆ**

f. Antennæ filiform, not verticillate-pilose . . . . **TACHYPORÌNÆ**
Antennæ capillary, verticillate-pilose . . . . **TRICHOPHYÌNÆ**

g. Anterior coxæ conical . . . . h
Anterior coxæ linear, transverse . . . . o

h. Anterior coxæ short i
Anterior coxæ large, prominent . . . . j

i. Tarsi two-jointed . . . . **LEPTOTYPHLÌNÆ**
Tarsi four-jointed . . . . **EVÆSTHETÌNÆ**

j. Vertex without ocelli . . . . k
Vertex with two ocelli . . . . **OMALIÌNÆ**

k. Last joint of labial palpi dilated, very large, crescent-shaped.
OXYPORÌNÆ
Last joint of labial palpi not, or not strongly, dilated l

l. Posterior coxæ conical . . . . m
Posterior coxæ transverse . . . . n

m. Palpi with the last joint very small, subulate . . . . . **PÆDERÌNÆ**
Palpi with the last joint equal to the preceding . . . . **PINOPHILÌNÆ**

n. Posterior trochanters small, one-fifth the length of the femora; head with a distinct neck . . . . **OXYTELÌNÆ**
Posterior trochanters large, one-third the length of the femora; head without a distinct neck . . . . **PHLŒOCHARÌNÆ**

o. Vertex without ocelli; elytra covering the greater part of the body.
PROTEINÌNÆ
Vertex with one ocellus; elytra only slightly surpassing the metasternum .... PHLŒOBIÌNÆ
Antennæ nine- or ten-jointed; tarsi three-jointed 88

88. Antennæ with a very abrupt club, received in cavities on the underside of the prothorax; body rather short, the elytra with several acutely elevated longitudinal ridges. (Micropéplus, Kalíssus, Nearc.) .... MICROPÉPLIDÆ
Antennæ without abrupt club, tarsi with the first joint very minute and concealed in the apex of the tibia; elytra without ridges. (Limulòdes, Am.) .... LIMULÓDIDÆ

89. Middle coxæ distant; epipleuræ wanting; elytra usually with a reticulate sculpture; no phosphorescent organs; usually flat beetles, widened behind and often with a bold color pattern. (Fig. 778). (Lỳcus, Calópteron, Pláteros, widespr.) ....LÝCIDÆ
Middle coxæ in contact; epipleuræ distinct; elytra not reticulate, rarely greatly reduced in size 90

90. Antennæ inserted at the sides of the front, before the eyes 91
Antennæ inserted on the upper part of the front or at the base of its anterior lobe; phosphorescent organs often present 93

91. Maxillary palpi flabellate; elytra very short; hind wings with a series of radiating veins; eyes almost meeting on the front (Atractócerus, widespr.) ....ATRÁCTOCÉRIDÆ
Maxillary and labial palpi simple, rarely greatly enlarged; elytra usually complete and the hind wings with normal venation 92

92. Maxillary and labial palpi enormously lengthened, the last joint nearly as long as the antennæ; slender, depressed species with the elytra extending to the middle of the abdomen (female). (Telegeùsis, N. Am.) .... TELEGEÙSIDÆ
Maxillary and labial palpi normal; elytra usually complete. Female usually larviform. (Drìlus, Halacogáster, Palæarc.; Selàsius, Ethiop.; Cerocósmus, Neotrop.; Karùmia, Persia: Drilocéphalus, Neotrop.). (Including KARUMÌIDÆ, ZARUDNIÓLIDÆ, HOMÁLÍSIDÆ, PRIONOCÉRIDÆ) .... DRÍLIDÆ

93. Head more or less completely covered by the prothorax; episterna of metathorax not sinuate on the inner side. (Lucìola, widespr.; Lucidòta, Photìnus, Photùris, Am.; Lámpyris, Palæarc., Ethiop.; Lamprócera, Neotrop.; Rhagophthálmus, As.). (Including RHAGOPHTHÁLMIDÆ) .... LAMPÝRIDÆ
Head not at all covered by the prothorax; episterna of metathorax sinuate on the inner side; antennæ of male sometimes flabellate. (Cántharis (= Teléphorus), widespr.; Podàbrus, Holarc. Chauliógnathus, Am.). (Including PHENGÓDIDÆ), PSEUDO-PHENGÓDIDÆ, TELEPHÓRIDÆ, PODABROCEPHÁL-

IDÆ) ....CANTHÁRIDÆ
94. Tarsi four-jointed on all pairs of legs (front ones three-jointed in
males of some Mycetophagidæ) 95
Tarsi with three joints or less 108
95. Wings fringed with long hairs; very small, highly convex beetles ..96
Wings not fringed 98
96. Hind coxæ in contact, with plates at least partially covering the
femora ....CLÁMBIDÆ
Hind coxæ distant, transverse, not laminate 97
97. Third joint of tarsi small, concealed in the bilobed second joint.
(Sàcium, cosmop.; Corỳlophus, Orthóperus, Árthrolips, widespr.).
(*CORYLÓPHIDÆ, CLYPEASTÉRIDÆ*) ..ORTHOPÉRIDÆ
First three joints of tarsi subequal, each bilobed. (Phænocéphalus,
Japan) ....PHÆNOCEPHÁLIDÆ
98. Abdominal sternites all free and movable 99
Sternites one to four firmly united, immovable 106
99. First tarsal joint greatly dilated, overlapping the very minute second
and third joints and a part of the long fourth joint; minute
elongate beetles with costate elytra. (Fig. 836). (Monœdus
(= *Adímerus*), Neotrop.). (*ADIMÉRIDÆ*)....MONŒDIDÆ
First tarsal joint not thus dilated 100
100. Front coxæ transverse; minute fungus-beetles (Cybocéphalus,
widespr.) ....CYBOCEPHÁLIDÆ
Front coxæ not transverse 101
101. Front coxæ globose 102
Front coxæ oval. (If conical, *cf.* Corynetidæ, couplet 79) 104
102. Tarsi slender, third joint distinct, but shorter than the second;
very small species. (If the cheeks bear projections, see Silvanidæ,
couplet 50; or Cucujidæ, couplet 50, if the body is greatly
flattened). (Fig. 817). (Mycetæa, Holarc., Ethiop.; Rhànis,
Nearc.; Liésthes, Palæarc.) ....MYCETÆIDÆ
Tarsi more or less dilated and spongy beneath; more or less
elongate beetles with hard body and strongly clubbed antennæ;
usually moderate-sized or large species 103
103. Front coxal cavities closed; metathoracic epimera separated by
a distinct suture; body elongate oval. (Tríplax, widespr.; Erótylus,
Ægithus, Brachysphænus, Mycotrètus, Neotrop.; Trítoma,
widespr.; Cyrtomórphus, Indomal.; Encaustes, Afr., Malay.;
Euxéstus, Malay.) ....EROTÝLIDÆ

a. Club of antennæ composed of distinct joints ....b
Club of antennæ solid, round, last joints reduced ..EUXESTÌNÆ
b. Last joint of maxillary palpi not transverse; first three joints of
tarsi not successively widened ....DACNÌNÆ
Last joint of maxillary palpi transverse; first three joints successively
widened c

c. Sides of mouth cavity carinate; maxillæ bidentate
           TRITOMÌNÆ, part
 Sides of mouth cavity forming flattened lobes ....d
d. Maxillæ bidentate ....EROTYLÌNÆ
 Maxillæ without teeth ....TRITOMÌNÆ

Front coxal cavities open; metathoracic epimera not separated; body elongate, slender. (Fig. 834). (Langùria, Acropteróxys, Am.; Adanástus, Palæarc., Indomal.; Doubledàya, Indomal.)
            LANGURÌIDÆ

104. Front coxæ almost in contact, prosternum more or less membranous, not visible between them; antennæ nine-jointed; small, convex, roughly sculptured beetles. (Georýssus, widespr.)
           GEORÝSSIDÆ
 Front coxæ well separated by the horny prosternum 105

105. Head more or less concealed by the projecting prothorax; last joint of tarsi usually very long; body cylindrical. (Cis, cosmop.; Enneárthron, widespr.; Hendecátomus, Holarc.; Rhopalodóntus, Palæarc.; Oròphius, Palæarc., Austr.; Polynesicis, Polynesia). (CIÒIDÆ, CÍSIDÆ) ....CÌIDÆ
 Head free, not covered by the prothorax; body oval, depressed, pubescent. (Litárgus, widespr.; Mycetóphagus, Holarc., Neotrop.). (TRITÓMIDÆ) .... MYCETOPHÁGIDÆ

106. Antennæ thickened, with a two- or three-jointed club; tibiæ simple, not dilated or spinose; not aquatic 107
 Antennæ with a large serrate, seven-jointed club (Fig. 812); front and middle tibiæ dilated and armed with rows of spines; small, subaquatic beetles. (Heterócerus, cosmop.; Litórimus, Micíllus, Palæarc.) ....HETEROCÉRIDÆ

107. Antennæ inserted under a distinct frontal ridge; front coxæ distant from the mesosternum. (Colýdium, Aulònium, Cérylon, widespr.) (Including MONVÉDIDÆ) ....COLYDÌIDÆ
 Antennæ inserted on the front; front coxæ inclosed behind by the mesosternum. (Murmídius, Bothríderes, Mychócerus, widespr.). (Including BOTHRIDÉRIDÆ) ....MURMIDÌIDÆ

108. Tarsi three-jointed 109
 Tarsi with less than three joints 119

109. Wings fringed with long hairs, or wanting; very small beetles...110
 Wings not fringed, or at most with a short fringe 112

110. Abdomen with only three sternites. Very small, highly convex beetles. (Sphærius, Holarc, Neotrop............SPHÆRÌIDÆ
 Abdomen with six or seven sternites 111

111. Antennæ slender, nine- to eleven-jointed, with whorls of long hairs; very minute, shining beetles, usually found on foliage. (Ptílium, Trichópteryx, Ptinélla, Acrótrichis, Palæarc., Am., Cephalopléctus) (TRICHOPTERÝGIDÆ) ....PTILÌIDÆ

Antennæ short, eight-jointed, thickened apically; very small, ovate, aquatic beetles. (**Hydróscapha**, Holarc.) ... **HYDROSCÁPHIDÆ**

112. Second joint of tarsi dilated; the third joint consisting really of two joints, the small, true third joint being fused with the base of the last joint, which thus appears as the third 113

Second tarsal joint not dilated 114

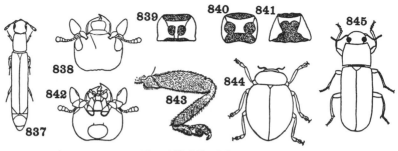

Figs. 837–845. Coleoptera

837. **Cylindrosella** (Fouts).
838. **Epilachna**, head from above (Silvestri) Coccinellidæ.
839. Prosternum of beetle, showing coxal cavities separated and closed behind (Wickham).
840. Prosternum of beetle, showing coxal cavities separated and open behind (Wickham).
841. Prosternum of beetle, showing coxal cavities confluent and open behind (Wickham).
842. **Epilachna**, head from below (Silvestri) Coccinellidæ.
843. **Epilachna**, hind leg (Silvestri) Coccinellidæ.
844. **Coccinella.** Coccinellidæ.
845. **Tenebrio** (Girault) Tenebrionidæ.

113. Tarsal claws usually dilated or toothed at the base; first sternite with curved coxal lines; mesothoracic epimeron triangular; small, rounded, convex usually brightly spotted beetles. "Ladybirds." A large widespread family. (**Coccinélla, Chilócoris, Hippodamìa, Scýmnus, Adàlia, Hyperáspis, Megílla, Ánatis, Epiláchna**). (Figs. 838, 842, 843, 844). (Including *CERASOMMATIDÌIDÆ*).

COCCINÉLLIDÆ

Tarsal claws simple; first sternite without coxal lines; mesothoracic epimeron quadrangular; small oblong or oval beetles, often with a striking color pattern, usually living in fungi. (**Endómychus**, widespr.; **Lycoperdìna**, Holarc.; **Aphorísta**, Nearc.; **Epípocus, Rhýmbus**, Am.; **Ámphix**, Neotrop.; **Sphærosòma**, Palæarc.; **Amphistérnus**, Indomal.) . . . . **ENDOMÝCHIDÆ**

114. Elytra entire 115

Elytra truncate, exposing the last abdominal segment 118

115. Mandibles with a long, styliform process in front, not fitted for biting; myrmecophilous species. (**Aculógnathus**, Austr.)
                                         ACULOGNÁTHIDÆ
    Mandibles of the usual biting form 116
116. Body broadly oval, convex; prothorax much widened behind; first three tergites more or less connate; very small beetles. (**Aphænocéphalus**, As.; **Discolòma** (= *Notiópygus*), Neotrop., Afr.). (*APHÆNOCEPHÁLIDÆ, PSEUDOCORYLÓPHIDÆ, NOTIOPÝGIDÆ*) ....**DISCOLÓMIDÆ**
    Body more elongate, the prothorax narrower, not widened behind 117
117. Abdominal sternites all free; wings with a short fringe of hairs (Fig. 808). (**Corticària**, widespr.; **Melanophthálma**, cosmop.; **Lathrídius, Cartódere,** Holarc.; **Enícmus,** Holarc., Austr.).
                                           LATHRIDÌIDÆ

a. Last three or four joints of the antennæ separately thickened, spindle-shaped, and set with long curved hairs........**DASYCERÌNÆ**
    Antennæ without long hairs at apex..........................b
b. Anterior coxal cavities closed behind............................c
    Anterior coxal cavities open behind......**HOLOPARAMECÌNÆ**
c. Anterior coxæ separate; head longer before the eyes; elytra often carinate ....**LATHRIDIÌNÆ**
    Anterior coxæ contiguous; head shorter before the eyes; elytra never carinate ....**CORTICARIÌNÆ**

Basal three sternites connate. (See couplet 107)
                                        A few **COLYDÌIDÆ**
118. Front coxæ subtransverse; maxillæ with a single lobe. (**Smicrips,** Am.) ....**SMICRÍPIDÆ**
    Front coxæ small, rounded; maxillæ bilobed; small flattened bark beetles. (**Monótoma**) ....**MONOTÓMIDÆ**
119. Tarsi two-jointed; antennæ eleven-jointed; metasternum very long; very small, elongate beetles, with the elytra oval. (**Jacobsònium,** Sumatra) ....**JACOBSONÌIDÆ**
    Tarsi consisting of a single joint: antennæ four-jointed; metasternum not greatly elongated; very small, broad species. (**Cyathócerus,** Neotrop.). (If both elytra and wings are wanting and body larviform, see couplet 198). (*LEPICÉRIDÆ*)
                                           CYATHOCÉRIDÆ
120. Front coxal cavities closed behind (Fig. 839) 121
    Front coxal cavities open behind (Fig. 840) 130
121. Tarsal claws simple 122
    Tarsal claws pectinate; usually elongate, convex, rather soft bodied and often thinly silky-pubescent beetles of small or moderate size; prothorax widened behind. (**Allécula,** cosmop.;

Hymenòrus, Palæarc., Am.; Cistèla, widespr.; Ctenìopus, Palæarc.; Lophópoda, Am.). (*ALLECÙLIDÆ*) ....CISTÉLIDÆ

122. Ventral segments (abdominal sternites) all freely movable. (If the mesosternum is carinate, compare some rare Silphidæ, couplet 82) 123

First two to four ventral segments more closely joined together, more or less fused or immovable 127

123. Antennæ 11-jointed 124

Antennæ 10-jointed 126

124. Prothorax cylindrical; small, soft-bodied beetles with long, slender antennæ and protruding eyes; elytra not completely covering the abdomen. (Pètria, Palæarc.) ....PETRÌIDÆ

Prothorax not cylindrical 125

125. Prothorax quadrate, not wider than the head; narrow-bodied beetles. (If body is greatly flattened, compare males of some Cucujidæ, couplet 50, and Silvanidæ, couplet 50). (Elácatis (= *Óthnius*), widespr.; Ábaba, Nearc.). (*ÓTHNÌIDÆ*).

ELACÁTIDÆ

Prothorax greatly expanded at the sides, much wider than the head. (Nílio, Neotrop.) ....NILIÓNIDÆ

126. Elytra entire; small convex beetles. (Sphíndus, Holarc., Neotrop.)

SPHÍNDIDÆ

Elytra truncate, exposing the pygidium; small, flattened beetles. (See couplet 34) ....Males of RHIZOPHÁGIDÆ

127. Five ventral segments 128

Six ventral segments, the first two immovably united; small black beetles. (Eurystèthus (= *Ægialìtes*), Nearc., California to Alaska, Persia). (*ÆGIALÍTIDÆ*) ....EURYSTÉTHIDÆ

128. Penultimate joint of tarsi spongy pubescent beneath; front coxæ prominent; slender, elongate, usually hairy, soft-bodied species, sometimes of metallic color. (Làgria, widespr.; Arthromàcra, Holarc.; Statìra, Am.; Nemostìra, Afr., Indomal.)...LAGRÌIDÆ

Penultimate joint of tarsi not spongy pubescent beneath; front coxæ short, not projecting from the cavities 129

129. Antennæ filiform or gradually clavate, the joints usually more or less bead-like, not concealed under the sides of the head; beetles of variable form, oval, elongate, or even pedunculate; usually hard-bodied, black or dark colored; moderate, large or small species. (Figs. 845, 846). A very large and widely distributed family. (Tenèbrio, Strongýlium, Hèlops, Bláps, Ásida, Bolitópha-gus, Diapèris, Eleòdes, Epítragus, Nyctóbates, Platýdema, Zópherus, Tentýria, Tribòlium, Meracántha). (Including *HELÓPIDÆ, OPÁTRIDÆ, PIMELÌIDÆ, BLÁPIDÆ, DIA-PÉRIDÆ, BÓRIDÆ, TRETOTHORÁCIDÆ, RHYSOPAUS-SIDÆ* ....TENEBRIÓNIDÆ

Antennæ strongly clavate, more or less completely concealed beneath the sides of the head, with large two-jointed club, geniculate at the base, with the first joint very long; middle tarsi sometimes four-jointed, very small, oval, flattened beetles living in ants' nests. (Cossyphòdes, Cossyphodìtes, Ethiop.; Cossyphodìnus, India) . . . . COSSYPHÓDIDÆ

130. Antennæ geniculate; elytra truncate behind, exposing two abdominal tergites; small, oval, hard-bodied species. (Acrìtus, Halacrìtus, widespr.; Aelètes, Neotrop.). (See couplet 44)
(Tribe Acritini) A few HISTÉRIDÆ

Antennæ not geniculate, except in male of Meloë (see couplet 146) 131

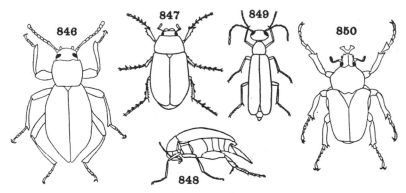

Figs. 846–853. Coleoptera

846. Eleodes (Hyslop) Tenebrionidæ.
847. Phyllophaga (Forbes) Melolonthidæ.
848. Mordellistena. Mordellidæ.
849. Epicauta (Bruner) Meloidæ.
850. Goliathus (Westwood) Cetoniidæ.

131. Head not strongly or suddenly narrowed or constricted behind the eyes; tarsal claws simple or cleft 132
Head strongly and suddenly constricted behind the eyes; if more gradually narrowed, the tarsal claws are pectinate 138

132. Middle coxæ not noticeably prominent 133
Middle coxæ very prominent, contiguous; prothorax without lateral margin; penultimate joint of tarsi dilated and with a dense brush of hairs beneath; slender, soft-bodied species. (Nacèrda, Asclèra, Sessínia, widespr.; Cálopus, Xanthróchroa, Holarc.; Óxacis, Am.; Œdémera, Palæarc.) . . . . ŒDEMÉRIDÆ

133. Antennæ received in grooves on the underside of the prothorax; small, oval, flattened beetles with the head partly concealed

in the prothorax; legs retractile. (Monómma, widespr.)
(*MONÓMMIDÆ*) .... MONOMMÁTIDÆ
Antennæ free, not received in grooves 134
134. Prothorax with a sharp lateral margin 135
Prothorax not margined laterally, narrowed behind, its disk
without impressions. (Myctèrus, Sphæriéstes (= *Salpíngus*),
Lissodérma, widespr.; Pỳtho, Holarc.). (*SALPÍNGIDÆ*)
PỲTHIDÆ
135. Epimera of mesothorax not reaching the coxæ, the coxal cavities
entirely surrounded by the sterna (males of a few genera). (See
couplet 52) .... CRYPTOPHÁGIDÆ, part
Epimera of mesothorax attaining the coxæ 136
136. Metasternum long; epimera of metathorax visible 137
Metasternum quadrate, epimera of metathorax covered. (Males
of a number of genera, see couplet 50) .... CUCÙJIDÆ, part
137. Prothorax widened toward the base, its disk with basal impressions; tarsal claws sometimes cleft or appendiculate; elongate or
broadly oval species. (Orchèsia, Phlœotrỳia, Serropálpus,
widespr.; Tetrátoma, Hallómenus, Melándrya, Ósphya, Holarc.;
Pénthe, Palæarc., Indomal.). (*MELANDRỲIDÆ, HALLO-
MÉNIDÆ*) .... SERROPÁLPIDÆ
Prothorax narrowed behind and in front, the sides rounded or
toothed; without basal impressions; tarsal claws simple; mandibles very large and powerful, porrect. Very large, elongate
beetles. (Trictenótoma, Ind., E. Ind.; Autócrates, S. As.)
TRICTENOTÓMIDÆ
138. Head prolonged behind and gradually narrowed; prothorax not
margined at the sides, as wide as the elytra at base; tarsal
claws pectinate, with a large appendage at base; medium-sized
slender beetles. (Cepháloon, Holarc.; Typítium, Nearc.; Sponí-
dium, Palæarc.) .... CEPHALÒIDÆ
Head suddenly narrowed behind 139
139. Prothorax with a sharp lateral margin 140
Prothorax rounded on the sides, without a sharp lateral margin . 142
140. Antennæ filiform 141
Antennæ pectinate (male) or subserrate (female); tarsal claws
serrate or toothed; elytra covering the abdomen. (Evaniócera,
Palæarc., Austr.; Pelecótoma, Holarc.)
Tribe EVANIOCERINI of RHIPIPHÓRIDÆ
141. Hind coxæ moderate or large, flattened; front coxæ without
trochantin; head placed vertically against the thorax; tarsal
claws simple, or cleft and pectinate; body usually conically
narrowed behind, the abdomen often prolonged and pointed at
tip; small pubescent beetles. (Fig. 848). (Mordélla, Mordel-
listèna, Anáspis, cosmop.; Tomóxia, widespr.; Tólida, Palæarc.)

(Including *ANASPIDIDÆ*) ....MORDÉLLIDÆ
Hind coxæ transverse; front coxæ with trochantin; body not
greatly narrowed behind; tarsal claws simple. (Scráptia, cosmop.;
Trotommídea, Trotómma, Palæarc.; Eválces, Neotrop.)
SCRAPTÌIDÆ

142. Base of prothorax narrower than the elytra 143
Base of prothorax as wide as the elytra; body broad, much
narrowed behind; elytra usually shortened and narrowed behind;
antennæ pectinate in the male, often serrate in the female.
Females sometimes much degenerate or even larviform. (Pele-
cotomòides, Rhipídius, widespr.; Macrosìagon, cosmop.;
Rhipíphorus (including *Myodìtes*), Holarc., Neotrop.)
RHIPIPHÓRIDÆ

143. Hind coxæ transverse, not prominent; tarsal claws usually
simple 144
Hind coxæ large and prominent 146

144. Eyes more or less emarginate; hind coxæ contiguous or nearly
so 145
Eyes elliptical, entire, rather coarsely granulated; hind coxæ
usually well separated. (Ánthicus, Tomóderus, cosmop.; Notóxus,
Formicòmus, Endòmia, widespr.; Lemòdes, Austr.)
ANTHÍCIDÆ

145. Head constricted far behind the finely granulated eyes. (Macràtria,
cosmop.; Pedìlus (= *Corphyra*), Stereopálpus, Holarc.)
PEDÍLIDÆ
Head constricted just behind the coarsely granulated eyes; tarsi
apparently with 4, 4, 3 joints, as the penultimate joint is extremely
minute; first two ventral segments immovably united. (Áderus
(*Hylóphilus*), cosmop.; Syzèton, Austr.). (*XYLOPHÍLIDÆ,
EUGLÉNIDÆ, HYLOPHÍLIDÆ*) ....ADÉRIDÆ

146. Tarsal claws simple; head horizontal; antennæ serrate, often
pectinate in the male (Fig. 797); body flattened; moderate-sized
beetles. (Dendròides, Schizòtus, Holarc.; Pyróchroa, Palæarc.;
Pseudopyróchroa, Palæarc., Indomal.) .....PYROCHRÒIDÆ
Tarsal claws toothed or cleft; head deflexed, with the front vertical;
elytra sometimes shortened; body plump, usually more or less
cylindrical; moderate or large beetles (Fig. 849). Blister beetles.
(Epicaúta, Lýtta (= *Cántharis*), Méloë, Cissìtes, widespr.; Zonìtis
(including *Nemógnatha*), cosmop.; Macróbasis, Am.; Hórnia,
Nearc.). (*CANTHÁRIDÆ, LÝTTIDÆ*) .... MELÒIDÆ

147. Submentum pedunculate; *i.e.* the mentum supported at its base
by a narrow portion or peduncle; antennæ eleven-jointed, serrate,
rarely pectinate; head prolonged into a broad muzzle; antennæ
and body usually pubescent; elytra shortened, exposing the

pygidium. (Fig. 853). Pea and bean weevils. (*MYLÁBRIDÆ,
LARÌIDÆ*) ....BRÙCHIDÆ

a. Mesopleural suture distinct, free from the meso-metapleural
suture; some of the tibiæ often with two spurs at apex ....b
Mesopleural suture vestigial, joining the meso-metapleural suture,
or closely approximate to it. (**Brùchus** *Mylàbris*, *Lària*),
Acanthoscélides, cosmop.) ....BRUCHÌNÆ

b. Pronotum without lateral carina; hind femora never greatly
thickened, their tibiæ straight c
Pronotum separated from the pleura by a lateral carina; hind
femora sometimes greatly thickened and their tibiæ arcuate ....d

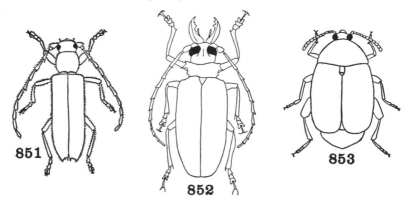

Figs. 851–853. Coleoptera

851. **Elaphidion** (Forbes) Cerambycidæ.
852. **Acanthophorus** (Gahan) Prionidæ.
853. **Bruchus** (Felt) Bruchidæ.

c. Pygidium and one or two tergites exposed behind the tip of the
elytra; antennæ of male pectinate or flabellate; tibiæ without spurs.
(**Kytorhìnus**) ....KYTORHINÌNÆ
Pygidium covered at base by the elytra; antennæ of both sexes
deeply serrate. (**Eubáptus**) ....EUBAPTÌNÆ

d. Hind femora not thickened, only half as broad as the coxa.
(**Amblýcerus, Spermóphagus,** widespr.) ......AMBLYCERÌNÆ
Hind femora greatly thickened, much broader than the coxa.
(**Pachýmerus, Caryóborus,** widespr.) ....PACHYMERÌNÆ

Submentum not pedunculate; head not prolonged into a broad
beak; antennæ rarely distinctly serrate, occasionally with more
than eleven joints, usually filiform or moderately thickened toward
apex 148

148. Antennæ usually long or greatly developed, frequently inserted on frontal prominences; front often vertical, large and quadrate; pronotum rarely margined; tibial spurs well developed; usually rather large, elongate or oblong beetles with parallel sides and pubescent upper surface. Longicorns 149

Antennæ moderate or short, not inserted on frontal prominences; front small, oblique, sometimes greatly inflexed; prothorax most frequently margined; tibial spurs usually wanting; small or of moderate size; body usually glabrous above and often very brightly colored or metallic; rather oval in form. Leaf-beetles 151

149. Prothorax sharply margined at the sides which commonly bear teeth or spines; labrum connate; front coxæ strongly transverse; inner lobe of maxillæ very small or obsolete; large or very large, considerably flattened, usually brown or black beetles. (Fig. 852). (Priònus, Holarc.; Macrótoma, widespr.; Mállodon, Orthosòma, Am.; Derancístrus, Pyròdes, Neotrop.). (Including *ANOPLO-DERMÁTIDÆ*) ....PRIÓNIDÆ

Prothorax very rarely margined at the sides; labrum free; front coxæ rounded, rarely strongly transverse; inner lobe of maxillæ more or less well developed; antennæ never pubescent 150

150. Front tibiæ obliquely grooved on the inner side; front coxæ never transverse; last joint of palpi usually pointed. (Fig. 791). (Monóchamus, Obèrea, widespr.; Sapérda, Holarc.; Dorcà-dion, Palæarc.; Oncíderes, Am.; Tetraòpes, Nearc.; Batócera, Afr., Austr.; Tragocéphala, Afr.; Platyomópsis, Austr.). (Including *BATOCÉRIDÆ*) ....LAMÌIDÆ

Front tibiæ not grooved; last joint of palpi never acute at tip; antennæ pubescent. (Fig. 851). (Leptùra, Callichròma, Xy-lótrechus, widespr.; Acmæops, Strangàlia, Phymatòdes, Rhàgium, Holarc.; Ebùria, Elaphídion, Cyllène, Am.)

CERAMBÝCIDÆ

151. Mouth placed anteriorly, the front normal; head porrect or vertical 152

Mouth inferior, the anterior part of the front prominent, so that the mouth is confined to the underside of the head and is small, hidden or nearly so 164

152. Antennæ widely separated at the base; elytra of hard texture ..153

Antennæ generally closely approximate at base, not widely sep-arated; elytra more or less soft in texture 163

153. Intermediate abdominal sternites not narrowed medially, the pygidium not exposed behind the elytra 154

Intermediate abdominal sternites narrowed medially, the pygid-ium usually exposed, declivous 158

154. Prothorax rounded on the sides, without distinct lateral margin; head produced, the eyes prominent; prosternum very narrow ..155

Prothorax with a distinct lateral margin (if rarely not margined, the antennæ are usually short, with the terminal joints transverse and more or less serrate); head not produced, the eyes not prominent; prosternum broad. (If antennæ are strongly clavate, compare a few Erotylidæ, couplet 103) 161

155. Antennæ not separated by the entire front of the head 156
      Antennæ separated by the entire front of the head 157

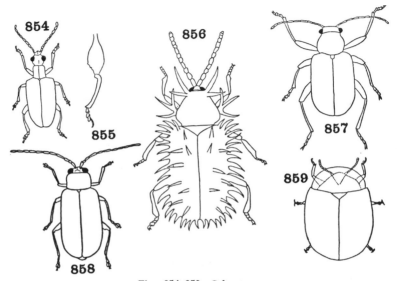

Figs. 854–859. **Coleoptera**

854. **Crioceris** (Jacoby) Crioceridæ.
855. **Sagra**, hind leg (Jacoby) Sagridæ.
856. **Hispella** (Fletcher) Hispidæ.
857. **Fidia** (Johnson and Hammar) Eumolpidæ.
858. **Diabrotica** (Chittenden) Galerucidæ.
859. **Cassida** (Jones) Cassididæ.

156. Prosternum very narrow, not distinct; body beneath clothed with dense silvery pubescence; first sternite as long as the others united; elongate, more or less metallic, semiaquatic beetles. (**Donàcia,** widespr.; **Hæmònia, Plateùmaris,** Holarc.) ......DONACÌIDÆ
      Prosternum distinct; body beneath not thus densely pubescent; first sternite shorter; less elongate beetles, not aquatic. (**Megá-scelis, Atelédera,** Neotrop.) ....MEGASCÉLIDÆ
157. Hind femora greatly thickened, their tibiæ curved; brilliantly metallic species of moderately large size. (Fig. 855). (**Sàgra,** Old World tropics; **Aulacóscelis,** Neotrop.) ....SÁGRIDÆ

Hind femora only slightly incrassated; much smaller and less brilliant insects, rarely metallic. (Fig. 854). (Crióceris, Lèma, cosmop.; Sigrísma, Ethiop.; Orsodácne, widespr.). (Including *ORSODÁCNIDÆ*) . . . . CRIOCÈRIDÆ

158. Antennæ short, the joints serrate 159
Antennæ long and generally filiform, never serrate, although sometimes shorter with the terminal joints thickened; small, cylindrical beetles of compact shape, with the head flat, perpendicular and invisible from above. (Cryptocéphalus, cosmop.; Pachýbrachys, cosmop., mainly Am.; Diorýctus, Indomal.; Cœnòbius, As., Afr.; Mónachus, Neotrop.; Bassàreus, Nearc.)
CRYPTOCEPHÁLIDÆ

159. Prothorax without grooves for the reception of the antennæ; elytra not tuberculate 160
Prothorax with grooves on the flanks for the reception of the antennæ; elytra tuberculate; body subquadrate or somewhat elongate; head flat, deeply inserted in the prothorax, invisible from above. (Chlàmisus, Éxema, widespr.; Fúlcidax, Neotrop.). (*FULCIDÁCIDÆ, CHLAMÝDIDÆ*) . . . . CHLAMÍSIDÆ

160. Apical joint of maxillary palpi pointed; hind femora with one or two teeth; last joint of tarsi and claws very long; body elongate, the head not concealed. (Megálopus, Neotrop.; Mastostèthus, Neotrop.; Temnáspis, Colobáspis, Afr., Indomal.)
MEGALOPÓDIDÆ
Apical joint of maxillary palpi more or less truncate; hind femora without teeth; claw joint normal; elongate, more or less cylindrical species with the head deflexed or perpendicular; elytra generally covering the pygidium. (Clỳtra, Gynandrophthálma, widespr.; Cyanìris, widespr.; Æthomórpha, Afr., Indo-Austr.; Aspidólopha, Indomal.; Coscinóptera, Bàbia, Am.) . . . . CLÝTRIDÆ

161. Third joint of tarsi deeply bilobed; front coxæ usually rounded . 162
Third tarsal joint entire, not bilobed; front coxæ transverse; body oval, convex; antennæ moderately thickened toward apex. (Fig. 790). (Chrysomèla, Plagiódera, Dorýphora, widespr.; Phytodécta, Phyllodécta, Holarc.; Leptinotársa (*L. decemlineàta*, Colorado potato-beetle), Polyspìla, Am.; Timárcha, Palæarc.; Pýrgo, Austr.)
CHRYSOMÉLIDÆ

162. Prothorax as wide as the elytra at base; legs compressed; femora with grooves into which the tibiæ can be placed; metasternum and abdomen grooved for the reception of the femora; short, very convex beetles, often brilliantly metallic. (Lamprosòma, Neotrop., As.; Lycnóphanes, Neotrop., Ethiop.)
LAMPROSOMÁTIDÆ
Prothorax generally narrower than the elytra; legs not compressed; abdomen not grooved for the reception of the femora;

more or less oblong, convex beetles. (Fig. 857). (Fídia, Coláspis, Am.; Chrýsochus, Adóxus, Holarc.; Chrysolámpra, As.; Nodóstoma, Triclìòna, Indomal.; Corynòdes, Colasposòma, Afr., Indomal.; Pària, Am., As.; Nodonòta, Am. Austr.)

EUMÓLPIDÆ

163. Hind femora slender, adapted for walking; tibiæ usually subcylindrical; tarsi slender, not retractile. (Fig. 858). (Lupèrus, Galerucélla, cosmop.; Galerùca, Holarc.; Monóxia, Cerótoma, Diabròtica, Trirhábda, Am.) ....GALERÙCIDÆ

Hind femora greatly thickened, adapted for leaping; tibiæ frequently sulcate externally, the tarsi retractile. (Áltica (= *Háltica*), Sýstena, Épitrix, Œdiónychus, widespr.). (*HALTÍCIDÆ*)

ALTÍCIDÆ

164. Head free, not retracted beneath the prothorax; body usually spinose, narrowed in front, broad and truncate behind. (Fig. 856). (Híspa, Afr. As.; Chálepus, Am.; Cephalòlia, Cephalodónta, Neotrop.; Gonóphora, Callíspa, Dactylíspa, Afr. As.) ..HÍSPIDÆ

Head concealed under the prothorax, which, with the elytra, is widely margined; body oval or nearly circular in outline. (Fig. 859). (Cássida, Coptocỳcla, widespr.; Chelymórpha, Am.; Hoplionòta, Ethiop., Indo-Austr.; Charídotis, Metrìona, Neotrop.; Aspidomórpha, Afr., Indo-Austr.) ....CASSÍDIDÆ

165. Tarsi apparently three-jointed, with the second joint lobed. (Fig. 877). (AGLYCYDERÒIDEA) 166

Tarsi apparently four-jointed, with the third joint lobed 167

166. Head without a distinct beak in either sex, wider than the anterior part of the pronotum; prothorax subquadrate, the sides straight and the pleuræ clearly separated from the notum. (Fig. 877). (Aglycýderes, Canary Isl., Austromal.)......AGLYCYDÉRIDÆ

Beak in female well developed; in male rarely attaining a length greater than its width; head narrower than the anterior part of the pronotum; prothorax oval, the sides bulging outwards and the pleuræ indistinctly separated from the notum. (Fig. 872). (Proterhìnus, Hawaii, Micronesia) ....PROTERHÍNIDÆ

167. Rostrum or beak extremely short and broad, scarcely developed; tibiæ with a series of teeth externally or the front ones produced into a stout curved process at tip; antennæ short with a broad club; small oval or cylindrical beetles. (SCOLYTÒIDEA) ...168

Beak of variable length, usually at least longer than broad, tibiæ simple, without teeth externally or process at tip; antennæ clubbed or not. (CURCULIONÒIDEA) 172

168. First joint of anterior tarsi shorter than the second, third and fourth together (Fig. 871); eyes oval, emarginate or divided; head narrower than the prothorax. (Fig. 864) 170

First joint of anterior tarsi very long (Fig. 875), longer than the second, third and fourth together; head broader than prothorax; eyes rounded (Fig. 865) 169

169. Third joint of front tarsi not lobed; anterior tibiæ with a prominent apical process and with rugosities on the ventral area. (Figs. 865, 867, 875). (Plátypus, tropicopol.; Tesserócerus, Neotrop.; Crossotársus, Afr., Indo-Austr.; Periómmatus, Afr.)
PLATYPÓDIDÆ
Third joint of front tarsi deeply lobed; anterior tibiæ more slender. (Chapuisia, Neotrop.) ....CHAPUISÌIDÆ

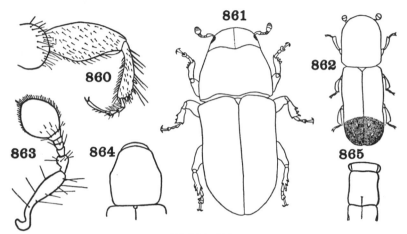

Figs. 860–865. Coleoptera

860. **Pityogenes,** front leg (Felt) Ipidæ.
861. **Dendroctonus** (Hopkins) Ipidæ.
862. **Xyleborus** (Hubbard) Ipidæ.
863. **Ips,** antenna (Felt) Ipidæ.
864. **Hylastes,** dorsal outline of head and prothorax (Felt) Ipidæ.
865. **Platypus,** dorsal outline of head and prothorax (Felt) Platypodidæ.

170. Front tibiæ without a prominent process on the outer apical angle. (Figs. 810, 861, 863, 864, 868, 870, 871). (Íps, Pityóphthorus, Hylesìnus, Hylástes, cosmop.; Dendróctonus, Cryptúrgus, Holarc.; Mìcracis, Am.). (Including *HYLESÍNIDÆ,* part) ......ÍPIDÆ
Front tibiæ with a prominent process on the outer apical angle. ..171
171. Front tibiæ without prominent rugosities on ventral area. (Figs. 788, 869). (Scólytus (= *Eccoptogáster*), widespr.; Scolytópsis, Camptócerus, Neotrop.). (Including *HYLESÍNIDÆ,* part)
SCOLÝTIDÆ
Front tibiæ with prominent rugosities on ventral area. (Fig. 866). (Scolytoplátypus) ...............SCOLYTOPLATYPÓDIDÆ

172. Antennæ not elbowed, without a distinct club although sometimes
     stouter toward tip; first joint not lengthened................173
     Antennæ straight or elbowed, always with a distinct club, the
     first joint much elongated...............................174
173. Antennæ 10-jointed, the last joint very elongate. (Cỳlas (*C. formi-
     càrius*, Sweet-potato weevil), widespr.; Myrmacícelus, Austr.)
                                                        CYLÁDIDÆ
     Antennæ 11-jointed; body very elongate; beak well developed at
     least in the female and often remarkably long and thin. (Fig.
     874). (Eùpsalis, Trachelìzus, widespr.; Brénthus, Rhaphìdor-
     rhýnchus, Neotrop.). (*BRÉNTIDÆ*)..........BRÉNTHIDÆ
174. Palpi flexible; labrum present.............................175
     Palpi rigid; labrum wanting ....CURCULIÓNIDÆ [1]

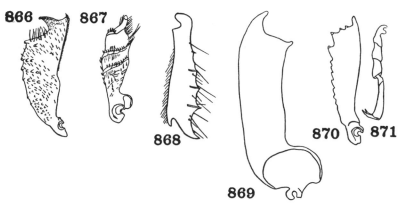

Figs. 866–871. Coleoptera

866. **Scolytoplatypus,** front tibia (Hopkins) Scolytoplatypodidæ.
867. **Platypus,** front tibia. Platypodidæ.
868. **Erineophilus,** front tibia (Felt) Ipidæ.
869. **Camptocerus,** front tibia (Hopkins) Scolytidæ.
870. **Ips,** front tibia (Hopkins) Ipidæ.
871. **Ips,** tarsus (Hopkins) Ipidæ.

a. Prothorax with a distinct acute or carinate lateral margin; antennæ straight, not geniculate...............................b
   Prothorax without a distinct lateral margin, rarely with the weak
   indication of one..c
b. Elytra short, exposing three dorsal abdominal segments; short,
   stout species. (Pterócolus, Am.).............PTEROCOLÌNÆ

[1] This very extensive family has been divided into a long series of subfamilies, the
limits of which are not agreed upon by different workers. Those generally recognized
are included in the following key.

Elytra completely covering the abdomen. (Oxycórynus, Neotrop.)
OXYCORYNÌNÆ

c. Antennæ straight, not received in grooves; club frequently with
separated joints . . . . .d
Antennæ geniculate, more or less completely elbowed; the beak
with grooves for the reception of the scape; club compact. . . . . . .j

d. Antennal club composed of completely separated joints. . . . . .e
Antennæ with the joints closely united into a compact, oval club. .f

e. Mandibles flat, toothed on inner and outer sides, tibiæ with short
terminal spurs; tarsal claws free, bifid or acutely toothed.
RHYNCHITÌNÆ
Mandibles stout, pincers-shaped; tibial spurs forming two strong
hooks; tarsal claws connate at base. . . . . ATTELABÌNÆ

f. Trochanters elongate, the femora attached to their apices and thus
separated from the coxæ; elytra completely covering the abdomen, concealing the pygidium; beak porrect, usually long; small
species. (Àpion, cosmop.) . . . . .APIONÌNÆ
Trochanters triangular, the femora contiguous with the coxæ. . . .g

g. Tips of elytra leaving the pygidium exposed. . . . . .h
Tips of elytra completely covering the abdomen. (Brachýcerus,
Palæarc., Ethiop.; Micrócerus, Bròtheus, Ethiop.).
BRACHYCERÌNÆ

h. First joint of antennæ no longer than the second; beak short, broad;
middle and hind coxæ widely separated; hind legs very long, fitted
for grasping; broad, short species. (Tachýgonus, Am.)
TACHYGONÌNÆ
First joint of antennæ longer than the second. i

i. Hind femora short, very broad, their outer margin crenulate and
strongly curved; small species with long, curved beak; joints of
antennal club less closely compacted than usual. (Allocórynus,
Am.) . . . . ALLOCORYNÌNÆ
Hind femora of the usual elongate, clavate form; beak short,
broad; large species. (Ithýcerus, Nearc.). (BÉLIDÆ, Leng).
ITHYCERÌNÆ

j. Abdomen of male with an apparent extra segment at tip; the
pygidium and anal segment separated by a suture; club of antennæ
usually annulated, sensitive and not shining; third joint of tarsi
usually deeply bilobed, with a brush beneath (rarely with narrow
setose tarsi in some subaquatic species). .k
Abdomen similar in both sexes, the pygidium not divided by a
suture as the anal segment of the male is at least partly free and
retractile; club of antennæ usually with its basal joint enlarged
or shining, or both, without or with indistinct sutures. . . . . .o

k. Mandibles with a deciduous cusp or projection which leaves an
oval scar when it falls off; beak never long and slender, not

received in the breast in repose. (*BRACHYRHÍNIDÆ, PSALI-DÍIDÆ*) .... **OTIORHYNCHÍNÆ**
Mandibles without scar or deciduous cusp; beak elongate, or if slender, received by the breast in repose 1

l. Prosternum not forming a triangular plate in front of the coxæ; simple or grooved to receive the beak .... m
Prosternum forming a triangular plate in front of the coxæ; beak received in the prosternum when in repose; tarsi usually narrow and bristly. (**Thecestérnus**, Holarc.; **Býrsops**, Palæarc.). (*BYR-SÓPIDÆ*) .... **THECESTERNÍNÆ**

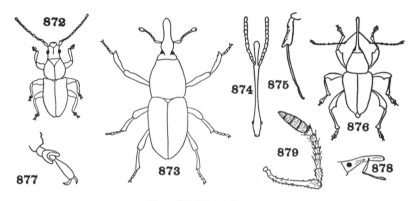

Figs. 872–879. Coleoptera

872. **Proterhinus** (Perkins) Proterhinidæ.
873. **Sitophilus** (Back and Cotton) Curculionidæ.
874. **Brenthus**, head from above (Berlese) Brenthidæ.
875. **Platypus**, tibia and tarsus of front leg (Felt) Platypodidæ.
876. **Balaninus** (Chittenden) Curculionidæ.
877. **Aglycyderes**, hind tarsus (Tillyard) Aglycyderidæ.
878. Curculionid Weevil, side of head.
879. **Sitones**, antenna (Silvestri) Curculionidæ.

m. Trochanters elongated, completely separating the base of the femora from the coxæ .... **NANOPHYÍNÆ**
Trochanters short, triangular; base of femora contiguous with the coxæ .... n

n. Beak short and stout, received between the front legs in repose; jumping species with short thickened hind femora.
ORCHESTÍNÆ
Beak usually elongate, slender and porrect, rarely concealed; hind femora not thickened for jumping .... **CURCULIONÍNÆ**

o. Pygidium covered by the elytra; mentum attached to a short quadrate gular peduncle .... **COSSONÍNÆ**

Pygidium exposed; peduncle of mentum long and narrow, the buccal cavity elongate. (Caléndra (=Sphenóphorus)). (CAL-ÁNDRIDÆ, RHÝNCOPHÓRIDÆ) .... CALÉNDRÌNÆ

175. Beak long, well developed, prothorax without lateral carinate margin or transverse ridge; elytra completely covering the pygidium; anterior coxæ conical. (Rhinómacer, Holarc.; Nemònyx, Palæarc.). (DOYDIRHÝNCHIDÆ, RHINOMACÉRIDÆ).

NEMONÝCHIDÆ

Beak very short; prothorax trapezoidal, with carinate lateral margin and usually a transverse raised line or ridge; pygidium exposed; anterior coxæ globose. (BRUCHÉLIDÆ, CHORÁGIDÆ, PLATYRRHÍNIDÆ, PLATYSTÓMIDÆ).... ANTHRÍBIDÆ

176. Lamellæ of antennal club not capable of closing together, usually not flattened, but forming a more or less comb-like mass (Fig. 814); only five abdominal sternites..........................177
Lamellæ of antennal club movable, flattened and capable of close apposition to form a solid club; six, or more rarely five, abdominal sternites 179

177. Mentum entire, ligula behind, or at the apex of the mentum; antennæ not curled in repose............................178
Mentum deeply emarginate, the ligula large, corneous, filling the emargination; labrum free; antennæ straight, curled in repose; large elongate, somewhat flattened, shining beetles with deeply lined elytra .... PASSÁLIDÆ

178. Ligula and maxillæ covered by the mentum; antennæ usually elbowed. (Fig. 814). Stag-beetles. (Dórcus, Platýcerus, Cerùchus, Lucànus, Holarc.; Nicàgus, Platyceròides, Nearc.; Odontólabis, As., Indomal.; Lámprima, Austr.) .... LUCÁNIDÆ
Ligula and maxillæ not covered; antennæ straight. (Sinodéndron, Holarc.) .... SINODÉNDRIDÆ

179. Side pieces of mesosternum attaining the coxæ; abdomen usually with six tergites 180
Side pieces of mesosternum not attaining the coxæ; abdomen with five tergites; body heavily sculptured, the elytra usually with distinct rows of tubercles; pygidium covered by the elytra; small or moderate, rarely large beetles. Skin-beetles. (Tróx, cosmop.; Gláresis, Holarc.; Cryptogènius, Neotrop.)......... TRÓGIDÆ

180. Abdominal spiracles placed in a line, each one in the membrane between the sternite and tergite and all of them coverd by the elytra; mentum and ligula separated by a suture.............181
At least some of the apical abdominal spiracles located on the sternites, below the connecting membrane; the last one usually not covered by the elytra; mentum and ligula usually connate 191

181. Hind tibiæ with a single apical spur; scutellum usually invisible; middle legs widely separated by their coxæ; clypeus expanded so

as to cover the mandibles and mouthparts; pygidium partly exposed; antennæ eight- or nine-jointed. (Onthóphagus, cosmop.; Scarabæus, Palæarc., Ethiop. (*S. sàcer*, Sacred scarabæus); Gymnopleùrus, Afr., As.; Cánthon, Tumble-bugs, Deltochìlum, Am.; Chœrídium, Am.; Pinòtus, Neotrop.; Còpris, widespr.; Phanæus, Am.). (*CÓPRIDÆ*) . . . . SCARABÆIDÆ
Hind tibiæ with two apical spurs; scutellum well developed; middle legs more approximated; clypeus of variable size, either concealing or exposing the mouthparts 182

182. Six abdominal sternites 183
Five abdominal sternites, or with the sutures between the sternites effaced 190

183. Antennæ with eleven joints 184
Antennæ with ten joints or less 185

184. Antennal club with three leaves; mandibles and labrum prominent; moderate-sized beetles usually with strongly striate elytra. (Fig. 815). (Bolbóceras, cosmop.; Athýreus, Neotrop., As.; Geotrùpes, widespr.; Lèthrus, Holarc.) . . . . GEOTRÙPIDÆ
Antennal club with many (5–7) leaves; moderately large, black, hairy beetles. (Pleócoma, Ácoma, Nearc.) (*ACLÓPIDÆ*).
                                                                    PLEOCÓMIDÆ

185. Antennæ ten-jointed; body more or less hairy 186
Antennæ nine-jointed 189

186. Antennal club bare and shining, sparsely hairy; epimera of metathorax large; conspicuously hairy beetles. (Amphícoma, Holarc.; Toxócerus, Gláphyrus, Palæarc.) . . . . GLAPHÝRIDÆ
Antennal club, at least on the apical two joints, pubescent and dull or opaque 187

187. Epimera of metathorax covered; abdominal sternites free; antennal club simple, lamellate 188
Epimera of metathorax visible; abdominal sternites connate; antennal club telescopic, the joints cupuliform. (Hybósorus, Holarc., Ethiop.; Liparòchrus, Austr.; Phæòchrous, widespr.)
                                                                    HYBOSÓRIDÆ

188. Eyes divided in front. (Hýbalus, Palæarc.; Órphnus, Ethiop., Ind.; Ægídium, Neotrop.) . . . . ÓRPHNIDÆ
Eyes entire. (Ochodæus, widespr.) . . . . OCHODÆIDÆ

189. Mandibles concealed beneath the clypeus. (Aphòdius, Atænius, Psammòdius, Saprosìtes, Oxyòmus, cosmop.; Eupària, Pleuróphorus, widespr.; Lorditomæus, Afr.) . . . . APHODÌIDÆ
Mandibles not covered by the clypeus. (Ægìalia, Holarc.; Eremàzus, Palæarc.) . . . . ÆGIALÌIDÆ

190. Abdomen retractile, whole body together with the legs capable of being contracted into a ball; small shining, more or less metallic species. (Acanthócerus, Cleonòtus, Am.; Philharmóstes, Afr.;

Pterorthochætes, Indo-Austr.) . . . . ACANTHOCÉRIDÆ
Body not retractile. Tribe Oncerini of the MELOLÓNTHIDÆ

191. Abdominal spiracles forming two rows which diverge only slightly behind, each row forming a nearly straight line; tarsal claws at least of hind legs usually of equal size and with a tooth, generally immovable; rarely with only one claw; epistoma transverse, separated from the front by a suture. (Figs. 816, 847). A large, widely distributed group. (**Melolóntha** (Cockchafers), **Oncócerus, Sérica, Diplotáxis, Phyllóphaga** (= *Lachnostérna*) (May-beetles, June-bugs), **Polyphýlla** and many others) . . . . MELOLÓNTHIDÆ
Abdominal spiracles forming two rows which diverge strongly behind, each row forming an angulate line 192

192. Front legs greatly lengthened, especially in the male; sides of prothorax dentate; tarsal claws equal; distal leaves of antennal club inclosing the proximal ones. (**Euchìrus,** Indomal.; **Cheirótonus, Propomàcrus,** As.) . . . . EUCHÍRIDÆ
Of a different conformation 193

193. Tarsal claws, at least of the hind legs, of equal length 194
Tarsal claws unequal, freely movable, the shorter one not bifid; pygidium exposed; usually large, often brightly colored beetles, usually no strong dimorphism between the sexes. (**Anómala,** cosmop.; **Popíllia,** widespr.; **Adorètus,** Old World; **Anisòplia,** Palæarc.; **Cotálpa, Plusiòtis, Pelidnòta,** Nearc.) . . . . RUTÉLIDÆ

194. Hind legs of male with the femora greatly swollen, the antennæ nine-jointed; female without elytra or wings. (**Páchypus,** Palæarc.)
PACHYPÓDIDÆ
Femora normal; female with elytra 195

195. Mandibles visible from above, more or less widened and blade-like; anterior coxæ transverse; large or very large beetles; highly dimorphic, the males often with large horns on the head and prothorax. Rhinoceros beetles. (**Dynástes, Orýctes**).
DYNÁSTIDÆ
Mandibles not visible from above, not widened or expanded; anterior coxæ usually strongly conical 196

196. Clypeus emarginate at the sides in front of the eyes, so that the base of the antenna is visible from above; antennæ ten-jointed . . 197
Clypeus not thus emarginate at the sides; antennæ nine-jointed. (**Phænómeris, Oxychìris,** Afr.) . . . . PHÆNOMÉRIDÆ

197. Epimera of metathorax visible from above between the hind angle of the prothorax and the humeral callus; lateral edge of elytra bent inwards near the base. (Fig. 850). Moderate-sized, or often large, frequently brightly colored beetles. (**Cetònia,** Palæarc.; **Cremastochìlus,** Nearc.; **Euphòria, Allorhìna, Cótinus,** Am.; **Golìathus** (Goliath beetle), Ethiop.; and many others).
CETONÌIDÆ

Epimera of metathorax not visible from above, elytra not sinuate; prothorax behind much narrower than the base of the elytra. (**Tríchius**, Holarc.; **Válgus**, widespr.; **Osmodérma**, Holarc.; **Gnórimus**, Palæarc.) .... **TRICHÌIDÆ**

198. Head more or less completely retracted within the prothorax; legs larviform, bearing a single claw...........................199
Head prominent, not retracted; legs of normal form with two tarsal claws. (See couplet 142)......A few female **RHIPIPHÓRIDÆ**

199. Body elongate, more or less uniformly cylindrical; thorax no broader than the abdomen; females of PHENGODINI (See couplet 93) (**Phengòdes**) .... Some **CANTHÁRIDÆ**
Body strongly flattened; prothorax triangularly narrowed in front, meso- and metathorax expanded laterally and much wider than the abdomen, the latter with processes extending from the sides of the segments. (**Dulitícola**, Borneo). "Trilobite larvæ" of Malaya. (See couplet 92)...........Some females of **DRÍLIDÆ**

KEY TO THE LARVÆ OF THE PRINCIPAL FAMILIES OF COLEOPTERA [1]

1. Aquatic, free-living species.................................2
Not aquatic 8
2. Head with the labrum wanting; mouthparts directed forwards....3
Labrum present; mouthparts directed more or less downwards.....7
3. Tarsus distinctly separated from the tibia, with one or two movable claws at the tip..4
Tarsus forming a claw-like joint at the end of the tibiæ; eight abdominal segments .... **HYDROPHÍLIDÆ**
4. Eight abdominal segments; free-swimming forms...............5
Ten abdominal segments; creeping forms......................6
5. Respiration by a pair of terminal spiracles..........**DYTÍSCIDÆ**
Respiration by ventral gills......................**PELOBÌIDÆ**
6. Tarsus with one claw; no gills; apical abdominal segment long; bifid at apex ....**HALÍPLIDÆ**

[1] The following key is based on one published by Blair in 1934. More complete and elaborate classifications and keys have been published and are listed in the bibliographic references cited on page 616. Although arranged in an unusual form and restricted to the families represented in Great Britain, Blair's key is based on intimate knowledge and is understandable to those without specialized knowledge of coleopterous larvæ. On account of the many structural adaptations seen in larvæ, but not reflected in adults, it is difficult or impossible to avoid the temptation of proposing arrangements that cannot be correlated with the generally acceptable classification based on the adult insects. Until such time as larval and adult classifications can be correlated, it seems unwise to introduce any families or subfamilies that cannot be supported by imaginal characters.

The larvæ of a number of groups of Coleoptera are still unknown and this key must be used with caution.

Tarsus with two claws; long leaf-like gills along the sides of the abdomen; apical abdominal segment armed with four hooks.
GYRÍNIDÆ

7. Antennæ very long and slender, many-jointed; body oval.
HELÓDIDÆ

Antennæ short, with few joints; body usually elongate, more rarely oval .... ÉLMIDÆ, DRYÓPIDÆ

8. Occurring in soil, litter on the ground, beneath carrion, decayed vegetable material, etc...................................9

Occurring on living plants, feeding on or in leaves, stems, in roots, etc., or boring in wood of living or dead trees...............26

9. Body long, cylindrical; usually predaceous.....................10

Body curved, commonly feeding on dung or roots or very rotten wood 23

10. Labrum absent; mouthparts projecting forwards................11

Labrum well developed, mouthparts directed more or less downwards 21

11. Tarsus present as a distinct joint, usually with two articulated claws 12

Tarsus forming a simple claw at the tip of the tibia............13

12. Larva living in a vertical burrow in the soil; body soft, only the head and thorax heavily sclerotized and pigmented; fifth abdominal segment with a dorsal tubercle; cerci wanting...CICINDÉLIDÆ

Larva free and active; abdomen usually with sclerotized and pigmented tergites and sternites; cerci usually jointed and movable.
CARÁBIDÆ

13. Cerci present 14

Cerci wanting 16

14. Spiracles with a single round opening; mandibles simple, without tooth before tip; cerci three-jointed.........STAPHYLÍNIDÆ

Each spiracle with two elongate openings; mandibles with a tooth before tip 15

15. Cerci two-jointed; apex of mandible not serrate; two or no ocelli.
HISTÉRIDÆ

Cerci long, three-jointed; apex of mandible serrate; usually six ocelli on each side of the head. (Helophorus). HYDROPHÍLIDÆ, part

16. Body with conspicuous spines or processes; sometimes greatly expanded and flattened; feeding on snails ....DRÍLIDÆ

Body smooth, without such projections......................17

17. Body surface opaque; mandibles with a channel on the inner surface 18

Body surface smooth and shining; tip of abdomen with one or a pair of short thorns .... ELATÉRIDÆ

18. Ninth abdominal segment unarmed..... 19

Ninth abdominal segment with a dorsal shield ending in two upturned points .... **MALACHÏIDÆ, DASÝTIDÆ**

19. Head retractile beneath pronotum 20

Head exposed from above, not retractile; body soft, with velvety
surface .... **CANTHÁRIDÆ**

20. Tip of abdomen with a protrusible brush; body leathery; feeding
mainly on snails .... **LAMPÝRIDÆ**

Tip of abdomen without terminal brush; mandible with deep groove,
splitting it to the base .... **LÝCIDÆ**

21. Cerci present .... **STAPHYLÍNIDÆ, SÍLPHIDÆ**

Cerci absent 22

22. Body smooth, hard and shining; ventral mouthparts free.

TENEBRIÓNIDÆ

Body softer; segmental constrictions well marked; small forms living
in wet mud .... **HETEROCÉRIDÆ**

23. Head capsule complete below behind the mouth cavity; body firmer
with feeble segmental constrictions 24

Head capsule incomplete ventrally; body soft, transversely ridged
or wrinkled 25

24. Spiracles each having a pair of elongate openings; median frontal
suture present .... **BÝRRHIDÆ**

Spiracles each opening through a plate with numerous perforations;
frontal suture wanting .... **DASCÝLLIDÆ**

25. Legs present, well developed; often large species ... **SCARABÆIDÆ**

Legs wanting, usually small species .... **CURCULIÓNIDÆ**

26. Free living forms (external feeders) 27

Internal feeders (leaf-miners, leaf-rollers, feeders in flower buds,
seeds and seed-heads, gall makers, etc.) 37

27. Body with a covering of slime, wax or living in a portable case ... 28

Body not thus protected 31

28. Covering slimy, black 29

Covering not slimy 30

29. Legs present (*Crióceris, Lèma*) .... Some **CHRYSOMÉLIDÆ**

Legs wanting .... Some **CURCULIÓNIDÆ**

30. Covering whitish, waxy; feeding on scale insects.

Some **COCCINÉLLIDÆ**

Covering in the form of a hard case constructed by the larva.

Some **CHRYSOMÉLIDÆ**

31. Legs present 32

Legs wanting, body green (*Phytónomus, Hypera*).

A few **CURCULIÓNIDÆ**

32. Body bearing branched processes or spines 33

Body without branched processes or spines 34

33. Body with a lateral fringe of processes; larva accumulating trash
which is held over the back by a caudal spine ...... **CASSÍDIDÆ**

Body with the spines extending over the dorsal surface.

EPILACHNÌNAE of the **COCCINÉLLIDÆ**

34. Body short, fusiform...35

    Body elongate, with parallel sides; a pair of spines at tip of abdomen 36

35. Active, predatory forms with rather long legs; head capsule complete below, behind the mouth cavity; feeding on aphids and scale insects on foliage.....................**COCCINÉLLIDÆ**

    Slow-moving forms, often gregarious, feeding on foliage.

    CHRYSOMÉLIDÆ

36. Body dark in color, clothed with erect hairs.........**LAGRÌIDÆ**

    Body pale yellow ....**BYTÚRIDÆ**

37. Leaf-miners, excavating burrows in the parenchyma of leaves, but not causing abnormal growths.............................38

    Feeding in flower buds, seed heads, sometimes causing deformation or abnormal growths (galls) in various parts of plants; occasionally feeding in leaves rolled by the parent beetles (leaf rollers). (If boring in wood, proceed to couplet 45)......................40

38. Legs present .... Some **HÍSPIDÆ**

    Legs wanting 39

39. Body widest at prothorax, tapering behind; head elongate, deeply inserted into the prothorax (*Bráchys*).......A few **BUPRÉSTIDÆ**

    Prothorax not widened; head rounded (*Orchéstes*).

    A few **CURCULIÓNIDÆ**

40. Gall-makers, living in abnormal growths...................41

    Not gall-makers 42

41. Body stout, arcuate, convex above........Some **CURCULIÓNIDÆ**

    Body slender, elongate, not arcuate; forming stem-galls in woody plants .... Some **CERAMBÝCIDÆ**

42. Developing in rolled leaves. (RHYNCHITÌNÆ and ATTELABÌNÆ).

    Some **CURCULIÓNIDÆ**

    Developing in flower heads, seeds or seed heads................43

43. Legs well-developed; feeding in flower heads .Some **NITIDÙLIDÆ**

    Legs vestigial or wanting.................................44

44. Legs completely wanting; tip of abdomen quadrilobate.

    Many **CURCULIÓNIDÆ**

    Legs minute; tip of abdomen with a transverse fold only; feeding in seeds, mainly of Leguminosæ...................**MÝLÁBRIDÆ**

45. Body more or less cylindrical or flattened, not curved.........46

    Body arcuate, convex dorsally..............................59

46. Legs vestigial or wanting................................47

    Legs well developed; head free............................51

47. Labrum present; mouthparts normal.......................48

    Labrum and mouthparts reduced; tips of mandibles divergent.

    MELÁSIDÆ

48. Head free; legs present, usually small........................49
    Head partly sunk into the prothorax........................50
49. Dorsal and ventral scansorial pads (discrete, roughened or spinose
    areas) present. (Some predatory Elateridæ will run out here; cf.
    couplet 17) .... LEPTURÌNÆ of the CERAMBÝCIDÆ
    Ventral scansorial pads wanting...........Most MORDÉLLIDÆ
50. Prothorax greatly enlarged and flattened; each spiracle opening
    through a group of small openings...........BUPRÉSTIDÆ
    Body of quite uniform width; scansorial pads (discrete, roughened
    or spinose areas) present on both dorsal and ventral sides of the
    body. (Some predatory Elateridæ will run out here; cf. couplet
    17) .... CERAMBÝCIDÆ
51. Four well developed legs, the hind pair modified into stridulating
    pads and not fitted for crawling.................PASSÁLIDÆ
    All six legs of similar form.................................52
52. Body not unusually slender; head capsule complete behind the
    mouth cavity 53
    Body very long and slender; head capsule incomplete behind.
                                            LYMEXÝLIDÆ
53. Labrum wanting 54
    Labrum distinct; ventral mouthparts free, prominent...........55
54. Body heavily sclerotized, cylindrical; without segmental constric-
    tions; tip of abdomen with a single or a pair of spinose processes.
    Wireworms .... ELATÉRIDÆ
    Body soft, hairy, tip of abdomen with dorsal plate produced into a
    pair of spines .... CLÉRIDÆ
55. Body rather heavily sclerotized; spiracles each with a single circu-
    lar opening 56
    Body of softer consistency................................58
56. Form convex, subcylindrical; last segment of abdomen simple and
    depressed or armed with a pair of upturned spines.
                              TENEBRIÓNIDÆ and CISTÉLIDÆ
    Body strongly depressed; tip of abdomen with a pair of backwardly
    directed spines 57
57. Eighth abdominal segment not lengthened.
                              PÝTHIDÆ and NITIDÙLIDÆ
    Eighth segment lengthened, as long as the two preceding together.
                                          PYROCHRÒIDÆ
58. Mola (a roughened expansion inwardly near base of mandible) well
    developed .... ŒDEMÉRIDÆ
    Mola absent ....SERROPÁLPIDÆ
59. Large or moderate-sized species; head free, with long antennæ; mid-
    dle and hind legs forming a stridulating organ; anal opening
    longitudinal .... LUCÁNIDÆ
    Small species; antennæ very small; legs not thus modified.......60

60. With legs 61
    Without legs .... CURCULIÓNIDÆ and SCOLÝTIDÆ
61. Head free from the thorax; body bearing minute spinules.
    ANOBÌIDÆ
    Head partly concealed in the prothorax 62
62. Spiracles on eighth segment of abdomen much larger than the other
    ones .... LÝCTIDÆ
    All spiracles of about the same size .... BOSTRÝCHIDÆ

LITERATURE ON COLEOPTERA

GENERAL

ALLUAUD, C. Catalogue of Coleoptera of Madagascar. In Grandidier, Hist. Nat. Madagascar, 21, 509 pp. (1900).

BALFOUR-BROWNE, F. British Water Beetles. London, Ray Soc. Vol. 1, 375 pp., 5 pls., 89 figs. (1940); vol. 2, 394 pp., 1 pl. (1950).

BARTHE, E. Tableaux analytiques illustrés des Coléoptères de la faune franco-rhénane. Various parts, Misc. Ent. Castenet-Tolosan, vols. 31, and later (1929-).

BLACKWELDER, R. E. Fourth Supplement to Leng Catalogue of Coleoptera of America. 146 pp. J. D. Sherman, Mt. Vernon, N. Y. (1939).
  Checklist of the Coleopterous Insects of Mexico, Central America, the West Indies, and South America. 5 Parts. Bull. U. S. Nat. Mus., No. 185, 925 pp. (1944-47).
  Fifth Supplement to Leng Catalogue of Coleoptera of America. 87 pp. J. D. Sherman, Mt. Vernon, N. Y. (1948).

BLATCHLEY, W. S. Coleoptera or Beetles of Indiana. Nature Publishing Co., Indianapolis (1910).

BÖVING, A. G. Classification of Beetles According to Larval Characters. Bull. Brooklyn Ent. Soc., 24, pp. 55-80 (1929).

BRADLEY, J. C. Manual of the Genera of Beetles of America North of Mexico. Daw, Illston & Co., Ithaca, 360 pp. (1930).
  Classification of Coleoptera. Coleopterists' Bull., 1, pp. 75-85, 1 pl. (1947).

BROUN, T. Manual of New Zealand Coleoptera. 1566 pp. Wellington (1880-93).

BRUCH, C. Catálogo de los Coleópteros de Argentina. Rev. Mus. la Plata, 19 (several parts) (1915).

CAILLOT, H. Fauna dichotomique des Coléoptères de Provence. Ann. Mus. Hist. Nat. Marseille, 23, pp. 1-174 (1930).

CALWER, C. G. Käferbuch. 6th edition, 1390 pp., Stuttgart (1916).

CASEY, T. L. Memoirs on the Coleoptera, 1-11, Lancaster, Pa. (1910-24). (Some parts are listed separately). (Deals with various groups of North American Coleoptera).

CHAGNON, G. Contribution à l'étude des Coléoptères de la province de Québec. Nat. Canad., 60, pp. 166-178, 202-213, 289-302, 319-330, 343-351, 2 pls., 4 figs. (1933); ibid., 61, pp. 18-26, 84-95, 99-110, 137-157, 182-198, 215-230, 269-282, 309-319, 85 figs. (1934).

Dibb, J. R. Field Book of British Beetles with Keys to Genera and Species. 197 pp. Browne & Sons, Hull, England (1948).

Fleutiaux, E., et al. Coléoptères des Antilles. Faun. Emp. Franç., 240 pp., 259 figs. (1947).

Forbes, W. T. M. The Wing-venation of Coleoptera. Ann. Ent. Soc. America, 15, pp. 328–352 (1922).
    The Wing-folding Patterns of the Coleoptera. Journ. New York Ent. Soc. 34, pp. 42–68; 91–138 (1926).

Fowler, W. W. British Coleoptera. 6 vols. London (1887–1913).
    Coleoptera, General Introduction and Cicindelidæ and Paussidæ. Fauna of British India (1912).

Gahan, C. J. and others. Coleoptera of India. Fauna of British India, 4 vols. (1906–1912). (An extensive work, covering a part of the coleopterous fauna of this region).

Ganglbauer, L. Die Käfer von Mitteleuropa. Vienna, 4 vols., (1892–1904). (Adephaga, Staphyliniformia and Clavicornia).

Gemminger, M. and B. Harold. Catalogus Coleopterorum. 12 vols., 3986 pp. Monaco (1868–76).

Guignot, F. Les Hydrocanthares de France. 1057 pp., 7 pls., 558 figs. Frères Douladoure, Toulouse (1931–33).

Hansen, V. Blødvinger, Klannere (Coleoptera). Danmarks Fauna, 44, pp. 1–192, 96 figs. (1938).

Hatch, M. H. Systematic Index to Keys for the Determination of Nearctic Coleoptera. Journ. New York Ent. Soc., 35, pp. 279–306. (Supplementary to the bibliography in Leng's catalogue).

Hayward, R. Classification of the Families of Coleoptera of North America. Trans. American Ent. Soc., 34, pp. 13–65 (1908).

Henshaw, S. Bibliography, in "Synopsis of North American Coleoptera." Appendix to Leconte and Horn, 1883, pp. 535–552 (1883).

Hinton, H. E. Monograph of Beetles Affecting Stored Products. 443 pp., 505 figs. British Mus. Nat. Hist., London (1945).

Horn, G. H. Coleoptera of Baja California. Proc. California Acad. Sci. (2), 4, pp. 302–449 (1895); 5, pp. 225–295 (1896); 6, pp. 367–381 (1897).

Houlbert, C. Encyclopédie Scientifique. Les Coléoptères d'Europe, France et Régions voisins. Paris (1922). (A continuing series).

Houlbert, C. and E. Barthe. Tableaux analytiques des Coléoptères de la faune franco-rhénane. Famille 84. Scarabeides. Misc. Ent., 34, pp. 49–96, 10 figs.; Ibid., pp. 129–160 (1933–35).

Hudson, G. V. New Zealand Beetles and their Larvæ. 236 pp., 17 pls. (1934).

Jeannel, R. Coléoptères. In Grassé, Traité de Zoologie, 9, pp. 771–1077, 346 figs. (1949).

Jeannel, R. and R. Paulian. Morphologie abdominale des Coléoptères et systematique de l'ordre. Rev. franç. Ent., 11, pp. 66–110; 131 figs. (1944).

Joy, N. H. British Beetles. xi + 143 pp., 21 figs. F. Warne & Co., London (1933).

Junk, W. Coleopterorum Catalogus. Berlin, and later, Lochem, Holland. (1910–). (The parts are listed separately under the families.)

Lacordaire, J. T. Genera des Coléoptères. 13 vols., Paris (1854–76).

Lameere, A. Classification des Coléoptères. Ann. Soc. Ent. Belgique, 44, pp. 355–377 (1900).

Précis de Zoologie, Coléoptères. Publ. Inst. zool. Torley-Rousseau, 5, pp. 273–395, 143 figs. (1938).

LECONTE, J. L. and G. H. HORN. Classification of the Coleoptera of North America. Smithsonian Misc. Coll., No. 507 (1883). (With an extensive list of literature on North American Coleoptera).

LEECH, H. B. Contributions toward a Knowledge of the Insect Fauna of Lower California. No. 11. Haliplidæ, Dytiscidæ, Gyrinidæ, Hydrophilidæ, Limnebiidæ. Proc. California Acad. Sci., (4)24, pp. 375–483 (1948).

LENG, C. W. Catalogue of the Coleoptera of America North of Mexico. J. D. Sherman, Mount Vernon, N. Y. (1920). (With a complete bibliography of the North American Coleoptera).

LENG, C. W. and A. J. MUTCHLER. Water Beetles (Dytiscidæ, Hydrophilidæ and Parnidæ) of Florida. Bull. American Mus. Nat. Hist., 38, pp. 73–116 (1918).

LENG, C. W., A. J. MUTCHLER and R. E. BLACKWELDER. Supplements to the Catalogue of Coleoptera of America. 1. 1919–24, 78 pp., (1927); 2 and 3. 1925–32, 112 pp. (1933); 4. 1933–38, 146 pp. (1939); 5. 1939–47, 87 pp. (1948).

LUCAS, R. Catalogus generum et subgenerum Coleopterorum. (Catalogue of such genera and subgenera as have been treated in the Genera Insectorum and the Catalogus Coleopterorum, Junk). Pt. 1, 696 pp., Berlin (1920).

LUIGIONI, P. I. Coleotteri d'Italia. [Catalogue]. Mem. Acad. Nuovi Lincei, (2)13, pp. 1–1160 (1929).

MANSOUR, K. On the Phylogenetic Classification of the Coleoptera. Bull. Soc. ent. Egypte, 17, pp. 190–203, 8 figs. (1933).

MEIXNER, J. Coleopteroidea. In Kükenthal, Handbuch Zoologie, 4, Heft 2, Lief. 2, pp. 1037–1132, 104 figs. (1934).

MIWA, Y. Systematic Catalogue of Formosan Coleoptera. Rept. Dept. Agric. Taihoku, Formosa, No. 55, xi + 359 pp. (1931).

PERRIER, R. and J. DELPHY. Faune de la France en tableaux synoptiques illustrés. 2me. édition. 6, Coléoptères (deuxième partie). Librairie Delagrave, Paris. 230 pp., 1100 figs. (1937).

PERRIER, R. et al. Coléoptères de la France. Faune de France, 5, 192 pp., 894 figs.; 6, 230 pp., 1100 figs. (1935–37).

REITTER, E. Fauna Germanica. Käfer. 5 vols., Stuttgart (1908–16).

REITTER, E. and others. Bestimmungs-Tabellen der europäischen Coleopteren. (About one hundred parts of this series have appeared in various journals. We are unable to cite them here, but references are contained in the Zoological Record and the Tierwelt Mitteleuropas.)

SCHEERPELTZ, O. and A. WINKLER. Coleoptera. In Tierwelt Mitteleuropas, 5, Lief. 2, pp. XII, 1–272 (1930).

SCHENKLING, S. and W. JUNK. Coleopterorum Catalogus. W. Junk, Berlin, (A complete synonymic catalogue of the Coleoptera of the World being published in parts by various authors, and we have listed the parts separately). (1910–40). Supplements to some parts have been issued and more will follow.

SCHULTZE, W. A Catalogue of Philippine Coleoptera. Philippine Journ. Sci., 11D, pp. 1–194 (1916).

SHARP, D., G. C. CHAMPION and others. Coleoptera. In Biologia Centrali-Americana. 7 vols. (1887–1909).

SHARP, D. and R. C. L. PERKINS. Coleoptera. In Fauna Hawaiiensis, 2, pt. 3 (1900).

WINKLER, A. Catalogus Coleopterorum regionis palæarcticæ. 1392 pp., Winkler and Wagner, Vienna (1924–30).

YAKOBSON, G. G. Key to Beetles of Russia (in Russian). Moscow and Leningrad Govt. Pub., 522 pp. (1927).

ADEPHAGA

AHLWARTH, K. Gyrinidæ. Coleop. Cat. Junk, pt. 21, 42 pp. (1910).

ANDREWES, H. E. Carabidæ. Fauna of British India, 1, 431 pp. (1929); 2, 323 pp. (1935).

Carabidæ. Catalogue of Indian Insects, Pt. 18, xii + 369 pp., Govt. India Centr. Publication Branch (1930).

Catalogue of the Coleoptera of Sumatra. Tijdschr. Ent., 76, pp. 319–382 (1933).

ARNOLD, W. Bestimmungstabellen europäischen Cicindelidæ. Koleopt. Rundsch., 25, pp. 113–124, 2 figs. (1939).

Bestimmungstabellen europäischen Carabidæ. Koleopt. Rundsch., 25, pp. 125–200 (1939).

ARROW, G. J. Rhysodidæ with Key to Known Species. Proc. Roy. Soc. London B, 11, pp. 171–183 (1942).

ATKINSON, E. T. Catalogue of Oriental Carabidæ. Journ. Roy. Asiatic Soc., 58, pp. 1–126 (1889).

BÄNNINGER, M. Monograph der Subtribus Scaritina (Carabidæ). Deutsch. ent. Zeit., 1939, pp. 126–161 (1939).

Ueber die australischen Tribus Pamborini, Ozaenini und die Subtribus Carenina (Carabidæ). Mitt. münchner. ent. Ges., 33, pp. 654–670 (1943).

BALFOUR-BROWNE, F. British Water Beetles. I. (Dytiscidæ and Hydrophilidæ). xix + 375 pp., 5 pls., 89 figs. Ray Soc., London (1940).

Genera of the Gyrinoidea and Their Genotypes. Ann. Mag. Nat. Hist., (11)21, pp. 103–111 (1945).

BARBER, G. W. and W. O. ELLIS. Cupedidæ of North America. Journ. New York Ent. Soc., 28, pp. 197–208 (1920).

BARTHE, E. and R. TARD. Cicindelidæ. Coléoptères de la faune franco-rhénane. Misc. Ent., 33, pp. 1–41, 23 figs. (1931).

BASILEWSKY, P. Carabidæ du Congo Belge. Bull. Mus. Hist. Nat. Belgique, 24, No. 5, 48 pp.; No. 33, 38 pp.; No. 52, 15 pp. (1948).

African Carabidæ. Mem. Soc. Ent. Belgique, 25, 57–105 (1948).

BRITTON, E. B. The Carabidæ of New Zealand. Part I.-Pterostichini. Trans. Proc. Roy. Soc. New Zealand, 69, pp. 473–508, 8 pls. (1940); Part II. Lebiini and Pentagonicini. Proc. Roy. Ent. Soc. London, B, 10, pp. 185–196, 11 figs. (1941).

Harpalini, Lebiini and Bembidiini in Hawaii. Proc. Hawaiian Ent. Soc., 13, pp. 235–254, 28 figs. (1947).

Cicindelidæ and Carabidæ from Southwestern Arabia. Exped. to Southwest Arabia, 1, pp. 87–125, British Mus. Nat. Hist. (1948).

CAZIER, M. A. Tiger Beetles of Lower California. American Mus. Novit., No. 1382, 28 pp. (1948).

CSIKI, E. Carabidæ, Carabinæ. Coleop. Cat. Junk, pts. 91, 92, 127, 648 pp. (1927–33).

    Carabidæ, Harpalinæ. Coleopt. Cat. Junk, pts. 97, 98, 104, 112, 115, 121, 124, 126, 1933 pp. (1928–1933).

DARLINGTON, P. J., JR. New West Indian Carabidæ, with a List of the Cuban Species. Psyche, 41, pp. 66–131, 1 pl. (1934).

    American Patrobini. Ent. Americana, 18, pp. 135–182, 5 pls., 4 figs. (1938).

    Paussid Beetles. Trans. American Ent. Soc., 86, pp. 47–142, 206 figs., 3 maps (1950).

DESNEUX, J. Paussidæ. Gen. Insectorum, fasc. 35, 34 pp. (1905).

DUPUIS, P. Carabidæ, Metriinæ and Mystropominæ. Gen. Insectorum, fasc. 116, 4 pp. (1911).

    Carabidæ, Apotominæ. Gen. Insectorum, fasc. 117, 4 pp. (1911).

    Carabidæ, Psydrinæ. Gen. Insectorum, fasc. 123, 2 pp. (1911).

    Carabidæ, Opisthiinæ. Gen. Insectorum, fasc. 126, 2 pp. (1912).

    Carabidæ, Nothiphilinæ. Gen. Insectorum, fasc. 134, 7 pp. (1912).

    Carabidæ, Pentagonicinæ. Gen. Insectorum, fasc. 145, 4 pp. (1913).

    Carabidæ, Peleciinæ. Gen. Insectorum, fasc. 146, 4 pp. (1913).

    Carabidæ, Hexagoniinæ. Gen. Insectorum, fasc. 147, 4 pp. (1913).

FENG, H. T. Classification of Chinese Dytiscidæ. Peking Nat. Hist. Bull., 8, pp. 81–146, 2 pls. (1933).

GESTRO, R. Rhysodidæ. Coleop. Cat. Junk, 1, 11 pp. (1910).

    Cupedidæ, Paussidæ. Coleop. Cat. Junk, 5, 31 pp. (1910).

GROUVELLE, A. Synopsis des Rhysodides. Rev. Ent., 22, pp. 85–145 (1903).

HAMILTON, C. C. Morphology, Taxonomy and Ecology of Larvæ of Holarctic Tiger-beetles. Proc. U. S. Nat. Mus., 65, Art. 17, 87 pp., 12 pls. (1925).

HANSEN, V. Biller (Haliplidæ, Dytiscidæ, Gyrinidæ). Danmarks Fauna, 34, pp. 1–233, 119 figs. (1930).

    Biller. Sandspringere og løbebiller (Cicindelidæ og Carabidæ). Danmarks Fauna, 47, 380 pp., 70 figs. (1941).

HAYWARD, R. Revision of Bembidium of North America. Trans. American Ent. Soc., 24, pp. 32–143 (1897).

    Revision of North American Species of Tachys. Trans. American Ent. Soc., 26, pp. 191–238 (1900).

HEBERDEY, R. F. and J. MEIXNER. Die Adephagen der östlichen Hälfte der Ostalpen. Verh. zool.-bot. Ges. Wien, 83, pp. 1–164 (1933).

HELLER, K. M. Fauna Sumatrensis. Jacobsoniidæ. Suppl. Ent. 15, pp. 111–112 (1927); and Ibid., 14, p. 127 (1926).

HETSCHENKO, A. Jacobsoniidæ. Coleopt. Cat. Junk, pt. 108, 1 p. (1930).

HEYNES-WOOD, M. and C. DOVER. Cicindelidæ. Cat. Indian Ins. Govt. India, Centr. Pub. Branch, Calcutta, pt. 13 (1927).

HORN, W. Cicindelidæ. Coleop. Cat. Junk, pt. 86, 345 pp. (1926).

    List of the Cicindelidæ of North America. Trans. American Ent. Soc., 56, pp. 76–86 (1930).

    2,000 Zeichnungen von Cicindelidæ. Ent. Beihefte, 5, pp. 1–71, 90 pls. (1938).

HOULBERT, C. Faune entomologique armoricaine. Coléoptères. Hydrocarabiques. (Hydaticiformes). Bull. Soc. sci. Bretagne, 11, hors série, 147 pp., 116 figs. (1934).

JEANNEL, R. Monographie der Bathysciinæ. Arch. Zool., 63, pp. 1–436 (1924).
    Monographie des Trechinæ. Abeille, 32, pp. 221–550; 33, pp. 1–592, 35, pp. 1–808 (1926–30).
    Les Bembidiides endogés. Rev. franç. Ent., 3, pp. 241–396, 245 figs. (1937).
    Les Migadopides. Rev. franç. Ent., 5, pp. 1–55, 76 figs. (1938).
    Les Calosomes. Mem. Mus. Hist. nat. Paris, (N.S.) 13, pp. 1–240, 8 pls., 208 figs. (1940).
    Coléoptères carabiques. 2 Pts. Faune de France, 39, pp. 1–571; 40, pp. 573–1173 (1941–42).
    Coléoptères carabiques de la région malgache. I. Faune Emp. franç., 6, pp. 1–372, 168 figs., 4 pls. (1946).
    Pselaphides de l'Afrique orientale. 226 pp., 103 figs. (1949).
    Pselaphides du Congo Belge et du Ruanda-Urundi. 275 pp., 121 figs. (1949).

KOLBE, H. Die Paussiden Südamerikas. Ent. Mitt., 9, pp. 131–141 (1920).

LAPOUGE, G. V. Carabidæ, Carabinæ. Gen. Insectorum, fasc. 192, 289 pp. (1929–30); fasc. 192B, pp. 293–580 (1931).

LENG, C. W. Revision of Cicindelidæ of Boreal America. Trans. American Ent. Soc., 28, pp. 93–186 (1902).

LENG, C. W. and W. BEUTENMÜLLER. Handbook of Cicindelidæ and Carabidæ of Northeastern America. Journ. New York Ent. Soc., 2, 4 (1894–96). (Several parts).

LIEBKE, M. Revision der Amerikanischen Arten der Unterfamilie Colliurinæ. Mitt. Zool. Mus. Berlin, 15, pp. 649–726, 62 figs. (1930).
    Die Carabiden-Tribus Colliurini. Festschr. Embrik Strand, 4, pp. 37–141, 145 figs. (1938).

LIU, G. Synopsis of Genera of First Ten Families of Chinese Coleoptera. Peking Nat. Hist. Bull., 8, pp. 19–38 (1933).

MATHESON, R. The Haliplidæ of North America, North of Mexico. Journ. New York Ent. Soc., 20, pp. 156–193 (1912).

NOTMAN, H. Review of Pseudomorphidæ and Rearrangement of the Adephaga. Proc. U. S. Nat. Mus., 67, art. 14, 34 pp. (1925).

OCHS, G. Gyrinidæ of the Philippine Islands. Philippine Journ. Sci., 24, pp. 81–86 (1924).
    Gyrinidæ. Catalogue of Indian Insects, Pt. 19, Govt. India Central Publication Branch. ii + 29 pp. (1930).
    Checklist of Neotropical Gyrinoidea. Rev. Ent., Rio de Janeiro, 19, pp. 565–567 (1948).

OLSOUFIEFF, G. Les Cicindelides de Madagascar. Part 2. Mém. Acad. malgache, 20, pp. 31–76, 1 map. 3 pls., 27 figs. (1934).

PERINGUEY, L. Revision of South African Carabidæ. Ann. South African Mus., 23, pp. 579–659 (1926).

PESCHET, R. Dytiscidæ et Gyrinidæ des îles mascareignes. Ann. Soc. Ent. France, 86, pp. 1–56 (1917).

RÉGIMBART, M. Monographie des Gyrinides. Ann. Soc. Ent. France, (6) 2, pp. 379–458; 3, pp. 381–482 (1882–83).

Gyrinidæ. Gen. Insectorum, fasc. 1, 12 pp. (1902).

REICHENSPERGER, A. Die Paussiden Afrikas. Abh. Senckenb. naturf. Ges., 479, 33 pp., 1 pl. (1948).

RIVALIER, E. Les Cicindèles du genre Lophyra. Rev. franç. Ent., 15, pp. 49–74 (1948).

ROESCHKE, H. Monographie der Tribus Cychrini (Carabidæ). Ann. Mus. Hist. Nat. Hungarici, 5, pp. 9–277 (1907).

ROUSSEAU, E. Carabidæ, Anthiinæ. Gen. Insectorum, fasc. 39, 19 pp. (1906).
Carabidæ, Mormolycinæ. Gen. Insectorum, fasc. 40, 5 pp. (1906).
Omophronidæ. Gen. Insectorum, fasc. 83, 5 pp. (1908).
Carabidæ, Promecognathinæ. Gen. Insectorum, fasc, 84, 4 pp. (1908).
Carabidæ, Pamborinæ. Gen. Insectorum, fasc. 85, 3 pp. (1908).
Carabidæ, Lorocerinæ. Gen. Insectorum, fasc. 86, 4 pp. (1908).

SANPERE, J. M. Contribución al estudio de los Carábidos de Sáhara español (Carabidæ). Eos, 23, pp. 103–164, 5 pls., 8 figs., 1 map (1947).

SHARP, D. On Aquatic Coleoptera or Dytiscidæ. Sci. Trans. Roy. Dublin Soc., (2), 2, pp. 179–1003 (1882).

SLOANE, T. G. The Classification of the Family Carabidæ. Trans. London Ent. Soc., 1923, pp. 234–250 (1923).

STRANEO, S. L. Revisione dei Cælostromini africani (Carabidæ). Mem. Soc. ent. ital., 21, pp. 21–164, 128 figs. (1942).

VAN DORSSELAER, R. Dytiscidæ and Haliplidæ of Belgium. Bull. Soc. Ent. Belgique, 1, pp. 68–119 (1919).

ZIMMERMANN, A. Die Schwimmkäfer des Deutschen entomologischen Museums, Berlin. Arch. f. Naturg., Jahrg. 83, pp. 68–249 (1917).
Amphizoidæ, Dytiscidæ, Haliplidæ and Hygrobiidæ. Coleop. Cat. Junk, pt. 71, 326 pp. (1920).
Die Halipliden der Welt. Entom. Blätt., 20, pp. 1–16 et seq. (several parts) (1924).
Monographie der paläarktischen Dytisciden (Noterinæ, Laccophilinæ, Hydroporinæ). Koleopt. Rundschau, 16, pp. 35–118 (1930); ibid., 19, pp. 153–193 (1933).

ZIMMERMANN, A. and L. GSCHWENDTNER. Monographie der paläarktischen Dytisciden (Colymbetinæ). Koleopt. Rundschau, 22, pp. 81–102 (1936); Ibid., 24, pp. 33–76 (1939).

HYDROPHILOIDEA

GUIGNOT, F. Coléoptères Hydrocanthares. Faune de France, 48, 287 pp. (1947).

HANSEN, V. Hydrophilidæ. Danmarks Fauna, 36, pp. 1–164 (1931).

KNISCH, A. Die exotischen Hydrophiliden des Deutschen Entomologischen Museums. Arch. f. Naturg., Jahrg. 85 A, Heft 8, pp. 55–88 (1923).
Hydrophilidæ. Coleop. Cat. Junk, pt. 79, 306 pp. (1924).

D'ORCHYMONT, A. Classification des Palpicornia. Ann. Soc. Ent. France, 88, pp. 105–168 (1919) and Rev. Zool. Africaine, 6, pp. 163–168 (1919).
Palpicornia. Cat. Indian Ins. Govt. India, Centr. Pub. Branch, Calcutta, pt. 14, 145 pp. (1927).

RÉGIMBART, M. Revision des Grands Hydrophiles. Ann. Soc. Ent. France, 1902, pp. 188–232 (1902).

STAPHYLINOIDEA

ARNETT, R. H. Revision of the Nearctic Silphini and Nicrophorini. Journ. New York Ent. Soc., **52**, pp. 1–24 (1944).

BERNHAUER, M. and K. SCHUBERT. Staphylinidæ. Coleop. Cat. Junk, pts. **19, 29, 40, 57, 67, 82**, 988 pp. (1910–26).

BLACKWELDER, R. E. Morphology and Subfamilies of Staphylinidæ. Smithsonian Misc. Coll., **94**, 102 pp., 30 figs. (1936).

     Generic Revision of Tribe Pæderini. Proc. U. S. Nat. Mus., **87**, No. 3069, pp. 93–135 (1939).

     Monograph of the West Indian Staphylinidæ. Bull. U. S. Nat. Mus., No. **182**, vii + 658 pp., 19 maps, 3 figs. (1943).

BRUNDIN, L. Microdota-Studien. Ent. Tidskr., **69**, pp. 8–66, 13 pls. (1948).

CALVERT, G. B. Monografia de los Scydmænidæ de Chile. Bol. Mus. nac. Chile, **16**, pp. 131–142 (1937).

CAMERON, M. Indomalayan Staphylinidæ. (New Species of Staphylinidæ from Singapore with Catalogue). Trans. Ent. Soc. London, 1920, pp. 347–413 (1921).

     Staphylinidæ. Cat. Indian Ins. Govt. India, Centr. Pub. Branch, Calcutta, pt. 6, 126 pp. (1925).

     Staphylinidæ. Fauna Sumatrensis. Tijdschr. Ent., **73**, 325–348 (1930).

     Staphylinidæ. Fauna of British India, 5 vols., 2272 pp., 12 pls., 378 figs. (1930–39).

CASEY, T. L. Synopsis of Scaphidiidæ. Ann. New York Acad. Sci., **7**, pp. 281–606 (1893).

     Synopsis of Scydmænidæ. Ann. New York Acad. Sci., **9**, pp. 285–548 (1897).

     Synopsis (partial) of North American Pselaphidæ. Ann. New York Acad. Sci., **9**, pp. 550–630 (1897).

     Revision of Pæderini (Staphylinidæ). Trans. Acad. Sci. St. Louis, **15**, pp. 17–248 (1905).

     Partial Revision of Aleocharinæ and Xantholinini (Staphylinidæ). Trans. Acad. Sci., St. Louis, **16**, pp. 125–434 (1906).

CSIKI, E. Scaphidiidæ. Coleop. Cat. Junk, pt. **13**, 21 pp. (1910).

     Platypsyllidæ. Coleop. Cat. Junk, pt. **18**, 35 pp. (1910).

     Scydmænidæ. Coleop. Cat. Junk, pt. **70**, 106 pp. (1919).

DESNEUX, J. Platypsyllidæ. Gen. Insectorum, fasc. 41, 9 pp. (1906).

FENYES, A. Staphylinidæ, Aleocharinæ. Gen. Insectorum, fasc. 173, 453 pp. (1918–1921).

GRIDELLI, E. La sistematica degli Xantholinini. Atti Mus. Stor. Nat. Trieste, **16**, pp. 65–80, 97–130 (1947).

HATCH, M. H. Studies on the Silphinæ. Journ. New York Ent. Soc., **35**, pp. 331–370 (1927).

     Liodidæ, Clambidæ. Coleop. Cat. Junk, pt. **105**, 100 pp. (1929).

HETSCHKO, A. Thorictidæ. Coleop. Cat. Junk, pt. **83**, 15 pp. (1926).

HORN, G. H. Synopsis of the Silphidæ of the United States. Trans. American Ent. Soc., **8**, pp. 219–322 (1880).

     Synopsis of the Dascyllidæ of the United States. Trans. American Ent. Soc., **8**, pp. 73–114 (1880).

JEANNEL, R. Les Catops de France. Rev. franç. Ent., **1**, pp. 2–24, 118 figs. (1934).

Monographie des Catopidæ. Mem. Mus. Hist. nat. Paris, (N.S.) **1**, 433 pp., 1027 figs. (1936).

Pselaphides. Faune de France, **53**, 421 pp. (1950).

JEANNEL, R. and M. H. Hatch. Silphidæ. Coleop. Cat. Junk, pts. **60, 95**, 244 pp. (1914–28).

JOHANSEN, J. P. Danish Staphylinidæ (in Danish). 600 pp. Copenhagen (1914).

McGRATH, R. M. and M. H. HATCH. Sphæritidæ and Histeridæ of Washington. Univ. Washington Publ. Biol., **10**, pp. 47–90 (1941).

OLSUFIEF, G. Synopsis of Leptinidæ. Rev. Russe Ent., **18**, pp. 81–90 (1923).

PARK, O. Study in Neotropical Pselaphidæ. Northwestern Univ. Stud. Biol. Sci. Med., No. **1**, x + 403 pp., 21 pls. (1942).

Pselaphidæ of Mexico. Bull. Chicago Acad. Sci., **7**, pp. 171–233 (1943).

Pselaphidæ from Brazil, Colombia, and Mexico, with Keys to Mexican Genera and Species. Ibid., **7**, pp. 277–327, 7 pls. (1944).

Further Studies in Pselaphidæ of Mexico and Guatemala. Ibid., **7**, pp. 331–443 (1945).

Checklist of Pselaphidæ of Guatemala. Ibid., **7**, pp. 457–462 (1946).

PORTEVIN, G. Revision des Necrophorini du Globe. Bull. Mus. Hist. Nat. Paris (1923–25). (Various parts).

Les grands Nécrophages du Globe. Encycl. Ent., pt. 6, 270 pp. (1926).

RAFFRAY, A. Australian Pselaphidæ. Proc. Linn. Soc. New South Wales, **25**, pp. 131–249 (1900).

Pselaphidæ. Gen. Insectorum, fasc. 64, 487 pp. (1908).

Pselaphidæ. Coleop. Cat. Junk, pt. **27**, 222 pp. (1911).

SCHEERPELTZ, O. Staphylinidæ. Coleopt. Cat. Junk, pt. **130**, pp. 1501–1881 (1934).

Bestimmungstabellen europäischen Käfer (Staphylinidæ). Koleopt. Rundsch., **25**, pp. 81–112; **26**, sep., 93 pp., 3 figs. (1939–40).

SCHENKLING, S. Sphæritidæ. Coleopt. Cat. Junk, pt. **117**, 2 pp. (1931).

SEEVERS, C. H. A New Subfamily of Beetles Parasitic on Mammals. Staphylinidæ, Amblyopininæ. Publ. Field Mus. Zool. Ser., **28**, pp. 155–172, 3 pls. (1944).

SEEVERS, C. H. and H. S. DYBAS. Synopsis of Limulodidæ. Ann. Ent. Soc. America, **36**, pp. 546–586, 5 pls. (1943).

VINSON, J. The Scaphidiidæ of Mauritius. Mauritius Inst. Bull., **2**, pp. 177–209, 23 figs. (1943).

CUCUJOIDEA

BÖVING, A. G. Remarks on Taxonomy of Cucujidæ. Zoologica, New York, **3**, pp. 197–221 (1921).

CASEY, T. L. Revision of Cucujidæ of North America. Trans. American Ent. Soc., **11**, pp. 69–112 (1884).

Classification of Cucujidæ. Mem. Coleop., pt. 7, pp. 111 et seq. (1915).

HETSCHENKO, A. Cucujidæ. Coleopt. Cat. Junk, pt. **109**, pp. 1–120 (1930).

RITSEMA, C. Helotidæ. Coleop. Cat. Junk, pt. **34**, pp. 104–106 (1911).

ZIKAN, J. F. Genus Parandra. Rev. Soc. Ent. Argentina, **14**, pp. 22–50 (1948).

CANTHAROIDEA

BLAISDELL, F. E. Generic Synopsis and Generic Revision of the Tribe Dasytini of North America. Trans. American Ent. Soc., **64**, pp. 1–31, 2 pls. (1938).

CHAMPION, G. C. Revision of Mexican and Central American Malachiidæ. Trans. London Ent. Soc., **1914**, pp. 13–127 (1914).

Revision of Mexican and Central American Chauliognathinæ. Trans. London Ent. Soc., **1914**, pp. 126–168 (1914).

Revision of the Mexican and Central American Telephoridæ. Trans. London Ent. Soc., **1915**, pp. 16–146 (1915).

CHAPIN, E. A. Classification of the Philippine Components of the Coleopterous Family Cleridæ. Philippine Journ. Sci., **24**, pp. 159–286 (1924).

DALLAS, E. D. Sinopsis de la Familia Karumiidæ. Rev. chilena Hist. nat., **33**, pp. 386–394, 2 pls. (1929).

GREINER, J. Malachiidæ. Coleopt. Cat. Junk, pt. **159**, 199 pp. (1937).

KLEINE, R. Die Lyciden der Philippinen-Inseln. Philippine Journ. Sci., **31**, pp. 33–109 (1926).

Coleoptera, Lycidæ. Nova Guinea, Leiden, **15**, pp. 91–195 (1926).

Die Lycidenfauna Javas. Treubia, **13**, pp. 245–290, 26 figs. (1931).

Brenthidæ and Lycidæ of China. Lingnan Sci. Journ., **7**, pp. 493–496 (1931).

Bestimmungstabelle der Lycidæ. Bestimm. Tab. europ. Col., Heft **123**, 90 pp. (1942).

KNULL, J. N. Cleridæ of Ohio. 82 pp., 13 pls. Columbus (1951).

LECONTE, J. L. Synopsis of Lampyridæ of the United States. Trans. American Ent. Soc., **9**, pp. 15–72 (1881).

LENG, C. W. and A. J. MUTCHLER. The Lycidæ, Lampyridæ and Cantharidæ of the West Indies. Bull. American Mus. Nat. Hist., **46**, pp. 413–499 (1922).

MJÖBERG, E. "Trilobite Larvæ" (Drilidæ). Psyche, **32**, pp. 119–154, 2 pls. (1925).

OLIVIER, E. Lampyridæ. Gen. Insectorum, fasc. 53, 74 pp. (1907).

Lampyridæ and Drilidæ. Coleop. Cat. Junk, pts. **9**, 68 pp.; **10**, 10 pp. (1910).

PIC, M. Étude des Malacodermes de l'Indochine. Fauna Indochine Français, fasc. 6, pp. 7–63 (1923).

Lampyridæ, Phengodinæ. Coleop. Cat. Junk, pt. **94**, 8 pp. (1927).

Drilidæ (Karumiidæ). Coleop. Cat. Junk, pt. **94**, 8 pp. (1927).

Dasytidæ, Melyrinæ. Coleop. Cat. Junk, pt. **103**, 32 pp. (1929).

SCHENKLING, S. Cleridæ. Gen. Insectorum, fasc. 13, 124 pp. (1903).

Cleridæ. Coleop. Cat. Junk, **23**, 174 pp. (1910).

Lymexylidæ, Telegeusidæ and Micromalthidæ. Coleop. Cat. Junk, pt. **64**, 14 pp. (1915).

WITTMER, W. Catalogue des Drilidæ. Rev. Soc. Ent. Argentina, **12**, pp. 203–221 (1944).

WOLCOTT, A. B. Generic Review of Subfamily Phyllobæninæ. Journ. New York Ent. Soc., **52**, pp. 121–152 (1944).

Catalogue of North American Beetles of the Family Cleridæ. Fieldiana, Zool., **32**, pp. 61–105 (1947).

MORDELLOIDEA

ARNETT, R. H. Preliminary Key to the Genera of Œdemeridæ of the World. Coleopt. Bull., **2**, pp. 13–14 (1948).

BETREM, J. G. Die Tribus der Horiini der Meloidæ. Treubia, **14**, pp. 85–101, 1 pl., 7 figs. (1932).

BLAIR, K. G. A Revision of the Pyrochroidæ. Ann. Mag. Nat. Hist., (8) **13**, pp. 310–326 (1914).

South African Œdemeridæ. Ann. South African Mus., **23**, pp. 353–375 (1926).

Pythidæ and Pyrochroidæ. Coleop. Cat. Junk, pt. **99**, 55 pp. (1928).

BORCHMANN, F. Eurystethidæ. Coleop. Cat. Junk, pt. **2**, 32 pp. (1910).

Meloidæ and Cephaloidæ. Coleop. Cat. Junk, pt. **69**, 208 pp. (1917).

CASEY, T. Synopsis of Anthicidæ of United States. Ann. New York Acad. Sci., **8**, pp. 624–838 (1895).

North American Cephaloidæ. Ent. News, **9**, pp. 193–195 (1898).

CROS, A. Les Meloidæ algériens. 6e Congr. int. Ent. Madrid, 1935, pp. 311–338 (1940).

CSIKI, E. Rhipiphoridæ. Coleop. Cat. Junk, pt. **54**, 29 pp. (1913).

Mordellidæ. Coleop. Cat. Junk, pt. **63**, 84 pp. (1915).

DENIER, P. C. L. Documentos para la clasificación de los Melóidos americanos. Bol. Mens. Minist. Agr. Nac. Argentina, **32**, pp. 36–52 (1933).

ERMISCH, K. Die Gattungen der Mordelliden der Welt. Ent. Blätt., **45–46**, pp. 34–92 (1949–50).

GRESSITT, J. L. Rhipiphoridæ from South China. Ann. Ent. Soc. America, **34**, pp. 525–536 (1941).

HORN, G. H. Œdemeridæ of Boreal America. Proc. California Acad. Sci., (2), **6**, pp. 382–421 (1896).

LILJEBLAD, E. Monograph of the Family Mordellidæ of North America. Misc. Publ. Zool. Univ. Mich., No. **62**, 229 pp., 7 pls. (1945).

MÉQUIGNON, A. Contribution à l'étude des Mordellides paléarctiques. Rev. franç. Ent., **13**, pp. 52–76, 18 figs. (1946).

MUTCHLER, A. J. and H. B. WEISS. Meloidæ of New Jersey. Circ. New Jersey State Dept. Agric., No. 76, 19 pp. (1924).

PIC, M. Euglenidæ. Gen. Insectorum, fasc. 8, 14 pp. (1902).

Euglenidæ. Coleop. Cat. Junk, pt. 14, 25 pp. (1910).

Pedilidæ. Coleop. Cat. Junk, pt. **26**, 27 pp. (1911).

Anthicidæ. Coleop. Cat. Junk, pt. **36**, 102 pp. (1911).

RAY, E. Studies on North American Mordellidæ, V. Pan-Pacific Ent., **23**, pp. 121–131, 15 figs. (1947).

RIVNAY, E. Revision of Rhipiphoridæ of North and Central America. Mem. American Ent. Soc., **6**, pp 1–48, 4 pls. (1929).

SCHENKLING, S. Œdemeridæ. Coleop. Cat. Junk, pt. **65**, 82 pp. (1915).

SMITH, J. B. Synopsis of Mordellidæ of the United States. Trans. American Ent. Soc., **10**, pp. 73–100 (1882).

SUMACOV, G. G. Catalogue des Mylabrina (Meloidæ) paléarctiques. Sitzungsber. naturf. Ges. Tartu, **37**, pp. 1–114 (1931).

VAN DYKE, E. C. Genera of North American Meloidæ. Univ. California Publ. Ent., **4**, pp. 395–474 (1928).

ELATEROIDEA

BEER, F. M. and M. H. HATCH. Buprestidæ of Washington. Univ. Washington Publ. Biol., **10**, pp. 93–142 (1941).

BLANCHARD, F. Revision of North American Throscidæ. Trans. American Ent. Soc. **43**, pp. 1–26 (1917).

BONVOULOIR, H. Monographie des Eucnémides. Ann. Soc. Ent. France, (4), **10**, supplement, 907 pp. (1871–75).

BURGEON, L. Catalogues de la faune entomologique du Congo belge. Coléoptères. — Buprestidæ. Ann. Mus. Congo belge, Zool., (3) Sect. ii, **5**, pp. 121–276 (1941).

BUYSSON, H. DU. Tableaux des Elateridæ de la faune franco-rhénane. Misc. Ent. Castanet-Tolosan, pp. 1–208 (1910–26).

CANDÈZE, E. DE. Monographie des Élatérides. 4 vols. and 3 suppl. Liège (1857–81).

CHAMBERLIN, W. J. Catalogue of the Buprestidæ of North America, North of Mexico. Corvallis, Oreg. 289 pp. (1926).

DALLA TORRE, K. W. Cebrionidæ. Coleop. Cat. Junk, pt. **25**, 18 pp. (1911). Cebrionidæ. Gen. Insectorum, fasc. 127, 17 pp. (1912).

DIETRICH, H. Elateridæ of New York State. Mem. Cornell Agric. Expt. Sta., No. **269**, 79 pp., 4 pls. (1945).

FISHER, W. S. Revision of West Indian Buprestidæ. Proc. U. S. Nat. Mus., **65**, art. 9, pp. 1–207 (1925).

Revision of North American Buprestid Beetles of the Tribe Chrysobothrini. Misc. Publ. U. S. Dept. Agric., No. **470**, 274 pp., 126 figs. (1942).

FLEUTHIAUX, E. Études sur les Mélasidæ. Ann. Soc. Ent. Belgique, **60**, pp. 93–104 (1920); **61**, p. 23, etc. (1921).

Catalogue raisonné des Mélasidæ des Îles Philippines. Ann. Soc. Ent. France, **95**, pp. 29–90 (1926).

Un genre des Eucnemididæ paléarctiques. Rev. franç. Ent., **2**, pp. 1–18 (1935).

Les Elatérides de l'Indochine française. Septième partie. XVII. — Subfamily Agriotinæ. Ann. Soc. ent. France, **108**, pp. 121–148 (1939).

Revision des Eucnémides de l'Indochine française. Notes Ent. chinoise, **11**, pp. 1–68; pp. 233–420 (1947).

HORN, G. H. Synopsis of Throscidæ of the United States. Trans. American Ent. Soc., **12**, pp. 198–208 (1885).

Monograph of Eucneminæ and Cerophytinæ of the United States. Trans. American Ent. Soc., **13**, pp. 5–38 (1886).

HYSLOP, J. A. Genotypes of Elateridæ of World. Proc. U. S. Nat. Mus., **58**, pp. 621–680 (1921).

KERREMANS, C. Buprestidæ. Gen. Insectorum, fasc. 12, 338 pp. (1903). Monographie des Buprestidæ. 7 vols. Brussels (1906–14).

KNULL, J. N. The Buprestidæ of Pennsylvania. Ohio Univ. Studies, **2**, No. 2, 71 pp. (1927).

OBENBERGER, J. Revision der paläarktischen Trachydinen (Buprestidæ) mit Beschreibungen exotischer Arten. Arch. Naturgesch., **82A** (11), pp. 1–73, 30 figs. (1916).

Revision of Pachyseloides Trachides (Buprestidæ) of America. Sbornik Ent. Odd. Narod. Praze, **13** (20), pp. 3–149 (1925).

Buprestidæ. Coleop. Cat. Junk, pts. **84, 111, 132, 143, 152, 157,** 1714 pp. (1926–37).

OLAVE, L. E. Revisión de los Buprestidos chilenos. Rev. chilena Hist. nat., **39,** pp. 349–376, 2 pls., 3 figs. (1935).

PIC, M. Rhipiceratidæ. Coleop. Cat. Junk, pt. **81,** 13 pp. (1925).

SCHENKLING, S. Elateridæ. Coleop. Cat. Junk, pts. **80** and **88,** 636 pp. (1925–27).

Plastoceridæ. Coleop. Cat. Junk, pt. **93,** 11 pp. (1927).

Melasidæ. Coleop. Cat. Junk, pt. **96,** 110 pp. (1928).

Cerophytidæ. Coleop. Cat. Junk, pt. **101,** 30 pp. (1928).

SCHWARZ, O. Elateridæ. Gen. Insectorum, fasc. 46, 370 pp. (1906).

Plastoceridæ. Gen. Insectorum, fasc. 50, 10 pp. (1907).

Elateridæ, pt. Gen. Insectorum, fasc. 51, 4 pp. (1907).

THÉRY, A. Les Buprestides de l'Afrique du Nord. Mém. Soc. Sci. nat. Maroc, **9,** pp. 1–586, 2 pls., 167 figs. (1928).

Buprestides nouveaux d'Afrique. Bull. Soc. Sci. nat. Maroc, **9,** pp. 139–171 (1929).

Buprestides de l'Inde. Ann. Soc. Ent. Belgique, **11,** pp. 149–172 (1930).

Les espèces de Buprestidæ africaines de la tribu des Chrysobothrini sous-tribu des Actenodæ. Bull. Soc. Sci. nat. Maroc, **13,** pp. 234–253, 11 figs. (1933).

THOMAS, C. A. Elateridæ of Pennsylvania. Journ. New York Ent. Soc., **49,** pp. 233–263 (1941).

VAN DYKE, E. C. Buprestidæ of Lower California. Proc. California Acad. Sci., (4) **24,** pp. 97–132 (1942).

VAN EMDEN, F. Rhipiceratidæ (Sandalidæ). Ent. Blätt., **37,** various parts (1931).

DRYOPOIDEA

BARTHE, E. Dryopidæ. Misc. Ent., **30,** pp. 211–274 (1928).

BOLLOW, H. Monographie der palæarktischen Drvopiden. Mitt. münchner. Ent. Ges., **28,** pp. 147–187, 61 figs.; **29,** pp. 319–391, 4 pls., 157 figs.; **30,** pp. 24–70, 105 figs.; **31,** pp. 1–88, 84 figs. (1938–41).

CARTER, H. J. and E. H. ZECK. A Monograph of the Australian Dryopidæ. Australian Zool., **6,** pp. 50–72 (1929).

DELÈVE, J. Dryopidæ du Congo belge. II-III. Dryopinæ, Elminæ. Rev. Zool. Bot. africaine, **31,** pp. 351–375, 12 figs. (1938).

HINTON, H. E. Classification of the Dryopoidea. Trans. Roy. Ent. Soc. London, **89,** pp. 133–184, 105 figs. (1939).

Revision of Elmidæ of Mexico. Novitat. Zool., **42,** pp. 217–396, 401 figs. (1940).

HORN, G. H. Synopsis of Heteroceridæ of the United States. Trans. American Ent. Soc., **17,** pp. 1–17 (1890).

ZAITZEV, P. Dryopidæ, Georyssidæ and Heteroceridæ. Coleop. Cat. Junk, pt. **17,** 68 pp. (1910).

DASCYLLOIDEA

BARBER, H. S. Raspberry Fruit Worms [Byturidæ]. Misc. Publ. U. S. Dept. Agric., No. 468, pp. 1–13 (1942).

BORCHMANN, F. Alleculidæ. Coleop. Cat. Junk, pt. 3, 80 pp. (1910).

CARTER, H. J. Revision of the Australian Cistelidæ. Proc. Roy. Soc. Victoria, 28, pp. 52–104 (1915).

CASEY, T. L. Synopsis of North American Cistelidæ. Ann. New York Acad. Sci., 6, pp. 9–214 (1892).

    Descriptive Catalogue of American Byrrhidæ. Memoirs on the Coleoptera, No. 3, pp. 1–69 (1912).

DALLA TORRE, K. W. Byrrhidæ, Dermestidæ and Nosodendridæ. Coleop. Cat. Junk, pt. 33, 96 pp. (1911).

FALL, H. C. Revision of Ptinidæ of Boreal America. Trans. American Ent. Soc., 31, pp. 97–296 (1905).

GROUVELLE, A. Byturidæ. Coleop. Cat. Junk, 56, 223 pp. (1913).

JAYNE, H. F. Revision of Dermestidæ of the United States. Proc. American Philos. Soc., 20, pp. 343–377 (1882).

MUTCHLER, A. J. and H. B. WEISS. New Jersey Dermestidæ. Circ. New Jersey Dept. Agric., No. 108, 31 pp. (1927).

PIC, M. Ptinidæ. Coleop. Cat. Junk, 41, 46 pp. (1912).

    Dascillidæ and Helodidæ. Coleop. Cat. Junk, 58, 52 pp. (1914).

WESTWOOD, J. O. Description of a New Genus of Coleopterous Insects. (Gnostidæ). Trans. Entom. Soc. London (n.s.) 3, pp. 90–94 (1854).

HISTEROIDEA

BICKHARDT, H. Histeridæ. Coleop. Cat. Junk, pt. 24, 137 pp. (1910).

    Histeridæ, part. Gen. Insectorum, fasc. 166a, 112 pp. (1916).

COOMAN, A. DE. Coléoptères Histeridæ d'Extrême-Orient, principalement du Tonkin. Notes Ent. chinoise, 8, pp. 41–46; pp. 291–333, 23 figs. (1940–41).

HETSCHKO, A. Synteliidæ. Coleop. Cat. Junk, 83, 15 pp. (1926).

HORN, G. H. Synopsis of Histeridæ of the United States. Proc. American Philos. Soc., 13, pp. 237–360 (1873).

MCGRATH, R. M. and M. H. HATCH. Histeridæ of Washington. Univ. Washington, Publ. Biol., 10, pp. 47–90 (1941).

PORTEVIN, G. Les Liodides de l'Inde. Encycl. Ent., Ser. B, Coleoptera, 1, pp. 75–83 (1926).

SCHENKLING, S. Niponiidæ. Coleopt. Cat. Junk, 117, 2 pp. (1931).

WENZEL, R. L. Classification of Histeridæ. Field Mus., Zool. Ser., 28, No. 2, pp. 51–151, 9 pls. (1944).

COLYDIOIDEA

ARROW, G. J. Contribution to Classification of the Coleopterous Family Endomychidæ. Trans. Ent. Soc. London, 1920, pp. 1–83 (1920).

BELON, R. P. Classification des Lathridiidæ. Rev. Ent. 1897, pp. 105–221 (1897).

    Récapitulation des Lathridiidæ de l'Amérique méridionale. Ann. Soc. Lyon, 46, pp. 137–192 (1900).

    Lathridiidæ. Gen. Insectorum, fasc. 3, pp. 40 (1902).

BLAISDELL, F. E. Revision of Endomychid Tribe Liesthini. Trans. American Ent. Soc., 56, pp. 375–390, 1 pl. (1930).

BRÈTHES, J. Coccinellides du British Museum, avec une nouvelle famille (Cerasommatidiidæ). An. Mus. Hist. Nat. Buenos Aires 33, pp. 195–214 (1925).

CARTER, H. J., and E. H. ZECK. Monograph of the Australian Colydiidæ. Proc. Linn. Soc. New South Wales, 62, pp. 181–208, 2 pls., 2 figs. (1937).

CASEY, T. L. Synopsis of Phalacridæ. Ann. New York Acad. Sci., 5, pp. 39–185 (1891).

Revision of American Coccinellidæ. Journ. New York Ent. Soc., 7, pp. 71–163 (1899).

Review of American Corylophidæ, Cryptophagidæ, Tritomidæ and Dermestidæ. Journ. New York Ent. Soc., 8, pp. 51–172 (1900).

CHATTERJEE, S. N. Nitidulidæ. Cat. Indian Ins. Govt. India, Centr. Pub. Branch, Calcutta, pt. 5, 40 pp. (1924).

CSIKI, E. Endomychidæ. Coleop. Cat. Junk, pt. 12, 68 pp. (1910).

Discolomidæ, Orthoperidæ, Phænocephalidæ and Sphæriidæ. Coleop. Cat. Junk, pt. 18, 35 pp. (1910).

Hydroscaphidæ and Ptiliidæ. Coleop. Cat. Junk, pt. 32, 61 pp. (1911).

DALLA TORRE, K. W. Ciidæ. Coleop. Cat. Junk, pt. 30, 32 pp. (1911).

DEANE, C. Trichopterygidæ of Australia and Adjacent Islands. Proc. Linn. Soc. New South Wales, 57, pp. 181–196, 17 figs. (1932).

DEELDER, C. L. Revision of the Erotylidæ of the Leiden Museum. Zool. Meded., 24, pp. 49–115, 5 figs. (1942).

FALCOZ, L. Cryptophagidæ de la faune franco-rhénane. Misc. Ent. Castanet-Tolosan, 32, pp. 49–144 (1929–30).

FALL, H. C. Revision of the Lathridiidæ of Boreal America. Trans. American Ent. Soc., 25, pp. 101–190 (1899).

FISHER, W. S. Revision of North American Bostrychidæ. Misc. Publ. U. S. Dept. Agric., No. 698, 157 pp. (1950).

FOWLER, W. W. Languriidæ. Gen. Insectorum, fasc. 78, 45 pp. (1908).

GROUVELLE, A. Nitidulidæ. Coleop. Cat. Junk, 56, 223 pp. (1913).

GUI, H. L. Coccinellidæ of Kansas. Proc. Kansas Ent. Soc., 1, pp. 26–37 (1928).

HEINZE, E. Tribus Cerylini und Metacerylini (Colydiidæ). Arb. morph. taxon. Ent., 11, pp. 19–32 (1944).

HELLER, K. M. Erotyliden der indo-australischen Region. Arch. Naturg., Jahrg. 84 A, Heft 8, pp. 1–121 (1920).

HETSCHKO, A. Catapochrotidæ and Moncœdidæ. Coleop. Cat. Junk, 83, pp. 12–13 (1926).

Lathridiidæ. Coleop. Cat. Junk, 85, 86 pp. (1926).

Colydiidæ. Coleop. Cat. Junk, 107, 124 pp. (1930).

Mycetophagidæ. Coleop. Cat. Junk, 108, 48 pp. (1930).

HINTON, H. E. Revision of Cerylonini of Borneo. Ann. Mag. Nat. Hist., (11)9, pp. 141–173 (1942).

HORN, G. H. Revision of Bostrychidæ and Colydiidæ of the United States. Proc. American Philos. Soc., 17, pp. 555–592 (1878).

Synopsis of the Monotomidæ of the United States. Trans. American Ent. Soc., 7, pp. 257–267 (1879).

Revision of Nitidulidæ of the United States. Trans. American Ent. Soc., 7, pp. 267–336 (1879).

Kapur, A. P. Revision of Tribe Aspidimerini (Coccinellidæ). Trans. Roy. Ent. Soc., 99, pp. 77–128 (1948).

Korschefsky, E. Coccinellidæ. Coleop. Cat. Junk, 118, 120, 659 pp. (1931–32).

Kraus, E. J. and A. D. Hopkins. Revision of Holarctic Lyctidæ. Bull. U. S. Dept. Agric., Bur. Ent., Tech. Ser. No. 20, pp. 111–138 (1911).

Kuhnt, P. Erotylidæ. Gen. Insectorum, fasc. 88, 139 pp. (1909).
    Erotylidæ. Coleop. Cat. Junk, 34, 103 pp. (1911).

Lesne, P. Revision des Bostrychides. Ann. Soc. Entom. France, 1896, pp. 95–127 and several later parts (1896–1906).
    Les Bostrychides de l'Afrique tropicale française. Encycl. Ent. pt 3, 301 pp. (1924).
    Bostrychidæ. Coleop. Cat. Junk, 161, 84 pp. (1936).

Leveille, A. Temnochilidæ. Coleop. Cat. Junk, 11, 40 pp. (1910).

Mader, L. Die Erotyliden von Peru. Stettin. ent. Zeitg., 105, pp. 95–117 (1944).

Matthews, A. Monograph of Trichopterygidæ, 188 pp. London (1872).
    Synopsis of North American Trichopterygidæ. Trans. American Ent. Soc., 11, pp. 113–156 (1884).
    Monograph of Corylophidæ and Sphæriidæ. London (1899).

Mequigon, A. Rhizophagidæ. Coleop. Cat. Junk, 61, 16 pp. (1914).

Oke, C. Aculagnathidæ, a New Family of Coleoptera. Proc. Roy. Soc. Victoria, 44, pp. 22–24 (1932).

Parsons, C. T. Revision of Nearctic Nitidulidæ. Bull. Mus. Comp. Zool., 92, pp. 119–278 (1943).

Pic, M. Anobiidæ. Coleop. Cat. Junk, 48, 92 pp. (1912).

Roberts, A. W. R. Taxonomy of the Erotylidæ. Trans. Roy. Ent. Soc. London, 88, pp. 89–118 (1939).

Schenkling, S. Derodontidæ. Coleop. Cat. Junk, 64, 14 pp. (1915).
    Cryptophagidæ. Coleop. Cat. Junk, 76, 92 pp. (1923).
    Languriidæ. Coleop. Cat. Junk, 100, 40 pp. (1928).
    Throscidæ. Coleop. Cat. Junk, 101, 30 pp. (1928).
    Aspidophoridæ, Anobiidæ. Coleop. Cat. Junk, 117, 20 pp. (1931).

Stehr, W. C. Coccinellidæ of Minnesota. Tech. Bull. Minnesota Agric. Expt. Sta., 75, 54 pp., 4 figs. (1930).

Timberlake, P. H. The Coccinellidæ of the Koebele Collection. Part I. Hawaii Plant Rec., 47, pp. 1–67 (1943).

Vaurie, P. North American Languriidæ. Bull. American Mus. Nat. Hist., 93, pp. 123–155 (1948).
    Meloidæ of Mexico. American Mus. Novit., No. 1477, 68 pp. (1950).

Villiers, A. Revision des Languriides de l'ancien Monde. Abeille, 37, pp. 1–316, 637 figs. (1945).

Zaitzev, P. Cyathoceridæ. Coleop. Cat. Junk, 17, 68 pp. (1910).

Zia, Y. On the Languridæ of the Provinces Kweichow and Yunnan. Sinensia, 4, pp. 15–37, 24 figs. (1933).
    Etude morphologique et systématique des Languriidæ du Tonkin. Thésis, Mem. Fac. Sci. Univ. Paris, 41 pp., 83 figs. (1934).

Zimmerman, E. C. Ciidæ of Southeastern Polynesia. Occ. Pap. Bishop Mus., 14, pp. 199–217 (1938).
    Bostrychidæ of Hawaii. Proc. Hawaiian Ent. Soc., 11, pp. 103–108 (1940).

TENEBRIONOIDEA

ANDRES, A. Catalogue of Egyptian Tenebrionidæ. Bull. Soc. Ent. Egypte, **1931**, pp. 74–125 (1931).

BAGUENA CORELLA, L. Estudo sobre los Aderidæ, Xylophilidæ, Hylophilidæ (Euglenidæ). Madrid Inst. Estud. africaines, xiv + 547 pp., 134 figs. (1948).

BLAISDELL, F. E. Revision of the Tribe Eleodini of U. S., Lower California and Adjacent Islands. Bull. U. S. Nat. Mus., **63**, 524 pp. (1909).

Subfamilies and Tribes of Nearctic Tenebrionidæ. Trans. American Ent. Soc., **65**, pp. 43–60 (1939).

Tenebrionidæ of Lower California. Proc. Calif. Acad. Sci., (4)**24**, pp. 171–287, 2 pls. (1943).

BORCHMANN, F. Elactidæ, Lagriidæ, Nilionidæ, and Petriidæ. Coleop. Cat. Junk, **2** (1910).

Die Lagriinæ. Arch. Naturg., Jahrg. **81A**, Heft 6, pp. 46–186 (1916).

Die amerikanischen Gattungen und Arten der Statirinæ (Lagriidæ). Arch. Naturg., Jahrg. **87A**, Heft 1, pp. 216–357 (1921).

Lagriidæ and Alleculidæ of Burma and British India. Ark. Zool., **33A**, 32 pp. (1941).

BROWN, W. J. Revision of North American Ægialiidæ. Canadian Ent., **63**, pp. 9–19, 42–49, 1 pl. (1931).

CARTER, H. J. Catalogue of Australian Tenebrionidæ. Australian Zoölogist, **4**, pp. 117–163, 280; 294 (1926).

CASEY, T. L. Revision of American Tentyrinæ (Tenebrionidæ). Proc. Washington Acad. Sci., **9**, pp. 275–522 (1907).

Revision of American Coniontinæ (Tenebrionidæ). Proc. Washington Acad. Sci., **10**, pp. 51–166 (1908).

CHATANAY, J. Tenebrionidæ, Zophosinæ. Gen. Insectorum, fasc. 176, 50 pp. (1921).

CSIKI, E. Melandryidæ. Coleop. Cat. Junk, **77**, 62 pp. (1924).

GEBIEN, H. Tenebrionidæ and Trictenotomidæ. Coleop. Cat. Junk, **15, 22, 28, 37**, 742 pp. (1910–11).

Monographie der südamerikanischen Camarien (Tenebrionidæ). Arch. Naturg. Jahrg. **83 A**, pt. 3, pp. 25–167 (1919).

Tenebrionidæ of Southwest Africa. Abh. Hamburg Univ., **5**, pp. 1–168 (1920).

Ueber einige Gruppen amerikanischen Tenebrioniden. Stettiner Ent. Zeitg., **89**, pp. 169–170 (1928).

Katalog der Tenebrioniden. Mitt. münchn. ent. Ges., **30**, pp. 785–786, 1061–1092 (1940); **34**, pp. 497–555 (1944).

HETSCHKO, A. Cossyphodidæ. Coleop. Cat. Junk, **83**, 15 pp. (1926).

Cossyphodidæ. Coleop. Cat. Junk, **108**, 1 p. (1930).

Cavicoxumidæ. Coleop. Cat. Junk, **108**, 76 pp. (1931).

HINTON, H. E. Synopsis of Tribolium. Bull. Ent. Res., **39**, pp. 13–55 (1948).

HORN, G. H. Revision of the Tenebrionidæ of North America. Trans. American Philos. Soc., **14**, pp. 253–404 (1870).

Synopsis of North American Lagriidæ. Trans. American Ent. Soc., **15**, pp. 26–48 (1888).

HOULBERT, C. and E. BARTHE. Tableaux analytiques des Coléoptères de la faune franco-rhénane. Melandryidæ. Misc. ent., 35, sep., pp. 1–32, 21 figs. (1934).

KASZAB, Z. Revision der Tenebrioniden-Tribus Platyscelini. Mitt. münchn. ent. Ges., 30, pp. 119–235, 1 map; pp. 896–1003, 3 pls., 160 figs. (1940).

Die indomalayischen Misolampinen (Tenebrionidæ). Ann. Hist. nat. Mus. hungarici, 34 Zool., pp. 1–44, 1 pl. (1941).

Beiträge zur Kenntnis der orientalischen Opatrinen (Tenebrionidæ). Mitt. münchn. ent. Ges., 32, pp. 1–43, 16 figs. (1942).

PIC, M. Scraptiidæ. Coleop. Cat. Junk, 26, 27 pp. (1911).

POUILLADE, J. Revision of Trictenotomidæ. Insecta, Rennes, 4, pp. 243–251 (1914).

REITTER, E. Subfamilies and Tribes of Palæarctic Tenebrionidæ. Wiener Ent. Zeitg., 36, pp. 53–66 (1917).

SCHENKLING, S. Monommidæ. Coleop. Cat. Junk, 117, 7 pp. (1931).

Sphindidæ. Coleop. Cat. Junk, 117, 4 pp. (1931).

SEMENOV, A. Synopsis of Platyopinæ (Tenebrionidæ). Horæ Soc. Ent. Rossicæ, 38, pp. 175–184 (1907).

ZIMMERMAN, E. C. Revision of the Hawaiian Alleculidæ. Proc. Hawaii Ent. Soc., 10, pp. 471–476 (1939).

CERAMBYCOIDEA

ACHARD, J. Lamprosomatidæ. Gen. Insectorum, fasc. 159, 13 pp. (1914).

Chrysomelidæ. Chlamydinæ and Sphærocarinæ. Gen. Insectorum, fasc. 160, 25 pp. (1914).

AURIVILLIUS, C. and A. LAMEERE. Cerambycidæ (s. lat). Coleop. Cat. Junk, 39, 73, 74, 1278 pp. (1912–1923).

BECHYNE, J. Chrysomelidæ et Halticidæ d'Angola. Rev. Suisse Zool., 55, pp. 533–548 (1948).

BLAKE, D. H. Revision of Myochrous. Proc. U. S. Nat. Mus., 101, No. 3271, pp. 1–64, 8 pls. (1950).

BOPPE, P. Cerambycidæ s. lat., part; Disteniinæ and Lepturiinæ. Gen. Insectorum, fasc. 178, 121 pp. (1921).

BREUNING, E. Etudes sur les Lamiaires. Novit. Ent., 4, pp. 1–96, 188 figs. and later continuations in vols. 7, 9, 10, 11, 12, 13, 14, 15, 16 (1936–46).

BRIDWELL, J. C. Subfamilies of Bruchidæ. Proc. Ent. Soc. Washington, 34, pp. 100–106 (1932).

The Genera of Beetles of the Family Bruchidæ in North America. Journ. Washington Acad. Sci., 36, pp. 52–57 (1946).

CHEN, S. H. Study of Chinese Halticinæ. Sinensia, 3, pp. 211–254, 14 figs. (1933).

Revision of the Halticidæ of Yunnan and Tonkin. Sinensia, 5, pp. 225–416, 85 figs. (1934).

A New Classification of the Leaf Beetles. Sinensia, 11, pp. 451–479, 30 figs. (1940).

CHUJO, M. Chrysomelid Beetles of Micronesia. Mem. Fac. Sci. Agric. Taihoku Imp. Univ., 24, pp. 281–334 (1943).

CLAVAREAU, H. Chrysomelidæ s. lat. Coleop. Cat. Junk, 59, 215 pp. (1914).

CRAIGHEAD, F. C. Larvæ of the Prioninæ. Rept. No. 107, Office of Secretary, U. S. Dept. Agric., 24 pp. (1915).
    Classification of Larvæ of North American Cerambycidæ. Bull. Canada Dept. Agric. Entom., No. 23, 238 pp. (1923).

DILLON, L. S. and E. S. The Tribe Monochamini in the Western Hemisphere (Cerambycidæ). Sci. Publ. Reading Pub. Mus., No. 1, 135 pp., 5 pls. (1941).
    The Tribe Onciderini (Cerambycidæ). Sci. Publ. Reading Pub. Mus., No. 5, xv + 186 pp., No. 6, pp. 189–413, 17 pls. (1945–46).
    Review of the Onocephalini (Cerambycidæ). Trans. American Ent. Soc., 72, pp. 27–48, 1 pl. (1946).
    The Tribe Dorcaschematini. Trans. American Ent. Soc., 73, pp. 173–298 (1948).

FATTIG, P. W. Chrysomelidæ of Georgia. Emory Univ. Mus. Bull., No. 6, 47 pp. (1948).

FISCHER, C. R. Os coleópteros phytóphagos da tribu Alurnini, pragas das palmeiras (Hispidæ). Rev. Ent., Rio de Janeiro, 5, pp. 257–292, 32 figs., 4 pls. (1935).

GILMOUR, E. F. and J. R. DIBB. Revision of Batocerini (Lamiidæ). Spolia Zeylan., 25, pp. 1–121 (1948).

GRESSITT, J. L. The Obriini of the Japanese Empire (Cerambycidæ). Ins. Matsumurana, 9, pp. 144–153 (1935).
    Plant-beetles (Chrysomelidæ, s. lat.) from West China. Lingnan Sci. Journ., 20, pp. 271–376, 8 pls. (1942).
    Chinese Chlamisidæ. Ann. Ent. Soc. America, 39, pp. 84–100, 1 pl. (1946).

GUÉRIN, J. Megalopodidæ Neotropicais. Rev. Brasil. Biol., 4, pp. 545–549 (1944).

HANSEN, V. Chrysomelidæ and Lariidæ. Danmarks Fauna, 31, pp. 1–279, Copenhagen (1927).

HEIKERTINGER, F. Gattung Crepidodera (Halticidæ). Koleopt. Rundsch., 31, pp. 15–80 (1948).

HEINZE, E. Africanische Crioceriden. Rev. Zool. Bot. africaine, 20, pp. 23–55 (1930).

HERFORD, G. M. Key to Bruchidæ of Economic Importance in Europe. Trans. Soc. British Ent., 2, pp. 1–32, 4 pls. (1935).

HOFFMANN, A. Bruchides et Anthribidæ. Faune de France, 44, 184 pp. (1945).

HOPPING, G. R. Revision of the Clytini of Boreal America (Cerambycidæ). Ann. Ent. Soc. America, 30, pp. 438–457, 3 pls. (1937).

HORN, G. H. Revision of the Bruchidæ of the United States. Trans. American Ent. Soc., 4, pp. 311–342 (1873).
    Synopsis of the Halticinæ of North America. Trans. American Ent. Soc., 16, pp. 163–320 (1889).
    The Eumolpinæ of Boreal America. Trans. American Ent. Soc., 19, pp. 195–234 (1892).
    The Galerucinæ of Boreal America. Trans. American Ent. Soc., 20, pp. 57–136 (1893).

JACOBY, M. Sagridæ. Gen. Insectorum, fasc. 14, 11 pp. (1903).
    Chrysomelidæ. Fauna of British India, Coleoptera, 534 pp. (1908).

JACOBY, M. and H. CLAVAREAU. Donaciidæ. Gen. Insectorum, fasc. 21 (1904).
Crioceridæ. Gen. Insectorum, fasc. 23, 40 pp. (1904).
Megascelidæ. Gen. Insectorum, fasc. 32, 6 pp. (1905).
Megalopodidæ. Gen. Insectorum, fasc. 33, 20 pp. (1905).
Clytridæ. Gen. Insectorum, fasc. 49, 88, pp. (1907).

KLEINE, R. Lycidæ. Catalogue of Indian Insects. Govt. India, Centr. Publication Branch. iii + 52 pp. (1931).

KNULL, J. N. Cerambycidæ of Ohio. Bull. Ohio Biol. Surv., No. 39, pp. 133–354, 29 pls. (1946).

LABOISSIÈRE, V. Revision des Gallerucini d'Europe et pays limitrophes. Ann. Ass. Nat. Levall.-Perret, 17, pp. 22–33, 29 figs.; 18, pp. 13–55, 7 figs.; 19, pp. 14–78, 15 figs. (1911–13).
Galerucinæ de la faune française. Ann. Soc. ent. France, 103, pp. 1–108, 54 figs. (1934).

LAMEERE, A. Prionidæ. Coleop. Cat. Junk, 52, 108 pp. (1913). Gen Insectorum, fasc. 172, 189 pp. (1919).

LANE, F. Esboço monographico dos Anoplodermideos (Prionidæ). Rev. Mus. paulista, 23, pp. 153–223, 9 pls. (1937).

LENG, C. W. Synopsis of Nearctic Cerambycidæ. Bull. Brooklyn Ent. Soc., 7, and Entomologica Americana, 1–6 (1884–1900) (various parts).
Revision of Donaciidæ of Boreal America. Trans. American Ent. Soc., 18, pp. 159–176 (1891).

LENG, C. W. and J. HAMILTON. The Lamiidæ of North America. Trans. American Ent. Soc., 23, pp. 101–178 (1896).

LINSLEY, E. G. A Revision of the Pogonocherini of North America (Cerambycidæ). Ann. Ent. Soc. America, 28, pp. 73–103, 1 pl. (1935).
Revision of the North American Necydalini (Cerambycidæ). Ann. Ent. Soc. America, 33, pp. 269–281 (1940).
Reclassification of the Tribe Obriini (Cerambycidæ). Journ. New York Ent. Soc., 48, pp. 367–377 (1940).

MATUSHITA, M. Zur Kenntnis der Cerambyciden des Japanischen Reichs. Journ. Fac. Agric. Hokkaido Univ., 34, pp. 157–445, 5 pls. (1933).

MAULIK, S. Hispidæ and Cassididæ. Fauna of British India, Coleoptera, Chrysomelidæ, 439 pp. (1919).
Chrysomelidæ and Halticidæ. Fauna of British India, 442 pp. (1926).
Galerucidæ. Fauna of British India, 648 pp., 144 figs. (1936).

MONRÓS, F. Revisión de los Megalopidæ argentinos. Rev. Soc. ent. Argentina, 13, pp. 150–217, 56 figs. (1947).
Chlamisid Beetles of the Neotropical Regions. Proc. U. S. Nat. Mus., 101, pp. 451–463 (1951).

PIC, M. Bruchidæ. Coleop. Cat. Junk, 55, 74 pp. (1913).

PLANET, L. M. Histoire naturelle des Longicornes de France. Encycl. Ent. Sér. A, 2. 386 pp. (1924), also suppl. 53 pp. (1927).

PLAVILSTSHIKOV, N. M. Cerambycidæ. Bestimmungstab. Europ. Coleop., Heft 112, pp. 1–230 (1934).

SCHAEFFER, C. Revision of the New World Donaciini. Brooklyn Mus. Sci. Bull., 3, 165 pp. (1925).

SPAETH, F. Cassididæ. Coleop. Cat. Junk, 62, 182 pp. (1914).
Fauna sumatrensis, Cassidinæ. Supplementa Ent., 13, pp. 1–108 (1926).

Swaine, J. S. and R. Hopping. Lepturini of North America. Pt. I. Bull. Nat. Mus. Canada, No. 52, 79 pp. (1928).

Villiers, A. Cerambycidæ de l'Afrique du Nord. Faun. Emp. franç., 153 pp., 275 figs. (1946).

Webb, J. L. A Preliminary Synopsis of Cerambycoid Larvæ. Tech. Ser., 20. pt. 5, Bur. Ent. U. S. Dept. Agric. (1912).

Weise, J. Hispidæ. Coleop. Cat. Junk, 35, 94 pp. (1911).
Chrysomelidæ. Coleop. Cat. Junk, 68, 255 pp. (1916).
Galerucidæ. Coleop. Cat. Junk, 78, 225 pp. (1924).
Hispidæ. Gen. Insectorum, fasc. 125, 124 pp. (1911).

Zikan, J. F. and W. A inseto-fauna do Itatiaia e da Mantiqueira. Bol. Minist. Agric. Rio de Janeiro, 33, pp. 1–50 (1944).

CURCULIONOIDEA AND SCOLYTOIDEA

Aurivillius, C. Rhyncophora. Svensk Insektfauna, 2, pp. 65–139, 15 figs. (1924).

Blackman, M. W. North American Scolytidæ, Subfamily Micracinæ. Bull. Mississippi Agric. Expt. Sta., Tech. Ser. No. 11, 130 pp. (1921).
Revision of Pityophthori of North America. Bull. New York Coll. Forestry, Syracuse, Tech. Pub. No. 25, pp. 185–208 (1928).

Blatchley, W. S. and C. W. Leng. The Rhyncophora or Weevils of North-eastern America. Nature Pub. Co. (1916).

Bovie, A. Curculionidæ, Entininæ. Gen. Insectorum, fasc. 69, 7 pp. (1908).
Curculionidæ, Cryptoderminæ. Gen. Insectorum, fasc. 70, 3 pp. (1908).
Curculionidæ, Alcidinæ. Gen. Insectorum, fasc. 71, 11 pp. (1908).
Curculionidæ, Læmosaccinæ. Gen. Insectorum, fasc. 89, 6 pp. (1909).
Curculionidæ, Gymnetrinæ. Gen. Insectorum, fasc. 92, 19 pp. (1909).
Curculionidæ, Nanophyinæ. Gen. Insectorum, fasc. 98, 11 pp. (1910).
Curculionidæ, Brachycerinæ. Gen. Insectorum, fasc. 99, 38 pp. (1910).

Bruck, C. R. Synoptic Revision of the Subfamily Hylesinæ (Scolytidæ) of Western North America. Bull. Southern California Acad. Sci., 35, pp. 38–51, 108–126, 8 pls. (1936).

Chamberlain, W. J. The Bark and Timber Beetles of North America. vi + 513 pp., 5 pls., 321 figs. State College, Corvallis, Oregon (1939).

Chittenden, F. H. Classification of Nut Curculios of North America. Ent. Americana, 7, pp. 129–207 (1926).

Dalla Torre, K. W. Aglycyderidæ and Proterhinidæ. Coleop. Cat. Junk, 31, 8 pp. (1911).

Dalla Torre, K. W. and A. Hustache. Curculionidæ, Ceuthorrhynchinæ. Ibid., 113, 150 pp. (1930).

Dalla Torre, K. W., and E. Voss. Curculionidæ, part. Ibid., 110, 84 pp. (1930).
Misoptiliinæ and Rhynchitinæ. Ibid., 157, 56 pp. (1937).

Davis, A. C. Review of the Tribe Ophryastini (Curculionidæ) of America, North of Mexico. Proc. U. S. Nat. Mus., 96, pp. 483–551, 29 figs. (1947).

Dietz, W. G. Revision of North American Anthonomini. Trans. American Ent. Soc., 18, pp. 177–276 (1891).
Revision of Ceutorhynchini of North America. Trans. American Ent. Soc., 23, pp. 387–480 (1896).

DODGE, H. R. Bark Beetles of Minnesota. Tech. Bull. Univ. Minnesota Agric. Expt. Sta., 132, 60 pp. (1938).

FALL, H. C. Revision of North American Species of Apion. Trans. American Ent. Soc., 25, pp. 105–184 (1898).

FIEDLER, K. Monograph of South American Conotrachelus. 365 pp. London, British Mus. Nat. Hist. (1940).

GÜNTHER, K. and F. ZUMPT. Curculionidæ, Subfamily Tanymecinæ. Coleop. Cat. Junk, 131, 131 pp. (1933).

HAEDO ROSSI, J. A. The Genus Brenthus in the Argentine. Notas Mus. La Plata, 13, Zool. No. 105, pp. 141–164 (1948).

HAGEDORN, M. Ipidæ. Gen. Insectorum, fasc. 111, 178 pp. (1910). Coleop. Cat. Junk, 4, 134 pp. (1910).

HOFFMANN, A. Curculionides. Faune de France, 52, 486 pp. (1950).

HOPKINS, A. D. Monograph of Pissodes. Bull. U. S. Dept. Agric. Tech. Ser., No. 20, 68 pp. (1911).

Monograph of Scolytidæ. Bull. U. S. Dept. Agric., Tech. Ser. No. 17, pt. 1, pp. 1–164 (1909); pt. 2, pp. 165–232 (1915).

Classification of Cryphalinæ. Ent. Rept. 99, U. S. Dept. Agric., 75 pp. (1915).

HUSTACHE, A. Curculionides de Madagascar. Bull. Acad. Malgache, Tananarive, 7, pp. 1–582 (1924).

Tableaux analytiques des Coléoptères de la faune franco-rhénane. Curculionidæ: Magdalini. Misc. ent., 35, sep. pp. 1–32 (1933).

Magdalinæ (Curculionidæ) de l'Amérique méridionale. Ann. Mag. Nat. Hist., (10) 19, pp. 198–248 (1937).

Curculionidæ, Barinæ. Coleop. Cat. Junk, 163, 291 pp. (1938).

Ceratopinæ Sud-Americains (Curculionides). Misc. ent., 39, pp. 89–99 (1938).

JORDAN, K. Les Anthribides de l'Indochine. Faune Ent. Indochine française, fasc. 6, pp. 71–113 (1923).

KLEINE, R. Die Brenthiden der Nederländischen Ost-Indischen Kolonien. Capita Zool., 2, pt. 4, 86 pp. (1926).

Brenthidæ. Cat. Indian Ins. Govt. India, Centr. Pub. Branch, Calcutta, pt. 11, 50 pp. (1926).

Die Brenthiden. Nova Guinea, Leiden, 15, pp. 214–274 (1926).

Brenthidæ. Coleop. Cat. Junk, 89, 94 pp. (1927).

Bestimmungstabelle der Brenthidæ. Ent. Zeit. Frankfort-am-M., 40–42 (1927–28). (In several parts).

Die Brenthiden der Philippinen-Inseln. Philippine Journ. Sci., 46, pp. 383–445, 16 figs. (1931).

Brenthidæ (Revised Edition). Gen. Insectorum, fasc. 207, 197 pp., 6 pls. (1938).

LEA, A. M. and A. BOVIE. Curculionidæ, Belinæ. Gen. Insectorum, fasc. 91, 13 pp. (1909).

LIEBKE, M. Die Brachyninæ des afrikanischen Festlandes. Mem. Soc. ent. Belg., 24, pp. 5–94, 102 figs. (1934).

LONA, C. Curculionidæ, Otiorhynchinæ. Coleop. Cat. Junk, 160, pp. 229–412; 162, pp. 413–600 (1938).

MARSHALL, G. A. K. Curculionidæ. Fauna of British India, Coleoptera, 367 pp. (1916).

Genera of the Tribe Cyphicerini. Ann. Mag. Nat. Hist., (11) 11, pp. 73–98; 433–462 (1944).
Curculionidæ of the Swedish Expedition to India. Novit. Zool., 42, pp. 397–473 (1948).
Munro, J. W. British Bark-beetles. Bull. Forestry Comm., No. 8, 77 pp., 10 pls., 32 figs. (1946).
Murayama, J. Révision des Ipides et Platypides de Corée. Journ. Chosen Nat. Hist. Soc., 11, pp. 6–38, 2 pls. (1934).
On the Platypodidæ of Formosa. Journ. Coll. Agric., Hokkaido Imp. Univ., 15, pp. 197–236 (1925).
Pape, P. Curculionidæ, Brachycerinæ. Coleop. Cat. Junk, 16, 36 pp. (1910).
Petri, K. Monograph of Palæarctic Hyperini. 208 pp., Berlin (1901).
Pierce, W. D. Weevils of the Superfamily Curculionoidea. Proc. Ent. Soc. Washington, 21, pp. 21–36 (1919).
Studies of Weevils. Proc. U. S. Nat. Mus., 51, pp. 461–473 (1917).
North American Weevils of the Superfamily Platystomoidea. Proc. U. S. Nat. Mus., 77, No. 2840, 34 pp., 5 pls. (1930).
Schedl, K. E. Die Einteilung der Pityophthorinæ. Arch. Naturgesch. (N.F.) 7, pp. 157–188, 35 figs. (1938).
Bestimmungstabellen palæarktischen Borkenkäfer (Scolytus). Zentralbl. Gesamt-Gebiet. Ent. Monogr., 1, 67 pp. (1948).
Schenkling, S. and G. A. K. Marshall. Curculionidæ, part. Coleop. Cat. Junk, 106, 62 pp.; 114, 62 pp.; 116, 56 pp. (1929–31).
Schönfeldt, H. Brenthidæ. Gen. Insectorum, fasc. 65, 88 pp. (1908); Coleop. Cat. Junk, 7, 57 pp. (1910).
Smith, J. B. Synopsis of Apioninæ of North America. Trans. American Ent. Soc., 11, pp. 41–68 (1884).
Spesivtzer, P. N. Scolytidæ of European Russia. Govt. Agric. Publ., Moscow, 103 pp., 162 figs. (1931). (In Russian)
Strohmeyer, H. Platypodidæ. Coleop. Cat. Junk, 44, 26 pp. (1912).
Chapuisiidæ. Gen. Insectorum, fasc. 162, 6 pp. (1914).
Platypodidæ. Gen. Insectorum, fasc. 163, 55 pp. (1914).
Swaine, J. W. Catalogue of North American Scolytidæ. Rept. New York State Ent., No. 24, pp. 76–159 (1909).
Classification of Canadian Bark beetles. Bull. Canada Dept. Agric. Ent., No. 14, pp. 7–143 (1918).
Tanner, V. O. Study of the Subtribe Hydronomi. Great Basin Nat., 4, pp. 1–38, 1 pl., 12 figs. (1943).
Van Emden, F. I. Key to Genera of Brachyderinæ of the World. Ann. Mag. Nat. Hist. (11) 11, pp. 503–532; 559–586 (1944).
Voss, E. Die Unterfamilien Attelabinæ und Apoderinæ. Stettiner Ent. Zeitg., 85, pp. 1–78; 191–304 (1925).
Monographie der Rhynchitinæ-Pterocolinæ. Stettiner ent. Zeitg., 94, pp. 108–136, 273–286; 95, pp. 109–135, 330–344; 99, pp. 59–117, 302–363 (1933–38); Kol. Rundsch., 19, pp. 25–56, 13 figs.; Deutsch. ent. Zeits., 1941, pp. 113–215 (1941).
Wagner, H. Curculionidæ, Apioninæ. Gen. Insectorum, fasc. 130, 109 pp. (1912).
Curculionidæ, Apioninæ. Coleop. Cat. Junk, 6, 81 pp. (1910).
Monographie der paläarktischen Ceuthorrhynchinæ (Curculionidæ).

Ent. Blätter, **34**, pp. 145–172, 279–290, 297–312, 4 figs.; **35**, pp. 35–58, 65–90, 185–208, 241–252, 273–291; **36**, pp. 65–81, 97–111 (1938–40).

WOLFRUM, P. Anthribidæ. Coleop. Cat. Junk, **102**, 145 pp. (1929).

ZIMMERMAN, E. C. Cryptorhynchinæ of the Society Islands (Curculionidæ). Occ. Pap. Bishop Mus., **12** (23), pp. 1–48, 4 figs. (1936).

    Key to the Genera of Hawaiian Anthribidæ. Proc. Hawaiian Ent. Soc., **10**, p. 152 (1938).

    Anthribidæ of Southeastern Polynesia. Occ. Pap. Bishop Mus., **14** (13), pp. 219–250, 1 fig. (1938).

    Cryptorhynchinæ of Rapa. Bull. Bishop Mus., **151**, pp. 1–75, 6 figs., 4 pls. (1938).

    Synopsis of the Genera of Hawaiian Cossoninæ (Curculionidæ). Occ. Pap. Bishop Mus., **15** (25), pp. 271–293, 2 figs. (1940).

SCARABÆOIDEA

ARROW, G. J. Fauna of British India. Lamellicornia (Cetoniidæ, Dynastidæ, Rutelinæ, in Fauna British India, **1–3**, 1137 pp. (1910–31).

    Acanthoceridæ, Glaphyridæ, Hybosoridæ, Ochodæidæ, Orphnidæ, Pleocomidæ and Trogidæ. Coleop. Cat. Junk, **43**, 66 pp. (1912).

    Notes on the Coleopterous Families Hybosoridæ and Trogidæ. Ann. Mag. Nat. Hist. (9) **15**, pp. 328–331 (1925).

    Horned Beetles. 154 pp. Junk, The Hague. (1951).

    Copridæ. Coleoptera Lamellicornia. Fauna of British India, xii + 428 pp., 13 pls. (1931).

    A Contribution to the Classification of the Coleopterous Family Lucanidæ. Trans. Roy. Soc. London, **83**, pp. 105–125, 1 pl., 5 figs. (1935).

BALTHASAR, V. Monographie der Trogidæ der palæarktischen Region. Festschr. 60 Geburtst. E. Strand, **1**, pp. 407–459, 1 pl. (1936).

BENESH, B. Systematic Revision of the Holarctic Genus Platycerus (Lucanidæ). Trans. American Ent. Soc., **72**, pp. 139–202 (1946).

BOUCOMOUT, A. Geotrupidæ. Gen. Insectorum, fasc. 7, 20 pp. (1902).

    Geotrupidæ. Coleop. Cat. Junk, **46**, 47 pp. (1912).

BROWN, W. J. Revision of North American Ægialiidæ. Canadian Ent., **63**, pp. 9–19 (1931).

BURGEON, L. Les Trichiini (Cetoniidæ) du Congo belge. Bull. Inst. colon. belge, **17**, pp. 563–613, 6 figs. (1946).

    Melolonthini et Pachydemini du Congo belge (Melolonthidæ). Rev. Zool. Bot. afr., **39**, pp. 230–273; 339–366, 66 figs. (1946).

CARTWRIGHT, O. L. American Species of Pleurophorus (Aphodiidæ). Trans. American Ent. Soc., **74**, pp. 131–145 (1948).

CAZIER, M. A. Revision of the Pachydemini of North America. Journ. Ent. Zool., **29**, pp. 73–87, 2 figs. (1937).

    Review of the Phileurini of America North of Mexico (Dynastidæ). Bull. Southern California Acad. Sci., **38**, pp. 169–187, 13 figs. (1940).

CHAPIN, E. A. Rutelidæ, Dynastidæ and Cetoniidæ of Cuba. Ann. Ent. Soc. America, **25**, pp. 285–308, 3 pls. (1932).

    Revision of the Melolonthidæ of Cuba. I, II. Ann. Ent. Soc. America, **25**, pp. 173–209, 3 pls.; 282–314, 3 pls. (1932).

Nomenclature and Taxonomy of Glaphyridæ. Proc. Biol. Soc. Washington, **51**, pp. 79–86 (1938).

Revision of the West Indian Aphodiidæ. Proc. U. S. Nat. Mus., **89**, pp. 1–41 (1940).

DALLA TORRE, K. W. Melolonthidæ. Coleop. Cat. Junk, **45, 47, 49, 50**, 450 pp. (1912–13).

DAWSON, R. W. Scarabæidæ of Nebraska. Univ. of Nebraska Studies, **22**, pp. 1–82 (1922).

DIBB, J. R. Synopsis of Australian Passalidæ. Trans. Roy. Ent. Soc. London, **87**, pp. 103–124, 2 figs. (1938).

DIDIER, R. Lucanides du globe. 309 pp., 212 figs. (1937). Atlas (1949).

FALL, H. C. Synopsis of Ochodæidæ of the United States. Journ. New York Ent. Soc., **17**, pp. 30–38 (1909).

FUCHS, C. Synopsis of Lucanidæ of United States. Bull. Brooklyn Ent. Soc. **5**, pp. 49–52; 57–60 (1882).

GILLET, J. J. E. Scarabæidæ, *s. str.* Coleop. Cat. Junk, **38**, 100 pp. (1911).

GRAVELY, F. H. Passalidæ. Mem. Indian Mus., **7**, pp. 1–144 (1918).

HESSE, A. J. Notes on Acanthoceridæ from Natal and Zululand. Ann. Natal Mus., **11**, pp. 377–393 (1948).

HINCKS, W. D. Revision of the Madagascar Passalidæ. Ann. Mag. Nat. Hist., (10)**13**, pp. 561–576 (1934).

HORN, G. H. Monograph of Aphodiinæ of the United States. Trans. American Ent. Soc., **14**, pp. 1–110 (1887).

HOULBERT, C. and E. BARTHE. Tableaux analytiques des Coléoptères de la faune franco-rhénane, Lucanidæ. Misc. ent., **34**, sep. pp. 1–28, 33 figs. (1932).

Tableaux analytiques des Coléoptères de la faune franco-rhénane, Scarabæidæ. Misc. ent., **34**, pp. 29–48, 29 figs. (1932); **35**, pp. 97–128 (1934).

HOULBERT, C. and E. MONNOT. Faune entomologique amoricaine, Coléoptères. Lamellicornes. Trav. Sci. Univ. Rennes, **13**, pp. 1–171 (1915).

JANSSENS, A. Revision des Onitides (Copridæ). Mém. Mus. Hist. nat. belgique, (2)**11**, pp. 1–204, 2 pls., 107 figs. (1937).

Copridæ du Congo Belge. Expl. Parc nat. Albert, Mus. de Witte (1933–35), **29**, 104 pp., 4 pls., 88 figs. (1939).

LEA, A. M. Australian Scarabæidæ, *s. str.* Rec. South Australian Mus., **2**, pp. 353–396 (1923).

LUEDERWALDT, H. Monographia dos Passalideos do Brasil. Rev. Mus. paulista, **17**, pp. 1–262, 2 pls., 26 figs. (1931).

Monographia dos Lucanideos brasileiros. Ibid., **19**, pp. 447–574, 4 pls. (1935).

MOREIRA, C. Insectos Coleópteros Passalideos do Brazil. Fauna brasiliense, N. S. No. 1, 52 pp. (1925).

NIIJIMA, Y. and E. KINOSHITA. Japanische Melolonthiden, II, III. Res. Bull. Coll. Exp. For. Hokkaido Imp. Univ., **2**, pp. 1–253, 7 pls., 11 figs.; **4**, pp. 1–97, 3 pls. (1923–27).

OHAUS, J. Euchiridæ, Rutelidæ and Phænomeridæ. Coleop. Cat. Junk, **66**, 241 pp. (1918).

Euchiridæ and Phænomeridæ. Gen. Insectorum, fasc. 195, 18 pp., 1 pl. (1933).

Rutelidæ. Gen. Insectorum, fasc. 199a, 171 pp., 6 pls. (1934).

OLSOUFIEFF, G. Les Phanæides. Insecta, **13**, pp. 5–202 (1924).

PAULIAN, R. Faune entomologique de Madagascar. Coleoptera Lamellicornia, Scarabæidæ, Acanthocerini, Trogini, Aulonocnemis, Hybosorini, Orphnini et Ochodæini. Bull. Acad. malgache, (N.S.) **19**, pp. 129–143 (1936).

Contribution à l'étude des Canthonides américains. Ann. Soc. ent. France, **108**, pp. 213–296, 18 figs. (1938).

Coléoptères Scarabéides. Faune de France, **38**, 240 pp., 445 figs. (1941).

Coléoptères Scarabéides de l'Indo-chine. Faune Emp. franç., **3**, 225 pp., 105 figs. (1945).

PIC, M. Eucinetidæ. Coleop. Cat. Junk, **58**, pp. 53–65 (1914).

RITCHER, P. O. Anomalini (Rutelidæ) of Eastern North America. Bull. Kentucky Agric. Expt. Sta., No. **442**, 27 pp. (1943).

Dynastidæ of North America. Ibid., No. **467**, 56 pp. (1944).

Copridæ of Eastern North America. Ibid. No. **477**, 23 pp., 3 pls. (1945).

Cetoniidæ of Eastern North America. Ibid., No. **476**, 39 pp., 3 pls. (1945).

Rutelidæ of Eastern North America. Ibid. No. **471**, 19 pp. (1945).

ROON, G. VAN. Lucanidæ. Coleop. Cat. Junk, **8**, 70 pp. (1910).

SAYLOR, L. W. Synoptic Revision of the United States Dynastidæ, Tribes Cyclocephalini and Oryctini. Journ. Washington Acad. Sci., **35**, pp. 378–386, 1 fig. (1945); **36**, pp. 16–21, 19 figs.; pp. 41–45, 10 figs. (1946); **38**, pp. 176–183, 240–243 (1948).

Scarabæoidea of Lower California. Proc. California Acad. Sci., (4)**24**, pp. 337–374 (1948).

SCHATZMAYR, A. Gli Scarabeidi coprofagi della Libia e dell'Egitto. Atti Soc. italiana Sci. nat., **85**, pp. 40–84 (1946).

SCHENKLING, A. Cetoniidæ. Coleop. Cat. Junk, **72**, 431 pp. (1921).

Trichiidæ. Coleop. Cat. Junk, **75**, 58 pp. (1922).

SCHMIDT, A. Aphodiidæ. Gen. Insectorum, fasc. 110, 155 pp. (1910).

Aphodiidæ. Coleop. Cat.. Junk, **20**, 111 pp. (1910).

Ægialiidæ. Coleop. Cat. Junk, **42**, 11 pp. (1912).

Scarabæidæ (*s. lat.* part) Ægialiinæ, Chironinæ, Dynamopinæ, Hybosorinæ, Idiostominæ, Ochodæinæ, Orphninæ. Gen. Insectorum, fasc. 150, 87 pp. (1913).

Aphodiidæ. Das Tierreich. Lief. **45**, 614 pp. (1922).

SILVERIO PEREIRA, F. Contribuição para o conhecimento da subfamília dos Pseudacanthinæ (Passalidæ). Arq. Zool. São Paulo, **3**, pp. 93–113, 6 figs. (1941).

LITERATURE ON LARVÆ OF COLEOPTERA

ANDERSON, W. H. Key to Larval Bruchidæ in the U. S. National Museum. Journ. Washington Acad. Sci., **29**, pp. 382–391 (1933).

BERTRAND, H. Les larves et nymphes des Dytiscides, Hygrobiides et Haliplides. Encycl. Ent., **10**, 368 pp. (1928).

BLAIR, K. G. Beetle Larvæ. Proc. Trans. South London Ent. Nat. Hist. Soc., **1933–34**, pp. 89–110, 3 pls. (1934).

BÖVING, A. G. and A. B. CHAMPLAIN. Larvæ of North American Cleridæ. Proc. U. S. Nat. Mus., **57**, pp. 576–649 (1920).

BÖVING, A. G. and F. C. CRAIGHEAD. Synopsis of the Principal Larval Forms of the Order Coleoptera. Ent. Americana, **11**, pp. 1–351, 124 pls. (1931).

Böving, A. G. and K. L. Henriksen. Larvæ of Danish Hydrophilidæ. Vidensk. Medd. naturh. Foren., **102**, pp. 27–162, 54 figs. (1938).

Boldori, L. Altri appunti sulle larve dei Trechini (Adephaga). Mem. Soc. ent. italiana, **10**, pp. 149–167, 3 figs. (1931).

Chu, H. F. Larvæ of Harpalinæ Unisetosæ (Carabidæ). Ent. Americana, **25**, pp. 1–70 (1945).

Gage, J. H. Larvæ of the Coccinellidæ. Illinois Biol. Monogr., **6**, pp. 1–62 (1920).

Gardner, J. C. M. Immature Stages of Indian Coleoptera. Ind. For. Rec., **17** (3), 10 pp., 2 pls. (Platypodidæ) (1932); **17** (8), 12 pp. 2 pls. (Carabidæ) (1932); **18** (9), 19 pp. 4 pls. (Bostrychidæ) (1933); **20** (8), 17 pp., 2 pls. (Scolytidæ) (1934); **20** (2), 48 pp. (Curculionidæ) (1934); (N.S.) **1**, pp. 1–23, 4 pls. (Scarabæoidea) (1935); (N.S.) **1**, pp. 79–83, 2 pls. (Eucnemidæ) (1935); (N.S.) **1**, pp. 139–150 (Brenthidæ) (1935).

List of Described Immature Stages of Indian Coleoptera. Ind. For. Rec., (N.S.) **7**, pp. 163–191 (1947).

Glen, R. Larvæ of Elaterid Beetles (Tribe Lepturoidini). Smithsonian Misc. Coll., **111**, No. 11, 246 pp., 40 pls. (1950).

Hansen, V. Biller. XII. Heteromerer. Larverne ved Sv. G. Larsson. Danmarks Fauna, **50**, 293 pp., 87 figs. (1945).

Hayes, W. P. Morphology, Taxonomy and Biology of Larval Scarabæoidea. Illinois Biol. Monogr., **12**, pp. 85–203, 15 pls. (1929).

Hennig, W. Uebersicht über die Larven der wichtigsten deutschen Chrysomelinen. Arb. physiol. angew. Ent., **5**, pp. 85–136, 2 pls., 52 figs. (1938).

Kemner, N. A. Staphyliden-Larven. Ent. Tidskr., **46**, pp. 61–77, 2 pls., 5 figs. (1925).

Larsson, S. G. Larver Biller. Danmarks Fauna, **44**, pp. 193–320, 101 figs. (1938).

Maulik, S. On the Structure of Larvæ of Hispine Beetles. Proc. Zool. Soc. London, **1932**, pp. 293–322, 12 figs. (1932).

D'Orchymont, A. Les larves des Hydrophilides. Ann. Biol. Lacustr., **6**, pp. 173–214 (1913).

Peyerimhoff, P. de. Les larves des Coléoptères d'après A. G. Böving et F. C. Craighead et les grands criteriums de l'ordre. Ann. Soc. ent. France, **102**, pp. 77–106 (1933).

Rees, B. E. Classification of Larvæ of North American Dermestidæ. Misc. Publ., U. S. Dept. Agric., **511**, 18 pp. (1943).

Ritchie, P. O. Key to Larvæ of Tribes and Species of Scarabæidæ (s. lat.). Ann. Ent. Soc. America, **41**, pp. 206–212 (1948).

Rymer-Roberts, A. W. Key to Principal Families of Coleopterous Larvæ. Bull. Ent. Res., **21**, pp. 57–72 (1930).

Van Emden, F. Bestimmungstabelle der Larven der Malacodermata — Sternoxia — Reihe. Bull. Ann. Soc. ent. Belgique, **72**, pp. 199–259, 3 pls. (1932).

Taxonomy of Rhyncophora Larvæ. Trans. Roy. Ent. Soc. London, **87**, pp. 1–37 (1938).

Key to British Cerambycid Larvæ. Ent. Monthly Mag., **75**, pp. 257–273; **76**, pp. 7–13 (1939–40).

Key to British Lamellicornia Larvæ. Ibid., **77**, pp. 117–127, 181–192 (1941).

Key to Genera of Larval Carabidæ. Trans. Roy. Ent. Soc. London, **92,** pp. 1–99, 100 figs. (1942).

Key to Families of Larvæ of British Beetles. Ent. Monthly Mag., **78,** pp. 206–272; **79,** pp. 209–223, 259–270 (1942–43).

VERHOEFF, K. W. Staphyliden-Larven. Arch. Naturg., **85A** (6), pp. 1–111, 2 pls. (1920).

Coleopteren-Larven, besonders der Clavicornia. Arch. Naturg., **89A** (1), pp. 1–109, 7 pls. (1923).

WADE, J. S. Contribution to a Bibliography of Described Stages of North American Coleoptera. Bur. Ent. Plant Quarantine, U. S. Dept. Agric., 114 pp. (Mimeographed) Washington (1935).

ORDER STREPSÍPTERA

(RHIPÍPTERA)

Small species parasitic on other insects, the adult males winged and free-living, but the larviform females only rarely leaving the body of their host. Male with the head free. Eyes well developed, sphæroidal, provided with large, highly convex, separated facets. Antennæ with three to seven joints, one or several of the joints prolonged into a long, lateral process (flabellum). Mouthparts reduced; mandibles often soft or minute; maxillæ fleshy; labium not developed. Prothorax greatly reduced in size, usually ring-like; mesothorax small, strongly transverse; metathorax very large. Fore wings reduced to small club-shaped appendages; hind wings very large and delicate, with a few, fine radiating veins, but without crossveins. Legs rather weak; the coxæ, especially of the front and middle legs very minute; tarsi with from five to two joints; often with the claws absent. Female with the mouthparts and antennæ vestigial; wings absent and usually also the legs and antennæ absent; head and thorax fused into one strongly flattened piece; sexual openings in the form of segmental, usually unpaired canals opening on several of the abdominal segments. Metamorphosis complete; larvæ undergoing hypermetamorphosis with an active long-legged first stage larva or triungulin; female remaining larviform in the reproductive stage.

Adults

1. Males 2
   Females 8
2. Tarsi five-jointed, with two claws; pro- and mesothorax short, transverse 3
   Tarsi with four joints or less and without claws...................4
3. Antennæ seven-jointed, the third and fourth joints prolonged laterally; metathoracic præscutum transverse, reaching the humeri and lying entirely in front of the other dorsal plates of the meta-

thorax; scutellum broadly rounded in front, longer than the præscutum. (Fig. 886). (**Triozócera**, Nearc., Neotrop.; **Méngea,** Oligocene (fossil)) .... MENGÈIDÆ
Antennæ six-jointed, third, fourth and fifth joints prolonged laterally; sixth elongate; metathoracic præscutum transverse-quadrate, not reaching the humeri, depressed and forming a sort of neck; lateral lobes of scutum reaching the metathorax; scutellum very long, narrowed and rounded in front. (Mengenílla Palæarc.; Austr.) .... MENGENÍLLIDÆ
4. Tarsi four-jointed 5
Tarsi with two or three joints................................7
5. Antennæ seven-jointed; fourth joint very short, fifth to seventh joints very long. (**Myrmécolax**, widespr., **Cænócholax**, Neotrop.). Parasitic on ants .... MYRMECOLÁCIDÆ
Antennæ with less than seven joints..........................6
6. Third and fourth joints of antennæ each with a long lateral projection; antennæ five-jointed; first joint of tarsi as long as the following three together. (**Corióxenos**, Ethiop., **Callipharíxenos**, Indomal.) .... CALLIPHARIXÉNIDÆ
Only the third joint with projection; first joint of tarsi shorter than the following three together. (**Stỳlops**, Holarc., **Hylécthrus**, Palæarc., **Xènos**, Palæarc., Am.). (Including *XÉNIDÆ* and *HYLÉCTHRIDÆ*) .... STYLÓPIDÆ
7. Tarsi three-jointed; antennæ seven-jointed. (**Halictóphagus**, widespr.; **Stenocranóphilus**, Holarc.; **Tridactylóphagus**, Ind.). (Including *DIOZOCERÁTIDÆ*) .... HALICTOPHÁGIDÆ
Tarsi with two joints; antennæ four-jointed, the third joint with a long projection at its base. (**Elénchus**, widespr.).
ELÉNCHIDÆ
8. Adult free-living, with legs, eyes and antennæ present...........9
Adult larviform, without legs, eyes or antennæ; never emerging from body of the host................................10
9. Antennæ five-jointed .... MENGÈIDÆ
Antennæ four-jointed .... MENGENÍLLIDÆ
10. Cephalothorax with hook-like projections behind the spiracles (male unknown). (**Stichótrema**, Austr.). Parasites of Orthoptera.
STICHOTREMÁTIDÆ
No such projections behind spiracles........................11
11. Cephalothorax greatly lengthened, with two pairs of spiracles, or with the head and thoracic segments distinct. Parasites of Hemiptera .... CALLIPHARIXÉNIDÆ
Cephalothorax with one pair of spiracles; thoracic sutures not distinct 12
12. Parasites of Hymenoptera .... STYLÓPIDÆ
Parasites of Homoptera or Gryllidæ......................13

13. Brood passage (opening through which the larvæ escape after hatching) a narrow, linear or oblong slit; thorax prominent.

HALICTOPHÁGIDÆ

Brood passage opening broad and semicircular; thorax ringlike, reduced behind the opening. Parasites of Fulgoroidea.

ELÉNCHIDÆ

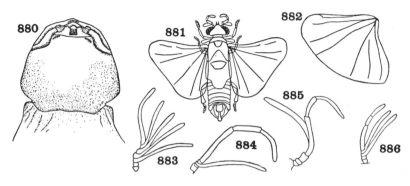

Figs. 880–886. Strepsiptera

880. **Xenos,** head of female (Brues) Stylopidæ.
881. **Stylops,** male (Pierce) Stylopidæ.
882. **Xenos,** wing of male (Kirby) Stylopidæ.
883. **Anthericomma,** antenna of male (Pierce) Halictophagidæ.
884. **Cænocholax,** antenna of male (Pierce) Myrmecolacidæ.
885. **Parastylops,** antenna of male (Pierce) Stylopidæ.
886. **Triozocera,** antenna of male (Pierce) Mengeidæ.

First Stage Larvæ (Triungulins)

1. Front and middle tarsi pulvilliform.............................2
   At least the middle tarsi setiform; with seta, but without pulvillus..4
2. Head behind with two long backwardly directed spines near the lower margin 3
   Head without such long spines. Parasites of wasps and bees.

STYLÓPIDÆ

3. Sternites of abdomen margined posteriorly with bristles.

MENGÈIDÆ, MENGENÍLLIDÆ

   Sternites with dentate posterior margin, but without marginal bristles. Parasites of Hemiptera..........**CALLIPHARIXÉNIDÆ**
4. Front tarsi pulvilliform; others setiform; three ocelli on each side of the head. Parasites of Orthoptera.....**STICHOTREMÁTIDÆ**
   All tarsi setiform. Parasites of Homoptera, especially Fulgoroidea, and of Gryllidæ.....**ELÉNCHIDÆ and HALICTOPHÁGIDÆ**

LITERATURE ON STREPSIPTERA

Bohart, R. M. Revision of Strepsiptera, with Special Reference to North America. Univ. California Publ., Ent. 7, pp. 91–160 (1941).

Leng, C. W. Catalogue of N. American Strepsiptera. Cat. Coleop., pp. 343–345 (1920).

Parker, H. L. and H. D. Smith. Notes on the Strepsipteron Eoxenes. Ann. Ent. Soc. America, 26, pp. 217–233; 27, pp. 468–479 (1933–34).

Pierce, W. D. A Monographic Revision of the Twisted-Winged Insects Comprising the Order Strepsiptera. Bull. U. S. Nat. Mus., 66, 232 pp. (1909). Strepsiptera. Gen. Insectorum, fasc. 121, 54 pp. (1911).
    The Comparative Morphology of the Order Strepsiptera, together with Records and Descriptions of Insects. Proc. U. S. Nat. Mus., 54, pp. 391–501 (1918).

Ulrich, W. Strepsiptera. In Tierwelt Mitteleuropas, 5, Lief. 1, Teil XIII, pp. 1–26, 46 figs. (1930).

ORDER HYMENÓPTERA

Moderate-sized, small or minute, rarely very large; four membranous wings, the fore pair larger and more completely veined; venation rather complete but not complex, sometimes greatly reduced; longitudinal veins greatly modified by peculiarities in branching and direction; head free, mandibulate, but the mouthparts usually adapted for lapping liquid food; antennæ variable, sometimes with very many or very few joints, in the higher forms usually with twelve or thirteen joints; eyes usually moderately large; ocelli nearly always present; prothorax not free; legs similar; tarsi nearly always five-jointed; abdomen usually with six or seven visible segments, the first segment fused with the thorax and not forming a part of the apparent abdomen; no cerci; ovipositor usually sting-like, sometimes saw-like, occasionally greatly elongate.

Metamorphosis complete; larvæ caterpillar-like in the more primitive families, legless in the higher forms; pupæ free, sometimes enclosed in a cocoon. Habits varied, phytophagous, predatory, or parasitic. Sawflies, Wood-wasps, Ichneumon-flies, Ants, Wasps and Bees.

There is no close agreement concerning the family divisions in the Chalastogastra, especially in the higher forms and it is probable that the future will see changes in grouping. Among the Terebrantia there is less difference of opinion. The Ichneumonidæ and Braconidæ include many diverse types and are of greater rank than most of the other families, but attempts to divide them have not been satisfactory. The wasps and bees on the other hand have been separated into families on far less important characters. Among the Ichneumonoidea and more primitive wasps, some of the family divisions are undoubtedly artificial and must be regarded as tentative only.

Adults

1. Abdomen broadly sessile, attached over a large area (Fig. 887); trochanters two-jointed (Fig. 896); hind wing with three basal cells. Suborder CHALASTOGÁSTRA (*SÝMPHYTA, SESSILI-VÉNTRES, PHYTÓPHAGA, BOMBÓPTERA*) 2
   Abdomen petiolate or subpetiolate, sharply constricted at the base, never broadly sessile (Figs. 891, 916, 935); trochanters one- or two-jointed; hind wing with less than three basal cells. Suborder CLISTOGÁSTRA (*APÓCRITA, PETIOLÀTA*) 17

2. Fore wings with three radial cells, *i.e.* two radial crossveins present; antennæ many-jointed, but with the three basal joints strongly developed, the third very long. (Fig. 892) . . . .**XYÉLIDÆ**

a. Intercostal vein free for its entire length, ending in a short fork; first transverse radial vein shorter than width of stigma . . . . . . .b
   Intercostal vein fused with subcostal vein, except at tip; first transverse radial vein longer than width of stigma (**Xyèla, Megaxyèla,** Holarc.) . . . . **XYELÌNÆ**

b. Fork of intercostal vein proximal to the first cubital cell; wings densely pubescent c
   Fork of intercostal vein distal to base of first cubital cell; wings bare or sparsely pubescent. (**Macroxyèla,** Nearc.; **Megaxyèla,** Holarc.)
   MACROXYELÌNÆ

c. Apical filament of antenna with nine to twelve joints. (**Pleuroneùra,** Holarc.) . . . . **PLERONEURÌNÆ**
   Apical filament of antenna composed of 24 or more joints. (**Xylècia,** Nearc.) . . . . **XYLECÌÌNÆ**

   Fore wings with only one or two radial cells; third antennal joint only rarely lengthened 3

3. Costal cell divided by a distinct longitudinal vein (the subcosta); antennæ slender, becoming very thin apically, many-jointed; radial cell with one crossvein; second abdominal tergite divided medially . . . . **PAMPHILÌIDÆ**

a. Tarsal claws with a short triangular basal tooth (**Cænolýda,** Palæarc.; **Cephálcia, Acantholýda,** Holarc.) . . . . **CEPHALCÌNÆ**
   Tarsal claws bifid at tip, the inner tooth long (**Pamphílius** (= *Lỳda*), **Neurótoma,** Holarc.) . . . . **PAMPHILÌÌNÆ**

   Costal cell not divided by a longitudinal vein 4

4. Anterior tibiæ with a single apical spur. (Wood-wasps). Superfamily SIRICÒIDEA 5
   Anterior tibiæ with two apical spurs. (Saw-flies). (Superfamily TENTHREDINÒIDEA) 9

5. Fore wings with only one closed cubital cell and one recurrent nervure; antennæ ten- or eleven-jointed, inserted much below the lower margin of the eyes, beneath a frontal ridge; vertex strongly tuberculate. (Orýssus (= Orússus), Eur., N. Am., Austr.; Ophrynòpus, Austr., S. Am.). (IDIOGÁSTRA, ORYSSÒIDEA, ORÚSSIDÆ) .... ORÝSSIDÆ
   Fore wings with two or three closed cubital cells; antennæ inserted above the lower margin of the eyes; two recurrent nervures; antennæ variable. (Figs. 888, 890) 6

6. Pronotum nearly truncate or weakly emarginate behind, its anterior portion not forming a vertical surface; abdomen more or less compressed. (Fig. 888) .... CÉPHIDÆ

a. Labial palpi three-jointed, longer than the four-jointed maxillary palpi. (Àthetocèphus, Madagascar) ...... ATHETOCEPHÌNÆ
   Labial palpi four-jointed, shorter than the six-jointed maxillary palpi. (Cèphus, Jànus, Holarc.) .... CEPHÌNÆ

   Pronotum deeply incurved or emarginate behind, its anterior part forming a more or less vertical surface; abdomen cylindrical....7

7. Parapsidal furrows present; fore wings with a crossvein (Sc) in the costal cell; no triangular plate at the apex of the abdomen; prothorax conical, the pronotum a narrow collar.............8
   Parapsidal furrows absent; fore wings without a crossvein in the costal cell; apex of the abdomen with a triangular or spear-shaped plate; prothorax subquadrate, the pronotum longer. Horntails. (Trèmex, cosmop.; Sìrex, Urócerus, Xèris, Holarc.). (Fig. 890). (UROCÉRIDÆ) .... SIRÍCIDÆ

8. Mesonotum divided by a transverse suture. (Syntéxis, Nearc.). (SYNTÉCTIDÆ) .... SYNTÉXIDÆ
   Mesonotum without a transverse suture .... XIPHYDRÌIDÆ

a. Pronotum with a distinct dorsal surface laterally; not deeply emarginate anteriorly when viewed from above. (Derecýrta, Neotrop.) DERECYRTÌNÆ
   Pronotum without a distinct dorsal surface laterally; deeply emarginate anteriorly when seen from above...................b

b. Maxillary palpi seven-jointed; inner margins of eyes very strongly convergent behind. (Moaxíphia, Austr.) ......MOAXIPHÌINÆ
   Maxillary palpi with six joints or less; inner eye-margins not, or weakly convergent behind c

c. Maxillary palpi six-jointed. (Brachýxiphus, Neotrop.; Nasoxíphia, Palæarc.) .... BRACHYXIPHÌNÆ
   Maxillary with four or five joints...........................d

d. Proepisterna long, in profile much longer than high............e
   Proepisterna short, in profile slightly longer than high. (Konòwia, Holarc.) ....XIPHYDRIÌNÆ, part

e. Maxillary palpi four-jointed (**Euxiphýdria**, Holarc.).
              EUXIPHYDRIÍNÆ
 Maxillary palpi five-jointed ....f
f. Labial palpi four-jointed. (**Hyperxíphia**, widespr.; **Palpixíphia**, Indomal.) ....**HYPERXIPHIÍNÆ**
 Labial palpi three-jointed. (**Xiphýdria**, Holarc....**XIPHYDRIÍNÆ**
9. Posterior margin of the pronotum straight or nearly so; mesonotum very short, never extending much behind the anterior margins of the tegulæ; second abdominal tergite divided medially. (**Megalodóntes**, Palæarc.) ....**MEGALODÓNTIDÆ**
 Posterior margin of the pronotum strongly curved, mesonotum longer, extending well behind the anterior margin of the tegulæ 10

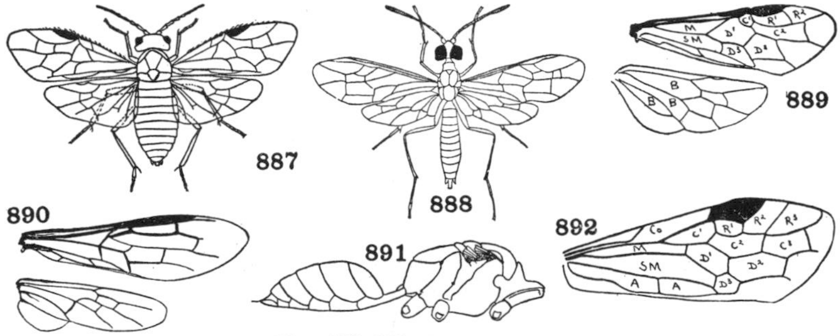

Figs. 887–892. Hymenoptera

887. **Cladius** (Chittenden) Tenthredinidæ.
888. **Cephus** (Marlatt) Cephidæ.
889. **Dolerus**, wings: M, median cell; R1, R2, marginal or radial cells; C1, **C2**, cubital or submarginal cells; D1, D2, D3, first, second and third discoidal cells; SM, submedian cell; B1, B2, B3, basal cells. Tenthredinidæ.
890. **Tremex**, wings. Uroceridæ.
891. **Chlorion**, lateral view of thorax and abdomen (Fernald) Sphecidæ.
892. **Xyela**, fore wing. Lettering as in fig. 889; Co, costal cell; A, A, anal cells (MacGillivray) Xyelidæ.

10. Antennæ clavate; transverse median and basal veins interstitial; abdomen more or less swollen or globose....................11
 Antennæ not clavate; filiform, serrate, or pectinate.............12
11. Radial cell divided by a crossvein (Fig. 889); abdomen angled laterally so that the tergites are sharply divided into a dorsal and ventral surface; abdomen of female strongly globose. (**Címbex**, **Trichiosòma**, Holarc.) .... **CIMBÍCIDÆ**
 Radial cell not divided; abdomen rounded laterally, not angled or carinate; abdomen not greatly swollen. (**Pérga**, **Xylopérga**, Austr.) .... **PÉRGIDÆ**

12. Antennæ with only three joints, the third very long, sometimes split in the male. (Árge (= Hylótoma), widespr.; Labidárge, S. Am.; Schizócera (= Sterictóphora), Eur., Am.). (HYLOTÓM-IDÆ) ....ÁRGIDÆ
    Antennæ with four or more joints..........................13
13. First discoidal cell petiolate above, i.e. the cubitus arising from the basal vein; antennæ four-jointed, the third joint very long. (Blasticótoma, one European species).....BLASTICOTÓMIDÆ
    First discoidal cell almost never petiolate above, the cubitus arising beyond the basal vein; antennæ with at least six joints........14
14. Radial cell simple, without a crossvein........................15
    Radial cell divided by a crossvein (Fig. 889); antennæ commonly filiform, rarely with some of the joints toothed or with projections, with at least seven and usually with nine joints. Cosmopolitan but scarce in the tropics. (Ametastègia, Blennocámpa, Caliròa, Hoplocámpa, Tenthrèdo, Allántus, Dólerus, Macròphya, Selándria, Fenùsa, Holarc.) .... TENTHREDÍNIDÆ

a. Female wingless; scutellum enlarged and covering the reduced mesonotum. (Cacosýndia, Palæarc.)......BLENNOCAMPÌNÆ, part
   Both sexes winged..b
b. Radial cell divided by a cross-vein...........................c
   Radial cell not divided by a cross-vein (see couplet 14).
                                                    NEMATÌNÆ
c. Anal cell in fore wings not petiolate..........................d
   Anal cell in fore wings petiolate...........BLENNOCAMPÌNÆ
d. Two cubital cells, the second very long and receiving both recurrent nervures .... DOLERÌNÆ
   Four, rarely three cubital cells...............................e
e. Basal vein and cubitus meeting the subcosta at the same point, or very nearly so .... SELANDRIÌNÆ
   Basal vein meeting the subcosta considerably before the base of the cubitus .... TENTHREDINÌNÆ

15. Antennæ filiform 16
    Antennæ of a different conformation, many-jointed, serrate in the female and pectinate in the male. (Diprìon (= Lophyrus) (Pine sawflies). Holarc.; Perreyia, Neotrop.; Pterygóphorus, Austr.). (Including PERREYÌIDÆ, PTERYGOPHÓRIDÆ, LOBOCERÁTIDÆ, LOPHÝRIDÆ) ....DIPRIÓNIDÆ
16. Antennæ nine-jointed. (Pachynématus, Pteronídea (= Ptéronus), Holarc.; Pontània (Willow gall sawflies); Nématus (N. erichsonii, Larch sawfly); Pristíphora; Diphádnus). (NEMATÌNÆ).
                                      Some TENTHREDÍNIDÆ
    Antennæ six-jointed; posterior tibiæ with preapical spurs. (Acordulécera, Am.) ....ACORDULECÉRIDÆ

17. Last abdominal sternite divided longitudinally, the ovipositor issuing some distance before the tip of the abdomen (Fig. 893) and provided with a pair of narrow sheaths which equal it in length. Trochanter divided into two distinct joints, except in some forms without stigma; fore wing either with or without a costal cell. (TEREBRĂNTIA) 18

Last abdominal sternite not divided longitudinally, the ovipositor issuing from the tip of the abdomen as a sting (rarely absent) without a pair of exserted sheaths (Fig. 894). Trochanter consisting of a single joint (Fig. 897), or if rarely divided, the second part is very closely attached to and not distinctly separated from the femur (except Trigonalidæ); fore wing always (except Rhopalosomatidæ) with a costal cell. Ants, Wasps and Bees. (ACULEATA) 73

18. Winged 19

Wingless or with the wings greatly reduced in size............59

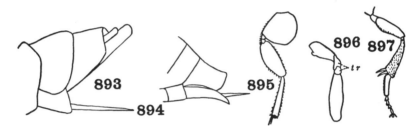

Figs. 893–897. Hymenoptera

893. **Ichneumon,** apex of abdomen, with ovipositor. Ichneumonidæ.
894. **Epeolus,** apex of abdomen, with ovipositor. Melectidæ.
895. **Elasmus,** basal segments of leg (Silvestri) Elasmidæ.
896. **Ichneumon,** basal segments of leg; tr. two-jointed trochanter (Sharp) Ichneumonidæ.
897. Hind leg of a bee (Riley).

19. Fore wings with a stigma which is usually triangular or rarely very slender or linear (Fig. 900); costal vein well developed as far as the stigma; abdomen usually with the sternites membranous and with a median fold; antennæ usually with more than sixteen joints; wing venation ordinarily well developed. Ichneumon-flies. (ICHNEUMONÒIDEA) (*TRĬSTEGA*) 20

Fore wings without a stigma, the marginal vein if present linear, not swollen to form a stigma; costal vein much thinner than the subcostal (Sc + R) (Figs. 906, 907); abdomen with the ventral surface hard and chitinous, without a median fold; antennæ with never more than eighteen joints and rarely more than thirteen; wings with very incomplete venation........................32

20. Costal and subcostal (Sc + R) veins separated, enclosing a narrow costal cell; abdominal sternites chitinized (Figs. 904, 905)......21
Costal and subcostal veins confluent, no costal cell (Fig. 900)....28

21. Mesonotum with a sharp median groove or linear furrow; notauli absent; abdomen elongate oval; body more or less cylindrical; ovipositor prominent, usually extremely long. (Megályra, Austr.; Dinápsis, S. Afr.). (Including DINÁPSIDÆ). MEGALÝRIDÆ
Mesonotum without median groove; or if with a median impressed area, also with notauli....................................22

22. Abdomen inserted on the thorax, far above the hind coxæ, commonly on a nipple-shaped protuberance; antennæ with 13 or 14 joints 23
Abdomen inserted normally, low down, at the apex of the thorax, and quite close to the hind coxæ.........................25

23. Fore wing with two recurrent nervures; two more or less completely closed cubital cells, the second one sometimes partly open, due to a partial loss of the apical intercubitus. (Fig. 904). (Aùlacus, Aulacostèthus, cosmop.) Parasites of beetles and saw-flies .... AULÁCIDÆ
Fore wing with one or no recurrent nervure; only one distinctly closed cubital cell, or none..............................24

24. Prothorax long, forming an elongate neck; abdomen long, gradually clavate; radial cell of fore wing long, pointed; fore wing folded lengthwise at rest. (Fig. 905). (Gasterúption, Rhydinofœnus, cosmop.; Hyptiogáster, Austr.). Parasites of wasps and bees .... GASTERUPTIÓNIDÆ
Prothorax short; body of abdomen short, orbicular, borne on a narrow cylindrical pedicel; radial cell short and broad, or absent; fore wing not folded. (Evània, cosmop.; Brachygáster, Eur.; Hýptia, Am.). Parasites of cockroach eggs..............EVANÌIDÆ

25. Two or three closed cubital cells........................26
Only one closed cubital cell, or none......................27

26. Antennæ with 18 joints or more; head large, quadrate. (See couplet 93) .... TRIGONÁLIDÆ
Antennæ with 12 or 13 joints. (See couplet 99).
RHOPALOSOMÁTIDÆ

27. Antennæ setaceous, multiarticulate, with 30 joints or more; abdomen long and slender; ovipositor long; hind femora swollen and toothed before the apex; head tuberculate above. (Stéphanus, cosmop.; Megíschus, tropicopol.; Hemistéphanus, S. A., Austr.; Diastéphanus, As., Afr., Austr.) ....STEPHÁNIDÆ
Antennæ 14-jointed; abdomen long and slender; ovipositor very short; hind femora without teeth; head not tuberculate above. (If the body of the abdomen is compressed, rounded (♀) or broadly ovate (♂), borne on a slender cylindrical petiole, com-

pare Roproniidæ, couplet 83). (Monómachus, S. Am., Austr.; Tetracònus, S. Am.) .... MONOMÁCHIDÆ

28. Mandibles widely separated, not meeting when closed, the tips concave, the teeth curving outward instead of inward. (Dacnùsa, Phænocárpa, Aphæreta, Alýsia, cosmop.; Lysiógnatha, N. Am.). (Including LYSIOGNÁTHIDÆ) .... ALYSÌIDÆ
Mandibles attached normally, their tips opposed and meeting when closed 29

29. Ventral abdominal segments soft and membranous, with a median fold 30
Ventral abdominal segments hard, heavily chitinized; scutellum armed with a sharp spiniform process. (Agriótypus, Holarc.).
AGRIOTÝPIDÆ

30. Fore wing with two recurrent nervures (except Ophionellus and Hymenopharsalia); first cubital and first discoidal cells not separated; all the abdominal segments freely movable, except in very rare cases. (Figs. 893, 896, 898, 902). A very large cosmopolitan family. (Including OPHIONÉLLIDÆ, MYERSÌIDÆ). This very large family is divided into a number of subfamilies and the current classification involves many exceptions. Recently the number of subfamilies has been greatly increased, with good reason, but we are unable to present here an adequate, workable key.
ICHNEUMÓNIDÆ
Fore wing with only one, or without any recurrent nervure (Fig. 900); usually with the second and third abdominal segments immovably united above 31

31. Abdomen extremely slender, three times as long as the head and thorax together, the segments freely movable; tip of propodeum prolonged beyond the hind coxæ. (Hymenopharsàlia, Ophionéllus, Am.). (See couplet 30)............. A few ICHNEUMÓNIDÆ
Abdomen shorter; propodeum not thus prolonged; venation sometimes considerably reduced. A large cosmopolitan family. (Including APHIDÌIDÆ, CAPITONÌIDÆ, PÁCHYLOMMÁTIDÆ, NÉORHACÓDIDÆ) .... BRACÓNIDÆ

a. Clypeus semicircularly emarginate below and forming with the mandibles a more or less circular opening or cavity............b
Clypeus not emarginate below, or at most with a broad, shallow emargination, not forming with the mandibles such an opening..i

b. Abdomen sessile, sometimes with the base considerably narrowed, but the first segment not forming a distinct petiole............c
Abdomen petiolate, the first segment greatly lengthened, at least three times as long as broad at apex, and often very long and slender with the remainder of the abdomen suddenly much wider; antennæ usually very slender. (Spàthius, widespr.; Stephanískus,

Ogmophásmus, Ethiop.; **Psenóbolus**, Neotrop.; **Cantharóctonus,** Nearc.). (Including *STEPHANISCÎNÆ*) ..... **SPATHIÎNÆ**
c. Head behind with the occiput, temples and cheeks rounded, without marginal line ....d
Head behind with a distinct carinate, raised marginal line which is always distinct on the sides although sometimes more or less obsolete either above or below............................e

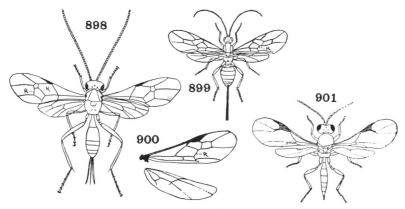

Figs. 898–901. Hymenoptera

898. Cryptus, R, R, recurrent nervures. Ichneumonidæ.
899. Microbracon (Hunter and Hinds) Braconidæ.
900. Rhogas, wings, R, recurrent nervure. Braconidæ.
901. Lysiphlebus. Braconidæ.

d. Nervulus (transverse median nervure) originating just basal to the basal vein or at the same point, rarely slightly further toward the apex of the wing; usually large species, often with colored wings. (Fig. 899). **Vípio, Microbràcon** (including **Habrobràcon**), **Iphiaulax, Glyptomórpha,** cosmop.; **Chelonogástra,** Ethiop., Indomal,; **Platybràcon,** Indomal.; **Gastrothèca,** Ethiop.). (Including *APHRASTOBRACONÎNÆ*) .... **BRACONÎNÆ**
Nervulus originating well beyond the lower end of the basal vein. (**Exothècus,** widespr.; **Spinària,** Ethiop., Indomal.; **Mesobràcon,** Ethiop.) .... **EXOTHECÎNÆ**
e. Fore wings with three submarginal cells, all completely formed; very rarely without wings.................................f
Fore wings with only two submarginal cells, the first sometimes incompletely formed; females occasionally wingless............h
f. Head cubical, large, and bulging behind the eyes, rarely slightly transverse. (**Doŕyctes, Dendrosòter, Odontobràcon,** widespr.). **DORYCTÎNÆ**

Head clearly transverse, usually much wider than long; not widened or bulging behind the eyes.................................g

g. Subdiscoidal vein arising at the upper corner of the second discoidal cell, forming a continuous line with the upper edge of this cell. (**Hormìus, Hormiópterus,** widespr.; **Chrémylus,** Palæarc.).
HORMIÌNÆ
Subdiscoidal vein originating from the outer side of the second discoidal cell which is angulate at the point of origin, this vein lying below the level of the upper side of the cell. (Fig. 900). (**Rhògas,** cosmop.; **Rhýssalus, Clinocéntrus; Gyroneùron,** Ethiop., Indomal.) .... **RHOGADÌNÆ**

h. Head, when seen from above, large, cubical; abdominal tergites almost always very clearly separated; female always winged; hind wing of male often with a stigma-like thickening on the costal margin. (**Hecábolus, Écphylus,** Holarc.; **Heterospìlus,** widespr.).
HECABOLÌNÆ
Head, when seen from above, strongly transverse, much wider than long; sutures of abdomen obsolete above except at the base; female commonly wingless; hind wing of male without false stigma. (**Pámbolus,** widespr.) .... **PAMBOLÌNÆ**

i. Abdomen with the tergites separated by distinct sutures, all the tergites beyond the third freely movable; if rarely all are fused, the abdomen is strongly clavate............................j
Abdomen with the tergites fused to form a rigid dorsal shell or carapace which is either entirely without sutures or with these indicated only as fine grooves...............................w

j. Abdomen sessile or subsessile; if the first segment is rarely elongate its lateral margins are straight; venation of wings not reduced...k
Abdomen petiolate, wing venation often much reduced in the smaller species x

k. Marginal cell either very narrow, or incompletely formed with the radial vein weak or wanting apically; second submarginal cell usually small or imperfectly formed.........................l
Marginal cell never much narrowed, second submarginal cell large and fully formed.......................................p

l. Marginal cell very narrow, the radial vein almost always distinct to the tip...m
Marginal cell not narrow, more or less incompletely formed apically ....n

m. Palpi very short; tarsi long, slender, with minute or very indistinct claws. Minute species parasitic on ants. (**Neoneùrus, Elasmosòma,** Holarc.) .... **NEONEURÌNÆ**
Palpi long, well developed; tarsi not unusually lengthened, with large, often toothed or pectinate claws. (**Crémnops, Disòphrys, Ágathis, Mícrodus, Órgilus,** cosmop.; **Braunsia,** Ethiop., Indomal.;

Eárinus, widespr.). (*AGATHÌNÆ*). (Including *ANEURO-BRACONÌNÆ*) .... AGATHIDÌNÆ

n. Second submarginal cell minute or incompletely formed; marginal cell wanting except at extreme base........................ o

Second submarginal cell large, although more or less weakly defined apically; apical part of marginal cell weakly defined, but the cell is clearly marked by a strongly curved and very delicately chitinized vein. (Cardiochìles, widespr.; Toxoneùron, Am.; Laminitársus, Malay.) .... CARDIOCHILÌNÆ

o. Radial vein consisting of two nearly equal sections with the stub of a third. (Neorhacòdes, Palæarc.). This group is by some placed in the Ichneumonidæ .... NEORHACODÌNÆ

Radial vein composed of only a single basal section. (Microgáster, Apantèles, Microplìtis, cosmop.; Mìrax, widespr.; Oligoneùrus, Neotrop.) .... MICROGASTRÌNÆ

p. Fore wings with three submarginal cells...................... q

Fore wings with only two submarginal cells.................... u

q. Legs long and slender, the spurs of the hind tibiæ often very long; body usually slender with the abdomen elongate; head strongly transverse. (Macrocéntrus, cosmop.; Zèle, Palæarc., Am.; Aulacocéntrum, Austrozèle, Australas.; Amicrocéntrum, Ethiop.; Neozèle, Neotrop.) .... MACROCENTRÌNÆ

Legs not long and slender, femora stout; abdomen usually stout and short, rarely elongate; tibial spurs not elongate; head large and thick in all forms with elongate abdomen................ r

r. Abdomen inserted low down on the propodeum, between the hind coxæ; usually small or minute species........................ s

Abdomen inserted distinctly above the hind coxæ; abdomen often elongate; head large, cubical, often with the vertex deeply impressed; rather large or moderate-sized species. (Hélcon, Gymnóscelus, Aspicólpus, widespr.; Eumacrocéntrus, Nearc.; Austrohélcon, Schauinslándia, Austr.; Cenocœlius, widespr.). (Including *CENOCŒLIÌNÆ*) .... HELCONÌNÆ

s. Marginal cell very short, its upper margin no longer than the stigma. (Ichneùtes, Holarc.; Próterops, widespr.; Ichneutídea, Proteropòides, Nearc.) .... ICHNEUTÌNÆ

Marginal cell long, much longer than the stigma................ t

t. Head above not margined; anal cell of fore wing without trace of a crossvein; clypeus often shallowly emarginate, leaving an elliptical opening between the mandibles when closed; second submarginal cell often much shorter above than below. (Òpius, cosmop.; Biósteres, Diachásma, Eurýtenes, widespr.; Rhinòplus, Ethiop.) .... OPIÌNÆ

Head margined above; anal cell of fore wing often with an incomplete crossvein; clypeus not emarginate, fitting close to the mandibles when closed; second submarginal cell rarely noticeably shortened above. (Diospìlus, widespr.; Dyscolètes, Holarc.; Eudiospìlus, Neodiospìlus, Ethiop.) .... DIOSPILÌNÆ

u. Second discoidal cell not completely closed below at apex, the posterior part of its outer side without the usual vein. (Brachístes (= Calýptus), Eubádizon, widespr.). (CALYPTÌNÆ).

BRACHISTÌNÆ

Second discoidal cell completely closed below at apex by a vein....v

v. Last section of radial vein curved, marginal cell very short, not nearly extènding to the wing tip. (Leìophron, Centístes, Holarc.; Centistìna, Ethiop.) .... LEIOPHRONÌNÆ
Last section of radial vein straight, the marginal cell long, extending almost to the tip of the wing. (Blàcus, widespr.; Pygóstolus, Holarc.) .... BLACÌNÆ

w. Fore wings with three cubital cells. (Chelònus, Chelonélla, Phanerótoma, Ascogáster, cosmop.; Sphæropyx, Palæarc.; Minánga, Pachychelònus, Ethiop.) .... CHELONÌNÆ
Fore wings with two closed cubital cells. (Triáspis (= Sigálphus), cosmop.). (SIGALPHINÆ) .... TRIASPIDÌNÆ

x. Hind wings with two closed basal cells, the second sometimes incomplete ....y
Hind wings with only one, or without any closed basal cell......aa

y. Fore wings with three submarginal cells, the second one always completely closed, their venation not reduced................z
Fore wings with only two submarginal cells; venation usually much reduced, the radial cell usually short. (Eùphorus, Holarc.; Perilìtus, Dinocámpus, widespr.; Eustalócerus, Cosmóphorus, Holarc.) .... EUPHORÌNÆ

z. Second submarginal cell about as long as high; antennæ long and slender, filiform; abdominal tergites separated by sutures. (Meteòrus, cosmop.) .... METEORÌNÆ
Second submarginal cell much longer than high; antennæ 18-jointed, the joints toward the apex bead-like; second tergite covering the whole abdomen beyond the petiole. (Helorimórpha, widespr.).

HELORIMORPHÌNÆ

aa. Abdomen inserted low down on the propodeum, between the hind coxæ; fore wings with one, two, or rarely three submarginal cells, the cubitus if present, not arising from the marginal cell. (Fig. 901). (Aphídius (= Íncubus), Pràon, Éphedrus, Trióxys, widespr.; Lysíphlebus, Holarc.). (INCUBÌNÆ)......APHIDIÌNÆ
Abdomen inserted high up on the propodeum, above the level of the hind coxæ; fore wings with two submarginal cells, the cubitus arising from the narrow, triangular marginal cell. (Paxylómma (= Pachylómma)) .... PAXYLOMMATÌNÆ

32. Sides of pronotum extending back to the tegulæ; antennæ not elbowed; marginal cell present, more or less complete; stigma very
rarely well developed. (Fig. 907). Gall wasps. CYNIPOI-
DEA 33
Pronotum not extending back to the tegulæ (except Mymaridæ)
(Fig. 910); antennæ more or less distinctly elbowed, often thickened apically, the basal joint usually much elongated: a well
defined quadrate or linear stigma (marginal vein) usually present. (Fig. 906). Chalcis-flies. (CHALCIDÒIDEA) 42
33. Dorsal abdominal plates (tergites) meeting along the venter and
completely enclosing all the ventral plates, except sometimes a
part of the hypopygium; parasitic species....................34
Dorsal abdominal plates usually extending well down on the sides
of the abdomen, but not meeting along the venter; all, or nearly
all of the ventral plates visible 41

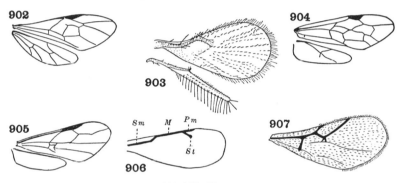

Figs. 902–907. Hymenoptera

902. **Ophion**, wings. Ichneumonidæ.
903. **Trichogramma**, wings (Girault) Trichogrammatidæ.
904. **Aulacus**, wings. Aulacidæ.
905. **Gasteruption**, wings. Gasteruptionidæ.
906. **Chalcid** fly, fore wing, diagrammatic. *Sm*, submarginal vein; *M*, marginal vein;
Pm, postmarginal vein; *St*, stigmal vein.
907. **Gall wasp**, fore wing, diagrammatic (Kieffer).

34. Fore wings with a well developed stigma, their venation greatly
reduced. (**Pterostígma**, Ethiop.) ......PTEROSTIGMÁTIDÆ
Fore wings without a distinct stigma.......................35
35. Hind femora stout, with a tooth below; ovipositor of female longer
than the body. (**Oberthuerella**, Ethiop.)
OBERTHUERÉLLIDÆ
Hind femora not swollen nor toothed; ovipositor very short.....36
36. Scutellum cupuliform, *i.e.*, with a cup-shaped elevation on the disk;

antennæ with 11–16 joints in the male, 13 in the female. (Eucòila, widespr.) .... EUCÒILIDÆ

Scutellum not cupuliform................................37

37. Abdominal petiole attached to the apex of the propodeum......38
Abdominal petiole attached far above the base of the hind coxæ; propodeum with a median furrow; fourth tergite much lengthened. (Liópteron, Pèras, Plastibàlia, Pseudibàlia). LIOPTÉRIDÆ

38. Second abdominal tergite about half as long as the abdomen; body not coarsely sculptured. (Chàrips, Nephýcta)....CHARÍPIDÆ
Second abdominal tergite less than half as long as the abdomen...39

39. Second tergite very narrow, tongue-shaped. (Aspìcera, Tavarèsia).
ASPICÉRIDÆ
Second tergite not tongue-shaped..........................40

40. Abdomen distinctly petiolate; second tergite slightly longer than the third. (Anácharis, Ægilops) ....ANACHARÍTIDÆ
Abdomen sessile, never with a distinct petiole. (Figìtes, Lonchídia).
FIGÍTIDÆ

41. Basal joint of the hind tarsi twice as long as the others united, second joint with a long process externally which reaches to the tip of the fourth joint; abdomen greatly compressed, curved like a pruning knife, much longer than the remainder of the body. Parasitic species. (Ibàlia, Eur., N. Am.).....IBALÌIDÆ
Basal joint of hind tarsi much shorter; second joint simple, without process. Mostly gall-making species, almost entirely Holarc. (Cỳnips, Aulacídea, Diástrophus, Rhodìtes, Disholcáspis, Amphíbolips) .... CYNÍPIDÆ

42. Hind wings exceedingly narrow, linear, the base forming a long stalk; ovipositor issuing barely before the tip of the abdomen; antennæ with the scape not greatly elongated, usually swollen and compressed and without ring joint; very minute species with long wing fringe 43
Hind wings never very narrow, not linear nor with a long stalk at the base; ovipositor issuing decidedly before the tip of the abdomen; antennæ elbowed (Figs. 909, 912, 913) with long scape and usually with from one to three minute ring joints; wing fringe almost always much shorter....................44

43. Prothorax reaching the tegulæ; spur of front tibiæ simple, not forming a strigil. (Mymarómma).........MYMAROMMÁTIDÆ
Prothorax not extending so far back as the tegulæ; front tibial spur forming a strigil. (Polynèma, Gonatócerus, Aláptus, Ánaphes) (Including LYMÆNÓNIDÆ) ....MYMÁRIDÆ

44. Tarsi five-jointed (rarely four-jointed or less in certain wingless males); axillæ with their anterior margins forming a more or less straight line, their sides not extended in front of the tegulæ (Fig. 908); spur of front tibia strong, curved..............45

Tarsi three- or four-jointed (five-jointed or heteromerous only in the females of one or two genera); axillæ extended strongly and obliquely forward at the sides, well in advance of the tegulæ (Fig. 910); spur of front tibia usually weak.................57

45. Head of female long, oblong, with a deep longitudinal groove above; front and hind legs very stout, the middle ones very much more slender; males almost always wingless, with stout, short, three- to nine-jointed antennæ. (Fig. 917). Tropicopolitan. Fig-insects. (**Blastóphaga** (*B. psènes* = *grossòrum*, Fig caprifier), tropicopolitan; **Ágaon, Ceratosòlen**, Old World; **Tétrapus**, Neotrop.; **Pleistodóntes**, Austr.) ....AGAÓNTIDÆ

Of a different conformation..............................46

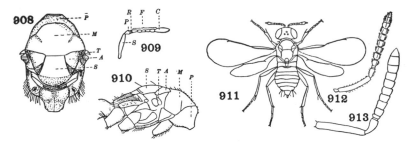

Figs. 908–913. **Hymenoptera**

908. **Pteromalus**, thorax from above. *P*, pronotum; *M*, mesonotum; *T*, tegula; *A*, axilla; *S*, scutellum. Pteromalidæ.
909. Chalcid fly, diagram of antenna. *P*, pedicel; *R*, ring-joints; *F*, funicle; *C*, club; *S*, scape.
910. **Eulophus**, thorax seen from side. Lettering as in Fig. 908. Eulophidæ.
911. **Coccophagus** (Howard) Eulophidæ.
912. **Dibrachys**, antenna of female. Pteromalidæ.
913. **Dibrachys**, antenna of male. Pteromalidæ.

46. Mesopleura rarely large, with an oblique femoral groove or impression; spur of middle tibia normal, not enlarged..........47

Mesopleura large, entire; flat, without femoral groove in the female and usually in the male; spur of middle tibia usually very large and stout, often fringed with minute spines internally. An extremely varied, abundant, cosmopolitan group. (**Eupélmus, Anástatus, Metapélma, Encýrtus, Ageniáspis, Hunteréllus, Copidosòma, Signíphora**). (Including *EUPÉLMIDÆ, SIGNIPHÓRIDÆ*, and *TANAOSTIGMÁTIDÆ*). (*EUTRICHOSOMÁTIDÆ*) .... ENCÝRTIDÆ

47. Hind tibiæ with two apical spurs...........................48

Hind tibiæ with a single apical spur; ovipositor rarely long; mandibles with three or four teeth at apex; small black, bronzed, or metallic species. (Figs. 908, 912, 913). A large cosmopolitan family. (Pterómalus, Díbrachys, Nasònia, Diglòchis, Pachyneùron, Spalángia). (Including *SPALANGÌIDÆ*).

PTEROMÁLIDÆ

48. Mandibles sickle-shaped, usually with one or two teeth within; thorax greatly elevated; scutellum usually much enlarged and produced behind; abdomen compressed, usually on a long, slender pedicel, the second segment very large. (Fig. 920). Cosmopolitan, but almost entirely tropical. (Kápala, Orasèma, Schizaspídia, Thoracántha, Stílbula). (*EUCHARÍTIDÆ*) . EUCHARÍDIDÆ

Mandibles strong and stout, generally with three or four teeth at apex; thorax not or very slightly elevated; axillæ separated from the mesonotum 49

49. Hind coxæ very large, long, five or six times larger than the front ones 50

Hind coxæ never very large, not conspicuously larger than the front ones 54

50. Hind coxæ more or less triangular in cross-section, sharply ridged above; hind femora usually simple, rarely swollen and with a tooth beneath; if denticulate beneath, the ovipositor is long 51

Hind coxæ cylindrical, long 52

51. Notauli present, ovipositor exserted, usually very long; abdomen not coarsely pitted or punctured. Cosmopolitan. (Tórymus (= *Callimome*), Diámorus, Monodontomèrus, Podágrion, Megastígmus (Seed chalcids), Idárnes). (*CALLIMÓMIDÆ*). (Including *PODAGRIÓNIDÆ*) . . . . TORÝMIDÆ

Notauli absent or obsolete; ovipositor hidden; abdomen of female conical, elongate, usually with rows of deep pits or large punctures. Mainly Eur. and N. Am. (Órmyrus, Tribæus).

ORMÝRIDÆ

52. Hind femora greatly swollen, and toothed or denticulate beneath, their tibiæ curved and oblique at apex; prothorax not elongate or narrowed 53

Hind femora not swollen, simple; all the legs very long and slender; abdomen extremely long and slender; prothorax much elongated, forming a narrow neck; ovipositor very long. S. Am. and Austr. (Leptofœnus (= *Pelecinélla*)). (*PELECINÉLLIDÆ*).

LEPTOFŒNIDÆ

53. Fore wings folded longitudinally in repose; ovipositor long, curving upwards and forward over the dorsum of the abdomen. (Leucóspis, cosmop.; Polistomórpha, S. Am.; Epexoclænòides, Ind.-Austr.) . . . . LEUCOSPÍDIDÆ

Fore wings not folded; ovipositor only very rarely long, and then not thus upcurved; tip of abdomen sometimes drawn out as a slender stiff process. (Fig. 914). Cosmopolitan, more abundant in the tropics. (**Chálcis, Phasgonóphora, Spilochálcis, Smìcra, Haltichélla, Dirrhìnus**) .... **CHALCÍDIDÆ**

54. Pronotum wide, quadrate, not or scarcely narrower than the mesonotum; mesonotum usually very coarsely sculptured 55
Pronotum narrower, usually much narrowed in front or transverse linear, rarely as wide as the mesonotum; mesonotum usually finely sculptured 56

55. Abdomen rounded or ovate, more or less compressed, second tergite never very large; the hypopygium usually produced in the female; black or yellowish species. Cosmopolitan. (**Harmolìta** (= *Isosòma*) (Joint-worms), **Eurýtoma, Decátoma, Áxima, Bruchóphagus, Rìleya**). (Figs. 916, 921) .... **EURYTÓMIDÆ**
Abdomen small, subtriangular, the second, or fused second and third tergite covering most of its surface; thorax very large; short, metallic or submetallic species. (Fig. 919). (**Perilámpus**, cosmop.; **Trichilogáster**, Austr.; **Chrysolámpus**, N. Am., Eur.).
PERILÁMPIDÆ

56. Mesepisternum not large and triangular; none of the femora noticeably swollen; small bronzed or green species. (**Semiotéllus, Lamprótatus, Miscogáster**, cosmop.; **Lèlaps**, Am.). (Including *TRIDÝMIDÆ*) .... **MISCOGÁSTRIDÆ**
Mesepisternum large and triangular; either the front or hind femora more or less swollen, and sometimes serrate; usually of metallic color. (Fig. 915). (**Chalcodéctus**, Am.; **Epistènia**, cosmop.; **Cleónymus, Cheirópachys**, Eur., N. Am.; **Ptinòbius**, N. Am.).
CLEONÝMIDÆ

57. Hind coxæ normal, not enlarged; mesopleura with a groove or impression 58
Hind coxæ much enlarged and dilated (Fig. 895), their femora compressed; marginal vein greatly elongated; very small, usually black species. (**Elásmus**, cosmop.; **Euryíschia**, Austr.).
ELÁSMIDÆ

58. Tarsi four-jointed (five-jointed or heteromerous in the females of one or two genera); wing hairs not placed in rows or lines; wings usually narrow. A very extensive but poorly known cosmopolitan family. (Figs. 910, 911, 918). (**Tetrástichus, Aphelìnus, Melittòbia, Ablèrus, Ootetrástichus, Epléctrus, Eùlophus**). (Including *TETRASTÍCHIDÆ, APHELÍNIDÆ, ELACHÉRTIDÆ* and *ENTEDÓNTIDÆ*) .... **EULÓPHIDÆ**
Tarsi three-jointed; wings broad, with the wing hairs usually arranged in bands or lines; marginal and stigmal veins united to form a strongly recurved stem (Fig. 903). (**Trichográmma** (= *Pentárthron, Oóphthora*)) ...... **TRICHOGRAMMÁTIDÆ**

59. Antennæ distinctly elbowed, the scape long and the flagellum generally swollen toward the tip (Figs. 909, 912, 913) 60

Antennæ not elbowed, usually filiform or tapering toward the
tip 69
60. Head with a deep triangular impression anteriorly............61
Head normal, without such impression......................62

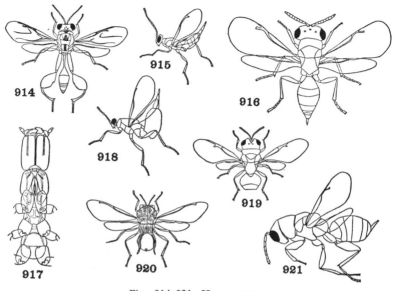

Figs. 914–921. Hymenoptera

914. **Xanthomelanus** (Ashmead) Chalcididæ.
915. **Trigonoderus** (Ashmead) Cleonymidæ.
916. **Bruchophagus** (Urbahns) Eurytomidæ.
917. **Sycophaga**, underside of head and thorax (Grandi) Agaontidæ.
918. **Paracrias** (Ashmead) Eulophidæ.
919. **Perilampus** (Ashmead) Perilampidæ.
920. **Kapala** (Ashmead) Eucharididæ.
921. **Bephratoides** (Brues) Eurytomidæ.

61. Abdomen short, of normal form, not pointed or enlarged apically.
    (Wingless males of Idarnini). (See couplet 51).

    Some **TORÝMIDÆ**

    Abdomen broadly sessile, much drawn out into a point apically,
    or broadened at tip. (Wingless males). (See couplet 45).

    AGAÓNTIDÆ
62. Pronotum as long as the mesonotum and scutellum together; abdo-
    men with only four visible segments. (A single species, Aliènus,
    S. Afr.) .... **ALIÉNIDÆ**
    Of different conformation..................................63

63. Tarsi five-jointed 64
   Tarsi four-jointed (see couplet 58).........A few EULÓPHIDÆ
64. Mesopleura large, entire, without a femoral groove. (See couplet
   46) ....A few ENCÝRTIDÆ
   Mesopleura with an oblique femoral groove or impression......65
65. Hind coxæ large, more or less triangular in cross-section, ridged
   above. (See couplet 51)..................A few TORÝMIDÆ
   Hind coxæ small, not ridged above.........................66
66. Femora of normal size, not greatly swollen on the front or hind
   legs; mesopleura small 67
   Femora of either the front or hind legs greatly swollen, mesopleura
   large, triangular. (See couplet 56)......A few CLEONÝMIDÆ
67. Hind tibiæ with a single apical spur. (See couplet 47).
                                    A few PTEROMÁLIDÆ
   Hind tibiæ with two apical spurs..........................68
68. Pronotum wide, quadrate. (See couplet 55).
                                    A few EURYTÓMIDÆ
   Pronotum narrow, usually narrowed in front or transversely linear.
   (See couplet 56)..................A few MISCOGÁSTRIDÆ
69. Abdominal petiole cylindrical, rarely very short; abdomen much
   compressed; antennæ frequently swollen apically or clavate....70
   Abdominal petiole, if well developed, arcuate, or curved toward
   the tip, rarely compressed; antennæ never enlarged apically....71
70. Tergites meeting along the venter and completely enclosing the
   sternites. (See couplet 40).................A few FIGÍTIDÆ
   Tergites not meeting along the venter; all, or nearly all the sternites
   visible. (See couplet 41)..................Some CYNÍPIDÆ
71. Second and third tergites immovably united; antennæ with more
   than twenty-four joints. (See couplet 31). A few BRACÓNIDÆ
   Second and third tergites freely movable like the other segments;
   very rarely indistinctly separated........................72
72. Abdominal petiole rather suddenly broadened and bent downward
   near the tip, its spiracles placed well beyond the middle. (See
   couplet 30)......................A few ICHNEUMÓNIDÆ
   Abdominal petiole very short or not of this conformation; very
   small black species. (Some apterous Aphidiinæ). (See couplet
   31) ....A few BRACÓNIDÆ
73. Pronotum extending entirely or almost back to the tegulæ, its
   hind angles usually not lobed, or the tegulæ absent; trochanters
   occasionally two-jointed 74
   Pronotum shortened (rarely extended in front as a neck), more
   or less collar-shaped (Figs. 891, 925), not extending back on the
   sides to the tegulæ, although each posterior angle is produced
   to form a lobe; trochanters always one-jointed..............126
74. First segment of abdomen forming a scale or node (Figs. 992, 923,

924, 926) or the first and second nodiform, and clearly separated both above and below from the gaster, or remainder of the abdomen 75

First segment of abdomen not scale-like; if nodiform and separated from the gaster by a constriction, the second segment forms a part of the gaster and is not separated from it both above and below 76

75. Hypopygium of male with an upturned spine; female wingless, but not dimorphic, without sterile worker caste; female with suture between mesonotum and pronotum, but without suture or impression between mesonotum and metanotum or propodeum. Insects not living in colonies. (**Apterógyna**, Afr., As.).

APTEROGÝNIDÆ

Hypopygium of male without an upturned spine; female dimorphic, the sterile form (worker) wingless, with the thoracic sutures lost or much reduced; the fertile form with the thoracic sutures all present; lower posterolateral corners of alitrunk (metapleura) each with a gland, usually indicated by the presence of a distinct bulla; external opening of gland with a dense fringe of short fine hairs. Insects living in colonies. Ants. (*FORMICÒIDEA, HETERÓGYNA*) .... FORMÍCIDÆ [1]

a. Apex of gaster (body of abdomen) with a small funnel-shaped circlet of hairs surrounding the opening of the poison gland. (Fig. 923). (**Prenólepis**, cosmop.; **Làsius, Formìca**, Holarc.; **Polýrhachis**, Old World tropics; **Camponòtus** (Wood-ants), cosmop.) ....FORMICÍNÆ

Apex of gaster with a slit-shaped orifice and without such funnel-shaped tuft ....b

b. Sting vestigial, not sclerotized (except *Aneuretus*); abdominal pedicel consisting of a single segment; no constriction between the second and third abdominal segments; species producing a secretion of aromatic rancid odor. (**Dolichodèrus**, cosmop.; **Dorymýrmex, Iridomýrmex** (*I. hùmilis*, Argentine ant), widespread).

DOLICHODERÍNÆ

Sting developed, sometimes very small, but capable of being exserted. Petiole of abdomen (pedicel) either consisting of two joints, or with the first segment forming a node and the second and third separated by a strong (very rarely weaker) constriction c

c. Pedicel of two segments, the petiole and postpetiole (Fig. 922);

---

[1] The ants form a very extensive, widespread, and dominant family divisible into a number of well-marked subfamilies, several of which are undoubtedly of equal rank with many of the families recognized in other groups. A table for their separation is given below, modified from a key by Wheeler.

frontal carinæ usually separated from each other; copulatory
organs of male almost always exserted.........................d
Pedicel consisting of a single segment, more rarely of two, but in
this case the frontal carinæ are very close to each other and do
not cover the insertions of the antennæ (Dorylinæ) or the mandibles are linear and denticulate (*Myrmecia*).................e

d. Antennæ 12-jointed in worker, female and male; clypeus not prolonged back between the frontal carinæ, its posterior margin
rounded; fore wings almost always with two closed cubital cells;
one of the tibial spurs on the middle and hind legs pectinate;
ocelli almost always present in the worker. (**Pseudomýrmex**
(=*Pseudomýrma*), neotrop.; **Pachysìma, Viticícola,** Afr.)
PSEUDOMYRMICÌNÆ
Clypeus almost always prolonged between the frontal carinæ; if
not, the spurs of the middle and hind tibiæ are simple or absent,
or the antennæ are 11-jointed in the worker and female, 12-jointed
in the male, and the fore wings have one closed cubital cell.
(**Pogonomýrmex** (Agricultural ants), Am.; **Myrmìca,** Holarc.,
Indo-Mal.; **Pheidòle, Monomòrium,** tropicopolitan; **Solenópsis**
(*S. geminàta,* Fire ant), cosmop.; **Átta** (Leaf-cutter ants), Neo-
trop.) .... **MYRMICÌNÆ**

e. Frontal carinæ very close to each other; almost vertical, not at all
covering the antennal insertions; abdominal pedicel of one or
two segments; genitalia of male almost always completely retractile. Legionary and Driver ants (Fig. 927). (**Dórylus, Ænìc-
tus,** Old World tropics; **Éciton,** Neotrop.)........**DORYLÌNÆ**
Frontal carinæ separated or close together, in the latter case being
dilated anteriorly to form an oblique or horizontal lamina, which
covers in part the insertion of the antennæ; abdominal pedicel
almost always of a single segment. Genitalia of male incompletely retractile. (Fig. 924). (**Pachycóndyla,** Neotrop.; **Myrmècia**
(Bull-dog ants), Austr.; **Stigmatómma,** widespr.; **Ponèra,** cosmop.; **Cerápachys; Odontómachus,** tropicopolitan). (Including
CERAPACHYÌNÆ) .... **PONERÌNÆ**

79. Wing venation very incomplete; radial cell if indicated very small, cubital vein $(R_4+R_5+M_1)$ entirely wanting; antennæ 11- to 14-jointed, usually strongly clavate in the female. (Fig. 932). (Paramèsius, Spilómicrus, Gálesus, Phænòpria, Trichòpria, cosmop.; Hoplòpria, Am.) .... DIAPRÌIDÆ

Wing venation more complete; radial cell large, but not always completely closed; cubital vein well developed except at apex; antennæ of males 10-jointed, of females 13-jointed. (Émbólemus, ($=Pedinómma$), Eur.; Myrmecomórphus, Eur., N. Am.; Ampulicimórpha, N. Am.) .... EMBOLÉMIDÆ

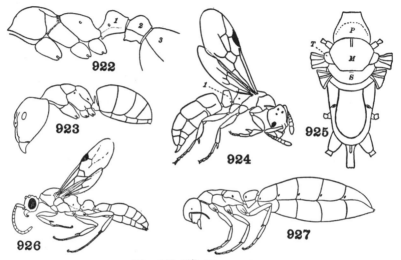

Figs. 922–927. Hymenoptera

922. **Myrmica**, profile view of thorax and base of abdomen; 1, 2, basal nodes of abdomen (first and second segments); 3, third abdominal segment. Formicidæ.
923. **Camponotus**, lateral outline of body (Wheeler) Formicidæ.
924. **Ponera**, female. 1, node or basal segment of abdomen (Wheeler) Formicidæ.
925. **Chlorion**, thorax from above. P, pronotum; M, mesonotum; S, scutellum; T, tegula (Fernald) Sphecidæ.
926. **Phyracaces**, male (Wheeler) Formicidæ.
927. **Eciton**, female (Emery) Formicidæ.

80. Antennæ composed of fourteen joints or more................81
    Antennæ composed of thirteen joints or less...................84
81. Basal joint of hind tarsi much shorter than the following joint; first abdominal segment as long as the head and thorax together; abdomen very long, filiform and composed of equal segments in the female; clavate in the male; large insects. (Fig. 930). (Pelecìnus, Am.) .... PELECÍNIDÆ

Basal joint of hind tarsi longer than the second joint; abdominal petiole very much shorter................................82

82. Head elongate; antennæ 22- to 40-jointed, inserted at the anterior margin of the head; females wingless. A small, widespread group of rare insects. (Sclerogíbba, Mystrocnèmis, Cryptobéthylus) .... SCLEROGÍBBIDÆ
Head short, broader than long; antennæ 14- or 15-jointed inserted at the middle of the face, far above the clypeus.............83

83. Basal vein complete; antennæ 14-jointed; abdomen strongly compressed. (Roprònia, N. Am., China)...........ROPRONÌIDÆ
Basal vein incomplete, its anterior portion wanting; antennæ 15-jointed; abdomen not compressed. (Helòrus, Eur., N. Am.). HELÓRIDÆ

84. Mandibles very short, with three large teeth, widely separated and not meeting when closed; when open, the tips are directed laterally; abdomen with only two (female) or four (male) visible tergites, the first covering most of the abdomen; sting very long, extended forward beneath the body. (Fig. 928). A single species. (Vanhórnia, N. Am.) .... VANHORNÌIDÆ
Mandibles in normal position, their tips opposing when closed....85

85. Antennæ inserted at the middle of the face, 13-jointed in both sexes; fore wings with a broad stigma and a closed, usually very small, radial cell; abdomen with a short cylindrical petiole, the second segment much longer than the others. (Fig. 931). (Proctotrỳpes (Sérphus), Phænosérphus, widespr.; Exallònyx, Holarc.). (SÉRPHIDÆ) .... PROCTOTRÝPIDÆ
Antennæ inserted near the mouth, close to the margin of the clypeus 86

86. Hind wing with a lobe at the anal angle, separated by a deep, slit-shaped notch; if the lobe and notch are inconspicuous, the body is metallic in color...............................87
Hind wing very narrow without anal lobe or slit-shaped notch...90

87. Abdomen with two to four, rarely five dorsal segments; venter concave; propodeum laterally with sharp keels or teeth; prothorax large, its posterior corners often distinctly separated from the tegulæ; ovipositor tubular, extensile, several-jointed; last large tergite frequently dentate; antennæ 13-jointed; body usually with coarse sculpture and of metallic color. Cuckoo-wasps. (Fig. 933). (Chrỳsis, cosmop.; Parnòpes, Ellámpus, Hédychrum, widespr.; Allocœlia, S. Afr.) .... CHRYSÍDIDÆ
Abdomen with six to eight visible segments, very rarely with only four or five; venter convex; body rarely with any coarse sculpture 88

88. Antennæ 10-jointed in both sexes; front tarsi of female usually pincers-shaped (Fig. 937); head broad, transverse, or subquadrate;

female frequently apterous with the thorax nodose. (Figs. 937,
938). (Drỳinus, Gonátopus, Ánteon, cosmop.; Aphélopus, Eur.,
N. Am.; Bócchus, N. Am.; Paradrỳinus, Austr.) . . . . DRYÍNIDÆ
Antennæ 12- to 13-jointed; front tarsi simple; head elongate or
rounded 89

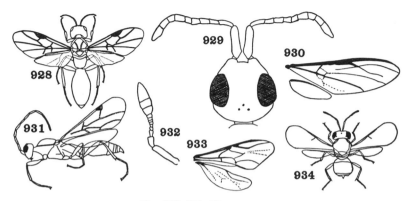

Figs. 928–934. Hymenoptera

928. **Vanhornia** (Crawford) Vanhorniidæ.
929. **Ceraphron,** head and antennæ. Ceraphronidæ.
930. **Pelecinus,** wings. Pelecinidæ.
931. **Proctotrypes** (Brues) Proctotrypidæ.
932. **Loxotropa,** antenna. Diapriidæ.
933. **Chrysis,** wings. Chrysididæ.
934. **Telenomus.** Scelionidæ.

89. Anal lobe of hind wing conspicuous; abdomen with seven or eight
visible dorsal segments; head usually elongate, oblong; small,
usually black or bronzed species, the females sometimes wingless.
(Béthylus, Mesítius, Perisiérola, widespr.; Siérola, Hawaii; Pristó-
cera, Épyris (*s. lat.*), Sclerodérma, Goniòzus, cosmop.).
BETHÝLIDÆ
Anal lobe of hind wing not conspicuous, separated by a minute
notch; abdomen with at most six segments visible from above.
(Cléptes, Eur., Am.; Mesitiópterus, Nearc.) . . . . . . CLÉPTIDÆ
90. Abdomen acute, or sharply margined along the sides 91
Abdomen rounded on the sides; wings, when present, with the
radial vein developed, but not complete, leaving the radial cell
open; no postmarginal vein. (Fig. 929). (Céraphron (*Callíceras*),
Lygócerus, Conostígmus, cosmop.; Megaspìlus, Holarc.). (*CAL-
LICERÁTIDÆ*) . . . . CERAPHRÓNIDÆ
91. Antennæ ten-jointed, rarely with fewer joints, but never more; front
wings without marginal or stigmal vein and usually without a

subcostal vein also. (**Platygáster** (including **Polygnòtus**), cosmop.; **Inostémma, Léptacis, Amblyáspis,** Eur., Am.).

PLATYGÁSTRIDÆ

Antennæ twelve- or eleven-jointed (if rarely seven- or eight-jointed, the club is unjointed, or if ten-jointed, the stigmal vein is present); marginal and stigmal veins usually present. (Fig. 934). (**Phanùrus, Telénomus, Caloteléia, Scèlio,** cosmop.; **Tèleas, Prosacántha, Hadronòtus,** widespr.; **Gryon,** Eur., Am.)......SCELIÓNIDÆ

92. Antennæ composed of fourteen or more joints.................93
  Antennæ with never more than thireeen joints; twelve-jointed in the female and thirteen-jointed in the male, except in rare instances when the number may be reduced. (VESPÒIDEA)....95

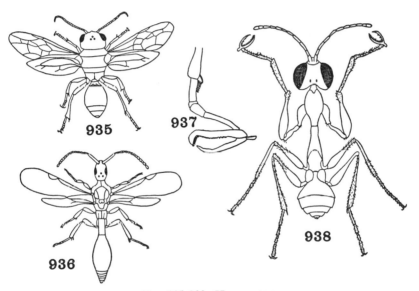

Figs. 935–938. Hymenoptera

935. **Seminota** (Schultz) Trigonalidæ.
936. **Belyta** (Fouts) Belytidæ.
937. **Gonatopus,** front tarsus of female. Dryinidæ.
938. **Gonatopus** (Misra) Dryinidæ.

93. Mandibles with four teeth, head large, quadrate; antennæ with at least 16 joints, usually more; hind wing with two large closed cells; moderate-sized, often brillliantly colored species. (Fig. 935). (**Trigónalys,** Palæarc.; **Lycogáster,** Am., E. Ind.; **Tapinógalos,** N. Am., S. Afr.; **Seminòta,** Neotrop.; **Bareogónalos,** N. Am.).

TRIGONÁLIDÆ

Mandibles with not more than three teeth; antennæ 14- or 15-jointed 94

94. Fore wing with a closed discoidal cell; apex of propodeum extending back beyond the insertion of the hind coxæ; antennæ not inserted on a large frontal prominence. (See couplet 27).

MONOMÁCHIDÆ

Fore wing always without a closed discoidal cell; propodeum not extended back beyond the insertion of the hind coxæ; antennæ inserted on a conspicuous frontal shelf or prominence; small black or brownish species. (Fig. 936). (Bélyta, Oxýlabis, Aclísta, widespr.; Pántoclis, cosmop.; Leptorháptus, Holarc.).

BELÝTIDÆ

95. First discoidal cell shorter than the submedian cell (usually very much so); fore wings very rarely folded; solitary species, never living in colonies..96

First discoidal cell very long, as a rule much longer than the submedian cell; fore wing almost always folded longitudinally when in repose; frequently social species, living in colonies. (Figs. 940, 941, 944, 946) ....VÉSPIDÆ [1]

a. Transverse median vein in hind wing straight or curved, not angulate; fore wing with two or three cubital cells, the marginal cell always truncate at apex; antennæ usually strongly clavate....b

Transverse median vein angulate; antennæ not noticeably swollen apically ....d

b. Anal lobe of hind wing elongate, more than half as long as the submedian cell. (Euparàgia, N. Am.).......EUPARAGIÍNÆ

Anal lobe of hind wing small, circular or oval, much less than half as long as the submedian cell................................c

c. Discoidal vein in hind wing obsolete or entirely absent. (Másaris, Palæarc.; Pseudomásaris, N. Am.; Trimèria, Neotrop.; Masariélla, Ceràmius, Ceramiòides, Afr.; Paràgia, Austr.)... MASARIDÍNÆ

Discoidal vein in hind wing present, fully developed. (Gayélla, Paramásaris, Neotrop., N. Am.)...............GAYELLÍNÆ

d. Second and third cubital cells each receiving a recurrent nervure. (Raphiglóssa, Palæarc., Afr.) ....RAPHIGLOSSÍNÆ

Second cubital cell receiving both recurrent nervures.............e

e. Mandibles short and broad, obliquely truncate and toothed at the apex, folding above one another under the clypeus or very slightly crossing ....f

Mandibles more or less elongate and knife-like, either crossing each other or extended forward to form a beak, their inner margins more or less toothed or notched................................j

---

[1] This varied and extensive family is divisible into several groups, some of which were formerly regarded as families, but now more generally as of only subfamily rank. A key to these, revised by Prof. Bequaert, is given below.

f. Tarsal claws bifid or toothed; middle tibiæ with one or two spurs; clypeus broadly truncate at apex; solitary wasps. (Zèthus, cosmop.; Làbus, Afr., Indo-mal.) .ZETHÌNÆ

Tarsal claws simple; middle tibiæ with two spurs, very rarely with one; true social wasps, living in colonies, the females often dimorphic as fertile females and sterile workers . . . . .g

g. Clypeus broadly truncate and more or less emarginate at the apex; first abdominal tergite vertically truncate anteriorly; hind wing without a lobe at the anal angle, the basal third strongly narrowed. Hornets; Yellow-jackets. (Véspa, Véspula, Palæarc., Nearc., Indo-mal.) . . . . VESPÌNÆ

Clypeus pointed at the apex, rarely rounded or straight, in which case the first abdominal tergite is not vertically truncate; hind wing usually with a lobe at the anal angle . . . . .h

h. Second abdominal segment broadly bell-shaped, its tergite and sternite completely or for the most part fused; first segment much narrower than the second; extensory muscle of the abdomen inserted on the propodeum in a narrow and much compressed slit. (One genus, Ropalídia (— Icària), Afr., Indo-Austr.). (RHOPALIDIÌNÆ) .ROPALIDIÌNÆ

Second abdominal segment of the usual shape, its tergite and sternite freely articulated i

i. Extensory muscle of the abdomen inserted on the propodeum in a narrow and much compressed slit; first abdominal segment never narrowed into a stalk; antennæ always of 12 joints in the female and 13 in the male. (Polístes, cosmop.; Gyróstoma, oriental). POLISTÌNÆ

Extensory muscle of the abdomen inserted on the propodeum in a broad, oval cavity; first abdominal segment often stalk-like; antennæ with 11 or 12 joints in the female and 12 or 13 in the male. (Polýbia, Chartérgus, Neotrop.; Mischocýttarus, Nectarìna, N. Am., Neotrop.; Belonogáster, Afr.; Polybiòides, Afr., oriental). POLYBIÌNÆ

j. Middle tibiæ with one apical spur (very rarely two or none); clypeus broadly rounded, truncate or emarginate at tip (very rarely pointed). A large cosmopolitan group. (Eùmenes, Odynèrus, Symmórphus, Ancistrócerus, Pterochìlus, cosmop.; Synàgris, Afr.; Pachýmenes, widespr.; Monòbia, N. Am., Neotrop.). EUMENÌNÆ

Middle tibiæ with two spurs; clypeus projecting in a round or sharp point. (Stenogáster (=Ischnogáster), Indo-Austr.). STENOGASTRÌNÆ

96. Flagellum of antennæ bare or with very short pubescence, not clothed with conspicuous hairs 97

Flagellum clothed with conspicuous hairs, as long as, or much longer than the width of the antennal joints. (**Plumàrius** (= *Konowiélla*), Chile, Argentina; **Myrmecopterìna** (= *Archihymen*), S. Afr.). (*KONOWIÉLLIDÆ, ARCHIHYMÉNIDÆ*).

PLUMARÌIDÆ

97. Mesopleura divided by an oblique suture into a lower and upper part; legs, including the coxæ very long; hind femora unusually long; middle tibiæ with two spurs. Spider hunting wasps. **Pómpilus** (= *Psammóchares*), **Pépsis** (Tarantula hawks), **Cerópales, Agènia,** widespr.). (*CEROPÁLIDÆ, PSAMMOCHÁRIDÆ*) .... **POMPÍLIDÆ**

Mesopleura not thus divided; legs shorter, the hind femora not usually extending to the apex of the abdomen 98

98. Meso- and metasternum forming together a flat plate which is divided by a transverse, more or less sinuous suture, and overlies the bases of the four posterior coxæ; wing membrane, beyond the closed cells, finely longitudinally wrinkled; hypopygium of male with three spines. Large, usually brightly colored wasps. (**Scòlia, Campsómeris** (= *Èlis*, auctt.), cosmop., mainly trop.).

SCOLÌIDÆ

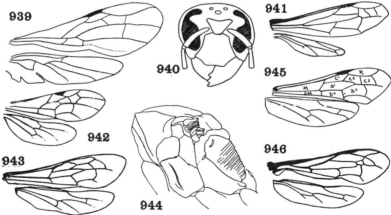

Figs. 939–946. **Hymenoptera**

939. **Paniscomima**, wings (Enderlein) Rhopalosomatidæ.
940. **Vespa,** head in front view (Schmiedeknecht) Vespidæ.
941. **Vespa,** wings. Vespidæ.
942. **Sphærophthalma,** wings. Mutillidæ.
943. **Elis,** wings of female. Tiphiidæ.
944. **Polistes,** lateral view of thorax (Bequaert) Vespidæ.
945. **Elis,** wings of male. *R*, radial or marginal cell; C_1, C_2, C_3, cubital or submarginal cells; D_1, D_2, D_3, discoidal cells; *M*, median cell; *SM*, submedian cell. Tiphiidæ.
946. **Eumenes,** wings. Vespidæ.

Meso- and metasternum not forming such a plate overlying all four posterior coxæ; sometimes provided with a pair of thin backwardly directed plates or laminæ which overlie the bases of the middle coxæ 99

99. Joints of antennal flagellum long and slender, each bearing at the apex two slender spines; joints of tarsi broadened and deeply lobed (female); hind wing with a prominent anal lobe and a deep axillary incision (Fig. 939). (**Rhopalosòma**, Am., Madagascar; **Paniscomìma**, Afr.; **Hymenochimæra**, India; **Rogezia**, Madagascar) . . . . RHOPALOSOMÁTIDÆ
   Joints of antennal flagellum not spined at tip, tarsi simple 100

100. Mesosternum with two laminæ that overlie or project between the bases of the middle coxæ and usually extend to the mid-line where they are separated by a median suture 101
   Mesosternum simple, without appendages behind, or with the laminæ reduced to a pair of minute tooth-like projections 104

101. Ocelli small 102
   Ocelli very large; nocturnal insects (males). (**Chyphòtes**, Am.). (See couplet 105) . . . . .A few MUTÍLLIDÆ

102. Males with apex of abdomen terminating in a single strongly upcurved spine (if there are 8 ventral abdominal segments and the pygidium is not deeply emarginate, see *Dimorphothynnus* and *Rhagigaster* in the Thynnidæ); females with a deep constriction between the first and second ventral abdominal segments. (Figs. 943, 945). (**Típhia**, cosmop.; **Paratíphia**, Am.; **Èlis** (= *Myzìne*), widespr.; **Pterómbrus** (= *Engycýstis*), Am.). (Including *PTERÓMBRIDÆ* and *MYZÍNIDÆ*) . . . . TIPHÌIDÆ
   Males with apex of abdomen not terminating in a single strongly upcurved spine (except *Dimorphothynnus* and *Rhagigaster*), otherwise armed or without spines; females (of *Anthobosca*) without a deep constriction between the first and second ventral abdominal segments 103

103. Pygidium of male of various forms, with or without spines; antennæ of male generally inserted under a frontal prominence, their sockets facing anteriorly or laterally instead of dorsally; wing venation of male complete and extending out to the tips of the wings, three closed cubital cells, the first usually divided at least partially by a spur from the first intercubitus; female wingless. (**Diámma**, **Rhagigáster**, **Dimorphothýnnus**, Austr.; **Elaphróptera**, **Encyrtothýnnus**, S. Am.; **Glyptometòpa**, N. Am.). THÝNNIDÆ
   Pygidium of male unarmed; antennæ of male not inserted under a frontal prominence, their sockets facing dorsally; female winged. (**Anthobòsca**, S. Am., Austr.; **Lálapa**, Nearc.). ANTHOBÓSCIDÆ

104. Hind wing with a prominent separated lobe at the anal angle...106
     Hind wing without a lobe at the anal angle, at most with an obtuse
     emargination at the posterior basal angle..................105
105. Cubital vein in hind wing originating beyond the transverse
     median vein; second abdominal segment separated from the first
     by a strong constriction both above and below; female winged.
     (Sierolomórpha, Nearc., Hawaii) ...... SIEROLOMÓRPHIDÆ
     Cubital vein in hind wing not originating beyond the transverse
     median vein; body almost always conspicuously pilose (Fig. 942);
     female wingless. Velvet ants. A widespread family occurring
     mainly in desert regions. (Mutílla, Palæarc., Ethiop., oriental;
     Dasymutílla, Photópsis, Am.; Traumatomutílla, Neotrop.; Ephu-
     tomórpha, Austr.) .... MUTÍLLIDÆ
106. Abdomen with the several segments separated by strong constric-
     tions (males) 107
     Abdomen without such constrictions, except between the first
     and second segments; hypopygium of male unarmed; female
     winged; sting long, enclosed in a tubular organ at base; body
     bare, marked with yellow or white. (Sapỳga, widespr.; Eusa-
     pỳga, Am.) .... SAPÝGIDÆ
107. Hypopygium of male armed with a strong, upcurved spine; female
     wingless, the thorax constricted into three parts. (Methòca, wide-
     spr.; Dryinópsis, E. Ind.).....................METHÓCIDÆ
     Hypopygium of male unarmed; female wingless, the thorax divided
     into two parts by a transverse suture. (Myrmòsa, Holarc.).
                                              MYRMÓSIDÆ
108. Thorax clearly divided above into three parts by sutures or sharply
     defined constrictions, or into two by a constriction; scutellum
     nearly always present 109
     Thorax with only one dorsal sclerite, or with two separated by a
     suture; no scutellum...................................124
109. Antennæ with 22 joints or more. (See couplet 82).
                           Females of the SCLEROGÍBBIDÆ
     Antennæ with 15 joints or less...........................110
110. Antennæ inserted on a frontal shelf or strong prominence.....111
     No shelf or strong prominence at the base of the antennæ......113
111. First segment of the abdomen forming a distinctly separated
     petiole 112
     Abdomen without a distinctly separated petiole. (See couplet 79).
                                       Some EMBOLÉMIDÆ
112. Antennæ usually 12-jointed. (See couplet 79).
                           Some females of the DIAPRÌIDÆ
     Antennæ usually 15-jointed. (See couplet 94).
                           Some females of the BELÝTIDÆ
113. Abdomen acute or sharply margined along the sides..........114

Abdomen without an acute or sharply margined edge along the sides 115

114. Antennæ 12- or 11-jointed (if rarely 7- or 8-jointed, the club is unjointed). (See couplet 91).
A few females of the SCELIÓNIDÆ
Antennæ 10-jointed, rarely with fewer joints, but never more. (See couplet 91) ....A few males of the PLATYGÁSTRIDÆ

115. Antennæ inserted low down, next to the border of the clypeus.. 116
Antennæ inserted at the middle of the face, far above the clypeus. (Paracòdrus). (See couplet 85).
A few females of the PROCTOTRÝPIDÆ

116. Antennæ 10- or 11-jointed................................117
Antennæ 12- or 13-jointed................................118

117. Front tarsi of female pincers-shaped; antennæ of male 10-jointed. (See couplet 88) .... Some DRYÍNIDÆ
Front tarsi of female not pincers-shaped; antennæ of male 11-jointed. (See couplet 90)...........Some CERAPHRÓNIDÆ

118. Head elongate, usually distinctly longer than wide; thorax divided by sutures, or if divided by constrictions, the head is much longer than wide. (See couplet 89). A few females of the BETHÝLIDÆ
Head almost always oval, slightly broader than high..........119

119. Abdomen with only four visible tergites. (See couplet 62).
ALIÉNIDÆ
Abdomen normal, with six to eight visible tergites............120

120. Wings present, though greatly reduced in size; tegulæ normally developed; thorax of normal form, divided by sutures.......121
Wings absent; tegulæ indicated only as minute tubercles; thorax generally of abnormal form, often divided by constrictions....122

121. Antennæ 13-jointed. (See couplet 105).
A very few males of the MUTÍLLIDÆ
Antennæ 12-jointed. (See couplet 97).
A very few females of the POMPÍLIDÆ

122. Mesosternum simple, without laminæ that overlie or project between the bases of the middle coxæ. (See couplet 107).
Females of the METHÓCIDÆ
Mesosternum with two laminæ that overlie or project between the bases of the middle coxæ..............................123

123. Abdomen with a distinct cylindrical petiole consisting only of the sternite, the first tergite capping its posterior end. (See couplet 101) (Females of Chyphòtes).............MUTÍLLIDÆ, part
Abdomen not petiolate; femora compressed. (See couplet 103).
Females of the THÝNNIDÆ

124. Pronotum separated from the remainder of the thorax by a suture 125

Pronotum fused with the remainder of the thorax, the entire thorax
without sutures above. (See couplet 105).

Females of the **MUTÍLLIDÆ**

125. Ocelli present. (See couplet 107). Females of the **MYRMÓSIDÆ**
Ocelli absent. (See couplet 101). Females of **Brachycístis.**

MUTÍLLIDÆ, part

126. Antennæ with 12 (female) or 13 (male) joints; very rarely with
12 in the male..127
Antennæ 10-jointed in both sexes; no closed cubital or discoidal
cells; front tarsi of female often pincers-shaped. (See couplet
88) ....**DRYÍNIDÆ**

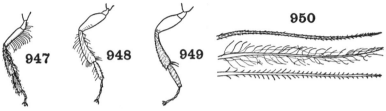

Figs. 947–950. **Hymenoptera**

947, 948, 949. Hind legs of bees (Smith) Apoidea.
950. Plumose or compound body-hairs of bees (Smith) Apoidea.

127. Hind tarsi slender, filiform, the first joint not broadened or thickened; abdomen often petiolate; all hairs on the body simple, unbranched. (SPHECÒIDEA) 128
Hind tarsi with the first joint thickened or flattened, often densely
hairy; abdomen always sessile; at least a part of the body-hairs
branched or plumose. Bees. (Figs. 947, 948, 949, 950, 964, 965).
(APÒIDEA (*ANTHÓPHILA*)) 146

128. Middle tibiæ with two apical spurs, both well developed......129
Middle tibiæ generally with only one well developed apical spur;
sometimes with two or none. When a second spur is well developed, the hind femora are widened at the tip (*Alysson, Didi-
neis*), or the mandibles are emarginate externally (*Dinetus*) ..135

129. Mesosternum produced into a forked process posteriorly; parapsidal furrows distinct; pronotum usually long, conically produced
in front, usually with a median groove, its posterior lobes often
approaching close to the tegulae. (**Ampùlex,** widespr.; **Rhinópsis,
Dolichùrus,** cosmop.) .... **AMPULÍCIDÆ**
Mesosternum not thus produced; parapsidal furrows indistinct or
wanting 130

130. Abdomen with a distinct, usually long, cylindrical petiole, which
at the base, at least, consists only of the sternite. (Figs. 891, 925,

951). (**Chlorìon** (=*Sphéx*, auctt.), **Scéliphron** (=*Pelopœus*),
Sphéx (*Ammóphila*), cosmop.; **Podalònia**).[1] . . . . . . **SPHÉCIDÆ**
Abdomen sessile or subsessile, never with a slender, cylindrical
petiole 131

131. Labrum free, well-developed, wider than long, triangular or semicircular, extending beyond the clypeus; sternauli on mesopleura
not complete. (**Stìzus, Sphècius,** cosmop.; **Exeìrus,** Austr.) (*EX-
EÍRIDÆ*) . . . . **STÍZIDÆ**
Labrum short, small, not or scarcely extending beyond the cly-
peus. (If the second cubital cell is petiolate and the hind angles
of the propodeum are neither acute nor spined, see *Exeirus,*
couplet 131) 132

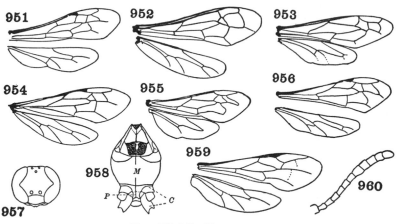

Figs. 951–960. **Hymenoptera**

951. **Chlorion,** wings. Sphecidæ.
952. **Eucerceris,** wings. Cerceridæ.
953. **Bembix,** wings. Bembicidæ.
954. **Cerceris,** wings. Cerceridæ.
955. **Tachytes,** wings. Larridæ.
956. **Gorytes,** wings. Gorytidæ.
957. **Trypoxylon,** front view of head (Kohl) Trypoxylidæ.
958. **Tachytes,** underside of thorax. *M,* mesosternum; *P,* its posterior process; *C,* coxæ
(Williams) Larridæ.
959. **Trypoxylon,** wings. Trypoxylidæ.
960. **Niteliopsis,** antenna of female (Williams) Larridæ.

132. Radial cell broadly truncate at apex and prolonged as a small,
weakly defined cell; antennæ inserted near the clypeus, very close
to the clypeal suture; eyes of male usually very large and con-

---

[1] As with many names for widely known genera of insects there is much disagreement concerning the proper application of Sphex, Chlorion and Ammophila.

tiguous above. (**Dimórpha** (=*Ástata*), cosmop.; **Diploplléctron,**
N. Am.) (*ASTÁTIDÆ*) .... **DIMÓRPHIDÆ**
Radial cell not appendiculate, pointed at apex 133

133. Antennæ inserted very near to the upper edge of the clypeus,
close to the clypeal suture; first segment of abdomen usually long,
slender, nodose at apex and separated from the second by a distinct constriction; second cubital cell not receiving a recurrent
nervure. (**Méllinus,** widespr.) .... **MELLÍNIDÆ**
Antennæ inserted on the face well above the margin of clypeus;
first segment of abdomen broad and stout; second cubital cell
receiving at least one recurrent nervure, usually two 134

134. Sternauli on mesopleura complete, usually deep; second cubital
cell with a distinct upper side, not triangular; propodeum rounded;
thorax smooth, not coarsely punctate. (Fig. 956). (**Gorỳtes,** cosmop.) .... **GORÝTIDÆ**
Sternauli wanting or indicated only anteriorly; second cubital cell
triangular or petiolate; propodeum with the upper hind angles
acute or produced as stout spines; thorax coarsely punctate.
(**Nýsson,** cosmop.) .... **NYSSÓNIDÆ**

135. Eyes deeply emarginate; one clearly defined cubital cell, abdomen
petiolate and gradually enlarged apically (**Trypóxylon,** cosmop.);
or two cubital cells, or three with the second petiolate (**Pìson,**
cosmop.; **Pisonópsis,** Nearc.; **Aulacóphilus,** Neotrop.). (Figs.
957, 959). (*TRYPOXYLÓNIDÆ*) .... **TRYPOXÝLIDÆ**
Eyes not deeply emarginate, or if emarginate, the second of the
three cubital cells is not petiolate 136

136. Fore wings with two or three completely closed cubital cells, the
veins enclosing them strong and sharply defined 137
Fore wings with not more than one closed cubital cell 143

137. Labrum large, free, triangularly elongated beyond the clypeus,
much longer than wide; radial cell simple, not appendiculate at
tip; ocelli more or less aborted. (Fig. 953). (**Bémbix** (=*Bém-
bex*), cosmop.; **Microbémbex, Bicýrtes** (=*Bembídula*), **Stíctia**
(=*Monédula*), **Steniòlia,** Am.) .... **BEMBÍCIDÆ**
Labrum small, usually entirely concealed by the clypeus; radial
cell sometimes with a crossvein clearly defined; ocelli, or at least
the anterior one, perfectly formed 138

138. Abdomen strongly constricted both above and below between the
first and second segments 139
Abdomen without a strong constriction above between the first
and second segments 140

139. Mesopleura with a vertical furrow which separates the prepectus
from the rest of the mesopleura; hind femora usually simple at
apex. (**Philánthus,** cosmop.; **Tráchypus,** Neotrop.; **Aphilánthops,**
Nearc.) .... **PHILÁNTHIDÆ**

Mesopleura without such a furrow, the prepectus not separated; hind femora with a projection below at apex. (Figs. 952, 954). (Cercèris, cosmop.; Eucercèris, Am.)............CERCÉRIDÆ

140. Hind femora produced below at apex as a flattened tubercle which overlaps the base of the tibia; abdomen sessile. (Álysson, Holarc., Neotrop.; **Bothynostèthus**, Am.; **Scapheùtes**, S. Am.).
ALYSSÓNIDÆ
Hind femora simple at apex, without projection.............141

141. Marginal cell not appendiculate and mandibles without an emargination externally; one, two, or three submarginal cells; eyes not emarginate on the inner edge. (**Stígmus, Psén, Mimèsa**, widespr.; **Pemphrèdon, Passalœcus**, Holarc.). (Including *MIMÉSIDÆ* and *PSÉNIDÆ*).........................PEMPHREDÓNIDÆ
Marginal cell appendiculate, or if not, the mandibles are emarginate externally...142

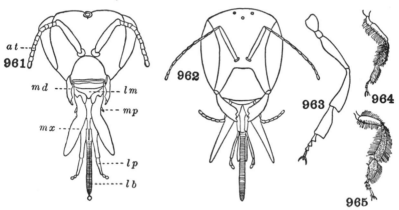

Figs. 961–965. Hymenoptera

961. Apis, head. *at*, antenna; *md*, mandible; *lm*, labrum; *mx*, maxillary palpus; *lp*, labial palpus; *lb*, labium. (Cheshire) Apidæ.
962. Head of long-tongued bee (Cockerell).
963. Apis, hind leg of worker (Smith) Apidæ.
964, 965. Hind legs of bees (Riley).

142. Second cubital cell present and not petiolate above; upper ocelli usually aborted or deformed. (Figs. 955, 958, 960). (**Táchytes, Lárra, Táchysphex**, cosmop.; **Palàrus, Lyròda**, widespr.; **Dinètus**, Eur.; **Sericóphorus**, Austr.).....................LÁRRIDÆ
Second cubital cell petiolate, or rarely absent; three perfectly formed ocelli; small species. (**Míscophus**, widespr.; **Plenóculus**, N. Am.). (*NITÉLIDÆ*)...........................MISCÓPHIDÆ

143. Postscutellum with two scale-like processes which project back;

propodeum above with a long spine or forked process; cubital and discoidal cells not distinctly separated. (**Oxýbelus**, cosmop.; **Belómicrus**, Holarc.) . . . . **OXYBÉLIDÆ**
Postscutellum and propodeum simple, without scales or spine . . 144
144. Hind wing with distinct cells 145
Hind wings without any closed cells. (**Nitèla**, Eur.). (See couplet 142) . . . . A few **MISCÓPHIDÆ**
145. Radial cell appendiculate; black, usually with yellow markings. (**Cràbro** (including **Eùplilis, Solènius,** and many subgenera), cosmop., mainly Holarc.; **Anacràbro**, N. Am.) . . . . **CRABRÓNIDÆ**
Radial cell simple, not appendiculate. (**Ammóplanus**, Holarc.). (See couplet 141) . . . . A few **PEMPHREDÓNIDÆ**

Apoidea [1]

146. Face between antennæ and clypeus with an area below each antenna, defined by a pair of vertical sutures below each antennal socket; tongue acute, usually short . . . . **ANDRÉNIDÆ**

a. Radial cell pointed at tip, or very narrowly rounded. (**Andrèna**, widespr., mainly Holarc.) . . . . **ANDRENÌNÆ**
Radial cell truncate at tip, bent away from the costal edge of the wing . . . . b
b. Stigma not or scarely developed; tips of hind femora in female enlarged and flattened. (**Oxæa**, Neotrop.) . . . . **OXÆÌNÆ**
Stigma well developed, of large or moderate size; tips of hind femora simple. (**Panúrgus**, widespr.; **Pérdita**, N. Am.; **Panurgìnus, Melittúrra,** Palæarc.) . . . . **PANURGÌNÆ**

Face without subantennal areas as there is only one vertical suture below each antenna, tongue usually long or of moderate length 147
147. Maxillary palpi inserted at or beyond the middle of the apical section of the tongue; mentum and submentum vestigial.
HALÍCTIDÆ

a. Clypeus short, usually not longer than the broadly rounded or truncate labrum; clypeus usually strongly convex. (**Dufoùrea, Halictòides,** Holarc.) . . . . **DUFOUREÌNÆ**
Clypeus longer than the labrum which is often medially pointed at tip in the female; clypeus not strongly convex . . . . b
b. Mesopleura divided by a well defined, vertical pre-episternal suture; third submarginal cell (when present) usually shorter than the

---

[1] There has long been wide disagreement concerning the classification of the Apoidea. Although the bees are abundant and well known, they appear to be undergoing rapid evolution and their taxonomy presents great difficulties. The key that follows is adapted from Michener, 1940.

first; face convex, protuberant. (**Halíctus, Sphecòdes,** cosmop.; **Augochlòra, Agapóstemon,** Am.) .... HALICTÌNÆ
Pre-episternal suture absent or vestigial; first and third submarginal cells subequal in length; face but little protuberant. (**Nòmia,** widespr.) .... NOMIÌNÆ

Maxillary palpi inserted at, or usually much before the middle; mentum and submentum present..........................148

148. Tongue of female, and usually of male, rounded, truncate, bilobed or bifid at tip; pre-episternal suture of mesopleura usually complete; middle coxæ much shorter than their distance from insertion of hind wing; submentum not V-shaped...**COLLÉTIDÆ**

a. Incision of anal lobe in hind wing before the middle of the lobe; pre-episternal suture incomplete below. (**Diphaglóssa, Policàna,** S. Am.) .... DIPHAGLOSSÌNÆ
Incision of anal lobe in hind wing at or beyond the middle of the lobe ....b

b. Pre-episternal suture complete c
Pre-episternal suture incomplete, wanting below. (**Stenotrìtus,** Austr.) .... STENOTRITÌNÆ

c. Palpi inserted beyond the middle of the galea of maxilla; no scopa nor pygidial plate. (**Chilócola,** Neotrop.).....**CHILOCOLÌNÆ**
Palpi inserted at or near middle of galea....................d

d. Clypeus not elongated, usually wider than high...............e
Clypeus lengthened above; scopa and pygidial plate absent; small, black, nearly hairless bees. (**Hylæus,** cosmop.; **Hylæòides,** Austr.). (*PROSOPÍDIDÆ*) .... HYLÆÌNÆ

e. Female with scopa; body conspicuously hairy; usually three submarginal cells; if only two, they are subequal. (**Collètes,** widespr.; **Caupolicàna** (=*Megacilíssa*), Am.; **Ptiloglóssa,** Neotrop.).
COLLETÌNÆ
Female without scopa; body with very short, sparse pubescence; two submarginal cells, the second much smaller. (**Euryglóssa,** Austr.) .... EURYGLOSSÌNÆ

Tongue acute at tip, often elongate; pre-episternal suture usually absent or present only at upper end; middle coxæ usually two-thirds as long as their distance from the insertion of hind wing; submentum V-shaped 149

149. Labial palpi with the first two joints simple, cylindrical; galeæ of maxillæ short; middle coxæ much shorter than their distance from the base of the hind wing......................**MELÍTTIDÆ**

a. Inner spur of hind tibiæ simple; radial cell in fore wing contiguous with the costal wing-margin, at least to near apex............b
Inner spur of hind tibiæ much widened, especially at base, and

fringed with a comb of long fine teeth; radial cell free from the costa for nearly half its length. (Ctenopléctra).

CTENOPLECTRÍNÆ

b. Stigma broad, triangularly narrowed at base; first joint of hind tarsi of female as broad as the tibiæ. (Macròpis, Holarc.).

MACROPIDÍNÆ

Stigma narrow, its sides subparallel...........................c

c. Three submarginal cells. (Melítta, widespr.; Dolichochìle, Nearc.).

MELITTÍNÆ

Two submarginal cells. (Hesperàpis, Dasýpoda, widespr.).

DASYPODÍNÆ

Labial palpi with the first two joints much lengthened and flattened, many times longer than the apical joints; galeæ very long, lanceolate; middle coxæ longer, over two-thirds as long as their separation from the base of the hind wing.................150

150. Labrum longer than broad, widened at the extreme base; subantennal sutures extending down from the outer side of the antennal socket; two submarginal cells; a pollen-collecting scopa usually present, on the underside of the abdomen.

MEGACHÍLIDÆ

a. Incision at margin of anal lobe in hind wing before the middle of the lobe; tibiæ smooth; tip of abdomen without a pygidial area. (Megachìle, cosmop.; Trachùsa, Holarc.; Ósmia, Heriades, Stèlis, Anthídium, widespr.) ....MEGACHILÍNÆ
Incision of anal lobe beyond the middle; tibiæ externally coarsely spiculate; male with pygidial plate, modified into a large spine in the female. (Lithúrgus, cosmop.)..........LITHURGÍNÆ

Labrum broader than long; if not so, then it is narrowed at base; subantennal sutures meeting the inner margin of the antennal socket; scopa, if present, nearly always on the hind legs. (Figs. 961–963) ....ÁPIDÆ

a. Pollen-collecting scopa of female on the hind legs only, or entirely absent in numerous parasitic forms........................b
Scopa present on underside of abdomen as well as on hind legs. (Fidèlia, Ethiop.) ....FIDELIÍNÆ

b. Scopa of female on the hind tibiæ usually the form of a corbicula (a bare, smooth area fringed with long, incurved hairs which hold the pollen-mass). Almost exclusively social species living in colonies, the females consisting of fertile individuals (queens) and infertile workers. (Figs. 961–963). (Àpis, Indomal. (A. mellífera, Honey-bee, cosmop.); Trígona, tropicopol.; Melípona, Chrysántheda, Euglóssa, Neotrop.; Bómbus, cosmop.; Psíthyrus,

Holarc., Neotrop.). (Including *EUGLÓSSIDÆ, CHRYSAN-THÉDIDÆ, BÓMBIDÆ*) . . . . **APÌNÆ**
Scopa not in the form of a corbicula. c

c. Pygidial plate usually present in both sexes; clypeus strongly protuberant, very deeply impressed at the sides; front coxæ usually only slightly transverse. (Anthóphora (=*Podalírius*), Eùcera, Melissòdes, Nómada, Diadàsia, Émphor, cosmop.; Melécta, Hemísia (=*Céntris*), widespr.). (Including *MELÉCTIDÆ*). (*PODALIRÌIDÆ*) . . . . **ANTHOPHORÌNÆ**
Pygidial plate absent, sometimes represented in the female by a flat spine; clypeus not protuberant, only weakly impressed at the sides; front coxæ transverse . . . . .d

d. Stigma vestigial, not thickened; distal part of wings wrinkled; large or very large, stout bees, boring in wood. (Xylócopa, tropicopol.) . . . . **XÝLOCOPÌNÆ**
Stigma large, well developed; wings with the surface smooth; small, slender species. (Cerátina, widespr.; Allódape, Afr., Austr., Asia) . . . . **CERATINÌNÆ**

Larvæ

At the present time it is impossible to give any reasonably complete or reliable key for the determination of the larvæ of the numerous families of Hymenoptera. Those of the suborder Chalastogastra have been quite extensively studied by several workers in Europe and in North America, and the grouping of these families below is based to a great extent on the work of Yuasa. Many of the larvæ of the other families have become so greatly specialized, modified, or reduced as a result of parasitism, maternal care, or from life as gall insects that the present, very incomplete knowledge affords no basis for a helpful key. Consequently references to habits have necessarily been introduced as differential characters, for the few of the higher forms that are included. It is thought, however, that the following summary will be helpful and reasonably reliable so far as it extends, although it must be borne in mind that the larvæ of only a small proportion of the species in any family are known, and that many families cannot be differentiated with assurance.

1. Body typically caterpillar-like (eruciform) (Figs. 966, 969), commonly with a color pattern; thoracic legs usually well developed, although sometimes much reduced; head much more strongly chitinized than the rest of the body; abdominal prolegs often present, entirely lost in some groups, but the body always retains an eruciform appearance. (Fig. 969). Antennæ and palpi almost always present and consisting of more than one joint. Mandibles strong, almost always with more than one tooth; ocelli frequently

present. Alimentary canal continous through the body (except probably Oryssidæ). Larvæ generally free living, feeding externally on plants, boring internally in plant tissue, occasionally forming galls; parasitic only in the Oryssidæ. Suborder CHALAS-TOGÁSTRA 2

Body legless, of a distinctly helpless, coarctate type, without color pattern; head not heavily chitinized; mouthparts and antennæ much reduced; palpi soft and papilliform; antennæ soft, unjointed;

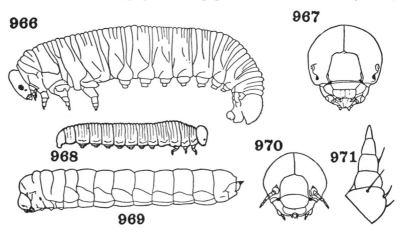

Figs. 966–971. Larvæ of Hymenoptera

966. **Neodiprion** (Middleton) Diprionidæ.
967. **Pteronidea,** head (Yuasa) Tenthredinidæ.
968. **Phyllotoma.** Tenthredinidæ.
969. **Tremex** (Yuasa) Siricidæ.
970. **Pamphilius,** head (Yuasa) Pamphiliidæ.
971. **Pteronidea,** maxillary palpus (Middleton) Tenthredinidæ.

mandibles weak, almost never with more than an apical tooth; ocelli absent; alimentary canal discontinuous, the mid-intestine and hind gut each closed and not connected with one another. (In some groups of Terebrantia and in some parasitic bees, hypermetamorphosis occurs and the first stage larvæ may be campodeiform or with much enlarged mandibles.) Larvæ not free-living, except in the first stage of some hypermetamorphic forms; parasitic, parasitoidal, or living upon a supply of food stored or fed by the mother, or by workers in the social groups; sometimes producing galls in plants. (Suborder CLISTOGÁSTRA) 30

2. Cerci present as distinctly segmented appendages..............3
    Cerci absent, or present as unjointed vestiges...................4

3. Cerci multiarticulate, setiform; larvæ feeding externally on leaves.
    a. Ocelli below and lateral to the antennæ. (Fig. 970).

    PAMPHILÌIDÆ

    b. Ocelli below or near the antennæ.... MEGALODÓNTIDÆ
    Cerci two-jointed, larva mining in the petioles of ferns.

    BLASTICOTÓMIDÆ

4. Abdominal prolegs present, well developed and distinctly jointed
    (except in a few leaf-mining forms)........................5
    Abdominal prolegs wanting; forms either feeding externally or
    boring in the stems or in woody plants or internal parasites of
    other insects; never leaf-miners...........................26

5. Ten pairs of prolegs, one on each abdominal segment; antennæ with
    six or seven joints................................XYÉLIDÆ
    Six to eight pairs of abdominal prolegs (Fig. 968); reduced or
    absent in leaf-mining and gall-making forms; antennæ with five
    joints or less...6

6. Thoracic legs normal in form, five-jointed; if reduced always with
    tarsal claws; prolegs usually well developed................7
    Thoracic legs fleshy, indistinctly four-jointed; no tarsal claws; pro-
    legs vestigial; larvæ leaf-miners.

    Some PHYLLOTOMÌNÆ; TENTHREDÍNIDÆ

7. Prolegs present on abdominal segments 2–8 and 10; antennæ elon-
    gate, usually five-jointed..................................8
    Prolegs absent on segment 8 or on both 7 and 8; if present on 8, the
    antennæ are one- or two-jointed...........................18

8. Legs five-jointed 9
    Legs four-jointed 17

9. Third abdominal segment divided dorsally by transverse grooves
    into six parts (annulets)..................................10
    Third abdominal segment dorsally with more or less than six annu-
    lets 13

10. Antennæ conical; five-jointed 11
    Antennæ not conical; three-jointed, the third joint erect and peg-
    like. (Fig. 966)........................Most DIPRIÓNIDÆ

11. Labrum bilaterally symmetrical; legs with the tibiæ shorter than
    the femora; tarsal claws short, strongly curved..............12
    Labrum distinctly asymmetrical, tibiæ longer than the femora; tarsal
    claws slender, only slightly curved.

    PHYLLOTOMÌNÆ; TENTHREDÍNIDÆ

12. Body rather robust, of uniform diameter throughout, with small
    distinct tubercles; tenth abdominal segment usually with several
    small protuberances above.

    Some BLENNOCAMPÌNÆ; TENTHREDÍNIDÆ

Body rather slender, tapering behind, without small distinct tubercles or protuberances.

Some **EMPHYTÌNÆ**; **TENTHREDÍNIDÆ**

13. Third segment with seven annulets on the dorsum; body without conspicuous branched spines or tubercles....................14
Third segment with five, rarely three or four annulets on dorsum; body with conspicuous branched spines or tubercles.

Some **EMPHYTÌNÆ**; **TENTHREDÍNIDÆ**

14. Antennæ short, one-jointed; labrum divided into three parts by a pair of longitudinal sutures......................**CIMBÍCIDÆ**
Antennæ five-jointed; labrum without a pair of longitudinal grooves 15

15. Prolegs provided with setæ; clypeus with three setæ on each side; labrum without a median longitudinal impression. Some **SELANDRIÌNÆ** and **EMPHYTÌNÆ**; **TENTHREDÍNIDÆ**
Prolegs without setæ; clypeus with two setæ at each side; labrum with or without median impression.........................16

16. Tibia small, distinctly shorter than the femur.

Some **SELANDRIÌNÆ**; **TENTHREDÍNIDÆ**
Tibia usually subequal to or longer than the femur.

TENTHREDINÌNÆ; **TENTHREDÍNIDÆ**

17. Prothorax, mesothorax and last abdominal segment above not narrowed behind......Some **EMPHYTÌNÆ**; **TENTHREDÍNIDÆ**
Body not thus ornamented; body often much narrowed behind. (Fig. 968) ..Some **PHYLLOTOMÌNÆ**; **TENTHREDÍNIDÆ**

18. Thoracic legs five-jointed..................................19
Thoracic legs with six joints, or with the first pair four-jointed and the others three-jointed......................**ÁRGIDÆ**

19. Anal prolegs present, often fused into a single median process....20
Anal prolegs wanting....................................25

20. Anal prolegs separate, present as a pair; antennæ with three to five joints 21
Anal prolegs fused; antennæ one-jointed.

SCOLIONEURÌNÆ; **TENTHREDÍNIDÆ**

21. Antennæ with five joints; last abdominal segment with several protuberances above.

Some **HOPLOCAMPÌNÆ**; **TENTHREDÍNIDÆ**
Antennæ with four, rarely three, joints; last abdominal segment without protuberances 22

22. First seven abdominal segments below each with an eversible gland; body often with numerous prominent setæ..................23
No eversible glands on the abdomen below; body never conspicuously setose 24

23. Body with numerous conspicuous tubercles, each bearing several

setæ of different lengths; setæ microscopically barbed; larvæ external feeders on leaves........CLADIÎNÆ; TENTHREDÍNIDÆ
Body usually without setigerous tubercles and never with tubercles bearing setæ of more than one size. Larvæ frequently leaf-rollers or gall-makers ....NEMATÎNÆ; TENTHREDÍNIDÆ

24. Antennæ four-jointed; third abdominal segment with five annulets.
Some HOPLOCAMPÌNÆ; TENTHREDÍNIDÆ
Antennæ one-jointed; third segment with three annulets. (Acordulécera) .... Some DIPRIÓNIDÆ

25. Antennæ three-jointed; third abdominal segment with four annulets; body not depressed; larvæ feeding externally or boring in fruits and leaf petioles.
HOPLOCAMPÌNÆ; TENTHREDÍNIDÆ
Antennæ one- or two-jointed; third segment with two annulets; body depressed; larvæ leaf-miners.
FENUSÌNÆ; TENTHREDÍNIDÆ

26. Thoracic legs large, well developed and distinctly jointed; larvæ gregarious, feeding on leaves......................PÉRGIDÆ
Thoracic legs vestigial, indistinctly jointed or entirely wanting; abdomen usually with a spine-like process at tip..............27

27. Ocelli present; antennæ with four or five joints; cerci present as minute one-jointed appendages; thoracic spiracles present; functional legs very small, indistinctly jointed...........CÉPHIDÆ
Ocelli absent; antennæ with three joints or less; cerci entirely absent 28

28. Antennæ with three joints. Larvæ wood-borers...XIPHYDRÌIDÆ
Antennæ with only a single joint............................29

29. Metathoracic spiracles large, functional; abdomen with a spine at tip; larvæ wood-borers ....SIRÍCIDÆ
Metathoracic spiracles vestigial, non-functional; abdomen without a spine at tip; larvæ parasitic on wood-boring insects. ORÝSSIDÆ

30. Parasitic species feeding internally in the eggs, nymphs, larvæ or pupæ of other insects................................31
Free living or feeding externally on other insects, spiders, etc. or on plant materials, sometimes within galls or in specially constructed cells or nests....................................32

31. Egg parasites ....Various CHALCIDÒIDEA; some
PROCTOTRYPÓIDEA especially SCELIÓNIDÆ
Parasites of nymphs, larvæ or pupæ or rarely of adult insects.
ICHNEUMONÒIDEA, many CHALCIDÒIDEA,
and PROCTOTRYPOIDEA; IBALÌIDÆ; some FIGÍTIDÆ

32. Living in galls formed in the tissues of plants. CYNÍPIDÆ and some FIGÍTIDÆ that are parasitic on them; a few CHALCI-DÒIDEA (some EURYTÓMIDÆ and a few PERILÁMPIDÆ)
Not in plant galls...33

33. Living attached externally on the bodies of immature or adult insects or spiders, sucking the body fluids through openings that they cut through the integument, occasionally crawling inside. . 34
Not external feeders attached to the bodies of other insects or spiders 35

34. Food-insect and feeder living in the cell, burrow or cavity in which the food-insect normally occurs when not parasitized; *i.e.* the food has not been removed from its normal habitat.
Most of the lower **VESPÒIDEA (SCOLÌIDÆ, TIPHÌIDÆ**, etc.); **DRYÍNIDÆ** (on Leaf-hoppers); **RHOPALOSOMÁTIDÆ; PELECÍNIDÆ; BETHÝLIDÆ**
Food-insects or spiders and feeder in a cavity, burrow, or specially constructed cell in which the food has been placed after being stung by the mother wasp; the cells or individual nests single, or if several cells are attached together, each is closed after being supplied with food and the larvæ receive no further care. Solitary Wasps. ....**POMPILÒIDEA, SPHECÒIDEA,** and most non-social **VÉSPIDÆ**

35. Solitary forms, living in specially constructed cells with a store of honey and pollen; the cells usually single, but if in small groups, each is separately sealed after completion and contains a single larva .... (**APÒIDEA**); a few **VÉSPIDÆ (MASARIDÌNÆ)**
Social forms, living in communal nests together with numerous others and attended by adult ants, bees or wasps of the same species 36

36. Living within hexagonal cells of papery material and fed by attendant wasps on malaxated insect-food...........Social **VÉSPIDÆ**
Not in hexagonal papery cells...............................37

37. Nests consisting of cells, hexagonal or rounded (bumble-bees), constructed of wax, often mixed with much earthy or other material. Social Bees .... **ÁPIDÆ**
Nests excavated in soil, in twigs, or other diverse locations, sometimes consisting of papery material or containing silk, but never with hexagonal cells; body usually provided with some simple, hooked or otherwise modified stiff setæ. Ants....**FORMÍCIDÆ**

LITERATURE ON HYMENOPTERA, GENERAL

ANDRÉ, E. and others. Spécies des Hyménoptères d'Europe et d'Algérie. 116 parts (1882–1920). (An extensive work, covering a number of families; we have not listed the parts separately).

ASHMEAD, W. H. Hymenoptera. In Fauna Hawaiiensis (1901).

BERLAND, L. Atlas des Hyménoptères de France, Belgique et Suisse. Nouv. Atlas Ent., no. 7, fasc. 1, 77 pp., 12 pls., 25 figs. (1947).

BERLAND, L. and others. Hyménoptères. Faune ent. France, 7, 213 pp., 712 figs. (1940).

BINGHAM, C. T. and C. MORLEY, Hymenoptera. Fauna of British India, 3 vols. (1897–1913).

BISCHOFF, H. Biologie der Hymenopteren. J. Springer, Berlin, 598 pp. (1927).

BÖRNER, C. Stammesgeschichte der Hautflügler. Biol. Zentralbl., **39**, pp. 145–186 (1919).

BROHMER, P. Hymenoptera. Fauna Deutschlands, pp. 129–404, 399 figs., 11 pls. (1932).

CAMERON, P. Biologia Centrali-Americana, Hymenoptera, **1**, pp. 1–487 (1883–1900); **2**, pp. 1–143 (1888–1900).
Hymenoptera orientalia. Mem. Manchester Philos. Soc. (various parts) (1889–1903).

CRESSON, E. T. Hymenoptera of Cuba. Proc. Ent. Soc. Philadelphia, **4**, pp. 1–196 (1865).
Synopsis of Families and Genera of Hymenoptera of America North of Mexico. Trans. Am. Ent. Soc., Suppl., 1887, 350 pp. (1887).

DALLA TORRE, K. Catalogus Hymenopterorum. 10 vols. Leipzig (1892–1902).

GINER MARÉ, J. Himenópteros de España. Apterogynidæ, Mutillidæ, Vespidæ, Eumenidæ, Masaridæ, Sapygidæ, Scoliidæ y Thynnidæ. 124 pp., 37 figs. (1944); 142 pp., 69 figs. (1945).

HANDLIRSCH, A. Insecta; Hymenoptera. In Kükenthal, Handbuch Zool., **4**, pp. 893–1036, 211 figs. (1933).

HEDICKE, H. Hymenoptera. In Tierwelt Mitteleuropas, **5**, Lief. 1, pp. XI, 1–246 (1930).

KIRBY, W. F. List of Hymenoptera of New Zealand. Trans. Ent. Soc. London, **1881**, pp. 35–50 (1881).

LAMEERE, A. Hyménoptères. Précis de Zoologie, Rec. Inst. zool. Torley-Rousseau, **5**, pp. 395–518, 114 figs. (1938).

MOCSÁRY, A. Literatura Hymenopterorum. Termes. Füzetek, **6**, pp. 7–122, (1882). (Extensive list, arranged alphabetically by authors).
Hymenoptera. Fauna Regni Hungariæ, Budapest, pp. 7–113 (1918).

MUESEBECK, C. F. W., R. V. KROMBEIN, H. K. TOWNES, et al. Catalogue of Hymenoptera of America North of Mexico. Agric. Monogr. **2**, U. S. Dept. Agric., 1420 pp. (1951).

PETERSON, A. Larvæ of Insects. An Introduction to Nearctic Species. Lepidoptera and Plant-infesting Hymenoptera. 315 pp., 84 pls. The Author, Columbus, Ohio (1948).

SCHMIEDEKNECHT, O. Die Hymenopteren Mitteleuropas. Jena (1930). (An earlier edition appeared in 1904).

VIERECK, H. L., A. D. MACGILLIVRAY, C. T. BRUES, W. M. WHEELER, and S. A. ROHWER. The Hymenoptera or Wasp-like Insects of Connecticut. Bull. State Geol. Nat. Hist. Surv., Connecticut, No. 22, 824 pp. (1916).

SUBORDER CHALASTOGASTRA

ASHMEAD, W. M. Classification of Horntails and Sawflies. (Chalastogastra). Canadian Ent., **30–36** (1898, 1903, 1904).

BENSON, R. B. Classification of Sawflies (Pterygophoridæ) and Revision of Australian Euryinæ. Trans. Roy. Ent. Soc. London, **82**, pp. 461–478, 9 figs. (1934).

On the Genera of the Cephidæ, and the New Family Syntexidæ. Ann. Mag. Nat. Hist., (10)16, pp. 535–553 (1935).

Genera of the Oryssidæ, with an Account of the African Species. Occ. Pap. Rhodesia Mus., no. 4, pp. 1–10, 10 figs. (1935).

Sawflies of the Subfamily Trichorhacinæ (Argidæ). Ann. Mag. Nat. Hist., (11)2, pp. 117–122, 12 figs. (1938).

Classification of Sawflies. Trans. Roy. Ent. Soc. London, 87, pp. 353–384, 47 figs. (1939).

Classification of the Siricidæ. Bull. Ent. Res., 34, pp. 125–151 (1943).

Classification of the Xyelidæ. Proc. Roy. Ent. Soc. London, (B) 14, pp. 34–37, 3 figs. (1945).

Classification of the Pamphiliidæ. Proc. Roy. Ent. Soc. London, (B) 14, pp. 25–33, 11 figs. (1945).

Classification of the Cephidæ. Trans. Roy. Ent. Soc. London, 96, pp. 89–108, 39 figs. (1946).

BENSON, R. B. and O. CONDE. Revision der neotropische Perreyinæ. Rev. Ent., Rio de Janeiro, 9, pp. 121–154 (1938).

BERLAND, D. Hyménoptères Tenthrédoides. Faune de France, 47, 496 pp., 418 figs. (1947).

BRADLEY, J. C. The Siricidæ of North America. Pomona Journ. Ent. and Zool., 5, pp. 1–30 (1913).

CAMERON, P. A Monograph of the British Phytophagous Hymenoptera. London, Ray Soc., 4 vols. (1882–1893).

ENSLIN, E. Tenthredinoidea. In Insekten Mitteleuropas, 3, pp. 95–213, Stuttgart (1914).

GUIGLIA, D. Catalogue of Oryssoidea. Ann. Mus. Civ., Genova, 62, pp. 85–111. (1943).

GUSSAKOVSKII, V. V. Insectes Hyménoptères. Chalastogastra. Faune de l'U.R.S.S., Inst. zool. Acad. Sci. U.R.S.S. (N.S.) 1, xviii + 453 pp., 82 figs. (1935).

HEDICKE, H. Siricidæ Hymenop. Cat. Junk, 6, 32 pp. (1938).

Xiphydriidæ. Hymenop. Cat. Junk, 7, 17 pp. (1938).

KLIMA, A. Syntexidæ, Pamphiliidæ, Cephidæ and Xyelidæ. Hymenop. Cat. Junk, 2, 3, 4, 147 pp. (1937).

KONOW, F. W. Lydidæ. Gen. Insectorum, fasc. 27, 27 pp. (1905).

Siricidæ. Gen. Insectorum, fasc. 28, 14 pp. (1905).

Tenthredinidæ. Gen. Insectorum, fasc. 29, 176 pp. (1905).

MAA, T. Synopsis of Asiatic Siricoidea. Notes Ent. chinoise, Mus. Heude, 13, pp. 11–189 (1949).

MALAISE, R. Tenthredinidæ of Sweden. Svensk Insektfauna, 13, 70 pp., 35 figs. (1931).

Tenthredinoidea of South-eastern Asia. Opusc. ent., Suppl., 4, 288 pp., 20 pls., 57 figs. (1945).

MORICE, F. D. Australian Sawflies. Trans. Ent. Soc. London, 1918, pp. 247–333 (1919).

NIELSEN, J. C. and K. HENRIKSEN. Danish Siricidæ and Sawflies (in Danish). Danmarks Fauna, pt. 18, 234 pp. (1915).

REICHERT, A. Tenthredinoidea von Leipzig. SB. naturf. Ges. Leipzig, 56–59, pp. 37–74 (1933).

RIES, D. T. Revision of Nearctic Cephidæ. Trans. American Ent. Soc., **63**, pp. 259–324 (1937).

ROHWER, S. A. Genera of Pamphiliinæ. Canadian Ent., **42**, pp. 215–220 (1910).

Classification of Chalastogastra. Proc. Ent. Soc. Washington, **13**, pp. 215–226 (1911).

Studies in Oryssoidea. Proc. U. S. Nat. Mus., **43**, pp. 141–158 (1913).

Genotypes of Sawflies and Woodwasps. Bull. U. S. Dept. Agric., Tech. Ser., **20**, pp. 69–109 (1911).

Nearctic Sawflies of the Genus Xyela. Proc. U. S. Nat. Mus., **45**, pp. 265–281 (1913).

ROHWER, S. A. and R. A. CUSHMAN. Idiogastra, a new Suborder of Hymenoptera. Proc. Ent. Soc. Wash., **19**, pp. 89–98 (1917).

ROSS, H. H. North American Sawflies of the Subfamily Dolerinæ. Illinois Biol. Monogr., **12**, pp. 211–320, 6 pls. (1931).

Xyelidæ of North America. Ann. Ent. Soc. America, **25**, pp. 153–169, 2 pls. (1932).

Generic Classification of Nearctic Sawflies. Illinois. Biol. Monogr., **34**, No. 94, 173 pp., 17 pls. (1937).

TAKEUCHI, K. A Revision of the Japanese Argidæ. Trans. Kansai Ent. Soc., **3**, pp. 27–42 (1932).

Tenthredinoidea of Saghalien, Tenthredo Acta Ent., **1**, pp. 53–108, 2 pls. (1936).

Systematic Study of the Suborder Symphyta (Chalastogastra). Tenthredo Acta Ent., **2**, pp. 393–439, 7 figs. (1938).

WAGNER, A. C. W. Symphyta des westlichen Norddeutschlands. Verh. Ver. naturw. Heimatsforsch., **28**, pp. 32–79 (1939).

YUASA, H. A Classification of the Larvæ of the Tenthredinoidea. Illinois Biol. Monogr., **7**, no. 4, Urbana (1922).

ICHNEUMONOIDEA

ASHMEAD, W. H. Classification of the Ichneumon Flies or the Superfamily Ichneumonoidea. Proc. U. S. Nat. Mus., **23**, 220 pp. (1900).

AYYAR, T. V. R. Catalogue of Indian Braconidæ. Rept. Proc. 5th Ent. Meeting, Pusa, pp. 352–362 (1923).

BAKER, C. F. Chelonini of the Philippines (Braconidæ). Philippine Journ. Sci., **31**, pp. 451–489 (1926).

BEIRNE, B. P. The Cephalic Structures and Spiracles of the Larvæ of the Ichneumonidæ. Trans. Soc. British Ent., **7**, pp. 123–190, 31 figs. (1941).

BERTHOUMIEU, V. Ichneumonidæ, Ichneumoninæ. Gen. Insectorum, fasc. 18, 87 pp. (1904).

BISCHOFF, H. Trigonaloidea. Hymenop. Cat. Junk, **5**, 18 pp. (1938).

BRADLEY, J. C. Family Roproniidæ. Ent. News, **16**, pp. 14–17 (1905).

The Evaniidæ. Trans. American Ent. Soc., **34**, pp. 101–194 (1908).

BRUES, C. T. South African Evaniidæ, Braconidæ, Alysiidæ and Plumariidæ, with Catalogue of Species. Ann. South African Mus., **19**, pp. 1–150 (1924).

Ethiopian Braconidæ, with a List of the African Species. Proc. Amer. Acad. Arts Sci., **61**, pp. 205–436 (1926).

CEBALLOS, G. Ichneumónidos de España (Cryptinæ). Trab. Mus. Cienc. Madrid, Zool., **56**, 206 pp., 102 figs. (1931).

CLÉMENT, E. Paläarktische Pimplinæ (Part). Festschr. E. Strand, **4**, pp. 502–569 (1938).

CRESSON, E. T. Species of the Subfamily Ichneumoninæ (Nearctic). Trans. American Ent. Soc., **6**, pp. 129–212 (1877).

CUSHMAN, R. A. Revision of American Cremastini. Proc. U. S. Nat. Mus., **53**, pp. 503–551 (1917).

North American Lycorini, Polysphinctini and Theroniini. (Ichneumonidæ). Proc. U. S. Nat. Mus., **58**, pp. 7–48 (1920).

Tribe Ephialtini. Proc. U. S. Nat. Mus., **58**, pp. 327–362 (1920).

New Oriental and Australian Ichneumonidæ, with key to Genera of Cryptinæ. Philippine Journ. Sci., **20**, pp. 543–595 (1922).

Genera of Paniscini (Ichneumonidæ). Proc. U. S. Nat. Mus., **64**, Art. 20, 48 pp. (1924).

Revision of the North American Ichneumon-flies of Mesostenus and related genera. Proc. U. S. Nat. Mus., **74**, Art. 16, 58 pp. (1929).

The Genus Lysiognatha. Journ. Washington Acad. Sci., **27**, pp. 438–444 (1937).

Ichneumon Flies of Subfamily Neorhacodinæ (Braconidæ). Proc. U. S. Nat. Mus., **88**, No. 3088, pp. 523–527 (1940).

Generic Revision of the Ichneumon-flies of the Tribe Ophionini. Proc. U. S. Nat. Mus., **96**, No. 3206, pp. 417–482, 8 pls. (1947).

CUSHMAN, R. A. and S. A. ROHWER. Holarctic Tribes of Ichneumoninæ. Proc. U. S. Nat. Mus., **57**, pp. 379–396 (1920).

North American Acænitini (Ichneumonidæ). Proc. U. S. Nat. Mus., **57**, pp. 503–523 (1921).

DAVIS, G. C. A Review of the Tryphoninæ. Trans. American Ent. Soc., **24**, pp. 193–348 (1897).

DUTT, G. R. Stephanidæ. Cat. Indian Ins. Govt. India, Centr. Pub. Branch, Calcutta, pt. 10, (1925).

ELLIOTT, E. A. Monograph of the Stephanidæ. Proc. Zool. Soc. London, **1922**, pp. 705–831 (1922).

ENDERLEIN, G., Die Braconiden-Subfamilie Mimagathidinæ. Zool. Anz., **28**, pp. 449–454 (1905).

Ueber die Klassifikation der Stephaniden. Zool. Anz., **28**, pp. 473–477 (1905).

Zur Kenntnis aussereuropäischen Braconiden (Key to Genera of Agathidinæ). Arch. Naturg., Jahr. **87A**, Heft 11, pp. 51–224 (1920).

FAHRINGER, J. Opuscula Braconologica. 2388 pp. Vienna. (A considerable number of parts have been published.) (1925–37).

FROGGATT, W. W. Notes on Megalyra. Proc. Linn. Soc. New South Wales, **31**, pp. 399–407 (1906).

GAHAN, A. B. Aphididiinæ of North America. Bull. 152, Maryland Agric. Expt. Sta., pp. 147–200 (1911).

Revision of North American Opiinæ (Braconidæ). Proc. U. S. Nat. Mus., **49**, pp. 63–95 (1916).

HEDICKE, H. Hymenop. Cat. Junk. Trigonalidæ, **5**, 18 pp. (1938); Evaniidæ, **9**, 50 pp.; Aulacidæ, **10**, 28 pp.; Gasteruptiidæ, **11**, 54 pp. (1939).

HEINRICH, G. Ichneumoninæ von Celebes. Mitt. Zool. Mus. Berlin, **20**, pp. 1–263, 8 pls. (1934).

    Ichneumoninæ de Madagascar. Mém. Acad. Malgache, **25**, 139 pp., **6** pls. (1940).

HOOKER, C. W. The Ichneumonidæ of the Tribe Ophionini. Trans. American Ent. Soc., **38**, pp. 1–176 (1912).

HOPPER, H. P. Revision of Trogini of United States and Canada. Trans. American Ent. Soc., **65**, pp. 307–346, 1 pl. (1940).

KIEFFER, J. J. Evaniidæ. Gen. Insectorum, fasc. 2, 13 pp. (1902).

    Stephanidæ. Gen. Insectorum, fasc. 77, 10 pp. (1908).

    Evaniidæ (including Aulacidæ and Gasteruptionidæ). Das Tierreich, Lief. **30**, 432 pp. (1912).

    Evaniiden der Philippinen. Philippine Journ. Sci., **11D**, pp. 317–346 (1914).

KRIECHBAUMER, J. Beitrag zu einer Monographie der Joppinen. Berliner Ent. Zeits., **43**, pp. 1–166 (1899).

KRIEGER, R. Revision of Pimpla and Allies (Ichneumonidæ). Ber. naturf. Ges, Leipzig, Jahrg. 1897–98, pp. 47–124 (1898).

    Ueber die Ichneumonidengattungen Neotheronia und Theronia. Zeits. Hym. Dipt., Jahrg. **5** and **6** (1905–06) (several parts).

    Die Ichneumonidengattung Lissopimpla. Zeitschr. Hym. Dipt. 1907, pp. 294–302 (1907).

LYLE, G. T. Catalogue of British Braconidæ. Trans. Roy. Ent. Soc. London, **81**, pp. 67–74 (1933).

MAO, Y.-T. Genus Cardiochiles in North America. Proc. U. S. Nat. Mus., **99**, pp. 229–266, 2 pls. (1949).

MARSHALL, T. A. Monograph of the British Braconidæ. Trans. Ent. Soc. London, (seven parts) (1885–99).

MEYER, N. F. Revision of Anomalini (Ichneumonidæ). Konowia, **10**, pp. 3–14, 4 figs. (1931).

    Revision der Tribus Ophionini (Ichneumonidæ). Konowia, **16**, pp. 15–24 (1937).

MORLEY, C. Ichneumonidæ of Great Britain, 3 vols. (1903–08).

    Catalogue of British Chalcididæ. London, 74 pp. (1910).

    Revision of Ichneumonidæ. London, British Mus. Nat. Hist. 4 pts. (1912–15).

    Notes on Braconidæ. XIII. Dacnusides. Entomologist, **57**, pp. 193–198; 250–255 (1924).

MUESEBECK, C. F. W. Revision of North American Apanteles. Proc. U. S. Nat. Mus., **58**, No. 2349, pp. 483–576 (1920).

    Revision of North American Neoneurinæ and Microgasterinæ. Proc. U. S. Nat. Mus., **61**, No. 2436, art. 15, pp. 1–76 (1922).

    Revision of North American Microbracon (Braconidæ). Proc. U. S. Nat. Mus., **67**, Art. 8, 85 pp. (1925).

    Revision of Braconinæ of North America. Proc. U. S. Nat. Mus., **69**, Art. 16, pp. 1–73 (1927).

    Genera of Euphorinæ (Braconidæ). Misc. Publ. U. S. Dept. Agric., No. **241**, 38 pp. (1936).

NIXON, G. E. J. Revision of the Spathiinæ of the Old World (Braconidæ). Trans. Roy. Ent. Soc., **93**, pp. 173–456, 1 pl., 283 figs. (1943).

Revision of European Dacnusini. Ent. Monthly Mag., **80**, pp. 88–108; 140–151; 193–200; 249–255, 162 figs.; **84**, pp. 207–224 (1944–48).

RIEGEL, G. T. The Wings of Braconidæ. Ann. Ent. Soc. America, **41**, pp. 439–449, 4 pls. (1948).

ROHWER, S. A. Tribe Xoridini (Ichneumonidæ). Proc. U. S. Nat. Mus., **45**, pp. 353–361 (1913).

North American Cenocœlius (Braconidæ). Canadian Ent., pp. 316–322 (1914).

North American Labenini, Rhyssini, Xoridini, Odontomerini, Phyto-dietini (Ichneumonidæ). Proc. U. S. Nat. Mus., **57**, pp. 405–474 (1921).

ROMAN, A. Systematische Stellung von Neorhacodes. Ent. Tidskr., **44**, pp. 169–174 (1923).

SAEGER, H. DE. Microgastrinæ (Braconidæ). Explor. Parc nat. Albert. Miss. de Witte (1933–35), fasc. **47**, 342 pp., 13 pls., 333 figs.; fasc. **50**, 245 pp. 201 figs. (1944–46).

Cardiochilinæ et Sigalphinæ (Braconidæ). Ibid., fasc. **53**, 272 pp., 306 figs. (1948).

SCHLETTERER, A. Revision of Gasteruptionidæ. Abh. zool.-bot. Ges. Wien, **35**, pp. 267–326 (1885).

Die Hymenopteren Gruppe der Evaniiden. Ann. k. k. naturh. Hofmus. Wien, **4**, pp. 107–180, 289–338, 373–546 (1889).

Revision of Stephanidæ. Berliner Ent. Zeitschr., **33**, pp. 71–160 (1889).

Die Hymenopteren-Gattungen Stenophasmus, Monomachus, Pelecinus, Megalyra. Berliner Ent. Zeitschr., **33**, pp. 198–250 (1889).

SCHMIEDEKNECHT, O. Opuscula Ichneumonologica. Blankenburg (1902–1931) (numerous fascicles and additions dealing with Palæarctic Ichneumonidæ).

Ichneumonidæ, Pimplinæ. Gen. Insectorum, fasc. **62**, 120 pp. (1908).

Ichneumonidæ, Cryptinæ and Ophioninæ, part. Gen. Insectorum, fasc. **34**, 71 pp.; fasc. **75**, 165 pp.; fasc. **114**, 100 pp. (1905, 1908, 1911).

Die Ichneumonidengattung Pimpla. Zeitschr. angew. Ent., **1**, pp. 396–478 (1914).

Deutschen Gattungen und Arten der Anomaloninen. Naturw. Zeits. Forst-u. Land-Wirtsch., **14**, pp. 97–116, 4 figs. (1931).

⌐puscula Ichneumonologica. Suppls. **10–21** (1931–34).

SCHULZ, W. A. Beitrag zur Kenntniss der Familie Pelecinidæ. S. B. Akad. Wiss., München, **33**, pp. 435–450 (1903).

Trigonalidæ. Gen. Insectorum, fasc. **61**, 24 pp. (1908).

Systematische Uebersicht der Monomachiden. Proc. 1st Congr. Entom., Brussels, pp. 405–424 (1911).

SÉYRIG, A. Pimplinæ de Madagascar. Mém. Acad. malgache, **11**, pp. 1–183, 17 pls., 1 map (1934).

Tryphoninæ de Madagascar. Ibid., **19**, 111 pp., 8 pls. (1934).

SMITH, C. F. Aphidiinæ of North America. Contrib. Zool. Ent. Ohio State Univ., No. **6**, xii + 154 pp., 17 pls. (1944).

STRICKLAND, E. H. North American Pezomachini (Ichneumonidæ). Ann. Ent. Soc. America, **5**, pp. 113–140 (1912).

SZÉPLIGETI, G. V. Braconidæ. Gen. Insectorum, fasc. **22**, 253 pp. (1904).

TELENGA, N. A. Insectes Hyménoptères. Vol. **5**, No. 2 (Braconidæ). Faune de l'U.R.S.S., xvi + 402 pp., 53 figs. (1936).

TOSQUINET, J. Ichneumonides d'Afrique. Mém. Soc. Ent. Belgique, **5,** 430 pp. (1896).

TOWNES, H. K. Revision of Pimplinæ of Eastern North America. Ann. Ent. Soc. America, **33,** pp. 283–323, 10 figs. (1940).

Catalogue and Reclassification of the Nearctic Ichneumonidæ. Mem. American Ent. Soc., No. **11,** pp. 1–925 (1944–45).

Nearctic Species of Stephanidæ. Proc. U. S. Nat. Mus., **99,** pp. 361–370 (1949).

Nearctic Species of Evaniidæ. Proc. U. S. Nat. Mus., **99,** pp. 525–539 (1949).

Nearctic Gasteruptiidæ. Proc. U. S. Nat. Mus., **100,** pp. 85–145 (1950).

TOWNES, H. K. and M. C. Revision of American Tryphonini. Ann. Ent. Soc. America, **42,** pp. 321–395, 397–447 (1949).

UCHIDA, T. Erster Beitrag zur Ichneumoniden Japans. Journ. Coll. Agric. Hokkaido Imp. Univ., **18,** pp. 43–173 (1926).

Beiträge zur Systematik der Tribus Accenitini Japans. Ins. Matsumurana, **9,** pp. 41–54 (1934).

VIERECK, H. L. Type Species of the Genera of Ichneumon Flies. Bull. U. S. Nat. Mus., **83,** pp. 1–186 (1914).

List of Families and Subfamilies of Ichneumonoidea. Proc. Biol. Soc. Washington, **31,** pp. 69–74 (1918); also Ibid., **32,** pp. 48 and 198 (1919).

WATERSTON, J. Dinapsidæ. Ann. Mag. Nat. Hist., (9) **10,** pp. 418–420 (1922).

CHALCIDOIDEA

ASHMEAD, W. H. Classification of Chalcid Flies or the Superfamily Chalcidoidea. Mem. Carnegie Mus., Pittsburgh, **1,** No. 4, pp. 225–551 (1904).

AYYAR, T. V. R. Check list of Indian Chalcidoidea. Spolia Zeylandica, **13,** pp. 235–254 (1925).

BURKS, B. D. Revision of the Tribe Chalcidini of North America. Proc. U. S. Nat. Mus., **88,** No. 3082, pp. 237–354, 14 figs. (1940).

CRAWFORD, J. C. Synopsis of North American Perilampidæ. Proc. Ent. Soc. Washington, **16,** pp. 69–76 (1914).

DEBAUCHE, H. R. Etude sur les Mymarommidæ et les Mymaridæ de la Belgique. Mém. Mus. Hist. nat. Belgique, No. **108,** 247 pp., 24 pls. (1948).

FERRIÈRE, C. Subfamily Cheiropachinæ. Mitt. Schweiz. Ent. Ges., **21,** pp. 516–530 (1948).

GAHAN, A. B. and M. M. FAGAN. Type Species of Genera of Chalcidoidea. Bull. U. S. Nat. Mus., **124,** 173 pp. (1923).

GAHAN, A. B. and C. FERRIÈRE. Notes on Some Gall-inhabiting Chalcidoids. Ann. Ent. Soc. America, **40,** pp. 271–302, 2 pls. (1947).

GEMIGNANI, E. V. Eucharidæ en la republica Argentina. An. Mus. Nac. Hist. Nat. Buenos Aires, **37,** pp. 277–290 (1933).

GHESQUIERE, J. Contribution à l'étude des Mymaridæ du Congo belge. Rev. Zool. Bot. africaine, **36,** pp. 317–328, 8 figs. (1942).

GIRAULT, A. A. Australian Hymenoptera Chalcidoidea. Mem. Queensland Mus., 365 pp. (1912–16). (Numerous parts and supplements dealing with all the families).

Systematic Monograph of the Signiphorinæ. Proc. U. S. Nat. Mus., **45,** pp. 189–233 (1913).

Revision of Trichogrammatidæ. Bull. Wisc. Nat. Hist. Soc., **11**, pp. 150–179; **12**, pp. 59–71 (1913–14).

North American Mymaridæ. Published by author, pp. 6–27. (1929).

GRANDI, G. Catalogo dei Agaonidi. Boll. Lab. Ent. Istit. Sup. Agrar., Bologna, **1**, pp. 107–235 (1928).

Second Edition, Revised. Boll. Ist. Ent. Bologna, **7**, pp. 214–240 (1935).

HOFFMEYER, E. B. Danischen Callimomiden (Torymidæ). Ent. Meddel., **17**, pp. 261–285, 11 figs. (1931).

HOWARD, L. O. New Genera and Species of Aphelininæ, with a Revised Table of Genera. Bull. U. S. Dept. Agric. Tech. Ser., No. 12, pt. 4, pp. 69–88 (1907).

ISHI, T. Encyrtidæ of Japan. Bull. Imp. Agric. Expt. Sta. Japan, **3**, pp. 79–160, 57 figs. (1928).

KIRBY, W. F. Synopsis of Genera of Eucharididæ. Journ. Linn. Soc., London, Zool., **20**, pp. 28–37 (1886).

KRYGER, J. P. The European Trichogrammatidæ. Ent. Meddel., **12**, pp. 257–354 (1918–19).

Mymaridæ of Palæarctic Region. Ibid., **26**, pp. 1–97 (1950).

MANI, M. S. Revision of Indian Leucospididæ. Rec. Indian Mus., **39**, pp. 287–302 (1937).

Chalcidoidea. Cat. Indian Insects, Pt. **23**, 170 pp. (1934).

Chalcidoid and other Hymenopterous Parasites from India. Indian Journ. Ent., **1**, pp. 69–99, 11 figs. (1939).

MASI, L. Sistematica degli Eunotini. Eos, **7**, pp. 411–459, 6 figs. (1931).

Chalcididæ of Formosa. Konowia, **12**, pp. 1–18 (1933).

Contributo alla conoscenza dei Dirhinini. Eos, **23**, pp. 39–78, 14 figs. (1947).

MAYR, G. Die europäischen Torymiden. Verh. zool.-bot. Ges. Wien, **24**, pp. 53–142 (1874).

Die europäischen Encyrtiden. Verh. zool.-bot. Ges. Wien, **25**, pp. 676–778 (1875).

MERCET, R. G. Fauna Iberica; Encírtidos. Mus. Nac. Cienc. Nat. Madrid, 732 pp. (1921).

Afelínidos de España. Rev. Biol. For. Limnol. (B), **2**, pp. 29–106, 9 figs. (1930).

RUSCHKA, F. Die europäischen Arten der mit Monodontomerus verwandte Gattungen. Zeits. angew. Ent., **9**, pp. 395–408 (1923).

Die europäischen Eucharidinæ und Perilampinæ. Deutsch. Ent. Zeits., 1924, pp. 82–96 (1924).

SANTIS, L. DE. Estudo monografico de los Afelínidos de la República Argentina. Rev. Mus. La Plata, **5**, Sect. Zool., pp. 23–280, 52 figs. (1948).

SCHLETTERER, A. Leucospididæ. Berliner Ent. Zeits., **35**, pp. 141–302 (1890).

SCHMIEDEKNECHT, O. Chalcidoidea. Gen. Insectorum, fasc. 97, 550 pp. (1909).

SCHMITZ, G. Chalcididæ. Explor. Parc nat. Albert. Miss. de Witte (1933–35), fasc. **48**, pp. 1–191, 17 pls. (1946).

WELD, C. J. Revision of American Leucospididæ. Proc. U. S. Nat. Mus., **61**, art. 6, pp. 1–43 (1922).

PROCTOTRYPOIDEA

ASHMEAD, W. H. A Monograph of the North American Proctotrypidæ. Bull. U. S. Nat. Mus., **45** (1893).
  Classification of the Pointed-tailed Wasps or the Superfamily Proctotrupoidea. Journ. New York Ent. Soc., **10**, p. 241; **11**, pp. 28 and 86 (1902–03).
BRUES, C. T. Scelionidæ. Gen. Insectorum, fasc. 80, 59 pp. (1908), with supplement by J. J. Kieffer.
CRAWFORD, J. C. A new Family of Parasitic Hymenoptera (Vanhorniidæ). Proc. Ent. Soc. Washington, **2**, pp. 63–64 (1909).
DEBAUCHE, H. R. Scelionidæ de la faune belge. Bull. Ann. Soc. ent. Belgique, **83**, pp. 255–285, 2 pls. (1947).
DODD, A. P. Revision of Australian Teleasinæ. Proc. Linn. Soc. New South Wales, **55**, pp. 41–91 (1930).
FOUTS, R. M. Revision of North American Platygasterinæ. Proc. U. S. Nat. Mus., **63**, art. 15a, pp. 1–145 (1924).
  Genus Trimorus (Scelionidæ) in North America. Proc. U. S. Nat. Mus., **98**, No. 3225, pp. 91–148 (1948).
KIEFFER, J. J. Revision des Scélionides. Ann. Soc. Sci. Brussels, **32**, pp. 111–250 (1908).
  Ceraphronidæ. Gen. Insectorum, fasc. 94, 27 pp. (1909).
  Serphidæ. Gen. Insectorum, fasc. 95, 10 pp. (1909).
  Belytidæ. Gen. Insectorum, fasc. 107, 47 pp. (1910).
  Diapriidæ. Gen. Insectorum, fasc. 124, 75 pp. (1911).
  Serphidæ. Das Tierreich, Lief. 42, 254 pp. (1914).
  Diapriidæ. Das Tierreich, Lief. 44, 627 pp. (1916).
  Scelionidæ. Das Tierreich, Lief. 48, 885 pp. (1926).
NIXON, G. E. J. Revision of the African Telenominæ. Trans. Roy. Ent. Soc. London, **83**, pp. 73–103, 1 pl., 14 figs. (1935).
  The African Species of Teleasinæ. Ann. Mag. Nat. Hist., (10) **17**, pp. 114–141, 161–191, 18 figs. (1936).
  Revision of British Proctotrupidæ. Trans. Roy. Ent. Soc. London, **87**, pp. 431–466, 71 figs. (1938).
TOWNES, H. The Family Roproniidæ. Proc. U. S. Nat. Mus., **98**, pp. 85–89, 1 fig. (1948).

CYNIPOIDEA

ASHMEAD, W. H. Classification of Cynipoidea. Psyche. **10**, pp. 7, 59, 140 (1903).
DALLA TORRE, W. and J. J. KIEFFER. Cynipidæ. Gen. Insectorum, fasc. 9–10, 84 pp. (1902).
  Cynipidæ. Das Tierreich, Lief. 24, 891 pp. (1910).
FULLAWAY, D. T. Monograph of the Gall Making Cynipidæ of California. Ann. Ent. Soc. America, **4**, pp. 331–380 (1911).
HEDICKE, H. and G. J. KERRICH. Revision of the Family Liopteridæ. Trans. Roy. Soc. London, **90**, pp. 177–225, 3 pls., 30 figs. (1942).
HOUARD, C. Les Zoocécidies de l'Amérique du Nord: Galles des Chênes. Lib. Sci., Hermann & Cie., 549 pp., 1893 figs. (1940).

KIEFFER, J. J. Cynipidæ. In Insekten Mitteleuropas, 3, pp. 1–94, Stuttgart (1914).

KINSEY, A. C. New Species and Synonymy of American Cynipidæ. Bull. American Mus. Nat. Hist., 42, pp. 293–317 (1920).

Phylogeny of Cynipid Genera and Biological Characteristics. Bull. American Mus. Nat. Hist., 42, pp. 357–402 (1920).

MORLEY, C. Synopsis of British Cynipidæ. Entomologist, 64, pp. 150–153; 183–186, 206–210, 248–250 (1931); Ibid., 65, pp. 15–18, 38–40, 63–65, 89–91, 108–113, 130–133 (1932).

ROHWER, S. A. and M. M. FAGAN. The Type Species of the Genera of the Cynipoidea. Proc. U. S. Nat. Mus., 53, pp. 357–380 (1917); 55, pp. 237–240 (1919).

TAVARES, J. S. Os Cynipides da Ibérica. Broteria, Ser. Zool., 26, pp. 25–53 (1930).

WELD, L. H. Cynipidæ; Genera of Liopterinæ and Oberthuerellinæ. Philippine Journ. Sci., 21, pp. 323–335 (1922).

ACULEATA, GENERAL

ASHMEAD, W. H. Classification of the Fossorial, Predaceous and Parasitic Wasps or the Superfamily Vespoidea. Canadian Ent., 32, 34, 35, 36, (1900–04). (Various parts published at intervals.)

BENSON, R. B., C. FERRIÈRE and O. W. RICHARDS. Generic Names of British Hymenoptera Aculeata, with List of Species. Generic Names of British Insects, Pt. 5, pp. 81–116. Roy. Ent. Soc. London (1937).

BERLAND, L. Hyménoptères Vespiformes. (Vespidæ, Bethylidæ, Dryinidæ, Embolemidæ). Faune de France, 19, pt. 2, 208 pp., Paris (1928).

BETHYLOIDEA

ASHMEAD, W. H. Rhopalosomidæ, a New Family of Wasps. Proc. Ent. Soc. Washington, 3, pp. 303–309 (1896).

BRUES, C. T. Note on the Hymenopterous Family Rhopalosomatidæ. Psyche, 33, pp. 18–19 (1926).

FULLAWAY, D. T. Revision of Hawaiian Sierola (Bethylidæ). Occ. Pap. Bishop Mus., Honolulu, 7, pp. 57–159 (1920).

KIEFFER, J. J. Dryinidæ. Gen. Insectorum, fasc. 54, 33 pp. (1907).

Bethylidæ. Gen. Insectorum, fasc. 76, 50 pp. (1908).

Bethylidæ. Das Tierreich, Lief. 41, 595 pp. (1914).

PERKINS, R. C. L. Leaf Hoppers and their Natural Enemies. Dryinidæ. Bull. Hawaiian Sugar Planters Expt. Sta., No. 1, pt. 1, pp. 1–69 (1905).

RICHARDS, O. W. The British Bethylidæ. Trans. Roy. Ent. Soc. London, 89, pp. 185–344, 111 figs. (1939).

Sclerogibbidæ. Proc. Roy. Ent. Soc., London, 8B, pp. 211–223 (1939).

CHRYSIDOIDEA

AARON, S. F. The North American Chrysididæ. Trans. American Ent. Soc., 12, pp. 209–248 (1885).

BERLAND, L. and F. BERNARD. Cleptidæ, Chrysididæ et Trigonalidæ. Faune de France, 34, 145 pp., 241 figs. (1938).

Bischoff, H. Chrysididæ. Gen. Insectorum, fasc. 151, 88 pp. (1913).

Bridwell, J. C. Family Alienidæ. Proc. Hawaiian Ent. Soc., 4, p. 117 (1919).

Ducke, A. As Chrysididas do Brazil. Cat. Faun. Brasiliera Mus. Paulista, São Paulo, 4, pp. 1–31 (1913).

Edney, E. B. Heteronychinæ (Chrysididæ) of South Africa. Occ. Pap. Nat. Mus. South. Rhodesia, No. 9, pp. 29–126, 67 figs. (1940).
  The Holonychinæ (Chrysididæ) of South Africa. Occ. Pap. Nat. Mus. South. Rhodesia, 2, pp. 168–205, 28 figs. (1947).

Mocsáry, A. Monographia Chrysidarum Orbis Terrarum Universi. Budapest, Soc. Franklinianæ (1889).

Trautmann, W. Die Goldwespen Europas. Weimar, 194 pp. (1927).

SCOLIOIDEA

André, E. Mutillidæ. Gen. Insectorum, fasc. 11, pp. 77 (1903).
  Bibliographie générale des Mutillides. Rev. Ent., 29, pp. 134–166 (1910).

Betrem, J. C. Monographie der Indo-australischen Scoliiden. Treubia, 9, suppl. 388 pp. (1928).
  Etude systématique des Scoliidæ de Chine. Notes Ent. chinoise, 8, pp. 47–188 (1941).

Bischoff, M. Konowiellidæ (Plumariidæ). Ent. Rundschau, Jahrg. 31, pp. 67–69 (1914).
  Monographie der Mutilliden Afrikas. Arch. Naturg., Jahrg. 86A, Hefte 1–5, 830 pp. (1920–21).

Blake, C. A. Monograph of the Mutillidæ of North America. Trans. American Ent. Soc., 13, pp. 179–286 (1886).

Bradley, J. C. Monograph of North American Mutillidæ. Trans. American Ent. Soc., 42, pp. 187–214; 309–336 (1916).
  Review of the Myrmosidæ. Trans. American Ent. Soc., 43, pp. 247–290 (1917).

Bradley, J. C. and J. Bequaert. Revision of Mutillidæ of Belgian Congo. Bull. American Mus. Nat. Hist. 58, pp. 63–122 (1928).

Cresson, E. T. Synopsis of North American species of Sapyga. Trans. American Ent. Soc., 8, pp. xx–xxi (1880).

Ducke, A. O Genero Pterombrus. Rev. Mus. São Paulo, 9, pp. 107–122 (1914).

Durán-Moya, L. Die Thynniden von Chile. Arch. Naturgesch. (N.F.), 10, pp. 71–176 (1941).

Dusnet Y Alonsa, J. M. Los Escólidos de la Peninsula Ibérica. Eos, 6, pp. 5–82 (1930).

Fattig, P. W. Mutillidæ of Georgia. Emory Univ. Bull., 1, 24 pp. (1943).

Fox, W. J. The North American Mutillidæ. Trans. American Ent. Soc., 25, pp. 219–292 (1899).

Guiglia, D. Gli Scoliidei della Liguria. Ann. Mus. Stor. Nat. Genoa, 52, pp. 424–460 (1928).

Hedicke, H. Tiphiidæ. Hymenop. Cat. Junk, 1, 32 pp. (1936).

Krombein, K. V. Studies in the Tiphiidæ. Revision of the Nearctic Myzininæ. Trans. American Ent. Soc., 64, pp. 227–292, 12 figs. (1938).
  Studies on the Tiphiidæ. Trans. American Ent. Soc., 65, pp. 415–465 (1940).

Revision of West Indian Myzininæ. Rev. Ent., Rio Janiero, 13, pp. 308–353, 7 figs. (1942).

MALLOCH, J. R. Systematic notes on North American Brachycistinæ. Proc. U. S. Nat. Mus., 68, Art. 3, pp. 1–28 (1926).

MICHA, I. Beitrag zur Kenntnis der Scoliiden. Mitt. Zool. Mus. Berlin, 13, pp. 1–156 (1927).

MICKEL, C. E. Monograph North American Dasymutilla. Bull. U. S. Nat. Mus., 134, pp. 39–340 (1928).

　　Mutillidæ of Eastern Asia. Lingnan Sci. Journ., 12, pp. 189–325 (1933).

　　Mutillidæ of Formosa. Ann. Ent. Soc. America, 26, pp. 381–423 (1933).

　　Mutillidæ of the Philippine Islands. Philippine Journ. Sci., 54, pp. 91–219, 1 pl. (1934).

　　The Mutillidæ of the Pacific Islands. Trans. Roy. Ent. Soc. London, 83, pp. 177–321, 6 figs. (1935).

OLSOUFIEFF, G. Révision systématique des Mutilles de Madagascar. Bull. Acad. malgache, (N.S.) 20, pp. 171–216, 2 pls. (1938).

PATE, V. S. L. Neotropical Sapygidæ, with a Conspectus of the Family. Acta zool. lilloana, 4, pp. 292–426 (1947).

　　Nearctic Tiphiidæ. Jour. New York Ent. Soc., 55, pp. 115–143 (1947).

SCHUSTER, R. M. Revision of Sphærophthalmine Mutillidæ. Ann. Ent. Soc. America, 39, pp. 692–703 (1946).

TURNER, R. E. Revision of the Thynnidæ of Australia. Proc. Linn. Soc. New South Wales, 32, pp. 206–290 (1907).

　　Thynnidæ. Gen. Insectorum, fasc. 105, 62 pp. (1910).

UCHIDA, T. Revision der japanischen Scoliiden. Jour. Fac. Agric. Hokkaido Univ., 32, pp. 229–262, 2 pls. (1934).

FORMICOIDEA

ARNOLD, G. Monograph of the Formicidæ of South Africa. Ann. South African Mus., 23, pp. 191–295 (1926). Also 14, pp. 159–270 (1916).

BINGHAM, C. T. Ants of British India. Fauna of British India, Hymenoptera, vol. 2 (1903).

BORGMEIER, T. Catálogo systemático e synonymico das Formigas do Brasil. Arch. Mus. Nac. Rio de Janeiro, 24, pp. 33–103 (1924) and Ibid., 27, pp. 69–164 (1927).

BROWN, W. L. Preliminary Generic Revision of the Higher Dacetini. Trans. American Ent. Soc., 74, pp. 101–129 (1948).

　　Revision of Dacetini. Mushi, 20, pp. 1–24 (1949).

　　Revision of Dacetini. American Midl. Naturalist (in press).

BROWN, W. L. and W. L. NUTTING. Wing Venation of Formicidæ. Trans. American Ent. Soc., 75, pp. 113–132 (1950).

BRUCH, C. Catálogo de los Formícidos Argentinos. Rev. Mus. La Plata, 19, pp. 211–234; 527–537 (1915).

COLE, A. C. Guide to the Ants of the Great Smoky Mountains in North Carolina and Tennessee. American Midl. Naturalist, 24, pp. 1–88, 7 pls., 17 figs. (1940).

CLARK, J. Myrmeciinæ of Australia. Comm. Sci. Indust. Res. Organ., Melbourne, 230 pp. (1951).

CREIGHTON, W. S. American Species of Solenopsis. Proc. American Acad. Arts and Sci., **66,** pp. 39–151 (1930).

The Ants of North America. Bull. Mus. Comp. Zool., **104,** pp. 1–585 (1950).

DONISTHORPE, H. ST. J. K. British Ants, their Life History and Classification, Routledge & Sons, London, 436 pp. (1927).

EMERY, C. Formicidæ, Dorylinæ. Gen. Insectorum, fasc. 102, 34 pp. (1910).

Formicidæ, Ponerinæ. Gen. Insectorum, fasc. 118, 125 pp. (1911).

Formicidæ, Dolichoderinæ. Gen. Insectorum, fasc. 137, 50 pp. (1913).

Fauna entomologica italiana, Formicidæ. Bull. Soc. Ent. Ital., **47,** pp. 79–275 (1916).

Formicidæ, Myrmicinæ. Gen. Insectorum, fasc. 174, 174A and B, 206 pp. (1921–22).

Formicidæ, Formicinæ. Gen. Insectorum, fasc. 183, 302 pp. (1925).

FOREL, A. Les Formicides. In Grandidier, Hist. Madagascar, **20,** pt. 2, 280 pp. (1891).

Les Formicides de l'Empire des Indes et de Ceylon. Journ. Bombay Nat. Hist. Soc., **8** and **9** (several parts). (1894–95).

Die Ameisen der Schweiz. Mitt. schweizerischen Ent. Ges. suppl. to **12,** 77 pp. (1915).

Cadre synoptique des Fourmis. Bull. Soc. Vaudoise Sci. Nat., **51,** pp. 229–253 (1917).

HOLGERSEN, H. The Ants of Norway. Medd. Zool. Mus. Oslo, No. **54,** pp. 165–203 (1944).

KARAVAJEV, V. Formicidæ der Ukraine. Trav. Inst. Zool. Biol. Akad. Sci. Ukraine, No. **1,** pp. 1–316, 68 figs. (1934–36).

LARSSON, S. G. Formicoidea. Danmarks Fauna, **49,** 190 pp., 100 figs. (1943).

LUEDERWALDT, H. Chave para determinar os Dorylineos Brasileiros. Rev. Mus. Paulista, **12,** pp. 229–257 (1920).

MENOZZI, C. Le formiche della Palestina. Mem. Soc. Ent. Italiana, **12,** pp. 49–113, 5 figs. (1933).

SANTSCHI, F. Fourmis de Cuba et de Panama. Rev. Ent., Rio Janeiro, **1,** pp. 265–282 (1931).

SMITH, M. R. Ants of Porto Rico. Journ. Agric. Univ. Porto Rico, **20,** pp. 819–875, 19 figs. (1936).

Generic and Subgeneric Synopsis of the Male Ants of the United States. American Midl. Naturalist, **30,** pp. 273–321, 60 figs. (1943).

Generic and Subgeneric Synopsis of the United States Ants, Based on the Workers. American Midl. Naturalist, **37,** pp. 521–647, 21 pls. (1947).

STITZ, H. Formicidæ. Die Insekten Mitteleuropas, **2,** pp. 1–111, Stuttgart (1914).

Ameisen oder Formicidæ. Tierwelt Deutschlands, **37,** 428 pp., 197 figs. (1937).

VAN PELT, A. F. Preliminary Key to Worker Ants of Florida. Florida Ent., **30,** pp. 57–65 (1948).

WEBER, N. A. Revision of North American Myrmica, with Synopsis of Palæarctic Species. Ann. Ent. Soc. America, **40,** pp. 437–474 (1947); **41,** pp. 267–308 (1948); **43,** pp. 189–226 (1950).

WHEELER, W. M. Ants, their Structure and Behavior. 663 pp. Columbia University Press, New York (1910).

Keys to the Genera and Subgenera of Ants. Bull. American Mus. Nat. Hist., New York, **45**, pp. 631–710 (1922).

WHEELER, W. M. and J. W. CHAPMAN. The Ants of the Philippine Islands. Pt. 1. Dorylinæ and Ponerinæ. Philippine Journ. Sci., **28**, pp. 47–71 (1925).

VESPOIDEA

BEQUAERT, J. Revision of the Vespidæ of the Belgian Congo. Bull. American Mus. Nat. Hist., **39**, pp 1–384 (1918).

Synopsis of the Vespinæ of America. Ent. Americana, **12**, pp. 71–138, 6 figs. (1932).

The Nearctic Wasps of the Subfamily Polybiinæ. Ent. Americana, **13**, pp. 87–148, 3 pls., 4 figs. (1933).

North American Ancistrocerus (Vespidæ). Ent. Americana, **23**, pp. 225–286 (1943).

Vespidæ of the Guianas, Particularly of British Guiana. Bull. Mus. Comp. Zool., **94**, pp. 247–304, 9 figs. (1944).

The Vespidæ of Venezuela. Bol. Ent. venezolana, **7** (3–4), pp. 123–240 (1948).

BEQUAERT, J. and F. RUIZ PEREZ. Revision of the Vespidæ of Chile. Part I. Gayellinæ and Zethinæ. Rev. chil. Hist. nat., **44**, pp. 214–223, 1 pl. (1940).

BLÜTHGEN, P. Paläarktischen Eumeniden. Deutsch. ent. Zeitschr., **1938**, pp. 434–495, 2 figs. (1938).

Europäischen Polistinen. Arch. Naturg., **B12**, pp. 94–129 (1946).

BOHART, R. M. Eumeninæ of Lower California. Proc. California Acad. Sci., (4) **24**, pp. 313–336, 1 pl. (1948).

BRADLEY, J. C. Taxonomy of the Masarid Wasps, Including a Monograph of the North American Species. Univ. California Publ., Tech. Bull., **1**, pp. 369–464 (1922).

BUYSSON, R. Monographie des Vespides. Ann. Soc. Ent. France, **73** and **74**, several parts, incomplete (1904–06).

DALLA TORRE, K. W. Vespidæ. Gen. Insectorum, fasc. 19, 108 pp. (1904).

DUCKE, A. Révision des guêpes sociales polygames. Ann. Mus. Nat. Hungarici, **8**, pp. 449–544 (1910).

Ueber Phylogenie und Klassifikation der sozialen Vespiden. Zool. Jahrb. Abth. f. Syst., **36**, pp. 303–330 (1914).

Catálogo das Vespas Sociaes do Brazil. Rev. Mus. Paulista, **10**, pp. 314–374 (1918).

ISELY, D. Synopsis of North American Eumenidæ. Ann. Ent. Soc. America, **10**, pp. 345–366 (1917).

LIU, C. L. Bibliographic and Synonymic Catalogue of Vespidæ of China. Nat. Hist. Bull. Peking, **11**, pp. 205–232, 331–350 (1937).

REID, J. A. Classification of the Larvæ of the Vespidæ. Trans. Roy. Soc. London, **92**, pp. 285–331, 137 figs. (1942).

SAUSSURE, H. Synopsis of American Wasps. Misc. Coll. Smithsonian Inst., Washington, No. 254 (1875).

ZAVATTARI, E. Materialien zu einer Monographie der Neotropischen Eumeniden. Arch. f. Naturg., **78A**, Heft 4, pp. 1–272 (1912).

POMPILOIDEA

ARNOLD, G. The Psammocharidæ (Pompilidæ) of the Ethiopian Region. Ann. Transvaal Mus., **14**, pp. 284–396, 1 pl., 61 figs.; **15**, pp. 41–122, 40 figs.; pp. 283–400, 4 pls., 85 figs.; pp. 413–483, 35 figs.; **18**, pp. 415–460, 77 figs. (1932–36).

BANKS, N. Psammocharidæ: Classification and Descriptions. Journ. New York Ent. Soc., **19**, pp. 219–237 (1911).

Psammocharidæ (Pompilidæ) of the Philippines. Proc. American Acad. Arts Sci., **69**, pp. 1–117 (1934).

Psammocharidæ (Pompilidæ) of British Guiana. Zoologica, New York, **29**, pp. 97–112 (1944).

Psammocharidæ (Pompilidæ) of Northern South America. Bol. Ent. venezolana, **4**, pp. 81–126 (1945).

Studies of South American Psammocharidæ (Pompilidæ). Bull. Mus. Comp. Zool., **96**, pp. 311–525, 3 pls., 2 figs.; **99**, pp. 371–486, 1 pl. (1946–47).

BRADLEY, J. C. Revision of American Pompilinæ. Trans. American Ent. Soc., **70**, pp. 23–157, 2 pls. (1944).

BRIMLEY, C. S. Pompilidæ of North Carolina. Journ. Elisha Mitchell Sci. Soc., **52**, pp. 107–131. (1930).

DREISBACH, R. R. Keys to Subfamilies and Tribes of Pompilidæ in North America and to the Genera in Michigan. Pap. Michigan Acad. Sci., **32**, pp. 239–247 (1946).

Key to American Species of Ceropales. Journ. New York Ent. Soc., **56**, pp. 233–238 (1948).

Generic Classification on Nearctic Pompilidæ. Papers Michigan Acad. Sci. Arts, **33**, pp. 63–71. (1949).

HAUPT, H. Monographie der Psammocharidæ von Mittel Nord- und Osteuropa. Beiheft, Deuts. Ent. Zeits. 1926–27, 367 pp.

Weiterer Ausbau meines Systems der Psammocharidæ. Mitt. zool. Mus. Berlin, **15**, pp. 109–197 (1929).

Classification of Psammocharidæ with Two Cubital Cells. Mitt. zool. Mus. Berlin, **16**, pp. 673–797 (1930).

Psammocharidæ mediterraneæ (Pompilidæ). Boll. Lab. Ent. Bologna, **7**, pp. 263–302, 18 figs. (1935).

Psammocharidæ der nordwestlichen Provinzen Chinas. Ark. Zool., **27A** (10), 21 pp., 12 figs. (1935).

HURD, P. D., JR. Californian Species of Pepsis. Univ. California Publ. Ent., **8**, pp. 123–150 (1948).

JUNCO Y REYES, J. J. Psammocharidos de España. (Pompilidæ). Eos, **20**, pp. 123–172, 7 pls., 33 figs. (1940).

LUCAS, R. Die Pompilidengattung Pepsis. Berliner Ent. Zeits., **39**, pp. 449–480 (1894).

SUSTERA, O. Die paläarktischen Gattungen der Psammocharidæ. Verh. zool.-bot. Ges. Wien, **62**, pp. 171–213 (1912).

WILCKE, J. De Nederlandse Pompilidæ. Meded. Landbhoogesch. Wageningen, **47**, 88 pp., 72 figs. (1943).

SPHECOIDEA

ARNOLD, G. The Sphegidæ of South Africa. Ann. Transvaal Mus., 9, 10, 12, 13, 14 (1922–31).
   Check-list of Ethiopian Sphegidæ. Transvaal Mus., Pretoria. 21 pp. (1930).
   Sphecidæ of Madagascar. Occ. Pap. South. Rhodesia Nat. Mus., 12, 193 pp., 139 figs. (1944).
ASHMEAD, W. H. Classification of Sphegoidea. Canadian Ent., 31, pp. 145, 161, 212, 238, 291, 345 (six parts) (1899).
BANKS, N. Cerceris (Philanthidæ) of the Western United States. Psyche, 54, pp. 1–35 (1947).
BAUMONT, J. DE. Les Pseninæ de la région paléarctique. Mitt. Schweiz. ent. Ges., 17, pp. 33–93 (1937).
BOUWMAN, B. E. De Graafwespen van Nederland. Levende Natuur, Amsterdam, 31, 32, 33 (numerous parts) (1927–28).
BRADLEY, J. C. North American Nyssonidæ. Trans. American Ent. Soc., 46, pp. 113–132 (1920).
CRESSON, E. T. Monograph of the Philanthidæ of North America. Proc. Ent. Soc. Philadelphia, 5, pp. 85–132 (1865).
FERNALD, H. T. The Digger Wasps of North America, Subfamily Chlorioninæ. Proc. U. S. Nat. Mus., 31, pp. 291–423 (1906).
FOX, W. J. The North American Pemphredonidæ. Trans. American Ent. Soc., 19, pp. 307–326 (1892).
   The North American Larridæ. Proc. Acad. Nat. Sci. Philadelphia, 1893, pp. 467–551 (1894).
   The Crabronidæ of Boreal America. Trans. American Ent. Soc., 22, pp. 129–226 (1895).
GINER MARÉ, J. Sphecidæ de España. Madrid, Inst. espan. Ent. 270 pp., 319 figs. (1943).
HONORÉ, A. M. Les Sphégides d'Egypte. Bull. Soc. Fouad 1er Ent., 26, pp. 25–80, 7 figs. (1942).
KOHL, F. Zur Kenntnis der Pemphredonen. Ann. naturh. Hofmus. Wien, 5, pp. 49–65 (1890).
   Die Larriden. Verh. zool.-bot. Ges. Wien, 34, pp. 171–268, 327–454 (1885).
   Monographie der Gattung Sphex. Ann. naturh. Hofmus. Wien, 5, pp. 77–194, 317–462 (1890).
   Die Hymenopterengattung Philanthus. Ann. naturh. Hofmus. Wien, 6, pp. 345–370 (1891).
   Über Ampulex Jur. und verwandten Hymenopterengattungen. Ann. naturh. Hofmus. Wien, 8, pp. 455–516 (1893).
   Zur Monographie der Gattung Sphex. Ann. naturh. Hofmus. Wien, 10, pp. 42–74 (1895).
   Die Gattungen der Sphegiden. Ann. naturh. Hofmus. Wien, 11, pp. 233–516 (1896).
   Monographie der Gattung Podium. Abh. zool.-bot. Ges. Wien, 1, Heft 4, pp. 1–101 (1902).
   Monographie der Gattung Ammophila. Ann. naturh. Hofmus. Wien, 21, pp. 228–382 (1906).

Die Crabronen der paläarktischen Region. Ann. naturh. Hofmus. Wien, **29**, pp. 1–453 (1915).

Die Hautflüglergruppe der Sphecinen. IV. Sceliphron. Ann. naturh. Hofmus. Wien, **32**, pp. 1–170 (1918).

LOHRMANN, E. Die Grabwespengruppe der Bembicinen. Mitt. Münchner. Ent. Ges., **34**, pp. 420–471 (1944).

MAIDL, G. and A. KLIMA. Sphecoidea. (Astatinæ-Nyssoninæ). Hymenop. Cat. Junk. **8**, 150 pp. (1939).

MALLOCH, J. R. Review of Pseninæ (Pemphredonidæ) of North America. Proc. U. S. Nat. Mus., **82**, Art. No. 26, 60 pp., 2 pls. (1933).

MELANDER, A. L. Synopsis of North American Species of Ammophila. Psyche, **10**, pp. 156–164 (1903).

MICKEL, C. E. A Synopsis of the Sphecoidea of Nebraska (Hymenoptera). Nebraska Univ. Studies, **17**, pp. 342–456 (1918).

MURRAY, W. D. The Genus Podalonia (Sphecidæ). Ent. Americana, **20**, pp. 1–82 (1940).

PARKER, J. B. A Revision of the Bembicine Wasps of America North of Mexico. Proc. U. S. Nat. Mus., **52**, pp. 1–155 (1917).

A Generic Revision of the Fossorial Wasps of the Tribes Stizini and Bembecini. Proc. U. S. Nat. Mus., **75**, art. 5, 203 pp. (1929).

PATE, V. S. L. Studies in Oxybeline Wasps. Ent. News, **40**, pp. 219–222 (1929).

The Generic Names and Type Species of Sphecoidea. Mem. American Ent. Soc., No. **9**, 103 pp. (1937).

Oxybelidæ of the Philippines. Philippine Journ. Sci., **64**, pp. 373–395 (1938).

Studies in Nyssonine Wasps. Trans. American Ent. Soc., **64**, pp. 119–125 (1938).

Generic Classification of Crabroninæ. American Midland. Naturalist, **31**, pp. 329–384 (1944).

The Pemphiledine Wasps of the Caribbees. Trans. American Ent. Soc., **73**, pp. 1–33, 1 pl. (1947).

PULKKINEN, A. Sphecidæ of Finland. Myrkkypistiäiset, Hym. Acul., **1**, pp. 1–168, 99 figs. (In Finnish). (1931).

RICHARDS, O. W. Sphecidæ and Bembicidæ of British Guiana. Trans. Roy. Ent. Soc. London, **86**, pp. 101–118 (1937).

Mischocyttarus in South America. Ibid., **95**, pp. 295–462 (1945).

ROHWER, S. A. North American Genera of Nyssonidæ. Proc. U. S. Nat. Mus., **59**, pp. 403–413 (1921).

SCHLETTERER, A. Die Hymenopteren Gattung Cerceris. Zool. Jahrb. Abth. Syst., **2**, pp. 349–510 (1887).

SCULLEN, H. A. Eucerceris. Pan-Pacific Ent., **24**, pp. 155–164 (1948).

SPOONER, G. M. British Species of Pseninæ. Trans. Roy. Ent. Soc. London, **99**, pp. 129–172 (1948).

VERHOEFF, P. M. F. Oxybelidæ of Netherlands. Tijdschr. Ent., **89**, pp. 158–208 (1946).

WILLIAMS, F. X. The Larridæ of Kansas. Kansas Univ. Sci. Bull., **8**, pp. 117–213 (1913).

Larridæ of the Philippines. Bull. Hawaiian Sugar Planters Assoc., No. 19, pp. 61–101 (1928).

WILLINK, A. Las especies argentinas de Bembicini. Acta zool. lilloana, **4**, pp. 509–651, 19 pls. (1947).

APOIDEA

ALFKEN, J. D. Die Bienenfauna von Ostpreussen. Schrift. Königsberg, **53**, pp. 114–182 (1912).
ARNOLD, G. Key to the African Genera of the Apidæ. Journ. Ent. Soc. Southern Africa, **9**, pp. 193–218 (1947).
ASHMEAD, W. H. Classification of Apoidea. Trans. American Ent. Soc., **26**, pp. 49–100 (1899).
BISCHOFF, H. Zur Kenntnis afrikanischer Schmartozerbienen. Deutsch. Ent. Zeitschr., 1923, pp. 585–603 (1923).
    Ein natürlichen System der Bienen. Deutsches ent. Zeits., **1934**, pp. 324–331, 3 figs. (1934).
BLÜTHGEN, P. Beiträge zur Kenntnis der afrikanischen Halictinæ. Zool. Jahrb. Abth. f. Syst., **55**, pp. 163–252 (1928).
    Aethiopischen Halictinæ. Mitt. zool. Mus. Berlin, **15**, pp. 495–542, 63 figs. (1930).
COCKERELL, T. D. A. North American Anthophoridæ. Trans. American Ent. Soc., **32**, pp. 63–116 (1906).
    Genera of Colorado Bees. Univ. Colorado Stud., **16**, pp. 99–126 (1928).
    Revision of Australian Apoidea. Australian Zool., **6**, pp. 137–156; 205–236 (1930); **7**, pp. 34–54, 206–218, 291–324 (1932); **8**, pp. 2–28 (1934).
    Xylocopidæ of the Philippines. Philippine Journ. Sci., **43**, pp. 265–275 (1930).
    African Anthophoridæ. Rev. Zool. Bot. africaine, **18**, pp. 331–343 (1930).
    African Xylocopidæ. Ibid., **18**, pp. 294–306 (1930).
    African Megachilidæ. Ibid., **19**, pp. 43–55 (1930).
    Bees of the Family Hylæidæ from the Ethiopian Region. Smithsonian Misc. Coll., **101**, No. 8, 15 pp. (1942).
DUCKE, A. Die Bienengattung Osmia. Ber. naturf. Ver. Innsbruck, **25**, pp. 1–323 (1900).
FRANKLIN, H. J. The Bombidæ of the New World. Trans. American Ent. Soc., **38**, pp. 177–486; **39**, pp. 73–200 (1912–13).
FRIESE, H. Monographie der Gattung Ceratina. Termes. Füzetek, **19**, pp. 34–65 (1896).
    Monographie der Gattung Panurgus. Termes. Füzetek, **20**, pp. 78–102 (1897).
    Monographie der Gattung Megacilissa. Ann. naturh. Hofmus. Wien, **13**, pp. 59–86 (1908).
    Monographie der Gattung Euglossa. Termes. Füzetek, **21**, pp. 117–172 (1899).
    Monographie der Gattung Exomalopsis und Tetrapedia. Ann. naturh. Hofmus. Wien, **14**, pp. 247–304 (1899).
    Monographie der Gattung Centris. Ann. naturh. Hofmus. Wien, **16**, pp. 237–350 (1901).
    Die Bienen Afrikas. Jenaische Denkschr., **14**, pp. 85–475 (1909).

Die Bienenfauna von Neuguinea. Ann. Mus. Hist. Nat. Hungarici, 7, pp. 179–288 (1909).

Megachilidæ. Das Tierreich, Lief. 28, 440 pp. (1911).

Die europäischen Bienen. Berlin (1922–23).

FRISON, T. H. The Bumblebees of the Philippine Islands. Philippine Journ. Sci., 27, pp. 113–121 (1925); 37, pp. 273–281 (1928).

Relationships of Bremidæ (Apinæ) of North America. Trans. American Ent. Soc., 53, pp. 51–78 (1927).

KIRBY, W. F. Monographia Apum Angliæ. 2 vols. Ipswich (1882).

LINSLEY, E. G. Studies in the Andrenidæ of North America. Proc. California Acad. Sci., (4) 23, pp. 263–282 (1938).

Revision of Nearctic Meaectinæ. Ann. Ent. Soc. America, 32, pp. 429–468 (1939).

LINSLEY, E. G., and C. D. MICHENER. Generic Revision of North American Nomadidæ. Trans. American Ent. Soc., 65, pp. 265–305, 4 pls. (1939).

LUTZ, F. E. and T. D. A. COCKERELL. Distribution and Bibliography of North American Bees (Apidæ, Meliponidæ, Bombidæ, Euglossidæ, Anthophoridæ). Bull. American Mus. Nat. Hist., 42, pp. 491–641 (1920).

MAIDL, F. Die Xylocopen des Wiener Hofmuseums. Ann. naturh. Hofmus. Wien, 26, pp. 249–330 (1912).

MEADE-WALDO, G. Prosopidinæ (Hylæinæ). Gen. Insectorum, fasc. 181, 45 pp., 1 pl. (1923).

METZ, C. W. Revision of the Genus Perosopis (Hylæus). Trans. American Ent. Soc., 37, pp. 55–156, 10 figs., 9 pls. (1911).

MEYER, R. Monographie der Apidæ-Sphecodinæ. Arch. Naturg., Jahrg. 85A, Heft 1–2, pp. 79–242 (1920).

MICHENER, C. D. Generic Revision of the American Osmiinæ with Notes on Old World Genera. American Midl. Naturalist, 26, pp. 147–167, 22 figs. (1941).

Morphology, Phylogeny and Classification of Bees. Bull. American Mus. Nat. Hist., 82, pp. 151–326 (1940).

Revision of American Species of Hoplitis. Bull. American Mus. Nat. Hist., 89, pp. 261–317 (1947).

Generic Classification of Anthidiine Bees. American Mus. Novit., No. 1381, 29 pp. (1948).

MOURE, J. Abejas de Batatais (Brazil). Arq. Mus. paranaense, 3, pp. 145–203 (1943).

Diphaglossinæ, particularmente Ptiloglossa. Ibid., 4, pp. 137–178, 1 pl., 9 figs. (1945).

MITCHELL, T. B. Revision of the Genus Megachile in the Nearctic Region. Trans. American Ent. Soc., 59, pp. 295–361; 61, pp. 1–44, 155–205; 62, pp. 117–166, 323–382; 63, pp. 45–83, 175–206, 381–426 (1934–37).

ROBERTSON, C. Synopsis of Panurgidæ. Psyche, 29, pp. 159–173 (1922).

RUIZ PEREZ, F. Apidologia chilena (Revision of Apoidea). Rev. chilena Hist. nat., 44, pp. 281–377, 1 pl. 3 figs. (1940).

SANDHOUSE, G. A. Type Species of Genera and Subgenera of Bees. Proc. U. S. Nat. Mus., 92, pp. 519–619 (1943).

SCHMIEDEKNECHT, O. Apidæ Europæ. 2 vols., 1112 pp. Berlin (1882–84).

SCHWARZ, H. F. Social Bees (Meliponidæ) of Barro Colorado, Canal Zone. American Mus. Novit., No. 731, 23 pp. (1934).

Meliponidæ of the Western Hemisphere. Bull. American Mus. Nat. Hist., **90**, 546 pp. (1948).

Indomalayan Trigona. Ibid., **76**, pp. 83–141. (1939).

SLADEN, F. W. L. The Humble-bee (British Bombidæ). 283 pp. Macmillan & Co., London (1915).

SMITH, H. S. Revision of Ceratinidæ of North and Middle America. Trans. American Ent. Soc., **33**, pp. 115–124 (1907).

Figs. 972–997. Larvæ and Pupæ of Various Insects

972. **Calosoma,** larva (Duncan) Coleoptera, Carabidæ.
973. **Dytiscus,** larva (Maxwell-Lefroy) Coleoptera, Dytiscidæ.
974. Caddis worm, larva (Duncan) Trichoptera, Phryganeidæ.
975. **Chrysopa,** larva (Chittenden) Neuroptera, Chrysopidæ.
976. **Phyllophaga,** larva (Forbes) Coleoptera, Melolonthidæ.
977. **Mallodon,** larva, ventral view. Coleoptera, Prionidæ.
978. Geometrid larva (Packard) Lepidoptera, Geometridæ.
979. **Hylastinus,** larva (Chittenden) Coleoptera, Scolytidæ.
980. **Melanotus,** larva (Forbes) Coleoptera, Elateridæ.
981. Saw-fly, larva (Maxwell-Lefroy) Hymenoptera, Tenthredinoidea.
982. **Acherontia,** larva (Maxwell-Lefroy) Lepidoptera, Sphingidæ.
983. **Mylabris,** larva (Howard) Coleoptera, Bruchidæ.
984. **Anatis,** larva (Britton) Coleoptera, Coccinellidæ.
985. **Simulium,** larva (Osborn) Diptera, Simuliidæ.
986. **Chrysobothris,** larva (Chittenden) Coleoptera, Buprestidæ.
987. **Culex,** larva (Dyar) Diptera, Culicidæ.
988. **Musca,** larva (Howard) Diptera, Muscidæ.
989. **Pulex,** larva (Chittenden) Siphonaptera, Pulicidæ.
990. **Gelechia,** pupa, underside (Hunter) Lepidoptera, Gelechiidæ.
991. **Simulium,** pupa (Miall) Diptera, Simuliidæ.
992. **Lyctus,** larva (Hopkins) Coleoptera, Lyctidæ.
993. **Sialis,** pupa (Davis) Neuroptera, Sialidæ.
994. **Cyllene,** pupa (Hopkins) Coleoptera, Cerambycidæ.
995. **Tipula,** larva (Needham) Diptera, Tipulidæ.
996. **Gelechia,** pupa, ventral side (Hunter) Lepidoptera, Gelechiidæ.
997. **Culex,** pupa (Knab) Diptera, Culicidæ.

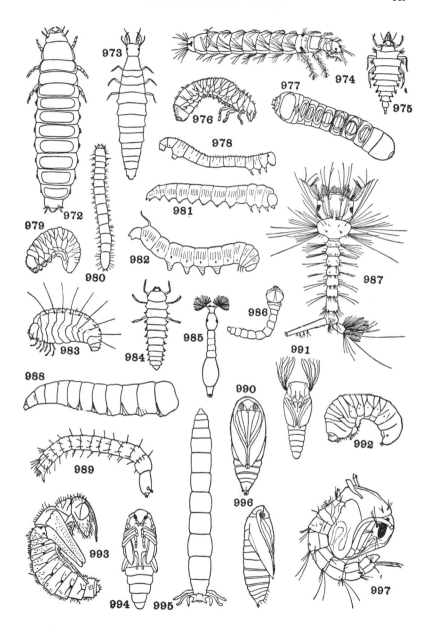

PART II

OTHER TERRESTRIAL ARTHROPODA

CONSPECTUS OF THE HIGHER GROUPS OF TERRESTRIAL
ARTHROPODS (EXCEPT INSECTS)

Class **ONYCHOPHORA**
  Order **MALACOPODA** (Peripatidæ, Peripatopsidæ)
Class **ARACHNIDA**
  Order **MICROTHELYPHONIDA**
    (Kœneniidæ)
  Order **PEDIPALPIDA**
    Suborder **Uropygi**
      (Thelyphonidæ, Schizomidæ)
    Suborder **Amblypygi**
      (Tarantulidæ, Charontidæ, Phrynidæ)
  Order **RICINULEI**
    (Ricinoididæ)
  Order **SCORPIONIDA**
    (Buthidæ, Scorpionidæ, Ischnuridæ, Diplocentridæ, Chactidæ,
      Vejovidæ, Bothriuridæ)
  Order **SOLPUGIDA**
    (Hexisopodidæ, Rhagodidæ, Eremobatidæ, Galeodidæ, Karshiidæ,
      Ceromatidæ, Solpugidæ, Melanoblossiidæ, Dæsiidæ, Ammo-
      trechidæ)
  Order **CHELONETHIDA**
    Suborder **Heterosphyronida** (Chthoniidæ, Dithidæ)
    Suborder **Diplosphyronida**
      NEOBISIOIDEA (Syarinidæ, Neobisiidæ, Hyidæ, Ideoroncidæ)
      GARYPOIDEA (Menthidæ, Olpiidæ, Garypodidæ)
    Suborder **Monosphyronida**
      CHELIFEROIDEA (Synsphyronidæ, Pseudogarypodidæ, Feaellidæ,
      Sternophoridæ, Cheliferidæ, Myrmochernetidæ, Chernetidæ,
      Atemnidæ, Cheiridiidæ)
  Order **PHALANGIDA**
    Suborder **Cyphophthalmi** (Sironidæ)
    Suborder **Laniatores** (Oncopodidæ, Triæuonychidæ, Assamiidæ,
      Phalangodidæ, Cosmetidæ, Gonyleptidæ)
    Suborder **Palpatores**
      PHALANGIOIDEA (Phalangiidæ)
      NEMASTOMATOIDEA (Acropsopilionidæ, Trogulidæ, Nemasto-
      matidæ, Ischyropsalidæ)
  Order **ARANEIDA**
    Suborder **Liphistiomorphæ**
    (Liphistiidæ, Heptathelidæ)

Suborder **Mygalomorphæ**
(Ctenizidæ, Dipluridæ, Paratropididæ, Theraphosidæ, Atypidæ,
Migadidæ, Barychelidæ, Pycnothelidæ)
Suborder **Hypochilomorphæ**
(Hypochilidæ)
Suborder **Dipneumonomorphæ**
(Œcobiidæ, Urocteidæ, Filistatidæ, Sicariidæ, Pholcidæ, Ar-
chæidæ, Palpimanidæ, Mimetidæ, Uloboridæ, Dictynidæ,
Erigonidæ, Tengellidæ, Eresidæ, Dinopidæ, Amaurobiidæ,
Psechridæ, Agalenidæ, Pisauridæ, Lycosidæ, Oxyopidæ,
Zodariidæ, Hersiliidæ, Theridiidæ, Leptonetidæ, Linyphiidæ,
Argiopidæ, Acanthoctenidæ, Ctenidæ, Zoropsidæ, Eusparassidæ,
Thomisidæ, Platoridæ, Selenopidæ, Drassodidæ, Homalony-
chidæ, Clubionidæ, Lyssomanidæ, Salticidæ, Segestriidæ, Dys-
deridæ, Oonopidæ, Hadrotarsidæ, Hahniidæ, Argyronetidæ,
Anyphænidæ, Ammoxenidæ, Prodidomidæ, Senoculidæ)
Suborder **Apneumonomorphæ**
(Telemidæ, Symphytognathidæ, Caponiidæ, Micropholcom-
matidæ)
Order **ACARINA**
Eupodoidea (Cryptognathidæ, Bdellidæ, Eupodidæ)
Trombidoidea (Trombidiidæ, Anystidæ, Erythræidæ, Cæculidæ,
Tetranychidæ, Cheyletidæ)
Hydrachnoidea (Halacaridæ, Hydrachnidæ, Hydrovolziidæ,
Limnocharidæ, Eylaidæ, Thermacaridæ, Protziidæ, Sperchon-
idæ, Pseudohydryphantidæ, Hydryphantidæ, Limnesiidæ,
Arrhenuridæ, Lebertiidæ, Atractideidæ, Hygrobatidæ, Teu-
toniidæ, Unionicolidæ, Pionidæ, Axonopsidæ, Ewingiidæ,
Hydrodromidæ, Mamersopsidæ)
Ixodoidea (Argantidæ, Nuttalliellidæ, Ixodidæ)
Parasitoidea (Holothyridæ, Spelæorhynchidæ, Spinturnicidæ,
Halarachnidæ, Parasitidæ, Dermanyssidæ, Dynichidæ, An-
tennophoridæ, Macrochelidæ)
Oribatoidea (Oribatidæ, Phthiracaridæ, Pelopidæ, Labidostomati-
dæ)
Acaroidea (Tarsonemidæ, Canestriniidæ, Sarcoptidæ, Listro-
phoridæ, Analgesidæ, Acaridæ, Podapolipodidæ, Scutacaridæ,
Cytoditidæ, Laminosioptidæ)
Demodicoidea (Eriophyidæ, Demodicidæ)
Opilioacaroidea (Opilioacaridæ)
Class **PENTASTOMIDA**
Order **CEPHALOBÆNODEA** (Cephalobænidæ)
Order **LINGUATULODEA** (Linguatulidæ)
Class **TARDIGRADA**
Order **HETEROTARDIGRADA**
(Halechiniscidæ, Echiniscidæ)
Order **EUTARDIGRADA**
(Milnesiidæ, Macrobiotidæ)
Class **PAUROPODA**
Order **HETEROGNATHA**

PAUROPODOIDEA (Polypauropodidæ, Pauropodidæ, Asphæridiopodidæ)

BRACHYPAUROPODOIDEA (Scleropauropodidæ, Brachypauropodidæ)

EURYPAUROPODOIDEA (Eurypauropodidæ)

Class **DIPLOPODA**

Subclass **PSELAPOGNATHA**

(Polyxenidæ)

Subclass **CHILOGNATHA**

Division OPISTHANDRIA

Order **LIMACOMORPHA**

(Glomeridesmidæ)

Order **ONISCOMORPHA**

(Sphærotheriidæ, Glomeridæ, Gervaisiidæ, Glomeridellidæ)

Division PROTERANDRIA

Superorder EUGNATHA

Order **POLYDESMOIDEA**

Suborder **Polydesmidea** (Polydesmidæ, Mastigonodesmidæ, Cryptodesmidæ, Stylodesmidæ, Oniscodesmidæ, Vanhoeffeniidæ, Peridontodesmidæ)

Suborder **Strongylosomatidea** (Strongylosomatidæ, Sphærotrichopidæ, Leptodesmidæ, Oxydesmidæ, Platyrhacidæ, Gomphodesmidæ, Sphæriodesmidæ, Rhacodesmidæ, Fontariidæ)

Order **NEMATOPHORA**

Suborder **Chordumidea** (Trachysomatidæ, Chamæosomatidæ, Metopidothrigidæ, Conotylidæ, Diplomaragnidæ, Caseyidæ, Underwoodiidæ, Chordeumidæ, Orobainosomatidæ, Faginidæ, Heteroporatiidæ, Verhœffiidæ, Heterolatzellidæ, Anthogonidæ Brachychæteumidæ, Anthroleucosomatidæ, Neatractosomatidæ, Pseudoclididæ, Rothenbuehleriidæ, Attemsiidæ, Opisthocheiridæ, Haplobainosomatidæ, Craspedosomatidæ)

Suborder **Stemmiulidea** (Stemmiulidæ)

Suborder **Striariidea** (Striariidæ)

Suborder **Lysiopetalidea** (Lysiopetalidæ, Dorypetalidæ, Callipodidæ)

Order **JULIFORMIA**

Suborder **Julidea** (Blaniulidæ, Julidæ)

Suborder **Spirobolidea** (Spirobolidæ, Rhinocricidæ, Trigoniulidæ, Pachybolidæ, Spiromimidæ)

Suborder **Spirostreptomorpha** (Spirostreptidæ, Harpagophoridæ, Odontopygidæ, Cambalidæ, Pseudonannolenidæ, Pericambalidæ, Cambalopsidæ, Physiostreptidæ)

Superorder COLOBOGNATHA

Order **PLATYDESMIFORMIA** (Polyzoniidæ, Siphonocryptidæ, Siphonophoridæ, Platydesmidæ, Siphoniulidæ)

Class **CHILOPODA**

Subclass **ANAMORPHA**

Order **SCUTIGEROMORPHA** (Scutigeridæ)

Order **LITHOBIOMORPHA**

LITHOBIOIDEA (Lithobiidæ, Henicopidæ)
CERMATOBIOIDEA (Cermatobiidæ)
CRATEROSTIGMOIDEA (Craterostigmidæ)
Subclass **EPIMORPHA**
    Order **GEOPHILOMORPHA** (Himantariidæ, Schendylidæ, Oryidæ,
        Mecistocephalidæ, Geophilidæ, Soniphilidæ, Neogeophilidæ,
        Gonibregmatidæ, Sogonidæ)
    Order **SCOLOPENDROMORPHA** (Scolopendridæ, Cryptopidæ)
Class **SYMPHYLA**
    Order **CEPHALOSTIGMATA**
        (Geophilellidæ, Scutigerellidæ, Scolopendrellidæ)

CLASS ONYCHÓPHORA

(MALACÓPODA, POLÝPODA, PROTRACHEÁTA)

Moderate-sized or rather large, soft bodied, caterpillar-like species. Body elongate, gently narrowed at the ends, convex above, flattened below, bearing from fourteen to more than forty pairs of short, similar, annulate, but not distinctly jointed legs. Integument transversely wrinkled, each fold bearing many somewhat regularly disposed papillæ. One pair of annulated antennæ. Mandibles blade-like, toothed and denticulate on the edge. Legs with a series of several transverse pads below near tip and two prominent apical claws. Excretory organs opening by a pore on the fourth and fifth pairs of legs. Sexual orifice near the posterior end of the body. Respiration by means of many long, unbranched tracheæ that open by minute spiracles scattered over the body.

1. Sexual opening lying between the last pair of legs or behind them (Figs. 999, 1000, 1001); color pattern of body more or less bluish or greenish, at least in part; dorsal body folds or wrinkles very irregular, numbering from thirteen to twenty-six to each segment . . . . **PERIPATÓPSIDÆ**

  a. Sexual opening between the last pair of legs, which are well developed; no papillæ at bases of the legs. (**Peripatòides, Ooperípatus, Symperípatus**, Austr.; **Opisthópatus**, S. Afr.; **Metaperípatus,** Chile) . . . . **PERIPATOIDÌNÆ**
    Sexual opening behind the last pair of legs; or between the last pair, in which case the last pair of legs are greatly reduced in size and structure. (**Peripatópsis**, equatorial Afr.; **Paraperípatus**, Malay.).
                                  PERIPATOPSÌNÆ

  Sexual opening lying between the penultimate pair of legs (Fig. 998); color pattern of body more or less brownish, reddish or purplish; dorsal body folds regular, numbering twelve (rarely twenty-four) to each segment . . . . **PERIPÁTIDÆ**

a. Legs bearing from three to seven small, more or less distinctly jointed, conical papillæ at tip above, near the base of the claws.

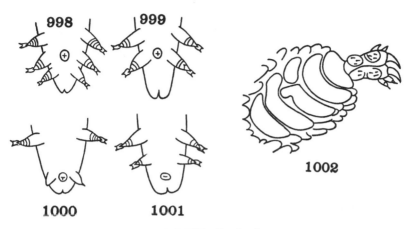

Figs. 998–1002. **Onychophora**

998. **Peripatus,** apical part of body (Bouvier) Peripatidæ.
999. **Peripatoides,** apical part of body (Bouvier) Peripatopsidæ.
1000. **Peripatopsis,** apical part of body (Bouvier) Peripatopsidæ.
1001. **Paraperipatus,** apical part of body (Bouvier) Peripatopsidæ.
1002. **Oroperipatus,** underside of fourth leg (Bouvier) Peripatidæ.

(Fig. 1002). (Macroperípatus, Epiperípatus, Plicatoperípatus, Perípatus, Oroperípatus, Neotrop.; Mesoperípatus, S. Afr.).

PERIPATÍNÆ

Legs bearing only two such papillæ at tip above, near the base of the claws; (Eoperípatus, Malay.; Typhloperípatus, Ind.).

EOPERIPATÍNÆ

LITERATURE ON ONYCHOPHORA

Bouvier, E. L. Monographie des Onychophores. Ann. Sci. Nat., (9) 2, pp. 1–383, 5, pp. 61–318 (1905–07).

Clark, A. H. Distribution of Onychophora. Smithsonian Misc. Coll., 65, No. 1, pp. 1–25 (1915).

Grassé, P. P. Onychophores. Traité de Zoologie, 6, pp. 3–37 (1949).

Lameere, A. Onychophores. Rec. Inst. zool. Torley-Rousseau, 2, Suppl., pp. 150–157, 4 figs. (1929).

Zacher, F. Onychophora. In Kükenthal and Krumbach, Handbuch der Zoologie, 3, Hälfte 2, Teil 4, pp. 79–138, 67 figs. (1933).

CLASS CRUSTÀCEA

ORDER ISÓPODA

As this group of Crustacea contains a small number of terrestrial forms, these have been included, especially since a few species occur abundantly in places where insects are commonly found. Two suborders are represented among the actually terrestrial species.

1. Body more or less depressed, coxæ of the walking legs developed into plate-like structures and fused with the tergites. (Suborder ONISCÒIDEA) 2

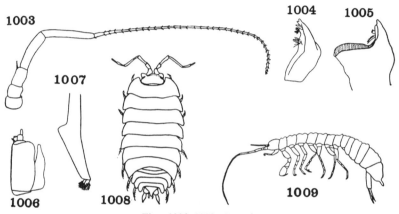

Figs. 1003–1009. Isopoda

1003. **Ligidium,** second antenna (Richardson) Ligiidæ.
1004. **Philoscia,** mandible (Richardson) Oniscidæ.
1005. **Haplophthalmus,** mandible (Richardson) Trichoniscidæ.
1006. **Porcellio,** maxilliped (Richardson) Oniscidæ.
1007. **Philoscia,** first maxilla (Richardson) Oniscidæ.
1008. **Porcellio** (Richardson) Oniscidæ.
1009. **Phreatoicus** (Richardson) Phreatoicidæ.

Body more or less compressed; coxæ small, the last six pairs free. (Fig. 1009). (**Phreatoicópsis, Hypsimetòpus**). (Suborder PHREATOICÒIDEA) .... **PHREATOÍCIDÆ**
2. Uropods not forming an operculum to cover the walking legs; abdominal segments freely movable.........................3
Uropods forming an operculum or cover which conceals the walking legs. (**Tỳlos**) .... **TÝLIDÆ**
3. Flagellum of second antennæ multiarticulate. (Fig. 1003). (**Lìgia, Ligídium**). (*LIGÝDIDÆ*) .... **LIGÌIDÆ**

Flagellum of second antennæ with not more than six joints 4
4. Mandible with the grinding surface well developed. (Fig. 1005)
(Trichoníscus, Tithanètes, Brackenrídgia, Haplophthálmus, Androníscus) . . . . TRICHONÍSCIDÆ
Mandible with the grinding surface small, poorly developed. (Fig. 1004) 5
5. Inner lobe of first maxillæ bearing only two or three plumose processes at its tip. (Fig. 1007) 6
Inner lobe of first maxillæ bearing four or more (usually many) plumose processes. (Eubèlum, Éthelum) . . . . .EUBÉLIDÆ
6. Terminal joints of maxillipeds small. (Fig. 1006) 7
Terminal joints of maxillipeds large, lamellar. (Scýphax, Scyphacélla) . . . . SCYPHÁCIDÆ
7. Body capable of being rolled into a perfect ball; head deeply immersed in the first thoracic segment; uropods short, not reaching beyond the tip of the abdomen. (Cùbaris (=Armadíllo), Armadillídium, Péntheus, Sphæroníscus, Uropòdias).
ARMADÍLLIDÌIDÆ
Body not capable of being rolled into a ball; head only slightly immersed in the first thoracic segment; uropods elongate, reaching beyond the apical abdominal segments. (Figs. 1004, 1006, 1007, 1008). (Oníscus, Porcéllio, Oroníscus, Philóscia, Synùropus, Tracheoníscus) . . . . ONÍSCIDÆ

CLASS ARÁCHNIDA

Moderate-sized, small or very small, rarely large Arthropoda. Body formed of two groups of segments, a cephalothorax and an abdomen, which are usually clearly separate although sometimes entirely fused. Cephalothorax rarely provided with any movable sutures; abdomen usually more or less freely articulated and formed of several similar segments, the apical portion sometimes forming a tail-like prolongation, or (spiders and mites) showing no sutures. Cephalothorax bearing six pairs of appendages, the first usually chelate; the second often hooked and fitted for chewing or crushing prey; this pair sometimes sensory or fitted for walking, usually terminated in claws. No antennæ. No compound eyes; several simple eyes (two to twelve) usually present. No wings. Respiration by tubular tracheæ or by tracheal book-lungs or both; very rarely without special respiratory apparatus. Development direct. Spiders, Mites, Ticks, Scorpions, Harvestmen, Tongue-worms.

KEY TO THE ORDERS OF ARACHNIDA

1. Abdomen distinctly segmented, no silk-spinning organs on the abdomen 2
Abdomen not segmented, or when rarely with distinct sclerites

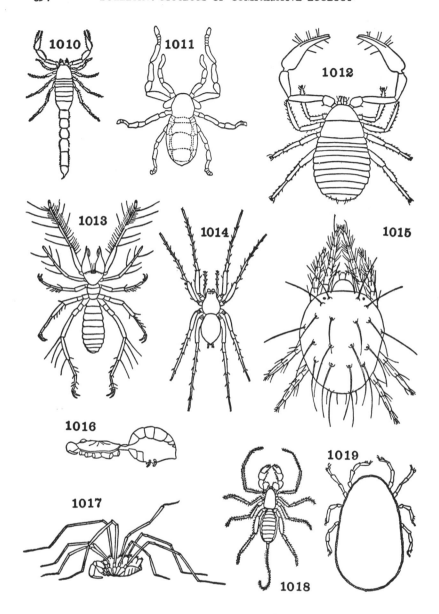

Figs. 1010–1019. **Various Arachnida**

1010. **Buthus** (Kraepelin) Scorpionida.
1011. **Cryptocellus** (Ewing) Ricinulei.
1012. **Chelifer** (Ewing) Chelonethida.
1013. **Galeodes** (Dufour) Solpugida.
1014. **Tegenaria** (Emerton) Araneida.
1015. **Tetranychus** (Woodworth) Acarina.
1016. **Liphistius** (Warburton) Araneida.
1017. **Protolophus** (Banks) Phalangida.
1018. **Thelyphonus** (Kraepelin) Pedipalpida.
1019. **Argas** (Bishopp) Acarina.

(Liphistiidæ) with spinning organs (spinnerets) located at the middle of the venter 9

2. Abdomen with the posterior segments forming a contrasting long tail-like prolongation 3

Post-abdomen not differentiated 5

3. Post-abdomen consisting of six segments, terminating in a prominent bulbous sting; abdomen broadly joined to the unsegmented cephalothorax; second ventral segment with a pair of comb-like organs; four pairs of book-lungs opening on the third to sixth sternites; pedipalpi stout, terminating in large pincers; legs fitted for walking, tarsi three-jointed. Distribution widespread, in warm dry countries. (Fig. 1010). Scorpions.

SCORPIÓNIDA (Page 701)

Post-abdomen very slender and many-jointed, not ending in a sting; abdomen narrowed at base, no comb-like ventral organs; tarsi of first legs many-jointed 4

4. Pedipalpi slender, similar to the walking legs; book-lungs wanting; three pairs of eversible sacs on sternites 4, 5 and 6; abdomen terminating in a long, many-jointed filament. Minute species, under 3 mm. in length. Delicate, pale colored, tropical species. (Fig. 1020) . . . . MICROTHELYPHÓNIDA (Page 697)

Pedipalpi very stout, contrasting with the very long first pair of legs; two pairs of book-lungs, opening on segments 2 and 3. Moderate to large species. Tropical. Whip-scorpions. (*THELYPHÓ-NIDA*) . . . . .PEDIPÁLPIDA (Page 698)

5. Abdomen constricted at base; front legs very long and with long tarsi; pedipalpi clawed at tip, not chelate; one pair of book-lungs, on the second segment. Tropical. (*SCHIZÓMIDA*).

PEDIPÁLPIDA (Page 698)

Abdomen broadly joined to the cephalothorax; front tarsi not elongate 6

6. Pedipalpi with large pincer-like claws; cheliceræ chelate, with a spinneret on the movable finger. Small flat species, usually liv-

ing under the bark of trees. (Fig. 1012). Pseudoscorpions, Book-scorpions . . . . **CHELONÉTHIDA** (Page 707)
Pedipalpi without pincer-like claws 7

7. Head distinct from the three-parted thorax; cheliceræ relatively large and powerful, their pincers opening up and down. Pale-colored, mostly nocturnal species, inhabiting hot dry regions. (Fig. 1013). Wind-scorpions, Solpugids.

SOLPÙGIDA (Page 705)

Cephalothorax not distinctly divided into head and segments; cheli-ceræ usually smaller, their pincers not moving dorsoventrally . . . 8

8. Abdomen usually eight-segmented as indicated by the tergites; cheliceræ usually exposed; two eyes usually present, often on tubercles; legs usually excessively long and slender. (Fig. 1017). Cosmopolitan, abundant. Harvestmen, Daddy-long-legs.

PHALÁNGIDA (Page 711)

Abdomen apparently four-segmented, with lateral as well as dorsal plates and with a small terminal several-jointed piece; cheliceræ concealed by a large, pendant hood formed by a movable plate in front of the carapace; eyes absent; legs only moderately long. (Fig. 1011). Tropical, rare species . . . . . . **RICINÙLEI** (Page 700)

9. Abdomen joined to the cephalothorax by a narrow short stalk, usually soft and weakly sclerotized, always provided with spin-ning organs. (Figs. 1014, 1016). Cosmopolitan. Spiders.

ARANÈIDA (Page 716)

Abdomen broadly fused with the cephalothorax. Widespread, often parasitic, frequently very small species. (Figs. 1015, 1019). Mites, Ticks . . . . **ACARÍNA** (Page 733)

LITERATURE ON ARACHNIDA

TREATISES ON THE WHOLE CLASS, OR DEALING WITH MORE THAN A SINGLE ORDER

BANKS, N. Synopsis of North American Scorpions, Solpugids and Pedipalpi. American Naturalist, **34**, pp. 421–427, (1900).

COMSTOCK, J. H. The Spider Book. Doubleday, Page & Co., Garden City, N. Y. (1912). (Contains also brief synopses of the North American repre-sentatives of several Orders of Arachnida in addition to the Araneida).

GRASSÉ, P. P. Onychophores, Tardigrades, Trilobitomorphes, Chélicérates. Traité de Zoologie, **6**, 979 pp., 719 figs. (1949).

KOCH, L. Arachniden Australiens. 1489 + 274 pp. Nürnberg (1869–89).

LAWRENCE, R. F. Arachnida of Southwest Africa, Pt. 2, Ann. S. Afr. Mus., **25**, pp. 217–312 (1928).

PETRUNKEVITCH, A. Orders of Arachnida. Sci. Pap. State Illinois, **3**, No. 2, 72 pp., 4 pls. (1945).

POCOCK, R. J. Arachnida. Fauna British India (1900).

Arachnida. In Biologia Centrali-Americana. 71 pp. (1902).

SIMON, E. Arachnides de France, **1–7** (1874–1914).

THORELL, T. Studi sui Ragni Malesi e Papuani. 4 parts. Genoa (1877–90).
WARBURTON, C. Arachnida, In Cambridge Natural History, 4, pp. 297–473
(1909).

ORDER MICROTHELYPHÓNIDA

(*PALPIGRÀDI; PALPIGRÀDA*)

Minute, delicate, elongate species with a long, jointed median appendage at the tip of the abdomen. Cephalothorax above consisting
of a large carapace which bears the pedipalps and the first three pairs of

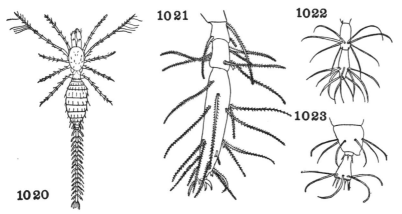

Figs. 1020–1023. Microthelyphonida

1020. **Kœnenia** (Wheeler) Kœneniidæ.
1021. **Kœnenia**, apical part of third leg (Börner) Kœneniidæ.
1022. **Kœnenia**, two joints of flagellum (Börner) Kœneniidæ.
1023. **Kœnenia**, apex of abdomen (Börner) Kœneniidæ.

legs, and a small, separate posterior section which bears the fourth pair
of legs. Cheliceræ large, chelate; pedipalps leg-like, nine-jointed, bearing
a pair of claws at tip. First pair of legs the longest, twelve-jointed, the
tarsi consisting of nine segments, terminated by a pair of claws. Second
and third legs seven-jointed; fourth eight-jointed, all with a pair of
claws at tip. Eyes absent. Mouth anterior. No book-lungs, but with a
pair of eversible sacs opening on the fourth to sixth abdominal segments
below. Abdomen elongate-oval, consisting of eleven segments, the third
to seventh segments larger than the others. Apex of abdomen bearing
a long, slender median appendage consisting of nine to fifteen moniliform joints, bearing sparse bristly hairs. (Figs. 1020, 1021, 1022, 1023).
One family. (**Kœnènia**, widespread in tropical and subtropical countries; **Allokœnènia, Kœneniòdes**, Ethiop.) . . . . **KŒNENÌIDÆ**

LITERATURE ON MICROTHELYPHONIDA

HANSEN, H. J. Biospeologica LIII. Palpigradi. Arch. Zool. Paris, 65, pp. 167–180 (1926) (with bibliography).
KÄSTNER, A. Palpigrada. In Kükenthal, Handbuch der Zoologie, 3, Hälfte 2, pp. 77–98 (1932).
KRAEPELIN, K. Palpigradi. Das Tierreich, Lief. 12, pp. 1–3 (1901).
ROEWER, C. F. Palpigrada. In Bronn's, Klassen und Ordnungen des Tierreichs, 5, Abt. IV, Buch 4, pp. 640–673 (1934).

ORDER PEDIPÁLPIDA

(PEDIPÁLPI)

Large or moderate-sized species with heavily chitinized integuments. Cephalothorax forming a solid carapace, or with two small thoracic segments separated by sutures. Chelicerae claw-like. Pedipalpi six-jointed, strong, sometimes very stout, clawed at apex or imperfectly chelate, sometimes very long; first pair of legs sensory in function, forming a long, many-jointed filament; other legs stouter and fitted for walking, the tarsi with claws at tip. Abdomen consisting of ten or eleven segments; sometimes with a long slender many-jointed median apical appendage or filament, sometimes rounded at apex and without appendage. Respiration by book-lungs in the second abdominal segment and sometimes also in the third. Restricted to warm countries. Whip-scorpions and Tailless whip-scorpions.

1. Cephalothorax elongate, longer than wide, its lateral margins more or less parallel except in front; last three segments of abdomen very small, the abdomen at apex with a median appendage, which is usually long and consisting of numerous joints, rarely short and one-jointed; femur and tibia of pedipalpi rarely spinose. (Suborder UROPYGI) 2
    Cephalothorax short and broad, more or less expanded laterally, the lateral margins strongly convex; abdomen blunt and rounded at apex, without a median appendage at apex; femur and tibia of pedipalpi strongly spinose. (Suborder AMBLYPYGI) (*PHRYNÍCHIDA*) 3
2. Cephalothorax dorsally with an undivided shield; eyes well developed, two close together on a tubercle in front and a group of three large ones toward each lateral margin; abdominal appendage long, filiform, consisting of many movable joints; tarsus of first pair of walking legs (second legs) seven-jointed and at least four times as long as the metatarsus; second and third segments of abdomen each with a pair of book-lungs. (Fig. 1018). (**Mimoscórpius, Tetrabàlius, Hypóctonus,** Malay.; **Thelýphonus,** In-

domal.; **Typopéltis,** As.; **Mastigopróctus, Thelyphonéllus,** Am.).
(*THELYPHÓNIDA*) .... THELYPHÓNIDÆ
Cephalothorax dorsally divided into a head and a free thoracic
segment separated by a membranous suture and bearing the third
and fourth pairs of legs; median eyes absent, at most one pair
of lateral eyes; abdominal appendage short, in female subcylindrical and divided into three or four scarcely movable joints; in
the male thickened and one-jointed; tarsi of first pair of walking
legs six-jointed, less than twice as long as the metatarsus (Figs.
1025, 1026); only one pair of book-lungs, in the second segment.
(**Schízomus,** Ethiop., Ind.; **Trithýreus,** Indomal., Ethiop., Nearc.)
(*SCHIZÓMIDA*) (*TARTÁRIDÆ*) ....SCHIZÓMIDÆ

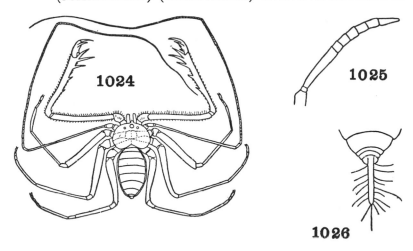

Figs. 1024–1026. Pedipalpida

1024. **Damon** (Pocock) Tarantulidæ.
1025. **Schizomus,** metatarsus and tarsus of first pair of legs of female (Graveley)
Schizomidæ.
1026. **Schizomus,** apex of abdomen. Schizomidæ.

3. Tibia of the fourth pair of legs divided by sutures into three or
four sections, the tarsus four or five-jointed; apical spurs of tibiæ
of pedipalpi extending laterally.............................4
Tibia of the fourth pair of legs not divided, or consisting of only
two sections; the tarsus four-jointed; apical spurs of tibiæ of pedipalpi directed forward. (Fig. 1024). (**Tarántula** (=*Phrynichus*)
Ethiop., Ind.; **Dàmon, Titanodàmon,** Ethiop.). (*PHRYNICH-*
ÌNÆ, Kræpelin 1899) .... TARANTÙLIDÆ

4. Tarsi five-jointed, with a pulvillus at the base of the claws; second abdominal tergite sometimes distinctly margined. Old World species. (Chàron, Indomal.; Charìnus, Ethiop., Malay., Galapagos; Catagèus, Stygophrỳnus, Indomal.; Sàrax, Austromal.).

CHARÓNTIDÆ

Tarsi four-jointed, without pulvillus; second tergite not margined. New World species. (Phrỳnus (= Tarántula), Hemiphrỳnus, Acanthophrỳnus, Heterophrỳnus, Am.) .... PHRỲNIDÆ

LITERATURE ON PEDIPALPIDA

BÖRNER, C. Pedipalpida. Zoologica, Heft 42 (1904).
GRAVELEY, F. H. Revision of the Oriental Subfamilies of Tarantulidæ. Rec. Indian Mus., 11, pp. 433–455 (1915).
    Indo-australian Thelyphonidæ. Rec. Indian Mus., 12, pp. 59–85 (1916).
KÄSTNER, A. Pedipalpi. In Kükenthal, Handbuch der Zoologie, 3, Hälfte 2, Lief. 4, pp. 1–98, 124 figs. (1932).
KRAEPELIN, K. Revision der Tarantuliden. Abh. naturh. Ver. Hamburg, 13, pp. 1–53 (1895).
    Revision der Uropygi. Abh. naturh. Ver. Hamburg, 15, 60 pp. (1897).
    Pedipalpida. Das Tierreich, Lief. 8, pp. 231–265 (1899).
WERNER, F. Pedipalpida. In Bronn's, Klassen und Ordnungen des Tierreichs, 5, Abt. IV, Buch 8, pp. 317–485, 186 figs. (1935).

ORDER RICINÙLEI

(MERIDOGÁSTRA, RHIGNOGÁSTRA)

Small or very small species with extremely thick, hard integument. Body elongate oval, without long tail-like prolongation at the apex of the abdomen but with a very short three segmented projection. Cephalothorax bearing anteriorly a large movable hood which when folded down completely hides the cheliceræ; cheliceræ chelate. Eyes absent. Pedipalpi five-jointed, short; geniculate at the apex of the femur; tarsus minute, opposed to a small projection at the tip of the tibia. Legs rather stout, the second pair the longest; tarsi of second to fourth legs five-jointed. Abdomen oval, broadly joined to the cephalothorax, consisting of nine segments, basal ones very short; three to six much longer; six to nine forming a very short retractile apical tubercle. Respiration by tubular tracheæ opening by a pair of spiracles at the sides of the cephalothorax above the third coxa. (Fig. 1011).

The living species form a single family. (Ricinòides (= Cryptostémma), Ethiop.; Cryptocèllus, Neotrop.). (CRYPTOSTEMMÁTIDÆ, HOLOTÉRGIDÆ, CURCULÒIDIDÆ, POLIOCHÉRIDÆ).

RICINÒIDIDÆ

LITERATURE ON RICINULEI

BOLIVAR Y PELTAIN, C. Un Ricinulideo de Mexico. Rev. Soc. Mexicana Hist. Nat., 2, pp. 197–209, 1 pl. (1942).
HANSEN, H. J. and W. SÖRENSON. Two Orders of Arachnida. 178 pp. Cambridge, Eng., University Press (1904).
EWING, H. E. A Synopsis of the Order Ricinulei. Ann. Ent. Soc. America, 22, pp. 583–600 (1929).
KÄSTNER, A. Ricinulei. In Kükenthal & Krumbach, Handbuch der Zoologie, 3, Hälfte 2, Lief. 5, pp. 94–116, 26 figs. (1932).
PETRUNKEVITCH, A. Ricinulei. Scientific Papers, State of Illinois, 3, No. 2, pp. 65–67 (1945).

ORDER SCORPIÓNIDA

(SCORPIÒNES)

Large or very large species. Cephalothorax and abdomen broadly attached; cheliceræ chelate; pedipalpi very large, bearing a large swollen chela at the apex. Cephalothorax with a pair of median eyes near the middle and a group of two to five lateral eyes at each side; rarely absent. Basal portion of abdomen broad, the five apical segments much narrower, forming a highly flexible postabdomen, the last segment of which bears a sting at apex and contains a poison gland. Four pairs of legs, each consisting of seven segments; tarsi three-jointed. Underside of abdomen at base with a pair of movable pectinate organs. Respiration by book-lungs opening by paired slits on the third to sixth abdominal segments. Mainly tropical species. Scorpions.

1. Sternum large, at least half as long as wide and often longer than wide, pentagonal or frequently much narrowed anteriorly; generally nearly as large as or larger than the genital plate which lies behind it. (Figs. 1031, 1032)..........................2
   Sternum much reduced in size, forming two narrow transverse or oblique plates that are sometimes barely visible, therefore much wider than long (Fig. 1033); tip of tarsus without a lobe at the side. (Bothriùrus, Brachiostérnus, Théstylus, Urophònius, Neotrop.; Cercophònius, Austr.) .... BOTHRIÙRIDÆ
2. Legs with a spine or thorn in the connecting membrane between the last two tarsal joints, only on the outer side; sternum pentagonal, not triangularly narrowed in front 3
   Legs with one or two spines or thorns internally and externally in the membrane between the second and last tarsal joints (Figs. 1027); sternum sometimes triangularly narrowed in front......6
3. Postabdomen (narrowed, tail-like, apical body segments) with the

four basal segments each bearing below a pair of longitudinal
keels near the median line..................................4
Postabdomen with only one median ventral keel. (Uródacus, Austr.;
Hemiscórpion, Palæarc.). (See couplet 5). SCORPIÓNIDÆ, part

4. Last segment of postabdomen with a distinct thorn or tubercle
below the sting; chela flat or rounded; last joint of tarsi with
two rows of spines beneath. (Diplocéntrus, Œclus, Neotrop.;
Nèbo, Palæarc.) ....DIPLOCÉNTRIDÆ
Last segment of postabdomen simple, without thorn or tubercle
beneath the sting 5

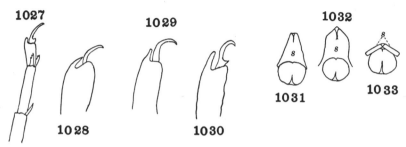

Figs. 1027–1033. Scorpionida

1027. **Centruroides**, tarsus of fourth leg. Buthidæ.
1028. **Pandinus**, tip of last tarsal joint. Scorpionidæ.
1029. **Vejovis**, tip of last tarsal joint. Vejovidæ.
1030. **Iomachus**, tip of last tarsal joint. Ischnuridæ.
1031. **Centruroides**, sternum. Buthidæ.
1032. **Pandinus**, sternum (Kraepelin) Scorpionidæ.
1033. **Bothriurus**, sternum (Kraepelin) Bothriuridæ.

5. Tip of last tarsal joint rounded or acute and produced on the
sides to form a lobe the edge of which forms an acute angle
with the apical projection that lies dorsally between the claws.
(Figs. 1028, 1032). ....SCORPIÓNIDÆ

a. Postabdomen with only a single median keel on the ventral side
of all segments ....b
Basal four segments each with a pair of keels on the ventral side
near the median line ....d

b. Last joint of tarsi simple, without rounded lateral lobes c
Last joint of tarsi with rounded lateral lobes. (Uródacus, Austr.)
URODACÌNÆ

c. Last joint of tarsi with an external spine at the apex. (Hetero-
scórpion, Madagascar) ...........HETEROSCORPIONÌNÆ
Last joint of tarsi without any thorns below, with two rows of
bristles. (Hemiscórpion, Palæarc.) ......HEMISCORPIONÌNÆ

d. Last joint of tarsi with rounded lateral lobes, the edges of which form an acute angle with the dorsal claw-fold; upper side of chela usually rounded, without a keel. (Scórpio, Palæarc., Ethiop.; Heterомètrus, Indomal.; Pandìnus, Ethiop.)

SCORPIONÌNÆ

Last joint of tarsi without rounded lobes; its edge forming a right angle with the claw-fold. (Lisposòma, Ethiop.)

LISPOSOMATÌNÆ

Tip of last tarsal joint more or less truncate, without rounded lobes, its apical edge forming a right angle with the dorsal projection between the claws; last tarsal joint below with spines or bristles. (Fig. 1030). (Ischnùrus, Hadógenes, Ethiop.; Opisthacánthus, Ethiop., Neotrop.; Hormùrus, Indoaustr.; Iómachus, Ethiop., Ind.) .... ISCHNÙRIDÆ

6. Three to five lateral eyes in a group at each side of the cephalothorax in front 7
Only two lateral eyes at each side of cephalothorax, or lateral eyes absent .... CHÁCTIDÆ

This family is divisible into five well-marked subfamilies as follows:

a. Basal four segments of postabdomen below with a single median, tuberculate keel; underside of body tuberculate. (Megacórmus, Neotrop.) .... MEGACORMÌNÆ
Basal four segments without a keel on the underside, or with two keels — one on each side of the median line .... b

b. Movable finger of chela with one or several rows of minute tubercles c
Movable finger of chela with oblique, non-overlapping rows of minute tubercles. (Superstitiònia, Nearc.)

SUPERSTITIONIÌNÆ

c. Movable finger of chela with numerous (7–14) irregular rows of minute tubercles. (Chærílius, Indomal.) .... CHÆRILIÌNÆ
Movable finger of chela with one or an irregular row of minute tubercles ....d

d. Chela flattened, its upper surface divided by a strong keel into two areas that lie at right angles to one another. (Euscórpius, Palæarc.)

EUSCORPIÌNÆ

Chela rounded or ridged, not thus divided into two areas that lie at a right angle to one another. (Cháctas, Bròteas, Neotrop.)

CHACTÌNÆ

7. Sternum more or less triangular, strongly narrowed in front; first tarsal joint of third and fourth pair of legs often with a thorn at tip; three or five lateral eyes; last segment of postabdomen often bearing a spine beneath the sting. (Figs. 1010, 1027, 1031).

(Bùthus, Palæarc., Ethiop., Indomal.; Isomètrus, Indoaustr.; Tìtyus, Centruròides, Am.; Anánteris, Neotrop.; Uropléctes, Ethiop., Indoaustr.; Isometròides, Austr., Lỳchas, Buthèolus, Palæarc., Parabùthus, Ethiop.) ....BÙTHIDÆ
Sternum with parallel sides, usually wider than long, with a deeply impressed median groove; three lateral eyes; last segment of postabdomen always without a spine beneath the sting. (Fig. 1029) ....VEJÓVIDÆ

a. Sternites of the four basal segments of postabdomen with a single median keel. (Syntròpis, Nearc.) ....SYNTROPÌNÆ
Sternites of the four basal segments of postabdomen with a pair of keels next to the median line ....b
b. Last joint of tarsi with a distinct spine (for walking). (Carabócto-nus, Hadruròides, Neotrop.) ....CARABOCTONÌNÆ
Last joint of tarsi without a spine for walking; this replaced by a pair of tubercles c
c. Basal attachments of pecten-teeth few in number, not over six; intermediary joints (fulcra) very small or vestigial ....d
Pecten-teeth with at least 8 bead-like basal attachments; fulcra distinct, also bead-like. (Vejòvis, Hadrùrus, Nearc.)
VEJOVÌNÆ
d. Edge of the movable finger of chela with many irregularly defined tuberculate serrations; movable finger of mandible with a conspicuous tooth below. (Jùrus, Palæarc.) ....JURÌNÆ
Edge of movable finger of chela with one or two rows of small tubercles; movable finger of mandible not toothed, one with as many as six very small teeth ....e
e. Edge of movable finger of chela with two rows of tubercles. (Scórpiops, Palæarc, Ind.; Parascórpiops, Malay.)
SCORPIOPSÌNÆ
Edge of movable finger of chela with only a single row of tubercles. (Uroctonus, Anuroctonus, Am.) ....UROCTONÌNÆ

LITERATURE ON SCORPIONIDA

Ewing, H. E. Scorpions of the Western United States. Proc. U. S. Nat. Mus., 73, No. 2730, 24 pp. (1928).
Gough, L. H. Key to Egyptian Scorpions. Cairo Ministry Agric. Egypt Bull. 76, 7 pp. (1927).
Hewitt, J. Survey of the Scorpion Fauna of South Africa. Trans. Roy. Soc. South Africa, 6, pp. 89–192 (1918).
Hoffman, C. C. Los Scorpiones de Mexico. An. Inst. Biol. Mexico, 3, pp. 243–282, 20 figs. (1932).
Kästner, A. Scorpione (Scorpionida). In Tierwelt Mitteleuropas, 3, Lief. 1, pp. II 1–3 (1928).

KRAEPELIN, K. Revision der Skorpione. Jahrb. Hamburg. wiss. Anst., **8**, pp. 1–144 (1891); **11**, pp. 1–248 (1894); **12**, pp. 1–24 (1895). Scorpionida. Das Tierreich. Lief 8, pp. 1–230 (1899).

LAWRENCE, R. F. The Scorpions of Natal and Zululand. Ann. Natal Mus., **10**, pp. 141–190, 32 figs. (1942).

MELLO-LEITÃO, C. DE. Escorpiões Sul-Americanos. Arq. Mus. Nac. Rio de Janeiro, **40**, pp. 7–468, 182 figs. (1940).

VACHON, M. La systématique des Scorpions. Mem. Mus. Hist. Nat., Paris, n.s. **13**, pp. 241–260, 64 figs. (1940).

WERNER, F. Scorpionida. In Bronn's, Klassen und Ordnungen des Tierreichs, **5**, Abt. IV, Buch 8, pp. 1–316, 390 figs. (1935).

ORDER SOLPÙGIDA

(SOLÍFUGÆ)

Large or moderately large, pale-bodied, very active species. Chelicerae very large, chelate, moving in a vertical plane. Cephalothorax bearing only one pair of legs, separated from three distinct thoracic segments to each of which a pair of legs is attached. Abdomen elongate, oval, consisting of ten segments, without terminal filament or appendage. Pedipalpi long, leg-like, six-jointed. Tarsus of pedipalpi and first pair of legs one-jointed; second to fourth legs with the tarsi often several-jointed; tarsi usually provided with claws. Respiration by tracheæ that open through spiracles behind the first pair of legs on both the first and second abdominal segments. Distribution tropical and subtropical, most generally in dry or arid regions.

1. Fourth pair of legs ending in a pair of claws as do the second and third pairs; basal portion of fourth pair of legs (including the coxæ and two trochanters) clearly shorter than the remainder of the leg (femur, tibia and two tarsal joints); fourth legs with the basal section of femur very much shorter than the apical section 2
   Fourth pair of legs without claws, these replaced by short spines; basal portion of fourth leg almost as long as the remainder of the leg; basal section of femur of fourth leg longer than the apical section. (**Hexìsopus, Chelipus,** S. Afr.) .HEXISOPÓDIDÆ
2. Metatarsus of first pair of legs spinose below; all tarsi one-jointed. (**Rhagòdes, Rhagodélla, Rhagídoca,** Ethiop., Ind.)
   RHAGÓDIDÆ
   Metatarsus of first pair of legs unarmed below 3
3. Tarsi of second and third pair of legs without an apical spine above the claws 4
   Tarsi of second and third pair of legs bearing a spine at tip above the claws. (**Eremóbates, Eremóstata, Erèmopus,** Western U. S., Centr. Am.) ....EREMOBÁTIDÆ

4. Tarsi of first pair of legs with two claws (sometimes more or less
   hidden by setæ) 5
   Tarsi of first pair of legs entirely without claws 7
5. Tarsal claws of the second to fourth pairs of legs hairy; tarsus of
   pedipalps movable. (Galeòdes, Galeodéllus, N. E. Afr. to Asia)
   GALEÓDIDÆ
   Tarsal claws of the second to fourth pairs of legs bare, without hairs;
   tarsus of pedipalps immobile 6

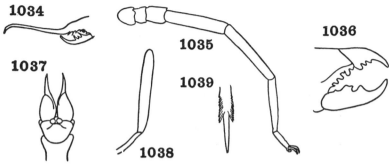

Figs. 1034–1039. Solpugida

1034. Gnossipus, chelicera in lateral view (Kraepelin) Solpugidæ.
1035. Solpugid, third leg (Ewing).
1036. Eremobates, chelicera in lateral view (Putnam) Solpugidæ.
1037. Eremobates, head in dorsal view (Putnam) Solpugidæ.
1038. Eremobates, tip of pedipalpus (Putnam) Solpugidæ.
1039. Solpuga, tip of flagellum of pedipalpus (Kraepelin) Solpugidæ.

6. Tarsi of second, third and fourth pairs of legs composed of a single
   joint. Old World species. (Kárschia, Barrélla, Gylíppus)
   KARSCHÏIDÆ
   Tarsi of second, third and fourth pairs of legs two-jointed. (Ceròma,
   Ceromélla, Ethiop.) ....CEROMÁTIDÆ
7. Tarsi of second and third legs one or two-jointed; fourth tarsi with
   not more than four joints 8
   Tarsi of second and third legs four-jointed, the fourth tarsi six- or
   seven-jointed. (Solpùga, Solpugyla, Zerriássa, Ferrándia, Ethiop.)
   SOLPÙGIDÆ
8. Flagellum of cheliceræ in male scale-like; movable finger of
   cheliceræ, at least in the female, with only a single tooth 9
   Flagellum of cheliceræ composed only of a brush of specialized
   bristles; finger of cheliceræ, at least in the female, with additional
   small teeth. (Melanoblóssia, Lawrencega, Ethiop.)
   MELANOBLOSSÏIDÆ

9. Flagellum of cheliceræ in the male movable so as to extend either forward or backward over the arc of half a circle. (Bìton, Gluviópsis, Ethiop., Palæarc.; Dæsia, Palæarc.) ...... DÆSÌIDÆ
Flagellum of male cheliceræ fixed, not movable. (Ammótrecha, Centr. Am.; Ammotréchula, Sw. U. S.; Pseudoclèobis, Neotrop.) AMMOTRÉCHIDÆ

LITERATURE ON SOLPUGIDA

KRAEPELIN, K. Zur Systematik der Solifugen. Mitt. naturh. Mus. Hamburg, 16, pp. 197–258 (1899).
Solpugida. Das Tierriech, Lief. 12, pp. 4–159 (1901).
HEWITT, J. A Short Survey of the Solifugæ of South Africa. Ann. Transvaal Mus., 7, pp. 1–76 (1919).
MELLO-LEITÃO, C. DE. Solifugos de Argentina. An. Mus. Argentina, 40, pp. 1–32, 12 pls. (1938).
PUTNAM, J. D. Solpugida of America. Proc. Davenport Acad. Nat. Sci., 3, 149 pp. (1882).
ROEWER, C. F. Solifuga. In Bronn's, Klassen und Ordnungen des Tierreichs, 5, Abt. 4, Buch 4, Lief. 1–5, pp. 1–723, 223 figs. (1932–34).
SIMON, E. Essai d'une Classification des Galéodes. Ann. Soc. Ent. France, 1879, pp. 93–154 (1879).

ORDER CHELONÉTHIDA

(PSEUDOSCORPIÓNIDA; PSEUDOSCORPIÒNES, CHERNETÍDEA)

Small or very small Arachnida with flattened body. Cephalothorax unjointed, although sometimes with distinct transverse grooves; abdomen with 11 or 12 tergites, each often composed of a pair of plates, narrowly separated along the median line. Cheliceræ two-jointed, chelate. Pedipalpi very large, six-jointed, much longer than the walking legs, their tarsi forming a much enlarged pincers-like grasping organ. Legs six-jointed, the tarsi one or two-jointed and the femur sometimes divided into two sections; tarsi with a pair of apical claws. Cephalothorax narrower than the abdomen which is often much widened; abdomen without any apical prolongation, joined to the cephalothorax along its entire base. Eyes two or four, placed near the sides of the carapace; sometimes wanting. Respiration by tracheæ opening by four spiracles placed just behind the second and third abdominal plates at the sides of the body. Genital aperture on the first sternite. Slow-moving carnivorous species of retiring habits, living under bark, stones, etc. False-scorpions; Book-scorpions.

1. Tarsi of first two pairs of legs one-jointed; of third and fourth legs two-jointed. Suborder HETEROSPHYRONIDA 2
Tarsi of all four pairs of legs with the same number of joints 3

2. Spiracles surrounded by a stigmal plate in the form of an incomplete elliptical band that is open on the side below the spiracle; basal section of the femora of the fourth pair of legs only slightly shorter than the apical section. (Dìtha, Heterólophus, widespr.) (*TRI-DENCHTHÓNIDÆ*) .... DÍTHIDÆ
Spiracles without a special plate; basal section of femora of fourth pair of legs much shorter than the apical section. (Chthònius, Holarc.; Tyrranochthònius, widespr.; Lechýtia, Neotrop., Ethiop.; Apochthònius, Nearc.) .... CHTHONÌIDÆ

3. Tarsi two-jointed. (Suborder DIPLOSPHYRÓNIDA) 4
Tarsi one-jointed (Fig. 1040). (Suborder MONOSPHYRÓNIDA) 10

4. Movable finger of cheliceræ clearly multidenticulate, without a true subapical lobe; carapace usually produced medially in front. (Superfamily NEOBISIÒIDEA) 5
Movable finger of cheliceræ with a single subapical lobe or tooth which is rarely secondarily subdivided, but never multidenticulate; carapace in front often somewhat emarginate, rarely if ever produced medially. (Superfamily GARYPODÒIDEA) 8

5. Venom apparatus present in the fixed finger of the claw only, the movable finger with a definite sheath for the reception of the venom-tooth 6
Venom apparatus present in both the fixed and movable fingers; a sheathing structure rarely present in either finger 7

6. Pleural membrane of abdomen smoothly longitudinally plicate, never granulate; femur of fourth pair of legs with an oblique cross-suture (rarely nearly perpendicular to the longitudinal axis). (Chìtra, Syarìnus, Hyarìnus, Nearc.) .... SYARÍNIDÆ
Pleural membrane granulate or granulate-striate; femoral articulation of fourth pair of legs truly vertical to the longitudinal axis of the femur-patella. (Neobísium, Microbísium, Holarc.; Blòthrus, Róncus, Palæarc.) .... NEOBISÌIDÆ

7. Pleural membrane of abdomen granulate; claw with twelve tactile setæ on the fingers. (Hỳa, Indomal.) .... HỲIDÆ
Pleural membrane of abdomen evenly longitudinally plicate; fingers of claw usually with many more than twelve tactile setæ. (Fig. 1043). (Ideoróncus, Bóchica, Neotrop.; Albìorix, N. Am.; Shravàna, Indomal.) .... IDEORÓNCIDÆ

8. Venom apparatus present in both the movable and fixed fingers of the claw; no sheathing structure on either claw to receive the venom-tooth 9
Venom apparatus present in the fixed finger of the claw only; a well developed sheathing structure present on the movable finger to receive the venom-tooth. (Ménthus, Nearc., Neotrop.). MÉNTHIDÆ

9. Pleural membrane of abdomen smoothly and evenly plicate; carapace not or rarely noticeably narrowed in front; sides of abdomen more or less parallel, the abdomen not greatly wider than the cephalothorax. (Ólpium, Palæarc.; Garypìnus, Am.; Seriànus, Nearc., Neotrop., Indomal.; Solìnus, Nearc., Austr.; Hòrus, Ethiop.; Xenólpium, Indoaustr.) .... OLPÌIDÆ
Pleural membrane prickly, granular, or irregularly wrinkled; carapace narrowed in front, clearly triangular; abdomen subovate, much broader than the cephalothorax. (Gárypus, Palæarc., Neo-

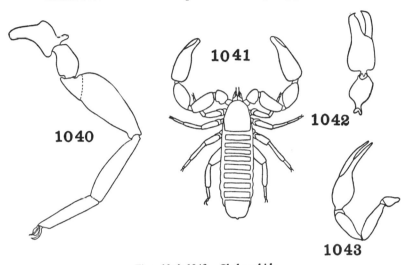

Figs. 1040–1043. Chelonethida

1040. **Chelifer,** fourth leg (Ewing) Cheliferidæ.
1041. **Chelifer** (Tullgren) Cheliferidæ.
1042. **Chelifer,** pedipalpus (With) Cheliferidæ.
1043. **Ideoroncus,** pedipalpus (With) Ideoroncidæ.

trop.; **Geogárypus,** Palæarc., Indomal.; **Lárca,** Holarc.; **Anagárypus,** Austromal.; **Maorigárypus,** Austr.) .... GARYPÓDIDÆ
10. Four well developed eyes 11
    Two eyes, sometimes imperfect, or none 13
11. Carapace in front of the eyes with at least two lobed projections; venom apparatus lacking on the chela; a movable joint between the basal and apical sections of the femora of the walking legs . . 12
    Carapace produced in front of the eyes, but without projecting lobes; venom apparatus present on both fingers of the chela; basal and apical sections of femora separated by a constriction, but immovably united. (**Synsphyrònus,** Austr.) . . . SYNSPHYRÓNIDÆ

12. Cephalothorax and abdomen not separated with one another by an articulation; pedipalpi of normal form. (**Pseudogárypus**, Nearc.) .... **PSEUDOGARYPÓDIDÆ**
  Cephalothorax and abdomen separated by an articulation; long basal joint of pedipalpi greatly thickened and arcuate. (**Feaélla**, Ethiop., Ind.) .... **FEAÉLLIDÆ**

13. Venom apparatus present in both the fixed and movable fingers of the chela 14
  Venom apparatus absent in either the movable or fixed finger of the chela 15

14. A median sclerite (pseudosternum) present between the coxæ of the walking legs; eyes entirely absent. (**Sternóphorus**, N. Am., Austr.) .... **STERNOPHÓRIDÆ**
  No pseudosternum; usually two eyes present or visible as vestiges; integument usually granulate; abdominal tergites usually divided by a median line of fracture. (**Chélifer**, cosmop.; **Lophochérnes**, Old World; **Wíthius**, Holarc.; **Rhacochélifer**, Palæarc.; **Cacodemònius**, Neotrop.) .... **CHELIFÉRIDÆ**

15. Venom aparatus present only on the movable finger of the chela . . 16
  Venom apparatus present only on the fixed finger of the chela 17

16. Cheliceræ externally with a pair of strongly clavate setæ; many other body bristles also clavate; carapace more or less triangular, wider than long; myrmecophilous species. (**Myrmochérnes**, S. Afr.). .... **MYRMOCHERNÉTIDÆ**
  Cheliceræ without such specialized clavate bristles, although some of the body bristles may be clavate; carapace usually somewhat longer than wide, more or less rounded in front. (**Chérnes**, Lamprochérnes, Palæarc.; **Chélanops**, **Lustrochérnes**, Am.; **Goniochérnes**, Ethiop.) .... **CHERNÉTIDÆ**

17. Carapace rounded in front, without lobes or projections. (**Atémnus**, Palæarc.; **Anatémnus**, Ethiop., Malay.; **Titanatémnus**, Ethiop.). .... **ATÉMNIDÆ**
  Carapace with a pair of angulate projections or lobes on its front margin. (**Cheirídium**, cosmop.; **Apocheirídium**, widespr.; **Neocheirídium**, Neotrop.) .... **CHEIRIDÌIDÆ**

LITERATURE ON CHELONETHIDA

BALZAN, L. Revisione dei Pseudoscorpioni de Paraguay. Ann. Mus. Civ. Genova (2), **29**, pp. 401–451 (1890).
  Pseudoscorpiones de Venezuela. Ann. Soc. Entom. France, 60, pp. 497–552 (1891).
BEIER, M. Pseudoscorpionida. In Kükenthal, Handbuch der Zoologie, 3, Hälfte 2, Lief. 5, pp. 117–192, 111 figs. (1932).
  Pseudoscorpionida. Das Tierreich, Lief. **57**, pp. 1–258, 271 figs.; **58**, pp. 1–294, 300 figs. (1932).

Revision der Chernetidæ. Zool. Jahrb. (Syst.), **64**, pp. 509–548, 15 figs. (1933).

Pseudoscorpioniden-Fauna der iberischen Halbinzel. Zool. Jahrb. (Syst.), **72**, pp. 157–202, 24 figs. (1939).

CHAMBERLIN, J. C. Synoptic Classification of False Scorpions, Part I. Ann. Mag. Nat. Hist. (10), **4**, pp. 50–80 (1929), **5**, pp. 1–48, and pp. 585–618 (1930).

The Arachnid Order Chelonethida. Stanford Univ. Publ. Biol. Ser., **7**(1), pp. 1–284, 71 figs. (1931).

False Scorpions from Yucatan Caves. Publ. No. **491** Carnegie Inst., pp. 109–121 (1938).

New and Little Known False Scorpions from the Pacific. Ann. Mag. Nat. Hist., (11)**2**, pp. 259–285 (1938).

CHAMBERLIN, J. C. and R. V. CHAMBERLIN. The Genera and Species of the Tridenchthoniidæ (Dithidæ). Bull. Univ. Utah, Biol. Ser., **9**(2), 67 pp., 17 figs. (1945).

COOLIDGE, K. R. List of North American Pseudoscorpionida. Psyche, **15**, pp. 108–114 (1908).

ELLINGSEN, E. Die Pseudoscorpione des Berliner Museums. Mitt. Zool. Mus. Berlin, **4**, pp. 355–423 (1910) (extensive bibliography).

Pseudoscorpions of South Africa. Ann. South African Mus., **10**, pp. 75–128 (1912).

FEIO, J. L. DE A. Novos Pseudoscorpiões de região neotropical. Bol. Mus. Nac. Rio de Janeiro, **44**, pp. 1–47 (1945).

KÄSTNER, A. Afterscorpione (Pseudoscorpionida). In Tierwelt Mitteleuropas, **3**, Lief. 1, pp. IV 1–13 (1928).

KEW, H. W. Synopsis of False Scorpions of Britain and Ireland. Proc. Roy. Irish Acad., **29**, Sec. B, No. 2 (1911), and Supplement, *Ibid.*, **33** (1916).

ROEWER, C. F. Chelonethida. In Bronn's, Klassen und Ordnungen des Tierreichs, **5**, Abt. IV, Buch 6, pp. 1–354, 259 figs. (1936–40).

WITH, C. J. Chelonethida of the Australian Region. Ann. Mag. Nat. Hist., (7) **15**, pp. 94–143 (1905).

Indian False-Scorpions. Kgl. Danske Vid. Selsk. Skrifter, **7**, pp. 1–124 (1906).

ORDER **PHALÁNGIDA**

(*OPILIÒNES*)

Usually moderate-sized species with long or very long legs. Cephalothorax not separated from the abdomen by a constriction, forming an unsegmented or very indistinctly segmented dorsal carapace. Abdomen segmented, with nine dorsal plates and fewer ventral ones. Head with two eyes, often on stalk-like tubercles. Cheliceræ three-jointed, chelate; rather long and sometimes thickened. Pedipalpi similar to the legs, but usually much shorter. Legs very long and slender; coxæ very large and firmly attached to the body. Respiration by tracheæ; one pair of spiracles opening ventrally near the base of the abdomen. Harvestmen, Daddy-long-legs.

1. Genital opening covered by a movable plate or operculum; openings of the scent glands situated at the side margin of the cephalothorax, not on tubercles 2
   Genital opening exposed, not covered by an operculum; scent glands each placed upon a conical protuberance at the sides of the cephalothorax. (Fig. 1045). (Suborder CYPHOPHTHÁLMI). (Sìro, Palæarc.; Ogòvea, Ethiop.; Miópsalis, Stylocéllus, Indomal.; Péttalus, Ind.) . . . . SIRÓNIDÆ

2. Pedipalpi stout, their tarsi with a strong grasping claw; apical joint of the tarsus of first and second pairs of legs with only one simple claw; the third and fourth tarsi with either two, or with a tridentate claw; sternite of first abdominal segment much reduced, not reaching in front of the hind coxæ; hind legs usually the longest. (Fig. 1044). (Suborder LANIATÒRES) 3

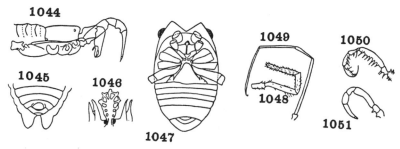

Figs. 1044–1051. **Phalangida**

1044. **Oncopus,** anterior part of body in profile (Roewer) Oncopodidæ.
1045. **Pettalus,** apical part of abdomen (Roewer) Sironidæ.
1046. **Ortholasma,** anterior part of cephalothorax (Roewer) Trogulidæ.
1047. **Acropsopilio,** underside of body (Roewer) Acropsopilionidæ.
1048. **Trogulidæ,** pedipalpus (Roewer) Trogulidæ.
1049. **Phalangiidæ,** pedipalpus (Roewer) Phalangiidæ.
1050. **Gonyleptidæ,** pedipalpus (Roewer) Gonyleptidæ.
1051. **Oncopodidæ,** pedipalpus (Roewer) Oncopodidæ.

Pedipalpi slender, palpiform, their tarsi with a weaker claw which is occasionally lacking; apical joint of all four tarsi with only one simple claw; sternite of first abdominal segment extending much in front of the hind coxæ; second pair of legs the longest. (Suborder PALPATÒRES) 8

3. Last four tergites freely movable, not fused .4
   All tergites except the apical one fused to form a scutum, the latter forming a movable anal plate. (Figs. 1044, 1051). (Óncopus, Gnómulus, Pelítnus, Indomal.) . . . . ONCOPÓDIDÆ

4. Third and fourth tarsi each with a pair of apical claws which are simple or furnished with curved teeth 5

Third and fourth tarsi each with a single three-pronged claw; or in partly grown specimens with a single claw furnished with denticles laterally. (**Triænònyx**, Neotrop.; **Sclerόbunus**, Nearc.; **Núncia, Soerensenélla**, Austr.; **Acumόntia**, Madagasc.; **Adæum, Ceratomόntia**, Ethiop.) ....**TRLÆNONÝCHIDÆ**

5. Pedipalpi carried with the tips curved backwards behind the patella, weakly armed; anterior margin of the cephalothorax below with five erect, conical teeth. (**Assàmia, Metassàmia**, Indomal.; **Trionyxélla**, Ind.; **Mérmerus**, Mal.; **Macrodampètrus, Dampètrus, Mosòia**, Austr.) ....**ASSAMÌIDÆ**

   Pedipalpi not curved, held straight forward or at most bent to the side of the cheliceræ; anterior margin of the cephalothorax sometimes sharply excavated, but never with five erect, conical teeth ..6

6. Tarsi of the third and fourth legs each with a false claw (pseudonychium) below the true claws........................7

   Tarsi of third and fourth legs without a pseudonychium. (**Beloníscus, Obaloniànus**, Indomal.; **Scotolèmon**, Palæarc.; **Phalangòdes**, Am.; **Zalmόxis**, Austr.; **Metabiántes**, Ethiop.).

   PHALANGόDIDÆ

   By some workers this family is given the rank of a superfamily, composed of a number of families. The following key includes these (designated here as subfamilies), as they have been outlined in a posthumous work of Sørensen, edited and published by Henriksen in 1932, after a lapse of some years.

a. Apical part of tarsi of the first pair of legs undivided.

   ERECANANÌNÆ

   Apical part of tarsi of the first pair of legs composed of two or three joints ....b

b. Scopula present c

   Scopula wanting ....f

c. Ocular tubercle present, distinctly separated; femora of first pair of legs not spinose......................................d

   Ocular tubercle not distinctly separated; scutum with five dorsal grooves ....e

d. Scutum with five dorsal grooves....................**SAMOÌNÆ**

   Scutum with four dorsal grooves................**ACROBUNÌNÆ**

e. Femur of first pair of legs armed with bristly spines. **IBALONIÌNÆ**

   Femur of first pair of legs not spiny..............**BIANTÌNÆ**

f. Ocular tubercle present..g

   Ocular tubercle absent..l

g. Femora of first pair of legs spiny or armed with setigerous tubercles; last joint of first tarsi bipartite...............**MINUÌNÆ**

   Femora of first pair of legs without spines or setigerous tubercles...h

h. Apical section of tarsi of first pair of legs tripartite..............i

   Apical section of first pair of tarsi bipartite....................j

 i. Scutum with five dorsal grooves............TRICHOMMATÎNÆ
  Scutum with four dorsal grooves................SARACINÎNÆ
 j. Maxillary lobe of coxæ of second pair of legs distinct, broad and
  porrect. (If small, see Minuinæ, couplet g).................k
  Maxillary lobe of second coxa wanting..........STYGNOPSÎNÆ
 k. Scutum with four dorsal grooves................EPEDANÎNÆ
  Scutum with five dorsal grooves............PHALANGODÎNÆ
 l. Femora of first pair of legs armed with bristly spines.
               PODOCTÎNÆ
  Femora of first pair of legs without bristly spines..............m
 m. Scutum with five dorsal grooves..........STYGNOMMATÎNÆ
  Scutum with four dorsal grooves...................DIBUNÎNÆ

7. Pedipalpi weak, their femur, tibia and tarsus broadly flattened
 and keeled, curved in front of and to the side of the chelceræ;
 all joints of the pedipalpi almost unarmed, without stout spines.
 (Libitòides, Metacynórta, Am.; Paravanònes, Cynórta, Cynórtula,
 Metarhaucus, Flírtea, Ergínulus, Neotrop.). (PALPÍNIDÆ).
                 COSMÉTIDÆ
 Pedipalpi very stout, their femur not flattened, their tibia and
 tarsus rounded, at most flattened beneath between the stout tibial
 and tarsal spines, not keeled; the pedipalpi porrect and not curved
 toward the cheliceræ. (Fig. 1050). (Discocýrtus, Metagynòdes,
 Eusárcus, Pachylòides, Wèyhia, Gonyléptes, Goniosòma, Cælopỳ-
 gus, Neotrop.) .... GONYLÉPTIDÆ
8. Tarsi of the pedipalpi always shorter than their tibiæ (Fig. 1048);
 without, or with only a very minute claw; maxillary lobe of the
 second coxa very small or absent, never freely movable; no accessory spiracles on the legs. (Superfamily NEMASTOMAT-
 ÒIDEA) 9
 Tarsi of the pedipalpi always longer than the tibiæ and always
 with a distinct, simple or pectinate claw; maxillary lobe of the
 second coxa distinct, freely movable, long and narrow; two accessory spiracles on the first to fourth tibiæ. (Fig. 1049). (Lacínius,
 Phalángium, Opílio, Holarc.; Cáddo, Nearc.; Mítopus, Odiéllus,
 Palæarc.; Rhampsinìtus, Ethiop.; Gagrélla, Indoaustr.). Superfamily PHALANGIÒIDEA) .... PHALANGÌIDÆ
9. Eyes large, highly convex, widely separated, not on a common
 ocular tubercle, placed one at each side of the cephalothorax.
 (Fig. 1047). (Acropsopílio, Neotrop.)..ACROPSOPILIÓNIDÆ
 Both eyes placed on a common median ocular tubercle..........10
10. Ocular tubercle separated distinctly from the anterior margin of the
 cephalothorax which is sharply truncate, exposing the cheliceræ
 and pedipalpi 11
 Ocular tubercle placed at the anterior margin of the cephalothorax
 and forming with it a large lobe which covers the cheliceræ and

pedipalpi from above. (Figs. 1046, 1048), (Trógulus, Dicranolásma, Palæarc.; Ortholásma, Dendrolásma, Nearc.).

TROGÙLIDÆ

11. First and second thoracic tergites fused together in the cephalothorax; first to fourth coxæ each with a series of tubercles before and behind. (Nemástoma, Holarc.; Crósbycus, Nearc.).

NEMASTOMÁTIDÆ

First thoracic tergite fused with the cephalothorax and forming a prosoma; second thoracic tergite free, not fused with the cephalothorax nor the first tergite; first to fourth coxæ without an anterior and posterior row of tubercles. (Ischyrópsalis, Palæarc.; Táracus, Sábacon, Tomicomèrus, Nearc.).........ISCHYROPSÁLIDÆ

LITERATURE ON PHALANGIDA

Banks, N. Synopsis of North American Phalangida. American Naturalist, 35, pp. 669–679 (1901).

Bishop, S. C. and C. R. Crosby. Phalangida of the Southeastern United States. Journ. Elisha Mitchell Soc., 1924, pp. 8–26 (1924).

Forster, R. R. Keys to New Zealand Genera of Opiliones. Rec. Dominion Mus. Wellington, 1, pp. 183–192 (1944).

Lawrence, R. F. The Harvest-Spiders (Opiliones) of South Africa. Ann. South African Mus., 29(2), pp. 342–508, 90 figs. (1931).

Mello-Leitão, M. Notas sobre Arachnideos Argentinos. Ann. Acad. Brasil. Sci., 3(2), pp. 83–97, 5 figs. (1931).

Notas sobre os Opilioes do Brasil. Bol. Mus. nac. Rio de Janeiro, 9(1), pp. 99–114 (1933).

Algumas notas sobre os Laniatores. Arch. Mus. nac. Rio de Janeiro, 36, pp. 87–116 (1935).

Phalangodoidea. Ann. Acad. Brasil. Sci., 10, pp. 135–145, 1 pl. (1938).

Palpatores Sul Americanos. Ibid., 10, pp. 317–337, 2 pls. (1938).

Oudemans, A. C. Ein neuer Stygobiont (Stygophalangiidæ). Zool. Anz., 103, pp. 193–198, 9 figs. (1933).

Roewer, C. F. Die Weberknechte der Erde. 1116 pp. G. Fischer, Jena (1923).

Weitere Weberknechte. Abh. Naturw. Ver. Bremen, 26, pp. 261–402 (1927).

Weberknechte (Opiliones). In Tierwelt Mitteleuropas, 3, Lief. 1, pp. V, 1–10 (1928).

Alte und neue Assamiidæ. Veröff. deutsch. Kolonial- u. Uebersee-Mus. Bremen, 1, pp. 1–168, 9 pls. (1935).

Phalangida (Opiliones). In Bronn's, Klassen und Ordnungen des Tierreichs, 5, Abt. IV, Buch 6, Lief. 1–3, pp. 1–348, 260 figs. (1936–40).

Phalangodidæ. Veröff. deutsch. Kolonial- u. Uebersee-Mus. Bremen, 2, pp. 81–169, 10 pls., 1 fig. (1938).

Ueber Gonyleptiden. Senckenbergiana, 26 (1–3), pp. 12–68, 9 pls. (1943).

Sørensen, W. Descriptiones laniatorum. Danske Vidensk. Skr. Natur. Math. (9), 3, pp. 199–422, 29 figs. (1932). Edited by K. L. Henriksen.

WALKER, M. E. Revision of Phalangida of Ohio. Ohio State Univ. Studies, Biol. Surv., Bull., 4, No. 4, pp. 153–175 (1928).

ORDER ARANÈIDA

Small or moderate-sized, rarely large Arachnida. Cephalothorax usually oval, the head frequently separated by an indistinct suture. Usually eight simple eyes, sometimes less or occasionally none. First pair of appendages (cheliceræ) hooked or chelate, each provided with a poison-gland opening near the tip. Second pair of appendages (pedipalpi) six-jointed, with one-jointed tarsi; similar to, but usually much shorter than the four pairs of walking legs which are seven-jointed. Tarsi two-jointed, clawed at tip and often with additional claws or bristles used for manipulating the web. Abdomen almost always entirely unsegmented, its integument thinly chitinized, attached to the cephalothorax by a very strongly constricted base. Respiration by book-lungs opening by one or two pairs of slits on the underside of the abdomen; tracheæ usually present in addition to book-lungs, opening by one or two spiracles on the abdomen below. Silk-spinning glands present, opening by short tubular organs on the abdomen below. Development direct, the young essentially like the adults. Spiders.[1]

1. Abdomen segmented above and showing several distinct segments posteriorly between the anal tubercle and spinnerets which are separated by a considerable space; six to eight spinnerets; fangs of cheliceræ moving up and down; two pairs of lungs. (Suborder LIPHISTIOMÓRPHÆ (=*MESOTHÉLÆ*)) 5
    Abdomen entirely unsegmented in the adult 2
2. Fangs of cheliceræ moving up and down (paraxial); four lungs. (Suborder MYGALOMÓRPHÆ) 6
    Fangs of cheliceræ moving in and out (diaxial) 3
3. Four lungs; cribellum and calamistrum present. (Suborder *HYPO-CHILOMÓRPHÆ*). (**Hypochìlus, Ectatostícta**).
    HYPOCHÍLIDÆ
    Not more than two lungs 4
4. One pair of lungs. (Suborder *DIPNEUMONOMÓRPHÆ*) 13
    Lungs wanting. (Suborder *APNEUMONOMÓRPHÆ*) 67
5. Eight spinnerets; lip longer than wide (**Liphístius, Anadiastothèle**).
    LIPHISTÌIDÆ

a. Lateral spinnerets with several joints .... **LIPHISTÌINÆ**
    Lateral spinnerets single-jointed .... **ANADIASTOTHELÌNÆ**

[1] The accompanying key follows the system adopted by Professor Petrunkevitch in his recent publications cited on page 732, with very few changes in nomenclature, some modifications of arrangement, the frequent omission of characters of lesser diagnostic value or more difficult recognition, and a few more recent additions.

Six spinnerets and a posterior colulus; lip wider than long. (Hepta-
thèla) .... HEPTATHÉLIDÆ
6. Claw-tufts wanting 7
   Claw-tufts present 12
7. All tarsi with a brush of hairs (scopula) beneath; claws pectinate
   in two rows; cheliceræ without rastellum (Pycnothèle, Lycìnus).
                                          PYCNOTHÉLIDÆ
   At least third and fourth tarsi without scopula..................8
8. Cheliceræ with a rastellum, *i.e.*, armed on outer side near tip with
   several rows of stout teeth; maxillary lobes wanting; three claws,
   upper ones similar, pectinate in a single or double row; four,
   rarely six, comparatively short spinnerets, the anterior more or less
   approximated; eight eyes, heterogeneous. (Actínopus, Ctenìza,
   Ídiops, Acáttyma, Brachybóthrium, Pachylomèrus). Trap-door
   spiders .... CTENÍZIDÆ

a. Lip immobile .... ACTINOPODÌNÆ
   Lip free ....b
b. Thoracic groove transverse; anterior spinnerets approximated.
                                           CTENIZÌNÆ
   Thoracic groove longitudinal; anterior spinnerets wide apart.
                                       BRACHYBOTHRIÌNÆ
   Cheliceræ without a rastellum.............................9
9. Lip free, posterior spinnerets very long and slender; maxillary lobes
   wanting; three claws, the upper ones pectinate in a single or
   double row; four or six spinnerets, the posterior pair very long;
   eight or six eyes, heterogeneous: species spinning webs. (Brachy-
   thèle, Evàgrus, Haplothèle, Hexùra, Diplùra, Áname, Tréchona,
   Macrothèle) .... DIPLÙRIDÆ

a. Sternum very long and narrow; anterior pair of spinnerets approximated. (Austr.) .... DOLICHOSTERNÌNÆ
   Sternum normal; anterior spinnerets wide apart...............b
b. Upper claws pectinate in a double row........... DIPLURÌNÆ
   Upper claws pectinate in a single row.......................c
c. Four spinnerets .... MACROTHELÌNÆ
   Six spinnerets ....d
d. Thoracic groove transverse .... HEXATHELÌNÆ
   Thoracic groove longitudinal .... HEXURÌNÆ

   Lip immobile; posterior spinnerets short and stout, or at least not
   slender 10
10. Six spinnerets, the anterior pair close together; maxillary lobes well
    developed; three claws, the upper ones pectinate in a single row;
    eight eyes in three groups, heterogeneous. (Átypus, Calómmata,
    Microhexùra) .... ATÝPIDÆ
    Four or two spinnerets....................................11

11. Four claws, the upper ones with one or several teeth, sometimes dissimilar; maxillary lobes wanting; four spinnerets; eight eyes in two rows, heterogeneous; body with simple hairs. (Cádmon, Mìgas, Moggrídgea, Pœcilomìgas). (*MÍGIDÆ*)...MIGÁDIDÆ

a. Thoracic groove simple, transverse; third tibia normal..........b
Thoracic groove more or less recurved, with a median arm; third tibia excavated .... PARAMIGADÌNÆ

b. Head not elevated .... MIGADÌNÆ
Head considerably elevated .... CALATHOTARSÌNÆ

Two claws with a single tooth each, sometimes with a vestigial third claw; four or two spinnerets; coxæ of pedipalpi with a vestigial maxillary lobe; eight eyes in a compact group, heterogeneous; body with scales and clubbed hairs. (Parátropis, Anisáspis, Anisaspòides) .... PARATROPÍDIDÆ

12. Last joint of posterior spinnerets very short; four or two spinnerets; cheliceræ often with several rows of stout teeth externally at apex (rastellum); claws similar, smooth or with a few teeth in a single row; eight eyes, heterogeneous. (Barychèlus, Diplothèle, Leptopélma, Sàson) .... BARYCHÉLIDÆ

a. Two spinnerets .... DIPLOTHELÌNÆ
Four spinnerets ....b

b. Eyes not in a compact group.....................SASONÌNÆ
Eyes in a compact group.......................................c

c. Eyegroup on a distinct tubercle; lateral eyes separated by less than their diameter .... LEPTOPELMATÌNÆ
Eyegroup not on a tubercle; lateral eyes separated at least by their diameter .... BARYCHELÌNÆ

Last joint of posterior spinnerets as long as, or often longer than the preceding joint; four spinnerets; claws similar, pectinate in a single row; cheliceræ without a rastellum; eight eyes in a compact group, heterogeneous. Tarantulas. (Theraphòsa, Aviculària, Eurypélma, Grammóstola, Eumenóphorus, Selenocósmia, Ornithóctonus). (*AVICULARÌIDÆ*) .... THERAPHÓSIDÆ

13. Cribellum and calamistrum present, at least in the female......14
Cribellum and calamistrum absent in both sexes................24

14. Anal tubercle large, two-jointed, with a fringe of long hair; eight eyes in a compact group. (Œcòbius)............ŒCOBÌIDÆ
Anal tubercle of normal form...............................15

15. Three claws; claw-tufts usually wanting....................16
Two claws; claw-tufts always present.......................23

16. Tarsi with trichobothria 17
Tarsi without trichobothria 19

17. First and second tarsi and metatarsi with a brush of hairs (scopula)

beneath; tarsi with two rows of trichobothria; six spinnerets; cheliceræ with teeth on both margins; three claws, the upper ones pectinate in a single row; eight eyes in two rows. (Tengélla, Themàcrys) .... TENGÉLLIDÆ

a. Cribellum divided; retromargin of cheliceræ with four teeth.
TENGELLÌNÆ
Cribellum entire; retromargin of cheliceræ with three teeth.
CALAMISTRULÌNÆ

All tarsi without scopula; no trichobothria, or with a single row...18

18. Trichobothria few, only on the tarsi; claw-tufts (a bundle of hairs at tip, just beneath claws) often present; three claws, the upper ones pectinate in a single row; eight eyes in two rows, homogeneous, diurnal. (Pséchrus, Fecènia, Stiphídion, Matáchia).
PSÉCHRIDÆ

a. Claw-tufts present .... PSECHRÌNÆ
Claw-tufts wanting ....b
b. Cribellum divided; lip wider than long.......... STIPHIDIÌNÆ
Cribellum entire; lip long..................... MATACHIÌNÆ

Trichobothria numerous, in one row on the tarsi, in two rows on metatarsi and tibiæ; cribellum divided. (Amauròbius, Amphigỳrum, Badúmna, Titanœca) .... AMAUROBÌIDÆ

a. Calamistrum composed of two parallel lines of curved hairs.
AMAUROBIÌNÆ
Calamistrum composed of a single line of curved hairs.
IXEUTICÌNÆ

19. Tracheal spiracle located far in advance of the spinnerets; cheliceræ connate at the base; one pair of lungs; eight eyes in a compact group, heterogeneous. (Filístata) .... FILISTÁTIDÆ
Tracheal spiracle close to the spinneret; cheliccræ free..........20
20. Eyes heterogeneous. (Dictỳna, Scotolàthys, Làthys, Myrópsis, Altélla, Chærèa) .... DICTỲNIDÆ

a. First row of eyes straight or nearly so............ DICTYNÌNÆ
First row of eyes so strongly procurved that it is almost semicircular .... MYROPSIDÌNÆ

Eyes homogeneous, diurnal 21
21. Cribellum divided; six spinnerets, the posterior pair longer and heavier than the anterior pair; three claws, the upper pair dissimilar, pectinate in a single row; eight eyes in three rows, of which the first is formed of four eyes. (Erèsus, Dórceus, Adonèa, Stegódyphus) .... ERÉSIDÆ

a. Head considerably elevated .... ERESÌNÆ
   Cephalothorax flat .... PENESTOMÌNÆ

   Cribellum entire; spinnerets more nearly equal; claws similar 22
22. Femora with trichobothria; eight eyes in two rows; orb-weaving
    species. (Ulóborus, Sýbota, Hyptiòtes, Miagrámmopes, Avellóp-
    sis) .... ULOBÓRIDÆ

   a. Carapace oval, with more or less curved sides ..... ULOBORÌNÆ
      Carapace angular ....b
   b. Sternum normal; legs stout .... HYPTIOTÌNÆ
      Sternum very long and peculiarly shaped, connected with the cara-
      pace between second and third coxæ by hard chitin; first legs
      stout, the others slender .... MIAGRAMMOPÌNÆ

   Femora and tarsi without trichobothria; eight eyes in three or two
   rows, the first row formed of four eyes, those of the second row
   often very large. (Dinòpis, Ménneus) .... DINÓPIDÆ
23. Eyes in two rows; first and second tarsi and metatarsi with a
    scopula; claw-tufts present; cribellum divided. (Zorópsis, Ræcius,
    Zorócrates) .... ZORÓPSIDÆ
    Eyes in three rows, none of the tarsi and metatarsi with scopula;
    claw-tufts present. (Acanthóctenus) .... ACANTHOCTÉNIDÆ
24. A pair of tracheal spiracles behind the lungs 25
    Tracheal spiracle single or wanting 28
25. Claws pectinate in a single row 26
    Claws pectinate in a double row 27
26. Third pair of legs directed backward; carapace connected with ster-
    num by intercoxal sclerotized bridges. (Dýsdera). DYSDÉRIDÆ
    Third pair of legs directed forward; carapace connected with ster-
    num by a soft membrane. (Segéstria) .... SEGESTRÌIDÆ
27. Six eyes or none; six spinnerets, the anterior ones approximated.
    (Orchéstina, Gamasomórpha, Òonops, Epéctris, Scaphiélla).
                                                    OONÓPIDÆ

   a. Abdomen soft .... OONOPÌNÆ
      Abdomen with hard shields .... GAMASOMORPHÌNÆ

   Eight eyes, heterogeneous; four spinnerets in a chitinous ring.
   (Hadrotársus, Gmógala) .... HADROTÁRSIDÆ
28. Cheliceræ separated from the mouthparts by a considerable space
    and inserted into the carapace by means of a foramen in the latter;
    eight or six eyes, only the anterior median ones diurnal; six or
    two spinnerets. (Archæa, Mecysmauchènius) .... ARCHÆIDÆ

   a. Eight eyes; six spinnerets .... ARCHÆÌNÆ
      Six eyes, two spinnerets .... MECYSMAUCHENIÌNÆ

Cheliceræ inserted close to the mouthparts, in rare cases separated from them by a short distance; carapace without foramen except in the above rare cases 29

29. Tracheal spiracle far in advance of the spinnerets..............30
Tracheal spiracle close to the spinnerets, or wanting............36

30. Two claws; claw-tufts present................................31
Three claws; claw-tufts wanting..............................32

31. Cheliceræ inserted on a common pedestal, without margins; legs without scopulæ; eyes on a tubercle. (**Ammóxenus**).
AMMOXÉNIDÆ
Cheliceræ normal, with oblique margins; legs with scopulæ; eyes not on a tubercle. (**Anyphæna**)..............**ANYPHÆNIDÆ**

32. Six spinnerets in a single transverse row. (**Hahnia**)..**HAHNÌIDÆ**
Arrangement of spinnerets normal...........................33

33. Cheliceræ connate at the base; indirect eyes in two groups of three. (See couplet 42) ....**PHÓLCIDÆ**, part
Cheliceræ free; eyes in two rows...........................34

34. Anterior edge of lip distinctly thickened.....................35
Anterior edge of lip not distinctly thickened. (**Argyronèta**).
ARGYRONÉTIDÆ

35. Cheliceræ with a stridulating ridge; eyes heterogeneous. (See couplet 48) ....**ERIGÓNIDÆ**, part
Cheliceræ without stridulating ridge; eyes homogeneous, diurnal. (See couplet 47) ....**ARGIÓPIDÆ**, part

36. Anal tubercle large, two-jointed, with a fringe of long hairs. (**Uróctea**) ....**UROCTÈIDÆ**
Anal tubercle normal 37

37. First and second tibia and metatarsus with a conspicuous row of long spines, the interspaces between with a row of much shorter, curved spines. (**Mimètus, Èro, Gélanor, Oárces, Phobetìnus**).
MIMÉTIDÆ
Without such spines 38

38. Two spinnerets 39
Four or six spinnerets.....................................40

39. Trichobothria wanting; first pair of legs often unusually heavy, with minute claws; pedipalp of female without claw. (**Lùtica, Otìothops, Palpimànus, Stenochìlus, Hermíppus**)..**PALPIMÁNIDÆ**
One or several trichobothria on the tarsi, metatarsi and tibiæ; first pair of legs not unusually heavy, with claws of normal size. (See couplet 50) ....**ZODARÌIDÆ**, part

40. Four spinnerets. (See couplet 50)...........**ZODARÌIDÆ**, part
Six spinnerets 41

41. Cheliceræ connate at base.................................42
Cheliceræ free 43

42. Tarsi normal; lip long; six nocturnal eyes in three pairs or eight

eyes in two rows, or eyes wanting. (Sicàrius, Scytòdes, Loxósceles, Plectreùrys, Diguètia, Drymùsa) .... SICARIIDÆ
Tarsi flexible, subsegmented; lip broad; eyes either in a compact group, or the six indirect eyes in two groups of three. Phólcus, Modísimus, Spermóphora, Psilóchoris, Physoglènes, Ninètis).
PHÓLCIDÆ

a. Head considerably elevated and clearly set off from the carapace; eyegroup much narrower than the width of the head.........b
Head not elevated; eyegroup almost as wide as head...........d
b. Triads wide apart; median eyes, if present, far from each triad.
PHOLCÌNÆ
All eyes closer together.......................................c
c. Posterior median eyes much smaller than posterior lateral eyes.
PRISCULÌNÆ
Posterior median eyes larger than or subequal to the other eyes.
BLECHROSCELÌNÆ
d. Triads wide apart, at anterior corners of carapace.
LEPTOPHOLCÌNÆ
Eyegroup compact ....e
e. Thoracic groove longitudinal; posterior row of eyes strongly re-curved .... PHYSOGLENÌNÆ
Thoracic groove wanting; posterior row of eyes strongly procurved.
NINETIDÌNÆ

43. Three claws; claw-tufts usually wanting......................44
Two claws; claw-tufts usually present........................55
44. Fourth tarsi with a ventral row of serrated bristles, forming a distinct comb; lip flat; legs without spines; upper claws similar, pectinate in a single row or smooth; eight, rarely six or four eyes in two rows, heterogeneous. (Steatòda, Latrodéctus, Argyròdes, Spíntharus, Therídion, Monèta, Crustulìna, Nicódamus).
THERIDIIDÆ

a. Abdomen with a hard shield...............................b
Abdomen soft ....d
b. Spinnerets surrounded by a chitinous wall....PHORONCIDIÌNÆ
Spinnerets not surrounded by a chitinous wall................c
c. Claws with a series of almost equally long teeth; six eyes.
PACULLÌNÆ
Claws smooth or teeth small and few; eight eyes.
PHOLCOMMATÌNÆ
d. Claws smooth or nearly so...............................e
Claws with well developed teeth...........................f
e. Tarsi very short; abdomen long.................MONETÌNÆ
Tarsi long; abdomen globose...................MYSMENÌNÆ

f. Claws with a row of almost equally long teeth . . . . g
The teeth of the claws increasing gradually in length distally i

g. Abdomen more or less oval, with a stridulating organ in the male.
ASAGENÌNÆ
Abdomen variable in shape, never with a stridulating organ . . . . . . h

h. Abdomen globular . . . . LATRODECTÌNÆ
Abdomen oval . . . . NICODAMÌNÆ

i. Lip immobile, either without suture or at most with a faint indication of one; abdomen of male with a stridulating organ.
ARGYRODINÌNÆ
Lip free; abdomen of male without stridulating organ.
THERIDIÌNÆ

No ventral comb on fourth tarsi, or if this is present the lip is
rebordered 45

45. Tarsi with at least one pair of spurious claws in addition to the true
claws 46
Spurious claws wanting 49

46. Lip immobile, not thickened, at apex; tarsi with onychium; six
eyes in a compact group, nocturnal; legs short with spines.
(Leptonèta, Merizócera, Ochyrócera, Psilodérces, Usòfila).
LEPTONÉTÌDÆ

a. Claw-tufts present; pedipalp of female with claw; maxillæ without
serrula . . . . LEPTONETÌNÆ
Claw-tufts wanting; pedipalp of female without claw; maxillæ with
serrula . . . . OCHYROCERATÌNÆ

Lip free, strongly rebordered at end; tarsi without onychium; eight
eyes, rarely six or none 47

47. Cheliceræ with stridulating ridges on outer surface; eyes heterogeneous 48
Cheliceræ without stridulating ridges; eyes usually homogeneous,
diurnal, rarely heterogeneous. Orb-weavers. (Argìope, Mèta,
Arànea (= Epeìra), Néphila, Leucaùge, Tetrágnatha, Theridiosòma, Gasteracántha). (EPEÍRIDÆ) . . . . ARGIÓPIDÆ

a. Femora with several trichobothria arranged in a single or double
row . . . . g
Femora without trichobothria . . . . b

b. Spinnerets surrounded by a conspicuous, chitinous wall; abdomen
hard, usually with spines, at least in females.
GASTERACANTHÌNÆ
Spinnerets never surrounded by a chitinous circular wall; abdomen
usually soft c

c. Cheliceræ with well developed boss . . . . d
Cheliceræ without boss, or boss rudimentary . . . . f

  d. Metatarsi with tarsi longer than patellæ with tibiæ..............e
     Metatarsi with tarsi shorter than, or at most, as long as patellæ
     with tibiæ .... ARANEÌNÆ
  e. Lip wider than long; posterior row of eyes strongly procurved.
                                                   ARGIOPÌNÆ
     Lip longer than wide; posterior row of eyes straight or recurved.
                                                   NEPHILÌNÆ
  f. Sternum broadly truncated behind...... THERIDIOSOMATÌNÆ
     Sternum pointed behind........................... METÌNÆ
  g. Tracheal spiracle close to spinnerets...... TETRAGNATHÌNÆ
     Tracheal spiracle more or less in advance of the spinnerets.
                                              GLENOGNATHÌNÆ

48. Maxillæ parallel, often widened at end; pedipalp of female with a
    claw; pedipalp of male without tibial apophyses; legs smooth or
    with fine spines; eyes heterogeneous. Sheet-web weavers. (Boly-
    phántes, Drapetísca, Labúlla, Linýphia, Tapinòpa).
                                                  LINYPHÌIDÆ
  a. Fourth tarsus without comb.....................LINYPHIÌNÆ
     Fourth tarsus with a ventral comb of serrated bristles.
                                                   NESTICÌNÆ

    Maxillæ converging; pedipalp of female without claw; pedipalp
    of male with at least one apophysis. (Erígone, Lophocarènum,
    Màso). (*MICRYPHÁNTIDÆ*) .... ERIGÓNIDÆ
  a. Tracheal spiracle far in advance of the spinnerets.
                                             TENNESSEELLÌNÆ
     Tracheal spiracle close to spinnerets...........................b
  b. Abdomen with scuta .... LOPHOCARENÌNÆ
     Abdomen soft c
  c. Anterior tibiæ and femora with two rows of fine, ventral spines.
                                                   MASONÌNÆ
     Of a different conformation.................................d
  d. Fourth metatarsus with a trichobothrium......... GONATIÌNÆ
     Fourth metatarsus without trichobothrium......... ERIGONÌNÆ

49. Chelceræ without a boss.................................50
    Cheliceræ with a distinct boss.............................51
50. Body flat; posterior spinnerets very long, with spinning tubes along
    the entire inner edge; head conspicuously marked off by the sulci
    and elevated above the carapace; legs long and thin. (Hersília,
    Hersilìola, Murrícia, Tàma) .... HERSILÌIDÆ
    Body not flat; posterior spinnerets much shorter than the anterior
    ones, often minute; head not elevated; legs normal or even stout;
    eyes in two or three rows. (Zodàrion, Storèna, Làches, Cryp-
    tothèle, Cithæron) .... ZODARÌIDÆ

a. Anterior tarsi with a scopula.............................b
Scopula wanting on all tarsi............................c
b. Six spinnerets subequal in length............... HUTTONÌNÆ
Six spinnerets; anterior pair much longer than posterior pair.
STORENOMORPHÌNÆ
c. Two claws .... CITHÆRONÌNÆ
Three claws ....d
d. Claws slightly dissimilar, smooth or with a single small tooth.
CRYPTOTHELÌNÆ
Claws with several teeth.................................e
e. Eyes in two rows, both rows procurved...........ZODARIÌNÆ
Eyes in three rows; the three indirect eyes of each side form an
excurved line .... CYDRELÌNÆ

51. Tarsal trichobothria in a single row, increasing in length distally;
legs without scopulæ; body with plumose hairs. (Fig. 1014).
(Agalèna, Tegenària, Cœlòtes, Cybæus, Rhoicìnus).
AGALÉNIDÆ

a. Posterior spinnerets considerably longer than anterior ones.
AGALENÌNÆ
Posterior spinnerets not longer than anterior ones..............b
b. Head narrow, directed forward and projecting considerably beyond
the cheliceræ .... PLECTOPHANÌNÆ
Head normal c
c. Trochanters not notched .... CYBÆÌNÆ
Trochanters deeply notched .... RHOICÌNÆ

Tarsal trichobothria in two rows, irregularly distributed or wanting 52
52. All eyes diurnal 53
Anterior lateral eyes nocturnal; all others diurnal; body with plumose
hairs. (Scnóculus) .... SENOCÙLIDÆ
53. Clypeus low; posterior row of eyes usually recurved; body without
scales; all trochanters strongly notched....................54
Clypeus high; posterior row of eyes usually very strongly procurved;
body with scale-like hairs; only the fourth trochanters slightly
notched; eight eyes, all diurnal. (Oxyòpes, Hamatáliva, Oxyo-
peìdon, Peucètia, Tappònia) .... OXYÓPIDÆ
54. Third (lower) claw smooth or with a single tooth; body hairs
usually simple; legs always formed for running forward. Wolf
spiders. (Lycòsa, Pardòsa, Allocòsa, Arctòsa, Piràta, Evíppa,
Hýppasa).. LYCÓSIDÆ

a. Lateral eyes on tubercles .... BRADYSTICHÌNÆ
Lateral eyes not on tubercles............................b

b. Anterior median eyes much larger than anterior lateral eyes and the first row of eyes very strongly recurved...**CYCLOCTENÌNÆ**
   Anterior median eyes not much larger than anterior lateral eyes and the first row of eyes either straight, or only gently recurved or procurved c

c. Sides of face vertical.......................... **PARDOSÌNÆ**
   Sides of face slanting..d

d. Posterior pair of spinnerets longer than anterior pair and their terminal joint as long as the basal joint; integument with plumose hair .... **HYPPASÌNÆ**
   Posterior pair of spinnerets with a short, rounded terminal joint and not much longer than anterior pair; integument with simple hair .... **LYCOSÌNÆ**

   Third claw with two or three teeth; body with plumose hairs; legs long; sometimes adapted for running laterally. (**Chiásmopes, Pisaùra, Thanatídius, Dolómedes, Thaumàsia, Thalássius**).
   PISAURIDÆ

55. Claw-tufts wanting 56
    Claw-tufts present 57

56. Legs fitted for running laterally. (See couplet 63).
    THOMÍSIDÆ, part
    Legs fitted for running forward. (See couplet 50).
    ZODARÌIDÆ, part

57. Sternum much wider than long, broadly truncate behind; body very flat; legs fitted for running laterally. (**Plàtor, Véctius, Doliomàlus**) .... **PLATÓRIDÆ**
    Sternum normal 58

58. Eight eyes in two rows, six in the first row, posterior pair wide apart; body flat; legs fitted for running laterally. (**Selenops**).
    SELENÓPIDÆ
    Only two or four eyes in the first row.......................59

59. Eyes heterogenous, only the anterior median pair diurnal........60
    Eyes homogeneous, diurnal 61

60. Eyes in two rows of four each; all tarsi with scopula; anterior spinnerets not unusually long. (**Drassòdes, Zelòtes, Gnaphòsa, Callílepis, Anágraphis, Hemiclœa**). (*DRÁSSIDÆ, GNAPHOSIDÆ*)..................................**DRASSÓDIDÆ**
    Eyes in three rows (4–2–2); tarsi without scopula or a weak one on first tarsi only; spinning tubes of anterior spinnerets unusually long and bunched together in the form of a brush. (**Prodídomus, Zimìris, Elelèis, Pródida**) .... **PRODIDÓMIDÆ**

a. Anterior spinnerets more slender than the posterior ones.
   PRODIDOMÌNÆ
   Anterior spinnerets stouter than the posterior ones.....**ZIMIRÌNÆ**

61. Posterior coxæ approximated; sternum oval or elongate; spurious claws wanting 62
Posterior coxæ widely separated by the sternum which is rounded; claws smooth; a pair of spurious claws present. (Homalónychus).
HOMALONÝCHIDÆ

62. Legs formed for running laterally..........................63
Legs formed for running forward..........................64

63. Tarsi without scopula; apical end of metatarsus with a hard, trowel-shaped sclerite preventing the extension of the tarsus beyond the axis of the leg; cheliceræ without scopula. (Stròphius, Stephanópsis, Philódromus, Dièta, Coriaráchne, Misùmena, Oxýptila, Synæma, Xýsticus). (Including *APHANTOCHÍLIDÆ*).
THOMÍSIDÆ

a. Lip lance-shaped, very long and narrow....**APHANTOCHILÌNÆ**
Lip normal ....b

b. Lip long and pointed, surpassing middle of maxillæ which are also long and pointed ....**STROPHIÌNÆ**
Lip shorter, truncated or rounded at the end; maxillæ also rounded or truncated at the end.................................c

c. First tarsi very wide at base, longer than metatarsi; claws minute or rudimentary ....**STIPHROPODÌNÆ**
All tarsi and claws normal................................d

d. Retromargin of cheliceræ with at least two teeth.
STEPHANOPSÌNÆ
Retromargin of cheliceræ smooth ....e

e. Integument with plumose or squamose hair ..**PHILODROMÌNÆ**
Integument with simple hair ....f

f. Claw-tufts formed by true spatulate hairs ....**DIETÌNÆ**
Claw-tufts wanting or formed by simple hairs .....**THOMISÌNÆ**

First and second tarsi with a scopula; apex of metatarsus with a soft membrane permitting the extension of the tarsus beyond the axis of the leg; cheliceræ with scopula. (Delèna, Spariánthis, Micrómmata, Heterópoda, Palístes, Clastes, Staìanus). (*SPARÁS-SIDÆ*)..............................**EUSPARÁSSIDÆ**

a. Tarsal claws smooth ....**HEMICLŒÌNÆ**
Tarsal claws pectinate ....b

b. Third and fourth pair of legs not conspicuously shorter than first and second pair c
At least third leg conspicuously shorter than first and second......h

c. Quadrangle of median eyes wider than long ....d
Quadrangle of median eyes longer than wide ....e

d. Spinnerets normal ....**EUSPARASSÌNÆ**
Spinnerets situated on a common cone-shaped or cylindrical base
SPARIANTHIDÌNÆ

e. Anterior median eyes largest.............. **MICROMMATÌNÆ**
    Lateral eyes largest ....f
f. Posterior row of eyes recurved ....**HETEROPODÌNÆ**
    Posterior row of eyes straight or procurved ....g
g. Posterior row of eyes straight or but slightly procurved
                                              PALYSTEÌNÆ
    Posterior row of eyes strongly procurved ....**CLASTEÌNÆ**
h. Anterior eyes close together ....**STAIANEÌNÆ**
    Anterior median eyes farther apart from each other than from the
    anterior lateral eyes ....**CHROSIODERMATÌNÆ**

64. Eyes in four rows of two each, those of third row minute.
    (**Lyssómanes**) ....**LYSSOMÁNIDÆ**
    Eyes in two or three rows 65
65. Eight eyes in three rows (4–2–2); anterior median eyes by far the
    largest, directed forward; eyes of second row the smallest, often
    minute; body usually with scales. (**Sálticus, Myrmaráchne,
    Marpíssa, Phidíppus, Dendryphántes, Pellènes, Áttus**).
    (**ÁTTIDÆ**) ....**SALTÍCIDÆ**

a. Retromargin of cheliceræ with a single, pointed tooth or smooth..c
    Retromargin of cheliceræ either with several teeth, or with a
    bicuspid or polycuspid tooth ....b
b. Retromargin of cheliceræ with several teeth ....s
    Retromargin of cheliceræ with a bicuspid or polycuspid tooth ....n
c. Ant-like .... **SYNAGELÌNÆ**
    Not ant-like ....d
d. First pair of legs peculiarly modified; patella longer than femur,
    metatarsus quite short ....**AGORIÌNÆ**
    Relative length of patella and metatarsus normal ....e
e. Third legs longer than fourth ....f
    Fourth legs longer than third i
f. Sternum broadly truncated in front ....g
    Sternum narrowed in front, its truncature narrower than base of
    lip ....h
g. Eyes of second row much nearer to anterior lateral eyes than to
    the eyes of the third row ....**HYLLÌNÆ**
    Eyes of second row either half-way between the anterior lateral eyes
    and the eyes of the third row, or nearer to the latter
                                              PLEXIPPÌNÆ
h. Eyes of second row much nearer to anterior lateral eyes than to the
    eyes of the third row.........................**THYENÌNÆ**
    Eyes of second row either half-way between the anterior lateral eyes
    and the eyes of the third row, or nearer to the latter.
                                              PELLENÌNÆ
i. Sternum broadly truncated in front ....j

Sternum narrowed in front, its truncature narrower than base of lip l

j. Carapace low .... **ITATÌNÆ**
Carapace high .... k

k. Posterior declivity of carapace very steep, sometimes even concave **COCCORCHESTÌNÆ**
Posterior declivity not so steep .... **HELIOPHANÌNÆ**

l. Eyes of second row much nearer to the anterior lateral eyes than to the eyes of the third row .... **DENDRYPHANTÌNÆ**
Eyes of second row either half-way between the anterior lateral eyes and the eyes of the third row, or but little nearer to the former .... m

m. Retromargin of cheliceræ nearly always smooth ...... **SITTICÌNÆ**
Retromargin of cheliceræ with a strong tooth ..... **SALTICÌNÆ**

n. Sternum long; ant-like spiders .... **PECKHAMIÌNÆ**
Sternum short; not ant-like .... o

o. Third legs longer than fourth .... p
Fourth legs longer than third .... q

p. Retromargin with a polycuspid tooth .... **SPILARGÌNÆ**
Retromargin with a bicuspid tooth............... **HASARIÌNÆ**

q. Sternum considerably narrowed in front .... **MÆVIÌNÆ**
Sternum broadly truncated in front .... r

r. Eyes of second row almost twice as near to the anterior lateral eyes as to the eyes of the third row .... **ZYGOBALLÌNÆ**
Eyes of second row either only a little nearer to the anterior lateral eyes, or half-way between them and the eyes of the third row, or even a little nearer to the latter................... **CYTÆÌNÆ**

s. Eyes of second row fairly large .... **BŒTHÌNÆ**
Eyes of second row quite small .... t

t. Sternum long; ant-like .... **MYRMARACHNÌNÆ**
Sternum short; not ant-like .... u

u. Carapace high and relatively short, with steep posterior declivity **MAGONÌNÆ**
Carapace relatively lower and longer, with posterior declivity not so steep .... **THIODINÌNÆ**

Of a different conformation 66

66. Eight eyes in two rows of four each; maxillary scopula not extending over the external surface. (Chiracánthium, Clubiòna, Gayénna, Liócranum, Corínna, Tráchelas, Castaneìra) .... **CLUBIÓNIDÆ**

a. Terminal joint of posterior spinnerets distinctly cone-shaped...... b
Terminal joint of posterior spinnerets rounded, often indistinct .. c

b. Maxillæ constricted in middle; lip long .... **CLUBIONÌNÆ**
Maxillæ as wide in middle as at end or even with convex outer edge; lip as wide as or wider than long .... **LIOCRANÌNÆ**

c. Maxillæ rounded at end; sternum distinctly rebordered on sides
CORINNÌNÆ
Maxillæ subtruncate at end; sternum not rebordered. .MICARIÌNÆ

Eyes in three rows, usually 2–4–2; if 4–2–2 those of second row are larger than those of the first row; maxillary scopula extending over the anterior surface. (Ctènus, Acanthèis, Calóctenus, Òdo)
CTÉNIDÆ

a. Lip wider than long .... CALOCTENÌNÆ
Lip longer than wide .... b
b. Spines on legs stout and moderately long, usually from three to five ventral pairs (rarely six) on anterior tibiæ .... CTENÌNÆ
Spines on legs unusually long and slender, usually more than six ventral pairs on anterior tibiæ .... ACANTHEÌNÆ

67. Two pairs of tracheal spiracles, or at least one anterior pair and a median posterior one also 68
One pair of tracheal spiracles; chelicerae fused. (Symphytógnathus)
SYMPHYTOGNÁTHIDÆ
68. Colulus present; lip immobile 69
Colulus wanting, posterior spinnerets longest; eight or two eyes; lip free. (Capònia, Nóps, Caponína, Diploglèna). .CAPONÌIDÆ

a. Tarsi single-jointed, without pulvillus .... CAPONIÌNÆ
Tarsi subsegmented, two-jointed .... NOPÌNÆ

69. Eyes wanting; anterior spinnerets largest. (Telema, Apneumonélla)
TELÉMIDÆ
Eight eyes. (Micropholcómma, Austr.)
MÌCROPHOLCOMMÁTIDÆ

LITERATURE ON ARANEIDA

Ausserer, A. Die Arachniden-Familie der Territelariæ. Verh. k. k. zool.-bot. Ges. Wien, 21, pp. 117–224 (1871), and 25, pp. 156–206 (1875).
Banks, N. Families and Genera of Araneida. American Naturalist, 39, pp. 293–323 (1905).
    Catalogue of Nearctic Spiders. Bull. U. S. Nat. Mus., No. 72, 80 pp. (1910).
Berland, L. Les Arachnides. Encyclopedie Entomologique, 16, 585 pp., Paris (1933).
Bishop, S. C. Revision of Pisauridæ of the United States. Bull. New York State Mus., No. 252, 140 pp. (1924).
Bösenberg, W. Die Spinnen Deutschlands. Zoologica, 14, Lief. 5, 6, pp. 385–465 (1901–03).
Bristowe, W. S. The Liphistiid Spiders. Proc. Zool. Soc. London, 1932, pp. 1015–1057, 6 pls., 11 figs. (1932).

The Classification of Spiders. Proc. Zool. Soc. London, **108B**, pp. 285–321 (1938).

BRYANT, E. B. The Salticid Spiders of Jamaica. Bull. Mus. Comp. Zool., **103**, pp. 161–210, 3 pls. (1950).

CAMBRIDGE, F. P. Spiders of the Genus Latrodectus. Proc. Zool. Soc. London, **1892**, pp. 247–261 (1892).

CHAMBERLIN, R. V. Revision of North American Lycosidæ. Proc. Philadelphia Acad. Nat. Sci., **60**, pp. 158–318 (1908).

North American Gnaphosidæ. Proc. Biol. Soc. Wash., **35**, pp. 145–172 (1922).

Two Genera of Trap-door Spiders. Bull. Univ. Utah, Biol. Ser., **3**, pp. 1–11, 2 pls. (1937).

Revision of Araneæ of New Zealand. Rec. Aukland Inst. Mus., **3**, pp. 69–78 (1944).

CHICKERING, A. M. The Spider Genus Tmarus (Thomisidæ) in Panama. Bull. Mus. Comp. Zool. **103**, pp. 211–256, 4 pls. (1950).

CHYZER, C. and L. KULCZYNSKI. Araneæ Hungaricæ. 2 vols. Budapest (1892–97).

COMSTOCK, J. H. The Spider Book. Doubleday Page & Co., Garden City, N. Y. (1912). Revision by W. J. Gertsch. 740 pp. (1940).

DAHL, F. Die Spinnen Norddeutschlands. Schr. Ver. Schleswig-Holstein, **5**, pp. 13–86 (1883).

Die Lycosiden Deutschlands. Abh. K. Leop. Car. deutsch. Akad. Naturf., **88**, pp. 179–678 (1908).

Salticidæ in Tierwelt Deutschlands, 3, Lief. 1, 55 pp. (1926).

DALMAS, COMPTE DE. Araignées de Nouvelle Zélande. Ann. Soc. Ent. France, **86**, pp. 317–430 (1918).

Synopsis des araignées de la famille des Prodidomidæ. Ann. Soc. Ent. France, **87**, pp. 279–340 (1918–19).

EMERTON, J. H. Therididæ of New England. Trans. Conn. Acad. Arts Sci., **6**, pp. 1–86 (1882).

Epeiridæ of New England. Trans. Conn. Acad. Arts Sci., **6**, pp. 295–342 (1884).

New England Lycosidæ. Trans. Conn. Acad. Arts Sci., **6**, pp. 481–505 (1884).

Dictynidæ of New England. Trans. Conn. Acad. Arts Sci., **7**, pp. 443–460 (1888).

Drassidæ, Agalenidæ and Dysderidæ of New England. Trans. Conn. Acad. Arts Sci., **8**, pp. 1–40 (1890).

New England Spiders of the Family Thomisidæ. Trans. Conn. Acad. Arts Sci., **8**, pp. 359–381 (1892).

Common Spiders of the United States. Boston (1902).

Supplement to New England Spiders. Trans. Conn. Acad. Arts Sci., **14**, pp. 173–236 (1909).

EXLINE, H. Araneida of Washington, Agelenidæ and Hahniidæ. Univ. Washington Publ. Biol., **9**, pp. 1–35, 5 pls. (1938).

FAGE, L. Biospeologica. Araneæ. Arch. Zool. exp. gen., **71**, pp. 99–291, 48 figs. (1931).

Fox, I. Nearctic Spiders of the Family Heteropodidæ. Journ. Washington Acad. Sci., **27**, pp. 461–474 (1937).

GERHARDT, U. and A. KAESTNER. Araneæ. In Kükenthal, Handbuch der Zoologie, 3, Pt. 2, pp. 497–656 (1938).

GERTSCH, W. J. Revision of the Misumeninæ of North America. Bull. American Mus. Nat. Hist., 76, pp. 277–442, 25 pls. (1939).

American Spiders. 500 pp., 111 pls. Van Nostrand, New York (1949).

GRAVELEY, F. H. Indian Lycosidæ. Rec. Indian Mus., 26, pp. 587–613 (1924).

HENTZ, N. M. Spiders of the United States. Collected writings, edited by J. H. Emerton. Boston Soc. Nat. Hist. (1875).

HICKMAN, V. V. A New Family of Spiders, Symphytognathidæ. Proc. Zool. Soc. London, 1931, pp. 1321–1328, 1 pl., 6 figs. (1931).

The Toxopidæ, a New Family of Spiders. Pap. Roy. Soc. Tasmania, 1939, pp. 125–130, 3 pls. (1940).

KASTON, B. J. Supplementary Notes of Family Names in the Araneæ. American Midl. Natural., 30, pp. 765–768 (1943).

Spiders of Connecticut. Connecticut Nat. Hist. Surv., 874 pp. (1948).

KEYSERLING, E. Die Spinnen Amerikas. Nürnberg. 1, Laterigradæ (1880); 2, Theridiæ (1884–86), 3, Brazilian Spiders (1891), 4, Epeiridæ (1892–93).

KOCH, L. Die Arachnidenfamilie der Drassiden. Heft 1–6, pp. 1–304, Nuremberg (1866).

KRATOCHVIL, J. Liste générale des Araignées cavernicoles en Yougoslavie. Acta Soc. Sci. nat. Moravicæ, 9(12), pp. 1–25, 2 pls. (1935).

LESSERT, R. Araignées du Kilimandjaro et du Mérou. Rev. Suisse Zool., 27, pp. 99–234 (1919). See also Rept. Kilimandjaro-Meru Exped. (1915).

MELLO-LEITÃO, M. Aphantochílidas e Thomísidas do Brasil. Arch. Mus. Nac. Rio de Janeiro, 31, pp. 1–359 (1929).

Oxyopideos do Brasil. Rev. Mus. Paulista, 16, pp. 489–536 (1929).

Mimetidos do Brasil. Ibid., 16, pp. 537–568 (1929).

PECKHAM, G. W. and E. G. Revision of North American Attidæ. Trans. Wisconsin Acad. Sci., 16, pp. 355–596 (1909).

PETRUNKEVITCH, A. Catalogue of American Spiders. Bull. American Mus. Nat. Hist., 29, pp. 1–809 (1911).

On Families of Spiders. Ann. Acad. Sci., New York, 29, pp. 145–180 (1923).

Arachnida from Panama. Trans. Conn. Acad. Sci., 27, pp. 51–248 (1925).

Systema Aranearum. Trans. Conn. Acad. Arts Sci., 29, pp. 1–270 (1928).

Spiders of Porto Rico. Trans. Conn. Acad. Arts Sci., 30, pp. 1–355; 31, pp. 5–191 (1930).

The Natural Classification of Spiders, Based on a Study of Their Internal Antomy. Trans. Conn. Acad. Arts Sci., 31, pp. 299–389, 13 pls. (1933).

Catalogue of American Spiders. Part I. Trans. Conn. Acad. Arts Sci., 33, pp. 133–338 (1939).

RAINBOW, W. J. Census of Australian Araneida. Rec. Australian Mus., 9, pp. 107–319 (1911).

Terretelariæ of Australia. Rec. Australian Mus., 10, pp. 187–270 (1914).

RAINBOW, W. J. and R. H. PULLEINE. Australian Trap-door Spiders. Rec. Australian Mus., 12, pp. 81–169 (1918).

REIMOSER, E. Catalog der paläarktischen Spinnen. Abh. zool.-bot. Ges. Wien, **10**, pp. 1–280 (1919).
Gnaphosidæ, Anyphænidæ, Clubionidæ. Tierwelt Deutschlands, **33**, pp. 1–99, 197 figs. (1937).

ROEWER, C. F. Spinnen (Araneida). In Tierwelt Mitteleuropas, **3**, Lief. 2, pp. VI 1–144, (1928).

SIMON, E. Aviculariides de l'Amérique du Nord. Act. Soc. Linn. Bordeaux, **44**, pp. 307–339 (1892).
Histoire naturelle des Araignées. Paris, 2 vols (1892–03).
Les Arachnides de France, **6**, pp. 979–1298, 526 figs. (1937).

SMITH, C. P. Theraphosidæ of California. Ann. Ent. Soc. America, **1**, pp. 207–250 (1908).

THORELL, T. Descriptive Catalogue of Spiders of Burma. London, British Museum, 404 pp. (1895).

TODD, V. Systematic and Biological Account of the New Zealand Megalomorphæ. Trans. Proc. Roy. Soc. New Zealand, **74**, pp. 375–407, 3 pls. (1945).

TUCKER, R. W. E. Drassidæ of South Africa. Ann. South African Mus., **19**, pp. 251–438 (1923).

WIEHLE, H. Theridiidæ. Die Tierwelt Deutschlands, **33**, pp. 119–222, 286 figs. (1937).

ORDER ACARÌNA

(ACÁRIDA)

Usually small or minute species of rounded or oval form, with the body not divided by any deep constrictions. Abdomen not segmented although occasionally with a large number of minute transverse ridges; very broadly joined to the cephalothorax from which it is sometimes separated by a suture. Cheliceræ usually two-jointed, frequently chelate. Pedipalpi with five joints or less, usually clawed or chelate, occasionally long and serving as tactile organs. Adults usually with four pairs of legs, occasionally with only two; larva almost always with three pairs. Legs with five to seven joints, usually ending in one or two claws. Eyes usually present, commonly as one or several at each side of the body; rarely with a median one. Respiration by tubular tracheæ opening by one or several pairs of spiracles, or through the integument only. Habits varied, vegetarian or carnivorous, frequently parasitic. Mites and Ticks.

The Acarina are an extremely large and diverse group, but have received comparatively little attention. The classification given below follows in general that of Banks with many of the changes made by Vitzthum and other later workers. The arrangement of water mites follows Viets. For an extensive treatment the reader is referred to Baker and Wharton: Introduction to Acarology. Many families in use by recent acarologists have been merged with the larger and better known families. It is to be expected that a more natural system will develop in the forthcoming years.

1. Body rounded, oval, rarely noticeably elongate; abdomen not annulate, vermiform nor prolonged behind; adult form with eight legs. (If rarely, some of the posterior legs are reduced or vestigial, see couplet 46) 4
   Body elongate or lanceolate, the abdomen vermiform, prolonged behind and annulate; often with only four legs; very minute forms living in plants, forming galls, or parasitic in the skin of mammals. (Superfamily DEMODICÒIDEA) 2

2. Body with four legs placed near the anteriòr end, each composed of five joints; plant-inhabiting species, usually forming deformations or galls. (Fig. 1055). (Eriòphyes (= Phytóptus) (E. pyri, Pear blister mite), Phyllocóptes, Anthocóptes, Tegonòtus, Epitrímerus). (PHYTÓPTIDÆ, PHYLLOCÓPTIDÆ)
   ERIOPHYÌDÆ
   Body with eight legs.......................................3

3. Legs modified for clinging to hairs or feathers, composed of more than three joints. (Listróphorus, Myocóptes). (See couplet 50)
   LISTROPHÓRIDÆ
   Legs attached to the anterior half of the body, each composed of only three joints; living in the skin of various mammals. (Démodex (D. folliculòrum, Follicle mite)). (Fig. 1056)
   DEMODÍCIDÆ

4. Adult with eight spiracles on the dorsal surface; body with indications of segmentation above. (Opilioácarus, Palæarc.)
   OPILIOACÁRIDÆ
   Four spiracles or less, or spiracles vestigial; body unsegmented, except for a single groove or constriction sometimes present between the cephalothorax and abdomen 5

5. Body at each side with a distinct spiracle upon a stigmal plate, usually below the lateral margin and above the third or fourth coxa or a little behind; palpi free; skin often coriaceous or leathery; tarsi often with a sucker 6
   No such spiracle on a stigmal plate on this part of the body 16

6. Hypostome (median portion of mouthparts) large, provided below with a large number of recurved teeth or barbs; ventral surface of body posteriorly with at least one pair of furrows extending backwards from the genital pore; skin leathery; large species usually parasitic on mammals, more rarely on birds or reptiles. (Superfamily IXODÒIDEA) 7
   Hypostome small, not toothed or barbed; venter without furrows; body often with coriaceous shields; posterior margin never crenulated nor fluted; eyes absent. (Superfamily PARASITÒIDEA) 8

7. Body above with a chitinous plate or scutum which almost covers the body of the male, but is reduced to a small plate near the

front of the body in the female; body below sometimes with ventral shields; mouthparts of adult clearly visible from above; stigmal plate behind the coxæ; tarsus with a pulvillus. (Figs. 1053, 1054, 1057, 1058). (Ixòdes, Dermacéntor Rhipicéphalus, Hæmaphỳsalis, Margáropus, Boóphilus, Amblyómma)

IXÓDIDÆ

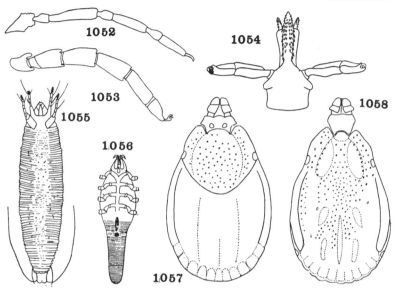

Figs. 1052–1058. Acarina

1052. Holosiro, leg (Ewing).
1053. Rhipicephalus, leg (Ewing) Ixodidæ.
1054. Ixodes, mouthparts (Nuttall) Ixodidæ.
1055. Eriophyes (Kendall) Eriophyidæ.
1056. Demodex (Banks) Demodicidæ.
1057. Rhipicephalus, female (Nuttall) Ixodidæ.
1058. Rhipicephalus, male (Nuttall) Ixodidæ.

The Ethiopian genus Nuttalliella with slightly sclerotized scutum is sometimes made the type of a distinct family.

NUTTALLIÉLLIDÆ

Body without scutum in either sex; without any ventral shield; mouthparts of adult almost entirely concealed from above; stigmal plate between coxæ of third and fourth legs; tarsi without pulvillus. (Fig. 1019). (Árgas, Ornithódorus). (*ARGÁSIDÆ*)

ARGÁNTIDÆ

8. Palpi not enlarged at tip; spiracles behind the coxæ of the third legs 9

Palpi with the last joint enlarged; a spiracle above the coxa of the
third leg; moderately large species. (Holòthyrus, Ethiop.,
Indoaustr.) ....HOLOTHÝRIDÆ

9. Genital aperture near the anus; mouthparts capable of being retracted within a large buccal cavity, which is near the anterior
end of the body and separated from the rest of the body by a
suture; living on bats. (Spelæorhýnchus, Neotrop.)
SPELÆORHÝNCHIDÆ
Genital aperture not or only slightly behind the hind coxæ; anterior part of body not separated by a suture; body rather broad
and flat, with relatively short legs 10

10. Spiracle and peritreme clearly on the ventral side of the body.
(Fig. 1060) 11
Spiracle and peritreme situated on the dorsum, or very nearly so;
legs short and very bristly, all with large caruncles, larva living
in body of female. (Fig. 1066). (Spintúrnix (= Pteróptus),
Periglíschrus, on bats). (PTEROPTÌNÆ) . .SPINTURNÍCIDÆ

11. Anus surrounded by a chitinous plate or shield; rarely parasitic on
mammals 12
Anus without a chitinous plate or shield; internal parasites in the
respiratory tract of mammals. (Halaráchne, in bronchi of seals;
Pneumonýssus, in lungs of monkeys). (Fig. 1062).
HALARÁCHNIDÆ

12. First pair of legs inserted outside the mouth opening; dorsal surface
of body not projecting in front of the camerostome; male genital
opening usually on the anterior margin of the sternal plate, sometimes in the middle 13
First pair of legs inserted in the mouth cavity with the oral tube;
dorsum of body projecting beyond the camerostome; male
genital opening in the sternal plate. Species often occurring on
insects. (Urópoda, Cílliba, Oplìtis, Polyáspis, Dínychus). (Including UROPÓDIDÆ, CILLÍBIDÆ, POLYASPÍDIDÆ)
DINÝCHIDÆ

13. Claw of cheliceræ usually without teeth, often stylate or needle-
like, the fixed arm always without a seta; tarsi of first pair of
legs with claws or caruncles; second legs of male without processes; anus of female usually at anterior end of anal shield; all
the chitinous shields rather weak and often not evident. Species
parasitic on birds, mammals and reptiles. (Dermanýssus (D.
gallìnæ, Chicken mite); Liponýssus, Lælaps, on mammals;
Ophionýssus, on snakes). (LÆLÁPTIDÆ). DERMANÝSSIDÆ
Claw of cheliceræ toothed, rarely stylate or needle-like, the fixed
arm usually with a seta. Species often occurring on insects, but
rarely on vertebrates 14

14. Body usually elongate; first pair of legs with or without claws; genital opening of male usually in front of the sternal plate; usually free-living species; rarely myrmecophilous 15
Body circular in outline, or nearly so; conspicuously hairy; first pair of legs greatly elongated and without claws; genital opening of male in the sternal plate; usually myrmecophilous species living externally on the bodies of ants. (**Antennóphorus, Echinomegístus, Antennomegístus**). (Including *PARAMEGIS-TIDÆ*) .... **ANTENNOPHÓRIDÆ**

15. First pair of legs with claws or caruncles, used for walking; second pair of legs often enlarged in the male; species free-living or parasitic, often on vertebrates (Figs. 1060, 1064). (**Parásitus** (= *Gámasus*) (*GAMÁSIDÆ*)............... **PARASÍTIDÆ**
First pair of legs without claws or caruncle, as long as or longer than the body and serving as sensory organs; second pair of legs in male rarely much enlarged; not parasitic on vertebrates. (Fig. 1059). (**Macrochèles, Holocelæno**) . . **MACROCHÉLIDÆ**

16. Body usually coriaceous, with few hairs; with a specialized seta arising from a pore near each posterior corner of the cephalothorax (pseudostigmatic organ, Fig. 1063); eyes absent, mouthparts and palpi usually very small; ventral openings of abdomen large; coxæ close together; tarsi without sucker. Species free-living, not parasitic. (Superfamily ORIBATÒIDEA) 17
Body nearly always of softer texture; pseudostigmatic organ absent 20

17. Body with a movable, wing-like expansion on each side near the middle. (**Pèlops**). (*PTEROGÁSTRIDÆ*) ..... **PELÓPIDÆ**
Body without such appendage 18

18. Cephalothorax and abdomen separated by a suture 19
Cephalothorax and abdomen not separated by a suture; mandibles very large and prominent. (**Labidóstoma**) (= *Nicoletiella*). (*NICOLETIÉLLIDÆ*) .... **LABIDOSTOMÁTIDÆ**

19. Cephalothorax loosely attached to the abdomen, so that it is freely movable; palpi four-jointed. (Fig. 1061). (**Phthirácarus, Protoplóphora, Mesoplóphora**). (Including *PROTOPLOPHÓRIDÆ, MESOPLOPHÓRIDÆ*). (*HOPLODERMÁTIDÆ*)
PHTHIRACÁRIDÆ
Cephalothorax immovably united with the abdomen; palpi five-jointed. (Figs. 1063, 1065). (**Oríbata, Oribatélla, Galúmna, Trizètes**). A large group, subdivided by some workers into numerous, poorly defined families. (*EREMAEIDÆ*)
ORIBÁTIDÆ

20. Aquatic species, living entirely in and laying their eggs in water and nearly always in fresh water; palpi four or five jointed; parasitic or free-living. Superfamily HYDRACHNÒIDEA . . 21

Terrestrial or parasitic species, never living in water, except certain parasitic species with two-jointed palpi and chelate hind legs 43

21. Basal attachment of the third and fourth pairs of legs strongly lateral in position, visible from above next to the lateral margin of the body, cephalothorax with two large posterior and two small lateral plates 22
Basal attachment of the third and fourth pairs of legs not visible from above 23

22. Palpi composed of five joints; red species. (Hydrovólzia)
HYDROVOLZÏIDÆ

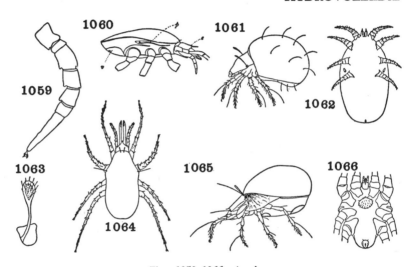

Figs. 1059–1066. Acarina

1059. **Macrocheles,** leg (Ewing) Macrochelidæ.
1060. **Parasitus** (Banks); *e,* epistoma; *p,* peritreme; *v,* anal plate. Parasitidæ.
1061. **Phthirácarus** (Banks) Phthiracaridæ.
1062. **Pneumonyssus** (Banks) Halarachnidæ.
1063. **Oribatidæ,** pseudostigmatic organ (Banks) Oribatidæ.
1064. **Parasitus** (Banks) Parasitidæ.
1065. **Oribatella** (Banks) Oribatidæ.
1066. **Spinturnix,** underside (Banks) Spinturnicidæ.

Palpi with only three or four joints; species living on marine algæ, not adapted for swimming. (**Halácarus, Porohalácarus, Soldanel·lònyx**). (Including *POROHALACÁRIDÆ*) . . HALACÁRIDÆ

23. Eyes placed near the middle of the vertex, connected by a transverse median chitinized structure 24
Eyes placed at the sides of the body, not connected across the vertex

by a chitinized structure, although sometimes with chitinous plates between them 25

24. Chitinized plate connecting the eyes forming a median band, *i.e.* much higher than wide; no swimming hairs on any of the legs; very soft-bodied species with thinly chitinized integument. (Limnóchares) ....LIMNOCHÁRIDÆ
Chitinized plate connecting the eyes forming a transverse band that is much wider than high; three anterior pairs of legs with swimming hairs. (Eylàis) ....EYLÀIDÆ

25. Legs six-jointed 26
Legs five-jointed; body with a dorsal shield; two lateral eyes and a median one. (Thermácarus, Holarc., in hot springs).
THÉRMACÁRIDÆ

26. Lateral eyes placed together on a chitinized tubercle or plate at each side of the head 27
Lateral eyes not placed together on a chitinized plate, although sometimes close together as a contiguous pair 32

27. Eye-plate free, not attached to any other plate. (Piersígia). (See couplet 24) ....EYLÀIDÆ, part
Eye-plate fused laterally to a chitinous plate which is produced medially behind 28

28. Body without a dorsal shield; legs without swimming hairs. (Prótzia, Calònyx, Partnùnia, Wandèsia) ......PROTZÌIDÆ
Body usually with dorsal shield; legs frequently with swimming hairs 29

29. Chelic<

æ styliform; beak produced, tubular. (Hydráchna, Bárgena)
HYDRÁCHNIDÆ
Cheliceræ with basal segment and opposable claw, not styliform; beak not produced 30

30. Second joint of palpi without a sharp projection inwardly 31
Second joint of palpi with a sharp projection inwardly. (Spérchon, Sperchonópsis) ....SPERCHÓNIDÆ

31. Body without a dorsal shield; body spinose. (Pseudohydryphántes)
PSEUDOHYDRYPHÁNTIDÆ
Body with a dorsal shield. (Hydryphántes, Thỳas, Viètsia, Pánisus, Georgélla, Diplodontus). (Including *THYÁSIDÆ*).
HYDRYPHÁNTIDÆ

32. Eyes separated, not forming contiguous double-eyes 33
Eyes united to form a double-eye at each side of the body 34

33. Fourth pair of legs with apical claws; palpi distinctly chelate at tip. (Hydrodròma, Oxópsis) ....HYDRODRÓMIDÆ
Fourth pair of legs without apical claws; palpi not chelate at tip. (Limnèsia, Limnesiélla, Duralimnèsia).........LIMNESÌIDÆ

34. Palpi simple at tip, without a stout hook 35
Last joint of palpi forming a stout hook which is opposable to the

broad tip of the preceding joint. (**Arrhenùrus, Thoracophorácarus, Mundamélla, Wùria**). (*ARRENÙRIDÆ*) . . ARRHENÙRIDÆ

35. Epimera of the fourth pair of legs with a large pore near the inner angle; tarsus of fourth leg pointed, without claws. (**Teutònia**)
      TEUTONÌIDÆ
      Epimera of the fourth leg without a pore 36

36. Second joint of palpi with a strong bristle inwardly which often arises from a sharp projection 37
      Second joint of palpi without a sharp projection or bristle 39

37. Third joint of palpi bearing five to seven stout bristles that are longer than the joint. (**Lebértia, Pilolebértia, Hexalebértia**)
      LEBERTÌIDÆ
      Third joint of palpi without such bristly hairs 38

38. Cheliceræ long, beak-like or extensile within a tube formed by the epistoma; carapace composed of several plates. (**Atráctides, Pseudotorrentícola**) . . . . .ATRACTIDÈIDÆ
      Cheliceræ of different conformation. (See couplet 37). (**Mamersópsis, Bandàkia**) .MAMERSÓPSIDÆ

39. Body strongly compressed from the sides, or narrowly elongate-oval; legs inserted one above another near the anterior end of the body; fourth pair of legs without apical claws. (See couplet 37). (**Óxus, Gnaphíscus, Frontípoda**) . . OXÌNÆ, LEBERTÌIDÆ
      Body not compressed nor narrowly elongate; legs inserted one behind another in the usual position .40

40. Epimera of the first pair of legs free, not fused medially behind the maxillæ 41
      Epimera of the first pair of legs completely fused. (**Hygróbates, Mégapus**) . . . . .HYGROBÁTIDÆ

41. First pair of legs bearing blunt bristles, usually placed in pairs on tubercles. (**Unionícola, Neumánnia, Huitféldtia**).
      UNIONICÓLIDÆ
      First pair of legs not thus bristly 42

42. Integument usually weak and thin, always without any pore-bearing shields; usually convex species. (**Féltria, Nautaráchna, Forélia Piòna Hydrochoreùtes**). (Including *FELTRÌIDÆ, NAUTARÁCHNIDÆ*) . . . . .PIÓNIDÆ
      Body with pore-bearing plates; usually flattened. (**Mìdea, Mideópsis, Brachýpoda, Atùrus, Álbia**). (Including *MIDEIDÆ, MIDEÓP-SIDÆ*). (*BRACHYPÓDIDÆ*) . . . . .AXONÓPSIDÆ

43. Palpi two-jointed, partly enclosing the cheliceræ; third and fourth pairs of legs in both sexes greatly thickened, the last two joints opposable to form grasping organs; tarsi without suckers; parasitic in the gills of hermit crabs. (**Ewíngia**, Nearc.) . .EWINGÌIDÆ
      Palpi with three or more joints; rarely the fourth pair of legs en-

larged to form a grasping organ in the male only, in which case
  the other tarsi bear suckers 44
44. Palpi small, three-jointed, adhering for some distance to the beak;
  body usually with ventral suckers at the genital opening or near
  the anal opening; eyes absent; tarsi often with suckers at tip;
  frequently parasitic. (Superfamily ACARÒIDEA) 45
  Palpi usually four or five-jointed, free; rarely with ventral suckers
  near the anal or genital openings; eyes present or absent; tarsi
  without suckers at tip; nearly always free living 54
45. Tracheæ absent, female without a clavate hair below at each side
  between the first and second pairs of legs 48

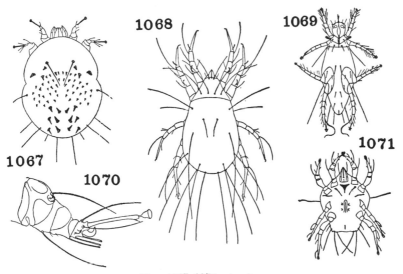

Figs. 1067–1071. **Acarina**

1067. **Sarcoptes** (Banks) Sarcoptidæ.
1068. **Acarus** (Banks) Acaridæ.
1069. **Pyemotes** (Banks) Tarsonemidæ.
1070. **Sarcoptes** (Banks) Sarcoptidæ.
1071. **Canestrinia** (Banks) Canestriniidæ.

Tracheæ present, no ventral suckers; legs terminated in claws;
  cephalothorax and abdomen clearly separated; female with a
  prominent clavate hair below on each side between the first
  and second pairs of legs; not parasitic on birds or mammals....46
46. Eight fully developed legs present 47
  Female with some of the posterior legs incompletely developed or
  absent. (**Podapólipus**) ....**PODAPOLIPÓDIDÆ**

47. Cephalothorax prolonged into a scutum which extends over the rostrum and front legs. (Scutácarus). ......SCUTACÁRIDÆ
Cephalothorax not thus prolonged anteriorly. (Tarsonèmus, Microdispódides, Pyémotes. (*Pediculòides*)). (Including *PYE-MÓTIDÆ*) ....TARSONÉMIDÆ

48. Not parasitic on birds or mammals; genital suckers usually present; integument usually without fine parallel lines 49
Parasites of birds or mammals; genital suckers absent; integument marked with fine parallel lines 50

49. Legs short; the tarsi of the first and second pairs without clavate hairs, terminating in suckers; species parasitic on insects. (Fig. 1071). (Canestrínia, Hemisarcóptes, Linòbia, Coleopteróphagus). (Including *HEMISARCÓPTIDÆ, LINOBÌIDÆ*)
CANESTRINÌIDÆ
Legs longer; tarsi of first and second pairs of legs externally near the base with a clavate hair; usually free-living, rarely parasitic on insects. (Fig. 1068). (Tyróglyphus, (= *Aleuròbius*), Rhizóglyphus, Histiostoma, Glyciphagus, Monieziélla Chætodactylus, Ácarus). (*TYROGLÝPHIDÆ*) ....ACÁRIDÆ

50. External parasites of mammals; legs or mouthparts modified to form clasping organs to cling to the hairs of the host. (Listróphorus, Labidocárpus, Schizocárpus, Myocóptes, Trichœcius)
LISTROPHÓRIDÆ
Species not living externally on the hair of mammals and without such specialized clinging apparatus 51

51. External parasites of birds, living on the plumage. (Análges, Freyàna, Pterólichus, Pterodéctes, Allóptes). (Including *PROCTOPHYLLÓDIDÆ*) ....ANALGÉSIDÆ
Internal parasites living in the skin or tissues of birds, and in or on the skin of mammals 52

52. Genital aperture of female longitudinal in position; species living in the skin or internal tissues of birds 53
Genital aperture of female transverse; skin parasites of mammals or birds. (Figs. 1067, 1070). (Sarcóptes (*Ácarus* auctt.) (Itch mites), Psoróptes, Chorióptes) (*ACÁRIDÆ* auctt., *PSOROPTIDÆ*) ....SARCÓPTIDÆ

53. Body without transverse suture or constriction; oval species. (Cytodìtes). (*CYTOLEÍCHIDÆ*) ....CYTODÍTIDÆ
Body elongate, with a distinct suture or constriction that separates the cephalothorax and abdomen. (Laminosióptes)
LAMINOSIÓPTIDÆ

54. Last joint of palpi opposable like a thumb to the preceding joint which is nearly always claw-like at tip (Fig. 1076); body often bearing many hairs. (Superfamily TROMBIDÒIDEA) 55

Palpi not thus modified; simple or rarely modified to hold prey; body with few hairs. (Superfamily EUPODÒIDEA) 60

55. Legs simple, without processes bearing spines; body without, or with inconspicuous chitinous shields 56

First and second pairs of legs with processes bearing spines; cephalothorax with a large, sculptured, median chitinous shield, abdomen with two or more similar shields; coxæ contiguous (Fig. 1075). (Cæculus) .... CÆCÙLIDÆ

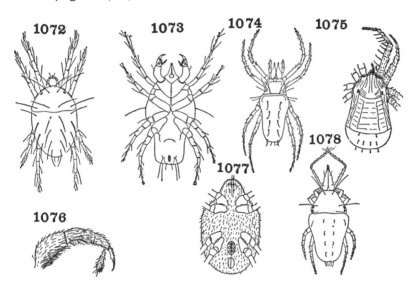

Figs. 1072–1078. Acarina

1072. **Tetranychus** (Banks) Tetranychidæ.
1073. **Cheyletus** (Banks) Cheyletidæ.
1074. **Rhagidia** (Banks) Eupodidæ.
1075. **Cæculus** (Banks) Cæculidæ.
1076. **Trombidium,** palpi (Banks) Trombidiidæ.
1077. **Smaris** (Banks) Erythræidæ.
1078. **Biscirus** (Banks) Bdellidæ.

56. Chelicera chelate or pincers-like at tip, with a movable claw opposable to the basal portion 57

Chelicera stylet-shaped or needle-like, retractile 58

57. Last joint of first pair of legs usually enlarged; cephalothorax with a median dorsal line or groove; legs inserted in two groups, the coxæ of the first two pairs placed far forward and those of the two posterior pairs in a second group far removed from the

first (Fig. 1076). Harvest mites. (Trombídium, Trombícula). (Including *TROMBICÙLIDÆ*) .... **TROMBIDÌIDÆ**
Last joint of first pair of legs not enlarged, often long; cephalothorax without median line or groove; coxæ of all legs usually closely approximated, forming a single group. (Anýstis, Tarsótomus, Geckòbia, Pterygosòma) (*PTÈRYGOSOMÁTIDÆ*) **ANÝSTIDÆ**

58. Last joint of legs not enlarged; cephalothorax without a median dorsal groove 59
Last joint of first and fourth pairs of legs enlarged; cephalothorax usually with a median dorsal groove; adults free-living, usually active and with long slender legs. (Fig. 1077). (Erythræus (= *Rhynchólophus*), Smàris, Fessònia, Átomus). (Including *SMÁRIDÆ*). (*RHÝNCHOLÓPHIDÆ*). ....ERYTHRÆIDÆ

59. Feeding on plants; all legs terminated by claws; body bristles or hairs usually simple. (Figs. 1015, 1072). Red spiders. (Tetránychus, Rhaphígnathus, Bryòbia (*B. praténsis*, Clover mite), Achèles, Stigmæus). (Including *RHAPHIGNÁTHIDÆ*) **TETRANÝCHIDÆ**
Predaceous or parasitic; claws often absent on one or more pairs of legs; body bristles often branched or pectinate. (Fig. 1073). (Cheylètus, Cheylètia, Cheyletiélla, Myòbia, Picòbia). (Including *MYOBÌIDÆ*) ....CHEYLÉTIDÆ

60. Cephalothorax and abdomen completely fused, the body showing no division into these two parts; no bristles on body above; palpi simple; last joint of first pair of legs not noticeably longer than the preceding joint; mouthparts covered by a large hyaline hood. (Cryptógnathus, Palæarc.) .....CRYPTOGNÁTHIDÆ
Cephalothorax and abdomen more or less distinctly separated; upper surface of body furnished with bristles; palpi sometimes geniculate; mouthparts without hood-like covering 61

61. Last joint of first pair of legs longer than the preceding joint, often twice as long; cephalothorax with four bristles, a pair in front and a more widely separated pair behind. (Fig. 1078). (Bdélla, Cunáxa, Cỳta, Eùpalus, Scírula). Including *CUNÁXI-DÆ*) ....BDÉLLIDÆ
Last joint of first pair of legs not or only slightly longer than the preceding joint; bristles of cephalothorax not arranged as above. (Eupòdes, Linopòdes, Tỳdeus, Rhagídia (Fig. 1074), Ereynètes, Teneríffia). (Including *TENERIFFÌIDÆ, RHAGIDÌIDÆ, PHYTOPTIPALPIDÆ, TYDEIDÆ*) ....EUPÓDIDÆ

LITERATURE ON ACARINA

ANDRÉ, M. Contribution à l'étude des Acariens libres. Trombididæ. Bull. Soc. Zool. Paris, **51**, pp. 175–228 (1926).

Le Genre Cæculus. Bull. Soc. Hist. Nat. Afrique du Nord, **26**, pp. 79–127. (1935).

ARAGÃO, H. DE B. Ixodidæ brasilieros e de alguns paizes limitrophes. Mem. Inst. Oswaldo Cruz, **31**, pp. 759–843, 1 pl., 4 figs. (1937).

BAGNALL, R. S. and J. W. H. HARRISON. A Catalogue of the British Eriophyidæ. Ann. Mag. Nat. Hist., (10) **2**, pp. 427–445 (1928).

BAKER, E. W. Cheyletidæ of United States National Museum. Proc. U. S. Nat. Mus.,·**99**, pp. 267–314, 12 pls. (1949).

BAKER, E. W. and J. BALOCK. Mites of the Family Bdellidæ. Proc. Ent. Soc. Washington, **46**, pp. 176–184. (1944).

BAKER, E. W. and G. W. WHARTON. An Introduction to Acarology. xiii+465 pp. Macmillan Co., New York (1952).

BANKS, N. Oribatoidea of the United States. Trans. Amer. Ent. Soc., **22**, pp. 1–16 (1895).

Catalogue of the Acarina of the United States. Proc. U. S. Nat. Mus., **32**, pp. 595–625 (1907).

Revision of Ixodoidea of the United States. Bull. U. S. Dept. Agric., Bur. Ent. Tech. ser., No. 15 (1908).

The Acarina or Mites. Rept. No. 108, U. S. Dept. Agric. 153 pp. (1915).

BEQUAERT, J. Synopsis des Tiques du Congo Belge. Rev. Zool. Bot. africaines, **20**, pp. 209–251 (1931).

Ixodoidea of North Eastern United States and Canada. Ent. Americana, **25**, pp. 73–232 (1946).

BERLESE, A. Acari, Miriopodi e Scorpione Italiani. Prostigmata, Cryptostigmata, Mesostigmata, Sarcoptidæ. 4 vols. (1882–1910).

Monografia del Genere Gamasus. Redia, **3**, pp. 68–304 (1905).

Trombidiidæ. Redia, **8**, pp. 1–291 (1912).

BRENNAN, J. M. and G. W. WHARTON. North American Neotrombicula. American Midl. Natural., **44**, pp. 153–197 (1950).

CANESTRINI, G. Prospetto dell' Acarofauna Italiana. Padova, 7 parts (1885–97).

CANESTRINI, G. and P. KRAMER. Demodicoidea. Das Tierreich, Lief. 7, pp. 1–3 (1899).

Sarcoptidæ. Das Tierreich, Lief. 7, pp. 4–193 (1899).

CHAMBERLIN, R. V. and S. MULAIK. Mites of the Family Neocaridæ. Proc. Biol. Soc. Washington, **55**, pp. 125–129, 2 pls. (1942).

COOLEY, R. A. and G. M. KOHLS. Argasidæ of North and Central America and Cuba. Monogr., American Midl. Natural., No. **1**, 152 pp., 15 pls., 57 figs. (1944).

Ixodes in North America. Bull. Nat. Inst. Health, **187**, p. 54 (1945).

COOREMAN, J. Canestriniidæ vivant sur des Coléoptères. Bull. Inst. Roy. Sci. Nat. Belgique, **26** (33), pp. 1–54 (1950).

EWING, H. E. Oribatoidea of Illinois. Bull. Illinois State Lab. Nat. Hist., **7**, pp. 337–389 (1909).

Synopsis of Beetle-mites (North America). Ann. Ent. Soc. America, **10**, pp. 117–132 (1917).

Classification of Mites. Ann. Ent. Soc. America, **15**, pp. 213–222 (1922).

Tarsonemidæ and Related Families. Canadian Ent., **54**, pp. 104–113 (1922).

Dermanyssid Mites of North America. Proc. U. S. Nat. Mus., **62**, art. 13, pp. 1–26 (1923).

New Parasitic Mites of the Superfamily Parasitoidea. Proc. U. S. Nat. Mus., **82**, art. 30, pp. 1–14 (1933).

Mites of the Family Cheyletidæ. Proc. U. S. Nat. Mus., **99**, No. 3258, pp. 267–320 (1949).

Revision of the Mites of the Subfamily Tarsoneminæ of North Africa, the West Indies, and the Hawaiian Islands. Bull. U. S. Dept. Agric., **653**, pp. 1–63, 25 figs. (1939).

The Trombiculid Mites. Journ. Parasitol., **30**, pp. 339–365, 8 figs. (1944).

FIELDING, J. W. Australasian Ticks. Service Publ. Australia, **9**, pp. 1–114 (1926).

FONSECA, F. DA. Der Schlangenparasit Ixobioides (Ixodorhynchidæ). Zeits. Parasitenkunde, **6**, pp. 508–527, 9 figs. (1934).

Monograph of Macronyssidæ (Liponissidæ). Proc. Roy. Soc. Zool. London, **118**, pp. 249–334 (1945).

GARMAN, P. Tetranychidæ of Connecticut. Bull. Connecticut Agric. Expt. Sta., New Haven, **431** (1940).

GEIJSKES, D. C. Beiträge zur Kenntnis der Europäischen Tetranychiden. Meded. Landb. Hoogesch., **42**, pt. 4, pp. 1–68, 44 figs. (1939).

GRANDJEAN, F. Les Microzetidæ. Bull. Soc. Zool. France, **61**, 60–93 (1936).

HAMMER, M. Oribatidæ of Greenland. Medd. om Gronland, **122**, pp. 1–210 (1944).

HIRST, S. Mites of the order Prostigmata (Trombidioidea) Found on Lizards. Jour. Linn. Soc. London, Zool., **36**, pp. 173–200. (1925).

Acari of the Genus Spinturnix. Proc. Zool. Soc. London, **1927**, pp. 323–338.

JACOT, A. P. Annotated Bibliography of the Oribatoidea. Tsingtao, pp. 1–60 (1929).

American Oribatid Mites, subfamily Galumninæ. Bull. Mus. Comp. Zool., **69**, pp. 1–37 (1929).

Genera of Pterogastrine Oribatidæ. Trans. American Micros. Soc., **48**, pp. 416–430 (1929).

Oribatid Mites of the Subfamily Phthiracarinæ of Northeastern United States. Proc. Boston. Soc. Nat. Hist., **39**, pp. 209–261 (1930).

Primitive Galumninæ of the Middle West. American Midland Nat., **14**, pp. 680–703 (1933).

The Galumnas of the Northeastern States. Jour. New York Ent. Soc., **42**, pp. 87–125 (1934.)

JAKOB, E. Die Verwandschaft der Zeckengattungen. Zeitschr. Morph. Ökol., **1**, pp. 309–372 (1924).

KEEGAN, H. L. Mites of the Subfamily Hæmogamasinæ (Lælaptidæ). Proc. U. S. Nat. Mus., **101**, pp. 41–55, 54 figs. (1951).

KEIFER, H. H. Eriophyid Studies. Bull. Dept. Agric. California, **27**, pp. 181–206; 301–323 (1938). (Also numerous other parts in the same journal).

KOENICKE, F. Nordamerikanische Hydrachniden. Abh. naturw. Ver. Bremen, **13**, pp. 167–226 (1900).

Acarinen- insbesondere Hydracarinen-System. Abh. naturw. Ver. Bremen, **20**, pp. 121–161 (1910).

Acarina. Süsswasserfauna Deutschlands, Heft 12, (1916).

LAWRENCE, R. F. Prostigmatic Mites of South African Lizards. Parasitology, **27**, pp. 1–45 (1935). Ibid. **28**, pp. 1–39 (1936).

LOMBARDINI, G. Chiave analitica ai sottordini alle superfamiglie ed alle famiglie degli Acari. Redia, **24**, pp. 199–217, 29 figs. (1938).

Canestriniidæ del America del Sud. Arthropoda, **1**, pp. 279–290 (1950).

LUNDBLAD, O. Süsswasseracarinen aus Dänemark. Vid. Selsk. Skr. Math.-natv. Afd. Copenhagen, (8) **6**, No. 2, 150 pp. (1920).

Die Hydracarinen Schwedens. Zool. Bidrag, **11**, pp. 185–535 (1927).

Südamerikanische Hydracarinen. Ibid., **13**, pp. 1–86 (1931).

Hydracarinen aus Java. Ent. Tidskr., **57**, pp. 145–157, 7 figs., 1 pl. (1936).

Neue Wassermilben aus Santa Catherina, Brasil. Zool. Anz., **116**, pp. 14–24; 200–211 (1936).

Die Hydrocaridenfauna Sudbrasiliens und Paraguays. K. Svenska Vetensk. Akad. Handl., (3) **19**, pp. 1–183, 5 pls., 82 figs.; **20**, pp. 1–171, 15 pls., 78 figs. (1941–43).

Uebersicht des Hydrachnellensystems. Zool. Bidrag. **20**, pp. 359–379 (1942).

MARSHALL, R. The Arrhenuri of the United States. Trans. American Micros. Soc., **28**, pp. 85–140 (1908).

McGREGOR, E. A. Red Spiders of America. Proc. U. S. Nat. Mus., **56**, pp. 641–679 (1919).

Nearctic Pseudoleptidæ. Mem. Southern California Acad. Sci., **3**, pp. 1–45. (1949).

Tetranychidæ. American Midl. Natural., **44**, pp. 257–420 (1950).

MICHAEL, A. D. Oribatidæ. Das Tierreich, Lief. 53, 93 pp. (1898).

British Oribatidæ. 2 vols. London, Ray Soc. (1883–87).

British Tyroglyphidæ, 2 vols. London, Ray Soc. (1901–03).

MOTAS, C. Hydracariens. Trav. Lab. Hydrobiol., Univ. Grenoble, **17**, pp. 75–140, 27 figs. (1925).

Hydracariens français. Ibid., **20**, pp. 1–370, 6 pls., 247 figs. (1928).

NALEPA, A. Eriophyidæ. Das Tierreich, Lief. 4, 74 pp. (1898).

Die Systematik der Eriophyiden. Verh. zool.-bot. Ges. Wien, **67**, pp. 12–38 (1917).

Index nominum Eriophyidarum Marcellia, Avellino, **20**, pp. 25–66 (1923).

Neuer Catalog der bisher beschriebenen Gallmilben. Marcellia, **25**, pp. 67–183 (1929).

NESBITT, H. H. J. Revision of the Family Acaridæ (Tyroglyphidæ). Canadian Journ. Res., **23**, pp. 139–188, 55 figs. (1945).

NEUMANN, L. G. Revision de la Famille des Ixodides. Mém. Soc. Zool. France, **9**, pp. 1–44; **10**, pp. 324–420; **11**, pp. 120–230; **12**, pp. 249–372 (1896–1901).

Ixodidæ. Das Tierreich, Lief. 26, 166 pp. (1911).

NEWELL, I. M. Halacaridæ of Eastern North America. Bull, Bingham

Oceanograph. Coll., Peabody Mus., Yale Univ., **10** (3), pp. 1–232 (1947).
Morphology and Systematics on Halarachnidæ. Bull. Bingham
Oceanogr. Coll. **10** (4), pp. 235–266 (1947).

NUTTALL, G. H. F. and C. WARBURTON. Ticks of the Belgian Congo. Bull.
Ent. Res., **6**, pp. 313–352 (1916).

NUTTALL, G. H. F., C. WARBURTON, W. F. COOPER, and L. E. ROBINSON.
A Monograph of the Ixodoidea. Cambridge University Press, London,
pt. 1 (1908); pt. 2 (1911); pt. 3 (1915).

OUDEMANS, A. C. New List of Dutch Acari. Tijdschr. Ent., **43** (1901); **45**
(1902).
Revision des Chélétines. Mém. Soc. Zool. France, **18**, pp. 36–144 (1906).
Families of Acarina. Tijdschr. Ent., **66**, pp. 49–85 (1923).
Analytical Key for the Classification of Families and Genera of Diacro-
tricha. Ent. Berich., **6**, pp. 226–235 (1924).
Kritisch historisch Overzicht der Acarologie. Tijdschr. Ent. Suppl. to
69, 500 pp. (1926).
Anystidæ. Arch. Naturg. (N.F.), **5**, pp. 364–446, 28 figs. (1936).

PAOLI, G. Monografia dei Tarsonemidi. Redia, **7**, pp. 215–281 (1911).

PIERSIG, R. Deutschlands Hydrachniden. Zoologica, Heft 22 (1897–1900).
Hydrachnidæ. Das Tierreich, Lief. 13, 336 pp. (1901).

RADFORD, C. D. Systematic Check List of Mite Genera and Type Species.
Sec. Ent., Union Internat. Sci. Biol. (C) **1**, pp. 1–252 (1950).

RAINBOW, W. J. A Synopsis of Australian Acarina. Rec. Australian Mus., **6**,
pp. 145–193 (1906).

SCHULZE, P. Ixodoidea. Biol. Tiere Deutschlands, Lief. 2 (1923).
Zecken (Ixodoidea). Tierwelt Mitteleuropas, **3**, Lief. 4, pp. X, 1–10
(1929.)

SELLNICK, M. Die Tardigraden und Oribatiden der ostpreussischen Moosrasen.
Schr. physik. Ges. Königsberg, **49**, pp. 317–350 (1908).
Oribatei (Oribatoidea). In Tierwelt Mitteleuropas, **3**, Lief. 4, pp. IX,
1–42 (1929).

SENEVET, G. Ixodoidés. Faune de France, **32**, pp. 1–100, 67 figs. (1937).

SOAR, C. D. Acarina or Mites. Watson's Micros. Rec., London, Nos. 6–9
(various parts).

SOAR, C. D., and W. WILLIAMSON. The British Hydracharina, 3 vols. Ray
Soc. London (1925–29).

SOUTHCOTT, R. V. Smarididæ. Proc. Linn. Soc. New South Wales, **70**, pp.
173–178 (1946). Australian Erythræidæ. Ibid., **71**, pp. 6–48 (1946).

STILES, C. W. and S. F. STANLEY. In Key-Catalogue of Parasites of Insectivora.
Bull. Nat. Inst. Health, Washington, No. **159**, pp. 791–911 (1932).

THON, K. Monographie der Hydrachniden Böhmens. Arch. naturw. Landes-
durchforsch. Prag, **12**, pt. 2, pp. 1–84 (1906).

THOR, S. Zur Systematik der Acarinenfamilien Bdellidæ, Eupodidæ und
Cunaxidæ. Ver. k. k. zool.-bot. Ges. Wien, **52**, pp. 159–165 (1902).
Einführung in das Studium der Acarina. In Dahl, Die Tierwelt
Deutschlands, Teil **22**, pp. 1–78, 146 figs. (1931).
Bdellidæ, Nicoletiellidæ, Cryptognathidæ. Das Tierreich, Lief. **56**,
pp. i–xiii, 1–87, 93 figs. (1931).
Norwegische Tydeidæ. Zool. Anz., **98**, pp. 69–91, 17 figs. (1932).
Acarina. Tydeidæ, Ercynetidæ. Das Tierreich, Lief. **60**, pp. i–xi, 1–84,

102 figs. (1933). Ibid., **60**, 87 pp. (1933). Ibid., **71**, 541 pp. (1941–47).

Die Prostigmatische Familie Eupodidæ. Zool. Anz., **101**, pp. 271–277 (1933).

Einteilung der Familie Trombidiidæ. Zool. Anz., **109**, pp. 107–112 (1935).

TRÄGÅRDH, I. Monographie der arktischen Acariden. Fauna Arctica, **4**, pp. 1–78 (1904).

Acarina from the Juan Fernandez Islands. Nat. Hist. Juan Fernandez and Easter Islands. Uppsala, **3**(4), pp. 553–628, 166 figs. (1931).

Comparative Morphology of Polyaspididæ. Zool. Bidrag, **20**, pp. 345–357 (1941).

Antennophoridæ and Megisthanidæ. Arkiv f. Zool., **34A**, no. 20, 10 pp. (1943).

Zur Systematik der Uropodiden. Ent. Tidskr., **65**, pp. 173–186, 14 figs. (1944).

Diarthrophallina on Passalid Beetles. Ent. Medd., **24**, pp. 307–394 (1946).

Classification of Mesostigmata. K. Fysiogr. Sällsk. Handl. (N.F.) 57, no. 4, pp. 1–37 (1946).

New Classification of the Mesostigmata. Lunds Universitets Arsskrift. (N.F. Avd. 2) 42, no. 4, 37 pp. (1946).

TROUESSART, E. L. Revision des Genres des Analgesinæ. Bull. Soc. Zool. Paris, **40**, pp. 207–223 (1916).

VIETS, K. Fortschritte in der Kenntnis der Hydracarinen (Bibliography). Arch. Hydrobiol. u. Planktonk., **8**, pp. 589–629 (1913); **9**, pp. 550–578 (1914).

Versuch eines Systems der Hydracariden. Zool. Anz., **69**, pp. 188–199 (1926).

Die Halacaridæ der Nordsee. Zeits. wiss. Zool., **130**, pp. 83–173 (1927).

Wassermilben (Aquatic Acarina). In Tierwelt Mitteleuropas, **3**, Lief. 4, pp. VIII, 1–57 (1928).

Halacaridæ. In Die Tierwelt der Nord- und Ostsee. XI C, 72 pp., Grimpe and Wagner, Berlin (1928).

Ueber eine an Krebskiemen parasitierende Halacaride aus Australien. Zool. Anz., **96**, pp. 115–120, 6 figs. (1931).

Wassermilben aus unterirdischen Gewässern (Hydrachnellæ et Halacaridæ). Zool. Anz., **102**, pp. 277–288, 10 figs. (1933).

Wassermilben oder Hydracarina. In Dahl, Die Tierwelt Deutschlands, **31–32**, 574 pp., 1100 figs. (1936).

Halacaridæ und Hydrachnellæ der Adria. Arch. Naturgesch., (N.F.) **8**, pp. 518–550, 22 figs. (1939).

VITZTHUM, H. G. Malayische Acari. Treubia, **8**, 1–2, pp. 1–198 (1926).

Acari aus Spanien. Senckenbergiana, Frankfurt-am-M., **8**, pp. 30–39 (1926).

Landmilben (Terrestrial Acarina). In Tierwelt Mitteleuropas, **3**, Lief. 3, pp. VII, 1–112 (1928).

Acari. In Kükenthal, Handbuch der Zoologie., **3**, Hälfte 2, pp. 1–160, 161 figs. (1931).

Terrestrische Acarinen der Deutschen Limnogischen Sunda-Expedition. Arch f. Hydrobiol., Suppl. **9**, pt. 2, pp. 59–134 (1931).

Milben aus der Nasenhöhle von Vögeln. Jour. Ornith., **83**, pp. 563–587 (1935).

Acarina. In Bronn's, Klassen und Ordnungen des Tierreichs, **5**, Abt. IV, Buch 5, 1011 pp., 522 figs. (1940–43).

WALTER, C. Die Hydracarinen der Schweitz. Rev. Suisse Zool., **15**, pp. 401–573 (1907).

WHARTON, G. W. et al. Terminology and Classification of Trombiculidæ. Journ. Parasitol., **37**, pp. 13–31, 8 figs. (1951).

WILLMANN, C. Moosmilben oder Oribatiden (Cryptostigmata). In Dahl, Die Tierwelt Deutschlands, Teil **22**, pp. 79–200, 364 figs. (1931).

WITH, C. J. Notostigmata a New Suborder of Acari. Vidensk. Medd. Natur. Foren. Copenhagen, **1904**, pp. 137–192 (1904).

WOLCOTT, R. H. A Review of the Genera of Water Mites. Trans. American Micros. Soc., **26**, pp. 161–243 (1905).

WOMERSLEY, H. A New Family, Spelæognathidæ. Ann. Mag. Nat. Hist., (10)**18**, pp. 312–315, 7 figs. (1936).

Australian Tyroglyphidæ. Rec. South Australian Museum, **6**, pp. 451–488 (1941).

Parasitoidea of Australia. Trans. Roy. Soc. South Australia, **66**, pp. 142–171 (1942).

Australian Listrophoridæ. Trans. Roy. Soc. South Australia, **67**, pp. 10–19, 5 figs. (1943).

Revision of the Microtrombidiinæ (Trombidiidæ) of Australia and New Guinea. Rec. South Australian Mus., **8**, pp. 293–355, 38 figs. (1944).

Australian Alycidae and Nanorchestidae. Trans. Roy. Soc. South Australia, **68**, pp. 133–143 (1944).

Leeuwenhoekiidæ of Australia and New Guinea. Trans. Roy. Soc. South Australia, **69**, pp. 96–113, 9 figs. (1945).

WOMERSLEY, H. and R. V. SOUTHCOTT. Smaridiidæ of Australia and New Zealand. Trans. Roy. Soc. South Australia, **65**, pp. 61–78 (1941).

ZAKHVATKIN, A. A. Tyroglyphidæ. Faure de l'U.S.S.R. Inst. Zool. Acad. Sci. Moscow, N. S. No. **28**, xii+475 pp., 705 figs. (1941).

ZUMPT, F. Lælaptidæ. Parsitology, **40**, pp. 298–303 (1950).

CLASS **PENTASTÓMIDA**

(*LINGUATÙLIDA*)

Rather large, elongate, vermiform, cylindrical or somewhat flattened animals. Body divided externally by constrictions into a large number of annuli or apparent segments; straight, bent or sometimes coiled. Mature form legless, but the embryo and very young animal with two or three pairs of short, imperfectly jointed legs. No antennæ. Mouth opening rounded or oval, situated close to two pairs of claw-like, movable chitinous hooks that arise from shallow pits. Respiratory organs wanting. Genital opening of male always at the base of the abdomen, of the female either at the base or apex of the abdomen; ovary or uterus either large and sac-like, or long, tubular and strongly sinuous or coiled, lying either above, below or twined about the alimentary tract. Metamorphosis slight, but evident. Parasitic; the adult form usually in the respiratory tract of reptiles, the immature one frequently in the tissues or internal organs of mammals. Tongueworms.

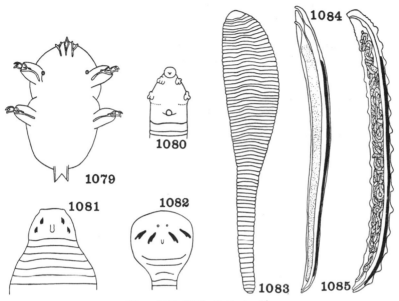

Figs. 1079–1085. Pentastomida

1079. "Pentastomum," young larva (Stiles) Linguatulidæ.
1080. Raillietiella, anterior extremity (Sambon) Cephalobænidæ.
1081. Sebekia, anterior extremity (Sambon) Linguatulidæ.
1082. Kiricephalus, anterior extremity (Sambon) Linguatulidæ.
1083. Linguatula (Sambon) Linguatulidæ.
1084. Cephalobænidæ, diagrammatic vertical section of body (Sambon) Cephalobænidæ.
1085. Linguatulidæ, diagrammatic vertical section of body (Sambon) Linguatulidæ.

The following classification is similar to that developed by Sambon, except that his subfamilies are regarded as families to render the divisions of this group more nearly on an equality with those of related classes.

1. Mouth opening lying in front of the oral hooks; genital opening of female at the anterior end of the abdomen, the uterus large and sac-like; salivary glands of moderate size; larva with three pairs of short legs. (Figs. 1080, 1084). (*RAILLIETIÉLLIDÆ*).
CEPHALOBÆNIDÆ

Three subfamilies may be distinguished as follows:

a. Anterior end of body forming a short, blunt beak. (**Cephalobæna,** Neotrop., in lungs of snakes)............**CEPHALOBÆNÌNÆ**
   Anterior end of body not forming a beak-like projection, rounded. .b
b. Body with two apical projections at the posterior end; posterior pair of oral hooks larger than the anterior ones. (Fig. 1080). (**Raillietiélla,** in reptiles and batrachians, widespr.).
   RAILLIETIELLÌNÆ
   Body without apical projections, bent downwards at posterior end; both pairs of oral hooks very small. (**Reighárdia,** in birds, Neotrop.) .... **REIGHARDIÌNÆ**

Mouth opening lying between or behind the oral hooks; genital opening of female at posterior end of abdomen, the uterus tubular, greatly elongated and irregularly coiled; salivary glands as long as the body; larva with only two pairs of legs. (Figs. 1079, 1081, 1082, 1083, 1085). (*POROCEPHÁLIDÆ*).
   LÌNGUATÙLIDÆ

This family includes three well-marked subfamilies, as follows:

a. Body cylindrical ....b
   Body flattened, fluke-like; more or less convex centrally above, the sides depressed; mouth hooks placed in an arch or curved line; alimentary canal following the axis of the body, the uterus twined about it. (**Linguátula,** in mammals, Holarc., Neotrop., Ethiop., Ind.; **Subtriquètra,** in crocodiles, Neotrop., Indomal.).
   LINGUATULÌNÆ
b. Body with well marked latero-ventral grooves; mouth hooks forming a trapezoid; alimentary canal sinuous, longer than the body. (Fig. 1081). (**Sebèkia,** in crocodiles, Neotrop., Ethiop., Indomal.; **Alòfia,** Malay., Ethiop.; **Leipèria,** in crocodiles, Ethiop., **Sambònia,** in lizards, Ethiop., Neotrop.; **Diesíngia,** in turtles, Neotrop., Indomal.) .... **SEBEKIÌNÆ**
   Without latero-ventral grooves; mouth hooks placed in a curve or arch; alimentary canal straight, not longer than the body. (Fig. 1082). (**Porocéphalus,** in snakes, Ethiop., Amer.; **Kiricéphalus,** in snakes, Amer., Indomal., Austr.; **Armíllifer,** in snakes and mammals, Ethiop., Indomal.; **Waddycéphalus,** Fiji).
   POROCEPHALÌNÆ

Note: **Pentastoma** and **Pentastomum** have in the past been used as more or less inclusive generic names for the adult and immature stages of various species.

LITERATURE ON PENTASTOMIDA

HEYMONS, R. Pentastomida. Kükenthal und Krumbach, Handbuch der Zoologie, **3**, pt. 1, pp. 69–131 (1926).
Zungenwürmer, in Tierwelt Mitteleuropas, **3**, Lief. 1, pp. 1–2 (1926).
Pentastomiden Australiens. Zeits. Parasitenk., **4**, pp. 409–430, 12 figs. (1932).
Pentastomida. In Bronn's Klassen und Ordnungen des Tierreichs, **5**, Buch 1, 628 pp., 148 figs. (1935).
Systematik der Pentastomiden. Zeits. Parasitenk., **12**, pp. 317–329, 3 figs.; 419–432, 7 figs. (1942).
HEYMONS, R. and H. VITZTHUM. Systematik der Pentastomiden. Zeits. Parasitenk., **8**, pp. 1–103, 36 figs. (1935).
SAMBON, L. W. A Synopsis of the Family Linguatulidæ. Journ. Trop. Med., **25**, pp. 188–206; 391–428 (1922).
STILES, C. W. and S. F. STANLEY. Pentastomida. In Key-Catalogue of Parasites of Insectivora, Bull. Nat. Inst. Health, Washington, No. **159**, pp. 829–834 (1932).

CLASS TARDÍGRADA

Very small or minute species, usually less than one mm. in length. Body more or less elongate oval, consisting of a head and four body-segments; integument tough and more or less transparent, not chitinous. Four pairs of short, fleshy, unjointed legs, each terminated by several claws or clavate vesicles. Cuticula usually forming distinct plates; often granulate or sometimes spinose. Mouthparts tubular, provided with a central piercing organ or stylet. Antennæ absent. Eyes absent, or present as two ocelli. Terrestrial or aquatic species; no special respiratory organs. Species capable of excessive and prolonged dessication without injury. Sexes separate; development from the egg direct, without metamorphosis. Water Bears.

1. Head bearing in front a pair of central and a pair of lateral cirri, in addition to two sensory appendages at each side. (Fig. 1086). (Order HETEROTARDÍGRADA) 2
   Head usually without such sensory appendages, or at least with only the four anterior ones present; the two at each side always wanting. (Order EUTARDÍGRADA). .3
2. Middle portion of leg capable of being withdrawn or telescoped within the basal part, the two parts separated by a distinct fold; legs without long, hooked claws. (Fig. 1086). (Suborder ARTHROTARDÍGRADA). (**Halechiniscus, Tetrakéntron,** Palæarc.; **Batíllipes,** Holarc.) . . . . **HALECHINÍSCIDÆ**
   Middle portion of leg only partly folding into the basal part; legs terminating in long, hooked claws. (Suborder ECHINISCHÓ-

DEA). (Echiníscus, cosmop.; **Pseudechiníscus,** widespr.; **Parechiníscus, Echiniscòides,** Palæarc.; **Oreélla,** Palæarc., Austr.).
ECHINÍSCIDÆ

3. Head entirely without sensory appendages. (Fig. 1088). (**Macrobiòtus, Hypsíbius,** cosmop.) .... **MACROBIÓTIDÆ**
Head with six rostral papillæ about the mouth and also with two papillæ below on each side. (Fig. 1087). (**Milnèsium** (=*Arctíscon*), cosmop.). (*ARCTÍSCIDÆ*) .... **MILNESÌIDÆ**

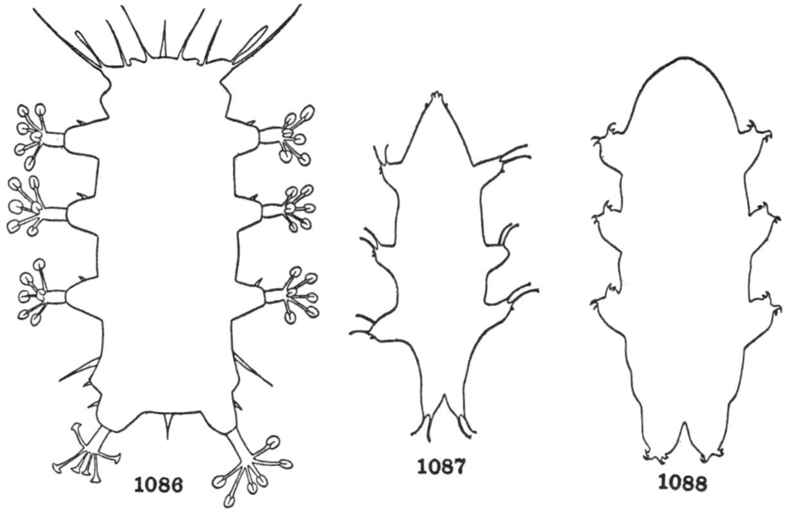

Figs. 1086–1088. Tardigrada

1086. **Batillipes** (Marcus) Halechiniscidæ.
1087. **Milnesium** (Marcus) Milnesiidæ.
1088. **Macrobiotus** (Marcus) Macrobiotidæ.

LITERATURE ON TARDIGRADA

AMMAN, J. Schweizerische Tardigraden. Berne (1908).
BOTEZAT, E. Die systematische Stellung der Tardigraden. Premier Congrès Nat. Naturalistes de Roumanie, **1928,** pp. 129–131 (1930).
CARLZON, C. Schwedische Tardigraden. Zool. Anz., **34,** pp. 137–142 (1909).
CUÉNOT, L. Tardigrades. Faune de France, **24,** pp. 1–96, 98 figs. (1932).
LAMEERE, A. Tardigrada, Linguatulida, Onychophora. Précis de Zool., Rec. Inst. zool. Torley-Rousseau, 2 (Suppl.), pp. 142–157, 12 figs. (1929).
MARCUS, E. Tardigrada. Tierwelt Deutschlands, **12,** 230 pp. (1928).

Tardigrada. In Bronn's Klassen und Ordnungen des Tierreichs, **5**, Abth. 4, Buch 3, 608 pp. (1929).

Tardigrada. Das Tierreich, Lief. 66, pp. i–xvii, 1–340, 360 figs. (1936).

MATHEWS, G. B. Tardigrada from North America. American Midl. Naturalist, **19**, pp. 619–627, 1 pl., 1 fig. (1938).

NEDERSTRÖM, P. Die aus Finland bekannten Tardigraden. Act. Soc. Faun. Flor. Fennica, **46**, No. 8, 25 pp. (1919).

RAHM, G. Tardigrada, Bärtierchen. Biol. Tiere Deutschlands., pt. 22, pp. 1–56, Geb. Bornträger, Berlin (1927).

Tardigraden in der Schweiz. Bull. Soc. Fribourg, Sci. Nat., **29**, pp. 169–174 (1930).

RICHTERS, F. Tardigrada. In Kükenthal und Krumbach, Handbuch der Zoologie, **3**, pp. 1–68 (1926).

CLASS **PAURÓPODA**

Very small species of elongate, rounded and more or less flattened form. Body composed of from six to ten segments, as indicated by the tergites, and bearing nine or ten pairs of legs in the adult stage. Antennæ branched apically; composed of four stout basal joints, the fourth bearing two elongate joints, one of which bears at tip a whip-like many-jointed flagellum and the other bears two such flagella. Mouthparts composed of a pair of mandibles, and one pair of maxillæ. Cerci bristle-like. Tracheæ absent; no respiratory organs.

1. Head and anal segment free and uncovered in dorsal view........2
   Head, anal segment and base of legs hidden from above by the strongly produced tergites; integument heavily sclerotized, thickly spinose or tuberculate and strongly pigmented. (Figs. 1090, 1092). (**Eurypaùropus**, Holarc.; **Sphæropaùropus**, Malay.). (Superfamily EURYPAUROPODÒIDEA) .... **EURYPAUROPÒDIDÆ**
2. Ocular areas of head exposed dorsally; last pair of tactile hairs the longest; terga weakly sclerotized, entire. (Superfamily PAURO-PODÒIDEA) 3
   Ocular areas of head not exposed dorsally; last pair of tactile hairs not longer than the first. (Superfamily BRACHYPAUROPO-DÒIDEA) 5
3. Legs of all pairs five-jointed. (**Polypaùropus**, Palæarc.). **POLYPAUROPÓDIDÆ**
   Legs of some of the intermediate pairs with six joints...........4
4. Legs of pairs 2–8 with six joints. (**Stylopaùropus**, Holarc.; **Paùropus**, widespr.) (Figs. 1089, 1091). ....**PAUROPÓDIDÆ**
   Legs of pairs 2–7 with six joints. (**Asphæridìopus**, Palæarc.). **ASPHÆRIDIOPÓDIDÆ**
5. Terga entire, strongly sclerotized and granular; the first to fifth with eight pairs of dorsal setæ. (**Scleropaùropus**, Holarc.). **SCLEROPAUROPÓDIDÆ**

Terga less strongly sclerotized, those of the first five segments divided longitudinally and transversely into four small plates, each bearing one pair of setæ. (**Brachypaùropus**, Holarc.).

BRACHYPAUROPÓDIDÆ

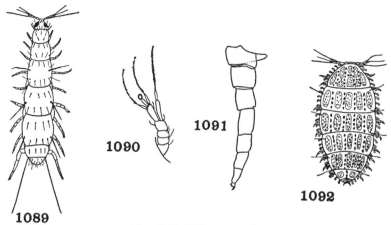

Figs. 1089–1092. **Pauropoda**

1089. **Pauropus** (Latzel) Pauropodidæ.
1090. **Eurypauropus**, antenna (Latzel) Eurypauropodidæ.
1091. **Pauropus**, leg (Ewing) Pauropodidæ.
1092. **Eurypauropus** (Latzel) Eurypauropodidæ.

LITERATURE ON PAUROPODA

BAGNALL, R. S. Classification of Pauropoda. Ann. Mag. Nat. Hist., (10)**16**, pp. 619–629, 2 figs. (1935).

KENYON, F. C. The Morphology and Classification of the Pauropoda. Tufts College Studies, No. 4 (1895).

LATZEL, R. Die Myriapoden der Œsterreichisch-Ungarischen Monarchie. Vienna, Alb. Hölder (1880–84).

REMY, P. Les Eurypauripodinæ. Bull. Mus. Hist. Nat., Paris, (2)**9**, pp. 252–257 (1937).

Pauropodes de France, d'Allemagne et des Balkans. Bull. Soc. Hist. Nat. Metz, **35**, pp. 153–178 (1938).

STARLING, J. H. Pauropoda from the Duke Forest, with List of Known Species. Proc. Ent. Soc. Washington, **45**, pp. 183–200, 5 figs. (1943).

CLASS **DIPLÓPODA**

Body long, comparatively narrow and of generally uniform width; cylindrical or at least not usually noticeably depressed or flattened. Eleven or more body segments or somites; thirteen or more pairs of legs; usually considerably more. Legs always more numerous than the dorsal segments, most of the apparent segments bearing each two pairs of legs, but the first three or four and the last one or two with only a single pair. Head with a pair of short, usually seven-jointed, antennæ, a pair of lateral eyes and a pair of mandibles; other mouthparts forming a plate-like structure (gnathochilarium). Eyes two, consisting of a group of ocelli. Legs usually six or seven-jointed, bearing an apical claw. Genital ducts opening between the second and third pairs of legs. Respiration through spiracles opening into paired pockets, one or two pairs corresponding to each of the somites. Seventh legs of the male usually modified into copulatory appendages. Somites often with paired repugnatorial glands, opening laterally.

Slow moving, usually vegetarian animals. A large group, more abundant in the tropics. Millipedes.

The System adopted here follows that of Attems in his "Myriopoda of South Africa." More recently the Diplopoda have been elaborately separated into very numerous families and an additional number of larger groups. As this excessive subdivision does not conform with the generally acceptable classification of other groups of Arthropoda, it has not been adopted in the following key.

1. Integument strongly chitinized, hardened by a deposit of calcareous material; body hairs if present simple, never in long tufts. (Subclass CHILÓGNATHA) 2
   Integumental bristles highly modified, short, scaly on body above, laterally forming long tufts; mandibles one-jointed; integument very weakly chitinized, not hardened by a deposit of calcareous material; usually eleven body segments and thirteen pairs of legs (rarely 12 and 17). (Subclass PSELAPÓGNATHA). (**Polýxenus,** cosmop.; **Saróxenus,** Ethiop.; **Lophopróctus,** widespr.; **Schindalmonòtus,** S. Afr.; **Macróxenus,** Palæarc.; **Trichopróctus,** Austr.) . . . . **POLYXÉNIDÆ**

2. Sternites divided into two parts, tracheæ dichotomously branched; male with one or two pairs of modified copulatory appendages (telopods) at the posterior end of the body, but without modified legs on the seventh segment. (OPISTHÁNDRIA) 3
   Sternites not divided; tracheæ not branched, but arising in tufts from the tracheal trunks; male with one or two pairs of modified legs (gonopods) on the seventh body segment. (PROTERÁNDRIA) 7

3. Body composed of 22 somites with 36 pairs of legs, not including one pair of telopods in the male; body not capable of being rolled into a ball. (Order LIMACOMÓRPHA). (**Glomeridésmus,** Neotrop.; **Termitodésmus,** Indomal.; **Zephroniodésmus,** Mal.).
   GLOMERIDÉSMIDÆ
   Body of twelve or thirteen somites; with 17 to 21 pairs of legs, not including two pairs of telopods in the male; body capable

of being rolled up into a ball so as to conceal the head and legs.
(Order ONISCOMÓRPHA) 4

4. Seventeen pairs of legs, not including the telopods of the male;
ocelli in a single row or wanting. (GLOMERÍDIA)..........5
Twenty-one pairs of legs, not including the telopods of the male;
ocelli numerous, in several rows. (Figs. 1095, 1096, 1097, 1098,
1099). (SPHÆROTHÈRIA). (Sphærothèrium, Globothèrium,
Ethiop.; Sphæropœus, Arthrosphæra, Indomal.; Cyliosòma,
Austr.) .... SPHÆROTHERÏIDÆ

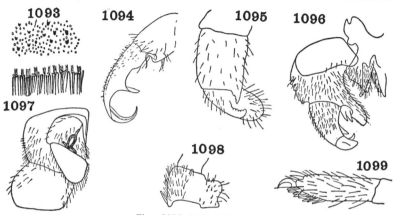

Figs. 1093–1099. Diplopoda

1093. Sphærotherium, pygidium and marginal bristles (Attems) Sphærotheriidæ.
1094. Sphæriodesmus, gonopod (Chamberlin) Sphæriodesmidæ.
1095. Sphærotherium, anterior gonopod (Attems) Sphærotheriidæ.
1096. Sphærotherium, posterior gonopod (Attems) Sphærotheriidæ.
1097. Sphærotherium, vulva (Attems) Sphærotheriidæ.
1098. Sphærotherium, coxa of fourth leg (Attems) Sphærotheriidæ.
1099. Sphærotherium, last joint of a leg (Attems) Sphærotheriidæ.

5. Seventeenth pair of legs of male with one to three small joints
beyond the large coxa. (Glómeris, Palæarc.; Rhopalómeris,
Apiómeris, Indomal.) .... GLOMÉRIDÆ
Seventeenth pair of legs of male with four or five small joints beyond the large coxa (Fig 127)............................6

6. Nineteenth pair of legs in male with the second and third joints
(prefemur and femur) simple, without a bristly projection; body
smooth. (Glomeridélla, Typhloglómeris, Glomerellìna, Palæarc.).
GLOMERIDÉLLIDÆ
Nineteenth pair of legs in male with a bristle-bearing projection on
the prefemur and femur; body often tuberculate or carinate.
(Gervàisia, Dodèria, Palæarc.) ....GERVAISÏIDÆ

7. First pair of legs of the seventh somite of the male modified into

gonopods, often the second pair of this somite also and the adjacent pairs on the sixth and eighth segments similarly modified; mouthparts with three pairs of palpal lobes. (EUGNATHA) . . 8
First pair of legs of the seventh somite of the male normal, not modified to form gonopods; mouthparts without palpal lobes. (COLOBÓGNATHA) 66

8. Anal segment without spinning styles or spinning glands; body of less than 23 or more than 40 somites 9
Anal segment with two or three pairs of spinning glands, opening by one to three pairs of spinning styles; body of 26 or more somites. (NEMATÓPHORA) 25

9. Nineteen to 22 body somites (usually 20); only the first pair of legs on the seventh somite of the male modified into gonopods; the gonopods inserted in a completely closed circular opening; body cylindrical, or flattened with lateral expansions. (POLYDESMÒIDEA) 10
More than 40 body somites; both pairs of legs of seventh somite of the male modified into gonopods, or the second pair absent; opening in which the gonopods are inserted never closed in front; body cylindrical. (JULIFÓRMIA) 52

10. Coxæ of the gonopods rather widely separated, but connected by broad, medially coalescent processes; the median part raised and keel-shaped. (POLYDESMÍDEA) 11
Coxæ of the gonopods close together, free or more or less connected but not by broad, medially keel-like, raised processes. (STRONGYLOSOMATÍDEA 17

11. Coxæ of the gonopods with a hooked process on the external margin; tergites broadly expanded at the sides, the lateral margins produced, with a number of sharp teeth, each tooth bearing a bristle. (Peridontodésmus, Neotrop.). PERIDONTODÉSMIDÆ
Of a different conformation 12

12. Head not or incompletley covered by the first tergite, which is generally small, not lengthened or enlarged 13
Head completely or almost completely hidden by the first tergite when seen from above; this tergite large 16

13. Coxa of gonopod bearing a long, annulate flagellum; posterior portion of each tergite with three transverse rows of bristles, which usually arise from small tubercles. (Mastigonodésmus, Schedoleiodésmus, Palæarc.) . . . . MASTIGONODÉSMIDÆ
Of a different conformation 14

14. Second tergite enlarged; posterior portion of tergites smooth or granulate, often densely clothed with setæ. (Oniscodésmus, Trigonóstylus, Oncodésmus, Neotrop.; Doratodésmus, Mal.; Hyperóthrix, Ethiop.) . . . . ONISCODÉSMIDÆ
Second tergite not enlarged 15

15. Gonopod with a brush of hairs inwardly near the tip and a seminal pouch which opens at the base of this brush. (Fig. 1100). (**Polydésmus,** Holarc.; **Brachydésmus, Epanerchòdus,** Palæarc.; **Opisthotrètus,** Mal.; **Opisthoporodésmus,** Austromal.).

POLYDÉSMIDÆ

Gonopod without brush of hairs or seminal pouch. (**Vanhoeffènia,** Ethiop.; **Gyrophállus,** Nearc.; **Trichopolydésmus,** Palæarc.).

VANHŒFFENÌIDÆ

1100   1101   1102

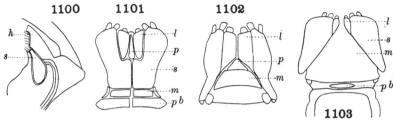

1103

Figs. 1100–1103. Diplopoda

1100. **Polydesmus,** gonopod: *h,* hair-brush; *s.,* seminal vesicle.
1101. **Blaniulus,** gnathochilarium: l, lingual lamellæ; p., promentum; s., stipes; pb., prebasilare. Blaniulidæ.
1102. **Xiphochætoporatia,** gnathochilarium. Lettering as in Fig. 1101.
1103. **Rhinocricus,** gnathochilarium. Lettering as in Fig. 1101.

16. Openings of the repugnatorial glands located on small, separate, transparent projections from the sides of some of the abdominal tergites (usually 5th, 7th, 9th, 10th, 12th, 13th and 15th). (**Stylodésmus,** Ethiop.; **Myrmecodésmus, Corypherépsis, Synoptùra,** Neotrop.; **Myxodésmus,** Mal.) . . . . **STÝLODÉSMIDÆ**
Openings of the repugnatorial glands very minute or not visible. (**Cryptodésmus,** Neotrop.; **Phenacóporus,** Austromal.; **Cryptocórypha,** Ethiop., Mal.; **Atopodésmus,** Austr.).

CRYPTODÉSMIDÆ

17. Coxa of the gonopod with a prominent curved horn-shaped process 18
Coxa of the gonopod without any such process; 20 body somites. (**Rhacodésmus,** Am.; **Acutángulus, Rhachidomórpha, Strongylodésmus,** Neotrop.) . . . . **RHACODÉSMIDÆ**

18. Certain joints of the anterior (or more) legs furnished with peculiar bristles that have a bulbously swollen base, and long slender or short nipple-shaped tip. (**Sphærotríchopus,** Austr.; **Pleonaràius, Semnosòma,** Neotrop.; **Scytonòtus,** Nearc., Austr.; **Icosidésmus,** Ethiop., Austr.; **Gnoméskelus,** Ethiop.).

SPHÆROTRICHÓPIDÆ

Legs destitute of such swollen bristles 19

19. Femur of the gonopod distinctly separated from the tibia by a strong constriction 20
Femur and tibia of the gonopod completely fused, without any line of demarcation.......................................22

20. Coxa of the gonopod long and slender; femur ovate, clothed with hairs; tibia usually with a long flagelliform process. (Strongylosòma, Palæarc.; Catharosòma, Habrodésmus, Neotrop.; Nedỳopus, Prionopéltis, Indomal.; Phæodésmus, Ethiop.; Australiosòma, Austr.) .... STRONGYLOSOMÁTIDÆ
Of a different conformation.................................21

21. Coxæ of the gonopods large, connected by a narrow band; femur with a large process that is often longer than the tibia and tarsus together. (Leptodésmus, Cyclorhábdus, Neotrop.; Ísaphe, Nearc.; Devíllea, Palæarc.) .... LEPTODÉSMIDÆ
Coxæ of the gonopods free, not connected with one another. (Oxydésmus, Metaphóricus, Orodésmus, Ethiop.) ....OXYDÉSMIDÆ

22. Lateral expansions of the tergites well developed or large, more or less horizontal......................................23
Lateral expansion of the tergites very strongly declivous, almost vertical; body very strongly convex above, its form highly adapted for curling up tightly. (Sphæriodésmus, Cyclodésmus, Colobodésmus, Neotrop.; Desmònus, Nearc.)....SPHÆRIODÉSMIDÆ

23. Legs of male with fleshy lobes beneath the claws; gonopod articulated at the end of the coxa; tergites without striking sculpture. (Gomphodésmus, Antíphonus, Aulodésmus, Ulodésmus Astrodésmus, Elaphógonus, Ethiop.) ....GOMPHODÉSMIDÆ
Legs of male without lobes beneath the claws................24

24. Tibia and tarsus of gonopods not separated. (Fontària, Holarc.; Rhysodésmus, Neotrop., Palæarc.; Mélaphe, Palæarc.; Pachydésmus, Nearc.; Tuberculàrium, Ethiop.; Asphalidésmus, Austr.).
FONTARÌIDÆ
Tibia and tarsus of gonopods usually separated by a distinct constriction; gonopod articulated at the end of the coxa. (Platýrhacus, Neotrop., Indoaustr.; Amplìnus, Pycnótropis, Neotrop.; Polýlepis, Mal.) .... PLATYRHÁCIDÆ

25. Body of 26–32 (usually 30) somites; repugnatorial glands absent..26
Body of 39 or more somites; repugnatorial glands present on the fifth and following somites.............................49

26. First tergite small; each somite above with three pairs of bristles arising from minute tubercles. (Superfamily CHORDEUMÒIDEA) 27
First tergite very large, its sides partly enclosing the head; body capable of being rolled into a spiral; some tergites with strong longitudinal carinæ; a few ocelli at each side of the head. (Superfamily STRIARIÒIDEA). (Striària, Nearc.). ....STRIARÌIDÆ

27. First four joints of antennæ short, subequal in length; fifth much longer and thicker, forming a club together with the apical joints; dorsum tuberculate or spinulose, very strongly convex; legs short and stout. (TRACHYZÒNA) 28
    First three joints of antennæ increasing in length, the second and third each much longer than the preceding joint; fourth at least twice as long as the first; legs long and slender. (XESTO-ZÒNA) 29
28. Body tuberculate, pale in color; 30 somites. (Trachysòma, Halleinosòma, Palæarc.) .... TRACHYSOMÁTIDÆ
    Body surface spinulose, dark in color; 28 somites. (Chamæosòma, Achrochórdum, Palæarc.) .... CHAMÆOSOMÁTIDÆ
29. Promentum present as a separate, more or less triangular sclerite in front of the mentum (Fig. 1102).......................30
    Promentum absent 45
30. Hind gonopod forming a large, stout, unjointed club..........31
    Hind gonopod never forming a stout, unjointed club; usually one- or two-jointed, or sometimes more or less like a walking leg, with three to six joints......................................32
31. Sides of body longitudinally striate; tergites without lateral expansions. (Càseya, Nearc.) .... CASEYIDÆ
    Sides of body not longitudinally striate; anterior tergites with carinate lateral expansions. (Underwoodia, Nearc.).
    UNDERWOODÌIDÆ
32. Hind gonopod with a long thread-like or flagelliform process....33
    Hind gonopod without such long process.....................34
33. Front gonopod with a filiform process like that of the hind gonopod; second pair of legs of female with the joints beyond the coxæ vestigial. (Heteroporàtia, Tessinosòma, Haploporàtia, Palæarc.) .... HETEROPORATÌIDÆ
    Front gonopod without such process; second pair of legs of female normally developed, similar to the other legs. (Verhœffia, Palæarc.) .... VERHŒFFÌIDÆ
34. Posterior pair of legs of eighth somite with coxal glands.......35
    Posterior pair of legs of eighth somite without coxal glands. (Fagìna, Palæarc.) .... FAGÍNIDÆ
35. Tarsi of male without papillæ..............................36
    Tarsi of third to seventh pairs of legs of male furnished with papillæ 38
36. Hind gonopods one- or indistinctly two-jointed...............37
    Hind gonopods three- or four-jointed. (Brachychæteùma, Scutógona, Macrochæteùma, Palæarc.)....BRACHÝCHÆTEÙMIDÆ
37. Tracheal pockets (the cavities next to the spiracles, leading into the tracheal tube) fused with the sternite and not movable. (Anthógona, Cranógona, Palæarc.)........ANTHOGÓNIDÆ

Tracheal pockets not anchylosed with the sternite, movable. (Anthroleucosòma, Pródicus, Palæarc.).
ANTHROLEUCOSOMÁTIDÆ

38. Coxæ of the front gonopods not forming a ring.............39
Coxæ of the front gonopods partly fused, forming together a ring which bears the unsegmented, movable part of the gonopod. (Heterolatzélla, Palæarc.) .... HETEROLATZÉLLIDÆ

39. Coxæ of the front gonopods without an elongate, flagelliform process or long, stalked pencil of hairs......................40
Coxæ of front gonopods each bearing an elongate, flagelliform process or a long, stalked pencil of hairs. (Neatractosòma, Trimeróphoron, Palæarc.) .... NEATRACTOSOMÁTIDÆ

40. Coxæ of the second pair of legs of the eighth segment without a horn-like projection internally; hind gonopods highly modified, wanting or one- to three-jointed, rarely four-jointed, and not resembling walking legs 41
Coxæ of second pair of legs of the eighth segment with a horn-like projection internally; hind gonopods four- to six-jointed and with claw, retaining the appearance of walking legs. (Pseùdoclis, Palæarc.; Cleidógona, Am.; Pseudotrèmia, Nearc.).
PSEUDOCLÍDIDÆ

41. Sternite bearing the second pair of legs of the sixth somite in the male, produced into a long, rod-shaped process; coxæ of front gonopods elongate, free or nearly so. (Rothenbuehlèria, Palæarc.).
ROTHENBUEHLERÌIDÆ
This sternite without rod-shaped prolongation; coxæ of front gonopods shorter, not extending beyond the remainder of the gonopod, frequently fused together...............................42

42. Coxæ of the second pair of legs of the sixth somite of the male elongate; rounded inwardly or without distinct process medially 43
Coxæ of second pair of legs of sixth somite of the male transverse, with one or two processes which extend to the apex of the sternite. (Attémsia, Syngonopòdium, Dendromonómeron, Haasea, Palæarc.) .... ATTEMSÌIDÆ

43. Sternite of the front gonopod obsolete or absent, never with a median process; the coxæ firmly united.....................44
Sternite of the front gonopod very large, bearing a long median process; the coxæ not fused with one another. (Opisthocheìron, Palæarc.) .... OPISTHOCHEÌRIDÆ

44. Coxæ of the front gonopods flat, not prominent; hind gonopods two- to four-jointed. (Haplobainosòma, Brœlemanneùma, Hispaniosòma, Palæarc.) .... HAPLOBAINOSOMÁTIDÆ
Coxæ of front gonopods prominent, forming a simple or two-parted

elevation. (Craspedosòma, Oxydáctylon, Macheirióphoron, Cera-
tosòma, Palæarc.) .... CRASPEDOSOMÁTIDÆ

45. Coxæ of the ninth pair of legs with glands; tarsi of the third to
seventh pairs of legs almost always bearing papillæ............46
Coxæ of the ninth pair of legs without glands; tarsi usually without papillæ 48

46. Body composed of 32 somites; tergites with prominent lateral expansions. (Diplomarágna, Syntelopodeùma, Palæarc.).
DIPLOMARÁGNIDÆ
Body composed of 28 or 30 somites; tergites without or with very
slight lateral expansions.................................47

47. Hind gonopods two-jointed; second pair of legs on the sixth and
eighth somites modified into accessory gonopods, not resembling
walking legs. (Chordeùma, Chordeumélla, Microchordeùma,
Orthochordeumélla, Palæarc.) .... CHORDEÙMIDÆ
Hind gonopods three- to five-jointed; second pair of legs on the
sixth somite normal, similar to the other walking legs. (Oro-
bainosòma, Brachybainosòma, Palæarc.).
OROBAINOSOMÁTIDÆ

48. First pair of legs of the eighth somite highly modified, reduced to
two- or three-jointed stumps; vertex of male bearing one or two
tufts of hairs. (Metopídothrix, Schedotrígona, Indo-austr.).
METOPIDOTHRÍGIDÆ
First pair of legs of the eighth somite normal, not modified or reduced; vertex of male without tufts of hairs. (Conotỳla, Tri-
chopétalum, Zygónopus, Nearc.; Apodígona, Neotrop.; Japano-
sòma, Palæarc.) .... CONOTỲLIDÆ

49. Promentum present as a separate sclerite in front of the mentum
(as in Fig. 1102); ocelli numerous. (Superfamily LYSIOPETA-
LÒIDEA) 50
Promentum absent; one or two ocelli at each side of the head.
(Figs. 1111, 1112). (STEMMIULÒIDEA). Stemmiùlus, Pros-
temmiùlus, Diopsiùlus, Ethiop.).............. STEMMIÙLIDÆ

50. Second pair of legs of female completely formed, similar to the
other walking legs; tracheal pockets of gonopods small, fused
to the gonopod. (Cállipus, Palæarc.)......... CALLIPÓDIDÆ
Second pair of legs of female greatly reduced, the segments beyond
the coxæ not developed; tracheal pockets of gonopods large,
not fused to the gonopod................................51

51. Gonopods very long, slender and strongly bent. (Dorypétalum,
Silvéstria, Cyphocállipus, Dorycállipus, Palæarc.).
DORYPETÁLIDÆ
Gonopods not noticeably long, not bent. (Lysiopétalum, Apfel-
béckia, Broelemánnia, Callipodélla, Palæarc.).
LYSIOPETÁLIDÆ

52. Stipites meeting for a distance along the median line, separating the promentum from the mentum (Fig. 1101). (Superfamily JULOIDEA) 53
Stipites not meeting along the median line, widely separated by the mentum or promentum; promentum if present in contact with the mentum...54

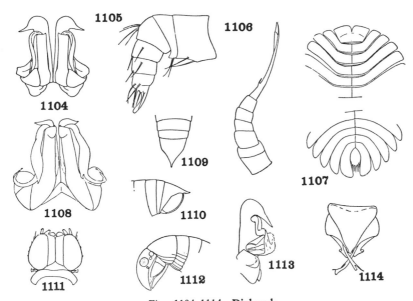

Figs. 1104–1114. Diplopoda

1104. **Diaporus,** gonopod (Chamberlin) Spirostreptidæ.
1105. **Siphonophora,** anterior gonopod (Chamberlin) Siphonophoridæ.
1106. **Siphonophora,** posterior gonopod (Chamberlin) Siphonophoridæ.
1107. **Platydesmus,** anterior and posterior ends of body (Chamberlin) Platydesmidæ.
1108. **Gymnostreptus,** gonopods (Chamberlin) Spirostreptidæ.
1109. **Paraiulus,** posterior end of body of male (Chamberlin) Blaniulidæ.
1110. **Paraiulus,** side view of posterior end of body of male (Chamberlin) Blaniulidæ.
1111. **Prostemmiulus,** gnathochilarium (Chamberlin) Stemmiulidæ.
1112. **Prostemmiulus,** head and first tergite (Chamberlin) Stemmiulidæ.
1113. **Orthoporus,** gonopod (Chamberlin) Spirostreptidæ.
1114. **Rhinocricus,** gonopods (Chamberlin) Rhinocricidæ.

53. Both pairs of gonopods lying in cavities; first pair of legs of male greatly reduced; body above usually with some longitudinal striation (**Julus**) .... **JULIDÆ**
Gonopods free, not sunk in depressions; first pair of legs of male usually four- to six-jointed; tergites without any longitudinal

striation. (Figs. 1109, 1110). (Blaniùlus, Chroneiùlus, Palæarc.; Nopoiùlus, Holarc., Neotrop.; Paraiùlus, Am.; Uroblaniùlus, Nearc.) (*PARAIÙLIDÆ*) .... BLANIÙLIDÆ

54. Promentum absent; mentum large, triangular, extending between the prebasilare and stipites which it separates widely (Fig. 1103); last joint of legs of male generally padded, but not the fourth or fifth joints. (Superfamily SPIROBOLÒIDEA) 55

Promentum present or absent; mentum surrounded at the sides by the stipites which extend backwards and lie in contact with the prebasilare. (SPIROSTREPTOMORPHA) 59

55. Hind gonopods connected to each other at base by the sternite and membranes; pores of repugnatorial glands usually opening on the anterior portion of the tergites. (TRIGONIULÍDEÆ) 56

Hind gonopods not united at base, sternite completely absent; pores of repugnatorial glands almost always opening on the posterior portion of the tergites. (SPIROBOLÍDEÆ) 58

56. Coxæ of hind gonopods completely chitinized 57

Coxæ of hind gonopods consisting of two rod-shaped thickenings meeting at a right angle with a membranous portion between them. (Trigoniùlus, Eucárlia, Cherástus, Ethiop., Indoaustr.; Mystálides, Ethiop., Malay.; Allopocóckia, Neotrop.). TRIGONIÙLIDÆ

57. Front gonopods short and broad. (Pachýbolus, Ethiop.; Microspiróbolus, Caríbolus, Neotrop.; Trachelomégalus, Eucentróbolus, Malay.) .... PACHYBÓLIDÆ

Front gonopods long and slender. (Spiromìnus, Pỳgodon, Ethiop.). SPIROMÍMIDÆ

58. Hind gonopods consisting of only a single joint, the coxa not distinctly separated or vestigial; first tergite more or less narrowed laterally. (Spiróbolus, Holarc.; Tylóbolus, Nearc.; Messicóbolus, Neotrop.; Pseudospiroboléllus, Indomal.; Spiroboléllus, Austromal.) .... SPIROBÓLIDÆ

Hind gonopods distinctly two-jointed; first tergite broadly rounded at the sides. (Fig. 1114). (Rhinócricus, Neotrop., Austromal.; Polyconóceras, Dinematócricus, Austromal.; Eurhinócricus, Cubóbolus, Neotrop.) .... RHINOCRÍCIDÆ

59. Mentum broadly triangular; its anterior angle lying far behind the front margin of the stipites. (Superfamily SPIROSTREPTÒI-DEA) 60

Mentum elongate-triangular, its anterior angle extending far forward, dividing the gnathochilarium completely to its anterior margin; first pair of legs of male modified. (Superfamily CAMBALÒIDEA) 62

60. Both sternites of the gonopod-bearing segment present, in spite of the atrophy of the hind gonopods. (ODONTOPYGÍDEÆ).

(Odontopỳge, Haplothỳsanus, Prionopétalum, Spinotársus, Ethiop.) .... ODONTOPÝGIDÆ
Sternite of the posterior part of the gonopod-bearing segment and the gonopod absent. (SPIROSTREPTÍDEÆ) 61

61. End of the gonopod flattened, almost always bearing on the edge a row of long, curved bristles; last somite without any spinose projection. (Figs. 1104, 1108, 1113). (Spirostréptus, Gymnostréptus, Diáporus, Orthóporus, Scaphiostréptus, Allóporus, Neotrop., Ethiop.) .... SPIROSTRÉPTIDÆ
End of the gonopod not thus flattened, without such bristles; anal segment almost always with a tail-like projection. (Harpagóphora, Ethiop.; Poratóphilus, Ethiop., Neotrop.; Thyropỳgus, Ethiop., Indomal.; Rhynchopróctus, Malay.) .... HARPAGOPHÓRIDÆ

62. Promentum present, separated from the mentum 63
Promentum not separated from the mentum; repugnatorial pores present on the fifth somite 65

63. Promentum divided into two halves by a longitudinal suture 64
Promentum not divided by a longitudinal suture. (Cámbala, Sámichus, Austr.; Nannolène, Epinannolène, Neotrop.; Julomórpha, widespr.). (Including NANNOLÉNIDÆ and EPINANNOLÉNIDÆ) .... CAMBÁLIDÆ

64. Repugnatorial pores absent on the fifth somite; hind gonopods three-jointed; front ones one-jointed, without bristles. (Pericámbala, Ind.) .... PERICAMBÁLIDÆ
Repugnatorial pores present on the fifth somite; hind gonopods wanting, the front ones two-jointed, the second joint strongly bristled. (Pseudonannolène, Neotrop.) .... PSEUDONANNOLÉNIDÆ

65. Posterior portion of tergites smooth; hind gonopods absent. (Physiostréptus, Holopodostréptus, Neotrop.). PHÝSIOSTRÉPTIDÆ
Posterior portion of the tergites with stout longitudinal carinæ or tubercles; hind gonopods present. (Cambalópsis, Cambalomórpha, Trachyiùlus, Ind.). (TRACHYIÚLIDÆ). CAMBALÓPSIDÆ

66. Sternites always, and pleurites often, free, i.e. connected by membranes with the adjacent parts 67
Tergites, pleurites and sternites completely coalesced; body cylindrical. (Siphoniùlus, Malay.) .... SIPHONIÙLIDÆ

67. Mentum and adjacent maxillary sclerites (gnathochilarium) consisting of a single plate or of several indistinctly defined pieces .. 68
Gnathochilarium possessing most of the parts typical of the Diplopoda (as in Fig. 1101). (Fig. 1107). (Platydésmus, N. Am.; Fiòria, Dolístenus, Palæarc.) .... PLATYDÉSMIDÆ

68. One or several ocelli at each side of the head; body not constricted on the base of each somite 69
Ocelli absent; body constricted at the base of each somite; repugnatorial pores opening on keels or tubercles. (Figs. 1105, 1106.)

(Siphonóphora, Indoaust., Ethiop., Neotrop.; Siphonorhìnus, Malay., Neotrop.) .... SIPHONOPHÓRIDÆ

69. Repugnatorial pores opening on the lateral lobes of the tergites; tergites divided by a median suture; head completely concealed by the first tergite. (Siphonocrýptus, Malay.).

SIPHONOCRÝPTIDÆ

Repugnatorial pores opening on the body of the tergites, far from the lateral margin; tergites without median suture; head partly free and visible. (Polyzònium, Orsíboe, Palæarc.; Siphonòtus, Austromal., Neotrop.; Burínia, Ethiop.) ...... POLYZONÌIDÆ

LITERATURE ON BOTH DIPLOPODA AND CHILOPODA (MYRIAPODA)

ATTEMS, C. Die indo-australischen Myriapoden. Arch. Naturg. Jahrg. 80A, Heft 4, pp. 1–398 (1914).

Chilopoda and Diplopoda in Kükenthal's Handbuch der Zoologie, 4, Lief. 1–4, pp. 17–402 (1926).

The Myriapoda of South Africa. Ann. South African Mus., 26, pp. 1–431 (1928).

Die Myriapodenfauna von Albanien und Jugoslavien. Zool. Jahrb. Abth. f. Syst., 56, pp. 269–356 (1929).

Leptodesmidæ und andere Polydesmiden. Zoologica, Heft 79, 149 pp. (1931).

BOLLMAN, C. H. Myriapoda of North America. Bull. U. S. Nat. Mus., 46, pp. 1–210 (1893).

CHAMBERLIN, R. V. The Chilopoda and Diplopoda of the West Indies. Bull. Mus. Comp. Zoöl. Harvard, 62, pp. 151–262 (1918).

The Myriapoda of the Australian Region. Bull. Mus. Comp. Zoöl. Harvard, 64, pp. 1–269 (1920).

COOK, O. F. The Myriapoda of Northwestern North America. Pap. Harriman Alaska Exped., 8, pp. 49–77 (1910).

LATZEL, R. Die Myriapoden der Oesterreichisch-Ungarischen Monarchie. Alb. Hölder, Vienna (1880–84).

UNDERWOOD, L. M. The North American Myriapoda. Ent. Americana, 1, pp. 141–151 (1885).

VERHOEFF, K. W. Diplopoda. Results of Dr. E. Mjöberg's Swedish Sci. Exped. to Australia. Ark. Zool., 16, No. 5, 142 pp. (1924).

WOOD, H. C. Myriapoda of North America. Trans. American Philos. Soc., 13, pp. 137–248 (1865).

LITERATURE ON DIPLOPODA

ATTEMS, C. System der Polydesmiden. Denkschr. math.-naturw. Kl. Kais. Akad. Wiss. Wien, 67, pp. 1–262 (1898); ibid., 68, pp. 1–186 (1899).

Ueber paläarktische Diplopoden. Arch. Naturg. Jahrg. 92A, No. 1, pp. 1–144; No. 2, pp. 145–256 (1927).

Diplopoden des Belgischen Congo. Polydesmoidea. Rev. Zool. Bot. Afr., 17, pp. 253–378 (1929).

Die Familie Leptodesmidæ und andere Polydesmiden. Zoologica, Stuttgart, **30**, Lief. 3–4, pp. 1–150, 245 figs. (1931).

Polydesmoidea. In Bronn's Klassen und Ordnungen des Tierreichs, Lief. **68**, pp. 1–300, 343 figs.; **69**, 1–487 pp., 509 figs. (1937–38).

Beiträge zur Kenntnis der Uiliden. Ann. naturh. Mus. Wien, **50**, pp. 294–327, 69 figs. (1939).

BRÖLEMANN, H. W. Essai de Classification des Polydesmiens. Ann. Soc. Ent. France, **84**, pp. 523–608 (1916).

Blaniulidæ. Arch. Zool. Paris, **61**, pp. 99–453 (1923).

Diplopoda. Faune de France, **29**, pp. 1–369, 750 figs. (1935).

CARL, J. Die Diplopoden-Fauna von Celebes. Rev. Suisse Zool., **20**, pp. 75–206 (1912).

CHAMBERLIN, R. V. Julidæ and Isobatidæ of North America. Proc. Biol. Soc. Washington, **34**, pp. 81–84 (1921).

The Millipedes of Central America. Proc. U. S. Nat. Mus., **60**, art. 8, pp. 1–75 (1922).

Diplopoda from Barro Colorado Island, Panama. Bull. Univ. Utah, Biol. Ser., **5**(6), pp. 1–16 (1940).

LOOMIS, H. F. Millipeds of Hispaniola. Bull. Mus. Comp. Zool., **80**, pp. 1–191, 75 figs., 3 pls. (1936).

New Millipedes of the United States. Bull. Mus. Comp. Zool., **92**, pp. 371–410 (1943).

POCOCK, R. J. Diplopoda, in Biologia Centrali-Americana, pp. 41–217 (1904–10).

SCHUBART, O. Tausendfüssler oder Myriapoda (Diplopoda). In Dahl, Tierwelt Deutschlands, Teil **28**, pp. 1–318, 480 figs. (1934).

VERHOEFF, K. W. Die Diplopoden Deutschlands. 8 parts, 640 pp. Leipzig (1910–14).

Zur Kenntnis italienischer Diplopoden. Zool. Jahrb. (Syst.), **60**, pp. 281–326, 3 pls. (1930).

Diplopoda. In Bronn's Klassen und Ordnungen des Tierreichs, **5**, Buch 2, Lief. 10, pp. 1523–1674, 82 figs. (1930); Lief. 11, pp. 1675–1834, 44 figs. (1931); Lief. 12–13, pp. 1837–2084 (1932).

Diplopoda, Symphyla, Pauropoda, Chilopoda. In Brohmer, Tierwelt Mitteleuropas, **2**, Lief. 3, pp. 1–120, 140 figs. (1934).

Zwei neue Myriapoden-Gattungen aus Indien. Zool. Anz., **117**, pp. 85–91 (1937).

Polydesmoideen, Colobognathen und Geophilomorphen aus Südafrika. Ann. Natal Mus., **9**, pp. 203–224, 42 figs. (1939).

Polydesmoidea and Colobognatha. Zool. Anz., **130**, pp. 104–119, 12 figs. (1940).

Ostasiatische Diplopoden aus Höhlen. Mitt. Hohlen- u. Karstforsch., **1941**, pp. 34–45, 15 figs. (1941).

Diplopoden der Insel Ischia. Zeits. Morph. Ökol. Tiere, **38**, pp. 147–196, 48 figs. (1941).

Über Gruppen der Leptodesmiden und neues System der Ordo Polydesmoidea. Arch. Naturgesch., (N.F.) **10**, pp. 399–415, 5 figs. (1941).

Ein cavernicole Familie der Diplopoden (Antroremyidæ). Zool. Anz., **139**, pp. 54–66, 13 figs. (1942).

Zur Kenntnis der Cambaliden. Zool. Anz., **145**, pp. 27–45, 19 figs. (1944).

Some Californian Chilognatha — Diplopoda. Bull. Southern California Acad. Sci., **43**, pp. 53–70, 2 pls. (1944).

CLASS **CHILÓPODA**

Body long, comparatively or very narrow, of nearly even width and dorsoventrally depressed; nineteen or more, sometimes many more body segments. Fifteen or more pairs of legs, inserted at the sides of the body and widely separated by sternal plates; never more than a single pair to any body segment; legs six- or seven-jointed, with a single apical claw, or with a flagellum in Scutigera. Head bearing a pair of long, many-jointed antennæ (14 joints or more); eyes composed of groups of ocelli, sometimes massed to form two apparently faceted eyes. Mandibles and two pairs of maxillæ present; appendages of first body segment greatly enlarged, forming a pair of large six-jointed poison-fangs (toxicognaths). Last two pairs of legs often greatly modified and directed backwards. Respiration through spiracles, the latter paired and located on the pleuræ or unpaired and located along the dorsal line. Genital ducts usually opening on the penultimate body segment. A widespread, moderately large group, of active carnivorous habits. Centipedes.

The system adopted here follows that of Attems in his account of "The Myriopoda of South Africa."

1. Nineteen body segments with fifteen pairs of legs; not more than seven segments bearing spiracles, the tracheæ not anastomosing; some of the tergites reduced so that never more than eight are present; newly hatched animals with seven pairs of legs. (Subclass ANAMÓRPHA) 2

   Twenty-five or more body segments with 21 or more pairs of legs, sometimes many more; nine or more pairs of spiracles, the tracheæ anastomosing; newly hatched animals with the full number of legs present in the adult. (Subclass EPIMÓRPHA).....6

2. Spiracles unpaired, seven in number; placed on the middle dorsal line near the posterior border of the tergites; eyes compound, with faceted surface; tracheæ not branched. (Fig. 1116). (Order SCUTIGEROMÓRPHA). (**Scutígera, Thereuónema, Parascutígera, Thereuópoda,** mainly tropical or subtropical).

   SCUTIGÉRIDÆ

   Spiracles paired, placed on the pleuræ between the tergites and the coxæ; eyes not compound; single ocelli or groups of ocelli or eyes absent; tracheæ branched. (Order LITHOBIOMÓRPHA).....3

3. Tergites of the leg-bearing segments alternately long and short, except at the middle of the body; those corresponding to legs

2, 4, 6, 9, 11 and 13 (not counting the jaws as legs) much smaller than the others. (Suborder LITHOBIOMORPHÍDEA)......4

Tergites of the leg-bearing segments not noticeably different in size, except the one bearing the jaws, which is shorter; in front of segments 4, 6, 8, 9, 11 and 13 with a greatly reduced, intercalary segment. (Suborder CRATEROSTIGMORPHÍDEA). (**Craterostígmus**, Austr.) .... **CRATEROSTÍGMIDÆ**

4. From one to five of the posterior pairs of legs with coxal glands opening by pores, legs usually spinose; ocelli, when present, placed near to the margin of the head. (Superfamily LITHO-BIÒIDEA) 5

No coxal glands opening by pores; legs without spines; ocelli widely separated from the margin of the head. (Superfamily CERMATOBIÒIDEA). (**Cermatòbius**, Ind.) **CERMATOBÌIDÆ**

5. Tibiæ of all legs without a spinose projection externally at tip. (Fig. 1117). (**Lithòbius**, Holarc., Ethiop.; **Monotarsòbius, Alokòbius, Polybóthrus**, Palæarc.; **Garíbius**, Nearc.; **Australòbius**, Palæarc., Indoaustr.; **Bothrópolys**, Holarc., Austromal.)
LITHOBÌIDÆ

Tibiæ of legs 11–14 with a spinose, tooth-like projection externally at tip. (**Hénicops**, Austr.; **Paralamýctes, Anopsòbius**, Neotrop., Ethiop., Austr.; **Zygethòbius**, Am.) ....**HENICÓPIDÆ**

6. Antennæ with 17–20 or more joints; four ocelli on each side, or more; 21–23 leg-bearing segments; 9, 10, 11 or 19 pairs of spiracles. (Order SCOLOPENDROMÓRPHA) 7

Antennæ 14-jointed; ocelli absent; 31–170 leg-bearing segments; all leg-bearing segments except the first and last with a pair of spiracles. (Order GEOPHILOMÓRPHA) 8

7. Eyes present, each composed of a group of four ocelli; tarsi two-jointed; sternites usually with a pair of longitudinal grooves, never with a transverse groove. (Fig. 1116) **SCOLOPÉNDRIDÆ**

a. Spiracular cavity divided into an inner and outer chamber by a tripartite or tufted partition. (**Scolopéndra, Chormocéphalus**, tropicopol.; **Campylostígmus**, Malay.; **Asanàda**, widespr.; **Arthrorhábdna**, Am., Austr.) ....**SCOLOPENDRÌNÆ**

Spiracular cavity simple, not divided. (**Otostígmus**, tropicopol.; **Rhysídia**, Indoaustr., Ethiop., Neotrop.; **Álipes**, Ethiop.)
OTOSTIGMÌNÆ

Eyes absent, or occasionally indicated by a pale spot; tarsi of legs 1–19 almost always one-jointed; sternites usually with a single median groove, never with a pair of grooves, often with one transverse groove. (Fig. 1118) ....**CRYPTÓPIDÆ**

a. Twenty-one pairs of legs; coxopleuræ usually without a spinose projection ....b

Twenty-three pairs of legs; coxopleuræ with a spiniform projection.
(**Scolopocrýptops,** Holarc., Neotrop.; **Otocrýptops,** widespr.;
Newpórtia, Neotrop.) .... SCOLOPOCRYPTOPÌNÆ

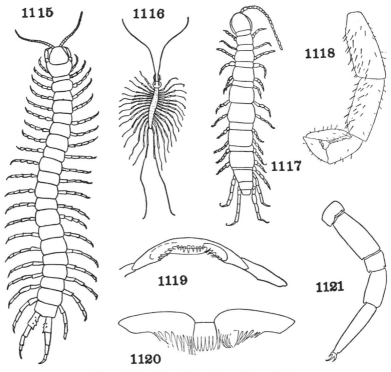

Figs. 1115–1121. Chilopoda and Symphyla

1115. **Scolopendra** (Newport) Scolopendridæ.
1116. **Scutigera** (Howard) Scutigeridæ.
1117. **Monotarsobius.** Lithobiidæ.
1118. **Cryptops,** last leg (Chamberlin) Cryptopidæ.
1119. **Soniphilus,** labrum (Chamberlin) Soniphilidæ.
1120. **Suturodes,** labrum (Chamberlin) Geophilidæ.
1121. **Scutigerella,** leg (Ewing) Scutigerellidæ.

b. Last leg-bearing segment lengthened, its legs very stout. (**Thèatops,**
Holarc.; **Plutònium,** Palæarc.) .... THEATOPÌNÆ
Last leg-bearing segment of normal size. (**Crýptops,** cosmop.;
Mìmops, widespr.; **Ánethops,** Nearc.) .... CRYPTOPÌNÆ

8. Mandible with several pectinate lamellæ and with or without a
dentate lamella 9

Margin of mandible simple, beset with one row of teeth; mandible with or without a dentate lamella 11

9. Mandible with one dentate lamella in addition to the pectinate lamellæ; labrum consisting of one piece; antennæ short, thick at base and gradually tapering, the basal joints with short hairs, but without long bristles. (**Himantàrium**, Palæarc., Ethiop.; **Mesocánthus**, Palæarc., Ethiop., Indomal.; **Haplóphilus**, **Bothriogáster**, Palæarc.) ....HIMANTARÌIDÆ
Mandible with pectinate lamellæ, but without any dentate lamella in addition 10

10. Labrum consisting of one piece, not especially broad; coxæ of first maxillæ completely fused. (**Òrya**, Palæarc.; **Orphnæus**, tropicopol.; **Ctenòrya**, Ethiop.; **Paròrya**, Nearc.) ... ORÌYIDÆ
Labrum tripartite; one small median tooth and two broad lateral pieces with strong edges at the sides of the cephalic pleuræ; coxæ of first maxillæ meeting at the median suture. (**Mecisto-céphalus**, Ethiop., Indoaustr.; **Prolammònyx**, **Dicellóphilus**, Palæarc.; **Árrup**, Nearc.; **Tygárrup**, Neotrop.)
MECISTOCEPHÁLIDÆ

11. Mandible with one dentate lamella; labrum consisting of one piece; antennæ filiform or clavate. (**Schendỳla**, Holarc., Neotrop., Mal.; **Escáryus**, Holarc.; **Nannóphilus**, Ethiop., Neotrop.; **Ballóphilus**, Ethiop., Austromal.; **Schendylùrus**, Palæarc., Ethiop., Neotrop.) ....SCHENDỲLIDÆ
Mandible without a dentate lamella 12

12. Coxæ of the first maxillæ fused, each bearing a median process and a one- or two-jointed apical portion 13
Coxæ of the first maxillæ completely separated, bearing a conical second joint; claws of anterior legs with a strong tooth. (**Neogeóphilus**, **Evallogeóphilus**, Neotrop.) (Including *AZYGÉ-THIDÆ*) ....NEOGEOPHÍLIDÆ

13. Labrum consisting of a single piece; antennæ generally flattened at the base and tapering 14
Labrum consisting of three parts, rarely more or less fused (Fig. 1119), the median piece sometimes partially fused with the lateral pieces; coxæ of the last legs not enlarged 15

14. Coxæ of the last pair of legs much enlarged, extending forward at the sides sometimes to the antepenultimate leg-bearing segment; paratergites (one or several rows of small plates between the tergites and the row of pleurites that bear the spiracles) generally present. (**Gonibrégmatus**, Austromal.; **Eucratònyx**, Indoaustr.; **Himantosòma**, Indomal.; **Macronicóphilus**, Neotrop.)
GONIBREGMÁTIDÆ
Coxæ of the last pair of legs not enlarged, not extending in front

of the last leg-bearing segment; paratergites absent. (Sogòna, Timpìna, Nearc.; Garrìna, Neotrop.) ....SOGÓNIDÆ

15. The median piece of the labrum, if present, not fused with the lateral pieces; in the middle the two larger and ventrally directed teeth lacking. (Fig. 1120). (Geóphilus, widespr.; Eurýtion, Ethiop., Neotrop., Austr.; Scolióplanes, Holarc.; Polygonàrea, Austr., Ethiop.; Aphílodon, Ethiop., Neotrop.; Hènia, Palæarc.; Pachymèrium, Holarc., Neotrop., Ethiop.) ....GEOPHÍLIDÆ

The median piece of the labrum at least partly fused with the lateral ones; two larger teeth in the middle, directed more or less ventrally. (Fig. 1119). (Soníphilus, Poáphilus, Nearc.)

SONIPHÍLIDÆ

LITERATURE ON CHILOPODA

See also Literature on Myriapoda, p. 768

ATTEMS, C. Myriapoda. Geophilomorpha. Das Tierreich, Lief. 52, 388 pp. (1929).

    Chilopoda, Scolopendromorpha. Das Tierreich, Lief. 54, 308 pp. (1930).

BAILEY, J. W. Chilopoda of New York State. Bull. New York State Mus., No. 276, 50 pp. (1928).

BRÖLEMANN, H. W. Chilopoda. Faune de France, 25, pp. 1–405, 481 figs. (1932).

BÜCHERL, W. Os quilopodos do Brasil. Mem. Inst. Butantan São Paulo, 13, pp. 49–362 (1939).

CHAMBERLIN, R. V. Chilopoda of California. Pomona Journ. Zoöl. Ent., 2, 3, 4 (1910–12). (Three parts).

    The Chilopoda of Brazil. Bull. Mus. Comp. Zoöl. Harvard, 58, pp. 151–221 (1914).

    The Centipedes of Central America. Proc. U. S. Nat. Mus., 60, Art. 7, pp. 1–17 (1922).

    The Ethnopolidæ of North America. Bull. Mus. Comp. Zoöl. Harvard, 57, pp. 385–437 (1925).

    Chilopoda of Alaska. Ann. Ent. Soc. America, 39, pp. 177–189 (1946).

KRAEPELIN, K. Revision der Scolopendriden. Jahrb. Hamburg Anst., Beiheft 2, Mitt. Mus. Hamburg, pp. 1–276 (1903).

POCOCK, R. I. Chilopoda. Biologia Centrali-Americana, pp. 1–40 (1896).

VERHOEFF, K. W. Chilopoda. Bronn's Tierreich, 5, Abth. 2, Lief. 83–99, pp. 83–537 (1915–18).

    Chilopoda. Ibid., 5, Abt. 2, Lief. 100, pp. 539–666 (1925).

    Chilognathen aus Nordwestitalien und andere mediterrane Diplopoden. Zool. Jahrb. (Syst.), 68, pp. 353–444, 6 pls. (1936).

CLASS SÝMPHYLA

Very small, delicate, elongate species with thin unpigmented integument. Body long, composed of fifteen to twenty-two similar segments; twelve pairs of short, five-jointed legs. Mouthparts consisting of a pair of mandibles and two pairs of maxillæ. Antennæ many-jointed, the joints short, more or less moniliform. Cerci stout, lanceolate, one-jointed or very indistinctly annulated. Respiration by tracheæ opening by a single pair of spiracles on the head. Usually in soil.

1. Fifteen to seventeen tergites; first pair of legs much smaller than the others 2
   Twenty-one to twenty-four tergites; first pair of legs almost as large as the others. (Geophilélla, Ribautiélla) . GEOPHILÉLLIDÆ
2. An intercalated segment without legs present behind the fourth, sixth and eighth segments only; posterior margin of tergites rounded, the corners rarely angulate; first pair of legs fully half as long as the others. (Figs. 11, 1121). (Scutigerélla, Hanseniélla, Tasmaniélla) .... SCUTIGERÉLLIDÆ
   An intercalated legless segment present behind segments four, six, eight, ten and twelve; posterior margin of tergites angulate laterally; first pair of legs usually imperfect and less than half as long as the others. (Scolopendrélla, Scolopendrópsis, Symphylélla) .... SCOLOPENDRÉLLIDÆ

LITERATURE ON SYMPHYLA

HANSEN, H. J. The Genera and Species of the Order Symphyla. Quart. Journ. Micr. Sci., **47**, pp. 1–101 (1903).

HILTON, W. A. Symphyla from North America. Ann. Ent. Soc. America, **24**, pp. 537–552, 1 pl. (1931).

LATZEL, R. Die Myriapoden der Oesterreichisch-Ungarischen Monarchie. Alb. Hölder, Vienna (1880–84).

MICHELBACHER, A. E. Notes on Symphyla. Ann. Ent. Soc. America, **32**, pp. 747–757 (1939).

Two New Genera of Symphyla. Ibid., **34**, pp. 139–150 (1941). Synopsis of Scutigerella. Ibid., **35**, pp. 267–288 (1942). Genera of Symphyla New to the United States. Ibid., **36**, pp. 139–150, 2 pls. (1943).

VERHOEFF, K. W. Symphyla. In Bronn's Klassen und Ordnungen des Tierreichs, **5**, Abt. 2, Buch 3, Lief. 1, pp. 1–120, 62 figs. (1933).

PART III

EXTINCT FAMILIES OF INSECTS

This section covers the extinct families of both living and extinct orders of insects. The keys of these families are intended to indicate only some of the more obvious taxonomic differences involved and to show the pattern of classification currently in use. They are not intended, on the other hand, to provide a means of identifying a fossil insect to its family. For this to be possible, extinct orders would need to be incorporated into the key to living orders, and extinct families into the keys to living families. Such an arrangement is impractical, since those characteristics used in the keys to living families are not usually preserved in the fossils.

A major problem in dealing with the fossils is the fragmentary nature of much of the material which has been described and for which families have been erected. The policy of establishing families "provisionally" for fragmentary specimens was set by Handlirsch and followed by him for many years, resulting in an extensive series of nondescript groups which cannot be included in keys. Such families are mentioned, however, under the order to which they apparently belong; or if their ordinal affinities are obscure, they are listed under *Insecta incertae sedis*.

Forty-four extinct orders of insects have been erected. Since the concept of any extinct category, whether an order or a genus, is largely an arbitrary one, there is much difference of opinion about the number of these orders that warrants recognition. Many have been reduced to suborders or synonymy by their own authors; others were only "provisionally" established for small fragments which did not provide evidence for their actual relationships. The remaining extinct orders are the controversial ones, since arguments for or against the recognition of each can be advanced. In the present volume only ten extinct orders are considered valid. The "provisional" orders have been either eliminated (and their families placed in *Insecta incertae sedis*) or included in other orders. A chronological list of extinct orders, with an indication of their treatment here, is given on p. 778.

A table of geologic periods is included for reference, with a list of the symbols used in the keys to indicate geologic ranges. The geologic distribution of existing orders is given under each order, including the few in which no extinct families are known.

1. **Palæodictyóptera** (Goldenberg, 1877), Cp-Pm.
2. **Megasecóptera** (Brongniart, 1885), Cp-Pm.
3. **Protodonàta** (Brongniart, 1885), Cp-Pm.
4. *Palæohemíptera* (Handlirsch, 1904), Pm. Hemiptera
5. *Protoblattòidea* (Handlirsch, 1906), Cp-Pm. Protorthoptera
6. *Hadentomòidea* (Handlirsch, 1906), Cp. Protorthoptera
7. *Sypharopteròidea* (Handlirsch, 1906), Cp. Incertæ sedis
8. *Mixotermitòidea* (Handlirsch, 1906), Cp. Protorthoptera
9. *Reculòidea* (Handlirsch, 1906), Cp. Protorthoptera
10. *Hapalopteròidea* (Handlirsch, 1906), Cp. Protorthoptera
11. **Protephemérida** (Handlirsch, 1906), Cp.
12. **Protohemíptera** (Handlirsch, 1906), Cp-Pm.
13. **Protorthóptera** (Handlirsch, 1906), Cp-Pm.
14. *Protomecóptera* (Tillyard, 1917), Tr. Mecoptera
15. *Paratrichóptera* (Tillyard, 1919), Tr. Trichoptera
16. *Paramecóptera* (Tillyard, 1919), Tr. Mecoptera
17. *Synarmogòidea* (Handlirsch, 1919), Cp. Protorthoptera
18. *Diaphanopteròidea* (Handlirsch, 1919), Cp. Megasecoptera
19. *Aeroplanóptera* (Tillyard, 1923), Tr. Orthoptera
20. *Protohymenóptera* (Tillyard, 1923), Pm. Megasecoptera
21. *Protocoleóptera* (Tillyard, 1923), Pm. Protelytroptera
22. *Miomóptera* (Martynov, 1927), Cp-Pm. Protorthoptera, Corrodentia, Protoperlaria
23. **Protoperlària** (Tillyard, 1928), Pm.
24. *Pruvostitóptera* (Zalessky, 1929), Pm. Protorthoptera
25. *Meganisóptera* (Martynov, 1931), Cp-Pm. Protodonata
26. *Permodonàta* (Zalessky, 1931), Pm. Odonata
27. **Protelytróptera** (Tillyard, 1931), Pm.
28. *Archodonàta* (Martynov, 1932), Pm. Incertæ sedis
29. *Protodíptera* (Tillyard, 1935), Pm. Mecoptera
30. *Hemipsocóptera* (Zalessky, 1937), Pm. Hemiptera
31. *Cnemidolestòidea* (Handlirsch, 1937), Cp. Protorthoptera
32. *Paraplecóptera* (Martynov, 1938), Pm. Protorthoptera
33. **Caloneuròdea** (Martynov, 1938), Cp-Pm.
34. **Glosselytròdea** (Martynov, 1938), Pm.
35. *Protocicádida* (Haupt, 1941), Cp-Pm. Protorthoptera, Incertæ sedis
36. *Protofulgórida* (Haupt, 1941), Cp-Pm. Protorthoptera, Incertæ sedis
37. *Archæhymenóptera* (Haupt, 1941), Cp. Palæodictyoptera, Incertæ sedis
38. *Palæohymenóptera* (Haupt, 1941), Cp. Megasecoptera
39. *Hemiodonàta* (Zalessky, 1943), Pm. Palæodictyoptera
40. *Perielytròdea* (Zalessky, 1943), Pm. Incertæ sedis
41. *Anisáxia* (Forbes, 1943), Cp. Palæodictyoptera
42. *Permodictyóptera* (Zalessky, 1944), Pm. Incertæ sedis
43. *Aphelophlèbia* (Pierce, 1945), T. Plectoptera
44. *Breyerídea* (Haupt, 1949), Cp. Palæodictyoptera

Chronological List of Extinct Orders of Insects. The orders printed in boldface are accepted as valid in this volume; others are included elsewhere as indicated. An explanation of abbreviations is given on page 779.

ERA	PERIOD	APPROXIMATE TIME (IN MILLIONS OF YEARS)	
		DURATION OF PERIOD	SINCE BEGINNING OF PERIOD
CENOZOIC (Age of mammals and man)	Quaternary	1	1
	Tertiary	69	70
MESOZOIC (Age of reptiles)	Cretaceous	50	120
	Jurassic	35	155
	Triassic	35	190
PALEOZOIC (Age of invertebrates and primitive vertebrates)	Permian	25	215
	Carboniferous { Upper	35	250
	Carboniferous { Lower	50	300
	Devonian	50	350
	Silurian	40	390
	Ordovician	90	480
	Cambrian	70	550

Table of Geologic Periods. The following symbols are used in the keys: Cp, Upper Carboniferous (Pennsylvanian); Pm, Permian; Tr, Triassic; J, Jurassic; K, Cretaceous; T, Tertiary; Q, Quaternary; R, Recent.

CONSPECTUS OF THE EXTINCT FAMILIES OF INSECTA

Subclass **APTERYGOTA**
    Order **PROTURA** (No fossil record)
    Order **THYSANURA** (Tr — Recent)
        (Triassomachilidæ)
    Order **ENTOTROPHI** (T — Recent)
        (No extinct families)
    Order **COLLEMBOLA** (K or T — Recent)
        (Protentomobryidæ)
Subclass **PTERYGOTA**
    Order **PALÆODICTYOPTERA** (Cp — Pm)
        (Dictyoneuridæ, Paoliidæ, Syntonopteridæ, Protagrionidæ, Calvertiellidæ, Fouqueidæ, Breyeriidæ, ThesoneuridæJ, Lamprotiliidæ, Polycreagridæ, Spilapteridæ, Apopappidæ, Eubleptidæ, Homothetidæ, Permoneuridæ, Rochlingiidæ)
    Order **MEGASECOPTERA** (Cp — Pm)
        Suborder **Eumegasecoptera**
            (Brodiidæ, Aspidothoracidæ, Bardohymenidæ, Foririidæ, Protohymenidæ, Scytohymenidæ, Sphecopteridæ, Mischopteridæ, Ischnoptilidæ, Corydaloididæ)
        Suborder **Paramegasecoptera**
            (Elmoidæ, Diaphanopteridæ, Martynoviidæ, Asthenohymenidæ, Biarmohymenidæ)
        Incertae sedis
            (Rhaphidiopsidæ, Prochoropteridæ, Kuĺojidæ, Parabrodiidæ, Carbonopteridæ, Campylopteridæ, Aspidohymenidæ)
    Order **PROTEPHEMERIDA** (Cp)
        (Triplosobidæ)
    Order **PLECTOPTERA** (Pm — Recent)
        Suborder **Permoplectoptera**
            (Protereismatidæ, Misthodotidæ, Doteridæ)
        Suborder **Euplectoptera**
            (Mesephemeridæ)
    Order **PROTODONATA** (Cp — Pm)
        (Erasipteridæ, Paralogidæ, Meganeuridæ)
    Order **ODONATA** (Pm — Recent)
        Suborder **Protozygoptera**
            (Kennedyidæ, Permolestidæ)
        Suborder **Archizygoptera**
            (Protomyrmeleontidæ)
        Suborder **Protanisoptera**
            (Ditaxineuridæ, Polytaxineuridæ)
        Suborder **Anisozygoptera**
            (Tarsophlebiidæ, Stenophlebiidæ, Heterophlebiidæ, Progonophlebiidæ, Liassophlebiidæ, Archithemistidæ, Sieblosiidæ)
        Suborder **Zygoptera**
            (Permagrionidæ, Zacallitidæ)

Suborder **Anisoptera**
   (Liassogomphidæ)
Incertae sedis
   (Mesophlebiidæ, Eosagrionidæ, Steleopteridæ, Camptotaxineuridæ)
Order **PROTOHEMIPTERA** (Cp — Pm)
   (Eugereonidæ, Homoiopteridæ, Lithomanteidæ)
Order **PROTOPERLARIA** (Pm)
   (Lemmatophoridæ)
Order **PLECOPTERA** (Pm — Recent)
   (Hypoperlidæ)
Order **PROTORTHOPTERA** (Cp — Pm)
   (Stenoneuridæ, Epideigmatidæ, Narkemidæ, Ischnoneuridæ,
   Spanioderidæ, Homoedictyidæ, Blattinopsidæ, Euryptilonidæ,
   Stereopteridæ, Protokollariidæ, Adeloneuridæ, Cacurgidæ,
   Probnisidæ, Protembiidæ, Chelopteridæ, Liomopteridæ,
   Palæocixiidæ, Atactophlebiidæ, Demopteridæ, Phenopteridæ,
   Ideliidæ, Sthenaropodidæ, Œdischiidæ, Adiphlebiidæ, Aeto-
   phlebiidæ, Anhomalophlebiidæ, Anthracothremmidæ, Api-
   thanidæ, Asyncritidæ, Climaconeuridæ, Cymenophlebiidæ,
   Emphylopteridæ, Epimasticidæ, Eucanidæ, Gerapompidæ,
   Geraridæ, Hadentomidæ, Hapalopteridæ, Kliveriidæ, Mixoter-
   mitidæ, Nemuropsidæ, Omalidæ, Pachytylopsidæ, Permocap-
   niidæ, Permotermopsidæ, Prostenoneuridæ, Protophasmatidæ,
   Prototettigidæ, Rachimentomidæ, Reculidæ, Roomeriidæ,
   Stenoneurellidæ, Stenoneuritidæ, Strephoneuridæ, Sylvaphle-
   biidæ, Sylviodidæ, Synarmogidæ, Tcholmanvissiidæ and
   Thoronysidæ)
Order **BLATTARIA** (Cp — Recent)
   (Archimylacridæ, Spiloblattinidæ, Mylacridæ, Pteridomylacridæ,
   Pseudomylacridæ, Cainoblattinidæ)
Order **CALONEURODEA** (Cp — Pm)
   (Caloneuridæ, Synomaloptilidæ, Euthygrammidæ, Permobiellidæ,
   Paleuthygrammidæ, Pleisiogrammidæ, Anomalogrammidæ)
Order **ORTHOPTERA** (Tr — Recent)
Suborder **Manteodea**
   (Triassomanteidæ)
Suborder **Grylloblattodea** (No fossil record)
Suborder **Saltatoria**
   (Locustopsidæ, Elcanidæ, Mesotitanidæ, Bintoniellidæ)
Suborder **Phasmatodea**
   (Necrophasmatidæ, Chresmodidæ, Ærophasmatidæ, Æroplanidæ)
Order **GLOSSELYTRODEA** (Pm)
   (Jurinidæ, Glosselytridæ)
Order **PROTELYTROPTERA** (Pm)
   (Elytroneuridæ, Megelytridæ, Blattelytridæ, Protelytridæ, Archely-
   tridæ, Protocoleidæ, Permofulgoridæ)
Order **DERMAPTERA** (J — Recent)
   (Protodiplatyidæ)
Order **EMBIODEA** (T — Recent)
   (No extinct families)

Order **ISOPTERA** (T — Recent)
(No extinct families)
Order **CORRODENTIA** (Pm — Recent)
(Permembiidæ, Palæomanteidæ, Delopteridæ, Zygopsocidæ,
Martynopsocidæ, Permopsocidæ, Dichentomidæ, Archipsyllidæ,
Lophioneuridæ, Zoropsocidæ, Asienthomidæ)
Order **ZORAPTERA** (No fossil record)
Order **MALLOPHAGA** (No fossil record)
Order **THYSANOPTERA** (Pm — Recent)
(Permothripidæ, Mesothripidæ)
Order **HEMIPTERA** (Pm — Recent)
Suborder **Homoptera**
(Archescytinidæ, Protopsyllidæ, Ipsviciidæ, Pereboriidæ, Coleoscy-
tidæ, Mesogereonidæ, Paleontinidæ, Prosbolopsidæ, Prosbolidæ,
Scytinopteridæ)
Suborder **Heteroptera**
(Paraknightiidæ)
Order **ANOPLURA** (Q — Recent)
(No extinct families)
Order **NEUROPTERA** (Pm — Recent)
Suborder **Sialodea**
(Archisialidæ, Permosialidæ)
Suborder **Raphidiodea**
(Permoraphidiidæ, Mesoraphidiidæ)
Suborder **Planipennia**
(Permoberothidæ, Mesochrysopidæ, Nymphitidæ, Prohemerobiidæ,
Permosisyridæ, Palæmerobiidæ, Permithonidæ, Kalligrammidæ,
Solenoptilidæ, Epigambriidæ)
Order **MECOPTERA** (Pm — Recent)
(Platychoristidæ, Anormochoristidæ, Belmontiidæ, Permotipulidæ,
Pseudopolycentropodidæ, Orthophlebiidæ, Archipanorpidæ,
Dobbertinidæ, Mesopsychidæ, Triassopsychidæ, Tillyarditidæ)
Order **TRICHOPTERA** (J — Recent)
(Prosepididontidæ, Necrotauliidæ)
Order **LEPIDOPTERA** (T — Recent)
(No extinct families)
Order **DIPTERA** (J — Recent)
Suborder **Nematocera**
(Protobibionidæ, Protoscatopsidæ, Pleciomimidæ, Protopleciidæ,
Pleciofungivoridæ, Paraxymiidæ, Eopleciidæ, Architipulidæ,
Eoptychopteridæ, Protorhyphidæ.
Suborder **Brachycera**
Division ORTHORRHAPHA
(Protocyrtidæ)
Division CYCLORRHAPHA
(Archiphoridæ)
Order **SIPHONAPTERA** (T — Recent)
(No extinct families)
Order **COLEOPTERA** (Pm — Recent)
Suborder **Adephaga**

(Tshekardocoleidæ, Permocupidæ, Sojanocoleidæ, Permor-
rhaphidæ)
Suborder **Polyphaga**
(Permophilidæ, Permosynidæ, Curculiopsidæ)
Order **STREPSIPTERA** (T — Recent)
(No extinct families)
Order **HYMENOPTERA** (J — Recent)
Suborder **Chalastogastra**
(Anaxyelidæ, Paroryssidæ, Myrmiciidæ)
Suborder **Clistogastra**
(Serphitidæ, Pelecinopteridæ, Ephialtitidæ)
Incertæ sedis (ordinal position doubtful)
(Ænigmatodidæ, Ampelipteridæ, Anorthoneuridæ, Archæoptilidæ,
Archæoptilitidæ, Bardapteridæ, Chaulioditidæ, Cheliphlebiidæ,
Coseliidæ, Cryptoveniidæ, Eohymenidæ, Heolidæ, Hyper-
megethidæ, Ideloblattidæ, Laspeyresiellidæ, Mecynopteridæ,
Megagnathidæ, Metropatidæ, Orthocostidæ, Perielytridæ, Per-
moneuridæ, Permothemidæ, Protermidæ, Pruvostitidæ, Ptero-
nidiidæ, Schuchertiellidæ, Strephoneuridæ, Stygnidæ, Sycop-
teridæ, Sylvaellidæ, Sypharopteridæ, Tillyardiellidæ, Tomiidæ,
Tshorkuphlebiidæ, Uralotermitidæ, Xenoneuridæ)

KEY TO EXTINCT ORDERS

1. Palæopterous insects, resting with wings outstretched, not folded
over abdomen, or if wings are folded over abdomen (some
Megasecoptera), the cerci are longer than entire body 2
Neopterous insects, resting with wings folded over abdomen; cerci
not longer than the abdomen 6
2. Wings with a complete set of main veins, showing alternation of
convexities and concavities 3
Wings lacking two main veins (posterior media, MP, and anterior
cubitus, CuA). (Including *MEGANISÓPTERA*)
(Cp-Pm) **PROTODONÀTA**
3. Mouth-parts mandibulate or without a conspicuous haustellate
beak 4
Mouth-parts haustellate, with a prominent beak. (*PSEUDO-
HEMÍPTERA*) .... (Cp-Pm) **PROTOHEMÍPTERA**
4. Wings with a fine archedictyon or with reticulated, irregular cross-
veins. (Including *HEMIODONÀTA, ANISÁXIA, PERMO-
DICTYÓPTERA, BREYERIDEA, ARCHÆHYMENÓPTERA*,
part) .... (Cp-Pm) **PALÆODICTYÓPTERA**
Wings with distinct cross-veins, not irregular or reticulate 5
5. Median caudal filament present ...... (Cp) **PROTEPHEMÉRIDA**
Median caudal filament absent. (Including *PROTOHYMEN-
ÓPTERA, DIAPHANOPTEROIDEA, PALÆOHYMEN-
ÓPTERA*) .... (Cp-Pm) **MEGASECÓPTERA**

6. Fore wing distinctly tegminous or elytrous 7
   Fore wing membranous 9
7. Fore wing with a conspicuous precostal area, and submarginal veins (subcosta, Sc, and posterior cubitus, CuP) following the distal half of wing margin . . . . . . (Pm-J) **GLOSSELYTRÒDEA**
   Fore wing at most with a small precostal area, and with no submarginal veins as above 8
8. Fore wing elytrous, with reduced and weak venation; anal area of hind wing much larger than the remigium. (Including *PROTO-COLEÓPTERA*) . . . .(Pm) **PROTELYTRÓPTERA**
   Fore wing tegminous, with normally developed venation; anal area of hind wing much smaller than remigium. (Including *PROTOBLATTÒIDEA, PRUVOSTITÓPTERA, MIXOTER-MITÒIDEA, SYNARMOGÒIDEA, HAPALOPTERÒIDEA, HADENTOMÒIDEA, RECULÒIDEA, CNEMIDOLEST-ÒIDEA, PARAPLECÓPTERA, MIOMÓPTERA*, part, *PROTO-CICADIDA*, part, *PROTOFULGORIDA*, part).
   (Cp-Pm) **PROTORTHÓPTERA,** part
9. Fore and hind wings similar in shape and venation.
   (Cp-Pm) **CALONEURÒDEA**
   Hind wing with a much larger anal area than the fore wing, and with more anal veins 10
10. Prothoracic paranotal lobes of adults always present and independent of each other; anal area of hind wing with not more than six veins; nymphs aquatic, with swimming legs. (Including *MIOMÓPTERA*, part)   (Pm) **PROTOPERLÀRIA**
    Prothoracic paranotal lobes of adults, when present, fused together; anal area of hind wing with several more than six veins; nymphs terrestrial. (See couplet 8). (Cp-Pm) **PROTORTHÓPTERA,** part

ORDER PALÆODICTYÓPTERA

(Including *ANISÁXIA, ARCHÆHYMENÓPTERA*, part, *PERMODICTYÓPTERA, BREYERIDEA, HEMIODONÀTA*)

Small to medium-sized palæopterous insects, related to the Plectoptera. Head small, antennæ setaceous; mouth-parts presumably mandibulate; prothorax with a pair of membranous paranotal lobes, independent of each other; legs slender, homonomous. Wings membranous; hind wing similar to fore wing or with a larger anal lobe; all main veins present in both wings; archedictyon or weak cross-veins present. Abdomen slender, terminating in a pair of conspicuous cerci. Immature stages unknown; metamorphosis presumably incomplete. Geological range: Upper Carboniferous to Upper Permian.

Nineteen families are sufficiently well known to be included in a key; five others (Apopappidæ, Eubleptidæ, Homothetidæ, Permoneuridæ,

Rochlingiidæ (Scepasmidæ)), all from Carboniferous strata, appear to be Palæodictyoptera but are very incompletely known.

1. Archedictyon present over nearly all of the wing surface 2
   Archedictyon absent or confined to a small part of wing surface ...3

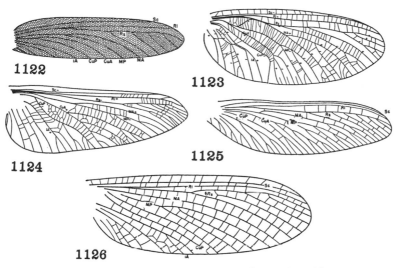

Figs. 1122–1126. **Palæodictyoptera and Protephemerida.**

1122. **Stenodictya,** Dictyoneuridæ. Sc, subcosta; R1, radius; Rs, radial sector; MA anterior media; MP, posterior media; CuA, anterior cubitus; CuP, posterior cubitus; 1A, first anal.
1123. **Lithoneura,** fore wing (Carpenter), Syntonopteridæ.
1124. **Thesoneura,** fore wing (Carpenter), Thesoneuridæ.
1125. **Homaloneura,** fore wing, Spilapteridæ.
1126. **Triplosoba,** fore wing, Triplosobidæ (Protephemerida).

2. Fore and hind wings nearly identical in shape and venation. (**Dictyoneùra, Stenodíctya** (Fig. 1122), **Microdíctya**). (Including *PEROMAPTÉRIDÆ, SAARLANDÌIDÆ, COCKEREL-LIÉLLIDÆ, ARCHÆMEGAPTÍLIDÆ*)
   (Cp) **DICTYONEÙRIDÆ**
   Hind wings with a much broader anal area than the fore wings.
   (Cp) **PAOLIÏDÆ**
3. Intercalary veins present. (**Syntonóptera, Lithoneùra** (Fig. 1123))
   (Cp) **SYNTONOPTÉRIDÆ**
   Intercalary veins absent 4
4. Anastomosis of at least two main veins present 5
   No anastomosis of main veins 6

5. MA anastomosed with Rs; Sc terminating on costa. (*PROTAG-RÌIDÆ*) .... (Cp) **PROTAGRIÓNIDÆ**
   CuA anastomosed with M; Sc terminating on radius
   (Pm) **CALVERTIÉLLIDÆ**
6. Cross-veins straight and very dense over nearly all of wing area. (Including *RHABDOPTÍLIDÆ*) ....(Cp) **FOUQUÈIDÆ**
   Cross-veins widely spaced and usually irregular 7
7. Sc terminating on radius ....(Cp) **BREYERÌIDÆ**
   Sc terminating on costal margin 8
8. Radial sector branched dichotomously 9
   Radial sector branched pectinately 10
9. Hind wing slender, tapering. (**Thesoneùra** (Fig. 1124))
   (Cp) **THESONEÙRIDÆ**
   Hind wing broad, apex blunt ....(Cp) **LAMPROTILÌIDÆ**
10. Subcosta terminating about two-thirds of wing length from base
    (Cp) **POLYCREÁGRIDÆ**
    Subcosta terminating near apex of wing. (**Dunbária, Spiláptera, Homaloneùra** (Fig. 1125), **Compsoneùra**). (Including *DUN-BARÌIDÆ, DOROPTÉRIDÆ, GRAPHIPTÍLIDÆ*)
    (Cp-Pm) **SPILÁPTÉRIDÆ**

ORDER **PROTEPHEMÉRIDA**

Insects of moderate size, related to the Palæodictyoptera and Plectoptera. Head small, body slender; cerci and median filament present; wings homonomous or nearly so; subcosta long; radial sector arising from the radius near wing base; anterior media, anterior cubitus and posterior cubitus not forked; radial sector and posterior media branched and with intercalary veins; cross-veins numerous. Immature stages unknown, but metamorphosis presumably incomplete. Geological range: Upper Carboniferous.

This order is known only by the family Triplosobidæ, consisting of one species (Fig. 1126). It appears to be more or less intermediate between the Palæodictyoptera and the true may-flies.

ORDER **MEGASECÓPTERA**

(Including *DIAPHANOPTERÒIDEA, PROTOHYMENÓPTERA, PALÆOHYMENÓPTERA*)

Medium-sized to large insects; wings equal or subequal with nearly identical venation; all main longitudinal veins present, forming an alternation of convexities and concavities. Head small; antennæ setaceous, of moderate length; pronotal lobes absent; legs usually slender, sometimes robust; three tarsal segments in Asthenohymenidæ, unknown in other families; abdomen slender; cerci at least as long as body; caudal filament absent. Metamorphosis incomplete. Geological range: Upper Carboniferous to Upper Permian.

This order appears to be related to the Palæodictyoptera and Plectoptera. The body structure is best known in the Asthenohymenidæ, which are much more specialized than the Carboniferous species. Immature stages, known only in Brodiidæ, are typical nymphs, with external wing buds. Adults of some families, comprising the suborder Eumegasecoptera, were unable to flex their wings over the body when resting; this is shown by their invariable occurrence with outstretched wings. Some others, the Paramegasecoptera, are found with wings flexed over the abdomen. This wing flexing probably originated independently of that in the true neopterous insects, and may have involved a very different mechanism.

The following key includes the most important families of the order. Several others (Raphidiopsidæ, Prochoropteridæ, Kulojidæ, Parabrodiidæ, Carbonopteridæ, Campylopteridæ and Aspidohymenidæ) have been established, but they are so unsatisfactorily known that they cannot be included in the key.

1. Wings outstretched at rest; radius straight or nearly so in proximal part of wing; cross-veins usually forming rows, only occasionally evenly distributed over wing; stem of cubitus and base of anterior cubitus usually remote from radius, never forming an angle divided by stem of media. (Suborder EUMEGASECÓPTERA) 2
   Wings held over abdomen at rest; radius with a more or less distinct bend not far from wing base; cross-veins distributed irregularly over wing, never forming distinct rows; stem of cubitus and base of anterior cubitus contiguous with stem of radius, the angle thus formed divided by stem of media (when present as an independent vein). (Suborder PARAMEGASECÓPTERA) . 11
2. Radial sector (Rs) and anterior media (MA) independent 3
   Radial sector and anterior media anastomosed at least for a short distance 6
3. Cross-veins numerous, evenly distributed over wing, not forming definite rows 4
   Cross-veins few, arranged to form at least one definite row 5
4. Wings distinctly petiolate . . . . (Cp) BRODÌIDÆ
   Wings not petiolate. (Aspidothòrax (Fig. 1130)).
                                        (Cp) ASPIDOTHORÁCIDÆ
5. Subcosta and radius crowded close to costal margin; cross-veins straight. (Calohỳmen, Sylvohỳmen)
                                        (Pm) BARDOHYMÉNIDÆ
   Subcosta and radius remote from each other and costal margin; most cross-veins sigmoidal . . . . (Cp) FORIRÌIDÆ
6. Subcosta and radius crowded together and close to costal margin . 7

Subcosta and radius remote from each other and from costal
   margin 8
7. Several cross-veins present. (Permohỳmen, Protohỳmen (Fig. 1134))
                           (Pm) PROTOHYMÉNIDÆ
   Cross-veins nearly absent ....(Pm) SCYTOHYMÉNIDÆ
8. Posterior media and anterior cubitus not anastomosed 9
   Posterior media and anterior cubitus anastomosed 10
9. One complete row of cross-veins. (Cyclocèlis, Sphecóptera (Fig.
   1131)) ....(Cp) SPHECOPTÉRIDÆ
   Two or three rows of cross-veins. (Psilothórax, Mischóptera (Fig.
   1129)) ....(Cp) MISCHOPTÉRIDÆ
10. One row of cross-veins ....(Cp) ISCHNOPTÍLIDÆ
   Three rows of cross-veins. (Corydalòides (Fig. 1133)).
                           (Cp) CORYDALÒIDIDÆ
11. Radial sector and anterior media independent. (Parélmoa (Fig.
   1128), Pseudélmoa) ....(Pm) ELMÒIDÆ
   Radial sector and anterior media with some anastomosis 12

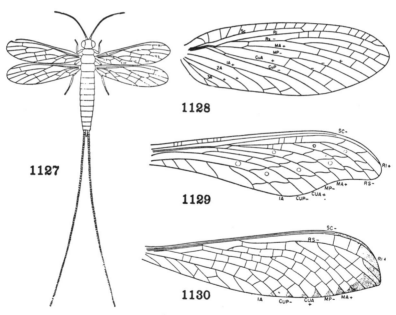

1128

1127

1129

1130

Figs. 1127–1130. Megasecoptera.

1127. **Asthenohymen** (Carpenter) Asthenohymenidæ.
1128. **Parelmoa,** fore wing (Carpenter) Elmoidæ.
1129. **Mischoptera,** fore wing (Carpenter) Mischopteridæ.
1130. **Aspidothorax,** fore wing (Carpenter) Aspidothoracidæ.

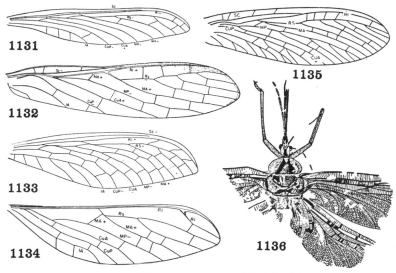

Figs. 1131–1136. **Megasecoptera** and **Protohemiptera**.

1131. **Sphecoptera**, fore wing (Carpenter) Sphecopteridæ.
1132. **Eumartynovia**, fore wing (Carpenter) Martynoviidæ.
1133. **Corydaloides**, fore wing (Carpenter) Corydaloididæ.
1134. **Protohymen**, fore wing (Carpenter) Protohymenidæ.
1135. **Diaphanoptera**, fore wing, Diaphanopteridæ.
1136. **Eugereon** (Lameere, after Dohrn) Eugereonidæ (Protohemiptera).

12. Posterior media (MP) with several branches. (**Diaphanóptera** (Fig. 1135)). (Including *DIAPHANOPTERÍTIDÆ*)
(Cp) **DIAPHANOPTÉRIDÆ**
Posterior media unbranched 13
13. Stem of media independent of anterior cubitus. (**Eumartynovia** (Fig. 1132), **Phaneroneùra**) ....(Pm) **MARTYNOVÌIDÆ**
Stem of media anastomosed with part of CuA 14
14. Proximal part of wing much narrower than middle part. (**Astheno-hỳmen** (Fig. 1127)) ....(Pm) **ASTHENOHYMÉNIDÆ**
Proximal part of wing about as wide as middle part.
(Pm) **BIARMOHYMÉNIDÆ**

ORDER **PROTODONÀTA**

(Including *MEGANISÓPTERA*)

Large to very large predaceous insects, resembling anisopterous Odonata, some (Meganeurinæ) having a wing-expanse of 750 mm. Head relatively small, with conspicuous eyes and large mandibles;

thoracic segments oblique, as in Odonata; legs spiny; abdomen long and slender; male with terminal claspers. Fore and hind wings hyaline, with similar venation, but the hind wing having a broader anal area; posterior media (MP) and anterior cubitus (CuA) absent or obsolescent; nodus, pterostigma and true arculus absent. Immature stages unknown, but metamorphosis was presumably incomplete. Geological range: Upper Carboniferous to Upper Permian. An incomplete wing (*Reisia*) from the Triassic of Germany appears to belong to the order but its assignment will remain questionable until more of the insect is known.

1. Cross-veins relatively few in number, forming only a few cells (Erasípteron) ....(Cp) **ERASIPTÉRIDÆ**
   Cross-veins very numerous, forming numerous small cells 2
2. Subcosta short, merging with costal margin at about mid-wing; R2 + 3 and R4 + 5 widely divergent after origin. (**Oligótypus** (Fig. 1137), **Parálogus**) ....(Cp-Pm) **PARALÓGIDÆ**
   Subcosta long, extending nearly to the apex of the wing; R2 + 3 and R4 + 5 diverge very gradually .(Cp-Pm) **MEGANEÙRIDÆ**

a. Precostal space long, extending nearly to mid-wing. (**Meganeùra**, **Meganeurópsis**) ....(Cp-Pm) **MEGANEÙRINÆ**
   Precostal space short, at most extending one-fourth wing length from the base. (**Tỳpus** (Fig. 1138), **Meganeùrula**)
   (Cp-Pm) **TYPÌNÆ**

ORDER **PROTOHEMÍPTERA**

(*PSEUDOHEMÍPTERA*)

Large palæopterous insects, related to the Palæodictyoptera, but having haustellate mouth-parts. Head small and narrow, with a prominent beak; labial and maxillary palps present; eyes small; thorax robust, abdomen slender; cerci long. Fore and hind wings hyaline, nearly homonomous; all main longitudinal veins present. Immature stages unknown, metamorphosis presumably incomplete. Upper Carboniferous to Lower Permian.

1. Wings with a conspicuous archedictyon, without distinct cross-veins. (**Eugèreon** (Fig. 1136)). (Including *MEGAPTÍLIDÆ*)
   (Cp-Pm) **EUGEREÓNIDÆ**
   Wings with distinct cross-veins, no archedictyon.................2
2. Radial sector (Rs) with not more than six branches; CuA forked. (**Homoióptera**). (Including *LITHOPTÍLIDÆ*).
   (Cp) **HOMOIOPTÉRIDÆ**
   Radial sector with 10 or more branches; CuA unbranched. (Including *LYCOCÉRCIDÆ*) ....(Cp) **LITHOMANTÈIDÆ**

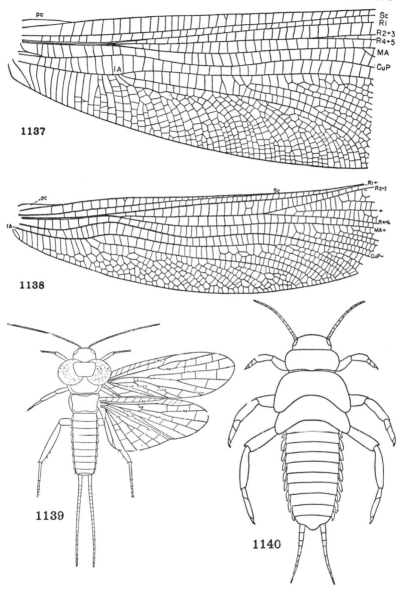

Figs. 1137–1140. Protodonata and Protoperlaria.

1137. **Oligotypus**, fore wing (Carpenter) Paralogidæ (Protodonata).
1138. **Typus**, fore wing (Carpenter) Meganeuridæ (Protodonata).
1139. **Lemmatophora** (Carpenter) Lemmatophoridæ (Protoperlaria).
1140. Nymph of Lemmatophoridæ (Carpenter) (Protoperlaria).

ORDER PROTOPERLÀRIA

(Including *MIOMÓPTERA*, part)

Small or medium-sized insects, related to the Plecoptera. Head relatively small, eyes large, antennæ long and multisegmental. Prothorax with prominent paranotal lobes, distinctly membranous and independent of each other. Pterothorax broad; wings membranous, the hind wing having an enlarged and folded anal area; in the hind wing the radial sector is anastomosed with the anterior media. Legs slender, sometimes tenuate, with five tarsal segments, the hind legs being somewhat longer than the others. Abdomen broad, terminating in prominent cerci. Nymphs aquatic, with lateral abdominal gills and swimming legs. Geological range: Lower Permian.

At present this order includes only the single family Lemmatophóridæ, represented by several genera in the Wellington Formation of Kansas and Oklahoma (Figs. 1139, 1140).

ORDER PROTORTHÓPTERA

(Including *PROTOBLATTÒIDEA; MIXOTERMITÒIDEA; HADENTOMÒIDEA; HAPALOPTERÒIDEA; PRUVOSTITÓPTERA; RECULÒIDEA, SYNARMOGÒIDEA; PARAPLECÓPTERA; CNEMIDOLESTÒIDEA; PROTOFULGÓRIDA*, part; *PROTOCICÁDIDA*, part; *MIOMÓPTERA*, part)

Small to large insects, related to the Orthoptera (*s.l.*), Blattaria and Protoperlaria. Head hypognathous, antennæ long and multisegmented; pronotal lobes either membranous or coriaceous, usually expanded to form a pronotal shield; abdomen with conspicuous cerci; legs variously modified, either cursorial or saltatorial, usually with five tarsal segments. Fore wings membranous or coriaceous, often with delicate covering of microtrichia; hind wing with an expanded anal area. Metamorphosis incomplete, though nymphal forms are little known. Geological range: Upper Carboniferous to Upper Permian.

Our conception of this group is very vague. Certain families merge with representatives of other orders (as Protoperlaria, Blattaria and Orthoptera), and up to the present time efforts to define the order have proven unsatisfactory. So, too, have the attempts to divide the order into subordinal categories. The following key includes those families which are well enough known to be presented in this way; it does not include the following families, which are based on fragmentary material, but which are referable to the order: Adiphlebiidæ, Aetophlebiidæ, Anhomalophlebiidæ, Anthracothremmidæ, Apithanidæ, Asyncritidæ, Climaconeuridæ, Cymenophlebiidæ, Emphylopteridæ, Epimasticidæ, Eucanidæ,

Gerapompidæ, Geraridæ, Hadentomidæ, Hapalopteridæ, Kliveriidæ, Mixotermitidæ, Nemuropsidæ, Omalidæ, Pachytylopsidæ, Permocapniidæ, Permotermopsidæ, Prostenoneuridæ, Protophasmatidæ, Prototettigidæ, Rachimentomidæ, Reculidæ, Roomeriidæ, Stenoneurellidæ, Stenoneuritidæ, Strephoneuridæ, Sylvaphlebiidæ, Sylviodidæ, Synarmogidæ, Tcholmanvissiidæ and Thoronysidæ.

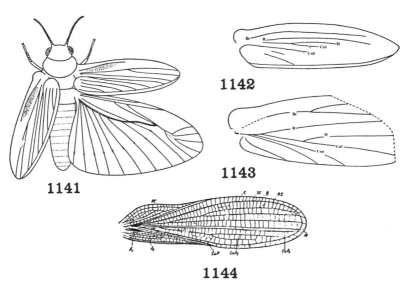

1142

1143

1141

1144

Figs. 1141–1144. Protelytroptera and Glosselytrodea.

1141. Protelytron (Carpenter) Protelytridæ.
1142. Parablattelytron, elytron (Carpenter) Blattelytridæ.
1143. Elytroneura, fore wing (Carpenter) Elytroneuridæ.
1144. Jurina, fore wing (Martynov) Jurinidæ (Glosselytrodea).

1. Precostal space present in fore wing............................2
   Precostal space absent in fore wing...........................3
2. Precostal area forming a prominent bulge; hind legs modified for jumping. (Œdíschia). (Including *HOMALOPHLEBÌIDÆ, PRUVOSTÍTIDÆ*) ....(Cp–Pm) **ŒDISCHÌIDÆ**
   Precostal area small, not forming a prominent bulge; hind legs cursorial. (**Archæacridìtes** (Fig. 1152), **Sthenarópoda**).
                                            (Cp) **STHENAROPÓDIDÆ**
3. Subcosta terminating on R1................................4
   Subcosta terminating on costal margin......................8
4. Cross-veins reticulate over most of fore wing.
                                            (Cp) **STENONEÙRIDÆ**
   Cross-veins simple over most of wing.......................5

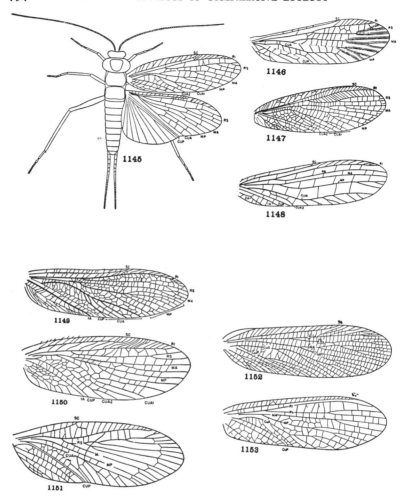

Figs. 1145–1153. **Protorthoptera**

1145. **Liomopterum** (Carpenter) Liomopteridæ.
1146. **Protembia,** fore wing (Carpenter) Protembiidæ.
1147. **Chelopterum,** fore wing (Carpenter) Chelopteridæ.
1148. **Probnis,** fore wing (Carpenter) Probnisidæ.
1149. **Demopterum,** fore wing (Carpenter) Demopteridæ.
1150. **Stereopterum,** fore wing (Carpenter) Stereopteridæ.
1151. **Sindon,** fore wing, Blattinopsidæ.
1152. **Archæacridites,** fore wing, Sthenaropodidæ.
1153. **Palæocixius,** fore wing, Palæocixiidæ.

5. Anal furrow strongly arched.:.........(Cp) EPIDEIGMÁTIDÆ
   Anal furrow nearly straight................................6
6. Wings broad, with wide costal area.........(Cp) NARKÉMIDÆ
   Wings narrow, with narrow costal area.....................7
7. Branches of posterior cubitus (CuP) directed along wing axis. (Including *ANTHRACOPTÍLIDÆ, CNEMIDOLÉSTIDÆ, EO-BLÁTTIDÆ*) ....(Cp) ISCHNONEÙRIDÆ
   Branches of CuP directed posteriorly.....(Cp) SPANIODÉRIDÆ
8. All cross-veins finely reticulate, forming an archedictyon over most of wing ....(Pm) HOMŒDICTYÌDÆ
   No archedictyon present 9
9. Some anastomosis of main veins present.....................10
   No anastomosis of main veins...............................15
10. Media (M) or its anterior branch anastomosed with Rs. (Síndon (Fig. 1151), Blattinópsis). (Including *ORYCTOBLATTÍNIDÆ, FAYOLIÉLLIDÆ, KLEBSIÉLLIDÆ*).
   (Cp–Pm) BLATTINÓPSIDÆ
   No anastomosis of M or its branches with radial sector (Rs); anterior cubitus (CuA) anastomosed with M or posterior media (MP) 11
11. CuA anastomosed with stem of M...........................12
   CuA anastomosed with posterior branch of M (MP) only.......13
12. Cross-veins absent or nearly so between branches of M and CuA.
   (Pm) EURYPTILÓNIDÆ
   Cross-veins well developed between branches of M and of CuA.
   (Stereópterum (Fig. 1150)) ....(Pm) STEREOPTÉRIDÆ
13. Costal area very narrow..........(Cp) PROTOKOLLARÌIDÆ
   Costal area distinctly broad..............................14
14. Radius (R1) unbranched distally ......(Cp) ADELONEÙRIDÆ
   R1 branched distally ....(Cp) CACÚRGIDÆ
15. Radial sector unbranched. (Próbnis (Fig. 1148)).
   (Pm) PROBNÍSIDÆ
   Radial sector at least forked..............................16
16. Terminal branches of Rs, MA and MP margined with faint lines.
   (Protémbia (Fig. 1146)). (*TELACTINOPTERÝGIDÆ*).
   (Pm) PROTEMBÌIDÆ
   Terminal branches of Rs, MA and MP without such lines......17
17. Most cross-veins between R1 and Rs reticulate 20
   Little or no reticulation between R1 and Rs 18
18. Cross-veins between R1 and Rs conspicuously slanted. (Chelópterum (Fig. 1147)) ....(Pm) CHELOPTÉRIDÆ
   Cross-veins between R1 and Rs more or less at right angles to these veins 19

19. Costal margin of fore wing markedly convex. (**Liomópterum** (Fig. 1145)) .... (Pm) **LIOMOPTÉRIDÆ**
Costal margin of fore wing straight or nearly so.
(Cp) **PALÆOCIXÌIDÆ**
20. Cross-veins in distal third of wing (excepting those between R1 and Rs) not reticulate 21
Cross-veins in distal third of wing reticulate.................22
21. MP branched almost to origin of MA.
(Pm) **ATACTOPHLEBÌIDÆ**
MP branched to only half its length. (**Demópterum** (Fig. 1149)).
(Pm) **DEMOPTÉRIDÆ**
22. MA unbranched. (Including *CAMPTONEURÍTIDÆ*) (*LEPÌ-IDÆ*). .... (Pm) **PHENOPTÉRIDÆ**
MA deeply forked. (Including *KHOSÁRIDÆ*).
(Pm) **IDELÌIDÆ**

ORDER CALONEURÒDEA

Small to large insects, related to the Protorthoptera and Orthoptera. Head hypognathous, of moderate size, antennæ long and slender; pronotal lobes absent; abdomen slender with a pair of short cerci; legs cursorial, slender, often tenuous, the posterior pair much longer than the others. Wings membranous and homonomous, there being no enlarged anal area in the hind wing; cross-veins numerous and strongly developed. Metamorphosis unknown, presumably like that of Orthoptera. Geological range: Upper Carboniferous to Upper Permian.

1. Four and veins present. (**Caloneùra** (Fig. 1154)). (Including *STHENAROCÉRIDÆ*) .... (Cp) **CALONEÙRIDÆ**
Less than four anal veins present...........................2
2. Anterior cubitus (CuA) and posterior cubitus (CuP) anastomosed for part of their lengths..........(Pm) **SYNOMALOPTÍLIDÆ**
CuA and CuP independent.................................3
3. CuP and first anal vein (1A) close together, CuA and CuP remote.
(Pm) **EUTHYGRÁMMIDÆ**
CuA and CuP close together for most of their lengths, CuP and 1A remote 4
4. CuA and CuP widely divergent at wing margin; cross-veins strongly convex. (**Permobiélla** (Fig. 1155))...(Pm) **PERMOBIÉLLIDÆ**
CuA and CuP not widely divergent at wing margin; cross-veins not markedly convex 5
5. Third anal vein (3A) long, extending to at least one quarter wing-length from base of wing. (**Paleuthygrámma** (Fig. 1156), **Aspidoneùra**) .... (Pm) **PALEUTHYGRÁMMIDÆ**
3A very short or absent......................................6

6. Subcosta (Sc) long, extending well beyond mid-wing.
(Pm) **PLEISIOGRÁMMIDÆ**
Sc short, ending before mid-wing. (Pm) **ANOMALOGRÁMMIDÆ**

ORDER GLOSSELYTRÒDEA

Small insects related to the Caloneurodea. Head small, antennæ long; fore wings tegminous; precostal area prominent; subcosta long, meeting with the posterior cubitus distally to form a compound submarginal

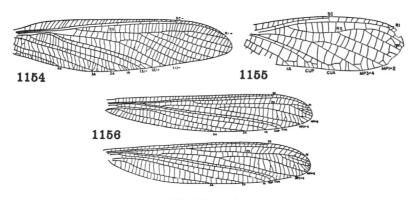

Figs. 1154–1156. **Caloneurodea**

1154. **Caloneura**, fore wing (Carpenter) Caloneuridæ.
1155. **Permobiella**, fore wing (Carpenter) Permobiellidæ.
1156. **Paleuthygramma**, fore (A) and hind (B) wings (Carpenter) Paleuthygrammidæ.

vein. Cross-veins numerous, usually reticulate in the precostal and anal areas. Hind wings unknown. Immature stages also unknown, but metamorphosis presumably incomplete. Geological range: Upper Permian to Jurassic.

1. Precostal area of fore wing with a submarginal vein along the anterior border. (**Jurìna** (Fig. 1144)).....(Pm–J) **JURÍNIDÆ**
Precostal area without such a submarginal vein.
(Pm) **GLOSSELŸTRIDÆ**

ORDER PROTELYTRÓPTERA

(*PROTOCOLEÓPTERA*)

Small insects, related to the Dermaptera and Blattaria. Head small but broad; eyes prominent, convex; antennæ short and thick, multisegmental; legs robust, spiny, with five tarsal segments; fore wings typically modified to form convex elytra (rarely flattened) with a true venation; hind wings longer and broader than fore wings, the expanded anal area having longitudinal and transverse folds; abdomen broad, terminating in a pair of short cerci. Immature stages unknown; metamorphosis presumably incomplete. Geological range: Upper and Lower Permian. The Protocoleidæ and Permofulgoridæ were originally placed in the order Protocoleoptera; they now appear to be protelytropterous (Tillyard, 1931), but are too little known to be included in the key to families.

1. Posterior sutural margin of fore wing (elytron) absent............2
   Posterior sutural margin of fore wing present.................3
2. Fore wing nearly flat; media (M) and anterior cubitus (Cu1) anastomosed proximally. (**Elytroneùra** (Fig. 1143)).
   (Pm) **ELYTRONEÙRIDÆ**
   Fore wing convex, forming a true elytron; media and anterior cubitus independent.................(Pm) **MEGELÝTRIDÆ**
3. Radial sector (Rs) absent in elytron. (**Permélytron, Parablattélytron** (Fig. 1142)). (Including *PERMELÝTRIDÆ*).
   (Pm) **BLATTELÝTRIDÆ**
   Radial sector present in fore wing..........................4
4. Anterior cubitus unbranched. (**Protélytron** (Fig. 1141), **Uralélytron**) ....(Pm) **PROTELÝTRIDÆ**
   Anterior cubitus with three branches....(Pm) **ARCHELÝTRIDÆ**

LITERATURE ON EXTINCT ORDERS OF INSECTS

BRONGNIART, C. Recherches pour servir à l'histoire des insectes fossiles des temps primaires. Text, 493 pp.; Atlas, 44 pp., 37 pls. St. Etienne, France (1893).

CARPENTER, F. M. The Lower Permian Insects of Kansas. Part 3. The Protohymenoptera. Psyche, **37**, pp. 343–374, 3 pls. (1930).

A Review of Our Present Knowledge of the Geological History of Insects. Psyche, **37**, pp. 15–34, 1 pl. (1930).

The Lower Permian Insects of Kansas. Part 2. The Orders Palæodictyoptera, Protodonata and Odonata. American Journ. Sci., (5) **21**, pp. 97–139, 6 figs. (1931).

The Lower Permian Insects of Kansas. Part 6. Delopteridæ, Protelytroptera and Plectoptera. Proc. American Acad. Arts Sci., **68**, pp. 411–504, 1 pl., 29 figs. (1933).

The Lower Permian Insects of Kansas. Part 7. The Order Protoperlaria. Proc. American Acad. Arts Sci., **70**, pp. 101–146, 2 pls., 11 figs. (1935).

The Lower Permian Insects of Kansas. Part 8. Additional Megasecoptera, Protodonata, Odonata, Homoptera, Psocoptera, Protelytroptera, Plecoptera and Protoperlaria. Proc. American Acad. Arts Sci., **73**(3), pp. 29–70, 2 pls., 27 figs. (1939).

Studies on Carboniferous Insects from Commentry, France. Part 1. Introduction and Families Protagriidæ, Meganeuridæ and Campylopteridæ. Bull. Geol. Soc. America, **54**, pp. 527–554 (1943).

The Lower Permian Insects of Kansas. Part 9. The Orders Neuroptera.

Raphidiodea, Caloneurodea and Protorthoptera (Probnisidæ) with Additional Protodonata and Megasecoptera. Proc. American Acad. Arts Sci., **75**, pp. 55–84, 1 pl., 15 figs. (1943).

Lower Permian Insects from Oklahoma. Part 1. Introduction and the Orders Megasecoptera, Protodonata and Odonata. Proc. American Acad. Arts Sci., **76**, pp. 25–54, 2 pls., 28 figs. (1947).

Early Insect Life. Psyche, **54**, pp. 65–85, 9 figs. (1947).

The Supposed Nymphs of the Palæodictyoptera. Psyche, **55**, pp. 41–50, 2 pls. (1948).

The Lower Permian Insects of Kansas. Part 10. The Order Protorthoptera: The Family Liomopteridæ and its Relatives. Proc. American Acad. Arts Sci., **78**, pp. 185–219, 3 pls., 11 figs. (1950).

Studies on Carboniferous Insects from Commentry, France: Part II. The Megasecoptera. Journ. Paleontol., **25**(3), pp. 336–355, 1 pl., 11 figs. (1951).

FORBES, W. T. M. The Protocoleoptera. Psyche, **35**, pp. 32–35, 4 figs. (1928).

The Origin of Wings and Venational Types in Insects. American Midl. Natural., **29**, pp. 381–405, 8 figs. (1943).

GUTHÖRL, P. Die Arthropoden des Saar-Nahe-Pfalz-Gebietes. Abhandl. Preuss. Landesanst., **164**, pp. 1–219 (1934).

HANDLIRSCH, A. Die fossilen Insekten und die Phylogenie der rezenten Formen. Ein Handbuch für Palaeontologen u. Zoologen. 1430 pp., 51 pls. Leipzig (1906–1908).

Revision der paleozoischen Insekten. Denkschr. Akad. Wiss. Math. Naturw. Kl., Wien, **96**, pp. 511–592, 91 figs. (1919).

Palaeontologie. In Schröder's Handbuch der Entomologie, **3**, pp. 118–306 (1920).

Fossilium Catalogus, **1**, Animalia, Pars 16, Insecta palaeozoica. 230 pp. Berlin (1922).

Neue Untersuchungen über die fossilen Insekten. Ann. naturh. Mus. Wien, **48**, pp. 1–140 (1937).

LAMEERE, A. Revision sommaire des insectes fossiles du Stéphanien de Commentry. Bull. Mus. Paris, **23**, pp. 141–200 (1917).

Pseudohémiptères. Précis de Zoologie, **4**, pp. 255–258 (1935).

MARTYNOV, A. V. Ueber eine neue Ordnung fossilen Insekten, Miomoptera nov. Zool. Anz., **72**, pp. 99–109 (1927).

Permian Fossil Insects of North-east Europe. Trav. Mus. Géol. Acad. Sci. URSS, **4**, pp. 1–118 (1928).

Permian Fossil Insects from Tikhije Gory. Order Miomoptera. Parts 1–2. Bull. Acad. Sci. URSS, **1930**, pp. 951–975; 1115–1134 (1930).

New Permian Insects from Tikhie Gory, Kazan Province. I. Palæoptera. Trav. Mus. Géol. Acad. Sci. URSS, **6**, pp. 69–86 (1930).

New Permian Insects from Tikhie Gory. II. Neoptera (excluding Miomoptera). Trav. Mus. Géol. Acad. Sci. URSS, **8**, pp. 149–212 (1931).

New Permian Paleoptera with the Discussion of Some Problems of Their Evolution. Trav. Inst. Paléozool. Acad. Sci., **1**, pp. 1–44 (1932).

Permian Fossil Insects from Kargala and Their Relationships. Trav. Inst. paléontol. Acad. Sci. URSS, **7**(2), 1–92, 20 figs. (1937).

Etudes sur l'histoire géologique et de phylogénie des ordres des insectes (Pterygota). le. partie. Paleoptera et Neoptera (Polyneoptera). Trav. Inst. paléontol. Acad. Sci. URSS, **7**(4), pp. 1–150, 1 pl., 70 figs. (1938).

Permian Fossil Insects from the Arkhangelsk District. Part V. The Family Euthygrammidæ and its Relationships with the Description of a New Genus and Family from Chekarda. Trav. Inst. paléontol. Acad. Sci. URSS, **7**(3), pp. 69–80, 5 figs. (1938).

On a New Permian Order of Orthopteroid Insects, Glosselytrodea. Bull. Acad. Sci. URSS, Ser. Biol., **1938**, pp. 187–206, 1 pl., 6 figs. (1938).

Permian Fossil Insects from Tshekarda. Trav. Inst. paléontol. Acad. Sci. URSS, **11**, pp. 1–62, 6 pls., 46 figs. (1940).

MARTYNOVA, O. M. Glosselytrodea from the Jurassic Shales of the Coal Bed Sogjuta. C. R. Acad. Sci. URSS, **39**, pp. 284–285, 2 figs. (1943).

PIERCE, W. D. Fossil Arthropods of California. 6. Two New Fossils from the Upper Miocene of the Fuente Hills. Bull. Southern Calif. Acad. Sci., **44**, pp. 3–6 (1945). [Aphelophlebia]

SCUDDER, S. H. A Classed and Annotated Bibliography of Fossil Insects. Bull. U. S. Geol. Surv. No. **69**, pp. 1–101 (1890).

TILLYARD, R. J. A Fossil Insect Wing Belonging to the New Order Paramecoptera, Ancestral to the Trichoptera and Lepidoptera, from the Upper Coal-Measures of Newcastle, N. S. W. Proc. Linn. Soc. New South Wales, **44**, pp. 231–256 (1919).

Mesozoic Insects of Queensland. No. 5. Mecoptera, the New Order Paratrichoptera, and Additions to Planipennia. Proc. Linn. Soc. New South Wales, **44**, pp. 194–212 (1919).

Kansas Permian Insects. Part 3. The New Order Protohymenoptera. American Journ. Sci., **8**, pp. 111–122 (1924).

Upper Permian Coleoptera and a New Order from the Belmont Beds, N. S. W. Proc. Linn. Soc. New South Wales, **49**, pp. 429–435, 2 pls., 1 fig. (1924).

Kansas Permian Insects. Part 5. The Orders Protodonata and Odonata. American Journ. Sci., **10**, pp. 41–73 (1925).

Kansas Permian Insects. Part 10. The New Order Protoperlaria; A Study of the Typical Genus Lemmatophora Sellards. American Journ. Sci., **16**, pp. 185–220 (1928).

Kansas Permian Insects. Part 11. Order Protoperlaria. Family Lemmatophoridæ. American Journ. Sci., **16**, pp. 313–348 (1928).

Kansas Permian Insects. Part 13. The New Order Protelytroptera. American Journ. Sci., **21**, pp. 232–266 (1931).

The Evolution of the Scorpion-flies and Their Derivatives. Ann. Ent. Soc. America, **28**, pp. 1–45 (1935).

ZALESSKY, G. Sur deux représentants permiens nouveaux de l'ordre des Protorthoptères. Ann. Soc. Ent. France, **103**, pp. 149–158 (1934).

Sur un représentant d'un nouvel ordre d'insectes permiens. [Hemipsocoptera]. Ann. Soc. géol. Nord, **61**, pp. 50–71, 6 figs. (1936).

A Representative of a New Order of Insects with Elytra. [Perielytrodea]. Priroda, **32**, pp. 70–71, 2 figs. (1943).

A Representative of a New Group of Insects from the Permian Deposits of the Urals. C. R. Acad. Sci. URSS, **44**, pp. 342–344, 2 figs. (1944).

Sur un représentant d'un nouveau ordre des hemiodonates de Permien de l'Oural. Moskov. Obshch. Isp. Prirody. Otd. Biol. B., **51**, pp. 63–70 (1946).

ORDER COLLÉMBOLA

The only extinct family known is Protentomobryidæ (Fig. 1157) from Canadian amber of uncertain age (Cretaceous or early Tertiary). The family is characterized by having a furcula which is not differentiated into manubrium, dentes and mucrones. Fragments of minute

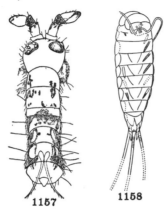

Figs. 1157–1158. **Collembola** and **Thysanura**

1157. **Protentomobrya** (Folsom) Protentomobryidæ (Collembola).
1158. **Triassomachilis** (Sharov) Triassomachilidæ (Thysanura).

arthropods (*Rhyniella*), from Devonian deposits of Scotland, have been referred to the Collembola, but their systematic position is problematical.

ORDER ENTÓTROPHI

No extinct families are known. Representatives of all three living families have been described from late Tertiary deposits of Arizona.

ORDER THYSANÙRA

The only extinct family is the Triassomachilidæ (Fig. 1158), from the Triassic beds of Russia. The other fossil representatives of the order, belonging to the Lepismatidæ and Machilidæ, occur in the Baltic amber.

LITERATURE ON COLLEMBOLA, ENTOTROPHI and THYSANURA — EXTINCT FAMILIES

Folsom, J. W. Collembola. In Insects and Arachnida from Canadian Amber. Univ. Toronto Stud., Geol. Ser. No. 40, pp. 14–17 (1937).

PIERCE, W. D. Fossil Arthropods from Onyx-Marble. Bull. Southern
California Acad. Sci., 50(1), pp. 44–49 (1950). [Entotrophi]
SCOURFIELD, D. J. The Oldest Known Fossil Insect. Proc. Linn. Soc. London,
152 sess., pp. 113–131 (1939–40). [Collembola]
SHAROV, A. G. Triassic Thysanura from Pre-ural. C. R. Acad. Sci. URSS, 61,
pp. 517–519, 2 figs. (1948).

ORDER PLECTÓPTERA

(Including *APHELOPHLÈBIA*)

Six extinct families of may-flies have been described, but one of these
(Ephemeropsidæ, Cretaceous) is known only from fragments. Nymphs,
presumably Permoplectoptera, have been found in several Permian deposits. The oldest known members of the order are from Lower
Permian rocks in Kansas. The family Aphelophlebodidæ (early Tertiary) is based on a minute fragment of a may-fly wing and cannot be
included in the key.

1. Fore and hind wings alike or very nearly so. (Suborder PER-
MOPLECTÓPTERA, Pm) 2
Hind wing much smaller than fore wing. (Suborder EUPLEC-
TOPTERA, Pm–R, with only one extinct family, having the
hind wing about two-thirds as long as fore wing).
(J) MESEPHEMÉRIDÆ
2. Costal brace small and weak . . . . (Pm) DOTÉRIDÆ
Costal brace well developed 3
3. CuA with a long triad. (**Protereísma** (Fig. 1159)).
(Pm) **PROTEREISMÁTIDÆ**
CuA with a very short triad at most . . . . (Pm) **MISTHODÓTIDÆ**

LITERATURE ON PLECTOPTERA — EXTINCT FAMILIES

CARPENTER, F. M. Jurassic Insects from Solenhofen in the Carnegie Museum
and the Museum of Comparative Zoology. Ann. Carnegie Mus., 21,
pp. 97–129, 11 figs. (1932).
The Lower Permian Insects of Kansas. Part 6. Delopteridæ, Pro-
telytroptera, Plectoptera and a New Collection of Protodonata, Odonata,
Megasecoptera, Homoptera and Psocoptera. Proc. Amer. Acad. Arts Sci.,
68, pp. 411–503, 1 pl., 29 figs. (1933).
COCKERELL, T. D. A. New Light on the Giant Fossil May-flies of Mongolia.
American Mus. Novit., No. 244, pp. 1–4 (1927).
TILLYARD, R. J. Kansas Permian Insects. Part 15. The Order Plectoptera.
American Journ. Sci., 23, pp. 97–134 (1932).
Kansas Permian Insects. Part 16. The Order Plectoptera (Cont'd.):
The Family Doteridæ, with a Note on the Affinities of the Order
Protohymenoptera. American Journ. Sci., 32, pp. 435–453, 4 figs. (1936).

ORDER **ODONÀTA**

Twenty-four extinct families of this order are sufficiently well-known to be assigned to suborders and to be included in the following key. The families Mesophlebiidæ, Eosagrionidæ, Steleopteridæ and Camptotaxineuridæ, though apparently odonate, are too incompletely known for inclusion. The first record of the order is in Lower Permian rocks.

1. Nodus absent 2
   Nodus present 4
2. At least two antenodals present; postnodals few in number; number of cross-veins relatively small. (Suborder PROTOZYGÓPTERA, Pm) 3
   Antenodals absent; postnodals numerous; number of cross-veins rela-

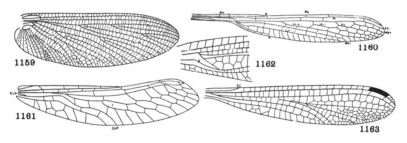

Figs. 1159–1163. **Plectoptera** and **Odonata.**

1159. **Protereisma,** hind wing (Carpenter), Protereismatidæ (Plectoptera).
1160. **Kennedya,** wing (Carpenter), Kennedyidæ (Odonata).
1161. **Ditaxineura,** fore wing (Carpenter), Ditaxineuridæ (Odonata).
1162. **Tarsophlebia,** base of fore wing (Carpenter), Tarsophlebiidæ (Odonata).
1163. **Protomyrmeleon,** wing (Martynov), Protomyrmeleontidæ (Odonata).

   tively large. (Suborder ARCHIZYGÓPTERA). (**Protomyrmèleon** (Fig. 1163). (Including *TRIASSAGRIÓNIDÆ*).
   (Tr–J) **PROTOMYRMELEÓNTIDÆ**
3. No nodal veinlets aligned below end of Sc; 1A short, terminating below end of Sc. (**Kennedya** (Fig. 1160)).
   (Pm) **KENNEDYIDÆ**
   Nodal veinlets aligned obliquely below end of Sc; 1A long, extending at least to middle of wing. (**Permoléstes**). (Including *PEREPALLÁGIDÆ*) .... (Pm) **PERMOLÉSTIDÆ**
4. Precostal area well developed, with an oblique brace-vein extending from the end of the precostal area to the radius; stem Rs+M nearly parallel to wing axis. (Suborder PROTANISÓPTERA, Pm) 5

Precostal area obsolescent, oblique brace-vein absent; stem Rs +M
oblique 6

5. Basal remnant of CuA present; antenodals few; cross-veins in distal
part of wing arranged in two gradate series. (Ditaxineùra (Fig.
1161)) .... (Pm) DITAXINEÙRIDÆ
Basal remnant of CuA absent; antenodals numerous; cross-veins in
distal part of wing irregularly arranged. (Including *PHOLIDOP-
TILÓNIDÆ, PERMÆSCHNIDÆ*).
(Pm) POLYTAXINEÙRIDÆ

6. Wings never petiolate; discoidal cell of fore wing subdivided into
a triangle and supratriangle. (Suborder ANISÓPTERA, J–R,
only one extinct family). (*GOMPHÍTIDÆ*).
(J) LIASSOGÓMPHIDÆ
Wings petiolate, subpetiolate, or non-petiolate; discoidal cell of fore
wing not subdivided into triangles........................7

7. Discoidal cell similarly formed in fore and hind wings. (Suborder
ZYGÓPTERA, Pm–R) 8
Discoidal cell differing in form in fore and hind wings. (Suborder
ANISOZYGÓPTERA, J–R) 9

8. Two antenodals; discoidal cell open. (Permágrion).
(Pm) PERMAGRIÓNIDÆ
At least ten antenodals; discoidal cell closed. (Zacallìtes).
(T) ZACALLÍTIDÆ

9. Anterio-distal angle of discoidal cell of hind wing obtuse.......10
Anterio-distal angle of discoidal cell of hind wing acute 12

10. Nodus well proximal to the middle of costal margin.
(T) SIEBLOSÌIDÆ
Nodus at middle of costal margin...........................11

11. Discoidal cell incomplete (open) in fore wing. (Tarsophlèbia, (Fig.
1162)) .... (J) TARSOPHLEBÌIDÆ
Discoidal cell closed in fore wing. (Including *ISOPHLEBÌIDÆ*).
(J) STENOPHLEBÌIDÆ

12. Discoidal cell of hind wing a simple quadrilateral, undivided 13
Discoidal cell of hind wing divided by a strut into a supratriangle
and triangle .... (J) HETEROPHLEBÌIDÆ

13. Wings of medium size (30–40 mm. long); subnodus placed slightly
distad from the nodus; M2 arising far distad from subnodus.
(J) PROGONOPHLEBÌIDÆ
Wings of large size (55–75 mm.); subnodus below nodus; M2 arising very close to subnodus................................14

14. Costal space crossed by only two hypertrophied antenodals, one on
each side of arculus, with a third weaker one occasionally at
extreme base .... (J) LIASSOPHLEBÌIDÆ
Costal space covered by a complete set of unspecialized antenodals.

(Including *PETROPHLEBÌIDÆ, SOLENOTHEMÍSTIDÆ, CÀMPTÈROPHLEBÌIDÆ*) .... (J) **ARCHITHÉMIDÆ**

LITERATURE ON ODONATA — EXTINCT FAMILIES

CARPENTER, F. M. The Lower Permian Insects of Kansas. Part 2. The Orders Palaeodictyoptera, Protodonata and Odonata. American Journ. Sci., (5) 21, pp. 97–139 (1931).

COWLEY, J. Descriptions of Some Genera of Fossil Odonata. Proc. Roy. Ent. Soc. London (B), 11, pp. 63–78 (1942).

FRASER, F. C. Note on the Classification of Zacallites balli Cockerell (Upper Eocene). Proc. Roy. Ent. Soc. London (B), 9, pp. 62–64, 2 figs. (1940).

HAGEN, H. A. Zwei Libellen aus der Braunkohle von Sieblos. Palaeontogr., 5, pp. 121–124, 1 pl. (1858).

Die Neuroptera des lithographischen Schiefers in Bayern. Palaeontogr., 15, pp. 1–40, 4 pls. (1866).

TILLYARD, R. J. The British Liassic Dragonflies (Odonata). Fossil Insects, No. 1. British Mus. (Nat. Hist.). 38 pp., 5 pls. (1925).

TILLYARD, R. J. and FRASER, F. C. A Reclassification of the Order Odonata. Based on Some New Interpretations of the Venation of the Dragonfly Wing. Austral. Zool., 9, pp. 125–396 (1938).

ORDER **PLECÓPTERA**

The only extinct family of this order is the Hypoperlidæ (Fig. 1168) from the Upper Permian of Russia. This differs from existing families of the order chiefly by having Rs arising near the base of the wing, instead of near mid-wing. The living family Eustheniidæ is recorded from the Upper Permian rocks of Australia, Tæniopterygidæ from the Jurassic beds of Turkestan, and other living families from the early Tertiary deposits (Baltic amber).

LITERATURE ON PLECOPTERA — EXTINCT FAMILIES

MARTYNOV, A. V. Permian Fossil Insects of North-East Europe. Rev. Mus. Geol. Acad. Sci. URSS, 4, pp. 57–59 (1928).

Liassic Insects from Shurab and Kisyl-Kiya. Trav. Inst. Paléontol. Acad. Sci. URSS, 7(1), pp. 158–160, 8 figs. (1937).

TILLYARD, R. J. Upper Permian Insects of New South Wales. V. The Order Perlaria or Stone-flies. Proc. Linn. Soc. N. S. W., 60, pp. 385–391 (1935).

ZALESSKY, G. M. A New Plecopteron from the Permian Depositions of the Ural. C. R. Acad. Sci. URSS, 60, pp. 1041–1043, 2 figs. (1948).

ORDER **BLATTÀRIA**

The classification of the fossil roaches is made difficult by our limited knowledge of their structure. Most specimens consist of isolated tegmina, the venation of which is highly variable. The following key, utilizing the tegminous venation, is based on the evolutionary changes that seem to have taken place since the group first appeared in the Middle Pennsylvanian (Upper Carboniferous) period. Two families, Pteridomylacridæ and Pseudomylacridæ (both Pennsylvanian), each based on a small fragment, are not included in the key; nor is the Cainoblattinidæ, based on a poorly preserved specimen in amber from China.

1. Subcosta distinct and well developed, extending at least as far as mid-wing (usually beyond), with forked veinlets; radius forked

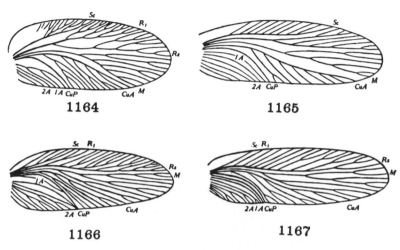

Figs. 1164–1167. Blattaria.

1164. **Archimylacris**, fore wing (Pruvost), Archimylacridæ.
1165. **Syscioblatta**, fore wing (Handlirsch), Spiloblattinidæ.
1166. **Triassoblatta**, fore wing (Tillyard), Mylacridæ.
1167. **Rhipidoblatta**, fore wing (Handlirsch), Mylacridæ.

dichotomously, R1 forming as conspicuous a part of the radial system as Rs; media forking at mid-wing or further distally. (Archimýlacris (Fig. 1164)). (*PALÆOBLÁTTIDÆ*).

(Cp–Pm) **ARCHIMYLÁCRIDÆ**

Sc either a distinct vein or appearing as a branch of the radial system, usually ending before mid-wing, radius not forked dichotomously, appearing merely as the most anterior branch of Rs; media forking at or before mid-wing 2

2. Sc a distinct vein, ending at mid-wing or slightly beyond, almost always with simple, pectinate veinlets; media forking near mid-wing; all branches of M directed posteriorly, forming a distinct

medio-cubital field, extending nearly in a straight line obliquely. (Spilobláttina, Permobláttina, Sysciobláttia (Fig. 1165)).

(Cp–Pm) SPILOBLATTÍNIDÆ

Sc rarely distinct, usually appearing as a branch of the radial system, and ending before mid-wing; subcostal veinlets (when present) few in number and not pectinately arranged; media forking before mid-wing, usually in proximal quarter of wing; a medio-cubital field (when present) curved or arched. (Mýlacris, Mesobláttina, Rhipidobláttina (Fig. 1167), Triassoblátta (Fig. 1166)). (Including *MESOBLATTÍNIDÆ, DIECHOBLATTÍNIDÆ, POROBLATTÍNIDÆ, NEOMYLÁCRIDÆ, IDIOMYLÁCRIDÆ, NEORTHOBLATTÍNIDÆ, OTTWEILERÌIDÆ, HEMIMYLÁCRIDÆ*) . . . . (Cp–J) MYLÁCRIDÆ

LITERATURE ON BLATTARIA — EXTINCT FAMILIES

GUTHÖRL, P. Neue Beiträge zur Insekten-Fauna des Saar-Carbons. Senckenbergiana, 18, pp. 82–112, 4 pls., 18 figs. (1936).

HANDLIRSCH, A. Die fossilen Insekten und die Phylogenie der rezenten Formen. Handb. Palæontol. u. Zool., pp. 181–301; 350–385; 427–435; 526–540; 662 (1906–08).

Beiträge zur Kenntnis der palæozoischen Blattarien. Sb. Akad. Wiss. Wien, Math.-naturwiss. Kl., 129, pp. 431–461, 8 figs. (1920).

PING, C. On a Blattoid Insect in the Fushun Amber. Bull. Geol. Soc. China, 11, pp. 205–207. (1932).

PRUVOST, P. La faune continentale du terrain houiller du Nord de la France. Mem. Carte Géol. France, pp. 130–247. Paris (1919).

TILLYARD, R. J. Kansas Permian Insects. Part 20. The Cockroaches, or Order Blattaria. Parts I, II. American Journ. Sci., 34, pp. 169–202, 17 figs.; pp. 249–276, 11 figs. (1937).

ORDER ORTHÓPTERA

SUBORDER SALTATÒRIA

Several extinct families of saltatorial Orthoptera have been described, the earliest record of the suborder being in Triassic rocks.[1] Five of these (Isfaropteridæ, Aboilidæ, Haglidæ, Pamphagopsidæ and Geinitziidæ, all Jurassic) are best included in the living family Prophalangopsidæ [2] (Zeuner, 1939). One other (Bintoniellidæ, Jurassic of England) is based on a small fragment. The three remaining families are separated as follows:

[1] The genus Elcanopsis from the Permian of Australia, though referred to the Saltatoria by some authors, is so incompletely known that even its ordinal position is questionable.

[2] Treated as a subfamily in the present volume.

1. Fore wing with cross-veins numerous and close together, giving the appearance of a fine network. (**Mesotìtan, Clatrotìtan**).
(Tr) **MESOTITÁNIDÆ**
Cross-veins few in number and widely spaced..................2
2. Rs and M of fore wing free from each other; Sc extending almost to apex. (**Locustópsis** (Fig. 1169)).....(Tr–J) **LOCUSTÓPSIDÆ**
Rs and M of fore wing fused; Sc not extending beyond mid-wing. (**Elcàna** (Fig. 1170)) .... (Tr–J) **ELCÁNIDÆ**

SUBORDER **PHASMATÒDEA**

Four extinct families of phasmids have been recognized, the oldest being from Triassic deposits. They are separated on the venation of the fore wing, as follows:

1. R dividing near mid-wing; wings narrowing to their ends.......2
Rs branching from R well before mid-wing; wings not narrowed to their ends...3

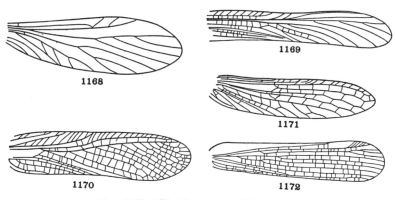

Figs. 1168–1172. Plecoptera and Orthoptera.

1168. **Hypoperla**, fore wing (Martynov), Hypoperlidæ (Plecoptera).
1169. **Locustopsis**, fore wing (Zeuner), Elcanidae (Orthoptera).
1170. **Elcana**, fore wing (Handlirsch), Elcanidæ (Orthoptera).
1171. **Necrophasma**, fore wing (Martynov), Necrophasmatidæ (Orthoptera).
1172. **Aerophasma**, fore wing (Martynov), Aerophasmatidæ (Orthoptera).

2. M dividing near wing base, well before origin of Rs; 1A terminating near mid-wing. (**Necrophásma**, Fig. 1171).
(J) **NECROPHASMÁTIDÆ**
M dividing almost at level of origin of Rs; 1A extending beyond mid-wing .... (J) **CHRESMÓDIDÆ**

3. Rs with three distal branches. (Aerophásma, Fig. 1172).
(J) AEROPHASMÁTIDÆ
Rs unbranched .... (Tr) AEROPLANIDÆ

SUBORDER MANTEODEA

Triassomanteidæ, from the Triassic deposits of Queensland, is the only extinct family of this suborder, and its assignment here is questionable because of the fragmentary condition of the fossil.

LITERATURE ON ORTHOPTERA — EXTINCT FAMILIES

MARTYNOV, A. V. A New Fossil Form of Phasmatodea from Galkino (Turkestan) and on Mesozoic Phasmids in General. Ann. Mag. Nat. Hist., (10) 1, pp. 319–328, 3 figs. (1928).
McKEOWN, K. C. New Fossil Insect Wings (Protohemiptera, Family Mesotitanidæ). Rec. Australian Mus., 20, pp. 30–37, 4 pls., 3 figs. (1937).
ZEUNER, F. E. The Recent and Fossil Prophalangopsidæ. Stylops, 4, pp. 102–108, 7 figs. (1935).
    Fossil Orthoptera Ensifera. 321 pp. Brit. Mus. (Nat. Hist.), London. (1939).
    The Fossil Acrididae (Orth. Salt.). Part I. Catantopinæ. Ann. Mag. Nat. Hist., (11) 8, pp. 510–522 (1941).
    The Locustopsidæ and the Phylogeny of the Acridodea. Proc. Roy. Ent. Soc. London (B), 11, pp. 1–18, 15 figs., 1 pl. (1942).

ORDER DERMÁPTERA

Only one extinct family has been described: Protodiplatyidæ, from Jurassic deposits of Turkestan. The group differs from all living families by having 5-segmented tarsi (posterior legs at least) and segmented cerci in the adult.

LITERATURE ON DERMAPTERA — EXTINCT FAMILIES

MARTYNOV, A. V. To the knowledge of Fossil Insects from Jurassic Beds in Turkestan. 2. Raphidioptera (Cont'd.), Orthoptera, Odonata, Neuroptera. Bull. Acad. Sci. URSS, 19, pp. 569–598 (1925).

ORDER EMBIÒDEA

No extinct families are referable to this order. The earliest record of the group is in Tertiary amber, in which the living family Notoligotomidæ occurs.[1]

[1] Davis, C. Taxonomic Notes on the Order Embioptera. XX. Proc. Linn. Soc. New South Wales, 65, pp. 533–542 (1940).

ORDER ISÓPTERA

No extinct families referable to this order have been recognized. The earliest record of the termites is in early Tertiary deposits, which have yielded specimens of Mastotermitidæ, Kalotermitidæ, Hodotermitidæ and Rhinotermitidæ.

ORDER CORRODÉNTIA

Eleven extinct families of this order are included in the following key. An additional family, Asienthomidæ (Jurassic of Turkestan), although

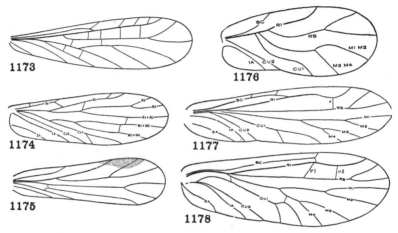

Figs. 1173–1178. **Corrodentia.**

1173. **Permembia,** fore wing (Tillyard), Permembiidæ.
1174. **Delopterum,** fore wing (Carpenter), Delopteridæ.
1175. **Zygopsocus,** fore wing (Tillyard), Zygopsocidæ.
1176. **Cyphoneura,** fore wing (Carpenter), Lophioneuridæ.
1177. **Dichentomum,** fore wing (Carpenter), Dichentomidæ.
1178. **Permopsocus,** fore wing (Carpenter), Permopsocidæ.

undoubtedly belonging to the order, is too incompletely known for inclusion in the key. The family Archæmiomopteridæ (Upper Carboniferous of Germany) can be placed in the Corrodentia only with much doubt. The oldest unquestionable record of the order is in Lower Permian strata of Kansas (Dichentomidæ and Permopsocidæ).

1. In fore wing, M and CuA anastomosed for a conspicuous part of their lengths 2
    M and CuA not anastomosed 4

2. Sc in fore wing terminating on costal margin 3
   Sc terminating on R1. (**Permémbia** (Fig. 1173)).
   (Pm) **PERMEMBÌIDÆ**
3. Several oblique veinlets between Sc and costal margin of fore wing,
   and also between R1 and Sc. . . . . . . (Pm) **PALÆOMANTÈIDÆ**
   Only one veinlet between Sc and costal margin and between Sc
   and R1. (**Delópterum** (Fig. 1174)). . . (Pm) **DELOPTÉRIDÆ**
4. Rs with four branches. (**Zygopsòcus** (Fig. 1175)).
   (Pm) **ZYGOPSÓCIDÆ**
   Rs with less than four branches 5
5. M with three branches. (*DINOPSÓCIDÆ*)
   (J) **MARTYNOPSÓCIDÆ**
   M with two or four branches 6
6. M with four branches 7
   M with two branches 9
7. Fork of CuA strongly arched, connected to M3 + 4 by a cross-vein.
   (**Permopsòcus** (Fig. 1178)) . . . . (Pm) **PERMOPSÓCIDÆ**
   Fork of CuA less arched, not connected with M3 + 4 by a cross-
   vein 8
8. Sc distinct and free from R1 for at least most of its length.
   (**Dichéntomum** (Fig. 1177)) . . . . (Pm) **DICHENTÓMIDÆ**
   Sc obsolescent or fused with R1 . . . . (J) **ARCHIPSÝLLIDÆ**
9. Main veins strongly curved, CuA sigmoidally curved. (**Cyphoneùra**
   (Fig. 1176), **Lophioneùra**) . . . . (Pm) **LOPHIONEÙRIDÆ**
   Main veins normal, CuA not sigmoidally curved.
   (Pm) **ZOROPSÓCIDÆ**

LITERATURE ON CORRODENTIA — EXTINCT FAMILIES

CARPENTER, F. M. The Lower Permian Insects of Kansas. Part 5. Psocoptera
   and Additions to the Homoptera. American Journ. Sci., **24**, pp. 1–22,
   11 figs. (1932).
   The Lower Permian Insects of Kansas. Part 6. Delopteridæ, Protely-
   troptera, Plectoptera, and a New Collection of Protodonata, Odonata,
   Megasecoptera, Homoptera and Psocoptera. Proc. American Acad. Arts
   Sci., **68**, pp. 411–504, 1 pl., 29 figs. (1933).
GUTHÖRL, P. Zur Arthropoden-Fauna des Karbons und Perms. Part 9.
   Palaeodictyoptera, Mixotermitoidea, Miomoptera und Blattariæ. Sencken-
   bergiana, **21**, pp. 320–324 (1939).
KARNY, H. H. Zur Systematik der Orthopteroiden Insekten. Zweiter Teil.
   Treubia, **12**, pp. 431–461 (1930).
MARTYNOV, A. V. Jurassic Fossil Insects from Turkestan. Part 6. Homoptera
   and Psocoptera. Bull. Acad. Sci. URSS, **20**, pp. 1349–1366, 9 figs. (1926).
TILLYARD, R. J. Kansas Permian Insects. Part 12. The Family Delopteridæ,
   with a Discussion of its Ordinal Position. American Journ. Sci., **16**,
   pp. 469–484, 11 figs. (1928).
   Upper Permian Insects of New South Wales. Part III. The Order

Copeognatha. Proc. Linn. Soc. New South Wales, **60**, pp. 265–279; 13 figs. (1935).

Kansas Permian Insects. Part 17. The Order Megasecoptera and Additions to the Palaeodictyoptera, Odonata, Protoperlaria, Copeognatha and Neuroptera. American Journ. Sci., **33**, pp. 81–110, 10 figs. (1937).

ORDER THYSANÓPTERA

Two extinct families of thrips have been established. One of these, Permothripidæ (Upper Permian beds of Russia), constituting the oldest record of the order, includes species resembling the existing Phlœothripidæ, but having short and thick antennæ. The other extinct family, Mesothripidæ (Jurassic deposits of Turkestan) includes species with very thick front femora and slender antennæ.

LITERATURE ON THYSANOPTERA — EXTINCT FAMILIES

MARTYNOV, A. V. Jurassic Fossil Insects from Turkestan. 7. Some Odonata, Neuroptera, Thysanoptera. Bull. Acad. Sci. URSS, **21**, p. 768 (1927).

A Find of Thysanoptera in the Permian Deposits. C. R. Acad. Sci. URSS, **3**, pp. 333–336, 4 figs. (1935).

ORDER HEMÍPTERA

SUBORDER HOMÓPTERA

Nineteen extinct families of Homoptera are included in the following key. Since much difference of opinion exists in the literature about their diagnostic characteristics, some changes in the synonymy of the families will probably become necessary as additional material is studied. The oldest record of the suborder is the Archescytinidæ, from Lower Permian rocks in Kansas.

1. Subcosta of fore wing free from R1 for its entire length, its termination on costal margin slightly proximal to that of R1a 2

    Subcosta of fore wing coalesced at least distally with R1, or obsolescent, not reaching the coastal margin near the termination of R1a 3

2. Ambient vein absent in fore wing. (**Archescýtina** (Fig. 1179)). (Including *MAUERÌIDÆ, URALOSCYTÍNIDÆ, PERMO-SCYTINÓPSIDÆ*) (*PERMOPSÝLLIDÆ*).

    (Pm) **ARCHESCYTÍNIDÆ**

    Ambient vein present in fore wing. (**Mesogèreon** (Fig. 1183)).

    (J) **MESOGEREÓNIDÆ**

3. CuA of fore wing in contact with stem R+M (or very nearly so) and anastomosed with M for some distance beyond the divergence of M from R 4

CuA free from R+M; or if in contact with it, there is no anastomosis of CuA and M beyond the point of this contact.........5
4. Fore wing membranous; costal margin not thickened.
(Pm) **PROTOPSYLLIDÌIDÆ**

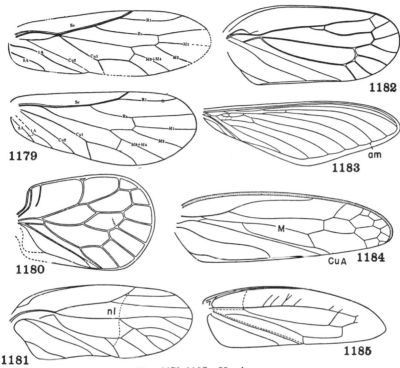

Figs. 1179–1185. Hemiptera

1179. **Archescytina,** fore and hind wings (Carpenter), Archescytinidæ.
1180. **Coleoscyta,** fore wing (Martynov), Coleoscytidæ.
1181. **Prosbole,** fore wing (Becker-Migdisova), Prosbolidæ.
1182. **Scytinoptera,** fore wing (Martynov), Scytinopteridæ.
1183. **Mesogereon,** fore wing (Tillyard), Mesogereonidæ.
1184. **Ipsviciopsis,** fore wing (Tillyard), Ipsviciidæ.
1185. **Paraknightia,** fore wing (Evans), Paraknightiidæ.

Fore wing leathery; costal margin thickened. (**Ipsvícia, Ipsvicíópsis**
(Fig. 1184)). (Including *PROCERCÓPIDÆ*).
(Pm–Tr) **IPSVICÌIDÆ**
5. Proximal part of fore wing distinctly leathery, distal part membranous; all veins with numerous distal branches in membranous
area of wing. (**Pereboria**).............(Pm) **PEREBORÌIDÆ**

Proximal part of fore wing having at most only a slightly different
texture from the distal part; veins with relatively few branches. .6
6. Fore wing about as broad as long. (Coleoscỳta (Fig. 1180)).
(Pm) COLEOSCÝTIDÆ
Fore wing much longer than broad 7
7. R1a of fore wing terminating at about mid-wing.
(J) PALEONTÍNIDÆ
R1a terminating much nearer apex............................8
8. First two anal veins of fore wing anastomosed distally.
(Pm) PROSBOLÓPSIDÆ
First two anal veins independent 9
9. Nodal line present. (Prósbole (Fig. 1181)). ·(Including SOJANO-
NEÙRIDÆ, PERMOGLÝPHIDÆ, PERMOCICADÓPSIDÆ).
(Pm) PROSBÓLIDÆ
Nodal line absent. (Scytinóptera (Fig. 1182)). (Including CICA-
DOPSÝLLIDÆ) .... (Pm) SCYTINOPTÉRIDÆ

SUBORDER HETERÓPTERA

Although several extinct families of Heteroptera have been erected,
almost all were "provisionally" established by Handlirsch, for very poorly
preserved fossils showing no satisfactory family characteristics. These
so-called families, all from Jurassic deposits, are as follows; Aphlebocor-
idæ, Apopnidæ, Archegocimicidæ, Cuneocoridæ, Diatillidæ, Eonabiidæ,
Hadrocoridæ, Hypocimicidæ, Pachymeridiidæ, Prosbascanionidæ, Progonocimicidæ, Protocoridæ, Psychrocoridæ and Sisyrocoridæ. The family
Triassocoridæ from Triassic rocks of Australia is also too incompletely
known for diagnosis. The only extinct family of the suborder which is
sufficiently well known for this purpose is Paraknightiidæ (Fig. 1185),
which is from Upper Permian deposits of Australia, and which consti-
tutes the earliest record of the suborder. These insects have well developed pronotal paranota, a short but broad embolium, extending as far as
the junction of R+M and lacking a nodal furrow. The problematical
family Dunstaniidæ, from Triassic beds of Australia, has been assigned
to both the Homoptera (Becker-Migdisova, 1949) and Heteroptera
(Tillyard, 1918; Evans, 1950).

LITERATURE ON HEMIPTERA — EXTINCT FAMILIES

BECKER-MIGDISOVA, H. E. Fossil Permian Cicadas of the Family Prosbolidæ
from the Sojana River. Trav. Inst. Paléontol. Acad. Sci. URSS, 11,
pp. 1–79 (1940).
    Contributions to the Knowledge of Comparative Morphology of the
Recent and Permian Homoptera. Bull. Acad. Sci. URSS, Biol. No. 6, 1946,
pp. 741–766 (1946).
    Mesozoic Homoptera from Central Asia. Trav. Inst. Paléontol. Acad.
Sci. URSS, 22, pp. 1–64, 1 pl., 33 figs. (1949).

CARPENTER, F. M. The Lower Permian Insects of Kansas. Part 4. The Order Hemiptera, and Additions to the Paleodictyoptera and Protohymenoptera. American Journ. Sci., (5)22, pp. 113–130, 8 figs. (1931).

The Lower Permian Insects of Kansas. Part 5. Psocoptera and Additions to the Homoptera. American Journ. Sci., (5)24, pp. 1–22, 11 figs. (1932).

The Lower Permian Insects of Kansas. Part 6. Delopteridæ, Protelytroptera, Plectoptera and a New Collection of Protodonata, Odonata, Megasecoptera, Homoptera, and Psocoptera. Proc. American Acad. Arts Sci., 68, pp. 411–503, 1 pl., 29 figs. (1933).

DAVIS, C. Hemiptera and Copeognatha from the Upper Permian of New South Wales. Proc. Linn. Soc. New South Wales, 67, pp. 111–122, 24 figs. (1942).

EVANS, J. W. Upper Permian Homoptera from New South Wales. Rec. Australian Mus., 21, pp. 180–198, 64 figs. (1943).

A New Fossil Homopteron from Kimbles Hill, Belmont (Upper Permian). Rec. Australian Mus., 21, pp. 431–432, 1 pl., 1 fig. (1947).

A Re-examination of an Upper Permian Insect, Paraknightia magnifica Ev. Rec. Australian Mus., 22, pp. 246–250, 15 figs. (1950).

HANDLIRSCH, A. Neue Untersuchungen über die fossilen Insekten. Teil I. Ann. Naturh. Mus. Wien, 48, pp. 1–140 (1937).

Neue Untersuchungen über die fossilen Insekten. Teil II. Ann. Naturh. Mus. Wien, 49, pp. 1–240, 16 pls. (1939).

MARTYNOV, A. V. To the Morphology and Systematical Position of the Family Palæontinidæ Handl., with a Description of a New Form from Ust-baley, Siberia. Ann. Soc. Paléont. Russie, 2, pp. 93–122, 1 pl. (1931).

Permian Fossil Insects from Arkhangelsk District. Part 5. Homoptera. Trav. Inst. Paléozool. Acad. Sci. URSS, 4, pp. 1–35, 1 pl., 35 figs. (1935).

Permian Fossil Insects from Kargala and Their Relationships. Trav. Inst. Paléontol., Acad. Sci. URSS, 7(2), pp. 1–92, 20 figs. (1937).

TILLYARD, R. J. Mesozoic and Tertiary Insects of Queensland and New South Wales. Publ. Queensland Geol. Surv. No. 253, pp. 31–35, 3 figs. (1916).

Mesozoic Insects of Queensland. No. 4. Hemiptera Heteroptera: The Family Dunstaniidæ. Proc. Linn. Soc. New South Wales, 43, pp. 567–592, 1 pl., 6 figs. (1918).

Mesozoic Insects of Queensland. No. 7. Hemiptera Homoptera. Proc. Linn. Soc. New South Wales, 44, pp. 857–896, 25 figs. (1919).

Mesozoic Insects of Queensland, No. 8. Hemiptera Homoptera (Cont'd.). The Genus Mesogereon. Proc. Linn. Soc. New South Wales, 46, pp. 269–284, 6 pls., 7 figs. (1921).

Upper Permian Insects of New South Wales. Part I. Introduction and the Order Hemiptera. Proc. Linn. Soc. New South Wales, 51, pp. 1–30, 1 pl., 27 figs. (1926).

ZALESSKY, G. Etudes des insectes permiens du bassin de la Sylva. III. Quelques nouveaux représentants des Protohymenoptera, Homoptera, Hemipsocoptera, Psocoptera, Protoperlaria, Isoptera et Protoblattoidea. Prob. Paléontol., 5, pp. 33–91, 3 pls., 45 figs. (1939).

ZALESSKY, M. D. Sur deux représentants nouveaux des Paléohémiptères du Permien de la Kama et du Perebore dans le bassin de la Pétchora. Bull. Acad. Sci. URSS, Physico-Math., 1930, pp. 1017–1027, 1 pl., 2 figs. (1930).

ORDER ANOPLÙRA

No extinct families are known. The only fossil record of the order is the occurrence of the living genus *Neohæmatopinus* in the Quaternary deposits of Siberia.[1]

ORDER NEURÓPTERA

SUBORDER SIALÒDEA

Only two extinct families, indicated in the key below, can be assigned to this suborder and even these are placed here with doubt. The earliest

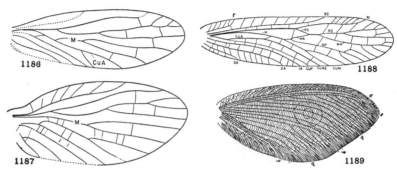

Figs. 1186–1189. **Neuroptera.**

1186. **Archisialis,** fore wing (Martynov), Archisialidæ.
1187. **Permosialis,** fore wing (Martynov), Permosialidæ.
1188. **Permoraphidia,** fore wing (Carpenter), Permoraphidiidæ.
1189. **Kalligramma,** fore wing (Handlirsch), Kalligrammidæ.

unquestionable representative (Corydalidæ) of the suborder is in the Baltic amber (early Tertiary).

1. CuA anastomosed with M. (**Archisìalis** (Fig. 1186)).
   (Pm) ARCHISIÁLIDÆ
   CuA free from M. (**Permosìalis** (Fig. 1187)).
   (Pm) PERMOSIÁLIDÆ

SUBORDER RAPHIDIÒDEA

Two extinct families belong here, one of which (Permoraphidiidæ) is the oldest record (Lower Permian) of the suborder.

[1] Dubinin, V. B. The Finding of Pleistocene Lice (Anoplura) and Nematodes in the Course of Investigations on the Bodies of Fossil Ground-Squirrels. C. R. Acad. Sci, URSS, 62, pp. 417–420, 3 figs. (1948).

1. Recurrent or submarginal costal vein present. (**Permoraphídia** (Fig. 1188)). .... (Pm) **PERMORAPHIDÌIDÆ**
No recurrent vein present. (**Mesoraphídia** (Fig. 1180)).
(Pm) **MESORAPHIDÌIDÆ**

SUBORDER **PLANIPÉNNIA**

The family Permoberothidæ, from the Lower Permian rocks of Kansas, is the oldest representative of this suborder. Twelve additional extinct families have been described, but two of them, Solenoptilidæ and Epigambriidæ (both Jurassic), are too little known to be included in the following key.

1. Cross-veins very numerous and close together over all but the marginal area of the wings. (**Kalligrámma** (Fig. 1189)).
(J) **KALLIGRÁMMIDÆ**
Cross-veins much less numerous........................2
2. Sc terminating on costal margin just beyond mid-wing; MA and MP parallel and close together, and separated by a groove. (**Permoberòtha** (Fig. 1191))........(Pm) **PERMOBERÓTHIDÆ**
Sc terminating further distally; MA and MP not parallel and not separated by a groove.................................3
3. At least one row of regularly arranged gradate cross-veins present in the fore wing. (**Mesochrysòpa, Chrysoleonìtes, Mesypochrỳsa** (Fig. 1192)). .... (J) **MESOCHRYSÓPIDÆ**
No gradate cross-veins present............................4
4. Rs with at least ten pectinate and parallel main branches........5
Rs with not more than eight main branches.................6
5. Distal part of R1 curved, following the curvature of the apical margin and terminating on the hind margin. (**Nymphìtes** (Fig. 1195)). .... (J) **NYMPHÍTIDÆ**
Distal part of R1 not so curved, terminating on the anterior margin just before wing apex. (**Kirgisélla, Actinophlèbia** (Fig. 1194)).
(J) **PROHEMEROBÌIDÆ**, part
6. Costal space at least twice as wide (at level of first branch of Rs) as the space between R1 and Rs. (**Permegalòmus, Palæmerobius** (Fig. 1197)). (Including *PERMOSISÝRIDÆ, PARASISÝR-IDÆ, SIALIDÓPSIDÆ*) .... (Pm) **PALÆMEROBÌIDÆ**
Costal space much less than twice as wide as the space between R1 and Rs 7
7. Sc terminating on R1. (**Permithòne** (Fig. 1193)).
(Pm) **PERMITHÓNIDÆ**
Sc terminating on costal margin. (**Prohemeròbius** (Fig. 1196)).
(J) **PROHEMEROBÌIDÆ**, part

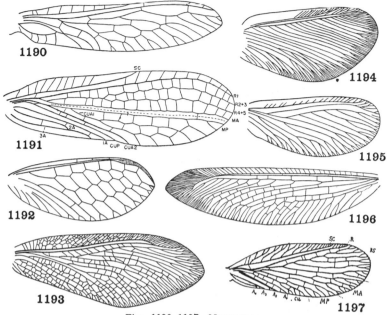

Figs. 1190–1197. Neuroptera.

1190. **Mesoraphidia**, fore wing (Martynov), Mesoraphidiidæ.
1191. **Permoberotha**, fore wing (Carpenter), Permoberothidæ.
1192. **Mesypochrysa**, wing (Martynov), Mesochrysopidæ.
1193. **Permithone**, fore wing (Tillyard), Permithonidæ.
1194. **Actinophlebia**, fore wing (Handlirsch), Prohemerobiidæ.
1195. **Nymphites**, hind wing (Carpenter), Nymphitidæ.
1196. **Prohemerobius**, fore wing (Handlirsch), Prohemerobiidæ.
1197. **Palæmerobius**, fore wing (Martynov), Palæmerobiidæ.

LITERATURE ON NEUROPTERA — EXTINCT FAMILIES

CARPENTER, F. M. A Jurassic Neuropteran from the Lithographic Limestone of Bavaria. Psyche, **36**, pp. 190–194, 1 fig. (1929).

The Lower Permian Insects of Kansas. Part 9. The Orders Neuroptera, Raphidiodea, Caloneurodea and Protorthoptera (Probnisidæ), with Additional Protodonata and Megasecoptera. Proc. American Acad. Arts Sci., **75**, pp. 55–84, 1 pl., 15 figs. (1943).

DAVIS, C. A New Species of Permithone (Neuroptera Planipennia) from the Upper Permian of New South Wales. Proc. Linn. Soc. New South Wales, **68**, pp. 11–12, 1 pl., 1 fig. (1943).

HANDLIRSCH, A. Die Fossilen Insekten. Handbuch f. Palaeontol. u. Zool., pp. 473–478; 604–612 (1906–08).

Neue Untersuchungen über die fossilen Insekten. Teil II. Ann. Naturh. Mus. Wien, **49**, pp. 1–240 (1939).

Martynòv, A. V. To the Knowledge of Fossil Insects from Jurassic Beds in Turkestan. 1. Raphidioptera. 2. Raphidioptera (cont'd.), Orthoptera (*s.l.*), Odonata, Neuroptera. Bull. Acad. Sci. Russie, **1925**, pp. 233–246, 9 figs.; pp. 569–598, 12 figs. (1925).

Jurassic Fossil Insects from Turkestan. 7. Some Odonata, Neuroptera, Thysanoptera. Bull. Acad. Sci. URSS, **1927**, pp. 757–768, 17 figs. (1927).

Permian Fossil Insects of North-east Europe. Trav. Mus. Géol. Acad. Sci. URSS, **4**, pp. 86–98, 8 figs. (1928).

New Permian Insects from Tikhie Gory. II. Neoptera (excluding Miomoptera). Trav. Mus. Géol. Acad. Sci. URSS, **8**, pp. 149–212, 29 figs. (1931).

Permian Fossil Insects from the Arkhangelsk District. Part II. Neuroptera, Megaloptera and Coleoptera. Trav. Inst. Paléozool. Acad. Sci., URSS, **2**, pp. 63–96, 19 figs. (1932).

Permian Fossil Insects from Kargala and Their Relationships. Trav. Inst. Paléontol., **7**(2), pp. 1–92, 19 figs. (1937).

Martynova, O. M. Two New Raphidioptera from the Jurassic Schists of Kara-Tau. Doklady Akad. Nauk SSSR, **56**, pp. 635–637 (1947). (Not seen).

Tillyard, R. J. Some New Permian Insects from Belmont, N.S.W. Proc. Linn. Soc. New South Wales, **47**, pp. 279–292, 2 pls., 6 figs. (1922).

Upper Permian Insects of New South Wales. Part 2. The Orders Mecoptera, Paramecoptera and Neuroptera. Proc. Linn. Soc. New South Wales, **51**, pp. 265–282, 2 pls., 18 figs. (1926).

The Panorpoid Complex in the British Rhætic and Lias. Fossil Insects, no. 3. British Mus. (Nat. Hist.), London. 79 pp., 1 pl., 31 figs. (1933).

ORDER MECÓPTERA

(Including *PROTOMECÓPTERA, PARAMECÓPTERA, PARATRICHÓPTERA*, part, *PROTODÍPTERA*)

Twenty-four extinct families have been erected in this order, which was a major one from the late Permian to the Jurassic periods. As more and more material has been studied, it has become apparent that fully one-third of these families fall into synonymy. The following key covers all families except five (Archipanorpidæ, Dobbertinidæ, Mesopsychidæ, Triassopsychidæ and Tillyarditidæ), which are too little known for inclusion. The Platychoristidæ, Anormochoristidæ and some Orthophlebiidæ, from the Lower Permian rocks of Kansas, are the oldest representatives of the order.

1. Costal space of fore wing with a complete series of oblique veinlets. (**Platychorísta** (Fig. 1198)). (*PROTOMERÓPIDÆ*).
   (Pm) **PLATYCHORÍSTIDÆ**
   Costal space with very few cross-veins, almost none oblique......2
2. Sc of fore wing terminating on R1.
   (Pm) **ANORMOCHORÍSTIDÆ**
   Sc terminating on costal margin............................3

3. Radius straight, without bend near origin of Rs.
                                    (Pm) BELMONTÌIDÆ
   Radius with a distinct bend near origin of R1 4
4. Only one or two anal veins in fore wing. (Permotípula (Fig. 1199)).
                                    (Pm) PERMOTÌPÙLIDÆ
   Three anal veins in forewing 5
5. Sc of fore wing very short, terminating at level of origin of Rs;
   fore wing triangular, with distinct tornus; hind wing much
   smaller than fore wing. (Pseudopolycéntropus (Fig. 1201)).
                        (J) PSEUDOPOLYCENTROPÓDIDÆ

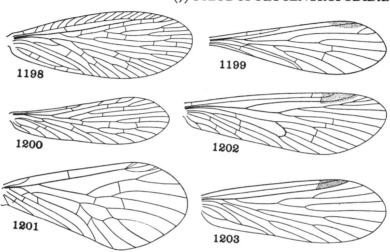

Figs. 1198–1203. Mecoptera and Trichoptera.

1198. **Platychorista**, fore wing (Carpenter), Platychoristidæ (Mecoptera).
1199. **Permotipula**, wing (Tillyard), Permotipulidæ (Mecoptera).
1200. **Permopanorpa**, fore wing (Carpenter), Orthophlebiidæ (Mecoptera).
1201. **Pseudopolycentropus**, fore wing (Martynov), Pseudopolycentropodidæ (Mecoptera).
1202. **Orthophlebia**, fore wing (Tillyard), Orthophlebiidæ (Mecoptera).
1203. **Necrotaulius**, fore wing (Tillyard), Necrotaulidæ (Trichoptera).

   Sc longer, usually extending beyond mid-wing; fore wing oval,
      without tornus; fore and hind wings subequal. (Permopanórpa
      (Fig. 1200), Permochorísta, Orthophlèbia). (Including *PERMO-
      CHORÍSTIDÆ, MESOPANÓRPIDÆ, CLADOCHORÍSTI-
      DÆ, PERMOPANÓRPIDÆ, PARACHORÍSTIDÆ, PETRO-
      MÁNTIDÆ, PROTOCHORÍSTIDÆ, PROTOPANÓRPIDÆ,
      AGETOPANÓRPIDÆ, LITHOPANÓRPIDÆ, NEORTHO-
      PHLEBÌIDÆ, STEREOCHORÍSTIDÆ*).
                        (Pm, Tr, J) ORTHOPHLEBÌIDÆ

LITERATURE ON MECOPTERA — EXTINCT FAMILIES

CARPENTER, F. M. The Lower Permian Insects of Kansas. Part 1. Introduction and the Order Mecoptera. Bull. Mus. Comp. Zool., 70, pp. 69–101, 5 pls., 3 figs. (1930).

MARTYNOV, A. V. Jurassic Fossil Mecoptera and Paratrichoptera from Turkestan and Ust-Balei (Siberia). Bull. Acad. Sci. URSS, 1927, pp. 651–666, 15 figs. (1927).

MARTYNOVA, O. M. Permian Mecoptera from Chekarda and Kargala. Bull. Acad. Sci. URSS, 1942, No. 1–2, pp. 133–149, 1 pl., 13 figs. (1942).

Variabilité individuelle des ailes de Mécoptères. Bull. Acad. Sci. URSS, 1948, No. 2, pp. 193–198, 5 figs. (1948).

TILLYARD, R. J. Mesozoic Insects of Queensland. No. 1. Planipennia, Trichoptera, and the New Order Protomecoptera. Proc. Linn. Soc. New South Wales, 42, pp. 175–200, 3 pls., 7 figs. (1917).

Mesozoic Insects of Queensland. No. 5. Mecoptera, the New Order Paratrichoptera, and Additions to Planipennia. Proc. Linn. Soc. New South Wales, 44, pp. 194–212, 1 pl., 6 figs. (1919).

The Evolution of the Scorpion-flies and Their Derivatives. Ann. Ent. Soc. America, 28, pp. 1–45, 23 figs. (1935).

Ancestors of the Diptera. Nature, 1937, pp. 66–67, 2 figs. (1937).

ORDER **TRICHÓPTERA**

(Including *PARATRICHÓPTERA*, part)

Only three extinct families are referable to this order. The Necrotauliidæ constitute the earliest record (Jurassic) of the group.

1. Fore wing with costal area broad, costal margin strongly curved; Rs with terminal branches.........(J) **PROSEPIDIDÓNTIDÆ**
   Costal area narrow, costal margin straight; Rs with four terminal branches. (**Necrotàulius** (Fig. 1203)). (Including *LIASSOPHÍLIDÆ*) ....(J) **NECROTAULÌIDÆ**

LITERATURE ON TRICHOPTERA — EXTINCT FAMILIES

HANDLIRSCH, A. Palæontologie. Handb. Ent., 3, pp. 199–200 (1920).

TILLYARD, R. J. The Panorpoid Complex in the British Rhætic and Lias. Fossil Insects, no. 3. Brit. Mus. (Nat. Hist.), London, pp. 1–79 (1933).

ORDER **LEPIDÓPTERA**

No extinct family is referable to this order. The family Eosetidæ (for the genus *Eoses*, Triassic beds of Australia) was originally placed here,[1]

[1] Tindale, N. B. Triassic Insects of Queensland. 1. Eoses, a Probable Lepidopterous Insect from the Triassic Beds of Mt. Crosby, Queensland. Proc. Roy. Soc. Queensland, 56, pp. 37–46, 1 pl., 3 figs. (1945).

but its position within the Panorpoid complex is uncertain. The earliest unquestionable Lepidoptera have been found in early Tertiary deposits (Tineidæ, Lyonetiidæ, Eriocraniidæ, etc.).

ORDER DÍPTERA

Twelve extinct families of Diptera have been established. The Eopleciidæ, Architipulidæ, Eoptychopteridæ and Protorhyphidæ constitute the earliest record of the order (Lower Jurassic).

SUBORDER NEMATÓCERA

1. Branches of media not forming a closed cell....................2
   Branches of media forming a closed cell......................8
2. Veins mostly limited to anterior half of wing.................3
   Veins distributed over posterior as well as anterior parts of wing...4
3. Rs extending to wing apex; Sc well developed. (Protobíbio (Fig. 1205)). .... (J) PROTOBIBIÓNIDÆ
   Apical part of wing without veins; Sc absent.
   (J) PROTOSCATÓPSIDÆ
4. Rs branched 5
   Rs unbranched. (Pleciomìma, Lycoriomìma (Fig. 1210)).
   (J) PLECIOMÍMIDÆ
5. All branches of Rs arising distad to cross-vein rm..............6
   At least one branch of Rs arising proximad to cross-vein rm......7
6. Basal part of Rs, from fork of R-Rs to rm, not less than four times the length of rm.....................(J) PROTOPLECÌIDÆ
   Basal part of Rs, from fork of R-Rs to rm, not more than three times as long as rm. (Pleciofungívora, Transversiplècia (Fig. 1207)).
   (J) PLECIOFUNGIVÓRIDÆ
7. Sc much shorter than half wing-length; M weak.
   (J) PARAXYMÌIDÆ
   Sc at least half of wing-length; M strong. (Eoplècia (Fig. 1209)).
   (J) EOPLECÌIDÆ
8. Wing slender, subpetiolate, about four times as long as broad. (Architípula, Liassotípula (Fig. 1204)). (J) ARCHITÍPULIDÆ
   Wing broadly oval, not more than three times as long as broad....9
9. Median cell almost one-half wing-length. (Eoptychóptera, Proptychóptera (Fig. 1206)).............(J) EOPTYCHOPTÉRIDÆ
   Median cell not more than one-quarter wing length.
   (J) PROTORHÝPHIDÆ

SUBORDER BRACHÝCERA

In the Division Orthorrhapha only one extinct family is known: Protocyrtidæ (Jurassic), in which the head is noticeably larger than in the Acroceridæ. In the Division Cyclorrhapha also only one extinct family is known: Archiphoridæ (Fig. 1208) (Jurassic), in which the branches of the media are not so reduced as in the true Phoridæ.

LITERATURE ON DIPTERA — EXTINCT FAMILIES

HANDLIRSCH, A. Handbuch der Entomologie, 3, pp. 202–206 (1920).
    Neue Untersuchungen über die fossilen Insekten. Teil II. Ann. Naturh.
Mus. Wien, 49, pp. 101–114 (1939).

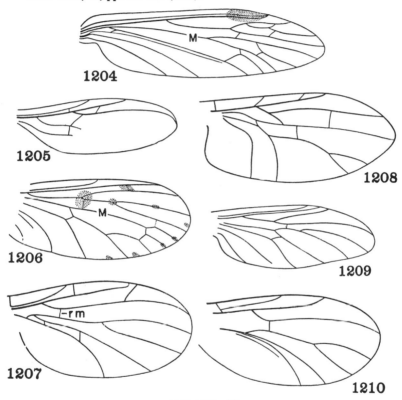

Figs. 1204–1210. **Diptera.**

1204. **Liassotipula,** wing (Tillyard), Architipulidæ.
1205. **Protobibio,** wing (Rohdendorf), Protobibionidæ.
1206. **Proptychoptera,** wing (Handlirsch), Eotychopteridæ.
1207. **Transversiplecia,** wing (Rohdendorf), Pleciofungivoridæ.
1208. **Archiphora,** wing (Rohdendorf), Archiphoridæ.
1209. **Eoplecia,** wing (Rohdendorf), Eopleciidæ.
1210. **Lycoriomima,** wing (Rohdendorf), Pleciomimidæ.

ROHDENDORF, B. B. Mesozoische Dipteren aus Kara-Tau. 1. Brachyceren und einige Nematoceren. Trav. Inst. Paléontol. Acad. Sci. URSS, **7**, pp. 29–67, 21 figs. (1938).
—— The Evolution of the Wing and the Phylogeny of Oligoneura (Diptera, Nematocera). Trav. Inst. Paléontol. Acad. Sci. URSS, **8**, pp. 1–102, 16 pls., 97 figs. (1946).
TILLYARD, R. J. The Panorpoid Complex in the British Rhætic and Lias. Fossil Insects, no. 3, British Mus. (Nat. Hist.), pp. 1–79 (1933).

ORDER SIPHONÁPTERA

No extinct families are known. The earliest record of the order is the living family Ctenopsyllidæ, in Lower Tertiary deposits (Baltic amber).[1]

ORDER COLEÓPTERA

The seven extinct families of Coleoptera are included in the following key. The Tschekardocoleidæ, Permocupidæ and Sojanocoleidæ constitute the earliest record of the order (Middle Permian of Russia).

1. Elytron with distinct veins...2
   Elytron without veins, at most having striæ on tubercles.........5
2. Elytron with a net-work of regular cells......................3
   Elytron with irregular cells...................................4
3. Cells of elytron forming a very fine mesh; Rs present. (**Tshekardocòleus** (Fig. 1211)).........(Pm) **TSHEKARDOCOLÈIDÆ**
   Cells of elytron forming a coarse net; Rs absent.
   (Pm) **PERMOCÙPIDÆ**
4. Cu extending to apex of elytron. (**Sojanocòleus** (Fig. 1212)).
   (Pm) **SOJANOCOLÈIDÆ**
   Cu extending to about middle of elytron.
   (Pm) **PERMORRHÁPHIDÆ**
5. Elytron with striæ or tubercles.............................6
   Elytron without striæ, tubercles or other sculpturing.
   (Pm) **PERMOPHÍLIDÆ**
6. Elytron with rows of tubercles. (**Curculióps** (Fig. 1213)).
   (Pm) **CURCULIÓPSIDÆ**
   Elytron with striæ. (**Ademosynòides, Permosỳne, Permocróssus** (Fig. 1214)) ....(Pm–Tr) **PERMOSÝNIDÆ**

LITERATURE ON COLEOPTERA — EXTINCT FAMILIES

MARTYNOV, A. V. New Permian Insects from Tikhie Gory. II. Neoptera (excluding Miomoptera). Trav. Mus. Géol. Acad. Sci. URSS, **8**, pp. 149–212, 29 figs. (1931).

[1] Hennig, W. Über einen Floh aus der Bernsteinsammlung des Herrn Scheele. Arb. Morph. Tax. Ent. Berlin-Dahlem, **6**, pp. 330–333 (1939).

Permian Fossil Insects from the Arkhangelsk District. Part ii.
Neuroptera, Megaloptera and Coleoptera, with the Description of Two
New Beetles from Tikhie Gory. Trav. Inst. Paléozool. Acad. Sci. URSS, 2,
pp. 63–96, 19 figs. (1932).

On Some New Materials of Arthropoda from Kuznetsk-Basin. Bull.
Acad. Sci. URSS, **1936,** pp. 1251–1264, 6 figs. (1936).

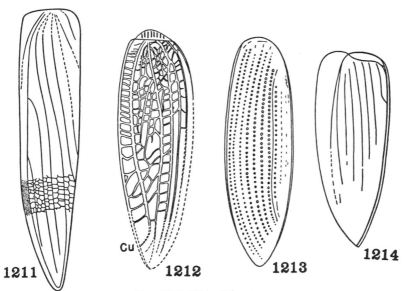

Figs. 1211–1214. **Coleoptera.**

1211. **Tshekardocoleus,** elytron (Rohdendorf), Tshekardocoleidæ.
1212. **Sojanocoleus,** elytron (Martynov), Sojanocoleidæ.
1213. **Curculiopsis,** elytron (Martynov), Curculiopsidæ.
1214. **Permocrossus,** elytron (Martynov), Permoscynidæ.

Permian Fossil Insects from Kargala and Their Relationships. Trav.
Inst. Paléontol. Acad. Sci. URSS, **7**(2), pp. 1–92, 20 figs. (1937).

ROHDENDORF, B. B. A New Family of Coleoptera from the Permian of the
Urals. C. R. Acad. Sci. URSS, **44,** pp. 252–253, 2 figs. (1944).

TILLYARD, R. J. Upper Permian Coleoptera and a New Order from the
Belmont Beds, New South Wales. Proc. Linn. Soc. New South Wales, **49,**
pp. 429–435, 2 pls., 3 figs. (1924).

ORDER **STREPSÍPTERA**

There are no extinct families in this order. Fossil representatives, belonging to the living family Mengeidæ, occur in early Tertiary amber.[1]

[1] Menge, A. Ueber ein Rhipidopteron und einige Helminthen im Bernstein.
Schrift. naturf. Ges. Danzig, (2) **1,** pp. 1–8 (1866).

ORDER HYMENÓPTERA

Six extinct families of this order have been established, but one of these, Ephialtitidæ (Jurassic of Spain), is too little known to include in the key. The families Anaxyelidæ, Paroryssidæ, and Myrmiciidæ, all from the Upper Jurassic, constitute the oldest record of the order.

SUBORDER CHALASTOGÁSTRA

1. Fore wing with three radial cells. (Anaxyèla (Fig. 1215)).
   (J) ANAXYÉLIDÆ
   Fore wing with one or two radial cells........................2

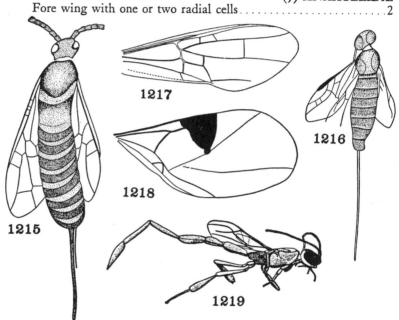

Figs. 1215–1219. Hymenoptera.

1215. **Anaxyela** (Martynov), Anaxyelidæ.
1216. **Paroryssus** (Martynov), Paroryssidæ.
1217. **Myrmicium,** fore wing (Carpenter), Myrmiciidæ.
1218. **Serphites,** fore wing (Brues), Serphitidæ.
1219. **Pelecinopteron** (Brues), Pelecinopteridæ.

2. Fore wing with one radial cell. (Parorýssus (Fig. 1216)).
   (J) PARORÝSSIDÆ
   Fore wing with two radial cells. (Myrmícium (Fig. 1217)).
   (*PSEUDOSIRÍCIDÆ* .... (J) MYRMICIIDÆ

SUBORDER CLISTOGÁSTRA

1. Antennæ with ten segments. (**Serphìtes** (Fig. 1218)).
   (K or T) **SERPHÍTIDÆ**
   Antennæ with 13 segments. (**Pelecinópteron** (Fig. 1219)).
   (T) **PELECINOPTÉRIDÆ**

LITERATURE ON HYMENOPTERA — EXTINCT FAMILIES

Brues, C. T. The Parasitic Hymenoptera of the Baltic Amber. Part 1. Bernstein-Forsch., **3**, pp. 1–178, 13 pls. (1933).
 Ichneumonoidea, Serphoidea, and Chalcidoidea. In Carpenter, *et al.*, Insects and Arachnids from Canadian Amber. Univ. Toronto Studies, Geol. Ser. No. 40, pp. 27–44, 3 figs. (1936).

Carpenter, F. M. Jurassic Insects from Solenhofen in the Carnegie Museum and the Museum of Comparative Zoology. Ann. Carnegie Mus., **21**, pp. 97–129, 11 figs. (1932).

Handlirsch, A. Die fossilen Insekten und die Phylogenie der rezenten Formen. Handb. Palaeontol. u. Zool., pp. 573–578 (1906–08).

Maa, T. A Synopsis of Asiatic Siricoidea with Notes on Certain Exotic and Fossil Forms (Hymenoptera Symphyta). Notes Ent. chinoise, Mus. Heude, **13**, pp. 17–19, 1 fig. (1949).

Martynov, A. To the Knowledge of Fossil Insects from Jurassic Beds in Turkestan. 3. Hymenoptera, Mecoptera. Bull. Acad. Sci. URSS, **1925**, pp. 753–762, 7 figs. (1925).

GLOSSARY OF SPECIAL TERMS [1]

This glossary is intended to include only such terms as are not easily understood from the figures referred to in the keys, and other words only when their meaning in the keys might not be readily ascertained from an ordinary English dictionary.

Abdòmen, the hindermost of the three main body divisions.

Acróstichal bristles, one, two or several longitudinal rows of minute bristles along the center of the mesonotum of some flies (*cf.* dorsocentral bristles).

Acùlea (-eæ), one of the numerous minute spines on the wing membrane of certain Lepidoptera.

Acùleate, (*a*) furnished with a sting; (*b*) beset with aculeæ.

Adventítious, not regular; accidental or additional.

Ædæagus, the male intromittent organ.

Álula (-læ), a small lobe, borne at the base of the wing (Diptera).

Amphipneùstic, having the first and last pairs of spiracles open and functioning.

Ànal, pertaining to the last abdominal segment or to the hind basal angle of the wing.

Ànal lobe, the rounded posterior part of the wing which includes the anal veins.

Ànal veins, in the typical wing the three most posterior main veins.

Ánnulated, incompletely divided into ring-like joints.

Ánnulus (-li), a ring or band.

Antecóxal sclerite, a part of the metasternum in front of the hind coxæ (Coleoptera).

Anténna (-næ), a pair of jointed sensory appendages of the head above the mouthparts.

Adfróntal plates, a pair of long oblique sclerites on the front of the head extending upwards from the base of the antennæ and meeting medially above (larvæ of Lepidoptera).

Antenòdal crossveins, crossveins along the costal border between the base and the nodus (Odonata).

Apneùstic, having all the spiracles closed and not functioning.

Appendículate cell, a small indistinct cell just beyond the apex of the marginal cell (Hymenoptera).

Ápterous, wingless.

Archedíctyon, a fine network of cuticular ridges on the wings of certain insects.

---

[1] Where the plural form is unusual the differing termination is given in parentheses added to the last common letter of the root. For additional definitions, the reader is referred to "Glossary of Entomology" by J. R. de la Torre Bueno, 326 pp. Brooklyn Entomological Society, New York (1937).

Árcuate, arched like a bow.

Árculus, a basal crossvein between the radius and cubitus (Odonata).

Arèola (-læ), **areóle,** a small closed cell in the forewing, enclosed by radial veins (Lepidoptera).

Arísta, a bristle-like process at or near the end of the antennæ (Diptera).

Aròlium (-ia), a terminal pad of the foot between the claws.

Àtrium (-ia), a cavity or enlarged entrance.

Atténuated, gradually tapering.

Auxíliary vein, the subcostal vein of Diptera, anterior to the radius.

Axílla (-læ), a triangular sclerite on each side of the scutellum (Hymenoptera).

Bàsal cells, the two cells proximal to the anterior crossvein and the discal cell (Diptera).

Bìfid, split into two parts.

Bìlobed, divided into two lobes.

Calamístrum, one or two rows of curved spines on the upper margin of the metatarsus of the hind legs (Araneida).

Calýpteres, small membranous disks under the base of the wings (Diptera).

Cámerostome, the opening through which the beak is extended in certain Acarina.

Campodèiform, having the form of Campodea (Thysanura), said of certain active carnivorous larvæ.

Cápitate, with a distinct knob at the tip.

Cárapace, the more or less fused dorsal sclerites of the cephalothorax (Arachnida). Also any fused series of sclerites covering a part of the body.

Cárinate, ridged, or furnished with a raised line or keel.

Cáruncle, a fleshy papillate or sucker-like appendage at the tip of the tarsus in certain Acarina.

Caudal filaments or **setæ,** thread-like processes terminating the abdomen.

Cell, a space in the wing bounded by veins.

Cephalothòrax, the combined head and thorax in Arachnida.

Cérci, a pair of appendages near the end of the abdomen.

Chætosèma, a series of short bristles on the head of certain Lepidoptera.

Cheek, the lateral part of the head between the eyes and the mouth.

Chèlate, pincers-shaped, having two opposable claws.

Chelíceræ, the first or most anterior pair of appendages in the Arachnida.

Chìtin, the horn-like material forming the hard parts of the body wall.

Clàvate, clubbed or enlarged at the tip.

Clàvus, an oblong basal part along the inner edge of the fore wings (Heteroptera, Homoptera).

Clýpeus, the sclerite bearing the labrum (Hymenoptera); a horseshoe-shaped sclerite under the margin of the mouth (Diptera).

Coárctate, with narrowed base and enlarged tip.

Coarctate pupa, a type of pupa in certain Diptera, enclosed in a hardened shell formed from the last larval moult-skin.

Cólulus, a slender or pointed organ lying in front of the spinnerets (Araneida).

Compréssed, flattened from side to side, as distinguished from depressed.

Cónnate, immovably united, fused.

Constrícted, narrowed in part.

Còrium, an elongate middle part of the fore wing (Hemiptera).

Córneous, horn-like in texture.

Córnicle, one of certain paired dorsal tubular processes on the posterior part of the abdomen of aphids.

Cósta, the front margin of the wing, considered as the first vein.

Cóstal àrea, the part of the wing immediately behind the front margin.

Cóstal cell, the space of the wing between the costa and the subcostal vein; formerly sometimes termed subcostal.

Cóxa (-xæ), the basal joint of the legs, sometimes quite fused with the body.

Cribéllum, a sieve-like spinning organ lying in front of the spinnerets (Arancida).

Cróchets, a series of spines on the prolegs of the larvæ of Lepidoptera.

Crossvein, any transverse vein connecting adjacent longitudinal veins.

Ctenídium (-ia), a comb-like row of bristles.

Cùbitus, the fifth of the main veins of the typical wing.

Cursòrial, fitted for running.

Declívity, the abruptly bent apex of the elytra (Coleoptera).

Decúmbent, bending downward.

Dentículate, with minute tooth-like projections.

Dichóptic, eyes not touching above (Diptera).

Dígitate, with finger-like processes.

Direct eyes, the anterior median pair of eyes in spiders.

Diúrnal eyes, in spiders, eyes that are dark colored.

Dórsal, pertaining to the upper surface or back of the body.

Dorsocéntral bristles, several longitudinal rows of bristles near the middle of the mesonotum, lateral to the smaller acrostichals (Diptera).

Ectopárasite, a parasite which lives on the exterior of animals.

Élytron (-ra), the horny fore wings, or wing covers, of beetles.

Empòdium (-ia), a single middle pad or bristle between the tarsal claws (Diptera).

Epímeron (-ra), the posterior portion of the pleura of a thoracic segment (Insecta). The sclerite to which the basal segment of the leg is attached (Arachnida, Diplopoda).

Epíphysis (-ses), a lappet-like process.

Epipleùra (-ræ), the infolded edge of the elytra (Coleoptera).

Epistérnum, the anterior portion of the pleura of a thoracic segment.

Épistome, the part of the face just above the mouth.

Epizòic, living as external parasites of animals.

Erùciform, having the body shaped like a caterpillar.

Exùviæ, the molt, or cast skin of an insect. Recently used as exuvia, exuviæ to differentiate the molts of a single from those of several instars, as in Coccoidea.

Eye-cap, a group of modified scales overhanging the eye (Lepidoptera).

Face, the front of the head, between the clypeus and antennæ.

Fàcial plate, the central part of the face (Diptera).

Fastígium, the upper edge or median ridge of the vertex (Orthoptera).

Fèmur (-émora), the thigh or third division of the legs.

Fíliform, hair-like, or filamentous, longer than setaceous.

Flabéllate, with fan-like processes or projections.

Flabéllum (-la), a leaf-like or fan-like process.

Flagéllum, the distal part of the antenna when lash-like.

Fontanél, a small, depressed, pale spot on the front of the head between the eyes (Isoptera).

Foràmen (-ámina), a small opening, orifice or puncture.

Fórcipate, bearing pincers, or pincers-shaped.

Frénulum, a strong spine or spines at the front basal angle of the hind wings (Lepidoptera).

Front, the forehead, between the antennæ, eyes and ocelli.

Frontàlia, the central strip of the front (Diptera).

Fróntal lùnule, a small crescent-shaped space just above the antennæ (Diptera).

Frónto-órbital bristles, several bristles along the front next to the eyes (Diptera).

Fundàtrix, a stem-mother or female of the first generation which founds a new colony (Aphidoidea).

Fúrcula, the forked springing appendage below the end of the abdomen (Collembola).

Gáster, the rounded part of the abdomen behind the basal node or nodes in ants (Hymenoptera).

Gèna (-næ), the cheek.

Genículate, abruptly bent, elbowed.

Genitàlia, the external sexual organs.

Gíbbous, puffed out; hunch-backed.

Glàbrous, bald, smooth, free of hairs.

Gnathochilàrium, a plate-like structure formed by the mouthparts, exclusive of the mandibles (Diplopoda).

Gónopod, a modified leg, serving as a copulatory appendage, on the seventh or adjacent body segments (Diplopoda).

Gonapóphysis (-ses), each of the short conical paired egg-laying processes terminating the abdomen; also applied to certain paired genital appendages in the male.

Graduated crossveins, an oblique row of crossveins forming steps across the wing (Neuroptera).

Grávid, filled with eggs.

Gùla, the median underpart of the head lying between the mouth and posterior foramen.

Gùlar suture, a longitudinal impressed line on each side of the gula or middle piece of the throat.

Hálter, a small knobbed appendage on each side of the thorax replacing the hind wings (Diptera).

Hàmus, a distinct abrupt spur-like vein in the hind wings of some Heteroptera.

Haústellate, formed for sucking, the mandibles not fitted for chewing.

Hemélytron (-ra), the heavily chitinized fore wing of Hemiptera.

Heterogèneous, of more than one type, as the eyes of certain spiders.

Heterómerous, differing in the number of joints in the three pairs of tarsi (*e.g.* 5, 5, 4), or in the structure of other repetitive parts.

Holóptic, having the eyes meeting above the antennæ (Diptera).

Homónomous, similar in form, function or development.

Hùmeral angle, the basal front corner of the wing.

Hyaline, more or less transparent.

Hypermetamórphosis, development in which two or more different types of larvæ follow one another in succeeding stages of growth.

Hypopleùral bristles, a more or less vertical row of bristles above each hind coxa (Diptera).

Hypopýgium, the last ventral plate; or the inflexed genitalia.

Hypostigmátic cell, a specialized cell located beneath the stigma of the wing of some Neuroptera.

Imàgo, the final, adult, or reproductive stage of an insect.

Inglùvial, pertaining to the crop.

Ínclinate, bent or directed toward the median line.

Ínquiline, an animal that occurs regularly in the nest or habitation of some other species.

Ínstar, any of the successive stages during metamorphosis, marked off by moltings.

Intercalary veins, a thickened fold which arises nearly mid-way between two preëxisting veins and which has no original connections with those veins.

Interfrontàlia, the central portion of the front of some flies when differentiated from the orbits.

Interfróntal bristles, minute bristles on the central part of the front (Diptera).

Interstítial, occurring between two segments, *e.g.* the trochanter, linking the coxa and femur; or coincident, as the ends of two veins.

Intra-àlar bristles, several bristles above the root of the wing lateral to the dorsocentrals (Diptera).

Júgum, a lobe-like process at the base of the fore wings overlapping the hind wings (Lepidoptera).

Labéllum (-la), the expanded tip of the proboscis (Diptera).

Làbial pálpus (-pi), a jointed sensory appendage at each side of the labium.

Làbium, the lower lip.

Làbrum, the upper lip, lying just below the clypeus.

Lamélla (-læ), a leaf-like plate.

Lámellate, bearing or composed of lamellæ.

Láminate, composed of leaf-like plates.

Lánceolate, tapering at each end, spear-shaped.

Lárva (-væ), the growing stages of an insect having a complete metamorphosis, after hatching from the egg and before the pupal period.

Lateral, at, toward, or pertaining to the sides of the body.

Lígula, the central part of the labium, borne by the mentum (Coleoptera).

Lòra (-ræ), the cheek (Homoptera).

Lung-book; lung sac, a respiratory sac, opening by a slit-shaped aperture on the ventral surface of the abdomen in certain Arachnida.

Lùnule, a small crescent-shaped piece just above the antennæ (Diptera).

Macrotríchia, the larger hairs on the surface of the wings.

Mandíbulate, with jaws fitted for chewing.

Marginal cell, one or more cells near the anterior margin of the wing, below the stigma (Hymenoptera).

Mask, the extensile labium of the nymphs of Odonata which forms an organ for grasping the prey.

Maxílla (-læ), the second pair of appendages belonging to the mouth, behind the mandibles or jaws.

Máxillary palpus, a finger-like jointed sensory appendage on each maxilla.

Mèdia, the fourth of the principal veins of the typical wing.

Mèdial, pertaining to the media.

Mèdian, lying along the middle line of the body.

Méntum, the part of the labium bearing the movable parts.

Mèsad, lying toward the median line.

Mesepistérnum (-na), the anterior of the oblique side pieces of the mesothorax.

Mesonòtum, the back or upper side of the mesothorax.

Mesopleùra (-ræ), the space between the root of the wings and the middle coxæ, consisting of episternum and epimeron (Diptera).

Mesostérnum, the middle part of the underside of the mesothorax.

Mesothòrax, the middle of the thoracic divisions, bearing the second legs and the fore wings.

Metamórphosis (-ses), the series of marked external changes through which an insect passes during its development, *e.g.* egg, larva, pupa, adult. Direct development entails no such changes. Incomplete metamorphosis lacks the pupal stage. Complete metamorphosis includes a pupal stage. See also hypermetamorphosis.

Metapneùstic, having only the posterior pair of spiracles open and functioning.

Metastérnum, the middle piece of the under side of the metathorax.

Metatársus (-si), the first joint of any tarsus, next to the tibia, also called basitarsus.

Metathòrax, the third division of the thorax, bearing the hind legs and the hind wings.

Micrópterous, with small or vestigial wings.

Microtríchia, the smaller abundant hairs that clothe the surface of the wings in some insects.

Molt, to cut off or shed the skin.

Moníliform, resembling a string of beads.

Nàiad, the nymph of aquatic insects.

Nàsus, the drawn-out forward part of the head of crane-flies.

Nàsute, a form of worker termite in which the head bears a snout-like projection in front.

Neuràtion, the arrangement of the veins of the wings, the venation.

Noctúrnal eyes, in spiders, eyes of a pearly white color.

Node, a swelling or knot-like knob.

Nòdus, a stout crossvein at or before the middle of the costal border of the wing (Odonata).

Notauli, a pair of longitudinal furrows on the mesonotum of certain Hymenoptera, lying nearer to the median line than the parapsidal furrows when both pairs of furrows are present.

Nòtum, the dorsal surface of the body, particularly of the thorax.

Nymph, the larval or growing stage of those insects that have no pupal period.

Océllus (-li), the simple eyes, usually three in number, on the upper part of the head; also the simple eyes of insect larvæ and of some other arthropods.

Ócciput, the back part of the head.

Onýchium (-ia), a pad between the tarsal claws.

Órbit, the part of the head immediately surrounding the eyes.

Óstioles, the paired lateral openings of the heart.

Ovipósitor, the egg-laying apparatus.

Pálpus (-pi), one or two pairs of jointed sensitive, finger-like processes borne by the mouth. See maxillary palpus and labial palpus.

Parafàcials, the sides of the face of some flies, when differentiated from the sunken central portion and the orbits.

Paranotal lobes, lateral extensions of the notum, exemplified by those on the pronotum of the Palæodictyoptera.

Parápsidal furrow, a longitudinal groove between the median line and each side of the mesonotum, lying near to the lateral margin (Hymenoptera). See notauli.

Párasite, an animal that feeds on or in some other living animal.

Paronýchium (-ia), a bristle-like appendage of the claws.

Péctinate, with branches like a comb.

Péndulous, hanging from one end.

Pedipálpi, pédipalps, the second of the paired appendages of Arachnida.

Peripneùstic, having a series of functional spiracles along each side of the body.

Péritreme, a chitinous plate surrounding the spiracle in certain mites.

Pétiolate, attached by a stalk or stem.

Phytóphagous, feeding on plants.

Plántula (-læ), a pad-like sole on the underside of the tarsi of certain insects.

Pleùrite, one of the side pieces of the body.

Plùmose, feathery.

Postèrior callósity, a swelling between the root of the wings and the scutellum (Diptera).

Postèrior cells, a variable number of cells extending to the hind margin of the wings, the first bounded inwardly by the anterior crossvein (Diptera).

Posthùmeral bristle, one or more bristles just behind the shoulder-swelling (Diptera).

Postnòdal crossveins, a series of short transverse veins next to the costal margin of the wing, beyond the nodus (Odonata).

Postscutéllum, a small transverse piece of the thorax immediately behind the scutellum.

Postvértical bristles, pair of minute bristles behind the ocelli (Diptera).

Preápical bristle, a bristle on the outside of the tibiæ just before the apex (Diptera).

Prebasilàre, a sclerite on the underside of the head, sometimes divided medially, lying behind the mentum (Diplopoda).

Prédatory, capturing living prey.

Prefúrca, the petiole of the second and third veins (R_4 and R_5) of Diptera.

Presùtural bristle, one or more dorsocentral bristles just in front of the transverse suture (Diptera).

Probóscis, the extended trunk-like or beak-like mouthparts.

Pròclinate, inclined forward.

Proepímeron (-ra), that part at the rear of the side of the prothorax next the coxæ.

Prógnathous, having the mouthparts projecting forwards.

Pròlegs, the fleshy abdominal legs of certain insect larvæ.

Proméntum, a median sclerite in the gnathochilarium, lying in front of the mentum or stipites (Diplopoda).

Pronòtum, the back or upper side of the prothorax.

Propleùra (-ræ), the side portion of the prothorax.

Propneùstic, having only the anterior pair of spiracles open and functioning.

Propòdeum, the large apical portion of the thorax, behind the wings and scutellum (Hymenoptera).

Prosòma, an anterior clearly separated section of the cephalothorax in certain Phalangida.

Prostérnum, the middle of the underside of the prothorax.

Prothorácic bristle, a bristle above each of the front coxæ (Diptera).

Prothòrax, the first division of the thorax, bearing the front legs.

Prùinose, coated with a hoary dust.

Pseùdopod, an outgrowth or projection of the body of certain larvæ, assisting in locomotion.

Pteropleùral bristles, bristles located on the sides of the body just beneath the root of the wings (Diptera).

Ptilìnum, a temporary bladder-like structure above the antennæ of certain Diptera.

Pulvíllus (-li), a pad beneath each tarsal claw.

Pùpa (-pæ), the resting stage of insects with complete metamorphosis, following the larva and preceding the adult.

Pupàrium, the oval, hardened covering of the pupa of the higher Diptera and some scale insects, formed of the larval or nymphal skin.

Pupíparous, giving birth to full-grown larvæ that are ready to pupate.

Pygídium, the last dorsal segment.

Ràdial, of or pertaining to the radius.

Ràdial cell, any cell in the wing bordered in front by a branch of the radius.

Ràdial séctor, the posterior of the two main divisions of the radius.

Ràdius, the third of the principal veins of the typical wing.

Raptòrial, fitted for grasping prey.

Rastéllum, a structure on the cheliceræ of certain spiders bearing numerous tooth-like projections.

Réclinate, pointing backward.

Recúrrent nervure, one or two transverse veins arising from the lower side of the submarginal cells (Hymenoptera).

Remigium, the wing area exclusive of the anal and jugal areas.

Réniform, kidney-shaped.

Reticulate, meshed, like net work.

Ròstrum, a beak or snout.

Scape, the basal joint or joints of the antennæ.

Sclèrite, any piece of the body wall bounded by sutures.

Scòpa, a brush on the underside of the abdomen, for collecting pollen (Hymenoptera).

Scópula, a brush of hairs or bristles (Araneida).

Scrobe, a groove or furrow, especially one on the mandible or one which receives the antenna.

Scutéllum, a somewhat triangular or crescentic sclerite just behind the mesonotum.

Sérrate, toothed along the edge, like a saw.

Séssile, (*a*) broadly attached; (*b*), incapable of movement from place to place.

Sèta (-tæ), a bristle or filament.

Setàceous, bristle-like, slender.

Shagreened, having a finely roughened surface.

Sínuous, S-shaped, winding back and forth.

Small-crossvein, a short crossvein extending from the base of the discal cell to the fifth posterior cell between M and Cu (Diptera).

Spátulate, broad at tip, narrowed at base.

Spínulated, furnished with very small spines.

Spíracles, breathing pores or external openings of the tracheal system.

Spurs, movable spines, usually two, at the end of the tibiæ.

Spùrious vein, an adventitious longitudinal vein crossing the anterior (r-m) crossvein (Diptera).

Squamopygídium, a plate formed by the fusion of several apical abdominal segments (Dermaptera).

Sternauli, a pair of lateral furrows on the mesothorax below the base of the wings (Hymenoptera).

Stérnite, the ventral piece of each abdominal segment.

Sternopleùral bristles, the bristles on the triangular pleural sclerite between the front and middle coxæ (Diptera).

Stígma, a thickening on the costal border of the wings near the apex.

Stípites (sing. stìpes), a pair of sclerites lying at each side of the gnathochilarium (Diplopoda).

Stridulàtion, a chirping or creaking noise.

Style, (*a*) a bristle-like process terminating the antennæ, thicker than the arista (Diptera); (*b*) short slender appendages on the underside of the abdomen (Thysanura).

Stỳliform, drawn out as a slender stiff process.

Subanténnal groove, a groove or grooves in the middle of the face (Diptera).

Subcósta, the second of the principal veins of the typical wing.

Submárginal cell, one or more cells lying behind the marginal cells, usually forming a second row below the anterior margin apically (Hymenoptera).

Submèdian cell, a long basal cell near the middle of the wing (Hymenoptera).

Subméntum, the basal part of the mentum.

Súlcate, grooved or furrowed.

Supraànal plate, a dorsal sclerite terminating the abdomen.

Sùture, a line separating the parts of the body wall.

Társus (-si), the foot, the jointed portion of the legs beyond the tibia.

Tégmen (-mina), the toughened fore wings of grasshoppers, etc.

Tégula (-læ), a small convex plate over the root of the fore wings (Hymenoptera).

Télepod, a modified leg, serving as a copulatory appendage, on one of the posterior body segments of male Diplopoda.

Télson, the last abdominal segment.

Tentòrial rods, several diverging chitinous rods within the posterior part of the head of certain dipterous larvæ.

Térgite, the dorsal piece of an abdominal segment.

Térmen, the outer, or distal margin of the wing.

Thèca, a sheath or sac-like covering.

Thòrax, the second of the main divisions of the insect body, between the head and the abdomen, bearing the legs and wings.

Tíbia (-iæ), the shin-joint of the legs, between the femur and the tarsus.

Tornus, the hind or inner angle of a wing.

Triad, a forked vein, with the fork divided by a middle member formed by the alignment of cross-veins.

Triangle, a small triangular cell near the base of the wing (Odonata).

Trichobóthria, minute sensory hairs on the tarsal joints of the legs of certain spiders.

Triúngulin, the active first-stage larva of the Strepsiptera and certain hypermetamorphic beetles.

Trochánter, the small second joint of the legs between the coxa and the femur.

Trochántin, a small piece between the sternum and the front coxa (Coleoptera).

Trúncate, ending squarely with sharply cut-off edge.

Týmpanal hoods, týmpanal bullæ, a pair of tubercles or swellings at the base of the abdomen in certain Lepidoptera.

Venàtion, the course of the veins or rod-like thickenings of the wings.

Véntral, pertaining to the underside of the body.

Véntral mémbrane, the skin-like tissue connecting the tergites and the sternites (Diptera).

Véntral ségments, the sternites of the abdomen.

Vérrucose, covered with minute warts or tubercles.

Vértex, the crown of the head.

Vertícillate, provided with whorls of fine hairs.

Vestígial, small, degenerate, not functional.

Vibríssa (-sæ), a bristle or bristles on each side of the mouth-opening in front (Diptera).

Vivíparous, bringing forth living young, not laying eggs.

INDEX TO GENERA AND HIGHER GROUPS

Illustrations are indicated by page numbers in bold face type.

Pompilus, 648
Pomposa, **103**, 105
Ponera, 641, **642**
Ponerinæ, 641
Pontania, 625
Pontomyia, 386, 388
Popa, 85
Popillia, 585
Poratophilus, 767
Porcellio, **692**, 693
Porina, 229
Porismus, 209
Poroblattinidæ, 807
Porocephalidæ, 752
Porocephalinæ, 752
Porocephalus, 752
Porohalacaridæ, 738
Porohalacarus, 738
Porotermes, 122
Porotermitinæ, 122
Porphyrops, 344
Porpocera, 327
Porricondyla, 316
Porsenus, 374
Porthetria, 247
Porydra, **405**
Potamanthidæ, 56, 59
Potamanthodes, 56
Potamanthus, 56, **60**
Potamida, 327
Potamidinæ, 327
Potamocorinæ, 183
Potanthus, 264
Poujadia, 244
Povilla, 56
Praon, 632
Praos, 117
Prebistus, 104
Precis, 268
Prenolepis, 640
Prepona, 268
Presibylla, 89
Preta, 151
Prexaspes, 104
Primicimex, 170
Pringleophaga, 271
Prionapteryx, 244
Prionoceridæ, 565
Prionelus, 316
Prionidæ, 575

Prionocyphon, **552**
Prionopeltis, 761
Prionopetalum, 767
Prionoxystus, **233**, 234
Prionus, 575
Prisculinæ, 722
Prisopus, 104
Prista, 330
Pristiphora, 625
Pristocera, 644
Privesa, 155
Probnis, **794**, 795
Probnisidæ, 795
Procampodea, 48
Procecidochares, 380
Procercopidæ, 813
Prochilidæ, 96
Prochilus, 96
Prochoropteridæ, 787
Prochyliza, 374
Prociphilus, 159
Procladius, 323
Proconia, 146
Proconiidæ, 146
Procris, 235
Procympiutus, 172
Proctacanthus, 339
Proctophyllodidæ, 742
Proctotrypes, 643, **644**
Proctotrypidæ, 643, 651
Proctotrypoidea, 663
Prodicus, 763
Prodida, 726
Prodidomidæ, 726
Prodidominæ, 726
Prodidomus, 726
Prodoxidæ, 252, 272
Prodoxus, 252, 272
Progonocimicidæ, 814
Progonophlebiidæ, 804
Prohemerobiidæ, 817
Prohemerobius, 817, **818**
Proisotoma, 52
Projapygidæ, 48
Projapyx, 48
Prolabia, 116
Prolammonyx, 773
Prolimacodes, 235
Promachus, 105, 339
Promiopteryx, 90

Pronuba, 252
Prophalangopsidæ, 807
Prophalangopsinæ, 94
Prophalangopsis, 94
Propomacrus, 585
Propsocus, 128
Proptychoptera, 822, **823**
Propyragra, **114**, 115
Prorates, 337
Proreus, 117
Prosacantha, 645
Prosarthria, **100**, 100
Prosbascanionidæ, 814
Prosbole, **813**, 814
Prosbolidæ, 814
Prosbolopsidæ, 814
Proscopia, 100
Proscopiidæ, 100
Prosepididontidæ, 821
Prosimuliinæ, 322
Prosimulium, 322
Prosomera, 105
Prosopididæ, 657
Prosopistoma, 59, **60**
Prosopistomatidæ, 57, 59
Prosopochrysa, 326
Prosopochrysinæ, 326
Prosotropis, 153
Prosparatta, 116
Prostemminæ, **176**
Prostemmiulus, 764, **765**
Prostenoneuridæ, 793
Prosthecina, 46
Protagriidæ, 786
Protagrionidæ, 786
Protanisoptera, 803
Proteininæ, 565
Protelytridæ, 798
Protelytron, **793**, 798
Protelytroptera, 797
Protembia, **794**, 795
Protembiidæ, 795
Protenor, 177
Protenthes, 323
Protentomidæ, 42
Protentominæ, 42
Protentomon, 42
Protentomobrya, **801**
Protentomobryidæ, 801
Protephemerida, 786

Schizaspidia, 636
Schizocarpus, 742
Schizocephala, 86
Schizocephalinæ, 86, 88
Schizocera, 625
Schizometopa, 352
Schizomida, 695, **699**
Schizomidæ, 699
Schizomus, **699,** 699
Schizoneura, 159
Schizophora, 351
Schizopinæ, 555
Schizopteridæ, 169
Schizotus, 573
Schizura, 239
Schmitzia, 388
Schoenbaueria, 322
Schœnobiinæ, 243
Schœnobius, 243
Schœnomyza, 360
Schœnophilus, 389
Scholastes, 371
Schreckensteinia, 259
Sciadocera, 341, **351**
Sciadoceridæ, 341
Sciara, **319,** 319, 396,
    397, 408, **409**
Sciaridæ, 319, 387, 396,
    408
Sciarinæ, 319
Sciapodinæ, 343
Sciapus, 343
Sciomyza, 367, **368**
Sciomyzidæ, 367
Sciomyzinæ, 367
Scione, 329
Sciopeza, 364
Sciophila, 318, **319**
Sciophilidæ, 318
Sciophilinæ, 318
Scipopus, 365
Scirtes, 553
Scirtotypus, 101
Scirula, 744
Sclerobunus, 713
Scleroderma, 644
Sclerogibba, 643
Sclerogibbidæ, 643, 650
Scleropauropodidæ, 755
Scleropauropus, 755

Scolia, 648
Scoliaphleps, 359
Scoliaula, 251
Scoliidæ, 648, 664
Scoliocentra, 374
Scolioneurinæ, 662
Scolioplanes, 774
Scolopendra, 771, **772**
Scolopendrella, 775
Scolopendrellidæ, 775
Scolopendridæ, 771
Scolopendrinæ, 771
Scolopendromorpha, 771
Scolopendropsis, 775
Scolopocryptopinæ, 772
Scolopocryptops, 772
Scolops, **152,** 154
Scolytidæ, 579, 591
Scolytoidea, 578
Scolytoplatypodidæ, 579
Scolytoplatypus, 579, **580**
Scolytopsis, 579
Scolytus, 579
Scoparia, 245
Scopariinæ, 245
Scopeuma, **355,** 359
Scopeumatidæ, 359
Scopeumatinæ, 359
Scopula, 237
Scorpio, 703
Scorpiones, 701
Scorpionida, 695, 701
Scorpionidæ, 702
Scorpioninæ, 703
Scorpiops, 704
Scorpiopsinæ, 704
Scotogramma, 247
Scotolathys, 719
Scotolemon, 713
Scraptia, 573
Scraptiidæ, 573
Scrupulaspis, 164
Scudderia, 96
Scutacaridae, 742
Scutacarus, 742
Scutare, 165
Scutellera, 179
Scutelleridæ, 179
Scutelleroidea, 179
Scutigera, 770, **772**

Scutigerella, **772, 775**
Scutigerellidæ, 775
Scutigeridæ, 770
Scutigeromorpha, 770
Scutogona, 762
Scutops, 371
Scydmænidæ, 563
Scydmænus, 563
Scymnus, 568
Scyphacella, 693
Scyphacidæ, 693
Scyphax, 693
Scythridæ, 260
Scythrididæ, 260, 280
Scythris, **259,** 260
Scytinoptera, **813,** 814
Scytinopteridæ, 814
Scytodes, 722
Scytohymenidæ, 788
Scytonotus, 760
Sebekia, **751,** 752
Sebekiinæ, 752
Sedulothrips, 139
Segestria, 720
Segestriidæ, 720
Selachops, 382
Selagena, 234
Selandria, 625
Selandriinæ, 625, 662
Selasoma, 329
Selasius, 565
Selenia, 238
Selenocosmia, 718
Selenopidæ, 726
Selenops, 726
Selidopogon, 339
Sematura, 237
Sematuridæ, 237
Semidalis, 207
Seminota, **645,** 645
Semioptila, 232
Semiotellus, 637
Semiothisa, 238
Semiramis, 337
Semniinæ, 244
Semnosoma, 760
Senoculidæ, 725
Senoculus, 725
Senotainia, 357
Seoptera, 369

INDEX TO COMMON NAMES

The number of vernacular, or common names in the present edition has been reduced to include only those very generally used in non-technical publications in the English language, especially in America. For those applied less frequently, and particularly for those coined as popular appellations for insect pests in the United States, the reader is referred to "Destructive and Useful Insects" by C. L. Metcalf and W. P. Flint, third edition, 1951, McGraw-Hill, New York.